MANUAL

OF THE

SOUTHEASTERN
FLORA

MANUAL

OF THE

SOUTHEASTERN FLORA

BEING DESCRIPTIONS OF THE SEED PLANTS GROWING NATURALLY
IN FLORIDA, ALABAMA, MISSISSIPPI, EASTERN LOUISIANA,
TENNESSEE, NORTH CAROLINA, SOUTH CAROLINA
AND GEORGIA

ILLUSTRATED

BY

JOHN KUNKEL SMALL

Part Two

[Facsimile Reprint of the 1933 Edition]

HAFNER PUBLISHING COMPANY
New York
1972

Published by
HAFNER PUBLISHING COMPANY
866 Third Avenue
New York, N.Y. 10022

Library of Congress Catalog Card Number: 72-75020

Printed in U.S.A. by
NOBLE OFFSET PRINTERS, INC.
NEW YORK 3, N. Y.

duced to scales, or almost wanting. Flowers mainly monoecious or dioecious, regular. Calyx of several sepals. Corolla of several petals, or often wanting. Androecium of more than one stamen, except when the staminate flowers are scattered over the inside of an involucre. Filaments distinct or united into a column. Anthers opening by longitudinal or transverse valves. Gynoecium of 2, 3, or 4, or rarely more, united carpels, superior. Styles, or stigmas, usually distinct and cleft or foliaceous, united by pairs in *Callitrichaceae*. Ovules 1, 2, or 3 in each cavity. Fruit capsular, achene-like, drupaceous or baccate. Seeds often carunculate.

Styles or stigmas distinct or mainly so, cleft or foliaceous : ovary 3-celled or rarely 1- or 2-celled : stamens several, except when on the inside of an involucre. Fam. 1. EUPHORBIACEAE.
Styles united by pairs : ovary 4-celled : stamen solitary. Fam. 2. CALLITRICHACEAE.

FAMILY 1. **EUPHORBIACEAE** — SPURGE FAMILY

Herbs, shrubs, or trees, often with milky sap. Leaves opposite, whorled, or alternate : blades simple and entire, toothed or lobed, or compound. Flowers monoecious or dioecious, solitary or variously clustered, or much reduced and in an involucre (*Euphorbia* and related genera). Calyx of 2–several sepals or obsolete. Corolla of 2–several petals or wanting. Androecium of few–many stamens. Fruit depressed or slightly elongate.—About 250 genera and 4,000 species, widely distributed.

Flowers not in an involucre : calyx of several sepals.
  Ovules, and seeds, 2 in each gynoecium-cavity.
    Corolla present : stamens 5.
    Corolla wanting : stamens 2 or 3.
      Plants monoecious or rarely dioecious : ovary 3-celled : fruit capsular or baccate.
      Plants dioecious : ovary 1- or 2-celled : fruit drupaceous.
  Ovules, and seeds, solitary in each gynoecium-cavity.
    Flowers, either staminate or pistillate, or both, in more or less elongate spikes or racemes, the pistillate basal.
      Corolla present in either staminate or pistillate flowers, or in both kinds (except in *Croton punctatus* and *C. texensis*).
        Stamens 5 to many : filaments distinct.
        Stamens 10 or fewer : filaments monadelphous.
      Corolla wanting.
        Gynoecium 2-carpellary : styles 2 : sepals distinct : herbs.
        Gynoecium 3–several-carpellary : styles 3–several, or gynoecium 2-carpellary and sepals united.
          Stamens 8–16.
          Stamens 1–5.
            Sepals valvate in the bud.
            Sepals imbricate in the bud.
    Flowers, either the staminate or the pistillate, or both, in cymes or corymbs, or in open racemes.
      Leaf-blades not peltate : filaments not repeatedly branched.
        Flowers borne in forking cymes.
        Flowers borne in racemes or panicles.
      Leaf-blades peltate : filaments repeatedly branched.
Flowers in involucres : calyx represented by a minute scale at the base of a filament-like pedicel : involucre and contents simulating a flower.
  Involucre regular or nearly so, not oblique.
  Involucre oblique and very irregular.

I. ANDRACHNEAE.

II. PHYLLANTHEAE.

III. DRYPETEAE.

IV. CROTONEAE.
V. DITAXEAE.

VI. MERCURIALEAE

VII. ACALYPHEAE.

VIII. TRAGIEAE.
IX. HIPPOMANEAE.

X. ADENOROPIEAE.
XI. MANIHOTEAE.
XII. RICINEAE.

XIII. EUPHORBIEAE.
XIV. PEDILANTHEAE.

I. ANDRACHNEAE

Evergreen dioecious shrubs or trees: flowers axillary, the staminate sessile, the pistillate pedicelled.   1. SAVIA.

II. PHYLLANTHEAE

Androecium and gynoecium surrounded by a disk at the base. Anthers opening horizontally: fruit capsular.
    Flower-bearing branches dilated, leaf-like, leafless or nearly so.   2. XYLOPHYLLA.
    Flower-bearing branches not dilated, leafy.   3. PHYLLANTHUS.
Anthers opening vertically: fruit baccate.   4. CICCA.
Androecium and gynoecium not surrounded by a disk at the base.   5. BREYNIA.

III. DRYPETEAE

Evergreen shrubs or trees.   6. DRYPETES.

IV. CROTONEAE

Ovary 3-celled or rarely 2-celled: capsule 3-celled or rarely 2-celled, 3-lobed or rarely 2-lobed, dehiscent: flowers in clusters, spikes, or racemes.   7. CROTON.
Ovary 1-celled: capsule 1-celled, achene-like, indehiscent: flowers scattered.   8. CROTONOPSIS.

V. DITAXEAE

Style once branched: petals distinct.   9. DITAXIS.
Style several times branched: petals united at the base.   10. CAPERONIA.

VI. MERCURIALEAE

Annual (or perennial) herbs.   11. MERCURIALIS.

VII. ACALYPHEAE

Annual or perennial monoecious or rarely dioecious herbs, or shrubs: flowers in axillary or terminal spikes or spike-like racemes, the pistillate flowers subtended by lobed bracts: stigmas much branched.   12. ACALYPHA.

VIII. TRAGIEAE

Perennial monoecious herbs, with erect or climbing stems, pubescent with often stinging hairs.   13. TRAGIA.

IX. HIPPOMANEAE

Gynoecium 3-carpellary, or rarely 2-carpellary (*Sapium*): styles 3, or rarely 2 (*Sapium*): fruit dehiscent.
    Receptacle with 3 horn-like projections under the capsule.   14. STILLINGIA.
    Receptacle with a central column.
      Calyx of the staminate flower present.
        Gynoecium 3-carpellary: stigmas 3: stamens usually 3.
          Capsule dry: seed with a caruncle: leaf-blades not biglandular at the base.   15. SEBASTIANA.
          Capsule fleshy: seed without a caruncle: leaf-blades biglandular at the base.   16. TRIADICA.
        Gynoecium 2-carpellary: stigmas 2: stamens 2.   17. SAPIUM.
      Calyx wanting or rudimentary.   18. GYMNANTHES.
Gynoecium 6–8-carpellary: styles 6–8: fruit indehiscent.   19. HIPPOMANE.

X. ADENOROPIEAE

Petals wanting: stamens 10 or more: calyx corolloid.   20. BIVONEA.
Petals present: stamens 10 or fewer: calyx not corolloid.   21. ADENOROPIUM.

XI. MANIHOTEAE

Large herbs, shrubs, or rarely trees, with usually large tuberous roots.   22. JATROPHA.

XII. RICINEAE

Annual herbs, or shrubs or trees, with large palmately lobed leaf-blades: capsule echinate.   23. RICINUS.

XIII. EUPHORBIEAE

Herbs, annual or perennial, unarmed, or partly woody plants. Glands of the involucres with petal-like appendages, these sometimes much reduced.
    Leaves all opposite: leaf-blades inequilateral, oblique at the base.   24. CHAMAESYCE.
    Leaves alternate or scattered at least below the inflorescence: stem topped by an umbel.

Annual or biennial: stipules narrow: bracts petal-like. 25. LEPADENA.
Perennial: stipules none: bracts not petal-like. 26. TITHYMALOPSIS.
Glands of the involucres without petal-like appendages, entirely naked, sometimes with crescent-like horns.
Stem topped by an umbel: stipules none: involucres in open cymes, each with 4 glands and entire or toothed lobes. 27. GALARHOEUS.
Stem not topped by an umbel: stipules gland-like: involucres in cluster-like cymes, each with a single gland or rarely 4 glands and fimbriate lobes. 28. POINSETTIA.
Shrubs with fleshy cactus-like branches, spine-armed. 29. EUPHORBIA.

XIV. PEDILANTHEAE

Fleshy plants with usually many stems, the involucres clustered at the ends of branches. 30. PEDILANTHUS.

1. **SAVIA** Willd. Shrubs or trees. Leaves alternate: blades thick, entire. Flowers green, dioecious; the staminate densely clustered, with 5 broad rounded sepals and 5 thin petals broadened upward: stamens 5, exserted. Pistillate flowers solitary or few together, with 5 broad sepals and 5 nearly similar petals: ovary 3-lobed; styles 2-parted. Capsule depressed.—About 6 species, West Indian.

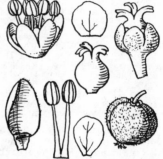

1. **S. bahamensis** Britton. Shrub or small tree, the bark pale-gray or whitish: leaf-blades typically obovate, varying to narrowly obovate or oval-obovate, 2–5 cm. long, pale-green, shining above, glabrous, short-petioled: staminate flower with orbicular-ovate sepals about 2 mm. long and cuneate or flabellate thin petals shorter than the sepals: pistillate flower with suborbicular sepals and petals about 2 mm. long: capsule spheroidal, 5–6 mm. long: seed 4–5 mm. long.—(MAIDEN-BUSH.)—Hammocks, lower Florida Keys.—(Bah.)—Spr.

2. **XYLOPHYLLA** L. Shrubs or small trees, with flattened leaf-like, usually distichous, branchlets. Leaves minute or obsolete. Flowers green, borne in clusters along the margins of the leaf-like branchlets. Staminate flowers mostly with 6 sepals and 3 stamens. Pistillate flowers mostly with 6 sepals and a 3-celled ovary. Fruit capsular.—About 10 species, West Indian and South American.

1. **X. angustifolia** Sw. Shrub 1–2 m. tall: flattened branches almost linear, varying to somewhat spatulate or lanceolate, commonly 4–10 cm. long: larger sepals of the staminate flower 1–1.5 mm. long: capsule 4–5 mm. broad. [*X. Epiphyllanthus* (Fl. SE. U. S.)]—(SWORD-BUSH.)—Hammocks, Key West, Fla.—(*W. I.*)—This and other species are cultivated for ornament in warm countries.

3. **PHYLLANTHUS** L. Herbs or partly woody plants. Leaf-blades entire. Flowers apetalous, green or purple-tinged. Staminate flowers with 5

or 6 sepals and usually 3 stamens. Pistillate flowers with 5 or 6 sepals and a 3-celled ovary. Fruit capsular.—About 60 species, mostly in tropical regions. Calyx of the pistillate flower about as large as that of the staminate, at anthesis,

or only slightly larger ; sepals scarcely accrescent in fruit.
  Stems solitary from a slender root, sometimes branched at
    the base. .... I. CAROLINENSES.
  Stems several or many from a thick woody root. .... II. PENTAPHYLLI.
Calyx of the pistillate flower much larger than that of the
  staminate, conspicuously accrescent. .... III. PLATYLEPIDES.

I. CAROLINENSES

Stem herbaceous : annual herbs.
  Branches erect or ascending.
    Mature pistillate sepals broadly linear to broadly spat-
      ulate ; calyx much wider than the capsule : seed about
      1 mm. long. .... 1. *P. carolinensis*.
    Mature pistillate sepals broadly ovate to broadly obo-
      vate : calyx as wide as the capsule or slightly wider :
      seed much less than 1 mm. long. .... 2. *P. pruinosus*.
  Branches recurved-spreading.
    Staminate sepals longer than wide : calyx of the pistil-
      late flower not reaching the middle of the capsule. ...... 3. *P. Niruri*.
    Staminate sepals wider than long : calyx of the pistil-
      late flower reaching above the middle of the capsule. ... 4. *P. lathyroides*.
Stem woody : short-lived shrub. .... 5. *P. Garberi*.

II. PENTAPHYLLI

Stems tufted on the root, slender-wiry : leaves numerous and
  approximate on the short branches : flowers usually approxi-
  mate. .... 6. *P. pentaphyllus*.

III. PLATYLEPIDES

Stems solitary or several from the thickened root : flowers few,
  borne in the upper leaf-axils, rather long-pedicelled. .... 7. *P. platylepis*.

1. P. carolinensis Walt. Plant 1–5 dm. tall, the stem glabrous: leaf-blades obovate to elliptic-obovate, rather gradually narrowed to the base: staminate calyx 1.5–2 mm. wide; sepals suborbicular:

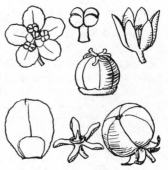

mature pistillate calyx 2.5 mm. wide; sepals broadly linear to broadly spatulate: capsule about 2 mm. wide.—Woods, river-banks, and roadsides, various provinces, Fla. to Tex., Mo., and Pa.—(*W. I.*)—Spr.–fall.

2. P. pruinosus Poepp. Plant 0.5–3.5 dm. tall: leaf-blades cuneate to obovate, abruptly narrowed at the base: staminate calyx 1.5–2 mm. wide; sepals suborbicular: mature pistillate calyx 2–2.5 mm. wide; sepals broadly ovate to broadly obovate: capsule about 1.5 mm. wide. [*P. saxicola* Small]—Low pinelands and hammocks, Everglade Keys, Fla. and the Florida Keys.—(*W. I.*)—All year.

3. P. Niruri L. Plant 1–3 dm. tall: leaf-blades thickish, elliptic or nearly so, rounded at the base: staminate calyx 1–1.5 mm. wide; sepals orbicular-ovate: mature pistillate calyx about 2 mm. wide; sepals broadly linear to linear-ovate: capsule about 2 mm. wide.—Pinelands and waste-places, pen. Fla. and the Keys.—(*W. I., Mex., C. A., S. A.*)—All year.—Sometimes used medicinally.

4. P. lathyroides H.B.K. Plant 2–6 dm. tall: leaf-blades thinnish, elliptic to obovate, acute or obtuse at the base: staminate calyx 1 mm. wide; sepals flabellate or reniform: mature pistillate calyx 2 mm. wide; sepals ovate to oval: capsule about 2.5 mm. wide.—Hammocks, S pen. Fla.—(*W. I., Mex., C. A., S. A.*)—All year.

5. **P. Garberi** Small. Plant 1–5 dm. tall: leaf-blades thickish, elliptic, sometimes narrowly so, or linear-elliptic: staminate calyx about 2 mm. wide; sepals ovate to orbicular-ovate: mature pistillate calyx 3 mm. wide; sepals elliptic to ovate: capsule 2.5–3 mm. wide. [*P. abnormis* (Fl. SE. U. S.)]—Coastal sand-dunes, pen. Fla. and the Keys.—All year.

6. **P. pentaphyllus** C. Wright. Plant 0.5–4 dm. tall: leaf-blades thinnish, mainly cuneate, often inequilateral: staminate calyx 1.5 mm. wide; sepals suborbicular: mature pistillate calyx about 3 mm. wide; sepals obovate to elliptic: capsule less than 1.5 mm. wide.—Pinelands, Everglade Keys, Fla. and lower Florida Keys.—(*W. I.*)—All year.

7. **P. platylepis** Small. Plant 1.5–4 dm. tall: leaf-blades obovate to elliptic-obovate: staminate calyx about 3 mm. wide; sepals elliptic to obovate: mature pistillate calyx about 6 mm. wide; sepals suborbicular to rhombic-orbicular, abruptly pointed: capsule 4–5 mm. wide.—Low hammocks, Gulf Hammock region, W pen. Fla.—All year.

4. **CICCA** L. Shrubs or trees. Leaf-blades entire. Flowers similar to those of *Phyllanthus*, but with vertically opening anther-sacs. Fruit baccate.— About 12 species, tropical.

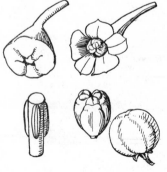

1. **C. disticha** L. Shrub or small tree, the branchlets spreading or drooping, glabrous: leaves various, those near the base of the branchlets with suborbicular to orbicular-ovate blades 1.5–3 cm. long, those above them with larger ovate to elliptic-lanceolate blades: larger sepals suborbicular to orbicular-obovate, 1.5–2 mm. long: berry depressed, 1.5–2 cm. broad.—(OTAHEITE-GOOSEBERRY. GOOSEBERRY-TREE.)—Pinelands and waste-places, Everglade Keys, Fla. and Florida Keys. Nat. of E. I. and cult.— (*W. I.*)—All year.—Plants usually bear an abundance of fruits. These are light-green and very acid. They are used for making pies, preserves, and wine. The root and leaves are medicinal.

5. **BREYNIA** Forst. Shrubs or trees. Leaves alternate: blades broad, entire. Flowers solitary in the axils, or the staminate few together. Staminate flower with a turbinate calyx-tube and 6 minute broad lobes surrounding the minute orifice: stamens erect, united, the narrow anthers opening vertically. Pistillate flower with a short, broad calyx-tube and 6 very broad imbricate lobes: overy 3-celled: styles very short: stigmas 2-lobed. Berry depressed.—About 15 species, natives of Asia and Oceania.

1. **B. nivosa** (W. J. Smith) Small. Shrub with irregularly and loosely branched stems, the branches dark-red: leaves somewhat distichously spreading; blades oval, varying to ovate or obovate, green and white, varie-

gated with red and pink; staminate calyx about 3 mm. wide, the lobes shallow: pistillate calyx 8–10 mm. wide, the lobes reniform: capsule 9–12 mm. broad.— (SNOWBUSH.)—Pinelands and waste-places. Everglade Keys, Fla.—Nat. of South Sea Islands, and cult.—(*W. I.*)—All year.—A very ornamental hedge-plant in pen. Florida. The leaves are well-colored and mottled with white. The flowers are mainly greenish and inconspicuous.

6. **DRYPETES** Vahl. Shrubs or trees. Leaf-blades entire or undulate-toothed. Flowers apetalous, green or brownish. Staminate flowers in rather dense clusters, with 4–8 sepals and 4–16 stamens. Pistillate flowers few in a cluster, with 4–8 sepals and a 1–2-celled ovary. Fruit a berry or a drupe.— About 10 species, West Indian and South American.

Sepals 4: gynoecium 2-carpellary: drupe subglobose, less than 15 mm. long.
1. *D. lateriflora.*
Sepals 5: gynoecium 1-carpellary: drupe elongate, over 15 mm. long.
2. *D. diversifolia.*

1. **D. lateriflora** (Sw.) Krug & Urban. Shrub, or tree becoming 10 m. tall, with brownish bark: leaf-blades elliptic or nearly so: stamens 4: drupe 9–11 mm. in diameter, red, ripe in spring or summer. — (GUIANA-PLUM.) — Hammocks, Everglade Keys, Fla. and Florida Keys.— (*W. I.*)—Fall–wint.—The sap-wood is yellow; the dark-brown heart-wood, close-grained, heavy, hard, but brittle, is used in cabinet-work.

2. **D. diversifolia** Krug & Urban. Shrub, or tree becoming 12 m. tall, with milk-white roughish bark: leaf-blades oblong, elliptic or oval: stamens 8: drupe 2–2.5 cm. long, ripe in fall. [*D. keyensis* Krug & Urban]—(WHITEWOOD.)—Hammocks, Cape Sable region, Fla. and Florida Keys.— (*W. I.*)—Spr.—The sap-wood is yellowish-brown; the brown and yellow streaked heart-wood, close-grained, heavy, hard, but brittle, is used in cabinet-work.

7. **CROTON** L. Shrubs or herbs. Leaf-blades entire, toothed, or lobed. Flowers mostly green, usually spicate or racemose. Staminate flower with 4–6, usually 5, sepals, small, often rudimentary, petals alternating with glands, and 6–many stamens, rarely less. Pistillate flower with 5–10 sepals, usually no petals and a 3-celled ovary. Fruit a capsule.—About 650 species, widely distributed in warm and tropical regions.

Staminate and pistillate flowers with petals.   I. ALABAMENSES.
Staminate flowers with petals, or both staminate and pistillate flowers without petals.
  Petals present in the staminate flowers, wanting or rudimentary in the pistillate.
    Plant with scaly foliage.
    Plant with stellate-pubescent foliage.   II. ARGYRANTHEMI.
      Pistillate calyx mostly not accrescent: leaf-blades entire.
        Leaves with blades of an ovate or elliptic type.   III. FRUTICULOSI.
        Leaves with blades of a linear or narrowly elliptic type.   IV. LINEARES.
      Pistillate calyx mostly accrescent: leaf-blades toothed or entire.   V. GLANDULOSI.
  Petals wanting in both the staminate and the pistillate flowers.   VI. PUNCTATI.

I. Alabamenses
Evergreen shrub, with leaf-blades silvery-scaly beneath.   1. *C. alabamensis.*
II. Argyranthemi
Perennial herb, the stem often branched at the base: leaves, beneath, and inflorescence silvery-scaly.   2. *C. argyranthemus.*

III. Fruticulosi
Shrub with slender branches: leaves with very slender petioles, the blades of an ovate or elliptic type.   3. *C. Berlandieri.*

IV. Lineares
Leaf-blades narrowly linear, glabrate above, yellow-pubescent beneath.   4. *C. linearis.*
Leaf-blades narrowly elliptic to broadly linear, stellate above, white-pubescent beneath.   5. *C. Fergusonii.*

V. Glandulosi
Leaves with prominently toothed blades.
  Calyx, and capsule, glabrous or merely with few short appressed stellate hairs.   6. *C. floridanus.*
  Calyx, and capsule, pubescent with long hirsute or hispid branching hairs.
    Leaf-blades shallowly crenate to shallowly serrate.
      Seed elliptic, minutely punctate, dull: leaf-blades crenate.   7. *C. arenicola.*
      Seed oval or ovoid, smooth and shining: leaf-blades serrate or crenate-serrate.   8. *C. glandulosus.*
    Leaf-blades coarsely crenate or crenate-dentate.   9. *C. miquelensis.*
Leaves with entire blades, except in *C. Engelmannii.*
  Pistillate flowers not pendulous from the base of the raceme.
    Lower leaves with lanceolate, oval, or ovate blades: sepals not hooded.
      Petioles long: tomentum of inflorescence purplish.   10. *C. capitatus.*
      Petioles short: tomentum of inflorescence yellowish.   11. *C. Engelmannii.*
    Lower leaves with linear or linear-lanceolate blades: sepals hooded.   12. *C. Elliottii.*
  Pistillate flowers early drooping from the base of the raceme.   13. *C. monanthogynus.*

VI. Punctati
Plant perennial, more or less woody: leaves stout petioled.   14. *C. punctatus.*
Plant annual, herbaceous: leaves with slender petioles..   15. *C. texensis.*

1. **C. alabamensis** E. A. Smith. Shrub 2–3 m. tall: leaf-blades evergreen, elliptic to elliptic-lanceolate, 5–8 cm. long, green and glabrate above, clothed beneath with silvery overlapping scales: staminate flowers 10–20; sepals and petals ciliate; stamens 10–25; pistillate flowers 4–7; sepals 3–4 mm. long; petals scaly without; glands 5: capsule 6–8 mm. long: seed oval, 5–7 mm. long.—River-bluffs of shale and limestone, Tuscaloosa and Bibb Counties, Appalachian Plateau, Ala.—Spr.

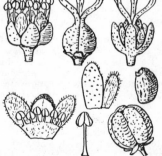

2. **C. argyranthemus** Michx. Perennial herb, 3–6 dm. tall: leaf-blades obovate to oval, or elliptic to elliptic-lanceolate above, 1–5 cm. long, blunt, scaly or glabrate above, clothed with silvery scales beneath: staminate flowers often 10–15; sepals lanceolate, acute; petals elliptic, scaly without; stamens mostly 10; filaments swollen at the base: pistillate flowers few; sepals partly united, acute; capsule globular or oval-globose, about 5 mm. long: seed less than 5 mm. long.—Sandhills and pinelands, Coastal Plain and SW provinces, Fla. to Tex. (N. M.?) and Ga.—Sum.

3. **C. Berlandieri** Torr. Shrub 3–8 dm. tall: leaf-blades ovate to elliptic, 2.5–3.5 cm. long, usually abruptly acute, the edges slightly repand and glandular, rounded or subcordate at the base, tomentose above when young, paler below: staminate flowers on slender pedicels, with 15–20 stamens (30–35 in western forms): pistillate flowers 2–6 at base of raceme, usually short-pedicelled; sepals elliptic-spatulate with sessile or short-stipitate marginal glands; styles 3, palmately 4-parted or twice 2-parted: capsule globose, 4–5 mm. high.—Sandy soil, thickets, and waste-places, Key West, Fla. and coastal region, S. Tex.—(*Mex.*)—Spr.–fall.

4. **C. linearis** Jacq. Shrub 6–20 dm. tall: leaf-blades narrowly linear, 4–7 cm. long, obtuse, dark-green and smooth above, yellowish-pubescent beneath: racemes 4–8 cm. long or longer: sepals 5–6, triangular: petals spatulate, surpassing the sepals, obtuse, ciliate: stamens about 15: pistillate racemes 4–5 cm. long, frequently exceeded by the leaves: sepals narrow, acuminate: capsule subglobose, 5 mm. high, yellowish-floccose: seed broadly elliptic, about 3 mm. long.—Pinelands and coastal sand-dunes, Everglade Keys, Fla. and Florida Keys.—(*W. I.*)—All year.—The leaves of this species are used for tea.

5. **C. Fergusonii** Small. Shrub 4–12 dm. tall: leaf-blades narrowly elliptic to broadly linear, 3–6 cm. long, blunt, entire, white-pubescent beneath, the upper surface channeled and green but minutely stellate: staminate flowers 12–25 in stout interrupted racemes 3–5 cm. long: sepals deltoid, acute: petals spatulate, 2.5–3 mm. long, surpassing the sepals, ciliate: stamens about 15: pistillate flowers about 6, in racemes 2–3 cm. long: capsule subglobose, about 5 mm. long: seed 3.5–4 mm. long.—Pinelands, S pen. Fla.—All year.

6. **C. floridanus** Ferguson. Herb 2–5 dm. tall: leaf-blades various, those of the lower leaves elliptic to ovate, those above elliptic to lanceolate, 1–2 cm. long, serrate-crenate: racemes 2–4 cm. long: staminate flowers inconspicuous; sepals ovate or elliptic-ovate; petals elliptic or nearly so, narrower than the sepals, ciliate; stamens about 10: pistillate flowers solitary or several below the staminate, subtended by deltoid bracts; sepals linear to oblanceolate or spatulate, accrescent: capsule oblong-oval, about 4 mm. long: seed oval, about 3 mm. long.—Sand-dunes, pen. Fla.—Spr.–fall.

7. **C. arenicola** Small. Herb 1.5–4.5 dm. tall: leaf-blades ovate to elliptic-ovate, 1–3 cm. long, blunt, coarsely toothed: staminate sepals elliptic or oval, acute; petals elliptic to oblanceolate: stamens 9–12: pistillate flowers solitary or 2–3 below the staminate; sepals spatulate, accrescent: capsule globose-oval, 4.5–5 mm. long: seed 3–3.5 mm. long.—Pinelands and sand-dunes, Everglade Keys, Fla. and Florida Keys.—All year.

8. **C. glandulosus** L. A tropical American species represented in our area by the following: *C. glandulosus septentrionalis* with coarsely-stellate foliage and serrate mainly elliptic leaf-blades, ranges in various provinces, from Fla. to Tex., Ia., and Va.; *C. glandulosus Simpsonii* with densely stellate foliage and coarsely serrate-crenate ovate leaf-blades, occurs in S pen. Fla. and on the Keys; *C. glandulosus angustifolius* with thinly appressed stellate foliage and linear remotely serrate upper leaf-blades, occurs in Fla. and Tex.—Spr.–fall or all year S.

9. **C. miquelensis** Ferguson. Herb 3–5 dm. tall: leaf-blades ovate to lanceolate, 2–4 cm. long, acute or acutish, crenate or dentate-serrate, finely pubescent beneath, biglandular at the base, slender-petioled: racemes sessile or nearly sessile, short: staminate flowers inconspicuous; sepals ovate; petals narrowly oblong, ciliate; stamens 8–10: pistillate flowers 3 or 4, subtended by ovate bracts; sepals lanceolate; petals obsolete or rudimentary: capsule globose, 3.5–4 mm. long: seed oval, 3–3.5 mm. long, the caruncle minute.—Woods and waste-grounds, W Fla. Nat. of S. A.—Spr.–fall.

10. **C. capitatus** Michx. Herb 5–20 dm. tall: leaf-blades various, those of the lower leaves oval, those of the upper elliptic, 2–5 cm. long, mucronate, entire, rounded or rarely cordate at the base, velvety above, densely stellate-tomentose and paler beneath: racemes 1–3 cm. long, with loose purplish-tinged tomentum: staminate flowers short-pedicelled; sepals 5, oval, nearly equal; petals 5, spatulate, ciliate; stamens 7–12; filaments pubescent below: pistillate flowers usually clustered below the staminate; sepals 6–8, elliptic to oblanceolate; styles 3, 2–3 times 2-cleft, 5–6 mm. long: capsule globular, 7–9 mm. long: seed suborbicular, 5 mm. long.—(HOGWORT. WOOLLY-CROTON.)—Waste-places, various provinces, Ga. to Tex., Ia., and S N. Y.—Spr.–fall or all year S. Introduced, at least eastward.

11. **C. Engelmannii** Ferguson. Herb 5–20 dm. tall: leaf-blades lanceolate, those of the lower leaves 10–20 cm. long (white in *C. Engelmannii albinoides* and broadly ovate), those of the upper much shorter, acute or somewhat acuminate, often shallowly and unevenly toothed, rounded or usually cordate at the base: racemes 5–15 cm. long, with yellow-tinged tomentum: staminate flowers distinctly pedicelled; sepals ovate, acute; petals spatulate, ciliate; stamens 9–12; filaments stellate-pubescent below: pistillate flowers usually 3, short-pedicelled; sepals 7–8, acuminate, the inner ones smaller; styles 3, twice 2-cleft, 6–10 mm. long: capsule depressed, 6–8 mm. long: seed oval-orbicular, 4.5–5 mm. long.—Dry soil, Coastal Plain, Fla. to Tex., Ark., and Ga.—Sum.–fall.

12. **C. Elliottii** Chapm. Herb 5–9 dm. tall: leaf-blades linear or linear-lanceolate, 4–5 cm. long, or shorter above, entire, usually blunt, 3-nerved at the narrowed base, velvety-stellate, gray-tomentose beneath, slender-petioled: racemes 1–2 cm. long: staminate flowers short-pedicelled; sepals 5, narrowly elliptic; petals linear, ciliate; stamens 8–10: pistillate flowers clustered; sepals 6–7, unequal; styles 3, twice 2-cleft, 2–3 mm. long: capsule globose, 4–5 mm. long, sometimes surpassed by the accrescent hooded sepals: seed oval, 3–4 mm. long. —Pinelands, Fla. to S. C.—Sum.–fall.—Rare.

13. **C. monanthogynus** Michx. Herb 3–5 dm. tall: leaf-blades various, those of the lower leaves suborbicular, those of the upper ovate to elliptic-ovate, 1–4 cm. long, or slightly longer, usually mucronate, entire: racemes about 1 cm. long: staminate flowers short-pedicelled; sepals 3–5, ovate; petals spatulate, ciliate; stamens 3–10: pistillate flowers 1–4 below the staminate, nodding at maturity; sepals 5, elliptic; ovary 2-celled: capsule ovoid or oval, 3–4 mm. long: seed solitary by the abortion of one ovule, 2.5–3.5 mm. long.— (PRAIRIE-TEA.)—Limestone outcrops and waste-places, various provinces, rarely Coastal Plain, Ga. to Tex., Ia., and Ind.—(*Mex.*)—Sum.–fall.

14. **C. punctatus** Jacq. Plant partly woody, 5–12 dm. tall: leaf-blades elliptic or ovate, 1–5 cm. long, entire or merely undulate: pistillate sepals triangular, nearly equal; stamens normally 12, barely exserted; filaments pubescent: pistillate flowers solitary or 2 or 3 together; sepals elliptic or cuneate, not accrescent: capsule subglobose, 5–8 mm. long: seed about 6 mm. long. [*C. maritimus* Walt.]—(SILVER-LEAF CROTON. BEACH-TEA.)—Sand-dunes, Coastal Plain, Fla. to Tex. and N. C.—(*W. I., Mex., C. A., S. A.*)—Sum.–fall or all year S.

15. **C. texensis** (Kl.) Muell. Arg. Plant herbaceous, 4–16 dm. tall: leaf-blades linear-lanceolate or elliptic, those of the staminate plant the narrower, 4–12 cm. long, entire, rounded or blunt at the apex: racemes few-flowered: staminate flowers in racemes 1–3 cm. long; sepals elliptic to ovate-elliptic; stamens 8–12; filaments pubescent: pistillate flowers 2–4-together or solitary; sepals triangular: capsule oval or globular, 4–6 mm. long: seed orbicular, 3–5 mm. long.—(SKUNK-WEED.)—Dry soil, low hills and plains, various provinces, Ala., to Ariz., Wyo., S. D., and Ill.—(*Mex.*)—Sum.–fall or all year S.

8. CROTONOPSIS Michx. Annual herbs, covered, except the upper surface of the leaves, with silvery appressed peltate stellate scales. Leaf-blades entire, upper surface with slender-rayed stellate hairs. Flowers monoecious, green or greenish-white. Staminate flowers with 5 sepals, 5 petals, and 5 stamens. Pistillate flowers with 3–5 sepals, no petals, and a 1-celled ovary. Fruit an achene-like capsule, erect.—Two species.—RUSHFOILS.

Staminate flowers with petals longer than the sepals: filaments longer than the sepals: spikes long, with 3–6 fruits: fruit ellipsoid, without veins on the sides, the scales with minute disks fringed with irregular lax stellately spreading rays: stellate hairs on upper surface of leaf with short rays.   1. *C. linearis.*
Staminate flowers with petals equalling the sepals: filaments shorter than the sepals: spikes short, with 1 or 2 fruits: fruit ovoid, with an evident vein on each side, the scales umbonate to tubercular-spiny, the margin with relatively uniform, appressed rays: stellate hairs on upper surface of leaf with long rays.   2. *C. elliptica.*

1. **C. linearis** Michx. Plant 3–8 dm. tall, the scales with small disks fringed with irregular lax stellately spreading rays: leaf-blades narrowly elliptic, linear-lanceolate, or linear: spikes elongate, with 3–6 fruits: staminate flower with ovate or oval sepals and spatulate petals: pistillate flower with linear or linear-lanceolate sepals; fruit ellipsoid, 2.5–3 mm. long, the stellate scales with blunt or spine-tipped disks; seeds 2–2.5 mm. long or more, slightly ridged, often bronze-colored. [*C. spinosa* Nash]— Dry acid sandy soil, flat rocks, and barren prairies, Coastal Plain and occasionally adj. provinces, Fla. to Tex., and S. C.—Spr.–fall.

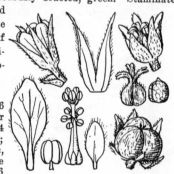

2. **C. elliptica** Willd. Plant 1–4 dm. tall, the scales with large disks surrounded by finely radiating closely appressed rays: leaf-blades ovate-elliptic, ovate-lanceolate, lanceolate or linear-lanceolate: spikes short, appearing axillary, bearing 1 or 2 fruits: staminate flower with obovate sepals and spatulate petals: pistillate flower with ovate sepals: fruit ovoid, 2.5–3.2 mm. long, the radiate scales with umbonate to tuberculate-spiny disks: seed about 2–2.5 mm. long, brown, smooth.—Dry sandy soil, various provinces, rarely Coastal Plain, Fla. to Tex., Kans., and Conn.—Sum.–fall.

9. DITAXIS Vahl. Shrubs or perennial herbs. Leaves alternate: blades entire or rarely toothed. Flowers inconspicuously bracted, green. Staminate flower with 4 or 5 sepals, 4 or 5 petals, and 10 stamens or sometimes fewer. Pistillate flower with a perianth similar to that of the staminate, but with smaller or rudimentary petals, and a 3-celled ovary. Capsule depressed.—About 20 species.

1. **D. Blodgettii** (Torr.) Pax. Plants 1–6 dm. tall: leaf-blades oval or elliptic, or those of the lower leaves spatulate, 1.5–4 cm. long: staminate calyx 7–8 mm. wide; sepals lanceolate; petals broadly elliptic, shorter than the sepals: mature pistillate sepals lanceolate to linear-lanceolate, 5–6

mm. long: capsule 4–5 mm. wide.—Pinelands and hammocks, Everglade Keys, Fla. Florida Keys.—All year.

10. CAPERONIA St. Hil. Herbs or partially woody plants, mostly monoecious. Leaves alternate: blades toothed. Flowers in elongate, interrupted spike-like racemes, green. Staminate flowers approximate, with 5, unequal sepals, 5 petals and 10 stamens or fewer through abortion. Pistillate flowers separated, with 5 sepals, 5 petals, smaller than those of the staminate flower, and a 3-celled ovary. Capsule 3-lobed, depressed. Seed without a caruncle.—About 20 species, tropical American.

1. **C. castaneàefolia** (L.) St. Hil. Plant 1 m. tall or less, with spreading or decumbent branches: leaf-blades obovate, elliptic, oval, elliptic-lanceolate or ovate, mostly 2–6 cm. long, rather coarsely toothed, petioled: larger staminate sepals about 2.5 mm. long: petals obovate, 3–3.5 mm. long: sepals and petals of the pistillate flowers smaller than those of the staminate: capsule depressed, 6–7 mm. wide: seed globose, about 3 mm. in diameter.—Wet soil, Everglades, about the Everglade Keys, pen. Fla.—(*W. I.*)—All year.

11. MERCURIALIS L. Herbs or parly woody mostly dioecious plants. Leaves opposite: blades often toothed. Flowers green, apetalous. Staminate flower with 3 sepals and 8–20 stamens. Pistillate flower with 3 sepals and a 2-celled ovary. Stigmas pinnatifid. Capsule 2-lobed.—About 7 species, natives of the Old World.—Dog's-mercuries.

1. **M. annua** L. Stem 2–6 dm. tall: leaf-blades ovate to lanceolate: staminate flowers in spikes which surpass the leaves: capsule 4–5 mm. broad, hispid.—(Herb-mercury.)—Waste-places, various provinces, Fla. to Tex., Ohio and Del., and locally further NE. Nat. of Eu. and Africa.—(*W. I.*)

12. ACALYPHA L. Herbs or shrubs, monoecious or sometimes dioecious. Leaf-blades entire or toothed. Flowers green (in our species). Staminate flower with 4 sepals and 8–16 stamens. Pistillate flower with 3–5 sepals and a 3-celled ovary, each flower subtended by a foliaceous bract. Capsule somewhat 3-lobed.—About 250 species most abundant in subtropical and tropical regions. — Spr.–fall, or all year S. — Three-seeded mercuries. Tar-weeds. Couple-caps.

Staminate and pistillate flowers in the same spike: capsule glabrous or pubescent.
  I. Corchorifoliae.
Staminate and pistillate flowers in separate spikes: capsule tuberculate-echinate.
  II. Ostryaefoliae.

I. CORCHORIFOLIAE

Plant annual.

Bracts subtending the pistillate flowers with 5–7, or rarely 9, long, elliptic to lanceolate, acute or obtusish lobes: leaves of the main stem with ovate or rhombic-ovate blades. — 1. *A. rhomboidea.*

Bracts subtending the pistillate flowers with 9–15 short lobes or teeth: leaves of the main stem with mostly ovate-lanceolate to linear blades.

Bracts of the pistillate flowers with lanceolate acute lobes: blades of the cauline leaves broadly to narrowly lanceolate, tapering to a blunt tip. — 2. *A. virginica.*

Bracts of the pistillate flowers with ovate to deltoid lobes: blades of the cauline leaves elliptic-lanceolate to linear, obtusish; petioles a fourth to a tenth as long as the blades. — 3. *A. gracilens.*

Plant perennial, prostrate: stems wire-like: seeds barely 1 mm. long. — 4. *A. chamaedrifolia.*

II. OSTRYAEFOLIAE

Mature pistillate spikes slender, interrupted, not plumose; bracts with lanceolate or subulate scabrous lobes: capsule depressed.

Bracts with lanceolate lobes about as long as the body: capsule about 3.5 mm. wide, echinate-tuberculate: seed tubercled. — 5. *A. ostryaefolia.*

Bracts with slender-subulate lobes much longer than the body: capsule about 2.5 mm. wide, sparingly pubescent: seed obscurely pitted. — 6. *A. setosa.*

Mature pistillate spikes stout, continuous, plumose; bracts with slender-caudate long-ciliate lobes: capsule globose-ovoid. — 7. *A. alopecuroidea.*

1. **A. rhomboidea** Raf. Stem 1–7 dm. tall: blades of the cauline leaves ovate to rhombic-ovate, 2–10 cm. long, glabrous except for a few long scattered hairs: bracts of the pistillate flowers, at least when young, with long stipitate whitish glands, ciliate, but not hispid: capsule 2.5–3 mm. in diameter: seeds 1.5–1.8 mm. long.— Woods and thickets, various provinces, Fla. to Nebr., Minn., Que., and Me.—Plant is reputed to have medicinal properties.

2. **A. virginica** L. Stem 2–5 dm. tall, with a few long spreading hairs, or often villous: blades of the cauline leaves broadly to narrowly lanceolate, 2–6 cm. long, finely toothed, finely pubescent: bracts of the pistillate flowers hispid on the veins and margins, usually not glandular: capsule 2.5–3 mm. in diameter: seed about 1.5 mm. long.—Woods and stream-banks, various provinces, Ga. to Tex., Mo., and Mass.

3. **A. gracilens** A. Gray. Stem 1–8 dm. tall, puberulent to pubescent with incurved or ascending hairs: blades of the cauline leaves elliptic-lanceolate to elliptic (or linear, often elongate-linear, in *A. gracilens Fraseri*), 1–6.5 cm. long, shallowly toothed, finely pubescent: bracts of the pistillate flowers sparsely beset with whitish or red sessile glands, ciliate to copiously pubescent: capsule about 2 mm. in diameter: seeds 1.5–2 mm. long.—Dry woods, hillsides, sandy banks, and old fields, various provinces, Fla. to Tex., Mo., Wisc., and Mass.

4. **A. chamaedrifolia** (Lam.) Muell Arg. Stem and branches mostly prostrate, 5–30 cm. long: blades of the upper leaves ovate to elliptic-lanceolate, 7–20 mm. long, crenate–serrate: larger bracts 4–6 mm. long, toothed: capsule

nearly 2 mm. in diameter.—Pinelands and sandy places, Everglade Keys, pen. Fla. and Florida Keys.—(*W. I.*).

5. **A. ostryaefolia** Ridd. Stem 3–8 dm. tall, closely fine-pubescent: leaf-blades ovate, 5–10 cm. long, serrate: larger bracts of the pistillate spike 4–5 mm. long, with lanceolate lobes: capsule about 3.5 mm. wide: seed broadly ovoid, 2 mm. long, finely tuberculate. [*A. caroliniana* Authors, not Ell.]— Thickets and waste-places, various provinces, Fla. to Tex., Kans., and N. J.— (*W. I., Mex.*)

6. **A. setosa** A. Rich. Stem 1 m. tall or less, usually glabrous: leaf-blades ovate or orbicular-ovate, 3–9 cm. long, rather finely serrate: larger bracts of the pistillate spike 3–4 mm. long, with slender-subulate lobes: capsule about 2.5 mm. wide: seed oval-ovoid, about 1.5 mm. long, obscurely pitted.—Woods, waste-places, and roadsides, pen. Fla. Nat. of Cuba.—(*W. I., Mex., C. A., S. A.*)

7. **A. alopecuroidea** Jacq. Stem mostly less than 1 m. tall, often widely branched, glandular-pubescent: leaf-blades ovate, usually broadly so, 2–8 cm. long, finely serrate: larger bracts of the pistillate spike about 8 mm. long, with slender-caudate long-ciliate lobes: capsule globose-ovoid; seed fully 1 mm. long, minutely pitted.—Waste-places and roadsides, Coastal Plain, Ala. Nat. of S. A.—(*W. I., Mex., C. A.*)

13. **TRAGIA** [Plum.] L. Herbs or shrubs. Leaf-blades entire, toothed, or lobed. Flowers green or purple, on a slender rachis, racemose. Staminate flower with 3–5 sepals and 1–3, or rarely more, stamens. Pistillate flower with 3–8 entire or pinnatifid sepals and a 3-celled ovary. Capsule prominently 3-lobed.—About 50 species, most abundant in tropical regions.—Spr.–fall or all year S.

Stem not twining: leaf-blades not conspicuously long-petioled.   1. *T. linearifolia.*
  Leaf-blades linear, entire.
  Leaf-blades broader and manifestly broadest above or below the middle.
    Leaves with more or less cuneately narrowed blades.   2. *T. urens.*
    Leaves, at least the lower ones, truncate or cordate at the base.
      Leaf-blades of a triangular or lanceolate type.   3. *T. urticaefolia.*
      Leaf-blades of a suborbicular, oval, or elliptic type.
        Leaf-blades slender-petioled, cordate or subcordate at the base, the teeth sharp.   4. *T. saxicola.*
        Leaf-blades sessile or very short-petioled, obtuse or truncate at the base, the teeth rounded.   5. *T. betonicaefolia.*
Stem twining: leaf-blades conspicuously long-petioled.   6. *T. macrocarpa.*

1. **T. linearifolia** Ell. Plant 1–5 dm. tall: leaf-blades linear, 3–12 cm. long, undulate: staminate calyx 3–3.5 mm. wide: mature pistillate calyx 5 mm. wide; sepals ovate: capsule 7–8 mm. wide, strigillose.—Pinelands and sandhills, Coastal Plain, Fla. to Ala.

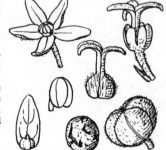

2. **T. urens** L. Plant 1–4 dm. tall, green: leaf-blades elliptic above the cuneate base to cuneate, 2–5 cm. long, irregularly few-toothed: staminate calyx about 3 mm. wide; sepals lanceolate to ovate: mature pistillate calyx 4–4.5 mm. wide; sepals linear: capsule 8-10 mm. wide, hirsutulous: seed 3.5–4 mm. long. [*T. innocua* Walt.]—Dry, often acid soil, Coastal Plain, Fla. to Tex. and S Va.

3. **T. urticaefolia** Michx. Plant 1–4 dm. tall: leaf-blades triangular or lanceolate, those of the lower leaves typically broadly lanceolate, 3–7 cm. long: staminate calyx 2.5–3 mm. wide; sepals ovate to suborbicular: mature pistillate calyx 11–12 mm. wide; sepals lanceolate: capsule 7–10 mm. wide, hirsutulous: seed 3.5–4 mm. long.—Dry sandy soil, Coastal Plain and occasionally adj. provinces, Fla. to Tex., Ark., Tenn. and S. C. (or Va. ?)

4. **T. saxicola** Small. Plant 0.5–2 dm. tall: leaf-blades suborbicular to broadly oval, 1–2.5 cm. long, crenate-dentate, finely and sharply many-toothed: staminate calyx 3–3.5 mm. wide; sepals linear to narrowly linear-lanceolate: capsule 7–8 mm. wide, hirsute.—Pinelands, Everglade Keys, pen. Fla. and Florida Keys.

5. **T. betonicaefolia** Nutt. Plant 1–3 dm. tall: leaf-blades orbicular to broadly elliptic, 2–4 cm. long, coarsely crenate-serrate, or somewhat lobed: mature pistillate calyx 4.5–5.5 mm. wide; sepals linear to linear-oblong: capsule mostly 8–9 mm. wide: seed about 4 mm. long.—Sandy soil, Coastal Plain, Fla. to La.

6. **T macrocarpa** Willd. Plant with twining stems: leaf-blades ovate, 5–12 cm. long, coarsely dentate-serrate: staminate calyx about 2.5 mm. wide; sepals ovate to orbicular-ovate: mature pistillate calyx 8–9 mm. wide; sepals elliptic or ovate-elliptic: capsule 12–16 mm. wide, finely pubescent: seed about 5 mm. long.—Dry or rocky soil and wooded bluffs, various provinces, Fla. to Tex., Mo., and Ky.

14. **STILLINGIA** Garden. Shrubs or herbs. Leaf-blades entire or toothed. Flowers monoecious, apetalous, in a green, yellow, or red spike. Staminate flower with 2 or 3 sepals and 2 or 3 stamens. Pistillate flower with 3 sepals and a 2- or 3-celled ovary. Fruit a capsule.—About 15 species, mostly American.—QUEEN'S-DELIGHTS. QUEEN'S-ROOTS.

Plant herbaceous.
  Capsule less than 10 mm. wide: seed 4–6 mm. long.
    Stem leaves with linear or essentially linear blades.   1. *S. angustifolia.*
    Stem leaves with spatulate or elliptic-spatulate blades. 2. *S. spathulata.*
  Capsule over 10 mm. wide: seed 7–9 mm. long.   3. *S. sylvatica.*
Plant shrubby.
  Spikes yellow; glands smaller than the bracts: seed coarsely
    reticulate.   4. *S. aquatica.*
  Spikes mainly red: glands as large as the bracts or larger:
    seed finely reticulate.   5. *S. tenuis.*

1. **S. angustifolia** (Torr.) S. Wats. Stem 2.5–6 dm. tall: leaf-blades linear or essentially so, 2–5 cm. long, crenulate-serrulate: spike 2–4.5 cm. long: capsule 5–6 mm. wide.—Sand-dunes and pinelands, pen. Fla. and Florida Keys.—All year.

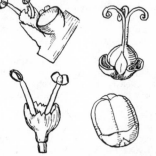

2. **S. spathulata** (Muell. Arg.) Small. Stem 3–7 dm. tall: leaf-blades spatulate to elliptic-spatulate, or linear-spatulate on the branches 7–15 cm. long, crenulate: capsule 7–9 mm. wide.—Sand-dunes and pinelands, Coastal Plain, Fla., Ala., and Ga.—All year.

3. **S. sylvatica** L. Stem 4–12 dm. tall: leaf-blades obovate, oval or elliptic, 3–11 cm. long, obtuse: capsule 12–15 mm. wide.—(QUEEN'S-ROOT.)—Dry, usually sandy, soil, Coastal Plain and adj. provinces, Fla. to Tex., Mo., and Va.—Sum.-fall.—The root is used medicinally.

4. **S. aquatica** Chapm. Short-lived shrub with wood lighter than cork, 6–20 dm. tall, stout-stemmed: blades of the upper leaves linear to linear-elliptic serrulate: spike stout, mainly yellow: capsule about 10 mm. wide.—(CORKWOOD.)— Ponds and wet pinelands, Coastal Plain, Fla. to Miss. and S. C.—Spr.–sum.

5. **S. tenuis** Small. Short-lived shrub with light brittle wood, 3–12 dm. tall, with slender stem not umbellately branched at the top: blades of the upper leaves narrowly linear, crenulate: spike slender, mainly red: capsule about 7 mm. wide.—Everglades, Fla.—All year.

15. **SEBASTIANA** Muell. Arg. Shrubs or rarely herbs. Leaf-blades entire or barely toothed. Flowers monoecious, apetalous. Staminate flower with a calyx of 3–5 sepals and 3, or rarely 4, stamens. Pistillate flower with 3 sepals and a 3-celled ovary. Fruit a dry capsule.—About 40 species, mostly tropical.

1. **S. ligustrina** (Michx.) Muell. Arg. Shrub 1–4 m. tall: leaf-blades elliptic or oval, 3–8 cm. long: spikes shorter than the leaves, green or yellowish: capsule depressed, nearly 1 cm. broad: seed subglobose, about 4 mm. long.—(SEBASTIAN-BUSH.)—Swamps, streambanks, and hammocks, Coastal Plain, Fla. to La., and N. C.—Spr.–sum.

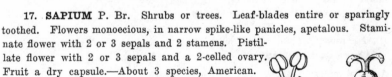

16. **TRIADICA** Lour. Shrubs or trees. Leaf-blades entire, usually broad. Flowers monoecious, in dense spike-like panicles, apetalous. Staminate flower with 2 or rarely 3 sepals and 3 stamens. Pistillate flower with 2 or 3 sepals and a 3-celled ovary. Fruit a fleshy capsule.—Few species, of tropical Asia.

1. **T. sebifera** (L.) Small. Tree resembling a poplar: leaf-blades broad, rhombic, acuminate, 4–8 cm. long, entire, long-petioled: spikes green: capsule about 1.5 cm. broad: seed 8–9 mm. long. [*Sapium sebiferum* (L.) Roxb.]—(CHINESE TALLOW-TREE.)—Hammocks and roadsides, Coastal Plain, Fla. to La. and S. C.—Nat. of E Asia and cult.—Spr.

17. **SAPIUM** P. Br. Shrubs or trees. Leaf-blades entire or sparingly toothed. Flowers monoecious, in narrow spike-like panicles, apetalous. Staminate flower with 2 or 3 sepals and 2 stamens. Pistillate flower with 2 or 3 sepals and a 2-celled ovary. Fruit a dry capsule.—About 3 species, American.

1. **S. glandulosum** (L.) Morong. Small tree or shrub, resembling a willow: leaf-blades linear-elliptic to narrowly elliptic, acute, 8–16 cm. long, serrulate, short-petioled: spikes green or yellowish: capsule about 1 cm. broad: seed 6–7 mm. long.—(MILK-TREE.)—Roadsides and waste-places, W. Fla. Nat. of S. A.—Spr.

18. GYMNANTHES Sw. Shrubs or trees. Leaf-blades entire or toothed. Flowers monoecious or rarely dioecious, apetalous. Staminate flower with a rudimentary or obsolete calyx and 2 or 3 stamens. Pistillate flower with a rudimentary calyx and a 3-celled ovary. Fruit a capsule.—About 12 species, American.

1. G. lucida Sw. Shrub, or tree becoming 10 m. tall: leaf-blades cuneate to elliptic-spatulate, or nearly elliptic, 4–10 cm. long, undulate or obscurely toothed near the apex, spikes shorter than the leaves, green; capsule depressed, about 1 cm. wide: seed ovoid, 6–8 mm. long.—(CRABWOOD.)—Hammocks, Everglade Keys, pen. Fla. and Florida Keys.—(*W. I.*)—Spr.—The sap-wood is bright-yellow: the dark-brown and yellow streaked heart-wood, close-grained, heavy, and hard, is used in cabinet work.

19. HIPPOMANE L. Trees. Leaf-blades entire or toothed, pinnately veined. Flowers on a simple rachis, forming a green spike. Staminate flower with 2 or 3 sepals and 2 or 3 stamens. Pistillate flower with 3 sepals and a 6–8-celled ovary. Fruit a drupe, with a sharply tuberculate stone imbedded in the pulp.

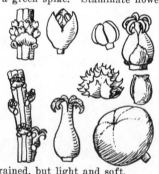

1. H. Mancinella L. Tree becoming 18 m. tall: leaf-blades ovate, elliptic, or oval, 4–10 cm. long: spikes 4–8 cm. long: drupe spheroidal, 2.5–3.5 cm. broad.—(MANCHINEEL.)—Hammocks, Everglade Keys and Cape Sable region, pen. Fla. and Florida Keys.—(*W. I., Mex., C. A., S. A.*)—The milky sap is a powerful irritant, a skin poison. The sap-wood is yellow or light-brown, the dark-brown heart-wood is close-grained, but light and soft.

20. BIVONEA Raf. Herbs or shrubs, often bristly-stinging. Leaf-blades entire, lobed, or divided. Flowers in forked cymes, white. Staminate flower with a corolla-like 5-lobed calyx and 10–30 stamens. Pistillate flower with a usually 3-celled ovary. Fruit a somewhat 3-lobed capsule. [*Cnidoscolus* Pohl.]—About 20 species, mostly in tropical America.

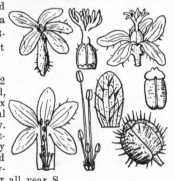

1. B. stimulosa (Michx.) Raf. Plant 1–12 dm. tall: leaf-blades 8–30 cm. broad, coarsely or finely lobed: staminate calyx with a cylindric tube, and lobes about equal in length: capsule 10–16 cm. long, bristly. [*Jatropha stimulosa* Michx.]—(SPURGE-NETTLE. FINGER-ROT. TREAD-SOFTLY.)—Dry woods, sandy hammocks, pinelands, and sand-dunes, Coastal Plain and adj. provinces, Fla. to Tex. and Va.—Spr.–fall or all year S.

21. ADENOROPIUM Pohl. Partly woody plants or herbs. Leaf-blades angled or lobed. Flowers monoecious, petaliferous, mostly red or purple. Staminate flower with 5 sepals, 5 small petals, and 8–10 stamens. Pistillate flower with a mainly 2–3-celled ovary. Fruit a capsule. [*Jatropha* L. in part.] —About 85 species, mainly tropical. All year.

Leaf-blades 3–5-lobed ; lobes toothed, glandular-ciliate : inflorescence pubescent.
1.· *A. gossypiifolium.*
Leaf-blades 9–11-lobed ; lobes entire or incised, eciliate : inflorescence glabrous.
2. *A. multifidum.*

1. A. gossypiifolium (L.) Pohl. Shrub 5–11 dm. tall: leaf-blades palmately 3–5-lobed, 8–15 cm. wide, the lobes broad, shallowly toothed and glandular-ciliate: cymules paniculate: petals scarcely twice as long as the sepals: capsule globular-ellipsoid, about 1 cm. long, slightly warty: seed 7–8 mm. long.—Roadsides and cult. grounds, Key West, Fla. Nat. of tropical regions and cult.—Like many of these plants this one is more or less poisonous when eaten, hence the popular name BELLY-ACHE BUSH.

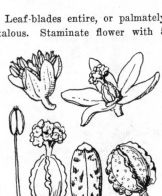

2. A. multifidum (L.) Pohl. Shrub 9–20 dm. tall: leaf-blades palmately 9–11-lobed, mostly 10–20 cm. wide, the lobes narrow, entire or incised, not ciliate: cymules corymbose: petals thrice as long as the sepals: capsule globose-obovoid, 2.5–3 cm. long, smooth: seed 18–25 mm. long.—Pinelands, Everglade Keys, Fla. Nat. of tropical regions and cult.—This plant, like its relatives, has been used in popular medicine and also as a hedge-plant. It is known as PHYSIC-NUT or CORAL-PLANT.

22. JATROPHA L. Shrubs or herbs. Leaf-blades entire, or palmately lobed or parted. Flowers monoecious, apetalous. Staminate flower with 5 sepals and 8 or 10 stamens. Pistillate flower often smaller than the staminate, with a 3-celled ovary, green or purple. Fruit a capsule. [*Manihot* Adans.]—About 80 species, South American.

1. J. Manihot L. Plants 9–16 dm. tall, with a very large root: leaf-blades 3–7 parted: flowers green or purple-tinged: capsules with crenate-undulate wings. [*M. Manihot* (L.) Karst.]—(CASSAVA.)—Roadsides, cult. grounds, and pinelands, Everglade Keys, Fla. and Florida Keys. Nat. of S. A., and cult.—(*W. I.*)—The large root yields starch in the form of cassava-meal

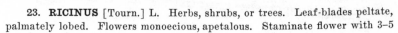

and tapioca. It contains a poison, however, which must be dissolved out before these products are edible.

23. RICINUS [Tourn.] L. Herbs, shrubs, or trees. Leaf-blades peltate, palmately lobed. Flowers monoecious, apetalous. Staminate flower with 3–5

sepals and numerous stamens, mainly yellow,
Pistillate flower with caducous sepals and a
3-celled ovary, green. Fruit a capsule.—
One species.

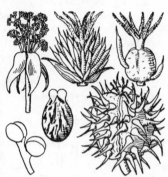

1. **R. communis** L. Small tree or shrub,
1–5 m. tall, the stem widely branched, or an
annual herb northward: leaf-blades nearly
orbicular, 6–11-lobed: capsule 12–16 mm. in
diameter.—(CASTOR-OIL PLANT. CASTOR-
BEAN. PALMA-CHRISTI.)—Pinelands, hammocks, roadsides, and waste-places, locally
escaped from gardens in various provinces,
throughout SE U. S. Nat. of Africa, and
cult.—(Widely distr.)—Sum.–fall or all year
S.—The seeds yield the castor oil of commerce.

24. **CHAMAESYCE** S. F. Gray. Annual or perennial herbs or shrubs.
Leaves opposite: blades oblique at the base. Involucres axillary or in axillary
cymes, each with 4 naked or appendaged glands, one sinus being glandless.
Capsule smooth, sometimes pubescent. Seed smooth or transverse-wrinkled.—
About 225 species, widely distributed.—SPURGES. EUPHORBIAS.—The flower-
like involucres have appendages to the marginal glands, either green tinged
with red, red, greenish-white or white. Some of the species have reputed
medicinal properties.

Leaf-blades entire.
    Plant with prostrate stems and branches.
        Leaves succulent: seed not angled, sometimes terete or nearly so.
                                                              I. POLYGONIFOLIAE.
        Leaves herbaceous or chartaceous: seed sharply
          angled.   II. CORDIFOLIAE.
    Plant with erect or ascending stems and branches.   III. BUXIFOLIAE.
Leaf-blades toothed, sometimes only at the apex.
    Capsule glabrous.
        Plant with prostrate stems and branches.   II. CORDIFOLIAE.
        Plant with erect or ascending stems and branches.   IV. HYSSOPIFOLIAE.
    Capsule pubescent.
        Involucres axillary to the leaves or leaf-like bracts.
           Stem, or branches, erect.   V. TRACYANAE.
           Stem, or branches, prostrate.   VI. MACULATAE.
        Involucres in peduncled clusters.   VII. HIRTAE.

I. POLYGONIFOLIAE

Seed 1.5 mm. long or more, somewhat 3-sided.
    Seed unequally 3-sided, covered with a silvery-gray bloom,
      usually 2 mm. long or more.   1. *C. polygonifolia.*
    Seed equally 3-sided, covered with a whitish or speckled
      bloom, usually about 1.5 mm. long.   2. *C. Ingallsii.*
Seed less than 1.5 mm. long, nearly terete.   3. *C. cumulicola.*

II. CORDIFOLIAE

Capsule, and ovary, glabrous.
    Leaf-blades, at least those of the stem or main branches,
      decidedly longer than wide, mainly elliptic to nar-
      rowly ovate.
        Involucre about 1.5 mm. long, broadly campanulate:
          leaf-blades thick and parchment-like.   4. *C. Chiogenes.*
        Involucre about 1 mm. long, narrowly campanulate:
          leaf-blades thin-herbaceous.   5. *C. Blodgettii.*
    Leaf-blades broadly ovate to orbicular.
        Appendages of the involucre-glands minute or obsolete.   6. *C. serpens.*
        Appendages of the involucre-glands petal-like.

Ultimate divisions of the inflorescence open, long-branched.   7. *C. cordifolia.*
Ultimate divisions of the inflorescence comparatively dense, raceme-like clusters.   7a. *C. Nashii.*
Capsule, and ovary, pubescent.
  Stem, branches, and leaves permanently and usually copiously pubescent.
    Plant with few stout or wiry branches, not forming dense mats.
      Foliage finely hirsute.
        Leaves of the branchlets much reduced in size, crowded : capsule with many long hairs.   8. *C. brachypoda.*
        Leaves of the branchlets not much reduced in size, not crowded : capsule with few short hairs.   9. *C. Mosieri.*
      Foliage canescent.   10. *C. Garberi.*
    Plant with many very slender, usually filiform branches, forming dense mats appressed to the ground.
      Branches strigillose : leaf-blades much longer than wide.   11. *C. Serpyllum.*
      Branches villous-hirsutulous : leaf-blades nearly or quite as wide as long.   12. *C. adhaerens.*
      than 4 mm. long), as wide as long or nearly so.   13. *C. deltoidea.*

III. BUXIFOLIAE

Stem, branches, and leaves glabrous.
  Twigs and leaves succulent : beach plant.   14. *C. buxifolia.*
  Twigs and leaves not succulent : pineland plants.
    Leaf-blades very broad : stem sparingly branched.   15. *C. Porteriana.*
    Leaf-blades rather narrow : stem much-branched and broom-like.   16. *C. scoparia.*
Stem, branches, and leaves pubescent.
  Single-stemmed woody plants, sometimes branched near the base : stem and leaves finely, usually sparingly canescent.
    Leaf-blades relatively small (on the main stem less than 4 mm. long), as wide as long or nearly so.   17. *C. adicioides.*
    Leaf-blades relatively large (on the main stem over 5 mm. long), twice as long as wide.   18. *C. keyensis.*
  Many-stemmed, wiry, cespitose plant : stem and leaves villous-hirsute.   19. *C. pinetorum.*

IV. HYSSOPIFOLIAE

Involucres in dense axillary cymes, the cymes rarely branched.   20. *C. hypericifolia.*
Involucres in loose cymes, rarely also with some axillary, the cymes much-branched.   21. *C. hyssopifolia.*

V. TRACYANA

Stem usually branched at the base and above, the branches and branchlets very leafy.   22. *C. Tracyi.*

VI. MACULATAE

Glands of the involucre with inconspicuous appendages.
  Capsule pubescent along the angles.   23. *C. prostrata.*
  Capsule pubescent all over, but often mainly so, below the middle.
    Leaf-blades twice as long as wide or less.
      Involucre not cleft on one side : seed sharply 4-angled, the faces with 3 or 4 prominent transverse ridges.   24. *C. maculata.*
      Involucre deeply cleft on one side : seed bluntly angled, the faces minutely roughened or nearly smooth.   25. *C. humistrata.*
    Leaf-blades thrice as long as wide.   26. *C. Mathewsii.*
Glands of the involucre, at least two of them, with petal-like appendages.
  Branches densely and copiously floriferous, the involucres crowded : leaves of the flowering branches much reduced in size, of a different shape from those of the stem, and usually acuminate.   27. *C. conferta.*
  Branches not densely or copiously flowered, the involucres not approximate : leaves of the flowering branches much reduced in size, but not changed in shape, rounded at the apex.   28. *C. adenoptera.*

VII. Hirtae

Plant erect: heads of involucres axillary, never terminal
  only, but rarely subtended by 2 or more leaf-like bracts.   29. *C. hirta.*
Plant prostrate: heads of involucres terminal, or terminating
  branches and subtended by 2 leaf-like bracts.   30. *C. gemella.*

1. **C. polygonifolia** (L.) Small. Leaf-blades narrowly elliptic to linear-lanceolate, fleshy: involucre between 1.5 and 2 mm. long: capsule globose-ovoid:
seed ellipsoid-ovoid, usually over 2 mm.
long.— (Seaside-spurge.) — Coastal sand-
dunes, Coastal Plain, and New England
Coast, Fla. to N. S.; also Great Lake Lowland, N. Y. to Wis.—Sum.–fall.

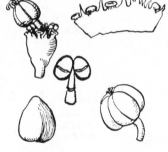

2. **C. Ingallsii** Small. Leaf-blades elliptic
to ovate-elliptic, fleshy: involucre between 1
and 1.5 mm. long: capsule depressed: seed
broadly ovoid or globose-ovoid, usually less
than 2 mm. long.—Coastal sand-dunes, Fla.
to Tex.

3. **C. cumulicola** Small. Branches prostrate, string-like, zigzag, glabrous; leaf-
blades elliptic to elliptic-ovate, veinless: involucre campanulate, about 1 mm. long, gla-
brous; appendages whitish and narrower than the glands or obsolete: capsule
about 2.5 mm. broad, glabrous: seed 1–1.3 mm. long, nearly terete, smooth.—
(Sand-dune spurge.)—Sand-dunes and scrub, Cape Romano region and lower
eastern coast, Fla.—All year.

4. **C. Chiogenes** Small. Leaf-blades narrowly ovate or elliptic, sometimes the
lower ones suborbicular: involucres about 1.5 mm. long; appendages mostly
smaller than the glands: capsule about 1.5 mm. broad: seed about 1 mm.
long, angled, the faces uneven.—Pinelands, lower Florida Keys.—All year.

5. **C. Blodgettii** (Engelm.) Small. Branches glabrous or nearly so: leaf-
blades narrowly ovate, elliptic, or spatulate: involucres about 1 mm. long, glabrous: gland-appendages white or pinkish, commonly slightly larger than the
glands: capsule fully 1.5 mm. broad, glabrous: seed about 1 mm. long.—Coastal
sand-dunes and low hammocks, S pen. Fla. and the Keys.—(*W. I.*)

6. **C. serpens** (H.B.K.) Small. Branches glabrous: leaf-blades orbicular,
orbicular-ovate, or ovate: involucres barely 1 mm. long; appendages mostly
smaller than the glands: capsule between 1 and 2 mm. broad: seed barely 1
mm. long, prominently angled.—Sandy woods, plains, and tablelands, various
provinces, Fla. to Tex., N. M., Ia., and Ill.—(*W. I.*)—Spr.–fall.

7. **C. cordifolia** (Ell.) Small. Branches glabrous: leaf-blades broadly elliptic
to ovate, or sometimes broadest below the middle: involucres fully 1 mm. long;
appendages mostly much larger than the green glands: capsule between 2 and
3 mm. broad, glabrous: seed fully 1 mm. long, gray, obscurely angled.—Sandy
hammocks and sandhills, Coastal Plain, Fla. to Tex. and S. C.—Spr.–fall.

7a. **C. Nashii** Small. Branches glabrous: leaf-blades broadly elliptic to ovate:
involucres nearly 1.5 mm. long; appendages narrow, delicate, white or greenish:
seed shallowly transverse-wrinkled.—Coastal sands and pinelands, pen. Fla. and
Florida Keys.—All year.

8. **C. brachypoda** Small. Branches hirsute or villous-hirsute, with many short
internodes: leaf-blades elliptic to ovate, hirsute: involucres fully 1 mm. long;

appendages much smaller than the red glands, or minute or obsolete: capsule about 2 mm. wide, pubescent: seed 1 mm. long, brown, obscurely angled.—Pinelands, Everglade Keys, Fla.—All year.

9. C. Mosieri Small. Branches prostrate, wiry, dark, villous-hirsutulous: leaf-blades orbicular-reniform to ovate, 4–8 mm. long, loosely-pubescent, acute or acutish: involucres campanulate, about 1 mm. long, pubescent; appendages red or deep-pink, some of them larger than the glands, others smaller, sometimes lobed: capsule globose-ovoid, about 1.5 mm. broad, sparingly pubescent: seed ovoid, about 1 mm. long, the faces nearly smooth.—Pinelands, Everglade Keys, S pen. Fla.—All year.

10. C. Garberi Small. Branches canescent: leaf-blades ovate or oval: involucres about 1.5 mm. long; appendages minute, or obsolete: capsule fully 1.5 mm. broad, pubescent: seed about 1 mm. long, reddish-brown.—Pinelands, hammocks, and sand-dunes, Everglade Keys and Cape Sable, pen. Fla. and Florida Keys. Adv. at Mobile, Ala.—All year.

11. C. Serpyllum Small. Branches puberulent-canescent, filiform, very numerous: leaf-blades deltoid or ovate-deltoid to triangular or triangular-ovate, 3–5 mm. long, obtuse: involucres about 1 mm. long; appendages very minute: capsule about 1.5 mm. broad, pubescent: seed less than 1 mm. long, yellowish or grayish.—Pinelands, lower Florida Keys.—All year.

12. C. adhaerens Small. Branches very numerous, forming closely prostrate mats, finely villous-hirsutulous, wiry-filiform: leaf-blades reniform to orbicular-ovate, or reniform-ovate, 2–3.5 mm. long, rounded at the apex, minutely pale-pubescent: involucres broadly campanulate or hemispheric, about 1 mm. long; appendages mere pale margins to the glands or obsolete: capsule fully 1.5 mm. broad, pubescent: seed ovoid, about 1 mm. long, the faces slightly wrinkled.—Pinelands, Everglade Keys, pen. Fla.—All year.

13. C. deltoidea (Engelm.) Small. Branches glabrous, closely appressed to the ground: leaf-blades deltoid-ovate or reniform, rarely minutely pubescent when young: involucres less than 1 mm. long, glabrous: glands yellow; appendages obsolete: capsule about 2 mm. broad, glabrous or sometimes sparingly pubescent: seed less than 1 mm. long, even, yellowish.—Pinelands, Everglade Keys, pen. Fla.—All year.

14. C. buxifolia (Lam.) Small. Branches, like the stem woody, 1 m. tall or less, glabrous, often purple, with long or short internodes: leaf-blades ovate to broadly elliptic or cuneate near the base of the stem, rather fleshy, 8–12 mm. long, obtuse or acutish, involute, rounded or subcordate, nearly sessile: involucres campanulate, about 1.5 mm. high, as long as the peduncles or shorter: glands transversely elliptic, 0.5 mm. broad: appendages whitish: capsule 2.5–3 mm. broad, glabrous.—Coastal sand-dunes and rocks along shores, S pen. Fla. and the Keys.—(*W. I.*)

15. C. Porteriana Small. Branches glabrous: leaf-blades ovate, or oval: involucres about 1 mm. long, glabrous: gland-appendages reddish, fully as long as the glands, or sometimes narrower: capsule about 2 mm. broad, glabrous: seed about 1 mm. long, markedly angled.—Pinelands, Everglade Keys, pen. Fla.—All year.

16. C. scoparia Small. Branches glabrous, pale: leaf-blades narrowly elliptic to narrowly ovate, 2–8 mm. long, obtuse or acutish, pale or glaucescent beneath: involucres about 1.5 mm. long, glabrous: gland-appendages white or pink, 2 of them prominent and 2 partly obsolete: capsule 1.5–2 mm. broad, glabrous: seed about 1 mm. long, grayish, scabrous.—Pinelands, lower Florida Keys.—All year.

17. **C. adicioides** Small. Shrub mostly less than 0.5 m. tall, finely pubescent with pale hairs, rather copiously branched above, zigzag: leaves numerous; blades ovate to oval, 2–3 mm. long, acute or acutish, entire, short-petioled: involucres campanulate, barely 1 mm. high, longer than the peduncles, minutely pubescent, deciduous: glands about 0.4 mm. broad: appendages obsolete: capsule pubescent, less than 1 mm. long.—Sandy shores and hammocks, Florida Keys.—All year.

18. **C. keyensis** Small. Branches erect or nearly so, finely pale-pubescent: leaf-blades elliptic-ovate, to elliptic, oval, or ovate, 3–9 mm. long: involucres turbinate, a little over 1 mm. long, finely pubescent; appendages white or pinkish, about as wide as the glands: capsule about 2 mm. broad, pubescent: seed nearly 1 mm. long.—Sand-dunes and pinelands, lower Florida Keys.—All year.

19. **C. pinetorum** Small. Branches villous-hirsute often ascending near the tips: leaf-blades reniform or deltoid to orbicular or ovate, conspicuously pubescent: involucres fully 1 mm. long, pubescent: glands green; appendages very narrow, even-edged: capsule fully 2 mm. broad, pubescent: seed 1 mm. long, transversely wrinkled, yellowish.—Pinelands, Everglade Keys, pen. Fla.—All year.

20. **C. hypericifolia** (L.) Small. Branches glabrous or nearly so, the ultimate ones slender: leaf-blades mainly elliptic, elliptic-lanceolate, or ovate, unequally serrate, usually nearly straight: involucres 1 mm. long or more: gland-appendages obovate to reniform, rather conspicuous: capsule fully 2 mm. wide, glabrous: seed brown or reddish-brown, about 1 mm. long.—Pinelands, waste-places, and roadsides, Coastal Plain, Fla. to Tex.—(*W. I., Mex., C. A., S. A.*)

21. **C. hyssopifolia** (L.) Small. Branches glabrous: leaf-blades elliptic, elliptic-ovate, elliptic-lanceolate, or sometimes linear-lanceolate, often slightly curved or even falcate, mostly 1–3 cm. long, usually toothed: involucres 1–1.5 mm. long, glabrous, few together in terminal cymes; appendages suborbicular or reniform, unequal: capsule 1.5–2 mm. wide, glabrous: seed gray, brown, or black, about 1 mm. long. [*Euphorbia brasiliensis* Lam. *E. nutans* Lag. *E. Preslii* Guss.]—(EYE-BANE.)—Hammocks, roadsides, fields, and waste-places, nearly throughout U. S. and S Can.—(*W. I., Mex., C. A., S. A.*)—Sum. or all year S.

22. **C. Tracyi** Small. Branches thinly canescent: leaf-blades elliptic to slightly broadest above the middle: involucres fully 1 mm. long, sparingly pubescent: gland-appendages minute, unequal and uneven: capsule nearly 2 mm. broad, slightly pubescent all over: seed less than 1 mm. long.—Sand-dunes and pinelands, Coastal Plain, Fla. to Miss.—Sum. or all year S.

23. **C. prostrata** (Ait.) Small. Branches pubescent: leaf-blades oval, obovate, or elliptic: involucres 1 mm. long or less, usually sparingly pubescent: appendages very narrow: capsule about 2 mm. broad, pubescent about the angles: seed 1 mm. long or less.—Sandy soil, Coastal Plain, Fla. to Tex.—All year.

24. **C. humistrata** (Engelm.) Small. Branches puberulent or finely pubescent: leaf-blades ovate-elliptic or sometimes narrower: involucres about 1 mm. long, pubescent: appendages white or red, commonly narrower than the glands: capsule about 1.5 mm. broad, pubescent: seed about 1 mm. long.—Dry or sandy soil, various provinces, W of Blue Ridge, Ala. to Tex., Nebr., Minn., Que., and N. Y.—Spr.–fall.

25. **C. maculata** (L.) Small. Branches like the stem puberulent or pilose: leaf-blades elliptic or ovate-elliptic, 8–12 mm. long: involucres mostly 1 mm.

long, pubescent; appendages white or red, narrow, nearly equal, entire: capsule less than 1.5 mm. wide, pubescent: seed nearly 1 mm. long, black beneath the pale coating.—(MILK-PURSLANE.)—Roadsides, cult. grounds, waste-places, and especially along railroads, various provinces, nearly throughout U. S. and S Can.—Spr.–fall or all year S.

26. **C. Mathewsii** Small. Branches prostrate, copiously loosely pubescent: leaf-blades broadly linear-elliptic to elliptic, 1–1.5 cm. long, with a black-purple blotch above, and scattered hairs beneath: involucres campanulate, slightly over 1 mm. long; appendages pale, very narrow, unequal, uneven: capsule about 1.5 mm. broad, pubescent: seed less than 1 mm. long.—Barren beaches, opposite Miami, Fla.—All year.

27. **C. conferta** Small. Branches villous: leaf-blades elliptic to ovate: involucres 1.5–2 mm. long, villous; gland-appendages red or magenta, 2 of them petal-like, much larger than the others, toothed: capsule less than 1.5 mm. broad, minutely pubescent: seed less than 1 mm. long, coarsely wrinkled.—Pinelands, Everglade Keys, pen. Fla.—All year.

28. **C. adenoptera** (Bertol.) Small. Branches closely villous: leaf-blades elliptic or ovate-elliptic: involucres 1–1.5 mm. long, finely pubescent; gland-appendages white or pink, petaloid, 2 of them much larger than the glands: capsule about 1.5 mm. broad, densely pubescent: seed about 1 mm. long, finely wrinkled.—Pinelands, S Fla.—Spr.–sum.

29. **C. hirta** (L.) Millsp. Branches closely pubescent: leaf-blades elliptic to elliptic-lanceolate, or somewhat triangular, often prominently blotched: involucres mostly in axillary clusters, 1 mm. long or less, minutely pubescent; gland-appendages imperfectly developed: capsule fully 1 mm. broad, finely pubescent: seed about 1 mm. long. [*C. pilulifera* (L.) Small]—Hammocks, roadsides, and cult. grounds, Coastal Plain, Fla. to Tex.—(*W. I., Mex., C. A., S. A.*)—All year.

30. **C. gemella** (Lag.) Small. Similar to *C. hirta* but smaller, and with more closely prostrate branches: leaf-blades elliptic to elliptic-lanceolate, mostly evenly green: involucres mostly in terminal clusters, about 1 mm. long, finely pubescent: gland-appendages white, narrower than the glands: capsule fully 1 mm. broad, often closely pubescent: seed less than 1 mm. long. [*C. pilulifera procumbens* (Boiss.) Small]—Hammocks, cult. grounds, roadsides, and waste-places, pen. Fla. and the Keys.—(*W. I., Mex., C. A., S. A.*)—All year.

25. **LEPADENA** Raf. Annual or biennial herbs, often topped by an umbel. Leaf-blades entire. Involucres in rather dense cymes, each with 5 conspicuously appendaged glands. Capsule pubescent. Seed wrinkled or tuberculate. [*Dichrophyllum* Kl. & Garcke.]—About 4 species, North American.—EUPHORBIAS.— SPURGES.

1. **L. marginata** (Pursh) Nieuwl. Plant 3–11 dm. tall: blades of the upper leaves obovate to ovate, like the bracts white-margined and conspicuous: involucre-glands with white appendages: capsule strigillose: seed 3–4 mm. long, coarsely wrinkled, obtuse. —(SNOW-ON-THE-MOUNTAIN.)—Dry soil and waste-places, various provinces, Ga. to N. C. and W; native from Tex. to N. M., Mont., and Minn.—Spr.–fall.—Extensively cultivated for the showy effect of the massed foliage which suggested the popular name.

26. TITHYMALOPSIS Kl. & Garcke. Perennial, mostly glabrous herbs often topped by an umbel. Leaf-blades entire. Involucres scattered or somewhat clustered in an umbel-like inflorescence, each with appendaged glands. Capsule smooth. Seed punctate.—About 18 species, North American.— EUPHORBIAS.—Some of the species, *T. corollata* and *T. Ipecacuanhae*, are used medicinally.

Leaves exceedingly numerous, approximate or imbricate.	1. *T. polyphylla.*
Leaves less numerous, never imbricate.	
Stem normally underground; branches of the inflorescence tufted; all leaves or bracts opposite.	
Glands of the involucre with inconspicuous margin-like appendages.	
Branches spreading or prostrate: leaf-blades fleshy.	2. *T. Ipecacuanhae.*
Branches erect or ascending: leaf-blades thin.	3. *T. gracilis.*
Glands of the involucre with conspicuous white appendages.	4. *T. eriogonoides.*
Stems erect, topped by the umbel-like inflorescence: leaves alternate on the inflorescence branches.	
Stem-leaves reduced to scales: bracts foliaceous.	5. *T. mercurialina.*
Stem-leaves with normally expanded blades.	
Inflorescence of scattered long-peduncled involucres.	
Involucres 2–4 mm. across the appendages.	
Stem-leaves with linear blades, fugacious.	6. *T. Curtisii.*
Stem-leaves with elliptic or lanceolate blades, persistent.	7. *T. exserta.*
Involucres 6–10 mm. across the appendages.	8. *T. zinniiflora.*
Inflorescence aggregated into terminal cymes or cymose clusters.	
Leaf-blades manifestly petioled, the petioles over 2 mm. long.	9. *T. apocynifolia.*
Leaf-blades sessile or nearly so, the petioles, if present, less than 1 mm. long.	
Involucres 3.5 mm. across the appendages or narrower.	10. *T. discoidalis.*
Involucres 4–8 mm. across the appendages.	
Appendages about as long as the involucre.	11. *T. olivacea.*
Appendages much longer than the involucre.	
Appendages longer than wide: leaf-blades relatively narrow.	12. *T. corollata.*
Appendages as wide as long or wider: leaf-blades relatively broad.	13. *T. paniculata.*

1. T. polyphylla (Engelm.) Small. Plant 0.5–2.5 dm. tall, the stems stout, often tufted, copiously leafy: leaf-blades linear or linear-spatulate, 5–15 mm. long: involucres 1.5–2 mm. long; gland-appendages white or pinkish, mostly reniform, crenate: capsule 4–5 mm. broad: seed about 2.5 mm. long, white.—Pinelands, pen. Fla.—All year.

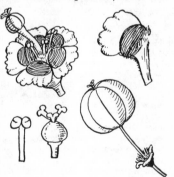

2. T. Ipecacuanhae (L.) Small. Plant 0.2–3 dm. tall, the stem slender, sparingly leafy: leaf-blades linear to orbicular, 1–7 cm. long: involucres 1.5 mm. long, or rarely longer: appendages of the glands very narrow or obsolete: capsule 4.5–5 mm. broad: seed 2.5 mm. long.—(IPECAC-SPURGE.)— Dry acid sand, often in pinelands, where vegetation is too sparse to carry fire, Coastal Plain and occasionally adj. provinces, Fla. to Tenn., Ind., and Conn.—Spr.–fall.

3. **T. gracilis** (Ell.) Small. Plant 1–3 dm. tall, the stems very slender, sparingly leafy: leaf-blades suborbicular to ovate or linear or rarely broader than long: involucres about 2 mm. long; appendages of the glands narrow: capsule 3–4 mm. broad: seed 2.5 mm. long.—Pinelands and sandhills, Coastal Plain, Fla. to S. C.—All year.

4. **T. eriogonoides** Small. Plant 1–3 dm. tall, the stem, diffusely branched: leaf-blades linear to linear-spatulate, 0.5–1.5 cm. long: involucres about 1 mm. long; appendages reniform to suborbicular, about 1 mm. broad: capsule about 4 mm. broad: seed about 2.5 mm. long.—Pinelands and roadsides, Coastal Plain, Fla. to N. C.—Spr.–fall.

5. **T. mercurialina** (Michx.) Small. Plant 1–4 dm. tall, often with several stems together: bracts oval, elliptic, or oblong-ovate, 2–9 cm. long: involucres 2 mm. long; appendages white, mostly narrower than the glands, undulate: capsule 5–6 mm. broad: seeds 2.5 mm. long, tuberculate.—Rocky woods, Coastal Plain and Appalachian provinces, Fla. to Ala., Tenn., and Ga.—Spr.–sum.

6. **T. Curtisii** (Engelm.) Small. Plant 1–5 dm. tall, the branches green: leaf-blades linear, 1.5–4 cm. long: involucres 1–1.5 mm. long: appendages white, reniform to orbicular-reniform, as wide as the glands or wider: capsule 4–5 mm. broad: seed about 2 mm. long.—Pinelands, Coastal Plain, Fla. to N. C.—Spr.–fall.

7. **T. exserta** Small. Plant 1–3 dm. tall, the branches reddish or purple: leaf-blades elliptic to lanceolate, 2–6 cm. long: involucres about 2 mm. long; appendages white, reniform, about as broad as the glands, or narrower: capsule long-exserted, 4–5 mm. broad: seed 3–3.5 mm. long.—Pinelands or coastal sands, Fla.—All year.

8. **T. zinniiflora** Small. Plant 3–5 dm. tall: leaf-blades linear-lanceolate to nearly linear, 2–5 cm. long, sessile or nearly so: involucres few, about 2 mm. long; appendages white or pink, suborbicular or 4-sided: capsule exserted, 4.5–5 mm. broad: seed about 2.5 mm. long.—Sandy soil, Coastal Plain, Fla. and Ala.—Spr.

9. **T. apocynifolia** Small. Plant 2–7 dm. tall: leaf-blades elliptic to oval, 2–7 cm. long, manifestly petioled: involucres numerous, about 1.5 mm. long; appendages white, orbicular to cuneate, or sometimes reniform: capsule about 5 mm. broad: seed 2.5 mm. long.—Sandy soil, Coastal Plain, Fla. to Miss. and N. C.—Sum.–fall.

10. **T. discoidalis** (Chapm.) Small. Plant 2–6 dm. tall: leaf-blades linear, 2–6 cm. long, sessile: involucres numerous, fully 1 mm. long; appendages white, reniform to ovate or 4-sided: capsule exserted, about 3 mm. broad: seed about 2 mm. long.—Pinelands, W Fla.—Sum.–fall.

11. **T. olivacea** Small. Plant olive-green, 2–7 dm. tall: leaf-blades elliptic, obovate-elliptic, or cuneate, 1–3 cm. long: involucres numerous, 1.5–2 mm. long; appendages white, reniform to ovate or cuneate: capsule slightly exserted, 3.5–4 mm. broad: seed 2.5 mm. long.—Sandy soil, Coastal Plain, Miss. to Tex.—Sum.–fall.

12. **T. corollata** (L.) Small. Plant bright-green, 2–9 dm. tall: leaf-blades linear, elliptic, or elliptic-spatulate, 2–4 cm. long: involucres numerous, conspicuous, 1–1.5 mm. long; appendages white, mostly cuneate or orbicular-cuneate: capsule exserted, 3.5–4.5 mm. broad: seed 2.5 mm. long.—(FLOWERING-SPURGE. TRAMP'S-SPURGE.)—Woods, fields, thickets, and roadsides, various provinces, Fla. to Tex., Minn., Ont., and Mass.—Sum.

13. T. paniculata (Ell.) Small. Plant deep-green, 3–9 dm. tall: leaf-blades elliptic to oval, 2–6 cm. long: involucres commonly few, about 1.5 mm. long: appendages white, suborbicular, somewhat reniform, or somewhat 4-sided: capsule 3–3.5 mm. broad: seed 2.5 mm. long.—Sandy or rocky woods, Coastal Plain and adj. provinces, Ga. and Ala. to N. C.—Spr.-fall.

27. GALARHOEUS Haw. Annual or perennial herbs or partially woody plants, the stem topped by an umbel. Leaf-blades entire or finely toothed. Stipules wanting. Involucres in open or compact cymes, each with 4 naked or appendaged glands. Capsule smooth or tuberculate. Seed pitted, grooved, reticulate, or smooth. [*Tithymalus* (Fl. SE. U. S.)]—About 250 species, widely distributed.—Sum.—SPURGES. EUPHORBIAS.

Leaf-blades entire.
  Leaves of the stem mainly opposite and decussate: capsule 1.5 mm. wide or more.
                                                        I. LATHYRI.
  Leaves of the stem alternate or scattered: capsule 1 cm.
    wide or less.
    Bracts or leaves of the inflorescence-branches (rays)
      opposite: rays simple or dichotomous.
      Stem topped by a repeatedly forked inflorescence.   II. PEPLI.
      Stem topped by an umbel-like simple or sparingly
        forked inflorescence.   III. CYPARISSIAE.
    Bracts or leaves of the inflorescence-branches (rays)
      alternate: rays trichotomous.   IV. TRICHOTOMI.
Leaf-blades serrulate.   V. OBTUSATI.

I. LATHYRI
Annual or biennial coarse plant: leaf-blades entire: glands
  of the involucre crescent-shaped.   1. *G. Lathyrus*.

II. PEPLI
Glands of the involucre without horn-like processes.
  Glands with erose-crumpled edges.   2. *G. floridanus*.
  Glands entire or merely undulate.
    Bracts of the rays longer than broad.
      Stem-leaves with narrowly oblanceolate to linear
        blades.   3. *G. inundatus*.
      Stem-leaves with obovate, spatulate, or oblanceo-
        late blades.   4. *G. telephioides*.
    Bracts of the rays fully as broad as long.   5. *G. Darlingtonii*.
Glands of the involucre lunate or crescent-shaped by horn-
  like processes.
  Surfaces of the seeds reticulate or rather finely and ir-
    regularly pitted.
    Stem-leaves with spatulate to ovate blades: bracts
      ovate-reniform or reniform: seeds pitted.   6. *G. commutatus*.
    Stem-leaves with linear blades: bracts deltoid: seeds
      reticulate.   7. *G. austrinus*.
  Surfaces of the seeds longitudinally grooved or with large
    pits in longitudinal rows: capsule with prominently
    keeled lobes.   8. *G. Peplus*.

III. CYPARISSIAE
Plants growing in dense colonies, the stems with numerous
  very narrow leaves, topped by a many-rayed umbel.   9. *G. Cyparissias*.

IV. TRICHOTOMI
Fleshy plant with few or many stems or branches.   10. *G. trichotomus*.

V. OBTUSATI
Capsule smooth.   11. *G. Helioscopia*.
Capsule warty.
  Leaves obtusely rounded at the tip, glabrous; seed retic-
    ulated.
    Blades of the cauline leaves with cordate or truncate
      blades, more or less auricled: glands of the invo-
      lucre stalked.   12. *G. obtusatus*.
    Blades of the cauline leaves narrowed to the base, not
      auricled: glands of the involucre sessile.   13. *G. arkansanus*.
  Leaves acute, pubescent beneath; seed smooth.   14. *G. platyphylla*.

1. **G. Lathyrus** (L.) Haw. Stem 2–12 dm. tall: blades of the upper leaves lanceolate to linear-lanceolate, 3.5–12 cm. long: bracts ovate to ovate-lanceolate: involucres 4–5 mm. long; lobes triangular, toothed at the apex, surpassing the broad crescent-shaped glands: capsule 1.5–2 cm. broad: seed ellipsoid, ovoid, 5–6 mm. long, wrinkled. — (MOLE-PLANT. CAPER-SPURGE. MYRTLE-SPURGE.)—Roadsides, cult. grounds, and waste-places, various provinces, N. C. to Tex., W. Va., and Conn. Nat. of Eu.—Spr.-sum.—Used medicinally. The seeds yield an oil similar to castor oil.

2. **G. floridanus** (Chapm.) Small. Stem 2–6 dm. tall: leaf-blades linear to narrowly lanceolate, 3–6 cm. long: bracts ovate to lanceolate: involucre 3.5–4 mm. long; lobes ovate, erose, surpassed by the flabellate glands which have crumpled edges: capsule 8–10 mm. broad: seed subglobose or spheroidal, 4 mm. broad, smooth.—Pinelands, Coastal Plain, M Fla. to Ala. and Ga.—Spr.-sum.

3. **G. inundatus** (Torr.) Small. Stem 1–5 dm. tall: leaf-blades narrowly oblanceolate to linear, or slightly broadest above the middle, 3–10 cm. long: bracts ovate to elliptic-lanceolate: involucre campanulate, 2–3 mm. long; lobes ovate, several toothed, about as high as the glands: capsule 6–7 mm. broad, smooth: seed subglobose or ovoid-globose, 3–3.5 mm. long, smooth.—Low pinelands, Coastal Plain, W Fla. to Ala.—Spr.

4. **G. telephioides** (Chapm.) Small. Stem 0.5–2.5 dm. tall: leaf-blades obovate, broadly spatulate, or oblanceolate, 2–5 cm. long: bracts ovate to deltoid: involucre broadly campanulate, about 2 mm. long; lobes half-orbicular, about as high as the glands: capsule 7–8 mm. broad, granular: seed subglobose, about 3 mm. in diameter.—Pinelands, near the coast, M Fla.—Spr.

5. **G. Darlingtonii** (A. Gray) Small. Stem 3–15 dm. tall: leaves few; blades oblanceolate to elliptic-lanceolate, 3.5–10 cm. long: bracts reniform to orbicular-reniform: involucre 3–4 mm. long; lobes ovate or quadrate, toothed or often notched; glands elliptic: capsule 8–9 mm. broad, warty: seed ovoid-globose, 3–4 mm. long.—Woods and thickets, Piedmont and occasionally adj. provinces, N. C. to N. J. (or N. Y.?).—Spr.-fall.

6. **G. commutatus** (Engelm.) Small. Stem decumbent, 1–4 dm. long: leaf-blades spatulate to ovate (or those of the upper ones somewhat lanceolate in *G. commutatus erectus*), 1–4 cm. long, with slender petiole-like bases; bracts reniform or ovate-reniform: involucre 2.5 mm. long; horns 1 mm. long or nearly so: capsule 3.5–4 mm. broad, smooth: seed ovoid, fully 2 mm. long, irregularly pitted.—(WOOD-SPURGE.)—Woods and stream-banks, various provinces, Fla. to Mo., Minn., and Pa.—Spr.-sum.

7. **G. austrinus** Small. Stem erect, 3–4 dm. tall: leaf-blades linear, mostly 2–5 cm. long, acute or acuminate, very short-petioled: bracts deltoid: involucre 1–1.5 mm. long; horns about 0.5 mm. long: capsule 3–3.5 mm. broad; smooth: seed ovoid, nearly 2 mm. long, finely reticulate.—Pinelands, W Fla.—Sum.

8. **G. Peplus** (L.) Haw. Stem erect, 1–3 dm. tall: leaf-blades elliptic or obovate, 1–4 cm. long: bracts ovate or triangular-ovate: involucre 1–1.5 mm.

long; horns less than 1 mm. long: capsule 2.5–3 mm. broad, smooth: seed ellip-soid or ovoid-ellipsoid, 1.5 mm. long or less, with 1–4 series of pits.—(PETTY-SPURGE.)—Roadsides, waste-places, and cult. grounds, various provinces, Ala. to Ia. and N. B.; also Calif. Nat. of Eu.—Spr.–fall.

9. **G. Cyparissias** (L.) Small. Stem often tufted, 1–3 dm. tall: leaves very numerous; blades linear, 2–4 cm. long, acute or acutish, entire: bracts ovate, deltoid, or reniform: involucre campanulate, about 2 mm. long, sessile; glands lunate, nearly 1 mm. wide: capsule 3-lobed, about 3 mm. wide, granular, the lobes rounded: seed ovoid, nearly 2 mm. long, smooth.—(CYPRESS-SPURGE.)—Fence-rows, roadsides, and waste-places, various provinces, E. U. S. Nat. of Eu. —Sum.–fall.

10. **G. trichotomus** (H.B.K.) Small. Stem 1–4 dm. tall: leaf-blades cuneate to elliptic, 0.5–1.2 cm. long: bracts similar to the leaves: involucre 2 mm. long; glands obreniform: capsule about 4 mm. broad, minutely wrinkled: seed sub-globose, fully 1.5 mm. in diameter.—Coastal sand-dunes, S pen. Fla. and the Keys.—(*W. I., Mex.*)—All year.

11. **G. Helioscopia** (L.) Haw. Stem 1–3.5 dm. tall: leaf-blades spatulate to cuneate, 1.5–4 cm. long, finely toothed near the rounded or emarginate apex: bracts of the rays cuneate to elliptic-cuneate: involucre turbinate-campanulate, about 1.5 mm. high, short-peduncled; glands transversely oval, about 0.5 mm. wide, unappendaged: capsule about 4 mm. broad, the lobes rounded: seed ovoid, nearly 2 mm. long, finely reticulate.—(WARTWEED.)—Fields, waste-places, and cult. grounds, various provinces, N. C. to Ill., Ore., Que., and N. Y. Nat. of Eu.—Sum.–fall.

12. **G. obtusatus** (Pursh) Small. Stem 3–6 dm. tall: leaf-blades spatulate-elliptic, 1–3 cm. long: bracts ovate: involucre 1–1.5 mm. long: capsule 3.5–4 mm. broad, warty: seed ellipsoid or orbicular-ellipsoid, 2 mm. long or less, faintly reticulate.—(WARTY-SPURGE.)—Dry soil, often in woods, various provinces, S. C. to Tex., Ia., and Pa.—Spr.–sum.

13. **G. arkansanus** (Engelm. & Gray) Small. Stem 2–5 dm. tall: leaf-blades spatulate or cuneate, 1–3 cm. long: bracts ovate to ovate-reniform: involucre about 1 mm. long: capsule 2.5–3 mm. broad, with elongate warts: seed ovoid-lenticular, 1.3–1.5 mm. long, finely reticulate.—Prairies and shaded banks, vari-ous provinces, Ala. to Tex., Colo., and Kans.—Spr.–sum.

14. **G. platyphylla** (L.) Small. Stem 2–10 dm. tall: leaf-blades oblanceolate, acute, cordate and auricled at the base, 2–5 cm. long, softly pubescent beneath especially at and near the margin, sometimes with scattered pubescence above: bracts obovate, triangular-ovate or reniform-ovate: involucre about 1.5 mm. long, cottony pubescent, the glands large, sessile: capsule 2.5–3 mm. broad with depressed worts: seed ovoid-lenticular with a slight dorsal keel, 2 mm. long, smooth.—Waste places and roadsides, various provinces, Lake Champlain and the Great Lake region, also central N. Y. and southern La. Nat. of Eu.—Spr.– early fall.

28. **POINSETTIA** Graham. Annual, biennial, or perennial herbs or woody plants. Leaf-blades entire, toothed, or lobed, those of the upper ones often like the bracts highly colored or discolored. Involucres solitary or cymose, each with 1, or rarely 3 or 4, unappendaged glands. Capsule smooth. Seeds tuberculate.—About 12 species, mostly tropical American.—Sum.–fall or all year S.—EUPHORBIAS. SPURGES.

Gland or glands of the involucre stalked: bracts and upper leaves barely if at all discolored.   1. *P. dentata.*

Gland of the involucre sessile or nearly so: bracts and upper leaves discolored at the base.
Bracts white or pale-pink at the base.   2. *P. geniculata.*
Bracts red, scarlet, or purple at the base.
  Leaves throughout the plant with very narrowly linear entire blades: plant glabrous: involucral glands mostly 3 or 4.   3. *P. pinetorum.*
  Leaves, at least those of the main stem, and the bracts, with broad, toothed, pandurate or pinnately lobed blades, those of the branches often narrow: plant pubescent: involucral glands mostly solitary.
    Broad leaves with toothed blades.   4. *P. heterophylla.*
    Broad leaves with pandurate or pinnately lobed blades.   5. *P. cyathophora.*

1. **P. dentata** (Michx.) Small. Stem 2–4 dm. tall, pubescent: leaf-blades 1–9 cm. long, ovate, lanceolate, or nearly linear: involucre 2.5–3 mm. long; glands usually solitary: capsule 4–4.5 mm. broad: seed prominently tuberculate.—Rich soil, dry hills, and plains, various provinces, rarely Coastal Plain, N. Fla. to N. M., Wyo., S. D., N. Y., and Va.

2. **P. geniculata** (Ortega) Small. Stem 3–9 dm. tall, glabrous or nearly so: leaf-blades elliptic or ovate, 4–9 cm. long, entire or obsoletely dentate: bracts often serrate or crenate: involucre 3–3.5 mm. long: capsule 4–5 mm. broad: seed ovoid, 3–3.5 mm. long.—Hillsides and roadsides, Rio Grande Region, Tex. and Fla. Keys.—(*W. I., Mex.*)

3. **P. pinetorum** Small. Stem 3–10 dm. tall, glabrous: leaf-blades narrowly elongate-linear, 4–15 cm. long: bracts entire: involucre turbinate, mostly less than 3 mm. long: capsule 2.5–3 mm. long: seed 2–2.5 mm. long, slightly tuberculate. [*P. havanensis* (Fl. SE. U. S.)]—Pinelands and sandy places, Everglade Keys, pen. Fla. and Florida Keys.—(*W. I.*)

4. **P. heterophylla** (L.) Small. Perennial, stem 3–12 dm. tall: leaf-blades obovate, elliptic, or ovate, or narrower, especially on the branches, 5–15 cm. long: involucre campanulate, mostly over 3 mm. long: capsule 3.5–4 mm. long: seed 3–3.5 mm. long, prominently tuberculate.—(PAINTED-LEAF. FIDDLER'S-SPURGE.)—Hammocks, wooded banks and rocky places, Coastal Plain, Fla. to Tex., Kans., Minn., and Ill.—(*W. I., Mex., C. A., S. A.*)

5. **P. cyathophora** (Murr.) Small. Annual, stem 1.5 m. tall or less, pubescent: leaf-blades elliptic or oval, varying to obovate or ovate, or narrower especially on the branches, 5–18 cm. long: involucre campanulate, 3.5–4 mm. long: capsule 4–4.5 mm. long: seed 3–3.5 mm. long, tuberculate.—(PAINTED-LEAF.)—Hammocks, cult. grounds, waste-places, and roadsides, Fla.—(*W. I., Mex., C. A., S. A.*)—A form, apparently of one or the other of the two preceding species occurs, perhaps as an immigrant in the Central States up into Kans., Minn., and Ill.

29. **EUPHORBIA** L. Very succulent cactus-like shrubs or trees, with angled or ribbed spine-armed jointed stems and branches. Leaves small or

minute, often scale-like, fleshy, early deciduous, or obsolete. Involucres solitary or
clustered, each with five mostly unappendaged glands. Capsule usually smooth.—
About 30 species, of the Old World.

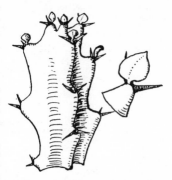

1. **E. lactea** Haw. Plants 1–5 m. tall,
copiously branched, the branches 3-angled,
the angles repand, with the faces whitish-
marbled: spines stout-subulate, 3–7 mm.
long, divergent: leaves between the spines;
blades suborbicular to orbicular-reniform,
2–4 mm. wide, glabrous, nearly sessile.—
(Mottled-spruge.)—Hammocks and waste-
places, Florida Keys. Nat. of E. I.—(*W.
I., Mex.*)—Frequently planted for ornament and for hedges in tropical regions.

30. **TITHYMALUS** Mill. Shrubs with fleshy branches. Leaves succulent: blades flat, entire or undulate-crisped. Involucres borne in dichotomous,
often contracted cymes, oblique and strongly
2-lipped, the lower lip much larger than the
upper. Capsule 3-lobed, the carpels often
keeled or horned.—About 30 species, tropical American. [*Pedilanthus* Neck.]

1. **T. Smallii** (Millsp.) Small. Plant 3–16
dm. tall or more, the stem and branches
sometimes zigzag: leaves spreading; blades
ovate to ovate-lanceolate, 4–11 cm. long: involucres 12–14 mm. long, mainly red, the two
terminal lobes broadly ovate, ciliolate: stamens and style exserted: capsule 6–7 mm.
long; seed 3–3.5 mm. long. [*P. tithymaloides*
(Fl. SE. U. S.) *P. Smallii* Millsp.]—(Jew-
bush. Red-bird flower.)—Hammocks and
pinelands, Everglade Keys, pen. Fla. and Florida Keys. Nat. of trop. Am., and
cult.—All year.—Used medicinally.

Family 2. CALLITRICHACEAE — Water-starwort Family

Herbs, often aquatics, with tender tissues. Leaves opposite: blades
entire, or 3-nerved. Flowers polygamous, minute, axillary, often minutely
bracted. Calyx wanting. Corolla wanting. Androecium of a single
stamen. Gynoecium of 4 united carpels. Ovary 4-celled. Fruit coriaceous, indehiscent, 4-lobed.—One genus.

1. **CALLITRICHE** L. Aquatic or more or less amphibious plants, the
opposite leaves often approximate or congested at the ends of the stem and
branches. Flowers inconspicuous, green.—About 20 species, of wide geographic
distribution.—Water-starworts.

Carpels permanently united: leaf-blades in terrestrial plants, or of floating leaves
in aquatics, obovate to spatulate and 3-veined.   I. Vernae.
Carpels, in fruit, separate nearly to the axis: leaf-blades uniformly linear and 1-veined.   II. Autumnales.

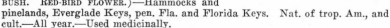

I. **Vernae**

Fruit manifestly pedicelled : leaves uniform.
Fruit about 0.8 mm. long: styles persistent. 1. *C. terrestris.*
Fruit about 0.7 mm. long: styles deciduous. 2. *C. Nuttallii.*
Fruit essentially sessile.
Styles much shorter than the fruit. 3. *C. palustris.*
Styles fully as long as the fruit.
Aquatic : fruit 1 mm. broad. 4. *C. heterophylla.*
Terrestrial : fruit 0.5 mm. broad. 5. *C. peploides.*

II. **Autumnales**

Submerged perennial, with leaf-blades notched at the apex. 6. *C. autumnalis.*

1. C. terrestris Raf. Terrestrial, fragrant in drying, the foliage scaleless: leaf-blades spatulate, 2–3 mm. long: fruit broader than long. [*C. Austinii* Engelm.]—Damp shaded soil, various provinces, rarely Coastal Plain, Ala. to Tex., Mo., Conn., and Va.—(*Mex.*)—Sum.-fall.

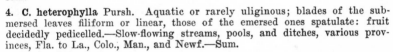

2. C. Nuttallii Torr. Terrestrial, the foliage scaleless: leaf-blades spatulate to elliptic, 2–4 mm. long: pedicels without scales: fruit broader than long.—Moist soil, Coastal Plain and occasionally adj. provinces, Ala. to La. and Ky.—Spr.-sum.

3. C. palustris L. Aquatic, the foliage scaly: blades of the submerged leaves linear, those of the emersed ones spatulate, shorter than the submersed ones: flower-stalks with 2 scales: fruit obovoid, about 1.5 mm. long. [*C. verna* L.] — (Water-chickweed.) — Ponds and streams, various provinces, U. S. and Can.—(*S. A., O. W.*)—Spr.-sum.

4. C. heterophylla Pursh. Aquatic or rarely uliginous; blades of the submersed leaves filiform or linear, those of the emersed ones spatulate: fruit decidedly pedicelled.—Slow-flowing streams, pools, and ditches, various provinces, Fla. to La., Colo., Man., and Newf.—Sum.

5. C. peploides Nutt. Terrestrial, the plant matted: leaf-blades uniform, obovate, oblanceolate, or elliptic: fruit sessile or nearly so.—Moist soil, various provinces, Fla. to Tex. and Ark.—Spr.-sum.

6. C. autumnalis L. Aquatic with stems 6–17 cm. long: leaf-blades narrowly linear, 5–12 mm. long: fruit orbicular-reniform, scarcely 2 mm. wide, 2-lobed, sessile.—Ponds, lakes, and streams, various provinces, La. to Colo., Ore., Man., and Que.—(*Eu.*)—Sum.-fall.

Order **SAPINDALES** — Sapindal Order

Shrubs or trees. Leaves various: blades simple and entire or toothed, or compound. Calyx of distinct sepals. Corolla of distinct petals, regular or rarely irregular, or wanting. Androecium of as many stamens as there are petals, or of twice as many, or rarely of more or fewer. Filaments distinct. Gynoecium of a single carpel, or of several united carpels. Ovary superior. Ovules 1 or 2, or several, in each cavity of the ovary, pendulous, with the raphe away from the axis of the ovary, or erect or ascending. Fruit various.—Exceptions to the woody plants are *Pachysandra* and *Cardiospermum*.

Corolla wanting: stamens 4 (in our genus): styles wanting.
                      Fam. 1. BUXACEAE.
Corolla present or if wanting (*Dodonaeaceae*) stamens
    6: styles present, distinct or united, rarely
    single.
Stigmas tufted or many-cleft.   Fam. 2. EMPETRACEAE.
Stigmas entire.
    Plant with resin-bearing tissues.   Fam. 3. SPONDIACEAE.
    Plant not resin-bearing.
        Leaf-blades simple, pinnately veined.
            Each cavity of the ovary with a single
              ovule.
                Flowers in racemes: fruit a dry
                   terete or a winged, coriaceous
                   drupe.   Fam. 4. CYRILLACEAE.
                Flowers not racemose: fruit a fleshy
                   drupe.   Fam. 5. AQUIFOLIACEAE.
            Each cavity of the ovary with 2 or more
              ovules.
                Disk present: corolla present.
                   Anthers introrse: seed often
                     arilled.   Fam. 6. CELASTRACEAE.
                   Anthers extrorse: seed not arilled. Fam. 7. HIPPOCRATEACEAE.
                Disk obsolete: corolla wanting. Fam. 8. DODONAEACEAE.
        Leaf-blades simple and palmately veined or
           compound.
           Leaves opposite.
              Fruit capsular.
                Flowers regular: fruit a mem-
                   branous, bladdery 3-lobed cap-
                   sule: leaf-blades pinnately com-
                   pound.   Fam. 9. STAPHYLEACEAE.
                Flowers irregular: fruit a leath-
                   ery globular capsule: leaf-
                   blades digitately compound. Fam. 10. AESCULACEAE.
              Fruit a samara.   Fam. 11. ACERACEAE.
        Leaves alternate, in our species.   Fam. 12. SAPINDACEAE.

FAMILY 1. **BUXACEAE** — Box FAMILY

Shrubs, trees, or perennial herbs. Leaves alternate or opposite, often persistent: blades simple. Flowers monoecious or dioecious. Calyx of several sepals or wanting. Corolla wanting. Androecium of 4–7 stamens. Gynoecium of 2–4 united carpels. Fruit a capsule or a drupe.—About 6 genera and 35 species, widely distributed.

1. **PACHYSANDRA** Michx. Herbs with leaves and flowers on separate branches. Leaves alternate, approximate. Flowers brownish, monoecious, spicate. Staminate flowers with 4 sepals and 4 stamens. Pistillate flowers with 4 or more sepals and a 3-celled ovary. Capsule 3-celled, 3-lobed. Seeds 2 in each cavity. Several species, mostly Asiatic.

1. **P. procumbens** Michx. Stem 1–3 dm. long: leaves evergreen; blades thickish, 3–12 cm. long, obovate, oval, or ovate, sometimes coarsely toothed: spikes 3–10 cm. long: flowers musk-scented, the pistillate few at the base of the spike: outer sepals ovate or elliptic, the inner broader, 4–6 mm. long: capsule subglobose, about 1 cm. in diameter, each carpel with a long curved beak.—(ALLE-GHENY-MOUNTAIN SPURGE.) — Rich woods, often in calcareous soils, various provinces, W. Fla. to La., Ky., and W. Va. —Spr.

FAMILY 2. **EMPETRACEAE** — Crow-berry Family

Shrubs, mostly resembling heaths. Leaves alternate or whorled, sometimes numerous and crowded. Flowers dioecious or rarely polygamous. Calyx of 2 or 3 sepals. Corolla of 2 or 3 petals, or wanting. Androecium of 2–4, mostly 3 stamens. Gynoecium of 2–several united carpels.— Three genera and few species, but widely distributed.

1. CERATIOLA Michx. Evergreen shrubs. Leaf-blades narrow, revolute and thus almost tubular. Flowers 2 or 3 in an axil. Sepals 2. Petals 2. Stamens 2. Ovary 2-celled. Drupe with 2 nutlets.—One species.

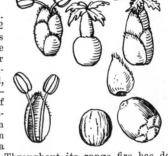

1. **C. ericoides** Michx. Shrub 3–15 dm. tall: leaves crowded and spreading, 8–12 mm. long: flowers red or yellowish: sepals about 1 mm. long: stamens exserted: drupe subglobose, 2–3 mm. in diameter, yellow or red.—(Rosemary.)—Dry pinelands, sandhills, and scrub, often in very acid soil, Coastal Plain, Fla. to Miss., and S. C.— Spr.–sum. or all year.—A peculiar shrub of somewhat uncertain relationship, but associated with the crowberries of northern North America. It resembles the heaths in habit and in the peculiarly pleasant aroma it gives off. It has two deadly enemies. Throughout its range fire has destroyed vast areas of it, while in lower peninsular Florida the parasitic woevine (*Cassytha*) is equally as destructive.—Specimens of this species collected at Palma Sola, Florida, have been described as *C. falcautla* Gandoger.

FAMILY 3. **SPONDIACEAE** — Sumac Family

Shrubs, trees, or vines, with a milky, resinous, often acid or caustic sap. Leaves alternate: blades simple or pinnately compound. Flowers monoecious, dioecious, or polygamous. Calyx of 3–6 sepals. Corolla of 3–5 petals, larger than the calyx. Androecium of 3–6, or rarely more, stamens. Gynoecium of 1, or 3–5 more or less united carpels. Fruit a drupe or a berry.—Sixty genera and 500 species, mostly tropical.

Gynoecium 1-carpellary: style single: ovary on a swollen receptacle: leaves with simple blades.   I. Mangifereae.
Gynoecium 3-carpellary: styles or stigmas 3: ovary not on a swollen receptacle: leaves with simple or compound blades.   II. Rhoedeae.

I. Mangifereae
Trees with narrow leaf-blades and panicled flowers.   1. Mangifera.

II. Rhoedeae
Ovary, and drupe, very oblique: style laterally oblique: leaves with broad simple blades.   2. Cotinus.
Ovary, and drupe, not oblique: style terminal: leaves with compound blades.
 Drupe somewhat elongate, the coats permanently united.   3. Metopium.
 Drupe depressed, the coats ultimately separating.
  Drupe with a glabrous or sparingly pubescent outer coat: stone ribbed.   4. Toxicodendron.
  Drupe with a copiously pubescent outer coat: stone smooth.
   Flowers polygamous, in terminal thyrsoid panicles appearing after the leaves.   5. Rhus.
   Flowers polygamo-dioecious, in solitary or clustered spikes in the axils, before the leaves.   6. Schmaltzia.

1. **MANGIFERA** L. Trees. Leaf-blades simple, relatively narrow. Flowers polygamo-dioecious, in stiff panicles, the branches not plumose. Sepals 4 or 5. Petals 4 or 5. Ovary oblique: style 1, lateral. Drupe ovoid to somewhat reniform, smooth: stone tenaciously fibrous-coated.—About 14 species, Asiatic.

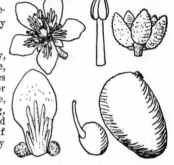

1. **M. indica** L. Leaf-blades leathery, elliptic to linear-elliptic or linear-lanceolate, mostly 1–3.5 dm. long, reticulate: panicles 1–4 dm. long: flowers greenish, yellowish, or red: sepals ovate: petals elliptic or obovate, 3.5–4 mm. long: drupe 5–10 cm. long, aromatic. — (MANGO.) — Hammocks and fields, S pen. Fla. and the Keys. Nat. of the E. I., and cult.—Spr.—Grown in many varieties for its esculent fruit.

2. **COTINUS** Adans. Shrubs or trees. Leaf-blades simple, relatively broad. Flowers mostly polygamous or dioecious, in loose panicles which often have plumose branches. Sepals 5. Petals 5. Ovary oblique: styles 3, eccentric. Drupe obliquely reniform, veiny: stone glabrous.— Two species, the following and one Eurasian.

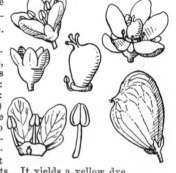

1. **C. americanus** Nutt. Shrub, or tree becoming 12 m. tall: leaf-blades membranous, obovate or oval, 4–15 cm. long: panicles 1–3 dm. long, the branches glandular-villous: sepals ovate: petals elliptic-ovate, green: drupe 5 mm. long. [*C. cotinoides* (Nutt.) Britton.]—(SMOKE-TREE.)—Rocky limestone hills, Interior Plateau provinces, Ala. to Ark. (or Tex?), Mo., and Tenn.—Spr.— The sapwood is whitish; the orange heartwood is coarse-grained, light and soft, but durable in contact with the soil as fence-posts. It yields a yellow dye.

3. **METOPIUM** P. Br. Shrubs or trees. Leaf-blades pinnate. Flowers dioecious, in open panicles. Sepals 5. Petals 5. Ovary equilateral. Styles united: stigma 3-lobed. Drupe not oblique. —Three species, West Indian.

1. **M. toxiferum** (L.) Krug & Urban. Shrub, or tree becoming 14 m. tall, with a very poisonous sap: leaflets 3–7; blades leathery, ovate, 3–9 cm. long: panicles 1–2 dm. long: sepals reniform or suborbicular: petals elliptic to ovate or oval yellow-green and often dark-lined within: drupe 10–15 mm. long.—(POISONWOOD. DOCTOR-GUM. CORAL-SUMAC.)—Hammocks, pinelands, and coastal sand-dunes, S. pen. Fla. and the Keys.—(W. I.)—Spr. or all year.—The sap is a powerful skin-poison. The sap-wood is yellow or light-brown; the dark-brown and

red-streaked heart-wood is heavy and hard, but not strong. A large tree in hammocks, a shrub, often with diffuse or depressed stems in pinelands.

4. **TOXICODENDRON** [Tourn.] Mill. Shrubs, trees, or woody vines, with poisonous sap. Leaf-blades pinnately compound. Flowers polygamous or dioecious, in rather dense panicles, white or greenish. Sepals 4–6. Petals 4–6. Ovary glabrous. Styles short. Drupe mostly glabrous, the sarcocarp wax-secreting. Seed ribbed.—About 20 species, North American and Asiatic.—Spr.–sum.—The sap is a powerful skin poison. Some of the species are used medicinally.

Leaf-blades 3-foliolate: vines or low shrubs: panicles of fruits spreading.
   Stems climbing or erect especially when young: blades
      of the leaflets coarsely toothed or entire, thin.   1. *T. radicans.*
   Stems erect: blades of the leaflets lobed, thickish.   2. *T. Toxicodendron.*
Leaf-blades 7–11-foliolate: tall shrub or tree: panicles of
   fruits drooping.   3. *T. Vernix.*

1. **T. radicans** (L.) Kuntze. Stem climbing by aërial roots: blades of the leaflets membranous, ovate to ovate-lanceolate, 3–20 cm. long: sepals ovate, 1–2 mm. long: petals elliptic to elliptic-ovate, 3–4 mm. long: drupe 3–6 mm. in diameter. [*Rhus radicans* L.]—(POISON-IVY. POISON-OAK.)—Woods, hammocks, thickets, fence rows, and swamps, various provinces, Fla to Miss., Nebr., Minn., and N. S.—(*W. I.*)

2. **T. Toxicodendron** (L.) Britton. Shrub, with densely pubescent twigs: blades of the leaflets ovate in outline or rarely obovate, 4–12 cm. long, coarsely crenate-lobed: panicles densely flowered: petals elliptic-lanceolate, about 2.5 mm. long: drupe depressed-globose. [*Rhus Toxicodendron* L.]—(POISON-OAK.) — Dry woods and pinelands, Coastal Plain and rarely adj. provinces, Fla. to Tex., Tenn., and N. J. The stems are simple or little branched. The leaflet-blades are much firmer in texture than in *R. radicans,* and strongly pubescent beneath.

3. **T. Vernix** (L.) Kuntze. Shrub or small tree: blades of the lateral leaflets elliptic, or oval, 4–15 cm. long, undulate: petals linear-elliptic, about 2 mm. long: drupes subglobose, about 5 mm. broad, in drooping panicles. [*Rhus Vernix* L. *Rhus venenata* DC.]—(POISON-SUMAC. THUNDERWOOD. POISON-ELDER. POISON-DOGWOOD. SWAMP-SUMAC.)—Non-alluvial swamps and wet woods, various provinces, Fla. to La., Minn., and Me.—The heart-wood, coarse-grained, light and soft, is brown streaked with yellow.

5. **RHUS** L. Shrubs or trees, not poisonous. Leaf-blades pinnately compound, several-foliolate. Flowers polygamous or dioecious, borne in terminal usually compact panicles, white or greenish-white. Sepals commonly 5. Petals commonly 5. Ovary pubescent. Style short. Drupe pubescent. Seed smooth and even.—About 125 species, natives of temperate and warm regions.—Spr.— SUMACS. The bark and leaves are sometimes used for tanning.

Rachis of the leaf wingless, terete or nearly so: fruiting panicles erect.
                                                  I. HIRTAE.
Rachis of the leaf winged: fruiting panicles nodding.   II. LEUCANTHAE.

I. HIRTAE

Foliage more or less glaucous or pale.
  Twigs, panicles, and drupes usually pubescent with soft very
    short hairs.
    Leaflets with acuminate, sharply serrate blades.   1. R. glabra.
    Leaflets with crenate-serrate blades, rounded at the apex.   2. R. Ashei.
  Twigs, panicles, and drupes bristly pubescent with long
    spreading hairs.   3. R. hirta.
Foliage densely pubescent with brownish hairs, not glaucous.   4. R. Michauxii.

II. LEUCANTHAE

Bark of the trunk gray, dull: petals about 2.5 mm. long: anthers
    broadly ellipsoid, scarcely 1 mm. long.
  Blades of the leaflets acuminate, and usually acute: leaf-
    rachis broadly winged.   5. R. Copallinum.
  Blades of the leaflets obtuse: leaf-rachis narrowly winged.   6. R. obtusifolia.
Bark of the trunk red, shining: petals about 3 mm. long:
    anthers linear-ellipsoid, fully 1 mm. long.   7. R. leucantha.

1. R. glabra L.   Shrub or tree becoming 6 m. tall, leaflets 11–31; blades
elliptic or lanceolate (that of the terminal one often ovate), 3–8 cm. long: petals
about 2 mm. long: drupe velvety, the stone
3–3.5 mm. long.—(SMOOTH-SUMAC. SCARLET-
SUMAC. RED-SUMAC.)—Dry rich soil and
thickets, various provinces, N Fla. to La.,
Minn., and N. S.—Spr.–sum.—The orange-
colored and green-streaked heart-wood is
coarse-grained, soft, and brittle. The fruiting panicles are erect.

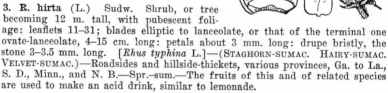

2. R. Ashei Small. Shrub with glaucous
stems: leaflets 13–17; blades elliptic to oval-
elliptic, 3–9 cm. long: stone of the drupe
about 3 mm. long. [*Rhus caroliniana* Ashe.
Not Mill.]—Sandy soil, Piedmont, N. C.—
Spr.

3. R. hirta (L.) Sudw. Shrub, or tree
becoming 12 m. tall, with pubescent foli-
age: leaflets 11–31; blades elliptic to lanceolate, or that of the terminal one
ovate-lanceolate, 4–15 cm. long: petals about 3 mm. long: drupe bristly, the
stone 3–3.5 mm. long. [*Rhus typhina* L.]—(STAGHORN-SUMAC. HAIRY-SUMAC.
VELVET-SUMAC.)—Roadsides and hillside-thickets, various provinces, Ga. to La.,
S. D., Minn., and N. B.—Spr.–sum.—The fruits of this and of related species
are used to make an acid drink, similar to lemonade.

4. R. Michauxii Sarg. Shrub with densely pubescent stems: leaflets 9–15;
blades elliptic, oval, or elliptic-ovate (that of the terminal one often ovate),
5–10 cm. long: stone of the drupe about 3.5 mm. long. [*Rhus pumila* Michx.
Not Meerb.]—(FALSE POISON-SUMAC.)—Sandy soil, Piedmont, Ga. to N. C.—
Spr.

5. R. Copallinum L. Shrub, or tree becoming 10 m. tall and 2.5 dm. in diameter, the bark thick, scaly: leaflets 9–21; blades elliptic to elliptic-lanceolate or
sometimes oval, 3–10 cm. long: stone of the drupe 2.5–3 mm. long.—(DWARF-
SUMAC. MOUNTAIN-SUMAC. BLACK-SUMAC. SHINING-SUMAC. SMOOTH-SUMAC.)
—Dry, often stony soil, and hillsides, various provinces, Fla. to Tex., Minn., and
Me.—Sum.—The heart-wood, light-brown streaked with green, is coarse-grained,
light and soft. The fruiting panicles are drooping.

6. R. obtusifolia Small. Shrub: leaflets 17–21; blades ovate to elliptic, 2–5
cm. long: petals about 2.5 mm. long: stone of the drupe 3.5–4 mm. long.—
Pinelands, Fla.—Spr.—sum. or all year S.

7. R. leucantha Jacq. Shrub, or tree becoming 9 m. tall, the bark thin, soft, smooth, peeling: leaflets 15–33; blades narrowly elliptic to linear-lanceolate, 3–9 cm. long: stone of the drupe about 3 mm. long.—(SOUTHERN-SUMAC.)—Hammocks, Everglade Keys, Fla.—(*W. I.*)—All year.

6. SCHMALTZIA Desv. Shrubs or trees, aromatic, not poisonous. Leaf-blades pinnately compound, usually 3-foliolate. Flowers polygamous or dioecious, in ament-like racemes or panicles before the leaves, yellowish-green. Sepals commonly 5. Petals commonly 5. Ovary pubescent: styles short. Drupe pubescent with crimson hairs, the sarcocarp not wax-secreting. Seed smooth and even.—About 8 species, North American.—SWEET-SUMACS.—The bark of some species is used medicinally.

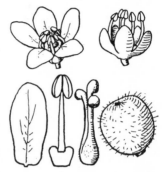

1. S. crenata (Mill.) Greene. Shrub with diffuse stems, 1–2.5 m. tall: leaflets 3; blade of the terminal one mostly ovate or obovate: flowers yellow: drupe 7–8 mm. in diameter. [*S. aromatica* (Ait.) Desv.]—(FRAGRANT-SUMAC. SWEET-SCENTED SUMAC.)—Dry woods, often in calcareous soils, various provinces, Fla. to La., Minn., and Ind.—Spr.—The genus *Schmaltzia* has been interpreted as made up of many species. All, except the present species have geographic ranges northward and westward of our range.

FAMILY 4. **CYRILLACEAE** — TITI FAMILY

Shrubs or trees. Leaves alternate, mostly evergreen: blades entire. Flowers perfect, borne in lateral or terminal narrow racemes or raceme-like panicles. Calyx of 4 or 5 persistent sepals. Corolla of 5 or 8 petals, white. Androecium of 5 or 10 stamens. Gynoecium of 2–5 united carpels: styles united: stigmas 2–5. Fruit a dry terete or winged nut-like drupe.—Three genera and about 12 species, American.

Panicles lateral: sepals equal: petals acute, narrowed upward: stamens 5: ovary 2-celled: fruit terete, not winged.   1. CYRILLA.
Panicles terminal: sepals unequal: petals obtuse, broadened upward: stamens 10: ovary 3- or 4-celled: fruit winged.   2. CLIFTONIA.

1. CYRILLA Garden. Shrubs or small trees, with pale close bark. Leaves with veiny blades at maturity. Panicles raceme-like, narrow, clustered, spreading in anthesis. Sepals acute or acuminate. Petals narrowed upward, clawless, about twice as long as the sepals. Stamens equal: filaments flattened. Style short. Fruit an almost terete spongy drupe, spreading.—Four or five species, the following and the others tropical American.—IRONWOODS. TITIS. RED-TITIS. WHITE-TITIS.

Leaves mostly 5–10 cm. long; blades thick-membranous: petals 3 mm. long or more: drupe conic-ovoid or ovoid.   1. *C. racemiflora.*
Leaves mostly 1–4 cm. long; blades coriaceous: petals less than 3 mm. long: drupe globose-ovoid or subglobose.
    Sepals ovate: anthers apiculate.   2. *C. parvifolia.*
    Sepals lanceolate: anthers notched.   3. *C. arida.*

1. C. racemiflora L.   Much branched glabrous shrub or small tree reaching a height of 10 m. and a maximum trunk diameter of 3 dm., semi-evergreen, the trunk clothed with a close pale or whitish bark: leaf-blades thick-membranous, oblanceolate, obovate, or nearly elliptic, 5–10 cm. long, obtuse, acute or acuminate, more or less strongly reticulate, lustrous above, dull and paler beneath: racemes slender, 8–15 cm. long: pedicels ascending or finally spreading: sepals ovate or ovate-lanceolate, 1 mm. long, acute: corolla white, 4–5 mm. broad: petals lanceolate or oblong-lanceolate, 3 mm. long or more, acute: drupe conic-ovoid or ovoid, 2.5–3 mm. long, obtuse, minutely granular: seeds narrowly ovoid.— (LEATHERWOOD. HE-HUCKLEBERRY. BLACK-TITI. MYRTLE.)—Swamps and stream-banks, Coastal Plain, and rarely adj. provinces, Fla. to Tex., Mo., and S. Va.—Spr.—The brown and red-tinged heart-wood is close-grained, heavy, and hard.   The flowers are an important source of honey.

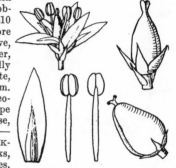

2. C. parvifolia Raf.   Glabrous evergreen compact, rigid, and much branched shrub 1–5 m. tall, evergreen: leaf-blades thin-coriaceous, oblanceolate or linear-oblanceolate, 1–4 cm. long, acute or apiculate, lustrous above, paler beneath, more or less reticulate: racemes slender, 3–8 cm. long: pedicels 1–2 mm. long, commonly surpassing the subulate bracts: sepals ovate, 1 mm. long, acute: corolla white, 3–4 mm. broad: petals broadly elliptic-lanceolate, 1.5–2 mm. long, more than twice as long as the sepals, obtuse, thickened at the base and above the midrib: stamens included: drupe subglobose or globose-ovoid, 1.5–2 mm. long, slightly granular.—Swamps and bays, Coastal Plain, N Fla. to La.—Sum.

3. C. arida Small.   Small tree, perhaps also a shrub, usually with vine-like branches: leaves evergreen, approximate near the ends of the branches: blades elliptic-spatulate, elliptic-oblanceolate, or narrowly elliptic, 1–3 cm. long, thick-coriaceous: panicles mostly 2–6 cm. long: sepals acuminate: petals elliptic-lanceolate about twice as long as the sepals, 2–2.5 mm. long: drupe globose-ovoid, often depressed, about 2 mm. long.—Scrub, inland sand-dunes, S lake region, Fla.—Sum.

2. **CLIFTONIA** Gaertn.   Shrubs or small trees, with dark scaly bark. Leaves with smooth blades.   Panicles raceme-like, stout, not clustered, erect in anthesis.   Sepals very broad and rounded, often reniform.   Petals broadened upwards, clawed, many times exceeding the sepals. Stamens unequal: filaments appendaged. Style wanting.   Fruit a winged nut-like drupe, nodding.—One species.

1. C. monophylla (Lam.) Sarg.   Shrub or tree becoming 8 m. tall: leaves evergreen; blades narrowly elliptic to elliptic-oblanceolate, oval, or obovate, 3–6 cm. long, pale or glaucous beneath: panicles 2–9 cm. long: flowers fragrant: sepals about 0.5 mm. long: petals spatulate, elliptic-obovate, or cuneate, 4–5 mm. long, or sometimes shorter: drupe ovoid to oval, 6–7 mm. long, the wings notched at both ends. [*C. ligustrina* Sims]—(TITI. BLACK-TITI. BUCK-

WHEAT-BRUSH. IRONWOOD.)—Non-alluvial swamps and bays, often in acid soil, Coastal Plain, N Fla. to La. and Ga.—Spr.—The brown and red-tinged heart-wood is close-grained and heavy, but brittle. The flowers are an important source of honey.

FAMILY 5. **AQUIFOLIACEAE** — HOLLY FAMILY

Shrubs or trees. Leaves alternate : blades simple. Flowers perfect or polygamous. Calyx of 4–6 persistent sepals. Corolla of 4–6 petals, often united at the base. Androecium of 4–6 stamens. Gynoecium of 4–8 united carpels. Fruit drupaceous.—Three genera and 300 species, in temperate and tropical regions.

1. **ILEX** L. Shrubs or trees. Leaves mostly persistent: blades entire or toothed. Flowers sometimes nearly dioecious. Sepals persistent. Corolla deciduous, white or greenish-white. Drupe with 4–8 nutlets.—About 280 species, mostly American.—HOLLIES.—The flowers of some species are an important source of honey. Some of the red-fruited species are used for decorations for winter festivals.

Fruit with smooth nutlets. — Subgenus I. PRINOS.
Fruit with ribbed or striate nutlets.
　Nutlets many-striate on the back : leaves deciduous :
　　blades thick-membranous or herbaceous. — Subgenus II. PRINOIDES.
　Nutlet few-ribbed or 1-grooved on the back : leaves
　　persistent, evergreen : blades coriaceous. — Subgenus III. AQUIFOLIUM.

I. PRINOS

Drupes black, except in a red-fruited form of *I. glabra* : leaves persistent ; blades leathery.
　Leaves with blades of an obovate or spatulate type prevailing ; petioles relatively short and stout.
　　Leaf-blades entire or distantly serrate above the middle, not spine-tipped : drupes mostly less than 6 mm. in diameter. — 1. *I. glabra.*
　　Leaf-blades spinescent-toothed above the middle or spine-tipped : drupes mostly over 6 mm. in diameter. — 2. *I. coriacea.*
　Leaves with blades of an ovate type prevailing ; petioles relatively long and slender. — 3. *I. Krugiana.*
Drupes red, orange-red, or scarlet : leaves deciduous ; blades herbaceous.
　Staminate and pistillate flowers on pedicels of about equal length. — 4. *I. verticillata.*
　Staminate flowers on conspicuously slender and long pedicels : the pistillate shorter-pedicelled. — 5. *I. laevigata.*

II. PRINOIDES

Staminate flowers solitary or clustered, without a common peduncle.
　Leaf-blades typically broadest above the middle.
　　Nutlets faintly ribbed and striate : leaf-blades glabrous or merely ciliate.
　　　Leaf-blades 3–9 cm. long : drupe shorter than the pedicel. — 6. *I. longipes.*
　　　Leaf-blade 1–2 cm. long : drupe longer than the pedicel. — 7. *I. Curtissii.*
　　Nutlets prominently ribbed and striate : leaf-blades pubescent beneath or usually so.
　　　Pedicel much longer than the drupe : drupes solitary or 2 together. — 8. *I. Cuthbertii.*
　　　Pedicel much shorter than the drupe : drupes more or less clustered. — 9. *I. decidua.*
　Leaf-blades broadest at the middle or below it.
　　Leaf-blades glabrous or with few hairs about the nerves : calyx glabrous without.
　　　Leaf-blades 2–7 cm. long, inconspicuously toothed : Carolinian.

Leaf-blades subcoriaceous: drupe 9–11 mm. in diameter.
Leaf-blades membranous: drupe 6–7 mm. in diameter.　　　　　　　　　　　　　　　　　　　10. *I. Buswellii.*
Leaf-blades 6–20 cm. long, conspicuously toothed:　　　11. *I. ambigua.*
　Alleghenian.　　　　　　　　　　　　　　　　　12. *I. monticola.*
　　Leaf-blades densely pubescent beneath: calyx pubescent.　13. *I. Beadlei.*
Staminate flowers several on a common peduncle.　　　14. *I. Amelanchier.*

III. Aquifolium

Leaf-blades entire or with a few appressed teeth near the apex.
　Leaf-blades linear or narrowly elliptic, or broader on
　　shoots, 1–4 cm. long.　　　　　　　　　　　　15. *I. myrtifolia.*
　Leaf-blades elliptic, oblanceolate, or obovate, 4–10 cm. long.　16. *I. Cassine.*
Leaf-blades toothed or sinuate.
　Teeth crenate.　　　　　　　　　　　　　　　17. *I. vomitoria.*
　Teeth spine-like, rarely only the terminal one present.
　　Leaf-blades cuneate or cuneate-obovate, with the teeth
　　　directed forward: nutlets oval, shallowly grooved and
　　　blunt-ridged.　　　　　　　　　　　　　18. *I. cumulicola.*
　　Leaf-blades oval, elliptic, or elliptic-obovate, with the
　　　teeth spreading: nutlets deeply grooved and sharp-
　　　ridged.　　　　　　　　　　　　　　　　19. *I. opaca.*

1. **I. glabra** (L.) A. Gray. Shrub 0.5–1.5 m. tall, with velvety-pubescent twigs: leaf-blades obovate, oblanceolate, elliptic, or oval, or rarely ovate, 1–5 cm. long, acute or obtuse, entire or distantly serrate above the middle, deep-green and lustrous above, short-petioled: staminate calyx fully 3 mm. wide: staminate corolla about 7 mm. wide: drupe 4–6 mm. in diameter, shorter than the stalks.—(Ink-berry. Evergreen-winterberry. Gallberry.)— Low pinelands, swamps, and prairies, often in acid soil, Coastal Plain and rarely adj. provinces, Fla. to La. and N. S.—Spr.– early sum.—An interesting form, rather smaller throughout than typical *I. glabra* occurs in pen. Florida. The drupe is red and rather pointed.

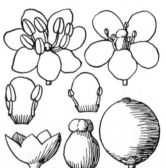

2. **I. coriacea** (Pursh) Chapm. Shrub 1–3 m. tall, glabrous or nearly so: leaf-blades obovate, elliptic, elliptic-oblanceolate, or oval, 2–9 cm. long, acute or usually short-acuminate, entire or with appressed spinescent teeth above the middle, dark-green and lustrous above, short-petioled: staminate calyx 3.5–4 mm. wide: staminate corolla 5.5–7 mm. wide: drupe globose, 6–8 mm. in diameter, black, shining. [*I. lucida* (Ait.) T. & G.]—(Large-gallberry.)— Non-alluvial swamps, Coastal Plain, Fla. to La. and S Va.—(Mex. (?))—Spr.

3. **I. Krugiana** Loesener. Shrub, or tree 11 m. tall, with glabrous twigs: leaf-blades elliptic or ovate, 4–7.5 cm. long, acuminate, mostly entire, deep-green and lustrous above, slender-petioled: staminate calyx about 3 mm. wide: staminate corolla 5–5.5 mm. wide: drupe 5.5–6.5 mm. in diameter, about as long as the stalk.—(Krug's-holly.)—Hammocks, Everglade Keys, Fla.—(W. I.)— Wint.

4. **I. verticillata** (L.) Gray. Shrub, or small tree sometimes 7 m. tall, with glabrous or slightly pubescent twigs: leaf-blades thickish, elliptic or oval, varying to ovate or obovate, 2–8 cm. long, acute or acuminate at both ends, more or less pubescent beneath, often strongly reticulate, serrate: staminate calyx about 2.5 mm. wide: staminate corolla 6–7 mm. wide: drupe 6–8 mm. in diameter, red.—(Black-alder. Winterberry. Fever-bush.)—Swamps and low woods, various provinces, Fla. to La., Mo., Ont., and N. S.—Sum.

5. I. laevigata (Pursh) A. Gray. Shrub, or small tree rarely 6 m. tall, with glabrous twigs: leaf-blades thinnish, elliptic or oval, or sometimes lanceolate or oblanceolate, 3–9 cm. long, acute or mostly acuminate, appressed-serrate, glabrous on both surfaces or sometimes sparingly pubescent on the veins beneath: staminate calyx 3.5–4 mm. wide: staminate corolla 6–7.5 mm. wide: drupe 8–18 mm. in diameter, orange-red.—(SMOOTH-WINTERBERRY. HOOP-WOOD.)—Swamps and wet woods, often in acid soil, various provinces, in Coastal Plain only N, Ga. to Pa., N. H., and Me.—Spr.–early sum.

6. I. longipes Chapm. Shrub or tree 7 m. tall, with widely spreading branches and glabrous twigs: leaf-blades rather coriaceous, nearly elliptic or oval but broadest slightly above the middle, often abruptly short-acuminate, obtuse or acute, dark-green above, glabrous or nearly so beneath at maturity, crenate-serrate, the teeth often tipped with appressed spine-like bristles: staminate calyx about 2.5 mm. wide: staminate corolla 6–7 mm. wide: drupe globose, red, 7–10 mm. in diameter.—Rocky banks, various provinces, Fla. to La., Tenn., and N. C.—Spr.

7. I. Curtissii (Fernald) Small. Shrub or small tree with spreading branches and glabrous twigs: leaf-blades thin-coriaceous spatulate to elliptic-spatulate, acute or obtuse, glabrous, obscurely crenate, short-petioled: flowers not seen: drupe globose, red, 4–5 mm. in diameter. [*I. decidua Curtissii* Fernald]—Hammocks, along rivers, Fla.—Spr.

8. I. Cuthbertii Small. Shrub or small tree with sometimes densely pubescent twigs: leaf-blades thickish, mainly obovate to nearly elliptic, obtuse, shallowly and usually inconspicuously toothed, permanently more or less pubescent on both sides, but especially so beneath: flowers not seen: drupe subglobose, 8–10 mm. in diameter.—Woods, Coastal Plain, Fla., and Ga.—Spr.

9. I. decidua Walt. Shrub, or small tree 10 m. tall, the twigs glabrous or nearly so: leaf-blades thickish, spatulate, oblanceolate, or nearly elliptic, 2–6 cm. long, obtuse or retuse at the apex, crenate-serrate, dark-green and glabrous above, paler and usually pubescent beneath: staminate calyx 2.5–3 mm. wide: staminate corolla 4.5–6 mm. wide: drupe globose, 7–9 mm. in diameter, orange or nearly scarlet.—(DECIDUOUS-HOLLY. BEAR-BERRY. POSSUM-HAW. WELK-HOLLY.)—Alluvial swamps, various provinces, Fla. to Tex., Kans., and Md.—Spr.—The creamy-white heart-wood is close-grained, heavy, and hard.

10. I. Buswellii Small. Shrub up to 3 m. tall, with numerous branches, the dark-purple twigs glabrous: leaf-blades elliptic, oval, or ovate, 2–3 cm. long, serrulate above the middle: drupe globose, 9–11 mm. in diameter, red shining—Hammocks, along the Caloosahatchee, Fla.—Wint.–spr.

11. I. ambigua (Michx.) Chapm. Shrub or small tree rarely up to 6 m. tall, the purple twigs glabrous: leaf-blades elliptic, oval, or suborbicular, 4–7 cm. long, serrulate or crenate-serrulate, at least above the middle: drupe globose-oval, 6–7 mm. in diameter, red. [*I. caroliniana* (Walt.) Trelease, not Mill.]—Hammocks, scrub, and sandhills, Coastal Plain and rarely adj. provinces, Fla. to Tex., Ark., (Mo. ?) and N. C.—Spr.

12. I. monticola A. Gray. Shrub, or tree 12 m. tall, with glabrous twigs (or with pubescent twigs and leaves in *I. monticola mollis*): leaf-blades thinnish, elliptic to oval, varying to broadest above or below the middle, 6–20 cm. long, acuminate, serrate, deep-green above, paler beneath, glabrous except on the nerves: staminate calyx 3–4 mm. wide: staminate corolla 4–5 mm. wide: drupe globose, about 1 cm. in diameter, bright-scarlet.—(MOUNTAIN-HOLLY. MOUN-TAIN-WINTERBERRY. HULVER.)—Woods, especially mountain slopes, Blue Ridge and more northern provinces, Ga. and Ala. to N. Y.—Spr.—The creamy-white heart-wood is close-grained, heavy, and hard.

13. I. Beadlei Ashe. Shrub or small tree, with pubescent twigs: leaf-blades elliptic, oval, or suborbicular, sometimes varying to slightly broader below the middle, 3–8 cm. long, acute or short acuminate, serrate, densely pubescent beneath and finely pubescent above: staminate calyx 2–2.5 mm. wide: staminate corolla 5–6 mm. wide: drupe oblong-globose, 8–10 mm. long.—Rocky woods, Blue Ridge to Appalachian Plateau, Ga. to Ala., Tenn., and N. C.—Spr.

14. I. Amelanchier M. A. Curtis. Shrubs with more or less persistently soft-pubescent foliage: leaf-blades leathery, elliptic, or elliptic-lanceolate, 4–8 cm. long, acute or short-acuminate, inconspicuously serrate, glabrous, dull and finely reticulate above, thinly tomentose beneath, acute or rounded at the base, 6–10 mm. long, pubescent: flowers not seen: drupe globose, 7–10 mm. in diameter, dull-red.—Sandy swamps, Coastal Plain, S. C.—Spr.

15. I. myrtifolia Walt. Shrub or small crooked tree, with smooth gray bark, and rigid branches: leaf-blades evergreen, leathery, narrowly elliptic or linear, or broader on shoots, 1–4 cm. long, apiculate, more or less revolute, dark-green and glabrous above, pale and usually glabrous beneath, short-petioled: calyx 1–1.5 mm. broad: corolla 4–5 mm. broad: drupe globose, about 6 mm. in diameter, red.—(YAUPON.)—Swamps and cypress ponds, Coastal Plain, Fla. to La. and N. C.—Spr.—A yellow fruited form is known.

16. I. Cassine L. Shrub, or small tree 12 m. tall, with smooth gray bark, usually pubescent twigs: leaf-blades leathery, oblanceolate or elliptic, or rarely obovate, 4–10 cm. long, obtuse, acute, or rarely retuse at the apex, more or less revolute, dark-green and glabrous above, pale and more or less pubescent beneath, or sometimes glabrous, rather slender-petioled: calyx 1.5–2 mm. broad: corolla 4–4.5 mm. broad: drupe globose, 6–8 mm. in diameter, red or sometimes nearly yellow. [*I. Dahoon* Walt.]—(DAHOON. YAUPON. CASSENA. HENDERSON-WOOD.)—Swamps, stream-banks, and hammocks, often in acid soils, Coastal Plain, Fla. to La. and S Va.—Spr. or all year S.—The pale-brown heart-wood is close-grained but light and soft.

17. I. vomitoria Ait. Shrub, or small tree 8 m. tall: leaf-blades leathery, oval or elliptic, sometimes elliptic-lanceolate on shoots, 1–2.5 cm. long, obtuse, crenate-serrate, deep-green and lustrous above, pale-green beneath: calyx 2 mm. broad: corolla 5–5.5 mm. broad: drupe globose, red, 5–6 mm. in diameter, longer than the pedicel. [*I. Cassine* Walt.]—(CASSENA. YAUPON.)—Sandy hammocks, sand-dunes, and sandhills, often in neutral soil, Coastal Plain and rarely adj. provinces, Fla. to Tex., Ark., and Va.—Spr.—The leaves contain caffeine. A decoction made from them was the ceremonial drink of the aborigines. The white heart-wood, turning yellow on exposure, is close-grained, heavy, and hard.

18. I. cumulicola Small. Shrub or small tree with fastigiate branches and pale-gray or whitish bark: leaf-blades 2.5–4.5 cm. long, more or less revolute, shallowly sinuate: sepals of the pistillate flowers acute or rather obtuse, eciliate, sometimes obscurely ciliolate: drupe globose, 7–8 mm. in diameter, deep-red: nutlets 5–6 mm. long. [*I. arenicola* Ashe]—Scrub, lake region, pen. Fla.—Spr.—Used locally for holiday decorations.—Additional species and varieties, apparently conspecific with this plant, have been described.

19. I. opaca Ait. Tree up to 15 m. tall, with spreading branches and pale-gray bark: leaf-blades 4–10 cm. long, flat or nearly so, rather deeply sinuate: sepals of the pistillate flowers acuminate, ciliate: drupe globose to ovoid-globose, 8–10 mm. in diameter, bright-red, or yellow, nutlets 6–7 mm. long.— (HOLLY. AMERICAN-HOLLY. WHITE-HOLLY.)—Woods, ravines, hammocks, bluffs, and river-banks, often in sub-acid soil, various provinces, Fla. to Tex., Mo., W. Va., and Mass., (Me.?).—Spr.—Collected in large quantities in winter.

FAMILY 6. **CELASTRACEAE** — STAFFTREE FAMILY

Shrubs or trees, or vines. Leaves alternate, opposite, or whorled: blades simple. Flowers perfect, polygamous, or dioecious, variously borne. Calyx of 3–5 sepals. Corolla of 3–5 petals. Androecium of 3–5 stamens borne on or under the disk. Gynoecium of 3–6 united carpels. Fruit a capsule, a drupe, or a berry. Seed often arillate.—About 45 genera and 375 species, widely distributed in temperate and warmer regions.

Fruits capsular, dehiscent.   I. CELASTREAE.
Fruits drupaceous, indehiscent.   II. RHACOMEAE.

I. CELASTREAE

Leaves opposite.
  Ovary 3–5-celled: capsule 3–5-lobed: 3–5-valved: aril red:
    anther-sacs divergent.   1. EUONYMUS.
  Ovary 2-celled: capsule not lobed, 2-valved: aril white:
    anther-sacs parallel.   2. PACHYSTIMA.
Leaves alternate.
  Climbing woody vines: ovary free.   3. CELASTRUS.
  Erect shrubs: ovary confluent with the disk.   4. MAYTENUS.

II. RHACOMEAE

Flowers perfect: ovary 4-celled: fruit oblique.   5. RHACOMA.
Flowers dioecious: ovary 2-celled: fruit not oblique.
  Leaves opposite: flower-clusters peduncled: calyx deciduous:
    drupe not lobed.   6. GYMINDA.
  Leaves alternate: flower-clusters sessile: calyx persistent:
    drupe lobed.   7. SCHAEFFERIA.

1. **EUONYMUS** [Tourn.] L. Shrubs, often weak-stemmed, trees, or rarely vines. Leaves opposite: blades entire or toothed. Flowers perfect. Sepals 4 or 5. Petals 4 or 5. Stamens 4 or 5, borne on the lobes of the disk: filaments very short: anther-sacs diverging. Stigmas 3–5. Capsules drooping.—About 65 species, in the north temperate zone.

Cymes mostly 1–3-flowered: sepals, petals, and stamens, typically 5: leaf-blades sessile or nearly so: capsule slightly lobed, warty.
  Sepals eciliate: petals orbicular-ovate or suborbicular, manifestly broad-clawed:
    capsule copiously warty.   1. *E. americanus.*
  Sepals erose-ciliate: petals orbicular-reniform, clawless:
    capsule sparingly warty.   2. *E. obovatus.*
Cymes mostly 5–many-flowered: sepals, petals, and stamens,
  typically 4: leaf-blades petioled: capsule deeply lobed,
  smooth.   3. *E. atropurpurea.*

1. **E. americanus** L. Erect or straggling shrub 2 m. tall or less: leaf-blades oval to lanceolate, 2–10 cm. long, acute or acuminate, crenate-serrate: calyx about 5 mm. wide: sepals usually 5, equal: corolla mostly over 1 cm. wide; petals greenish or greenish-purple: filaments arising from the edge of the disk; anthers fully 1 mm. wide: seed-body 4.5–5.5 mm. long.— (STRAWBERRY-BUSH.)—Rich woods, bluffs, and hammocks, various provinces, N pen. Fla. to Tex., Nebr., and N. Y.—Spr.–sum.

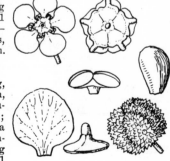

2. **E. obovatus** Nutt. Shrub with trailing, often rooting branches: leaf-blades thin, obovate, 2–6 cm. long, mostly obtuse, crenulate-serrulate: calyx about 4 mm. wide; sepals usually 5, erose-ciliate, equal: corolla mostly less than 8 mm. wide; petals greenish-purple, about 3 mm. wide: filaments arising from the top of the disk: anthers fully 1

mm. wide: seed-body 4–5 mm. long.—(RUNNING STRAWBERRY-BUSH. RUNNING-EUONYMUS.)—Shaded banks and low grounds, various provinces, Tenn. to Ill., Ont., and W N. Y.—Sum.—The rough red fruits of this and of the preceding species, suggested the name strawberry-bush.

3. **E. atropurpureus** Jacq. Erect shrub, or tree becoming 8 m. tall: leaf-blades elliptic, oval, ovate, or obovate, 5–16 cm. long, short-acuminate, serrate: calyx about 4 mm. wide; sepals usually 4, in unequal pairs: corolla mostly less than 1 cm. wide; petals dark-purple: filaments arising from the top of the disk; anthers less than 1 mm. wide: seed-body 8–9 mm. long.—(BURNING-BUSH. WAAHOO. SPINDLE-TREE. STRAWBERRY-BUSH. ARROW-WOOD. BLEED-ING-HEART.)—Woods and thickets, various provinces, Ala. (or Fla.?) to Okla., Mont., and N. S.—Spr.—The bark of the root is used medicinally. The white heart-wood, often tinged with yellow, is very close-grained, heavy, and hard. The dangling fruits are pinkish-purple.

2. **PACHYSTIMA** Raf. Shrubs. Leaves opposite, evergreen: blades toothed or entire. Flowers perfect. Sepals 4. Petals 4. Stamens 4, borne below the disk: filaments short: anther-sacs nearly globular. Stigmas 2.—Two species, North American.

1. **P. Canbyi** A. Gray. Diffuse and creeping, 1–4 dm. tall: leaf-blades linear, linear-elliptic or rarely oblanceolate, 0.5–2 cm. long, serrate: petals white, about 1.5 mm. long: capsule ellipsoid, about 4 mm. in diameter. — (MOUNTAIN-LOVER. RAT-STRIPPER. CLIFF-GREEN.)—Limestone cliffs and shaded banks, Blue Ridge and Appalachian Plateau, N N. C. to Ohio and Va.—Spr.—Its closest relative grows in the N Rocky Mountains.

3. **CELASTRUS** L. Vines with woody stems. Leaves alternate, deciduous: blades membranous, broad, entire or toothed. Flowers inclined to be dioecious, racemose or paniculate. Sepals 5. Petals 5. Stamens 5, borne at the sinuses of the disk. Capsules in drooping clusters.— About 30 species, most numerous in Asia.

1. **C. scandens** L. Diffuse climber: leaf-blades elliptic or oval, varying to ovate or obovate, 6–10 cm. long, serrate: panicles drooping: corolla greenish, about 8 mm. broad: capsule subglobose, about 1 cm. in diameter, orange, 3-valved, the scarlet seeds persistent and conspicuous in early winter. — (STAFF-TREE. SHRUBBY-BITTERSWEET. CLIMBING-BITTERSWEET. WAXWORK. GNOME'S GOLD.)—Thickets, woods, and fence-rows, various provinces, Ga. to La., Okla., Man., and Me.—Spr.–sum.—The bark is used medicinally. The ripe fruits are used for interior decoration in winter.

4. **MAYTENUS** Molina. Shrubs or trees. Leaves alternate, persistent: blades leathery, entire or toothed. Flowers polygamous or dioecious, solitary

or clustered. Sepals 5. Petals 5. Stamens 5, borne beneath the disk. Capsule erect.— About 10 species, tropical American.

1. M. phyllanthoides Benth. Shrub or tree: leaf-blades obovate to elliptic-oblanceolate, 2–4 cm. long: hypanthium broadly turbinate: sepals reddish: corolla 2–3 mm. broad, white or greenish-white: capsule obovoid or ellipsoid, 8–12 mm. long: seeds exposed by the recurved capsule valves, red.— Hammocks and sand-dunes, coast of lower pen. Fla. and Florida Keys, and lower Rio Grande region, Tex.—(*W. I., Mex., C. A.*)— Spr.–sum.—The leaves yield gutta-percha.

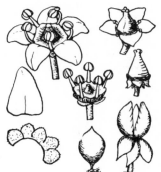

5. RHACOMA L. Shrubs or small trees. Leaves alternate, opposite, or whorled, persistent: blades entire or toothed. Flowers perfect, few together or solitary in axillary peduncled cymes. Sepals 4 or 5. Petals 4 or 5. Stamens 4 or 5, borne between the lobes of the disk. Drupe smooth.—About 12 species, tropical American.

Leaf-blades crenate or entire: cymes long-stalked (10–15 mm.) 1. *R. Crossopetalum.*
Leaf-blades spiny toothed: cymes short-stalked (3–5 mm.) 2. *R. ilicifolia.*

1. R. Crossopetalum L. Erect shrub or tree, with glabrous twigs: leaf-blades obovate or rarely somewhat elliptic, 1–4 cm. long, shallowly crenate or entire: cymes long-peduncled: petals oval or obicular, 1 mm. long or less, red or purplish: drupe obovoid, 5–6 mm. long, red.—Hammocks and sand-dunes, coasts of S. pen. Fla. and the Keys.—(*W. I.*).—All year.

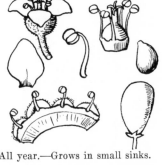

2. R. ilicifolia (Poir.) Trelease. Depressed shrub with pubescent twigs: leaf-blades oval or ovate, 10–15 mm. long, coarsely spiny toothed: cymes short-peduncled: petals suborbicular, less than 1 mm. long, red: drupe subglobose, 3–4 mm. long, red.— (CHRISTMAS-BERRY.)—Pinelands, Everglade Keys, Fla. and Florida Keys.—(*W. I.*).—All year.—Grows in small sinks.

6. GYMINDA Sarg. Shrubs or trees, the twigs 4-angled. Leaves opposite, persistent: blades mostly entire. Flowers dioecious, in axillary cymes. Sepals 4, or rarely 3. Petals 4, or rarely 3. Stamens 4, borne without a disk. Drupe smooth.— Two species, the following and 1 in C. A.

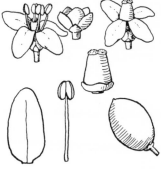

1. G. latifolia (Sw.) Urban. Shrub or small tree: leaf-blades obovate to elliptic-obovate, 2–4 cm. long, bright-green (or glaucous above in *G. latifolia glaucifolia*): petals elliptic to obovate-elliptic, 1.5–2 mm. long, white: drupe ellipsoid to ovoid, 7–8 mm. long, bluish-black. — (FALSE-BOXWOOD.) — Hammocks, Florida Keys.—(*W. I., Mex.*)—The dark heart-wood is heavy, and hard.

7. SCHAEFFERIA Jacq. Shrubs or trees, the twigs terete. Leaves alternate, persistent: blades entire. Flowers dioecious, in axillary clusters. Sepals 4. Petals 4. Stamens 4, borne without the disk. Stigmas recurved. Drupe tuberculate.—Five species, tropical American.

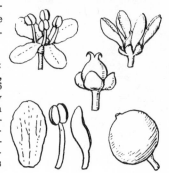

1. **S. frutescens** Jacq. Shrub or small tree: leaves not clustered; blades elliptic, oval, elliptic-obovate, or elliptic-oblanceolate, 4–6 cm. long, shining above: flowers manifestly pedicelled, greenish: drupe about 5 mm. in diameter.—(Boxwood. Yellow-wood.)—Hammocks, lower eastern coast of Fla. Everglade Keys, and Florida Keys.—(W. I.)—Spr.—The bright-yellow heart-wood is close-grained and heavy. It is sometimes used as a substitute for boxwood in engraving.

FAMILY 7. **HIPPOCRATEACEAE** — HIPPOCRATEA FAMILY

Shrubs or trees, or vines. Leaves opposite: blades simple. Flowers perfect, in axillary racemes, panicles, or cymes. Calyx of 5 persistent sepals. Corolla of 5 petals. Androecium of mostly 3 stamens. Gynoecium of 3 united carpels. Fruit a berry, a drupe, or a capsule, of 3 or fewer carpels cohering at the base. Seeds flattened.—Three genera and 170 species, mostly tropical.

1. **HIPPOCRATEA** L. Trees or woody vines. Leaf-blades leathery. Sepals and petals 5. Stamens 3: filaments dilated at the base and partly united. Capsule lobed. Seeds winged. About 70 species, tropical America.—Spr.–sum.

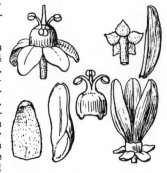

1. **H. volubilis** L. Climber: leaf-blades elliptic, varying to ovate or obovate, 5–14 cm. long, crenate-serrate: corolla 5–6 mm. broad, white: mature carpels broadly obovate, 2.5–3 cm. long. [*H. ovata* Lam.]—Hammocks, stream-banks, and shores, S pen. Fla. and the Keys.—(W. I.)—Wint.–sum.—In both hammocks and mangrove swamps the stems of this liane clambering over shrubbery or climbing to the tops of trees are much-branched, often diffusely so. The branches and branchlets hook or coil and thus bind the mass of growth into an impenetrable network.

FAMILY 8. **DODONAEACEAE** — VARNISH-LEAF FAMILY

Shrubs or trees. Leaves alternate: blades simple. Flowers polygamous or polygamo-dioecious, variously borne. Calyx of 3–5 sepals. Corolla wanting. Androecium of 5–8 stamens. Disk obsolete. Gynoecium of 3 or 4 united carpels. Fruit a reticulated septicidal capsule. Seeds subglobose or somewhat flattened.—Only the following genus.

1. **DODONAEA** [Plum.] L. Erect shrubs or trees, with usually viscid foliage. Leaf-blades broadened upward. Flowers green, yellow, or purplish. Capsule winged.—About 50 species, tropical and subtropical.—Spr. or all year. —VARNISH-LEAVES.

Leaf-blades spatulate to elliptic: fruit 10–30 mm. wide.
  Leaf-blades narrowly spatulate: fruit less than 2 cm. wide: seed 2–2.5 mm. in
    diameter.   1. *D. jamaicensis*.
  Leaf-blades broadly spatulate to elliptic: fruit over 2 cm.
    wide: seed 3–3.5 mm. in diameter.   2. *D. viscosa*.
Leaf-blades cuneate to obovate-cuneate: fruit 5–7 mm. wide.   3. *D. microcarya*.

1. **D. jamaicensis** DC. Shrub 1–4 m. tall: leaves 3–11 cm. long; blades narrowly spatulate, gradually narrowed to the base: sepals elliptic or oval, 2.5–3

mm. long, ciliolate: anthers about as long as the sepals: fruits 10–16 mm. long, deeply notched at the apex: seed orbicular-lenticular, 2–2.5 mm. in diameter.—Pinelands, hammocks, and coastal sand-dunes, pen. Fla. and the Keys.—(*W. I.*)—All year.

2. **D. viscosa** L. Shrub 2–5 m. tall: leaves 8–15 cm. long; blades broadly spatulate to elliptic, gradually or abruptly narrowed at the base: sepals ovate or oval, 2.5–3 mm. long: anthers rather shorter than the sepals: fruit 23–30 mm. long, deeply notched at the apex: seed orbicular-reniform, 3–3.5 mm. in diameter.—Woods and hammocks, pen. Fla.— (*W. I., Mex., C. A., S. A.*)—Sum.–fall.

3. **D. microcarya** Small. Shrub or small tree: leaves 2–5 cm. long; blades cuneate to obovate-cuneate: sepals smaller than in the two preceding species: fruit 5–7 mm. wide, emarginate at the apex: seed subglobose, nearly 2 mm. in diameter.—Hammocks, lower Florida Keys.—Fall.

FAMILY 9. **STAPHYLEACEAE** — BLADDERNUT FAMILY

Shrubs or trees. Leaves mostly opposite: blades pinnately compound. Flowers perfect or polygamous, racemose or paniculate, drooping. Calyx of 5 sepals. Corolla of 5 equal petals. Androecium of 5 stamens. Gynoecium of 2 or 3 partially or wholly united carpels. Fruit an inflated capsule.—Five genera and 22 species, widely distributed.

1. **STAPHYLEA** L. Shrubs or small trees. Leaf-blades pinnate, often 3-foliolate. Racemes cluster-like, drooping. Sepals and petals nearly erect. Capsule bladdery, 2- or 3-lobed.—About 6 species, of the north temperate zone.

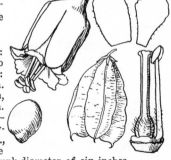

1. **S. trifolia** L. Shrub or small tree: leaflets 3: blades oval or elliptic, varying to ovate or obovate, 5–10 cm. long, serrate: racemes 5–10 cm. long: sepals 7–10 mm. long: petals spatulate, surpassing the sepals, green and cream striped: capsule 4–6 cm. long, the lobes apiculate.— (BLADDERNUT)— Rich woods and stream-banks, various provinces, rarely Coastal Plain, Ga. to Okla., Kans., Minn., and Que.—Spr.—Near the southern end of its range it may attain a trunk-diameter of six inches.

Family 10. **AESCULACEAE** — Buckeye Family

Shrubs or trees. Leaves opposite: blades palmately compound. Flowers polygamous, in terminal racemes or panicles. Calyx of 5 partially united sepals. Corolla of 4 or 5 unequal clawed petals. Androecium of 5–8 stamens. Gynoecium of 3 united carpels. Fruit a leathery loculicidal capsule.—Two genera and about 15 species, North American and Asiatic.

1. **AESCULUS** L. Shrubs or trees. Leaf-blades palmately 5–11-foliolate. Petals with their claws mostly in the calyx-tube. Filaments slender. Capsule smooth or echinate.—About 24 species, North American and Asiatic.—Buckeyes. Horse-chestnuts.

Panicle much elongate and narrow: corolla of petals not very different in shape: stamens several times longer than the calyx.   Subgenus I. Macrothyrsus.
Panicle short and thick: corolla of very differently shaped petals: stamens twice or thrice as long as the calyx.
    Upper petals with small rounded blades much shorter than the elongate claw: ovary and capsule smooth and glabrous.   Subgenus II. Pavia.
    Upper petals with spatulate blades about as long as the claw: ovary and capsule soft-prickly.   Subgenus III. Euaesculus.

I. Macrothyrsus
Shrub with erect, slender, elongate panicles of white flowers.   1. *Ae. parviflora.*

II. Pavia
Calyx tubular: broad petals not twice as long as the calyx.   2. *Ae. Pavia.*
Calyx campanulate: broad petals more than twice as long as the calyx.   3. *Ae. octandra.*

III. Euaesculus
Tree: blades of the leaflets serrate: flowers pale-yellow, in short panicles.   4. *Ae. glabra.*

1. **Ae. parviflora** Walt. Shrub: leaflets 5–7; blades elliptic-oblanceolate to obovate, 5–18 cm. long: calyx 5–7 mm. long: corolla white: petals 16–20 mm. long: capsules globular, 2.5–3 cm. in diameter. — (Bottlebrush-buckeye.) — Rich woods, Coastal Plain and adj. provinces, W Fla. to Ala. and S. C.—Spr.

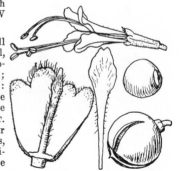

2. **Ae. Pavia** L. Low shrub or small tree: leaflets 5–7 or rarely 3; blades oval, oval-ovate, oblanceolate, or elliptic-lanceolate: calyx 8–12 mm. long or rarely longer; tube about 5 times as long as the lobes: narrow petals 3.5–4 cm. long, the claws more than twice as long as the calyx: capsule 3–5 cm. in diameter.—(Firecracker-plant. Red-buckeye. Scarlet-buckeye.)—Rich or dry woods, Coastal Plain and adj. provinces, Fla. to Tex., SE Mo., and Va.—Spr.—Additional species, related to *Ae. Pavia* have been proposed.

3. **Ae. octandra** Marsh. Shrub or large tree: leaflets mostly 5; blades oblanceolate to elliptic: calyx 12–16 mm. long or rarely shorter; tube about 8 times as long as the lobes: narrow petals 2.5–3 cm. long, the claws less than twice as long as the calyx: capsule 3–6 cm. in diameter. [*Ae. flava* Ait.]—(Yellow-buckeye. Sweet-buckeye. Large-buckeye.)—Rich woods and river banks, various provinces, Ga. to Tex., Ia., and W Pa.—Spr.—Additional species, related to *Ae. octandra*, have been proposed.—The creamy-white heart-wood is close-grained, soft, and light. It is used for artificial limbs and various utensils.

4. Ae. glabra Willd. Tree: leaflets 5, or rarely 7; blades elliptic to elliptic-oblanceolate: calyx 6–8 mm. long: corolla pale-yellow; lateral petals 11–12 mm. long: capsule 3–7 cm. in diameter.—(Ohio-Buckeye. Fetid-Buckeye.)— Woods, various provinces, rarely Coastal Plain, Ala. to Okla., Kans., Mich., and W Pa.—Spr.—The wood is used for artificial limbs and various utensils.

FAMILY 11. **ACERACEAE** — Maple Family

Shrubs or trees. Leaves opposite: blades simple or compound. Flowers perfect or polygamous, in cymes, racemes, or panicles, or often in congested clusters. Calyx of 4 or 5, or rarely more, deciduous sepals. Corolla of 4 or 5, or rarely more, petals, or wanting. Androecium of as many stamens as there are sepals or twice as many. Gynoecium of 2 more or less united carpels. Fruit 2 nutlets with wings (samaras).—Six genera and more than 100 species, in the north temperate zone.

Leaf-blades simple: flowers polygamous, monoecious, andromonoecious, or androdioecious; disk present: anthers ellipsoid or oval, not tipped.
 Flowers in terminal racemes or panicles: stigmas shorter
  than the style.   1. Acer.
 Flowers in lateral or terminal clusters: stigmas as long
  as the style or longer.
  Flowers filiform-pedicelled, in drooping clusters appearing with the leaves: sepals united into a lobed
   cup-like calyx, the staminate and pistillate similar.   2. Saccharodendron.
  Flowers sessile or short-pedicelled, in dense lateral involucrate clusters, appearing before the leaves.
   Sepals united, the staminate and pistillate calyx
    very distinct: petals wanting.   3. Argentacer.
   Sepals distinct, those of the staminate and pistillate flowers similar: petals present.   4. Rufacer.
Leaf-blades pinnately compound: flowers dioecious: disk
 wanting: anthers linear, minutely tipped.   5. Negundo.

1. ACER L. Shrubs or trees. Leaf-blades broad, coarsely toothed or 3–5-lobed. Flowers borne in terminal racemes or panicles, appearing after the leaves, polygamous. Calyx of usually 5 distinct or slightly united sepals. Petals 5, narrower or broader than the sepals. Stamens exserted or included: stigmas shorter than the style.—About 30 species, North American and Eurasian.—Spr.—Maples. Acers.

Flowers in erect panicles: petals linear or linear-spatulate, about twice as long as
 the sepals.   1. *A. spicatum.*
Flowers in drooping racemes: petals obovate, about as long
 as the sepals or slightly longer.   2. *A. pennsylvanicum.*

1. A. spicatum Lam. Shrub, or small tree 10 m. tall, the bark thin, relatively smooth: leaf-blades mostly longer than broad, mainly 3-lobed, sometimes with 2 additional lobes near the base, serrate, glabrate above, paler and more or less tomentulose beneath, cordate or subcordate: panicles many-flowered: pedicels spreading, 6–10 mm. long, or longer at maturity: petals yellow: stamens exserted: fruit green, about 2.5–3.5 cm. broad, the wings of the samaras spreading at about 90 degrees.—(Mountain-Maple. Low-maple.)—Damp rocky woods, Blue Ridge and more northern provinces, Ga. to Man. and Newf.—Spr.-early sum.—The heart-wood is soft, and light.

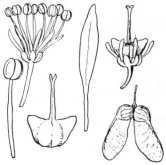

2. A. pennsylvanicum L. Shrub or tree, rarely over 11 m. tall, the bark relatively smooth, longitudinally striped: leaf-blades sometimes broader than long, 1–3 dm. broad, deep-green, with 3 nearly erect acuminate lobes, sometimes with 2 additional lobes, finely or doubly serrate, glabrous above, finely pubescent beneath, rounded or subcordate at the base: racemes relatively few-flowered: pedicels not spreading, 5–10 mm. long: petals pale-green or yellowish-green, obovate, slightly surpassing the elliptic sepals: stamens included: fruit bright-green, 3.5–5.5 cm. broad, glabrous, the wings of the samaras spreading at an angle of about 120 degrees.—(MOOSEWOOD. MOUNTAIN-ALDER. STRIPED-DOGWOOD. STRIPED-MAPLE.)—Rocky woods, Blue Ridge and more northern provinces, Ga. to Ont. and N. S.—Spr.—The heart-wood resembles that of *A. spicatum.*

2. **SACCHARODENDRON** Nieuwl. Trees or shrubs. Leaf-blades 3–5-lobed. Flowers in terminal umbels, somewhat precocious, appearing with the leaves, andromonoecious, long-pedicelled. Calyx campanulate, the lobes mostly shorter than the tube. Petals none. Stamens exserted: anthers ellipsoid or oval. Stigmas mostly longer than the style.—About 6 species, North American.—MAPLES. ACERS.—The sap of some of the species, particularly of *S. nigrum* and *S. barbatum*, is rich in sugar—the source of maple sugar.

Leaf-blades glabrous or sparingly pubescent and glaucous beneath.
  Leaf-blades with 3–5 acute or acuminate, often toothed lobes.   1. *S. barbatum.*
  Leaf-blades with 3 blunt few-toothed lobes.   2. *S. floridaum.*
Leaf-blades downy pubescent beneath, not glaucous.
  Leaf-blades green beneath: calyx campanulate: samaras green.   3. *S. nigrum.*
  Leaf-blades greenish, tinged with red beneath: calyx hemi-
    spheric: samaras red.   4. *S. leucoderme.*

1. **S. barbatum** (Michx.) Nieuwl. Tree sometimes 40 m. tall, the bark usually separating in coarse scales at maturity, the twigs red-brown: leaf-blades firm, mostly with 5 sinuate-toothed lobes, 8–15 cm. in diameter, deep-green above, pale or glaucous beneath, with an open shallow sinus: flower-clusters yellowish-green: calyx campanulate, about 5 mm. long; sepals obtuse: samaras slightly spreading, 3.5–4 cm. long. [*Acer saccharum* Marsh. *A. barbatum* Michx.] — (SUGAR-MAPLE. HARD-MAPLE. ROCK-MAPLE. SUGAR-TREE.)—Rich woods, rocky slopes, and stream-banks, various provinces, rarely Coastal Plain, Ga. to Tex., Man., and Newf.—Spr.—The light-brown heart-wood is close-grained, tough, hard, and strong.—*Acer saccharum* Marsh. is merely a misspelling of *A. saccharinum* L.

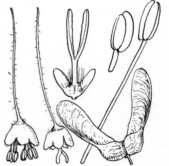

2. **S. floridanum** (Chapm.) Nieuwl. Tree rarely over 18 m. tall, the bark rather close, but rough in age, chalky-white: leaf-blades rather broader than long, 5–6 cm. broad, with 3–5 blunt undulate lobes about as long as the body, deep-green above, glaucous and more or less pubescent beneath, truncate and shallowly cordate at the base: flower-clusters yellowish: pedicels sparingly pubescent at least until the fruit matures: calyx campanulate, 1–1.5 mm. long: samaras green, 1.5–2 cm. long, sparingly pubescent near the base; wings rather widely spreading. [*Acer saccharinum floridanum* Chapm. *A. floridanum* Pax]—(HAMMOCK-MAPLE.)—Rich woods, bluffs, and hammocks, Coastal Plain and rarely adj. provinces, Fla. to La. and S. C. Naturalized in N. C. Reported from Va.—Wint.–spr.

3. **S. nigrum** (Michx. f.) Small. Tree sometimes 30 m. tall, the bark dark, coarsely flaky, the twigs light orange-brown: leaf-blades mainly broader than

long, often 15–20 cm. broad, relatively thin, deep-green above, scarcely paler and more or less downy beneath, with 3–5 entire or merely undulate lobes; basal sinus closed by the overlapping lobes: calyx campanulate, about 5 mm. long; sepals rounded: samaras 3–4 cm. long, slightly spreading. [*Acer nigrum* Michx. f.]—(BLACK-MAPLE.)—Woods, open slopes, and fields, various provinces, Ga. to La., Minn., Ont., and N. H.—Spr.—The wood is nearly similar to that of *S. barbatum*.

4. **S. leucoderme** (Small) Nieuwl. Shrub, or tree reaching a height of 8 m., the bark smooth, white: leaf-blades broader than long, or rarely orbicular in outline, mostly 4-lobed, sometimes imperfectly 5-lobed, 4–9 cm. in diameter, cordate or truncate, with a rather open and shallow sinus, dark-green, glabrous and marked with light nerves above, greenish, tinged with red, prominently nerved and velvety (especially to the touch) beneath, the lobes acute or acuminate (the fourth or fifth when present, obtuse), each, or the terminal one only with 2 obtuse teeth: flower clusters yellow: calyx 2 mm. long: samaras red; wings elliptic-spatulate, 1–2 cm. long, red, conspicuous, parallel or nearly so. [*A. leucoderme* Small]—(CHALK-MAPLE.)—Rocky river-banks, woods, and cliffs, inner edge of Coastal Plain and Piedmont, Ga. to La., Ark. and N. C.—Spr.—The heart-wood is very close-grained and hard. The trunk is often crooked.

3. **ARGENTACER** Small. Trees. Leaf-blades mostly 3-lobed. Flowers in dense lateral clusters, subtended by an imbricate involucre, very precocious, appearing long before the leaves, androdioecious, sessile or nearly so. Calyx various, that of the staminate flowers narrow and elongate, that of the pistillate short and broad, the lobes shorter than the tube. Petals wanting or minute. Stamens long exserted: anthers ellipsoid. Stigmas longer than the style.—One species.

1. **A. saccharinum** (L.) Small. Tree rarely 36 m. tall, the bark flaky at maturity, gray, or that of the twigs reddish-brown: leaf-blades about as long as broad, 10–15 cm. long, with 3–5 prominent incised lobes longer than the body, silky when young, glabrate, bright-green above, glaucous or silvery-white beneath, truncate or cordate at the base: calyx greenish or yellowish: samaras 5–6 cm. long, tomentose, or glabrate at maturity, green, at length, widely spreading. [*Acer dasycarpum* Ehrh.]—(SILVER-MAPLE. WHITE-MAPLE. SOFT-MAPLE.)—Woods, river-banks, and alluvial soil, various provinces, N Fla. to La., Okla., N. D., Ont., and N. B.—Wint.-spr.—The pale-brown heart-wood is close-grained and hard, but brittle.

4. **RUFACER** Small. Trees. Leaf-blades coarsely toothed or 3–5-lobed. Flowers in dense lateral clusters subtended by an imbricate involucre, appearing long before the leaves; androdioecious, short-pedicelled. Calyx of usually 5 distinct or nearly distinct sepals. Petals somewhat smaller than the sepals. Stamens, in the staminate flowers, exserted: anthers oval. Stigmas longer than the style.—About 6 species, North American.—MAPLES. ACERS.

Leaf-blades glabrous or glabrate beneath: samaras less than 4 cm. long: wings rather spreading.
  Leaf-blades prominently and sharply lobed, the lobes prominently toothed: samaras mostly less than 3 cm. long. 1. *R. rubrum*.

Leaf-blades mostly shallowly 3-lobed, the lobes shallowly
   toothed: samaras mostly over 3 cm. long.   2. *R. carolinianum.*
Leaf-blades copiously woolly beneath: samaras over 4 cm. long:
   wings tending to converge.   3. *R. Drummondii.*

1. R. rubrum (L.) Small.   Tree sometimes 35 m. tall, the bark dark-gray and
fissured on the trunk, smooth and pale or white-gray on the branches: leaf-

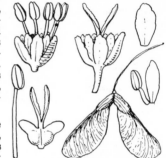

blades commonly broader than long, deep-
green above, pale or glaucous beneath,
mostly shallowly 5-lobed, rather evenly serrate, cordate at the base: flower-clusters red
or yellowish: sepals nearly distinct: petals
narrower than the sepals: samara-wings commonly red.—(RED-MAPLE.   SWAMP-MAPLE.
WATER-MAPLE.   SCARLET-MAPLE.) — Woods
and swamps, various provinces, Fla. to Tex.,
Man., and N. B.—Wint.–spr.—The heart-
wood is close-grained and very heavy.

2. R. carolinianum (Walt.) Small.   Tree
resembling *R. rubrum*, but usually smaller,
the bark of the trunk pale-gray: leaf-blades
as long as broad, or longer, mostly shallowly
3-lobed, but sometimes merely toothed, dark-green above, pale beneath, unevenly
serrate, rounded or subcordate at the base: flower-clusters red or yellowish: sepals
nearly distinct: petals about as broad as the sepals: samara-wings usually diverging at less than 45 degrees.—(CAROLINA-MAPLE.   RED-MAPLE.   SOUTHERN RED-
MAPLE).—Moist, often acid, soil, Coastal Plain and occasionally adj. provinces
S Fla., to Tex., Mo., and N. J.—Wint.–spr.—The wood is nearly similar to that
of *R. rubrum.*

3. R. Drummondii (Hook. & Arn.) Small.   Tree reaching a height of 26 m.,
the bark pale or whitish, rough on the trunk: leaf-blades thick, mostly broader
than long, 8–15 cm. broad or sometimes smaller, coarsely and irregularly
toothed, deep-green above, white and woolly beneath, rounded or cordate at
the base: flower-clusters red: sepals nearly distinct, elliptic or slightly narrowed upward: petals nearly like the sepals only narrower: samaras over 4
cm. long, the wings tending to converge.—(RED-MAPLE.)—River swamps,
Coastal Plain and rarely adj. provinces, Fla. to Tex., Mo., and Ga.—Spr.—
The wood is nearly similar to that of the two preceding species.

5. NEGUNDO [Ray] Ludwig-Boehmer.   Trees.   Leaf-blades pinnately
compound.   Flowers dioecious, the staminate in lateral clusters, long-pedi-

celled; the pistillate in lateral racemes.
Sepals 5, partly united.   Petals wanting.
Stamens exserted: anthers linear, minutely
appendaged at the tip.   Stigmas much
longer than the style.—Three or four species,
North American.

1. N. Negundo (L.) Karst.   Tree becoming
25 m. tall, with light-green twigs: leaflets
3–9; blades oval, ovate, or ovate-lanceolate,
often 5–12 cm. long, coarsely toothed:
flowers greenish, drooping: samaras 2.5–3.5
cm. long.—(BOX-ELDER.   ASH-LEAVED MAPLE.
WATER-ASH.)—Low woods and stream-banks,
various provinces, Fla. to Tex., Man., Ont., and Me.—Spr.—The whitish heart-
wood, close-grained, but soft, is made into wooden-ware and cheap furniture.

Family 12. **SAPINDACEAE** — Soapberry Family

Shrubs, trees, or vines. Leaves alternate in our species: blades simple or pinnate, sometimes 1-foliate. Flowers dioecious, polygamous, or polygamo-dioecious, or rarely perfect, borne in racemes, panicles, or corymbs. Calyx of 4 or 5 sepals. Corolla of 4 or 5 petals or wanting. Disk sometimes gland-bearing. Androecium mostly of 5 or more stamens. Gynoecium of 2–4 more or less united carpels. Fruit capsular or baccate. —About 125 genera and over 1,000 species.

Vines: fruit bladdery. — Tribe I. CARDIOSPERMEAE.
Shrubs or trees: fruit not inflated.
Fruit baccate, not stipitate. — Tribe II. SAPINDEAE.
Fruit capsular, loculicidal, stipitate. — Tribe III. CUPANIEAE.

I. CARDIOSPERMEAE
Climbers with tendrils and herbaceous or woody stems: capsule inflated, with 1 seed in each cavity. — 1. CARDIOSPERMUM.

II. SAPINDEAE
Petals appendaged, longer than the calyx.
Fruit lobed, the carpels nearly distinct: petals with short claw-like bases. — 2. SAPINDUS.
Fruit not lobed, the carpels united: petals with long claw-like bases. — 3. TALISIA.
Petals unappendaged, about as long as the calyx.
Ovary 2-celled: leaflets 2, 4 or 6: calyx persistent. — 4. EXOTHEA.
Ovary 3-celled: leaflets 3: calyx deciduous. — 5. HYPELATE.

III. CUPANIEAE
Shrub or tree: leaflets with toothed blades. — 6. CUPANIA.

1. **CARDIOSPERMUM** L. Herbaceous or woody vines. Leaves alternate: blades biternate or decompound. Flowers polygamo-dioecious, irregular. Sepals 4. Petals 4, unequal, white. Disk one-sided, with 2 glands opposite the lower petals. Stamens 8. Capsules bladdery.—About 15 species, of the warmer parts of America.—BALLOON-VINES. HEART-SEEDS.

Capsule subglobose, obovoid, globose-obovoid, or oval, slightly longer than wide, not angled: blades of the leaflets rather large and acute or acuminate.
Outer sepals glabrous: seed about 5 mm. in diameter, the aril reniform: leaflets glabrous or nearly so. — 1. *C. Halicacabum.*
Outer sepals pubescent: seed about 3.5 mm. in diameter, the aril heart-shaped: leaflets finely pubescent. — 2. *C. keyense.*
Capsule obpyramidal and lobed, wider than long: blades of the leaflets small, usually decidedly acuminate. — 3. *C. microcarpum.*

1. **C. Halicacabum** L. Twigs glabrous or sparingly pubescent: blades of the leaflets lanceolate to ovate, acute to acuminate, coarsely serrate and incised, sparingly pubescent or glabrous: calyx glabrous; outer sepals about 2 mm. long, rounded: petals 3.5–4.5 mm. long: capsule subglobose to obovoid or globose-obovoid, about as wide as long, 3.5–4.5 cm. in diameter, short-stipitate.—(HEART-PEA.)—Wasteplaces and cult. grounds, various provinces, Fla. to Tex., Kans., and Del. Nat. of trop. Am.—(*W. I., Mex., C. A., S. A.*)—Sum. or all year S.—The root is medicinal.

2. **C. keyense** Small. Twigs closely and finely pale-pubescent: blades of the leaflets ovate, more or less lobed or incised, and crenate, or crenate-serrate, acute to somewhat acuminate, copiously fine-pubescent:

calyx similar to that of *C. Halicacabum*, but outer sepals pubescent: petals 3.5–4 mm. long: capsule subglobose to oval, 3–3.5 cm. in diameter, mostly longer than wide, rather long-stipitate.—Hammocks, Florida Keys.—All year.

3. C. microcarpum H.B.K. Twigs glabrous or obscurely fine-pubescent: blades of the leaflets lanceolate to ovate-lanceolate, decidedly acuminate, incised and coarsely toothed, glabrous or with scattered hairs: calyx glabrous or nearly so; outer sepals 1–1.5 mm. long: petals 2–3 mm. long: capsule broadly obpyramidal, 1.5–2 cm. wide, not stipitate.—Hammocks, pinelands, and swamps, S pen. Fla. and the Keys, and S Tex.—(*W. I., Mex., C. A., S. A.*)—All year.

2. SAPINDUS [Tourn.] L.   Shrubs or trees.   Leaves alternate: blades pinnate.   Flowers polygamous, regular.   Sepals 4 or 5.   Petals 4 or 5, appendaged, white or greenish.   Stamens 8–10.   Baccate fruit not elongate, lobed.—About 10 species, American and Asiatic.—Wint.–spr.—The fruits contain saponin.

Leaf-rachis winged: blades of the leaflets obtuse, at least not acuminate: petals short-clawed.   1. *S. Saponaria*.
Leaf-rachis wingless: blades of the leaflets acuminate: petals long-clawed.   2. *S. marginatus*.

1. S. Saponaria L.   Shrub, or tree becoming 10 m. tall: leaflets 4–7; blades elliptic, oval, or obovate, 3–12 cm. long; leaf-rachis winged: mature carpels globose, 14–18 mm. in diameter.—(SOAP-BERRY.   FALSE-DOGWOOD.)—Hammocks, pen. Fla. and the Keys.—(*W. I., Mex., C. A., S. A.*)—All year.—The light-brown heart-wood is close-grained, hard, and heavy.

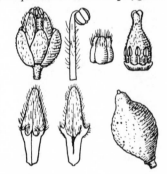

2. S. marginatus Willd.   Tree 10–15 m. tall, the twigs and inflorescence pubescent: leaflets 7–13; blades lanceolate to elliptic-lanceolate, 5–15 cm. long: leaf-rachis margined above: mature carpel globose, 10–15 mm. in diameter. — (WILD-CHINA.   SOAPBERRY.) — Hammocks, near the coast, Fla., Ga. and S. C.   Adv. elsewhere.—Spr.—The light-brown heart-wood is close-grained, heavy, and strong, being easily split it is used for making light frames and baskets.—*S. manatensis* Radlk. seems to be a form of this species.

3. TALISIA Aubl.   Shrubs or trees.   Leaves alternate, the rachis wingless: blades pinnate, the leaflet-blades slightly inequilateral.   Flowers polygamo-dioecious, regular.   Sepals 5.   Petals 5, appendaged.   Stamens 5–7, or usually 8.   Baccate fruit somewhat elongate, not lobed.— About 33 species, all but the following exclusively South American.

1. T. pedicellaris Radlk.   Small tree with puberulent twigs: leaflets 4–6; blades elliptic to elliptic-ovate, 5–9 cm. long, acuminate, short-petioled: panicle small, the branches pubescent: petals ovate to ovate-lanceolate, 4–5 mm. long, green or yellowish: fruits ovoid or ellipsoid, 1.5–2 cm. long, papillose.—Brickell hammock, Miami, Fla.—(*S. A.*)—Spr.

4. EXOTHEA Macfadyen. Shrubs or trees. Leaves alternate; blades equally pinnate. Flowers mostly polygamous, irregular. Sepals 5. Petals 5, unappendaged, short-clawed. S t a m e n s mostly 8. Baccate fruit not lobed.—One species.

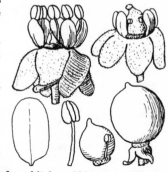

1. **E. paniculata** (Juss.) Radlk. Tree or shrub: leaflets 2–4, or rarely 6; blades elliptic, 5–13 cm. long, entire: buds clove-shaped: sepals 3–4 mm. long: petals white, smaller than the sepals: fruit subglobose, 10–13 mm. in diameter, orange turning purple. —(INKWOOD. IRONWOOD. BUTTER–BOUGH.) —Hammocks, pen. Fla. and the Keys.— (*W. I.*)—The light-brown heart-wood, close-grained, heavy and very hard, is used for cabinet work, boat-building, and small articles. The trees flower in wint. and spr. Has been carried far up the coast and planted on kitchenmiddens by birds.

5. HYPELATE P. Br. Shrubs or trees. Leaves alternate: blades 3-foliate. Flowers polygamo-dioecious. Sepals 5. Petals 5, unappendaged, clawless. Stamens 8–10. Baccate fruit not lobed.—One species.

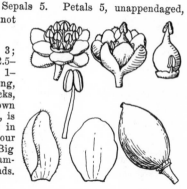

1. **H. trifoliata** Sw. Tree: leaflets 3; blades spatulate to narrowly obovate, 2.5–4.5 cm. long: petals white, suborbicular, 1–1.5 mm. long: fruit ovoid, 5–7 mm. long, black. — (WHITE-IRONWOOD.) — Hammocks, Florida Keys.—(*W. I.*)—The dark-brown heart-wood, close-grained and very heavy, is used for cabinet-work, tool-handles, and in boat-building. The largest trees in our range occur on Umbrella Key. On Big Pine Key specimens of this typically ham-mock plant are scatted in the pinelands. The trees flower in spr. and sum.

6. CUPANIA [Plum.] L. Shrubs or trees. Leaves alternate: blades pin-nate. Flowers polygamo-dioecious, regular. Sepals 4 or 5, rarely 3 .or 6. Petals 4 or 5, sometimes appendaged; or wanting. Stamens 8, or 5, 6, 10, or 12. Capsule 2–4-lobed.—About 32 species, tropi-cal American.

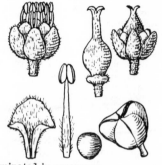

1. **C. glabra** Sw. Tree: leaflets 6–12; blades oblong with a cuneate base, 6–11 cm. long, crenate or crenate-serrate above the middle: sepals ovate, 2–2.5 mm. long: petals cuneate-flabellate, 2–2.5 mm. long, green, often tinged with yellow or red: capsule turbinate 11–14 mm. broad, stipitate.— Hammocks, Big Pine Key, Fla.—(*W. I.*)— Spr.—This is one of the trees discovered about a century ago on the Florida Keys, and up to several years ago thought to be exterminated in our range.

Order RHAMNALES — Rhamnal Order

Shrubs, trees, or vines. Leaves typically alternate. Flowers regular, sometimes imperfect or incomplete. Calyx present. Corolla present or wanting. Androecium of as many stamens as there are sepals. Gynoecium of 2 or more united carpels. Ovary superior or nearly so. Fruit a capsule or a berry, or drupaceous.

Sepals manifest: petals involute or wanting: fruit capsular, berry-like, or drupaceous. Fam. 1. FRANGULACEAE.
Sepals minute or obsolete: petals valvate: fruit baccate. Fam. 2. VITACEAE.

Family 1. **FRANGULACEAE** — Buckthorn Family

Shrubs, trees, or vines. Leaf-blades simple, pinnately veined. Flowers perfect or polygamous, or sometimes dioecious. Calyx of 4 or 5 sepals. Corolla of 4 or 5 petals, or wanting. Androecium of 4 or 5 stamens opposite the petals. Gynoecium of 2 or 3 united carpels. Fruit capsular, berry-like, or drupaceous, sometimes separating into nutlets.—About 50 genera and 600 species, of temperate and tropical regions.

Fruit wingless.
    Fruit drupaceous, pulpy, with a 1–4-celled stone.   Tribe I. ZIZYPHEAE.
    Fruit dry or berry-like, with 2–4 separate nutlets.   Tribe II. RHAMNEAE.
Fruit winged.   Tribe III. GOUANIEAE.

I. ZIZYPHEAE

Petals wanting.
    Sepals crested.   1. KRUGIODENDRON.
    Sepals not crested.   2. REYNOSIA.
Petals present.
    Petals hooded and clawed, broadly rounded at the apex.   3. ZIZYPHUS.
    Petals involute, sessile, obtuse or acute.   4. BERCHEMIA.

II. RHAMNEAE

Fruit pulpy.
    Hypanthium flattish: disk conspicuous.   5. SAGERETIA.
    Hypanthium cup-like: disk inconspicuous, lining the hypanthium.   6. RHAMNUS.
Fruit dry.
    Sepals inflexed: petals on slender claws.   7. CEANOTHUS.
    Sepals spreading: petals sessile, involutely folded over the filaments.   8. COLUBRINA.

III. GOUANIEAE

Vine with tendril-like twigs.   9. GOUANIA.

1. KRUGIODENDRON Urban. Shrubs or trees. Leaves nearly opposite: blades entire. Flowers perfect, green. Sepals 5, crested within. Petals wanting. Stamens 5: filaments longer than the anthers. Drupe apiculate.—One species.

1. K. ferreum (Vahl) Urban. Shrub, or small tree 9 m. tall, the bark ridged: leaf-blades ovate or oval, 3–6 cm. long: sepals ovate: drupe subglobose or oval, 5–8 mm. long, black. [*Rhamnidium ferreum* (Vahl) Sarg.] — (BLACK-IRONWOOD.) — Hammocks, lower E coast of Fla., Everglade Keys, and Florida Keys.—(*W. I.*)—Spr.—The orange-brown heart-wood, hard and very heavy, is used locally for cabinet-work. The geographic range of this species is not as wide as its relative the darling-plum, for it has not yet been found on the lower western coast of Fla.

2. **REYNOSIA** Griseb. Shrubs or trees. Leaves opposite: blades entire. Flowers perfect, green. Sepals 5, crestless. Petals wanting. Stamens 5: filaments longer than the anthers. Drupe apiculate.—About 9 species, West Indian.

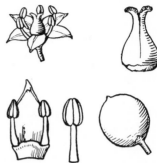

1. **R. septentrionalis** Urban. Shrub, or tree 9 m. tall, the bark scaly: leaf-blades elliptic, varying to ovate or obovate: sepals deltoid or ovate-deltoid: drupe subglobose, oval, or obovoid, 1.5–2 cm. long, purple or nearly black.—(RED-IRONWOOD. DARLING-PLUM.)—Hammocks, Everglade Keys, Fla. and Florida Keys.—(*W. I.*)—Spr.–sum.— The fruit is edible.—The dark-brown heart-wood, close-grained and very hard, is used locally for cabinet-work.—The fruits are pleasantly flavored.

3. **ZIZYPHUS** Juss. Shrubs. Leaves alternate: blades three-ribbed, entire, or sometimes shallowly toothed. Flowers perfect. Sepals 5, keeled within. Petals 5, hood-like. Stamens 5, opposite the petals. Drupe fleshy, edible, with a 1–3 celled stone. About 40 species, most abundant in the Old World tropics.

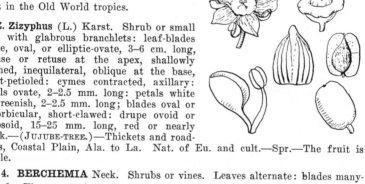

1. **Z. Zizyphus** (L.) Karst. Shrub or small tree, with glabrous branchlets: leaf-blades ovate, oval, or elliptic-ovate, 3–6 cm. long, obtuse or retuse at the apex, shallowly toothed, inequilateral, oblique at the base, short-petioled: cymes contracted, axillary: sepals ovate, 2–2.5 mm. long: petals white or greenish, 2–2.5 mm. long; blades oval or suborbicular, short-clawed: drupe ovoid or ellipsoid, 15–25 mm. long, red or nearly black.—(JUJUBE-TREE.)—Thickets and roadsides, Coastal Plain, Ala. to La. Nat. of Eu. and cult.—Spr.—The fruit is edible.

4. **BERCHEMIA** Neck. Shrubs or vines. Leaves alternate: blades many-ribbed. Flowers perfect or polygamous. Sepals 5, flat. Petals 5, involute, sessile. Stamens 5, often shorter than the petals. Drupe somewhat flattened, slightly longer than thick.—About 10 species, the following and the others in tropical Asia and Africa.

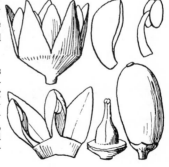

1. **B. scandens** (Hill) Trelease. Glabrous climber with wide-spreading branches: leaf-blades oval, elliptic, or sometimes varying to lanceolate, 4–8 cm. long, entire or un-dulate-crenate: sepals longer than the hy-panthium: petals greenish-yellow, obovate, about as long as the sepals: drupe ellipsoid or ovoid-ellipsoid, 6–8 mm. long. [*B. volu-bilis* DC.]—(SUPPLE-JACK. RATTAN-VINE.)

—Swamps and low hammocks, Coastal Plain, and occasionally adj. provinces, Fla. to Tex., Mo., and Va.—Spr.

5. SAGERETIA Brongn. Shrubs with diffuse branches. Leaves opposite or nearly so: blades of firm-texture, finely toothed. Flowers perfect. Sepals 5, keeled within. Petals 5, concave, short-clawed. Stamens 5, about as long as the petals. Drupe separating into 3 leathery nutlets.—About 10 species, mostly Asiatic.

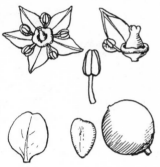

1. **S. minutiflora** (Michx.) Trelease. Pubescent, spinescent shrub: leaf-blades ovate or orbicular-ovate, 1–5 cm. long: spikes 1–4 cm. long: calyx 2–2.5 mm. broad: petals orbicular, ovate, about ½ as long as the sepals, white: drupe subglobose, 7–9 mm. in diameter.—(Buckthorn.)—Calcareous hammocks and bluffs, Coastal Plain, Fla. to Miss. and N. C.—Spr.—The flowers are very fragrant.

6. RHAMNUS [Tourn.] L. Shrubs or trees. Leaves alternate: blades entire or toothed, many-ribbed. Flowers perfect or polygamo-dioecious, green. Sepals 4 or 5, keeled within. Petals 4 or 5, commonly concave, clawless, shorter than the sepals, or wanting. Stamens 4 or 5, included: anthers acute. Drupe berry-like, not lobed, with 3 or 4 nutlets.—About 90 species, of warm and temperate regions.—Spr.—BUCKTHORNS.

Flowers usually dioecious: nutlet deeply grooved on the back; raphe dorsal: cotyledons leaf-like. 1. *R. lanceolata.*
Flowers perfect: nutlet not grooved; raphe lateral: cotyledons thick. 2. *R. caroliniana.*

1. **R. lanceolata** Pursh. Shrub 1–2 m. tall: leaf-blades elliptic, elliptic-lanceolate or sometimes oval, 2.5–9 cm. long: calyx about 3 mm. broad: petals about ½ as long as the sepals: drupe 5–7 mm. in diameter.—River-banks and moist hillsides, various provinces, rarely Coastal Plain, Ala. to Tex., Ia., and Pa.

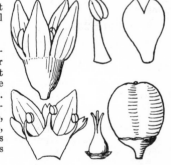

2. **R. caroliniana** Walt. Shrub, or tree becoming 11 m. tall: leaf-blades elliptic or slightly obovate, 5–12 cm. long: calyx about 4 mm. broad: petals about ½ as long as the sepals: drupe black, 10–11 mm. in diameter. —[INDIAN-CHERRY. YELLOW-WOOD. POLE-CAT-TREE.)—Shaded banks and hillsides, often in calcareous soils, various provinces, Fla. to Tex., Kans., and Va.—The bark is medicinal. The light-brown heart-wood is close-grained, light but rather hard.

7. CEANOTHUS L. Shrubs or trees. Leaves alternate: blades usually toothed, commonly 3-ribbed. Flowers perfect, white. Sepals 5, keelless. Petals 5, longer than the sepals, clawed, the blades hooded. Stamens 5, exserted: anthers emarginate. Drupe lobed, separating into 3 carpels.—About 55 species, North American.—RED-ROOTS.

Leaf-blades toothed, membranous or nearly so.
  Erect shrubs: leaves deciduous.
    Common peduncle elongate.
      Leaves 3–10 cm. long: corolla about 5 mm. wide.   1. *C. americanus.*
      Leaves 1–3 cm. long: corolla about 4 mm. wide.   2. *C. intermedius.*
    Common peduncle abbreviated.
      Twigs and branches viscid-puberulent: lower surface of the leaf-blades glabrous or with few scattered hairs.   3. *C. ovatus.*
      Twigs and branches copiously pubescent: lower surface of the leaf-blades closely and permanently pubescent.   4. *C. pubescens.*
  Low decumbent shrub: leaves 5–10 mm. long, persistent.   5. *C. serpyllifolius.*
Leaf-blades entire, fleshy.   6. *C. microphyllus.*

1. **C. americanus** L. Shrub 2–9 dm. tall: leaf-blades ovate to ovate-lanceolate or rarely orbicular-ovate, prominently serrate: sepals about 1.5 mm. long: petals about 2 mm. long: fruit 5–6 mm. broad. —(NEW JERSEY TEA. RED-ROOT. RED-SHANK.)—Dry woods and hillsides, various provinces, Fla. to Tex., Man., and Me.— Spr.–sum.—The leaves were used as a tea substitute in colonial times. The root is used medicinally.

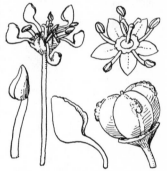

2. **C. intermedius** Pursh. Shrub 3–10 dm. tall: leaf-blades ovate to elliptic-ovate, or nearly elliptic, finely serrate: sepals about 1 mm. long: petals about 1.5 mm. long: fruit 4–5 mm. broad.—(RED-ROOT.)—Pinelands and woods, Coastal Plain and occasionally adj. provinces, Fla. to La., Tenn., and Ga.—Spr.

3. **C. ovatus** Desf. Shrub 2–6 dm. tall: leaf-blades thinnish, elliptic, oval, or ovate, 1.5–6 cm. long, somewhat veiny: sepals ovate, about 1.5 mm. long: petals about 2 mm. long.—Sandy woods, various provinces, Fla. to Tex., Minn., Vt., and Ga.—Spr.

4. **C. pubescens** (T. & G.) Rydb. Shrub similar to *C. ovatus* in habit: leaf-blades relatively thick, ovate-elliptic to narrowly elliptic, usually prominently veined: sepals deltoid, about 1 mm. long: petals about 2 mm. long.—Dry soil, various provinces, rarely Coastal Plain, Ga. to Tex., Mich., and Va.—Spr.

5. **C. serpyllifolius** Nutt. Shrub with diffuse or decumbent, very slender or filiform branches: leaf-blades elliptic to ovate-elliptic, serrulate, strigose beneath: sepals mostly 1 mm. long and obtuse: petals about 1.5 mm. long.— Pinelands, Coastal Plain, Fla. and Ga.—Spr.—Rare.

6. **C. microphyllus** Michx. Plant 3–6 dm. tall, diffuse: leaf-blades suborbicular, oval, or elliptic, 3–6 mm. long: sepals acute or abruptly pointed: petals about 1.5 mm. long: anthers brown: fruit depressed, 4–5 mm. wide.—Dry pinelands and sandhills, Coastal Plain, Fla., Ala., and Ga.—Spr.

8. **COLUBRINA** L. C. Rich. Shrubs or trees. Leaves alternate: blades entire or toothed, sometimes 3-nerved at the base. Flowers perfect. Sepals 5, spreading, often keeled. Petals 5, folded around the stamens, clawless. Sta-

mens 5: anthers notched. Drupe slightly 3-lobed, the carpels separating at least at the top.—About 15 species, with one exception tropical American.—Fall–spr. or all year.—The bark of some species is used as a substitute for hops.

Leaf-blades rather evenly pinnately veined: seeds shining, black.   I. AMERICANAE.
Leaf-blades 3-ribbed from the base: seeds gray, dull.   II. ASIATICAE.

I. AMERICANAE.

Leaf-blades mostly of an ovate type, neither prominently reticulate, nor copiously
    pubescent all over.
      Drupe 4–6 mm. in diameter: pedicel abruptly dilated into the hypanthium: leaf-
        blades glabrate; at most not rusty tomentose.   1. *C. reclinata.*
      Drupe 8–10 mm. in diameter: pedicel gradually dilated into
        the hypanthium: leaf-blades rusty-tomentose beneath.   2. *C. Colubrina.*
Leaf-blades mostly of an elliptic type, prominently fine reticulate,
    and copiously pubescent all over.   3. *C. cubensis.*

II. ASIATICAE.

A diffuse shrub, the dark-green leaf-blades shining.   4. *C. asiatica.*

1. C. reclinata (L'Her.) Brongn. Shrub or small tree becoming 20 m. tall, with puberulent twigs: leaf-blades ovate-elliptic or rarely oval or obovate, 3–8 cm. long: sepals about 2 mm. long: petals about 1.5 mm. long, yellow or greenish-yellow: drupe slender-pedicelled, seated on the hypanthium. — (NAKED-WOOD. SOLDIER-WOOD.)—Hammocks, Everglade Keys, Fla. and Florida Keys.—(*W. I.*)—The dark-brown heart-wood is close-grained, heavy, and hard.

2. C. Colubrina (Jacq.) Millsp. Shrub or tree, with rusty-tomentose twigs: leaf-blades ovate, elliptic, or rarely oblanceolate, 5–15 cm. long: sepals about 2.5 mm. long: petals somewhat longer than those of *C. reclinata*, yellow, sometimes red-tinged: drupe stout-pedicelled, partly immersed in the deep hypanthium.—(WILD-COFFEE.)—Hammocks, Everglade Keys, Fla. and Florida Keys.—(*W. I.*)

3. C. cubensis (Jacq.) Brongn. Shrub or small tree, with closely fine-pubescent twigs: leaf-blades elliptic, mostly 4–9 cm. long, prominently ribbed: sepals nearly 1.5 mm. long: petals about 1 mm. long: drupe slender-pedicelled, immersed in the hypanthium nearly or quite to the middle.—Hammocks, Everglade Keys, Fla.—(*W. I.*)—Rarely occurs as a woody vine climbing high into trees.

4. C. asiatica (L.) Brongn. Shrub with weak, diffuse or prostrate branches and glabrous twigs or sometimes erect and tree-like; leaf-blades ovate, 4–9 cm. long, acuminate or sometimes acute, crenate-serrate, glabrous, dark-green and shining above, truncate or cordate at the base, slender-petioled: sepals about 2 mm. long: petals nearly as long as the sepals, greenish: drupe subglobose, 7–10 mm. in diameter.—Hammocks and shores, S pen. Fla. and the Keys. Nat. of Asia.

     9. GOUANIA Jacq. Shrubs or vines. Leaves alternate: blades broad. Flowers polygamous, the inflorescence-branches often tendril-bearing. Sepals

5, spreading. Petals 5, clawed, the blades
scoop-like. Stamens 5, each surrounded by
a petal. Drupe capsule-like, 3-winged, separating into 3 carpels.—About 40 species,
widely distributed in the tropics.

1. G. lupuloides (L.) Urban. Climber:
leaf-blades oval or elliptic, varying to ovate,
3–9 cm. long: spikes 6–15 cm. long: petals
1 mm. long, short-clawed, yellowish or
greenish-yellow: drupe depressed, about 10
mm. broad. [*G. domingensis* L.]—(Chew-
stick.)—Hammocks, S pen. Fla. and the
Keys.—(*W. I., Mex., C. A., S. A.*)—The
wood is used for cleaning the teeth.—Spr.–
sum.

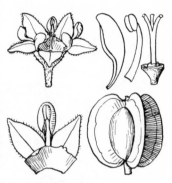

Family 2. **VITACEAE** — Grape Family

Vines, sometimes bushy or tree-like, usually with tendrils. Leaves
alternate, or the lower ones opposite: blades simple or compound.
Flowers perfect, polygamous, or dioecious, in flat-topped or elongate
clusters. Calyx of 4 or 5 sepals, or obsolete. Corolla of 4 or 5, often
caducous, petals, or wanting. Androecium of 4 or 5 stamens opposite the
petals. Gynoecium of usually 2 united carpels. Fruit a berry.—About 10
genera and 500 species, widely distributed.

Hypogynous disk present, either annular, cup-shaped, or glandular: leaf-blades simple or ternately compound.
    Petals cohering into a cap, caducous, never separating.
      Bark shreddy: pith interrupted by diaphragms at the
        nodes: tendrils forking.   1. Vitis.
      Bark not shreddy: pith continuous through the nodes:
        tendrils simple.   2. Muscadinia.
    Petals distinct, spreading.
      Floral envelopes mostly in 4's: disk 4-lobed: plant-
        tissues fleshy.   3. Cissus.
      Floral envelopes mostly in 5's: disk entire or nearly
        so: tissues not fleshy.   4. Ampelopsis.
Hypogynous disk wanting or obsolete: leaf-blades digitately
   5–7-foliolate.   5. Parthenocissus.

1. VITIS [Tourn.] L. Woody vines. Leaf-blades palmately lobed, angled
or coarsely toothed. Flowers in elongate racemes or panicles, green. Calyx
minute. Petals cohering. Berry juicy, mostly edible. Seed pyriform.—About
40 species, widely distributed in warm and temperate regions.—Spr.—Grapes.
—Some species have been cultivated in many varieties from very ancient times,
for the fruit. Some of our native species are represented in many hybrids which
are grown commercially for their fruits.

Leaf-blades green and glabrous beneath at maturity, or merely cobwebby about the
   nerves or in their axils.
    Leaf-blades merely toothed, or sometimes angled or shal-
      lowly lobed.
      Low shrub.   1. *V. rupestris.*
      Elongate, trailing or climbing vines.
        Shoots terete, glabrous or early becoming so: leaf-
          blades usually lustrous above.   2. *V. cordifolia.*
        Shoots angled, pubescent throughout the year:
          leaf-blades not lustrous on either side.   3. *V. Baileyana.*
    Leaf-blades prominently lobed.
      Lobes and sinuses of the leaf-blades acute: berries
        with a bloom.   4. *V. vulpina.*

Lobes of leaf-blades acuminate: sinuses obtuse: berries destitute of any bloom.   5. *V. palmata.*
Leaf-blades at maturity densely woolly, or glaucous and
sparingly cobwebby-flocculent beneath.
  Lower surface of leaf-blades very glaucous, and pale,
glabrate, the veins tawny pubescent.   6. *V. bicolor.*
  Lower surface of leaf-blades more or less woolly or cobwebby.
    Leaf-blades cobwebby or flocculent beneath at ma-
turity.
      Young foliage gray-cobwebby or white-tomentose:
leaf-blades gray-cobwebby beneath.   7. *V. cinerea.*
      Young foliage ferrugineous-pubescent, at least on
the nerves of the leaf-blades.
        Berry 12 mm. or more in diameter.   8. *V. Linsecomii.*
        Berry 5–6 mm. in diameter.
          Twigs and petioles tomentose: panicle-
branches felty-flocculent, at least during
anthesis.   9. *V. rufotomentosa.*
          Twigs, and often petioles, glabrous or
nearly so: panicle-branches not felty-
flocculent.   10. *V. aestivalis.*
    Leaf-blades felt-like or densely tomentose beneath at
maturity.
      Tendrils, or flower-clusters, intermittent, usually
every third node without tendril or inflorescence.
        Leaf-blades densely tomentose with white
hairs: berries less than 12 mm. in diameter.   11. *V. coriacea.*
        Leaf-blades densely tomentose with rusty or
tawny hairs.   12. *V. Simpsonii.*
      Tendrils continuous, usually every node with a ten-
dril, or inflorescence.   13. *V. Labrusca.*

1. V. rupestris Scheele. Stems 1–2 m. tall: leaf-blades commonly broader than
long, reniform to ovate-reniform, 4–10 cm. in diameter, coarsely toothed and

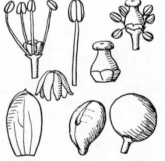

rarely slightly, and sometimes somewhat
irregularly, lobed, and with an abrupt tip at
the apex, mostly lustrous above, glabrous or
sparingly pubescent on the veins beneath,
somewhat glaucescent on both sides: panicles 2–10 cm. long, slender, not dense:
berry subglobose, 7–14 mm. in diameter,
purple-black, somewhat glaucous, pleasant-
tasted. — (SAND-GRAPE. SUGAR-GRAPE.) —
River-banks and hillsides, various provinces,
N of Coastal Plain, Tenn. to Tex., Mo., Pa.,
and Va.

2. V. cordifolia Lam. Leaf-blades thin,
deep-green, longer than broad, commonly
ovate in outline, rarely 3-lobed or 3-angled
near the apex, rather coarsely and irregularly toothed, glabrous or sometimes
sparingly pubescent beneath when young, more or less deeply cordate at the
base (persistent and lustrous in *V. cordifolia sempervirens*): panicles 1–3 dm.
long, commonly drooping: berry globose, 8–10 mm. in diameter, black under
a slight bloom, pleasantly acid, persistent.—(FROST-GRAPE. CHICKEN-GRAPE.)—
Woods, thickets, and stream-banks, various provinces, Fla. to Tex., Nebr., Wis.,
and N. Y.

3. V. Baileyana Munson. Leaf-blades thinnish but firm, ovate or orbicular-
ovate, 5–10 cm. long, glabrous and somewhat rugose above in age or pubescent
on the nerves beneath, toothed, otherwise entire or angularly 3-lobed near the
apex, cordate at the base: panicles 8–13 cm. long, compact: berry globose, 7–10
mm. in diameter, black, destitute of bloom or nearly so.—Woods and mountain
slopes, Blue Ridge and Appalachian Plateau, Ga. to Ala. and W. Va.

4. V. vulpina L.   Leaf-blades thin, commonly longer than broad, 5–20 cm. broad, mostly sharply 3-lobed and coarsely and irregularly toothed, glabrate or pubescent on and about the nerves beneath, cordate or nearly truncate at the base, the teeth and lobes acuminate: panicles 6–20 cm. long, often much branched: berry globose, 8–10 mm. in diameter, very dark with a copious bloom, the pulp sour.—(RIVERSIDE-GRAPE.   FROST-GRAPE.)—Rocky banks and along streams, various provinces, rarely Coastal Plain, Ala. to Miss., Colo., Man., N. B., and Md.

5. V. palmata Vahl.   Leaf-blades thin, deeply 3–5-lobed and very coarsely toothed, green and glabrous on both sides or glaucescent beneath and sparingly pubescent on the nerves, cordate at the base: panicles 5–12 cm. long, slender: berry subglobose, 7–10 mm. in diameter, black, destitute of any bloom.—(RED-GRAPE.   CAT-GRAPE.)—Sandy banks and rocky places, various provinces, Tenn. to La., Tex., and Ind.

6. V. bicolor Le Conte.   Leaf-blades thinnish, mostly longer than broad, 1–3 dm. in diameter, 3–5-lobed, shallowly toothed, glabrous above, pale and very glaucous and glabrous beneath or the veins usually pubescent, glabrous or glabrate at maturity: panicles 5–10 cm. long, commonly long-peduncled: berry globose, 10–14 mm. in diameter, black beneath the bloom, rather sour but pleasant-tasted.—(SUMMER-GRAPE.   BLUE-GRAPE.   WINTER-GRAPE.)—Rocky woods and river-banks, various provinces, N of Coastal Plain, Ala. to Mo., N. H., and N. C.

7. V. cinerea Engelm.   Leaf-blades thinnish, mostly longer than broad, 8–20 cm. in diameter, shallowly toothed, otherwise entire, or distinctly angularly 3-lobed near the apex, cowebby above or glabrous and rugose in age, more or less softly pubescent beneath with ashy or dark-brown webby hairs, cordate at the base: panicles 1.5–3 dm. long, irregular, drooping: berry subglobose, 10–14 mm. in diameter, black, barely glaucous, rather numerous.—(DOWNY-GRAPE.   SWEET WINTER-GRAPE.)—Woods and stream-banks, various provinces, Fla. to Tex., Nebr., and Ill.

8. V. Linsecomii Buckl.   Leaf-blades firm, as long as broad or a little longer than broad, 3-lobed and toothed, cordate, glabrate above, densely cobwebby or glabrate beneath (glaucous-blue beneath, except the rusty veins, in *V. Linsecomii lactea*): panicles 5–10 cm. long: berry subglobose, mostly 12–20 mm. in diameter, black beneath the bloom, pleasantly tasted.—Dry oaklands, various provinces, Tenn. to La., Tex., and Mo.

9. V. rufotomentosa Small.   Leaf-blades suborbicular to ovate-orbicular, 10–20 cm. long, or sometimes shorter, dull-green above, finely and closely tomentose on the veins, otherwise cobwebby beneath, especially rusty on and about the nerves, rather coarsely and irregularly toothed, cordate at the base: panicles rather small, or ample, sometimes 2.5–3 dm. long: peduncles much shorter than the panicles: berry black, with little or no bloom, often 5–6 mm. in diameter.—(WILD-GRAPE.)—Hammocks, Coastal Plain, Fla. to La.

10. V. aestivalis Michx.   Leaf-blades varying from broader than long to longer than broad, 1–3 dm. in diameter, angularly or deeply 3–5-lobed, shallowly toothed, dull-green and glabrate above, more or less densely, often unevenly, cobwebby or flocculent beneath, with rusty or brown hairs, cordate; petioles usually glabrous: panicles 1–2.5 dm. long, often conspicuously elongate and rather simple: berry globose, 8–10 mm. in diameter, black, under a bloom, with a tough skin, and pulp varying from sweet to very astringent.—(SUMMER-GRAPE.   PIGEON-GRAPE.)—Thickets and rocky places, various provinces, Fla. to Tex., Kans., and N. H.

11. V. coriacea Shuttlw. Leaf-blades reniform to suborbicular in outline, 3–10 cm. broad, shallowly toothed, angularly lobed (those of shoots often deeply lobed), becoming glabrate above, felty beneath, cordate or truncate and subcordate: panicles 5–12 cm. long: berry subglobose, less than 12 mm. in diameter, pleasantly acid.—Hammocks, pen. Fla.—(*W. I.*)

12. V. Simpsonii Munson. Leaf-blades suborbicular in outline, 5–18 cm. broad, prominently or mostly deeply 3–5-lobed, and shallowly toothed, glabrate above, more or less densely tawny- or rusty-tomentose beneath: panicles 5–10 cm. long, usually compact: berry commonly 15 mm. in diameter, black, mostly 4-seeded.—Sandy soil, especially in scrub and on shell mounds, pen. Fla.

13. V. Labrusca L. Leaf-blades thickish, suborbicular to broadly ovate, mostly longer than broad, shallowly toothed or scalloped, otherwise entire, or 3-lobed near the apex, glabrate above, densely tomentose or felty beneath: panicles 5–12 cm. long, usually simple: berry globose, 1.5–2 cm. in diameter, amber to purple, with a slight bloom, the skin and tough pulp sweet and musky, or astringent.—(FOX-GRAPE. PLUM-GRAPE.)—Thickets and woods, various provinces, Ga. to Miss., Ind., and Vt.

2. **MUSCADINIA** Small. Vines. Leaf-blades angled or coarsely toothed. Flowers in racemes or panicles, green. Calyx minute. Petals cohering. Berries rather juicy, ultimately edible.—Two species.—SCUPPERNONGS.

Berries 1.5–2.5 cm. in diameter; the skin and pulp tough, the latter musky: seed 6–9 mm. long.   1. *M. rotundifolia.*
Berries 1–1.5 cm. in diameter; the skin and pulp tender, the latter acid: seed 3–5 mm. long.   2. *M. Munsoniana.*

1. M. rotundifolia (Michx.) Small. Leaf-blades firm or leathery, suborbicular to ovate-orbicular, 4–9 cm. in diameter or larger, usually acuminate, coarsely toothed, glabrous, except the axils and sometimes the nerves beneath, cordate: berry subglobose, dull-purple, without bloom, with musky pulp, the bunches globular.—(MUSCADINE. SOUTHERN FOX-GRAPE. SCUPPERNONG.)—Thickets, swamps, river-banks, and hammocks, various provinces, Fla. to Tex., Kans., and Del.—(*Mex.*)—Spr.–sum.

2. M. Munsoniana (Simpson) Small. Leaf-blades thinnish, but rather firm, suborbicular or reniform, 4–8 cm. broad, coarsely toothed, glabrous, except the axils of the vein beneath, persistent, cordate at the base: berry globose, 1–1.5 cm. in diameter, nearly black under a slight bloom or shining, the skin and pulp tender, acid: seed 3–5 mm. long.—[*?Vitis peltata* Raf.]—(BULLACE-GRAPE.)—Hammocks and scrub, Fla. and Ga.—(*W. I.*)—Spr.–fall, or all year S.

3. **CISSUS** L. Fleshy vines. Leaf-blades simple or 3-foliolate. Flowers in small cymes, green. Petals spreading. Berry inedible.—About 225 species, tropical.—Spr.–sum. or all year S.—POSSUM-GRAPE.

Leaf-blades 3-foliolate, the leaflets coarsely toothed.
  Flowers in trichotomous cymes: berry thickest above the middle.
                                                                1. *C. incisa.*
    Flowers in compound umbel-like cymes: berry thickest below
      the middle.   2. *C. trifoliata.*
Leaf-blades simple, distantly serrate.   3. *C. sicyoides.*

1. C. incisa Desmoul. Plant glabrous: leaf-blades 3-foliolate; leaflets pale-green, very fleshy, 3–10 cm. long, coarsely toothed and incised, the terminal one sometimes 3-lobed, the lateral ones 2-lobed, all more or less cuneately narrowed at the base, on stout petiolules: berry obovoid or obovoid-globose, 10–12 mm. long, apiculate.— (MARINE-IVY.)—Sand-dunes and hammocks, various provinces, Fla., except the Florida Keys, to Tex., Kans., and Mo.—Sum.

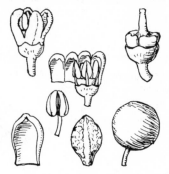

2. C. trifoliata L. Plant glabrous: leaf-blades 3-foliolate; leaflets 1–3 cm. long, sub-orbicular varying to ovate or obovate, often flabellate: berry globose-ovoid or ovoid, abruptly pointed, 5–7 mm. in diameter, dark-purple. [*C. acida* L.]—(SORREL-VINE.)— Hammocks, mostly near the coast, S pen. Fla. and the Keys.—(*W. I., Mex., C. A., S. A.*)—Sum.

3. C. sicyoides L. Plant pubescent: leaf-blades ovate or elliptic-ovate, 2–8 cm. long, acute or often acuminate: berry subglobose, about 1 cm. in diameter, black. —The inflorescence is often infected by a fungus, *Ustilago Cissi*, which trans-forms the flowers into cigar-shaped bodies.—Hammocks, S pen. Fla. and the Keys.—(*W. I., Mex., C. A., S. A.*)—Spr.-fall or all year S.

4. AMPELOPSIS Michx. Woody vines. Leaf-blades simple or bipin-nate; flowers in flat cymes, green. Petals spreading. Berry inedible.—About 15 species, of temperate and tropical regions.

Leaf-blades simple: ovary not surpassing the disk but nearly free from it.
　Calyx scarcely lobed: petals elliptic, about 2.5 mm. long.　　1. *A. cordata.*
　Calyx prominently lobed: petals broadly ovate or sub-
　　orbicular, about 1.5 mm. long.　　　　　　　　　　　2. *A. heterophylla.*
Leaf-blades bipinnate: ovary surpassing the disk, the latter
　mostly adnate to it.　　　　　　　　　　　　　　　　3. *A. arborea.*

1. A. cordata Michx. Leaf-blades ovate or triangular-ovate, 4–12 cm. long, shallowly serrate, long-petioled: style slender: berry 6–8 mm. in diameter, bluish or greenish-blue. [*Cissus Ampelopsis* Pers.] —River-banks and woods, various provinces, Fla. to Tex., Nebr., and Va.—Spr.

2. A. heterophylla Sieb. & Zucc. Leaf-blades broadly ovate, or deltoid in outline, 3–8 cm. long, crenate, short petioled: style stoutish: berry light-blue or white, dark-spotted.—Cult. grounds, various provinces, Ga. to N. C. and locally elsewhere. Nat. of E. Asia and cult.—Sum.-fall.

3. A. arborea (L.) Rusby. Leaf-blades bi-pinnate, 1–2 dm. long; leaflets several or many, the blades ovate, often broadly so or cuneate-obovate, 1–3 cm. long, coarsely toothed, incised, or lobed: berry 10–13 mm. in diameter, dark-purple. [*Cissus stans* Pers.]—(PEPPER-VINE.)—Hammocks, low thickets and swamps, Coastal Plain and occasionally adj. provinces, Fla. to Tex., Mo., and Va.—(*W. I., Mex.*)—Spr.-fall.

5. PARTHENOCISSUS Planch. Vines, the tendrils often disk bearing. Leaf-blades digitately compound. Flowers in compound cymes, green. Petals spreading. Berry inedible.—About 10 species, North American and Asiatic.— VIRGINIA-CREEPERS. WOODBINES. AMERICAN-IVIES.

Twigs, tendrils, and leaves pubescent.   1. *P. hirsuta.*
Twigs, tendrils, and leaves glabrous.   2. *P. quinquefolia.*

1. P. hirsuta (Donn.) Small. Leaflets 5; blades oval, elliptic, or ovate, acute or short-acuminate, coarsely toothed above the middle, all except the terminal one: berry 7–8 mm. in diameter, dark-blue, with a slight bloom, slightly pulpy: seed 5 mm. long, glossy, notched at the top, with a conspicuous spatulate raphe.—Rocky places, various provinces, Ga. to Tex.—(*Mex.*)— Spr.

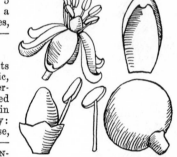

2. P. quinquefolia (L.) Planch. Leaflets 5; blades usually thinnish, oval or elliptic, the lateral ones inequilateral, coarsely serrate above the middle with rather appressed teeth: tendrils with disks: berry 8–9 mm. in diameter, deep-blue with scant bloom, pulpy: seed 4–4.5 mm. long, prominently rugose, mostly rather dull, with an orbicular raphe.— (VIRGINIA-CREEPER. WOODBINE. AMERICAN-IVY.)—Woods, thickets, sand-dunes, and hammocks, various provinces, Fla. to Tex., Man., and Que.—(*W. I., Mex.*)—Spr. or all year S.—The bark is used medicinally.

ORDER **MALVALES** — MALVAL ORDER

Herbs, shrubs, or trees. Leaves alternate or opposite: blades simple, often lobed and toothed. Flowers mostly perfect, regular and involucrate. Calyx of distinct or partially united sepals. Corolla of distinct petals. Androecium of numerous monadelphous or grouped stamens. Gynoecium of several distinct or united carpels. Fruit capsular, follicular, berry-like, or nut-like.

Stamens numerous (in our genera).
    Stamens distinct or in several groups: anthers 2-celled.
                                                          Fam. 1. TILIACEAE.
    Stamens monadelphous: anthers 1-celled.   Fam. 2. MALVACEAE.
Stamens as many as the sepals.   Fam. 3. BUETTNERIACEAE.

FAMILY 1. **TILIACEAE** — LINDEN FAMILY

Shrubs or trees, or rarely herbs. Leaves mostly alternate: blades simple. Flowers usually perfect. Calyx of 4 or 5 sepals. Corolla of 4 or 5 petals which sometimes bear a petaloid scale at the base. Androecium of usually numerous stamens, sometimes of as many or twice as many as the sepals. Gynoecium of 2–several united carpels. Fruit capsular, nut-like, or berry-like.—About 35 genera and 275 species, widely distributed.

Peduncles or pedicels without a conspicuous bract: filaments not forked: fruit capsular.
    Petals inserted with the stamens: capsule often silique-like.   1. CORCHORUS.
    Petals inserted below the stamens, at the base of an elevated
      receptacle: capsule subglobose.   2. TRIUMFETTA.

Peduncles each with a conspicuous adnate bract: filaments forked:
    fruit nut-like.
                                                                    3. TILIA.

1. **CORCHORUS** [Tourn.] L. Herbs or small shrubs. Leaf-blades serrate.
Sepals 5, or rarely 4, unappendaged at the tip. Petals 5 or rarely 4, naked at
the base, larger than the sepals, yellow. Anther-sacs contiguous. Ovary elongate. Ovules numerous. Capsule many-seeded.—About 40 species, mostly tropical.—JUTES. JEW'S-MALLOWS.—The fibrous bark of some species form at least
part of the jute of commerce.

Capsule long (4 cm. or more) and narrow, neither angled nor winged: leaf-blades
    without basal appendages, the teeth not bristle-tipped: seed about 1 mm. long.
    Petals of a spatulate type, often linear-spatulate: capsule
        with a single beak.   1. *C. orinocensis.*
    Petals of an obovate type, often rhombic-obovate: capsule
        with 4 tooth-like beaks.   2. *C. siliquosus.*
Capsule short (2 cm. or less) and stout, angled and winged:
    leaf-blades with a pair of basal bristle-tipped appendages, the
    teeth bristle-tipped: seed much less than 1 mm. long.   3. *C. acutangulus.*

1. **C. orinocensis** H. B. K. Stem usually sparingly branched: leaf-blades ovate,
elliptic, or lanceolate, 2–6 cm. long, acute or acutish, crenate-serrate, short-
petioled: flower-clusters sessile: sepals linear
to narrowly linear-lanceolate, 5–6.5 mm. long
or rarely longer: petals spatulate, mostly
4.5–6 mm. long: capsule slender, 4–7 cm.
long, subulate-beaked, finely pubescent.—
Hammocks, waste-places, and roadsides,
Coastal Plain and southwestern provinces,
Fla. to Tex. and Ariz.—(*W. I., Mex., C. A.,
S. A.*)—All year.

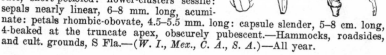

2. **C. siliquosus** L. Stem often widely
much-branched: leaf-blades ovate, oval-
ovate, or elliptic-lanceolate, mostly 1–3 cm.
long, sometimes longer, mostly acute, serrate, short-petioled: flower-clusters sessile:
sepals nearly linear, 6–8 mm. long, acumi-
nate: petals rhombic-obovate, 4.5–5.5 mm. long: capsule slender, 5–8 cm. long,
4-beaked at the truncate apex, obscurely pubescent.—Hammocks, roadsides,
and cult. grounds, S Fla.—(*W. I., Mex., C. A., S. A.*)—All year.

3. **C. acutangulus** Lam. Stem finely pubescent, 1 m. tall or less, widely
branched: leaf-blades elliptic-ovate, ovate, or orbicular-ovate, 2.5–7.5 cm. long,
acute or acutish, crenate-serrate, slender-petioled: flower-clusters nearly sessile:
sepals linear to linear-lanceolate, 4–4.5 mm. long: petals spatulate, 4–5 mm.
long: capsule stout, 1–2 cm. long, the angles winged, each with 5 spreading or
recurved beaks.—Waste-places and roadsides, W Fla. Nat. of E. I.—(*W. I.,
S. A.*)—Spr.–fall.

2. **TRIUMFETTA** [Plum.] L. Herbs or shrubs. Leaf-blades mostly
toothed and lobed. Sepals 5, often appendaged at the tip. Petals 5, each with
a pit at the base, often shorter than the sepals, yellow, or rarely wanting.
Anther-sacs contiguous. Ovary globular. Ovules few. Capsules few-seeded.—
About 70 species, of warm and tropical regions.—BURWEED.

Twigs hirsute: capsule-body glabrous or with scattered hairs: the prickles as long
    as its diameter or longer.   1. *T. semitriloba.*
Twigs softly pubescent: capsule-body cinereous-tomentulose: the
    prickles shorter than its diameter.   2. *T. Bartramia.*

1. T. semitriloba Jacq. Plants stellate-tomentose, 1–2 m. tall: leaf-blades ovate, rhombic, or suborbicular, serrate, angulate or 3-lobed, 3–8 cm. long: sepals linear, 5–6 mm. long, or longer: petals cuneate-spatulate or linear-spatulate: capsule-body 4–5 mm. in diameter, rigidly prickle-armed.—Pinelands, hammocks, and cult. grounds, pen. Fla. and the Keys. Nat. of S. Am.—(*W. I., Mex., C. A., S. A.*)— The bark yields a fiber similar to jute.

2. T. Bartramia L. Plants pubescent, fully 2 m. tall or less, usually widely branched: leaf-blades reniform, suborbicular, ovate or elliptic, commonly 1 dm. long or less, 3–5-lobed and toothed, cuneate to nearly truncate at the base; petioles shorter than the blades: panicles elongated, much interrupted: sepals linear or nearly so, 5–6 mm. long: petals spatulate, commonly shorter than the sepals: capsule-body 2.5–3.5 mm. in diameter, weakly prickled-armed.—Cult. grounds, waste-places, and roadsides, W Fla. Nat. of trop. Am.—(*W. I.*)—Spr.–fall.

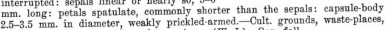

3. TILIA L.[1] Trees with roundish stoutish branchlets without terminal buds, the large acute axillary buds covered with numerous imbricate scales. Leaves deciduous: blades long-petioled, cordate, truncate, or cuneate at base, generally more or less oblique, mucronate-crenate: stipules caducous. Flowers in axillary or terminal cymes or corymbs, the peduncle more or less adnate to a reticulate bract. Sepals 5, distinct, alternate with the five white or yellow petals opposite each one of which in our species, stands a spatulate staminodium or petal-like scale. Stamens borne in clusters of five on the receptacle: filaments united at base and adnate to the staminodia, forked near apex, each branch bearing an extrorse anther-sac. Ovary sessile, 5-celled: stigmas 5. Fruit woody, nut-like, sometimes ribbed, 1-celled, 1- or 2-seeded, globose or subglobose.—About 65 species, in the Northern Hemisphere.—Spr.–early Sum.— BASSWOODS. LINDENS.—The wood is soft, light, pale, and straight-grained, and the inner bark is fibrous. The flowers are fragrant and yield fine honey, and are used medicinally. The European-lime, *Tilia europaea* L., without staminodia in the flowers, is often planted, and yields lime-flower oil used as a perfume. The leaves are variable in shape and pubescence, marked differences sometimes being found on the same tree. Leaves from suckers and new shoots are not so serviceable in identification as those on flowering branches.

Leaf-blades pubescent beneath at maturity.
　Hairs, when present, all stellate and closely appressed.
　　Leaf-blades with brown or rusty pubescence beneath.
　　　Leaf-blades obliquely cordate at the base.
　　　　Bracts mostly gradually narrowed to a peduncle
　　　　　above the base. 　　　　　　　　　　　　　　　　　1. *T. neglecta.*
　　　　Bracts mostly abruptly narrowed to or nearly
　　　　　to the base of the peduncle. 　　　　　　　　　　2. *T. caroliniana.*
　　　Leaf-blades obliquely truncate at the base.
　　　　Bracts 1–1.5 cm. wide. 　　　　　　　　　　　　　　3. *T. porracea.*
　　　　Bracts over 1.5 cm. wide. 　　　　　　　　　　　　　4. *T. georgiana.*
　　Leaf-blades with white, gray, or silvery-gray pubescence beneath. (Sometimes brown in No. 7).

[1] Contributed by Benjamin Franklin Bush.

Bracts mostly gradually narrowed to the pe-
  duncle above the base.
  Sepals pubescent on the outside, with short,
    felt-like hairs.
  Sepals nearly glabrous outside, with few   5. *T. Michauxii.*
    scale-like hairs.   6. *T. truncata.*
Bracts mostly abruptly narrowed to the base
  of the peduncle.
  Leaf-blades gray or silvery-gray beneath.   7. *T. heterophylla.*
  Leaf-blades white beneath.   8. *T. eburnea.*
Hairs on branchlets, peduncles, and pedicels long and
  spreading.   9. *T. lasioclada.*
Leaf-blades glabrous beneath at maturity.
  Bracts more or less pubescent at anthesis.
    Bract 0.5-2 cm. wide.   10. *T. littoralis.*
    Bract 3-4 cm. wide.   11. *T. glabra.*
  Bracts glabrous at anthesis.
    Leaves not glaucous beneath: cymes loosely few-flow-
     ered.   12. *T. leucocarpa.*
    Leaves glaucous beneath: cymes compactly many-
     flowered.
     Bract 1.5-2 cm. wide: stmainodia erose. 13. *T. floridana.*
     Bract 3-4 cm. wide: staminodia entire. 14. *T. australis.*

1. T. neglecta Spach. Tall tree, with deeply furrowed and scaly reddish-
brown bark, often pendulous branches, and slender glabrous branchlets: leaf-
blades thick, acute or abruptly acuminate,
obliquely concave, or unsymmetrically cordate at base, coarsely mucronate-crenate,
dark-green, smooth and lustrous above, covered below, except on the midrib and veins
with a short persistent pubescence and with
conspicuous axillary tufts, 10–15 cm. long,
8–12 cm. wide: flowers 5–15 together in
long-branched glabrous cymes: peduncles
slender, glabrous, the free portion 3–4 cm.
long: bract narrow, long-attenuate to the
base, rounded at the apex, glabrous, 7–11
cm. long, 2–4 cm. wide: sepals broadly
ovate, ciliate, glabrous without, pilose with
long white hairs within, half as long as the
lanceolate petals. [*T. americana* Marsh. Not

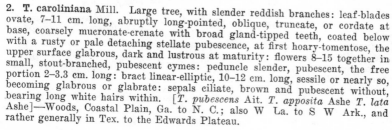

L.]—Rich moist ground, often in woods, various provinces, rarely Coastal Plain,
N. C. to N Miss., N. Y., Que., and W Mass.

2. T. caroliniana Mill. Large tree, with slender reddish branches: leaf-blades
ovate, 7–11 cm. long, abruptly long-pointed, oblique, truncate, or cordate at
base, coarsely mucronate-crenate with broad gland-tipped teeth, coated below
with a rusty or pale detaching stellate pubescence, at first hoary-tomentose, the
upper surface glabrous, dark and lustrous at maturity: flowers 8–15 together in
small, stout-branched, pubescent cymes: peduncle slender, pubescent, the free
portion 2–3.3 cm. long: bract linear-elliptic, 10–12 cm. long, sessile or nearly so,
becoming glabrous or glabrate: sepals ciliate, brown and pubescent without,
bearing long white hairs within. [*T. pubescens* Ait. *T. apposita* Ashe *T. lata*
Ashe]—Woods, Coastal Plain, Ga. to N. C.; also W La. to S W Ark., and
rather generally in Tex. to the Edwards Plateau.

3. T. porracea Ashe. Tree: leaf-blades on flowering branches elliptic-ovate,
8–10 cm. long, taper-pointed, about twice as long as broad, cuneate at base or
rounded on one side, mucronate-crenate with gland-tipped teeth, dull blue-green
above, pale grayish-green below, the early appressed straight pubescence deciduous by flowering time, or a little easily detached fascicled pubescence remaining; corymbs 7–15 flowered, pubescent; peduncle slender, pubescent, the
free portion 2–3.5 cm. long; bract linear-elliptic or lingulate, often falcate,
finally glabrous, 4–8 cm. long, narrowed to the rounded sessile base: sepals

pubescent without, long silky within at the base, three-fourths as long as the elliptic, obtuse petals, not longer than the staminodia.—Hammocks, Okaloosa Co., Fla.

4. T. georgiana Sarg. Small tree, with the slender branchlets at first pale-pubescent and rusty, ultimately red-brown and glabrous: leaf-blades ovate, abruptly short-pointed, cordate, oblique, or truncate at base, coarsely mucronate-crenate, reddish and tomentose when unfolding, ultimately dark yellow-green and scabrate above and covered below with a thick pale or reddish tomentum, or glabrous in autumn, conspicuously reticulate-veined: flowers 10–15 together in pubescent compact corymbs: peduncle slender, densely pubescent, the free portion 2.5–4 cm. long: bract linear-elliptic to spatulate, pubescent or becoming nearly glabrous, 6.5–10 cm. long: sepals ovate, half as long as the lanceolate-acuminate petals.—Hammocks, Coastal Plain, C Fla. to S. C.

5. T. Michauxii Nutt. Tree similar to *T. heterophylla*, but the leaf-blades longer and narrower, generally abruptly acute and obliquely cordate, the vein-axils generally without axillary tufts: flowers in puberulent cymes; peduncle glabrescent, the free portion 3.5–5 cm. long: bract oblanceolate to spatulate, occasionally linear-elliptic, 9–12 cm. long: sepals pubescent and ciliate without, tomentose within: petals lanceolate.—Woods, various provinces, though rarely Coastal Plain or higher mountains, Ga. to Miss., Ark., Mo., S Ill., and S N. Y.

6. T. truncata Spach. Large tree, with stout glabrous branchlets, which are bright-red the first season and later brown, the bark of the trunk furrowed and scaly: leaf-blades ovate or ovate-elliptic, or triangular-ovate, abruptly acuminate, obliquely cordate at the base, deeply crenate-serrate, dark-green and lustrous above, hoary-tomentose below, 10–18 cm. long, 8–10 cm. wide: flowers 7–10, in glabrous cymes: peduncle glabrous, slender, the free portion 3.5–4 cm. long: bract elliptic, obtuse, glabrous, 5–7 cm. long: sepals ovate, pale-pubescent outside, silky inside, half as long as the lanceolate petals. [*T. cinerea* Raf. *T. monticola* Sarg.]—Wooded hills, Blue Ridge to Appalachian Plateau, N. C. to Tenn. and Va.

7. T. heterophylla Vent. Large tree, with slender, glabrous reddish or yellowish-brown branchlets: leaf-blades ovate, gradually narrowed to the acuminate apex, obliquely truncate or slightly cordate at base, pubescent above at unfolding but at maturity dark-green and glabrous above, with the lower surface covered with thick firmly attached pale (sometimes brown) tomentum, the vein-axils with rusty tufts, mucronate-crenate with gland-tipped teeth, 8–12 cm. long; flowers 10–12 together in pubescent more or less corymbs; peduncle glabrous, the free portion generally 3–4 cm. long, or sometimes less: bract linear-elliptic to oblanceolate or spatulate, unsymmetrically cuneate at base, finally glabrous, 10.5–15 cm. long: sepals pale-pubescent without, villous within: petals lanceolate. [*T. tenera* Ashe]—Wooded slopes, various provinces, though rarely Coastal Plain or higher Appalachians, N Fla. to S Ind. and W. Va.

8. T. eburnea Ashe. Tall tree, with dark gray-brown furrowed bark on the trunk and smooth silver-gray bark on the branches, the twigs stout, 5–6 mm. thick, soft, glabrous, occasionally sparingly glaucous, those of the first season bright-green, brown, or red-brown, becoming gray the second year, the buds large and glaucous: leaf-blades ovate or round-ovate, 8–14 cm. long, abruptly acuminate, obliquely cordate or truncate at the base, sharply mucronate-crenate, thick, dark-green and glabrous above, densely pubescent beneath with soft ivory-white hairs which are sometimes deciduous by autumn: bract linear-elliptic or spatulate, 10–20 cm. long, or occasionally shorter, glabrate above, often pubescent beneath, nearly sessile: ovary coarsely brown-pubescent.—Rich soil and cool glens, various provinces, N W Fla. to N. C., in Coastal Plain only in the former State.

9. T. lasioclada Sarg. Large tree, becoming 20 m. tall: leaf-blades thick, ovate, 10–15 cm. long, abruptly acuminate, finely mucronate-crenate with gland-tipped teeth, bright-green and lustrous above, covered below with a thick, pale-brown or rufous, easily detached stellate pubescence: petioles at first with long spreading hairs mixed with fascicled hairs: flowers mostly 10–15 together in small, branched cymes shorter than the bract, the branches with long spreading hairs, the free portion 2.5–3 cm. long; bract linear-elliptic to spatulate, abruptly tapering to a short peduncle: sepals acute, pubescent without, villose within, about one-third as long as the lanceolate acuminate petals, about the same length as the staminodia.—Rich soil, Coastal Plain and Piedmont, Fla. to S. C., so far as known only the Valleys of the Apalachicola and Savannah Rivers—Distinct from all other American species in its long and spreading hairs on the branchlets, veins of the leaves, and the peduncle and branches of the inflorescence.

10. T. littoralis Sarg. Tree, the branchlets slender, reddish or purplish and pale-pubescent the first season, becoming glabrous and light gray-grown: leaf-blades ovate, 8–12 cm. long, 8–10 cm. wide, abruptly short-pointed, unsymmetrically rounded on one side at base, and cuneate at the other, finely serrate, at first tomentose, soon glabrous and even glaucous beneath, pale yellow-green above, only the vein-axils bearing conspicuous rusty tufts: flowers 9–15 together in small compact pubescent cymes: peduncle somewhat pubescent, the free portion 2–2.5 cm. long: bract oblanceolate, 5–17.5 cm. long, glabrous but for the ciliate margins and pubescent midrib beneath: sepals pale-pubescent without, villose on the margins and with long white hairs within: petals acuminate.—Coast and Sea-Islands of Ga.

11. T. glabra Vent. Tall tree, with stout, red, ultimately glabrous branchlets: leaf-blades broadly ovate, 10–18 cm. long, 10–15 cm. wide, abruptly acuminate, cordate, obliquely-cordate, or truncate at base, coarsely serrate-crenate with gland-tipped teeth, at first coated with pale tomentum, soon glabrous, dark yellow-green above, pale beneath, the vein-axils without axillary tufts: flowers 10–15 together in broad, slender-branched, nearly glabrous cymes: peduncle stout, glabrous, red, the free portion 2.5–4 cm. long: bract elliptic to obovate, gradually narrowed to the base, 8–16 cm. long: sepals one-third shorter than the lanceolate petals. [*T. venulosa* Sarg. *T. fulva* Raf.]—Cool upland woods, Blue Ridge and Appalachian provinces, N. C. to Tenn., and E Ky.

12. T. leucocarpa Ashe. Small tree, with pale furrowed bark, narrow crown, and rather slender, glabrous, orange or red-brown branchlets: the winter-buds dull-red, ovoid: leaf-blades thin, variously ovate, 10–15 cm. long, 8–10 cm. wide, abruptly painted unsymmetrically cordate or truncate at base, coarsely mucronate-crenate with glandular teeth, on unfolding dark-red and sparsely pubescent, soon glabrous or with small axillary tufts in the vein-axils beneath, dark-green above, pale and lustrous beneath: flowers usually 10–12, or sometimes as many as 40 together in long-branched pubescent cymes: peduncle glabrous: bract linear-lingular, sometimes broadly-lingular, 8–10 cm. long, usually 1.5 cm. wide, or occasionally 2.5 cm. broad, nearly sessile: sepals acute, rusty-tomentose without, glabrous within. [*T. nuda* Sarg.]—Woods, Coastal Plain and adj. provinces, Ala. to E Tex., S E Okla., and S W Ark.—Closely similar to *T. americana* L., of the northern States, differing chiefly in its densely tomentose pedicels.

13. T. floridana Small. Small tree, with furrowed bark and slender red-brown or yellowish glabrous branchlets: leaf-blades broadly ovate, 6–12 cm. long, 5–10 cm. wide, acuminate at apex, truncate or cordate at the unsymmetrical base, or variously oblique, coarsely mucronate-crenate with rather large teeth, the mucro exceedingly long, reddish and tomentose in unfolding, but at maturity dark and glabrous above, pale below, or sometimes with a silvery-white bloom, sometimes tufted in the vein-axils: cymes compact, few-flowered: peduncle pubescent, the free portion 2–4 cm. long, pedicels hoary-tomentose: bract linear-elliptic to nearly spatulate, often falcate, glabrous, 8–16 cm. long, mostly narrow: sepals hoary-tomentose without, two-thirds as long as the lanceolate petals. [*T. crenoserrata* Sarg. *T. alabamensis* Ashe]—Rich woods, various provinces, but not in the higher mountains, W Fla. to Tex., S E Okla., Ky., and W N. C. —(*Mex.*)

14. T. australis Small. Tree becoming 20 m. tall: leaf-blades relatively thin, ovate to oval-ovate, 7–17 cm. long, abruptly acuminate, crenate-mucronate with prominently gland-tipped teeth, deep-green above, glaucous beneath and essentially glabrous, cordate or nearly truncate at base: peduncle glabrous, the free portion 2–4 cm. long; bract lingulate, relatively large, often 4 cm. broad, peduncled, glaucous and glabrous beneath: sepals about three-fifths as long as the petals: staminodia linear-spatulate.—Wooded hillsides, Blue Ridge to Appalachian provinces, Ala. to N. C.

FAMILY 2. **MALVACEAE** — MALLOW FAMILY

Herbs, shrubs, or trees. Leaves alternate: blades simple, palmately veined. Flowers perfect. Calyx of 5 more or less united valvate sepals. Corolla of 5 convolute petals. Androecium of numerous monadelphous stamens. Gynoecium of several united, often whorled, carpels. Fruit capsular or sometimes baccate.—About 45 genera and 900 species, widely distributed.

Fruit of several radially disposed carpels which separate from each other at maturity.
  Carpels as many as there are stigmas: staminal-column anther-bearing at the summit.
    Stigmas short, capitate or truncate.   Tribe I. SIDEAE.
    Stigmas elongate, usually filiform, introrse.   Tribe II. MALVEAE.
  Carpels one half as many as there are stigmas: staminal-column anther-bearing on the upper part, but not at the lobed or truncate summit.   Tribe III. URENEAE.
Fruit a loculicidal capsule or rarely indehiscent.   Tribe IV. HIBISCEAE.

I. SIDEAE

Seeds 2–several in each carpel.
  Involucel wanting.
    Carpels leathery or parchment-like, not bladdery.   1. ABUTILON.
    Carpels membranous, bladdery.   2. GAYOIDES.
  Involucel of 3 bractlets.   3. MODIOLA.
Seeds solitary in each carpel.
  Involucel of 2 or 3 bractlets.   4. MALVASTRUM.
  Involucel wanting.   5. SIDA.

II. MALVEAE

Petals notched at the apex: carpels beakless, without internal processes.   6. MALVA.
Petals erose at the apex: carpels beaked, with an internal process above the seed.   7. CALLIRRHOE.

III. URENEAE

Carpels dry, achene-like.
  Involucel wanting: inflorescence capitate.   8. MALACHRA.
  Involucel of several bractlets: inflorescence axillary or racemose.
    Involucel of 5 partially united bractlets: carpels spiny all over.   9. URENA.
    Involucel of 5–15 distinct bractlets: carpels unarmed or with 1–3 spines on the back.
      Mature carpels spine-armed.   10. PAVONIA.
      Mature carpels spineless, sometimes cuspidate.   11. MALACHE.
Carpels forming a drupe-like berry, but separating at maturity.   12. MALVAVISCUS.

IV. HIBISCEAE

Styles distinct, spreading: seeds usually reniform.
  Capsule as long as broad or much longer, the cavities 2-many-seeded.
    Bractlets of the involucel distinct.
      Calyx not bladdery, surrounding the base of the capsule, persistent or deciduous.
        Calyx cup-like, persistent, nearly equally 5-lobed.   13. HIBISCUS.
        Calyx spathe-like, split on one side and deciduous about the base.   14. ABELMOSCHUS.
      Calyx bladdery-inflated, scarious and conspicuously veined.   15. TRIONUM.
    Bractlets of the involucel united into a lobed cup.   16. PARITI.
  Capsule much depressed, the cavities 1-seeded.   17. KOSTELETZKYA.
Styles united: seed not reniform.
  Bractlets of the involucels entire, rather inconspicuous.
    Sepals wholly united or nearly so: capsule indehiscent.   18. THESPESIA.
    Sepals merely united at the base: capsule loculicidal.   19. CIENFUEGOSIA.
  Bractlets of the involucels laciniate, conspicuous.   20. GOSSYPIUM.

1. **ABUTILON** [Tourn.] Mill. Herbs, shrubs, or rarely trees. Leaf-blades entire, toothed, or lobed. Involucel wanting. Sepals 5, united below. Petals 5, often yellow. Carpels 5–30, beaked at maturity.—About 100 species, mostly in tropical regions.—INDIAN-MALLOWS.—The bark yields a fiber. The plants, especially the flowers, are mucilaginous.

Carpels 11 or more: fruit hirsute at the top: mature carpels short-beaked or merely mucronate.
  Plant annual: petals yellow.   1. *A. Abutilon.*
  Plant perennial: petals pink, salmon-pink, or red, or yellow above a purple base.
    Petals yellow above a purple base: mature carpels less than 15 mm. long: seed merely minutely stellate.   2. *A. hirtum.*
    Petals pink, salmon-pink or red: carpels mostly over 15 mm. long; seed hirsute.   3. *A. pauciflorum.*
Carpels 10 or fewer: fruit finely pubescent or puberulent at the top: mature carpels slender-beaked.   4. *A. permolle.*

1. **A. Abutilon** (L.) Rusby. Stem 3–18 dm. tall, velvety-pubescent: leaf-blades suborbicular to ovate or reniform-orbicular, 9–30 cm. long: calyx-lobes abruptly pointed: petals yellow, 10–15 mm. long: carpels 15–20 mm. long. [*A. Avicennae* Gaertn.] — (INDIAN-HEMP. VELVET-LEAF.)—Roadsides, cult. grounds, and waste-places, various provinces, Fla. to Tex., S. D., and Me. Nat. of Asia.—(*W. I.*)

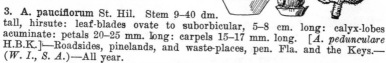

2. **A. hirtum** Sweet. Stem 1–3.5 dm. tall, velvety-canescent, and somewhat villous-hirsute: leaf-blades ovate to suborbicular, 2–15 cm. long: calyx-lobes acute or acuminate: petals 15–20 mm. long: carpels 8–10 mm. long. Coastal sands, pen. Fla. and the Keys.—(*W. I., E. I.*)—All year.

3. **A. pauciflorum** St. Hil. Stem 9–40 dm. tall, hirsute: leaf-blades ovate to suborbicular, 5–8 cm. long: calyx-lobes acuminate: petals 20–25 mm. long: carpels 15–17 mm. long. [*A. pedunculare* H.B.K.]—Roadsides, pinelands, and waste-places, pen. Fla. and the Keys.—(*W. I., S. A.*)—All year.

4. **A. permolle** (Willd.) Sweet. Stem 5–16 dm. tall, velvety-tomentose: leaf-blades ovate, 2.5–10 cm. long: petals yellow, 10–15 mm. long: carpels

11–12 mm. long.—(INDIAN-MALLOW.)—Coastal hammocks, cult. grounds, and roadsides, pen. Fla. and the Keys.—(*W. I.*)—All year.

2. GAYOIDES Small. Herbs, sometimes vine-like. Leaf-blades commonly toothed. Involucel wanting. Sepals 5, united below. Petals 5, usually yellow. Carpels numerous, beakless at maturity.—One species.

1. G. crispum (L.) Small. Stem and branches 3–9 dm. long: leaf-blades ovate, 1–5 cm. long, mostly acute or rather obtuse: calyx-lobes rather abruptly pointed: mature carpels angled at the summit.—Pinelands, hammocks, waste-places, and cult. grounds, Coastal Plain, Fla. and southwestern provinces, Tex. to Ariz.—(*W. I., Mex., C. A., S. A.*)—All year.—*G. imberbe* (Fl. SE. U. S.) has merely velvety pubescent foliage. It seems otherwise to be the same as *G. crispum* and occupies the same geographic range.

3. MODIOLA Moench. Herbs. Leaf-blades palmately lobed or divided. Involucel present. Sepals 5, united below. Petals 5, entire. Carpels many, transversely 2-celled, beaked at maturity, the faces smooth or merely wrinkled.—One species.

1. M. caroliniana (L.) G. Don. Branches spreading or prostrate, 1–7 dm. long: leaf-blades 2–6 cm. long, with coarsely serrate or incised lobes: calyx-lobes ovate or ovate-lanceolate: petals scarlet, obovate or oval-obovate, 6–10 mm. long: head of fruit depressed. [*M. multifida* Moench.] — Low grounds, waste-places, and roadsides, Coastal Plain and occasionally adj. provinces, Fla. to Tex. and Va.—(*W. I., Mex., C. A., S. A.*)— Sum.—The petals are sometimes orange.

4. MALVASTRUM A. Gray. Herbs or partly woody plants. Leaf-blades entire, lobed, or parted. Involucel of distinct bractlets, or wanting. Sepals 5, partially united. Petals 5, variously colored. Carpels 5 or more, 1-celled, beaked or beakless.—About 75 sepecies, American and African.— FALSE-MALLOWS.

Plant annual: 1. *M. angustum.*
Plant perennial:
    Flowers solitary in the axils or in terminal inter-
       rupted spikes or spike-like racemes: stem
       strigose.
      Mature carpels beakless, sometimes with a mere
        protuberance behind the apex.   2. *M. corchorifolium.*
      Mature carpels with a subulate beak behind the
        apex.   3. *M. coromandelianum.*
    Flowers in congested terminal and axillary spikes:
      stem hirsute.   4. *M. spicatum.*

1. **M. angustum** A. Gray. Stem 1-3 dm. tall; leaf-blades elliptic-lanceolate
to linear-elliptic, 2-4 cm. long, remotely serrate: calyx-lobes broadly triangular:
petals yellow, about equalling the calyx-
lobes: carpels 5 or 6, pubescent.—(YELLOW
FALSE-MALLOW.)—Dry soil and rocky hills,
various provinces, rarely Coastal Plain, Ala.
to Kans., Ia., and Tenn.—Sum.

2. **M. corchorifolium** (Desr.) Britton.
Stem 3-9 dm. tall; leaf-blades ovate to
elliptic-lanceolate, 2-6 cm. long, coarsely
serrate: calyx-lobes triangular-ovate, acuminate: petals orange-yellow: carpels hispidulous. [*M. Rugelii* S. Wats.]—Hammocks,
waste-places, and cult. grounds, pen. Fla.
and the Keys.—(*W. I.*)

3. **M. coromandelianum** (L.) Garcke. Stem
3-9 dm. tall: leaf-blades orbicular-ovate to elliptic-ovate, 2-8 cm. long, sharply
serrate: calyx-lobes triangular-ovate: petals light-yellow: carpels hirsute on
top. [*M. americanum* (L.) Torr.]—Hammocks, roadsides, cult. grounds and
waste-places, Coastal Plain, Fla. to Tex.—(*W. I., Mex., C. A., S. A., O. W.*)

4. **M. spicatum** (L.) A. Gray. Stem 3-9 dm. tall: leaf-blades ovate to
deltoid-ovate, 3-8 cm. long, crenate-serrate, or sometimes slightly lobed: calyx
densely pubescent; lobes triangular-lanceolate, 3-4 mm. long: petals orange,
8-11 mm. long: carpels 3 mm. long, the tip inflexed.—Sandy soil, Coastal
Plain, Fla. and Tex.

5. **SIDA L.** Herbs or partially woody plants. Leaf-blades usually
toothed. Involucel usually wanting. Sepals 5, partially united. Petals 5,
pale, often yellow. Carpels 5 to many, 1-celled, commonly singly or doubly
beaked.—About 100 species, widely distributed.—The bark of some species
yields a strong fiber.

Leaf-blades palmately lobed: corolla white: calyx terete at the base.—Subgenus PSEUDO-NAPAEA.	I. HERMAPHRODITAE.
Leaf-blades merely toothed: corolla colored: calyx angled.— Subgenus MALVINDA.	
Flowers or flower-clusters in leafy involucres at the ends of the branches.	II. CILIARES.
Flowers or flower-clusters axillary or sometimes in terminal panicles.	III. SPINOSAE.

I. HERMAPHRODITAE

Tall perennial: lobes of the leaf-blades toothed.	1. *S. hermaphrodita.*

II. CILIARES

Diffuse perennial, somewhat resembling a *Stylosanthes* in habit: flower-clusters leafy-involucrate.	2. *S. ciliaris.*

III. SPINOSAE

Stems or branches decumbent or prostrate.	3. *S. procumbens.*
Stems erect or ascending.	
Leaf-blades cordate.	4. *S. cordifolia.*
Leaf-blades acute, rounded, or truncate at the base.	
Leaf-blades ovate to cuneate or lanceolate.	
Mature carpels with 1 tooth each: peduncles, at least those arising from the stem, much longer than the pedicels.	5. *S. rhombifolia.*
Mature carpels with 2 teeth each: peduncles shorter than the pedicels or only slightly longer.	

Stem-leaves with petioles less than 1 cm.
   long.   6. *S. carpinifolia.*
Stem-leaves with petioles over 1 cm. long. 7. *S. spinosa.*
  Leaf-blades linear or linear-elliptic.
    Leaf-blades and calyx with red margins.
      Leaf-blades of a narrowly linear type: ma-
        ture carpels 4–5 mm. high.   8. *S. Elliottii.*
      Leaf-blades broader: mature carpels 3–4 mm.
        high.   9. *S. rubromarginata.*
    Leaf-blades and calyx with green margins, not
      discolored.   10. *S. leptophylla.*

1. **S. hermaphrodita** (L.) Rusby. Plant erect, 9–40 dm. tall: leaf-blades palmately 3–7-lobed: calyx-lobes triangular: petals white: mature carpels 6–7 mm. long. [*S. Napaea* Cav.]—(VIRGINIA-MALLOW.)—River-banks and rocky slopes, various provinces N of Coastal Plain, Tenn. to Ohio, Pa., and Va.—Sum.

2. **S. ciliaris** L. Plant with diffuse branches 1–3 dm. long; leaf-blades elliptic to cuneate, 1–4 cm. long, serrate: calyx-lobes triangular: petals reddish-purple: mature carpels 5–8, 2–2.5 mm. long.—Hammocks and open places, Florida Keys and S Tex.—(*W. I., Mex., C. A., S. A.*)—All year.

3. **S. procumbens** Sw. Plant with tomentose branches, 1–6 dm. long: leaf-blades suborbicular to ovate, 1–2.5 cm. long, crenate: calyx-lobes deltoid-acuminate: petals yellow, 4–6 mm. long: mature carpels often 5, about 2 mm. long, puberulent. [*S. supina* L'Her.]—Hammocks and waste-places, Florida Keys.—(*W. I., Mex., C. A., S. A.*)—All year.

4. **S. cordifolia** L. Plant 6–15 dm. tall, the stem and branches velvety-tomentose: leaf-blades ovate or suborbicular, 4–10 cm. long, irregularly crenate: calyx-lobes triangular: petals tawny-yellow, 5–7 mm. long: mature carpels often 10–12, about 3 mm. long, retrorse-pubescent.—Pinelands, hammocks, waste-places, and roadsides, pen. Fla. and the Keys; also Gulf seaports.—Nat. of trop. Am. (*W. I., Mex., C. A., S. A.*)—All year.

5. **S. rhombifolia** L. Plant 5–12 dm. tall, the branches puberulent or glabrate: leaf-blades rhombic, elliptic-obovate, or oblanceolate, 1.5–8 cm. long, serrate: calyx-lobes triangular: petals pale-yellow or sometimes red-blotched at the base: mature carpels 10–12, about 5 mm. long.—Roadsides and waste-places, Coastal Plain, Fla. to Tex. and N. C.—Spr.-fall or all year S.

6. **S. carpinifolia** L. f. Plant 3–9 dm. tall, the branches puberulent or glabrate: leaf-blades lanceolate, oblong-ovate, or ovate, 2–10 cm. long, irregularly serrate: calyx-lobes triangular: petals yellow to white: mature carpels 8–10, about 4 mm. long.—Pinelands, hammocks, and cult. grounds, Coastal Plain, Fla.—Spr.-fall or all year S.

7. **S. spinosa** L. Plant 1–6 dm. tall, pubescent: leaf-blades elliptic to ovate or ovate-lanceolate to linear-lanceolate, 1–5 cm. long, serrate: calyx-lobes triangular: corolla pale-yellow or orange: mature carpels about 5, 4 mm. long.—(INDIAN-MALLOW. FALSE-MALLOW. PRICKLY-SIDA.)—Roadsides, cult. grounds,

and waste-places, various provinces, Fla. to Tex., Ia., and Me.—Nat. of trop. Am.—(*W. I., Mex., C. A., S. A.*)—Sum.

8. S. Elliottii T. & G. Plant 3–5 dm. tall or sometimes depressed: leaf-blades linear or nearly so, 2–7 cm. long, serrate: calyx-lobes triangular: petals deep-yellow: mature carpels 8–12, 4–5 mm. long, rugose-reticulated on the back.—Pinelands and edges of hammocks, Coastal Plain, Fla. to Miss., Mo., and Va.—Sum.

9. S. rubromarginata Nash. Plant 5–10 dm. tall: leaf-blades varying from narrowly obovate to elliptic or oblong-lanceolate, 1.5–5.5 cm. long, serrate: calyx-lobes triangular: petals light-orange: mature carpels 8–10, 3–4 mm. long, rugose-pitted on the back.—Sandy pinelands, Fla.—Spr.–fall.

10. S. leptophylla Small. Plant 9–13 dm. tall, thinly pubescent: leaf-blades linear to linear-elliptic, 2–10 cm. long, sharply serrate: calyx-lobes triangular: petals light orange: mature carpels about 4 mm. long.—Sandy soil, Coastal Plain, Ga. to La.—Spr.–fall.

6. MALVA [Tourn.] L. Herbs. Leaf-blades lobed or dissected. Involucel of usually 3 bractlets. Sepals 5, partially united. Petals 5, sometimes eroded. Carpels many, 1-celled, beakless, the faces radially striate or ribbed at maturity.—About 30 species, natives of the Old World.—MALLOWS.—The leaves and flowers of some species are mucilaginous and are used medicinally.

Corolla less than 2 cm. broad: bractlets linear to lanceolate.
  Branches procumbent: carpels finely pubescent and smooth on the back.   1. *M. rotundifolia.*
  Branches erect or ascending: carpels glabrous and reticulated on the back.   2. *M. parviflora.*
Corolla over 2 cm. broad: bractlets elliptic to ovate-lanceolate.   3. *M. sylvestris.*

1. M. rotundifolia L. Plant depressed: leaf-blades obscurely lobed, crenate-dentate; calyx-lobes ovate to triangular-ovate: petals light-blue, pink, or white, 9–14 mm. long: carpels 1.5–2 mm. long.— (CHEESES. LOW-MALLOW.)—Cult. grounds, waste-places, and roadsides, various provinces, throughout U. S. and S Can. Nat. of Eu.—Spr.–sum.

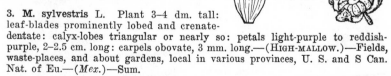

2. M. parviflora L. Plant erect or ascending: leaf-blades angularly or obtusely lobed and crenate: calyx-lobes triangular: petals white or purple-tinged, 3.5–7 mm. long: carpels 2–2.5 mm. long.—Waste-places, various provinces, Fla. to Tex., Calif., and B. C. Nat. of Eu.—(*Mex.*)—Sum.

3. M. sylvestris L. Plant 3–4 dm. tall: leaf-blades prominently lobed and crenate-dentate: calyx-lobes triangular or nearly so: petals light-purple to reddish-purple, 2–2.5 cm. long: carpels obovate, 3 mm. long.—(HIGH-MALLOW.)—Fields, waste-places, and about gardens, local in various provinces, U. S. and S Can. Nat. of Eu.—(*Mex.*)—Sum.

7. CALLIRRHOË Nutt. Herbs, resembling species of *Malva.* Leaf-blades lobed, cleft, or dissected. Involucel of distinct bractlets, or wanting.

Sepals 5, united below. Petals 5, sometimes erose-fimbriate. Carpels 10–20, 1-celled, more or less beaked, the faces smooth or reticulate at maturity.—About 8 species, North American.—POPPY-MALLOWS.

Peduncles several-flowered.	1. *C. triangularis.*
Peduncles 1-flowered.	
Involucels present.	2. *C. Papaver.*
Involucels wanting.	3. *C. alceoides.*

1. C. triangulata (Leavenw.) A. Gray. Stem 3–9 dm. tall, rough-pubescent: leaf-blades triangular-ovate to triangular-hastate, 3–1.5 cm. long, those of the lower ones crenate or lobed: calyx-lobes deltoid-ovate: petals deep-purple, 2–2.5 cm. long: carpels 3.5–4 mm. long.— (CLUSTERED POPPY-MALLOW.)—Dry woods, various provinces, rarely Coastal Plain, Ala. to Tex., Minn., Ill., and N. C.—Spr.–sum.

2. C. Papaver (Cass.) A. Gray. Stem with decumbent branches 2–7 dm. long, strigillose or glabrate: leaf-blades 3–5-lobed or 3–5-parted: calyx-lobes lanceolate to elliptic-lanceolate, 1–1.5 cm. long: petals red-purple, 2–4.5 cm. long: carpels 3 mm. long.—Sandy woods, Coastal Plain, Fla. to Tex. and Ga.—Spr.–sum.

3. C. alceoides (Michx.) A. Gray. Stem with strigillose branches 2–5 dm tall: leaf-blades palmately lobed or incised: calyx-lobes triangular or triangular-lanceolate, less than 1 cm. long: petals pink or rose, 1–1.5 cm. long: carpels 4 mm. long.—Dry soil, various provinces, Ala. to Tex., Nebr., and Ky.—Spr.–sum.

8. MALACHRA L. Herbs or woody plants, sometimes with stinging hairs. Leaf-blades lobed. Involucel wanting. Sepals 5, partially united. Petals 5, broad. Carpels 5, 1-celled, beakless, the faces reticulate-veiny.—About 6 species, tropical American.

| Bracts acuminate: calyx-lobes acuminate, with rather weak hairs. | 1. *M. urens.* |
| Bract acute: calyx-lobes setaceous-tipped, with stout hairs. | 2. *M. alceifolia.* |

1. M. urens Poit. Stem 2–6 dm. tall, more or less branched and spreading, finely pubescent in lines and with coarse simple or branched hairs: leaf-blades ovate to lanceolate, sometimes slightly 3-lobed, 3–10 cm. long, rather coarsely dentate or dentate-crenate: flower-clusters sessile or nearly so: calyx-lobes with acuminate tips: petals 6–12 mm. long, light-yellow, orange, or red, usually sparingly pubescent: carpels about 3 mm. long: seed nearly as wide as long.—Roadsides, cult. grounds, and waste-places, S pen. Fla. and the Keys.—(*W. I.*)—All year.

2. M. alceifolia Jacq. Stem mostly 3–10 dm. tall or diffusely branched and spreading, finely soft-pubescent all over and with stiff forking hairs: leaf-blades suborbicular to ovate, sometimes 3-lobed, 3–15 cm. long, rather finely dentate or crenate; flower-clusters manifestly short-peduncled: calyx-lobes with setaceous tips as long as the body or longer: petals 11–16 mm. long, bright-yellow, pubescent without and ciliate: carpels about 4 mm. long: seed much longer than wide.—Waste-places, roadsides, and pinelands, S pen. Fla.—(*W. I., Mex., C. A., S. A.*)—All year.

9. **URENA** [Dill.] L. Shrubs or partly woody herbs. Leaf-blades angled or lobed. Involucel present. Sepals 5, united below, and often partially adnate to the bractlets. Petals 5, yellow, pink, or purplish. Carpels 5, or rarely more, 1-celled, indehiscent, usually bristly with barbed spines.—Three species, tropical.

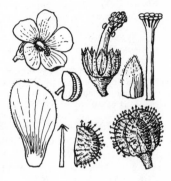

1. **U. lobata** L. Stem mostly 1–2 m. tall, tomentose: leaf-blades suborbicular to oval, shallowly lobed and serrulate: bractlets linear-lanceolate, 3–5 mm. long: calyx about as long as the involucel: petals pink or rose, about 2 cm. long: carpels 4–5 mm. in diameter.—Hammocks, waste-places, and roadsides, Fla. Nat. of E. I.—(*W. I., Mex., C. A., S. A.*)—The bark yields a fiber; the flowers are used medicinally.

10. **PAVONIA** Cav. Shrubs or woody herbs. Leaf-blades angled or lobed. Involucel present. Sepals 5, partially united. Petals 5, often showy. Carpels 5, 1-celled, spine-armed.—About 60 species, mostly tropical.

Carpels 3-awned, the awns barbed: leaf-blades of an ovate type: calyx-lobes lanceolate to ovate-lanceolate.   1. *P. spinifex.*
Carpels awnless and pointless: leaf-blades of a hastate type: calyx-lobes broadly ovate.   2. *P. hastata.*

1. **P. spinifex** (L.) Cav. Shrub 1–3 m. tall, hirsute and strigillose: leaf-blades ovate to elliptic-ovate, 5–10 cm. long: bractlets linear to lanceolate: calyx-lobes lanceolate to ovate-lanceolate: petals yellow, 2.5 cm. long: mature carpels 5–6 mm. long, the spines slender-subulate.— Sandy woods, hammocks, and shell-mounds, Coastal Plain, Fla. to S. C.—Spr.–sum.— Formerly this mallow was thought to be confined to the coastal regions in Florida, and suspected as being an introduction. However, in recent years it has been found in the wildest hammocks of the interior.

2. **P. hastata** Cav. Plant 9–20 dm. tall, roughish-canescent: leaf-blades of a hastate type, 2–5 cm. long: bractlets ovate to obovate, 4–5 mm. long: petals 15–25 mm. long, mainly pale red: carpels 4 mm. long. [*P. LeContei* T. & G.]—Sandy soil, Coastal Plain, Ga. Nat. of S. A.—(*W. I.*)— Spr.–fall.

11. **MALACHE** B. Vogel. Shrubs or partly woody plants. Leaf-blades broad, remotely serrate or repand, 3-ribbed. Involucel of 6–8 bractlets or more.

854 MALVACEAE

Sepals 5, partially united. Petals 5, pale.
Carpels with a median crest at the apex and
2 lateral cusps.—Three species, tropical
American.

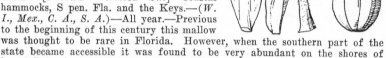

1. M. scabra B. Vogel. Plant 1–3 m. tall,
puberulent: leaf-blades ovate to elliptic-
ovate, 6–15 cm. long: bractlets elliptic-
lanceolate: calyx-lobes ovate: petals greenish-yellow or whitish, 2–2.5 cm. long: mature
carpels about 10 mm. long, reticulate on the
back. [*Pavonia racemosa* Sw.]—Coastal
hammocks, S pen. Fla. and the Keys.—(*W.
I., Mex., C. A., S. A.*)—All year.—Previous
to the beginning of this century this mallow
was thought to be rare in Florida. However, when the southern part of the
state became accessible it was found to be very abundant on the shores of
bays. It is often copiously and intricately branched.

12. **MALVAVISCUS** Dill. Shrubs, trees, or partially woody plants.
Leaf-blades entire, toothed, or angulately lobed. Flowers horizontal or nodding, peduncled. Involucel of 7–12 narrow
bractlets. Sepals 5, partly united. Petals
5, each with a lateral auricle. Carpels 5,
ultimately forming a baccate fruit.—About
10 species, tropical American.

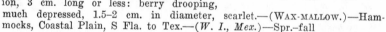

1. M. Drummondii T. & G. Stem 8–19 dm.
tall, tomentose: leaf-blades suborbicular,
angulately 3–5-lobed, softly pubescent:
bractlets of the involucel about 9, linear or
linear-spatulate, 5–6 mm. long: calyx tubular-campanulate, about 1 cm. long; lobes
triangular, often deltoid, or sometimes ovate,
shorter than the tube, acute: petals vermilion, 3 cm. long or less: berry drooping,
much depressed, 1.5–2 cm. in diameter, scarlet.—(WAX-MALLOW.)—Hammocks, Coastal Plain, S Fla. to Tex.—(*W. I., Mex.*)—Spr.–fall

13. **HIBISCUS.** L. Herbs, shrubs, or trees. Leaf-blades entire, lobed,
or parted. Involucel of several, rarely 3, distinct bractlets. Sepals 5, more
or less united. Petals 5, white, colored or variegated. Carpels forming a
5-valved capsule.—About 180 species, widely distributed.—ROSE-MALLOWS.—
The bark of some species yields a fiber, and the leaves are used as pot-herbs.

Corolla cylindric or the petals merely spreading at the tip: seed woolly.
  I. TUBIFLORI.
Corolla funnelform to rotate: seeds glabrous or hirsute.
  Bractlets of the involucel dilated or forked at the apex.   II. FURCELLATI.
  Bractlets of the involucel entire, not dilated at the
    apex.
    Herbs, often tall perennials.
      Involucel and calyx herbaceous, not succulent.
        Corolla broadly funnelform or campanulate;
          petals mainly pink or white.
        Calyx and involucel finely spinescent.   III. CANNABINI.

Calyx and involucel glabrous or softly
pubescent.
Corolla rotate; petals red.
Involucel and calyx succulent.
Shrubs or trees.
Corolla open-funnelform: leaf-blades lobed.
Corolla with a short funnelform tube and a large
rotate limb: leaf-blades merely toothed.

IV. GRANDIFLORI.
V. COCCINEI.
VI. SABDARIFFAE.

VII. SYRIACI.

VIII. ROSAE-SINENSES.

I. TUBIFLORI
Shrub with slender branches and nodding flowers.

1. *H. pilosus.*

II. FURCELLATI
Leaves softly pubescent; blades shallowly lobed; petals 8
cm. long or more.
Leaves harshly pubescent; blades deeply lobed: petals 7
cm. long or less.

2. *H. furcellatus.*

3. *H. aculeatus.*

III. CANNABINI
Erect bright-green plant, the leaf-blades with narrow
coarsely toothed lobes: bractlets very slender: calyx-
lobes slenderly attenuate from a broad base.

4. *H. cannabinus.*

IV. GRANDIFLORI
Leaf-blades glabrous.
Leaf-blades pubescent at least beneath.
Capsule glabrous.
Corolla pink: capsule blunt.
Corolla white, with a crimson eye: capsule beaked.
Capsule pubescent.
Leaf-blades closely whitish-pubescent beneath.
Leaf-blades closely and minutely stellate-
canescent beneath: capsule beaked.
Leaf-blades lanceolate to ovate, toothed.
Leaf-blades as wide as long, 3–5-lobed, the
lobes toothed:
Leaf-blades loosely stellate-tomentose beneath:
capsule rounded or truncate at the tip.
Leaf-blades brownish-pubescent beneath.

5. *H. militaris.*

6. *H. Moscheutos.*
7. *H. oculiroseus.*

8. *H. incanus.*

9. *H. grandiflorus.*

10. *H. lasiocarpus.*
11. *H. mutabilis.*

V. COCCINEI
Leaf-blades with 5–7 narrow elongate more or less incised
lobes.
Leaf-blades merely toothed or with 3–5 prominent, but
short and broad lobes.

12. *H. coccineus.*

13. *H. semilobatus.*

VI. SABDARIFFAE
Plant more or less suffused with red, the 3–5 leaf-lobes
shallowy toothed: succulent calyx-lobes elongate.

14. *H. Sabdariffa.*

VII. SYRIACI
Leaf-blades typically cuneate at the base: short-pedicelled.

15. *H. syriacus.*

VIII. ROSAE-SINENSES
Leaf-blades rounded to cordate at the base: flowers long-
peduncled.

16. *H. Rosa-sinensis.*

1. **H. pilosus** (Sw.) Fauc. & Rendle. Plant 3–18 dm. tall, stellate-hirsute:
leaf-blades triangular-ovate or angulately 3-lobed, crenate, 1–4 cm. long: bractlets linear or nearly so, 7–9 mm. long: calyx-
lobes acuminate: petals crimson, 2–2.5 cm.
long: capsule fully 1 cm. long. [*H. spiralis*
Cav. *H. tubiflorus* DC.]—Hammocks, Florida Keys.—(*W. I., Mex.*)—All year.

2. **H. furcellatus** Lam. Plant 9–25 dm. tall,
finely gray-tomentose: leaf-blades orbicular-
ovate to ovate or lanceolate, 5–15 cm. long,
angulate or 3–5-lobed, crenate: bractlets
narrow, 1–2 cm. long, not bristly: calyx-
lobes lanceolate to triangular-lanceolate:
petals pink or rose-purple, 8–10 cm. long:
capsule ovoid, about 2.5 cm. long, copiously
strigose.—Sandy shores, Indian River, Fla.
—(*W. I., S. A.*)—All year.

3. **H. aculeatus** Walt. Plant 9–20 dm. tall, very rough-pubescent: leaf-blades angulate, 3–5-lobed or 3–5-parted, 4–12 cm. in diameter, the lobes rhombic to spatulate, coarsely toothed: bractlets linear, about 15 mm. long, bristly: calyx-lobes lanceolate, bristly ciliate: petals yellow or cream-colored, except the purple base, 7–8 cm. long: capsule conic-ovoid, about 1.5 cm. long or rarely longer, stellate-pubescent and hispid.—Pinelands, Coastal Plain, N Fla. to La. and S. C.—Sum.

4. **H. cannabinus** L. Plant 3–22 dm. tall, sparingly pubescent: leaf-blades palmately 3–7-parted, the divisions linear to elliptic, unevenly toothed: bractlets narrowly linear, flat, bristle-margined or spiny: calyx-lobes lanceolate, long-acuminate, rather thin, bristle-margined or spiny: petals white or pink, sometimes darker-colored, and purple at the base: capsule conic, 1.5–2 cm. long, strigose.—(AMBAREE. BASTARD-JUTE. BROWN INDIAN-HEMP.)—Hammocks and cultivated grounds, pen. Fla. and the Keys. Nat. of the O. W. tropics.—(*W. I.*)—All year.

5. **H. militaris** Cav. Plant 9–20 dm. tall, glabrous or nearly so: leaf-blades ovate to broadly lanceolate in outline, 6–16 cm. long, serrate-dentate and hastately 3–5-lobed: bractlets 1.5–2 cm. long: calyx-lobes ovate: petals pink with a purple blotch: capsule ovoid, 2–3 cm. long, glabrous: seeds velvety.—(HALBERD-LEAVED ROSE-MALLOW. SWEATING-WEED.)—Alluvial swamps and river-banks, various provinces, Fla. to La., Minn., and Pa.—Sum.–fall.

6. **H. Moscheutos** L. Plant 8–20 dm. tall, velvety-tomentose: leaf-blades lanceolate to broadly ovate, dentate-serrate and often angulately 3–5-lobed: petals mainly pink, 10–12 cm. long: capsule ovoid, 2.5–3 cm. long.—(SWAMP ROSE-MALLOW. SEA-HOLLYHOCK. MARSH-MALLOW.)—Brackish and fresh marshes, Coastal Plain, and occasionally adj. provinces, Fla. to Tex. and Conn., also Central Lowland, Mo. to S Ont.—Sum.–fall.

7. **H. oculiroseus** Britton. Plant similar to *H. Moscheutos* in habit: leaf-blades lanceolate to ovate, unequally toothed: petals white, except the purple spot at the base: capsule conic-ovoid, 2.5–3 cm. long.—Marshes, various provinces, N Ala. to N. J. and N. Y.—Sum.–fall.

8. **H. incanus** Wendl. Plant 9–20 dm. tall, pale or gray velvety-tomentose: leaf-blades ovate to lanceolate, dentate-serrate: petals white, sulphur-yellow, or pinkish, with a crimson base, 8–10 cm. long: capsule ellipsoid-ovoid, 2.5–3 cm. long, finely hirsute.—Swamps, Coastal Plain, Fla. to Ala. and Md.; perhaps in the interior.—Spr.–sum.

9. **H. grandiflorus** Michx. Plant 8–21 dm. tall, velvety-tomentose: leaf-blades hastately 3-lobed, the lobes irregularly toothed: bractlets linear, 1.5–2 cm. long, not bristly: calyx about twice as long as the bractlets: petals 12–15 cm. long, pink, purple, or red at the base: capsule ovoid, 2–5.3 cm. long, coarsely hirsute.—Marshes and wet hammocks, Coastal Plain, Fla. to Miss. and Ga.—Spr.

10. **H. lasiocarpus** Cav. Plant 9–20 dm. tall, densely stellate-tomentose: leaf-blades ovate, 5–14 cm. long, serrate-dentate: bractlets linear, 2.5–3 cm. long, bristly: calyx lobes triangular lanceolate, little longer than the bractlets: petals white or pink with a dark base, 6–10 cm. long: capsule about 2.5 cm. long.—Swamps, various provinces, Ga. to Tex., Mo., and Ill.—Spr.–sum.

11. **H. mutabilis** L. Shrub, sometimes tree-like, scurfy-pubescent with brownish hairs: leaf-blades suborbicular in outline, cordate at the base, angu-

lately 3–5-lobed, the broad lobes unevenly toothed: bractlets narrowly linear, 2–2.5 cm. long: calyx-lobes ovate: petals white or pink, becoming deep-red: capsule 2.5 cm. long.—(COTTON-ROSE.)—Waste-places and pinelands, S Fla. and S La. Nat. of China.—(*W. I., Mex., C. A., S. A.*)—Spr.–sum.

12. **H. coccineus** Walt. Plant 9–30 dm. tall, glabrous: leaf-blades with linear or lanceolate lobes 4–25 cm. long: bractlets 2.5–3 cm. long: calyx 4–5 cm. long; lobes acuminate: petals crimson or deep-red: capsule globose-ovoid, 2–2.5 cm. long, reticulate.—Swamps, near the coast, Fla. to Ala. and Ga.—Sum.

13. **H. semilobatus** Chapm. Plant similar to that of *H. coccineus* in habit: leaf-blades orbicular or ovate, coarsely toothed and 3–5-lobed, 8–15 cm. in diameter: bractlets 2–2.5 cm. long: calyx 4–5 cm. long; lobes acute: petals crimson: capsule about 2.5 cm. long.—Swamps, near the coast, E Fla.— Spr.–fall.

14. **H. Sabdariffa** L. Plant 6–26 dm. tall, the foliage red throughout: leaf-blades digitately 3–5-lobed, the lobes crenate-serrate, the teeth shallow: bractlets linear to linear-lanceolate, very thick, sparingly pubescent, juicy: calyx-lobes lanceolate, like the bractlets dark-red, very thick, copiously fine-pubescent within: petals pink with a dark base: capsule ovoid, 1.5–2 cm. long, pubescent.—(JAMAICA-SORREL. ROSELLE.)—Pinelands, hammocks, and waste-places, Everglade Keys, Fla. and Florida Keys. Nat of the O. W. trop. and cult.—(*W. I., Mex., C. A., S. A.*)—All year.—The succulent tissues contain much mucilage, coloring matter, and an acid, all of which combines to make an excellent jelly. The succulent calyces are cooked and served as ''cranberries.''

15. **H. syriacus** L. Shrub or small tree, minutely pubescent when young: leaf-blades 3-lobed, coarsely crenate, 3–12 cm. long: bractlets linear or linear-spatulate, 10–20 mm. long: calyx-lobes triangular-ovate: petals rose-purple, or white, usually with crimson blotches at the base: capsule ellipsoid-ovoid, 2–2 5 cm. long.—(SHRUBBY-ALTHAEA. ROSE-OF-SHARON.)—Roadsides, fields, and thickets, various provinces, Fla. to Tex. and Conn. Nat. of western Asia and cult.—Sum.–fall.

16. **H. Rosa-Sinensis** L. Shrub or small tree, usually sparingly pubescent: leaf-blades ovate to ovate-lanceolate, rounded or abruptly narrowed at the base, coarsely and unequally toothed: bractlets narrowly linear: calyx-lobes lanceolate, more pubescent within than without: petals rose-red or of other colors: capsule 2–2.5 cm. long.—(SHOE-BLACK PLANT. CHINESE-ROSE.)— Fields, waste-places, and roadsides, pen. Fla. Nat. of China and cult.— (*W. I.*)—All year.—Extensively grown as an ornamental in warm and tropical countries. It is represented by many color forms. The flowers yield a black dye.

14. **ABELMOSCHUS** Medic. Herbs, usually large and coarse, mostly annual. Leaf-blades entire or lobed. Flowers solitary and terminal. Involucel of 4–many narrow bractlets. Sepals united into a long spathe-like calyx which splits and falls away from the fruits. Petals 5, broad. Carpels elongate, forming a long and narrow pointed capsule. Seed glabrous.—About 12 species, tropical.

Leaf-blades with short broad lobes: bractlets of the involucel linear, caducous:
1. *A. esculentus.*

Leaf-blades with long narrow lobes: bractlets of the involucel
elliptic or elliptic-lanceolate, persistent: 2. *A. Manihot.*

1. A. esculentus (L.) Moench. Plant 9–20 dm. tall, hirsute: leaf-blades
1–3 dm. broad, with 5–7 ovate, lanceolate, or oblanceolate, coarsely toothed or
incised segments: corolla greenish-yellow:
capsule columnar, 9–21 cm. long.—(OKRA.
GUMBO.)—Waste-places, gardens, and cult.
grounds, Coastal Plain, Fla. to Tex. Nat.
of Africa and cult.—(*W. I.*)—Spr.–fall.—
The unripe capsules are a very mucilaginous
esculent.

2. A. Manihot (L.) Medic. Plant usually
20–25 dm. tall, ultimately glabrous: leaf-
blades 1–4 dm. in diameter, with 5–9
coarsely toothed or again lobed segments:
corolla pale yellow with a dark eye: capsule
ellipsoid, 4–8 cm. long.—Waste-places, cult.
grounds, and river-banks, Coastal Plain,
Fla. to Tex. Nat. of Asia and cult.—Sum.–
fall.

15 TRIONUM Medic. Annual pubescent herbs. Leaf-blades palmately 3–5-lobed. Flowers solitary at the ends of the branches. Involucels
of several–many narrow bractlets: sepals 5,
united into a ribbed and shallowly lobed
calyx, which is persistent and inflated at
maturity. Petals 5, broad. Carpels forming
a short capsule which is included in the persistent calyx. Seed glabrous.—One species.

1. T. Trionum (L.) Wooton & Standley.
Plant 1–4 dm. tall, hispid: leaf-blades ovate
to suborbicular in outline, pedately 3–5-lobed
or 3–5-parted, the lobes coarsely toothed or
incised: bractlets about 1 cm. long: calyx-
lobes triangular: petals yellow or whitish
with a purple or brown-purple blotch: cap-
sule about 1.5 cm. long. [*Hibiscus Trionum* L.]—(FLOWER-OF-AN-HOUR. BLAD-
DER-KETMIA.)—Roadsides, fields, and waste-places, various provinces, Fla. to
N. M., S. D. and N. S. Nat. of Eu. and cult.—Sum.–fall.

16. PARITI Adans. Shrubs or trees, resembling *Hibiscus* in habit, but
with the bractlets of the involucel united into a lobed cup.—About 4 species
tropical.—Spr. or all year.

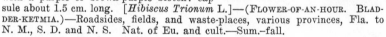

Petals straight or spreading at the tip, pure-yellow, becoming reddish-pink: capsule velvety: seeds papillose.   1. *P. tiliaceum.*
Petals strongly recurved, bronze or orange and blood-red toward
the center, becoming very dark-red: capsule hirsutulous: seed
hirsutulous.   2. *P. grande.*

1. P. tiliaceum (L.) St. Hil. Shrub or large tree, the young parts velvety-
tomentose: leaf-blades thick, suborbicular to orbicular-ovate, mostly 1–2 dm.

long, blunt entire, grayish-tomentose beneath: calyx-lobes lanceolate to triangular-
lanceolate: corolla campanulate or tubular-
campanulate; petals broadly obovate or
orbicular-obovate, pure-yellow, becoming reddish-pink: capsule velvety, beaked, 1–2 cm.
long, nearly or quite as long as the sepals.—
(Mahoe).—Shore hammocks and sand-dunes
coasts of southern pen. Fla. and the Florida
Keys.—(*W. I., Mex., C. A., S. A.*)

2. **P. grande** Britton.   Tree with wide-
spreading branches; the young parts thinly
pubescent: leaf-blades thin or thinnish, suborbicular, mostly 1.5–3 dm. long, sharp-
pointed, more or less crenate, thinly pubes-
cent beneath or glabrous: calyx-lobes lanceolate: corolla rotate-campanulate:
petals spatulate to narrowly obovate, bronze or orange along the edges and
blood-red toward the center, becoming very dark-red: capsule hirsutulous,
beakless, larger than in *P. tiliaceum*, much shorter than the sepals.—(Mahoe)
—Sandy shores, S pen. Fla.—(*W. I.*)

17. **KOSTELETZKYA** Presl.   Herbs or partly woody plants.   Leaf-
blades angulate-lobed, hastate, or sagittate.   Involucel of 7–10 bractlets, or
obsolete.   Sepals 5, partly united.   Petals 5.   Carpels forming a depressed
capsule.—About 8 species, of temperate and tropical America.—Spr.–fall or
all year S.—Fen-roses.

Corolla pink; petals 3–4 cm. long: calyx over 1 cm. wide, surpassing the capsule.
  Stem and leaves copiously pubescent.
    Calyx merely stellate-canescent: upper part of the stem'
      sparingly scabro-pubescent.   1. *K. virginica.*
    Calyx densely stellate-hirsute as well as canescent: upper
      part of stem densely pubescent, usually velvety.   2. *K. althaeifolia.*
  Stem and leaves glabrous or sparingly pubescent.   3. *K. smilacifolia.*
Corolla white; petals about 1 cm. long: calyx less than 1 cm.
  wide, surpassed by the capsule.   4. *K. pentasperma.*

1. **K. virginica** (L.) A. Gray.   Foliage pubescent with stellate hairs but
not velvety, often scabrous: leaf-blades 3–15 cm. long, ovate to ovate-hastate,
serrate-dentate, the lateral lobes triangular,
acute: calyx-lobes lanceolate or elliptic-
lanceolate, acute or acuminate: petals pink,
2–4 cm. long: capsule about 10 mm. broad:
seed 3.5–4 mm. long.—(Salt-marsh mallow.)—Marshes and wet hammocks, Coastal
Plain and rarely adj. provinces, Fla. to La.
and N. Y.

2. **K. althaeifolia** (Chapm.) A. Gray. Foliage mainly velvety-pubescent; leaf-blades
ovate to ovate-lanceolate or nearly lanceolate, 5–15 cm. long, acuminate, irregularly
dentate, the lower ones angularly 3-lobed,
cordate, the upper ones truncate or subcordate at the base: calyx-lobes lanceolate,
acuminate: petals pink, about 4 cm. long: capsule 12–15 mm. broad: seed about
3 mm. long.—Swamps, hammocks, Coastal Plain, Fla. to Tex. and N. C.—(*W. I.*)

3. **K. smilacifolia** A. Gray.   Foliage nearly glabrous: leaf-blades 5–10 cm.
long, those above the base of the stem hastate, with a linear-lanceolate or linear

entire or denticulate middle lobe and linear or nearly linear reflexed entire
or toothed basal lobes; calyx-lobes lanceolate or ovate-lanceolate, acute or
slightly acuminate, about as long as the bractlets: petals 2.5–3.5 cm. long,
bright-pink: capsule hispid, fully 1 cm. broad, surpassed by the sepals: seed
nearly 3.5 mm. long.—Low pinelands, W pen. Fla.

4. **K. pentasperma** (Bert.) Griseb. Foliage pubescent with stinging-hairs:
stem up to 2 m. tall, widely branched: leaf-blades lanceolate to ovate-lanceolate or ovate, with the larger ones sometimes slightly lobed, 2.5–9 cm. long,
serrate, slender-petioled: calyx bristly-pubescent; lobes ovate, acute, exceeding
the bractlets: petals about 1 cm. long, white: capsule nearly 1 cm. broad, surpassing the sepals: seed about 2.5 mm. long.—Hammocks, Cape Sable region,
Fla.—(*W. I.*)—All year.

18. **THESPESIA** Soland.   Shrubs or trees, resembling species of
Hibiscus. Leaf-blades entire or angulate-lobed. Involucel of 3–5 narrow
deciduous bractlets.   Sepals 5, partially or
wholly united.   Petals 5, showy.   Carpels
united into a mostly indehiscent capsule.—
About 8 species, tropical.

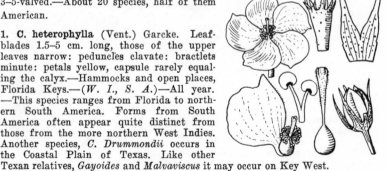

1. **T. populnea** (L.) Soland. Low tree or
shrub: leaf-blades ovate, 5–12 cm. long:
calyx cup-like: petals 5–7 cm. long, yellow
and purple: capsule depressed, 3–4.5 cm.
broad.—(SEASIDE-MAHOE.   PORTIA-TREE.)—
Shore hammocks and sand dunes, Everglade
Keys, Fla. and Florida Keys.   Nat. prob.
of the O. W. tropics, and cult.—(*W. I.*)—
All year   A sacred tree in some countries.
This tree grows luxuriantly on shores of
bays and inlets. By its elongate, spreading lower branches it makes almost impenetrable thickets. Large crops of fruits continuously increase its dense growth.

19. **CIENFUEGOSIA** Cav. Shrubs or woody herbs, resembling species
of *Hibiscus.* Leaf-blades entire or lobed. Involucels of 3–many bractlets.
Sepals 5, united below. Petals 5. Capsule
3–5-valved.—About 20 species, half of them
American.

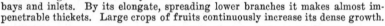

1. **C. heterophylla** (Vent.) Garcke. Leaf-
blades 1.5–5 cm. long, those of the upper
leaves narrow: peduncles clavate: bractlets
minute: petals yellow, capsule rarely equaling the calyx.—Hammocks and open places,
Florida Keys.—(*W. I., S. A.*)—All year.
—This species ranges from Florida to northern South America. Forms from South
America often appear quite distinct from
those from the more northern West Indies.
Another species, *C. Drummondii* occurs in
the Coastal Plain of Texas. Like other
Texan relatives, *Gayoides* and *Malvaviscus* it may occur on Key West.

20. **GOSSYPIUM** L. Herbs, shrubs, or trees. Leaf-blades palmately
lobed or rarely entire. Involucel of 3 large bracts. Sepals 5, united into a
cup-like calyx. Petals 5, usually dark-colored at the base. Capsule 5-valved.—

About 40 species, tropical.—COTTONS.—The bark of the root of some species is medicinal; the hairs of the seeds constitute cotton; the seeds yield oil.

Seed 4–5 mm. broad, glabrous, that is, completely separable from the wool: lobes of
  the leaf-blades mostly longer than the body.   1. *G. barbadense.*
Seed 6–7 mm. broad, woolly: lobes of the leaf-blades mostly
  shorter than the body.
    Wool tawny: plant woody: foliage closely pubescent with
      very short hairs.   2. *G. hirsutum.*
    Wool white: plant herbaceous: foliage if pubescent, hirsute.   3. *G. herbaceum.*

1. G. barbadense L. Shrub with glabrous twigs, often 2 m. tall or more: leaf-blades with 3–5 lanceolate or ovate-lanceolate lobes: corolla pale-yellow: capsule ovoid, acute, 3.5–5 cm. long.—(SEA-ISLAND COTTON.)—Thickets, old fields, and hammocks, Coastal Plain, Fla. to La. Nat. of trop. Am. and cult.—Seeds black, smooth when the long fibers are removed.

2. G. hirsutum L. Shrub or small tree, with usually hirsute twigs: leaf-blades 4–11 cm. wide, sometimes pubescent, 3-lobed, the lobes ovate to deltoid, as long as the body of the leaf or very short: calyx becoming 1–1.5 cm. wide: corolla creamy-white except the purplish base, but becoming pink; petals 3–5 cm. long: capsule ovoid, 2.5–3 cm. long: seed with tawny cotton.—(WILD-COTTON.)— Hammocks, sand-dunes, and kitchen-middens, S pen. Fla. and the Keys.—(*W. I., Mex., C. A., S. A.*)—All year.

3. G. herbaceum L. Plant glabrous, or with long scattered hairs: leaf-blades with 3–5 triangular or ovate lobes: corolla creamy white, becoming pink; petals 5–7 cm. long: capsule subglobose: seed with white cotton.— (COMMON COTTON. UPLAND-COTTON.)—Fields, thickets, and waste places, vaious provinces, Fla. to Tex., Ark., and S Va Nat. of Asia, and cult.— (*W. I., Mex., C. A., S. A.*)—Sum.

FAMILY 3. **BUETTNERIACEAE** — CHOCOLATE FAMILY

Shrubs or trees, or herbs, often resembling *Malvaceae.* Leaves alternate: blades simple. Flowers mostly perfect. Calyx of 5, or rarely fewer, sepals. Corolla of 5, or rarely fewer, petals, or wanting. Androecium of as many stamens as there are sepals, or more. Staminodia sometimes present. Gynoecium of 5, more or less united carpels, or fewer. Fruit capsular or follicular.—About 45 genera and over 600 species, mostly tropical.

Corolla present.
  Petals with flat blades.
    Gynoecium of 5 united carpels: styles 5, not eccentric: stigmas capitate.
      Involucel wanting: capsule angular or pyramidal,
        loculicidal.   1. MOLUCHIA.
      Involucel of 3 or more bractlets: capsule globose,
        loculicidal and septicidal.
        Styles distinct: flowers and fruits mostly in interrupted spike-like panicles.   2. MELOCHIA.
        Styles partly united: flowers and fruits mostly in
        a terminal cluster.   3. RIEDLEA.
    Gynoecium of a single carpel: style 1, eccentric: stigma
      brush-like.   4. WALTHERIA.
  Petals with hooded blades.   5. AYENIA.
Corolla wanting.   6. FIRMIANA.

1. **MOLUCHIA** Medic. Herbs, shrubs, or small trees. Leaf-blades toothed. Involucel wanting. Sepals 5, united at the base. Petals 5, marcescent. Filaments united at the base. Styles 5, distinct. Capsules 5-valved, angled.— About 6 species, tropical.

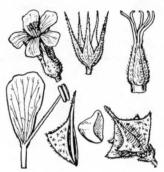

1. **M. tomentosa** (L.) Britton. Much-branched shrub up to 2 m. tall, the foliage densely pale stellate-tomentose: leaf-blades ovate, lanceolate, or linear-lanceolate, 1.5–6 cm. long, crenate or serrate-crenate, prominently veined beneath: calyx-lobes acuminate: petals mostly rose-purple, about 1 cm. long: capsule 6–8 mm. long, beaked, with 5 shoulder-like blades: seed 1.5 mm. long. [*Melochia tomentosa* L.]—(Broom-wood.)— Pinelands, S pen. Fla. and S Tex.—(*W. I., Mex., C. A., S. A.*)—Spr.–fall.

2. **MELOCHIA** [Dill.] L. Herbs or shrubby plants Leaf-blades toothed and sometimes also slightly-lobed. Involucel present. Sepals 5, partly united. Petals 5, marcescent. Filaments well united. Styles 5, distinct. Capsule primarily loculicidally 5-valved.—About 25. species, tropical and subtropical.

1. **M. corchorifolia** L. Stem up to 1.5 mm. glabrous or sparingly pubescent, virgately branched: leaf-blades ovate to ovate-lanceolate, irregularly serrate and often slightly 3-lobed, long-petioled: flower-clusters dense: calyx-lobes acute: petals purple, or with the claw yellowish, 4–7 mm. long: capsule subglobose, 4–4.5 mm. in diameter. [*M. hirsuta* (Chapm. Fl.) not Cav.]—Old fields, cult. grounds and waste-places, various provinces, Fla. to Tex., and S. C.—Spr.–fall.

3. **RIEDLEA** Vent. Herbs or low woody shrubs. Leaf-blades toothed. Involucel of 3 bractlets. Flowers in terminal and axillary clusters. Sepals 5, partly united. Petals 5, marcescent. Filaments partly united. Styles 5, partly united. Capsule 5-valved.—About 20 species, mostly tropical American.

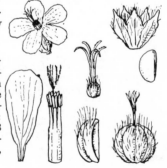

1. **R. hirsuta** (Cav.) DC. Stem diffusely branched, the branches decumbent or ascending, up to 1.5 m. long, hirsute and often with some appressed hairs: leaf-blades ovate to lanceolate, serrate, short-petioled: calyx-lobes ovate to deltoid, 9–13 mm. long: petals violet: capsule subglobose, about 3 mm. in diameter. [*Melochia hirsuta* Cav.]— Pinelands, S pen. Fla.—(*W. I., Mex., C. A., S. A.*)—All year.

4. WALTHERIA L. Herbs, shrubs, or trees. Leaf-blades toothed. Involucel of 3-bractlets. Sepals 5, united to the middle or above it. Petals 5, loosely spreading, narrow, slender-clawed, yellow. Stamens 5: anthers with 2 sacs: staminodia wanting. Ovary 1-celled. Capsule smooth, often pubescent, longer than thick.—About 35 species, tropical American.

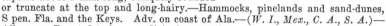

1. W. americana L. Stem erect or rarely diffuse and prostrate, 6–16 dm. long, often much-branched: leaf-blades ovate or orbicular-ovate, 1–8 cm. long, serrate or dentate-serrate, stout-petioled: flowers in dense axillary clusters: calyx 4–5 mm. long at maturity; lobes triangular to lanceolate or subulate-lanceolate, mostly nearly as long as the tube or shorter: petals 3–4 mm. long: capsule about 2 mm. long, obliquely rounded or truncate at the top and long-hairy.—Hammocks, pinelands and sand-dunes, S pen. Fla. and the Keys. Adv. on coast of Ala.—(*W. I., Mex., C. A., S. A.*)— All year.—Reputed to have medicinal properties.

5. AYENIA L. Herbs often partially woody. Leaf-blades toothed. Involucel wanting. Sepals 5, slightly united. Petals 5, converging, the claws involute. Stamens 5; anthers with three parallel sacs. Staminodia present. Ovary 5-celled. Capsule muricate, depressed.—About 10 species, tropical American.

Petals 6–6.5 mm. long; blades about 1.5 mm. wide; appendages stout, over 0.5 mm. long. 1. *A. euphrasiaefolia.*
Petals 4–4.5 mm. long: blades about 1 mm. wide; appendages slender, less than 0.5 mm. long. 2. *A. pusilla.*

1. A. euphrasiaefolia Griseb. Tap-root stout: stem prostrate: leaf-blades predominately suborbicular to reniform, 0.5–1 cm. long, sharply few-toothed: calyx about 3 mm. long: petals reddish: capsule 4–5 mm. in diameter: seed bluntly tuberculate.—Pinelands, Everglade Keys, Fla. and lower Florida Keys.—(*W. I.*)— All year.

2. A. pusilla L. Tap-root slender: stem erect or ascending: leaf-blades predominantly elliptic to elliptic-ovate, 1–2.5 cm. long, rather bluntly many-toothed: calyx about 2 mm. long; lobes ciliate: petals red: seed sharply tuberculate.—Waste-places, Everglade Keys, Fla. and Key West. Perhaps introduced from the W. I.; also in rocky places, W Tex.—(*W. I., Mex., C.A., S. A.*)—Spr.-fall.

6. FIRMIANA Marsigli. Shrubs or trees. Leaf-blades entire or lobed. Flowers unisexual or polygamous. Sepals 5, or rarely 4, often petaloid.

Petals wanting. Staminal-column broad.
Carpels nearly distinct. Stigmas peltate.
Capsule opening before maturity, the carpels
stellately spreading.—About 10 species,
Asiatic.

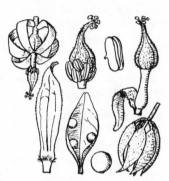

1. F. platanifolia (L.) R. Br. Tree becoming 12 m. tall, or a shrub: leaf-blades
1–3 dm. broad, palmately 3–5-lobed: panicle
commonly 2–3 dm. long: sepals linear:
carpels 6–9 cm. long. [*Sterculia platanifolia* L.]—(CHINA PARASOL-TREE. JAPANESE
VARNISH-TREE. BOTTLE-TREE.) — Roadsides,
woods, thickets, and fields, Coastal Plain,
Fla. to Tex. and S. C. Nat. of eastern Asia
and cult.—Spr.—Like the tallow-tree (*Tri-
adica*) this Asiatic tree is extensively naturalized in the Coastal Plain of South
Carolina and less abundantly within the range given above. In open places
the trunk may be widely branched, in the dense growth of large colonies the
trunks are usually pole-like.

ORDER **HYPERICALES** — HYPERICAL ORDER

Herbs, shrubs, or trees. Leaves various. Flowers mostly perfect,
complete and regular (irregular in Violaceae), sometimes involucrate.
Calyx of distinct or essentially distinct sepals. Corolla of distinct petals
(partially united in Fouquieriaceae), rarely wanting. Androecium of
several united carpels. Ovary superior, mostly with parietal placentae.
Fruit capsular, baccate, or drupaceous.

Stamens united into a tube which surrounds or encloses the gynoecium.
  Placentae parietal.   Fam. 1. CANELLACEAE.
  Placentae axial.   Fam. 2. CLUSIACEAE.
Stamens distinct.
  Styles wanting: stigmas introrse.
    Placentae axial: herbs or shrubby plants.   Fam. 3. ELATINACEAE.
    Placentae basal: shrubs or trees.   Fam. 4. TAMARICACEAE.
  Styles present, distinct or united: stigmas terminal.
    Styles distinct or partially united or coherent
      until maturity, if united to the stigmas, then
      grooved.
      Stigmas not brush-like: endosperm little or
        none.
        Herbs or shrubby plants, with opposite or
          whorled leaves.   Fam. 5. HYPERICACEAE.
        Shrubs or trees, with alternate leaves.   Fam. 6. THEACEAE.
      Stigmas brush-like: endosperm copious.   Fam. 7. TURNERACEAE.
    Styles wholly and permanently united.
      Corolla regular.   Fam. 8. CISTACEAE.
      Corolla irregular, the petals markedly unequal
        and one of them spurred; stamens 5.   Fam. 9. VIOLACEAE.

FAMILY 1. **CANELLACEAE** — WILD CINNAMON FAMILY

Trees. Leaves alternate: blades entire, pellucid-punctate. Flowers
perfect. Calyx of 3 thick imbricate sepals. Corolla of 4–12 narrow petals,
or wanting. Androecium of numerous stamens, the filaments united into
a tube around the pistil. Gynoecium of 2–5 united carpels. Fruit a
berry.—Five genera and 7 species, in tropical America and Africa.

1. CANELLA P. Br. Trees with gray bark. Leaf-blades leathery. Flowers in cymes. Petals 5. Stamens mostly 15–20, the tube projecting beyond the anthers. Ovary 1-celled. Berry subglobose.—One species.

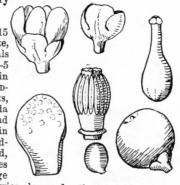

1. C. Winteriana (L.) Gaertn. Trees 5–15 m. tall: leaf-blades oblanceolate, spatulate, or elliptic-spatulate, 3–10 cm. long: sepals 2.5–3 mm. broad: petals 5, elliptic, 4.5–5 mm. long, purple: berry about 10 mm. in diameter, crimson or nearly black.—(WILD-CINNAMON. CINNAMON-BARK.)—Hammocks, Cape Sable region, pen. Fla. and Flórida Keys.—(W. I.)—Sum.–fall.—The leaves and bark are spicy-aromatic, and are used in medicine and as a condiment. The red-brown heart-wood is close-grained, very hard, and very heavy. The contrast of the cymes of purple flowers and the deep-green foliage is striking. The clusters of almost black berries also render the tree conspicuous.

FAMILY 2. CLUSIACEAE — BALSAM-TREE FAMILY

Shrubs or trees. Leaves opposite: blades entire. Flowers mostly dioecious or polygamous. Calyx of 2–6 imbricate sepals. Corolla of 4–9 petals. Androecium of numerous stamens, the filaments wholly or partly united. Gynoecium of 2 or more united carpels. Fruit baccate, drupaceous, or capsular.—About 25 genera and over 250 species, mostly tropical.

1. CLUSIA L. Shrubs or trees, often epiphytic, at least when young. Leaf-blades leathery. Flowers solitary or few together. Petals 4–9. Ovary 8–10-celled. Capsule leathery or fleshy.—About 80 species, tropical American. —BALSAM-APPLES. FAT-PORKS. MONKEY-APPLES.—Incomplete specimens of both the following species were collected on Big Pine Key and Key West many years ago.

Flowers yellow: fruits slightly elongate or globular: stigmas 12–14.　　1. C. flava.
Flowers white or pink: fruits depressed: stigmas 6–8.　　　　　　　　2. C. rosea.

1. C. flava Jacq. Tree, sometimes 20 m. tall: leaf-blades cuneate-obovate, 1–1.5 dm. long, many-ribbed: sepals suborbicular: petals yellow, obovate, 2.5–3 mm. long: capsule slightly elongate or globular.—Hammocks, Key West, Fla.; not collected in recent years.—(W. I.)

2. C. rosea L. Tree similar to C. flava in habit, but leaves rather larger: petals white or pink: capsule depressed.—Hammocks, Big Pine Key, Fla.; not recently collected.— (W. I.)—Among the several shrubs and trees discovered on the lower Florida Keys in the earlier part of the past century and then "lost," the two balsam-apples appear to be the only ones not yet rediscovered. They may yet be found in the hammocks not visited in recent years. Their discovery was due to the activities of a resident botanist, Dr. Blodget, of Key West.

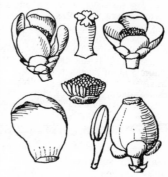

Family 3. ELATINACEAE — Water-wort Family

Herbs or partly woody plants. Leaves opposite. Flowers perfect. Calyx of 2–5 imbricate sepals. Corolla of 2–5 petals. Androecium of 2–5, or sometimes 10, stamens. Gynoecium of 2–5 carpels. Fruit a capsule.—Two genera and 30 species, widely distributed.

1. **ELATINE** L. Wholly succulent plants. Leaf-blades commonly entire. Sepals ribless. Ovary 2–4-celled: styles 2–4. Capsule membranous, 2–4-celled.—About 10 species, natives of warm regions.

1. **E. americana** (Pursh) Arn. Stem 1–5 cm. long: leaf-blades cuneate-obovate to elliptic, 1–5 mm. long: flowers greenish: sepals 2, obtuse: petals 2: stamens 2; capsule subglobose, about 1 mm. in diameter.— (WATER-WORT. MUD-PURSLANE.) — Ponds and slow streams, various provinces, Tenn. to Tex., Minn., Ont., and N. C.—Sum.—The petals may sometimes be pink-tinged. The plants, creeping on mud, resemble diminutive chickweeds and pimpernels.

Family 4. TAMARICACEAE — Tamarisk Family

Shrubs or trees, or partially herbaceous plants. Leaves alternate: blades entire, often scale-like. Flowers mainly perfect, sometimes in profuse panicles. Calyx of 5, or 4 or 6, sepals. Corolla of 5, or 4 or 6, petals. Androecium of 5 or many stamens. Gynoecium of 2–5 united carpels. Ovary 1-celled. Fruit a capsule—Four genera and 90 species, of Africa and Eurasia.

1. **TAMARIX** L. Irregularly branching evergreen shrubs or trees. Leaves scale-like, clasping or sheathing. Flowers borne in plume-like panicles. Capsule many-seeded.

1. **T. gallica** L. Small tree or shrub, with weak branches, the branchlets clothed with the imbricate leaves: panicles with numerous spikes: sepals about 0.5 mm. long: petals white or pinkish: capsule about 1 mm. long. —(TAMARISK.) — Roadsides, waste-places, and stream-banks, various provinces, Fla. to Tex., Ark., and S. C.—Nat. of Eu.—(W. I.)—Spr.–sum.—This species is widely cultivated and is naturalized in the Coastal Plain and adjacent provinces. It appears in several forms, varying with green or glaucous foliage, slender or stout branchlets and long or short racemes.

Family 5. HYPERICACEAE — St. John's-wort Family

Shrubs or herbs. Leaves opposite: blades mostly punctate, entire or nearly so, sometimes scale-like. Flowers perfect. Calyx of 4 or 5, sometimes unequal sepals. Corolla of 4 or 5, yellow, pink, or purple-tinged petals. Androecium of few or many stamens, sometimes grouped, the groups sometimes alternating with the glands. Gynoecium of 3–7 united carpels. Fruit a capsule.—Ten genera and more than 300 species, mostly in temperate and tropical regions.

Sepals 4, in more or less unequal pairs : petals mostly 4.
    Pairs of sepals very unequal in size or shape or both, the outer pair enclosing the capsule.   1. ASCYRUM.
    Pairs of sepals nearly equal in size and shape, much surpassed by the capsule.   2. CROOKEA.
Sepals and petals mostly 5.
    Petals yellow.
      Plants without basal branches, or with elongate ones with opposite leaves : petals deciduous : capsule not dehiscent to the base.
        Leaves with flat, more or less spreading blades.   3. HYPERICUM.
        Leaves reduced to erect or appressed, minute or slightly elongate scales, without blades.   4. SAROTHRA.
      Plants with clusters of short branches with crowded, decussate, bladeless leaves at the base, and wiry, remotely scaly flowering stems which terminate in slender-branched cymes : petals marcescent : capsule dehiscent to the base.   5. SANIDOPHYLLUM.
    Petals pink, sometimes tinged with green or purple.   6. TRIADENUM.

1. ASCYRUM L. Shrubs. Sepals 4, very unequal. Corolla yellow, Stamens not in groups. Styles relatively short. Capsule included in the calyx.—Seven species, American.—ST. PETER'S-WORTS. ST. ANDREW'S-CROSSES.

Styles 2 : inner sepals very small, petal-like or obsolete.
    Peduncles reflexed at maturity : calyx without bractlets, conspicuously surpassing the leaves.   1. A. pumilum.
    Peduncles not recurved : calyx subtended by a pair of bractlets, not conspicuously surpassing the leaves.
      Outer sepals ovate at maturity : capsule included.   2. A. hypericoides.
      Outer sepals elliptic at maturity : capsule exserted at the tip.   3. A. linifolium.
Styles 3–4 : inner sepals slightly smaller than the outer.
    Outer sepals obtuse or rounded at the apex.
      Leaf-blades predominately cuneate or obovate-cuneate, sessile : outer sepals suborbicular.   4. A. cuneifolium.
      Leaf-blades predominantly of an elliptic or oval type, somewhat clasping : outer sepals broadly ovate-or-bicular.   5. A. stans.
    Outer sepals acute or acuminate at the apex.
      Leaf-blades predominately of an ovate type : outer sepals quite different from the leaves.   6. A. Edisonianum.
      Leaf-blades predominately of an elliptic or linear-elliptic type : outer sepals resembling the leaves.   7. A. tetrapetalum.

1. **A. pumilum** Michx. Shrub, depressed, the short stems often matted: leaf-blades oval, obovate, or linear-elliptic, 3–9 mm. long: outer sepals ovate to suborbicular, 6–10 mm. long, the inner obsolete or nearly so: petals yellow, obovate: capsule about 5 mm. long.—Pinelands, Coastal Plain, Fla. and Ga. to Miss.—Spr.–sum.

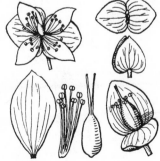

2. **A. hypericoides** L. Shrub, diffuse: leaf-blades linear, often narrowly so, 5–15 mm. long: outer sepals cuneate-obovate to elliptic or elliptic-lanceolate, 7–9 mm. long, the inner petaloid: petals pale-yellow: capsule 7–8 mm. long.—(ST. ANDREW'S-CROSS.)—Dry woods, thickets, and hammocks, various provinces, Fla. to Tex., Nebr., and Mass.—(W. I.)—Spr.–fall or all year.

3. A. linifolium Spach. Shrub, mostly erect: leaf-blades linear-spatulate to oblanceolate, elliptic, or obovate-elliptic, 1–3.5 cm. long: outer sepals ovate to elliptic-ovate, 6–9 mm. long, the inner petaloid: petals bright-yellow: capsule 5–8 mm. long.—Pinelands, Coastal Plain, Fla. to Tex., Ark., and S. C.— (*W. I.*)—Spr.–fall or all year.

4. A. cuneifolium Chapm. Shrub 1–2 dm. tall: leaf-blades cuneate or obovate, 5–20 mm. long: inner sepals elliptic or nearly so: petals yellow: capsule broadly ovoid.—Low pinelands, Coastal Plain, Fla. to Miss.—Sum.–fall.

5. A. stans Michx. Shrub 3–9 dm. tall, the stem simple above the base or sparingly branched: leaf-blades broadly elliptic, varying to obovate obtuse: petals bright-yellow: inner sepals lanceolate, short-acuminate: capsule ovoid, 8–10 mm. long.—Acid swamps and moist sandy soil, Coastal Plain and adj. provinces, rarely Blue Ridge, Fla. to Tex., Tenn., and N. Y.—Sum.–fall.

6. A. Edisonianum Small. Shrub 3–6 dm. tall, the stem often much-branched: leaf-blades narrowly elliptic to linear-elliptic, acute: petals yellow: inner sepals linear-lanceolate, long-acuminate: capsule narrowly ovoid, 4–6 mm. long.— Pinelands S pen. Fla.—Spr.–sum.

7. A. tetrapetalum (Lam.) Vail. Shrub 2–9 dm. tall: leaf-blades ovate to oval: outer sepals resembling the leaf-blades, the inner elliptic to lanceolate: petals bright-yellow; capsule about one-half as long as the sepals.—Low pinelands and swamps, Coastal Plain, Fla. and S Ga.—Spr.–fall or all year.

2. CROOKEA Small. Shrubs resembling species of *Ascyrum*, evergreen. Sepals 4, nearly equal. Stamens numerous: filaments distinct. Styles relatively long. Capsule not included. One species.

1. C. microsepala (T. & G.) Small. Branching shrub, with erect, ascending, or decumbent stems less than 1 m. tall: leaves numerous; blades cuneate to linear-cuneate or narrowly elliptic, 6–14 mm. long, rounded at the apex, often slightly revolute, sessile: flowers showy, 2–2.5 cm. broad: sepals linear to elliptic, obtuse: petals 4, yellow, unequal, the smaller elliptic, the larger obovate, obtuse: capsules conic-elliptic, 7–8 mm. long, much surpassing the sepals: seeds less than 1 mm. long, striate and pitted. [*Ascyrum microsepalum* T. & G. *Hypericum microsepalum* (T. & G.) A. Gray] —Low pinelands, edges of woods, and fence-rows, Coastal Plain, N Fla. and S Ga.—Spr.

3. HYPERICUM [Tourn.] L. Herbs or shrubs. Leaves more or less black-dotted. Sepals 5, essentially equal. Corolla yellow: petals inequilateral or nearly equilateral. Stamens mostly in groups. Style relatively long. Capsule not included.—About 210 species, widely distributed.—St. John's-worts.—Some species are used medicinally.

Stamens few or several, 5–12, usually in 3 clusters: petals copper-yellow.
1. Canadensia.
Stamens numerous, 15–40, distinct or in clusters.
Styles 3, or rarely 4: capsule 3-celled or 1-celled and with 3 more or less intruding placentae.

Capsule 1-celled or incompletely 3-celled.
  Capsule with parietal placentae, 1-celled.   II. VIRGATA.
  Capsule incompletely 3-celled by the intrusion of the
    placentae.   III. AMBIGUA.
Capsule completely 3-celled.
  Herbs, perennial, often stoloniferous: stem simple or
    sparingly branched.   IV. MACULATA.
  Shrubs with tap roots: stem much-branched.   V. PROLIFICA.
Styles 5: capsule 5-celled.   VI. LOBOCARPA.

I. CANADENSIA

Leaf-blades linear.   1. *H. canadense.*
Leaf-blades ovate, oval, or oblong.
  Sepals obtuse or somewhat acute: leaf-blades obtuse.   2. *H. mutilum.*
  Sepals acuminate: leaf-blades acute.   3. *H. gymnanthum.*

II. VIRGATA

Styles distinct: stigmas capitate.
  Foliage glabrous: sepals not ciliate.
    Sepals conspicuously imbricate, at least the outer
      broadest at the base: leaf-blades broadest about
      the middle.   4. *H. denticulatum.*
    Sepals not conspicuously imbricated, at least the
      outer broadest about the middle: leaf-blades
      broadest about the base.   5. *H. acutifolium.*
  Foliage tomentose: sepals ciliate.   6. *H. setosum.*
Styles coherent, at least below: stigmas minute.
  Corolla 18 mm. broad or more: capsules over 6 mm.
    high.   7. *H. dolabriforme.*
  Corolla less than 18 mm. broad; capsules less than
    6 mm. high.
    Capsules broadest at the top, about as long as the
      sepals.   8. *H. turgidum.*
    Capsules broadest at the base.
      Sepals obtuse: seeds striate and pitted.   9. *H. opacum.*
      Sepals acute or acutish: seeds transversely
      wrinkled.   10. *H. cistifolium.*

III. AMBIGUA

Sepals very small or at least not foliaceous.
  Leaves never in conspicuous axillary clusters; blades
    relatively broad.
    Sepals obtuse or merely acutish.
      Sepals less than ½ as long as the petals: cap-
        sules 6–7 mm. long.   11. *H. nudiflorum.*
      Sepals over ½ as long as the petals: capsules
        12–13 mm. long.   12. *H. apocynifolium.*
    Sepals manifestly acute or acuminate.   13. *H. adpressum.*
  Leaves in conspicuous axillary clusters; blades nar-
    row.
    Leaves of the axillary clusters mostly much
      smaller than the main pair; blades neither
      subulate, nor fleshy.
      Cymes in terminal congested corymbs: buds
        broadly ovoid: mountain species.   14. *H. glomeratum.*
      Cymes in elongated narrow panicles: buds
        conic: lowland species.
        Leaves linear-oblong, spatulate or oblanceo-
        late.   15. *H. ambiguum.*
        Leaves narrowly linear or narrowly linear-
        spatulate.   16. *H. galioides.*
    Leaves of the axillary clusters about as large as
      the main pair or slightly shorter; blades
      subulate or linear-subulate, fleshy, about as
      thick as wide.
      Sepals as long as the petals or fully ½ as
        long: leaves mostly over 10 mm. long.   17. *H. fasciculatum.*
      Sepals less than ½ as long as the petals:
        leaves mostly less than 10 mm. long.   18. *H. aspalathoides.*
Sepals foliaceous.
  Leaf-blades cordate-clasping.   19. *H. myrtifolium.*
  Leaf-blades more or less narrowed to the sessile or
    short petioled base.
    Flowers sessile: buds ovoid-globose.   20. *H. aureum.*
    Flowers pedicelled: buds conic.   21. *H. splendens.*

IV. MACULATA

Corolla less than 15 mm. broad.
  Leaf-blades short-petioled or merely sessile, with a rounded base. ... 22. *H. subpetiolatum.*
  Leaf-blades sessile and more or less clasping. ... 23. *H. punctatum.*
Corolla over 15 mm. broad.
  Upper leaves and bracts with ovate or ovate-lanceolate blades: petals spotted all over. ... 24. *H. pseudomaculatum.*
  Upper leaves and bracts with oblong blades: petals spotted around the edges.
    Sepals and petals merely dotted: capsules usually less than 6 mm. high. ... 25. *H. perforatum.*
    Sepals and petals striped with black: capsules usually over 6 mm. high.
      Corolla about 3 cm. broad: styles filiform. ... 26. *H. graveolens.*
      Corolla 1.5–2 cm. broad: styles subulate. ... 27. *H. Mitchellianum.*

V. PROLIFICA

Stems diffusely spreading or decumbent. ... 28. *H. Buckleyi.*
Stems erect, relatively tall.
  Flowers few in narrow panicles: corolla over 1.5 cm. broad. ... 29. *H. prolificum.*
  Flowers numerous in rather corymb-like panicles: corolla less than 1.5 cm. broad. ... 30. *H. densiflorum.*

VI. LOBOCARPA

Much-branched shrub, with numerous small flowers and a 5-lobed capsule. ... 31. *H. lobocarpum.*

1. **H. canadense** L. Plant 1–6 dm. tall: leaf-blades 3-nerved: sepals lanceolate or linear-lanceolate, 3–5 mm. long: petals 3–6 mm. long: capsule 4–8 mm. long, acute.—Moist, often acid, soil, various provinces, rarely Coastal Plain, Ga. to Ala., Wis., Man., and Newf.—Sum.

2. **H. mutilum** L. Plant 1–8 dm. tall: leaf-blades oblong-ovate to ovate, or sometimes oblong, 5-nerved: sepals elliptic to elliptic-lanceolate: petals about 3.5 mm. long: capsule 2–3 mm. long, obtuse.—(DWARF ST. JOHN'S-WORT.)—Wet sand and miry places, various provinces, Fla. to Tex., Man., and N. S.—Sum.-fall.

3. **H. gymnanthum** Engelm. & Gray. Plant 2–9 dm. tall: leaf-blades ovate, 5–7 nerved: sepals lanceolate: petals 3–6 mm. long: capsule about 4 mm. long.—Moist places and wet sandy soil, various provinces, Fla. to Tex., Mo., Mich., and N. C.—Sum.

4. **H. denticulatum** Walt. Plant perennial, 2–9 dm. tall: leaf-blades elliptic or nearly so, 1–3 cm. long, acute, (oval and relatively shorter, with the sepals oval to ovate, in *H. denticulatum ovalifolium*): sepals more or less foliaceous, lanceolate, elliptic-lanceolate or slightly broadened upward, 4–10 mm. long: petals copper-yellow, 5–10 mm. long: capsule ovoid, about 4 mm. long. [*H. virgatum* Lam.]—(COPPERY ST. JOHN'S-WORT.)—Acid sandy soil and pinelands, various provinces, Fla. to Ill. and N. J.—Sum.

5. **H. acutifolium** Ell. Plant perennial, 2–6 dm. tall: leaf-blades narrowly lanceolate to linear-lanceolate, 1–2.5 cm. long, acuminate: sepals linear to linear-lanceolate, 3.5–5 mm. long: petals copper-yellow, 5–6 mm. long: capsule ovoid, about 4 mm. long.—Low pinelands, Coastal Plain and occasionally adj. provinces, Fla. to Miss., Tenn., and N. C.—Sum.

6. **H. setosum** L. Plant annual or biennial, 3–6 dm. tall: leaf-blades elliptic, oval or ovate-lanceolate, 3–15 mm. long: sepals oval, ovate, or ovate-lanceo-

late, 2.5–3.5 mm. long: petals yellow, 5–6 mm. long: capsule oval or ovoid-oval, 4–5 mm. long. [*H. pilosum* Walt.]—Moist pinelands, Coastal Plain, Fla. to La. and N. C.—Sum.

7. **H. dolabriforme** Vent. Plant perennial, woody, 2–5 dm. tall: leaf-blades linear or nearly so, 2–5 cm. long: sepals foliaceous, lanceolate to ovate-lanceolate, 6–10 mm. long: petals yellow, 8–11 mm. long: capsule conic-ovoid, 7–9 mm. long.—Dry hillsides, various provinces N of Coastal Plain, Ala. to Mo., Ky., and Ga.—Spr.-sum.

8. **H. turgidum** Small. Plant perennial, woody, 3–6 dm. tall: leaf-blades almost linear to linear-lanceolate, 1–2.5 cm. long: sepals ovate to elliptic, 3–4 mm. long: petals yellow, 6–8 mm. long: capsule subglobose, about 3.5 mm. long, turgid.—Wooded slopes, Appalachian provinces, Ala.—Sum.

9. **H. opacum** T. & G. Plant perennial, woody, 3–16 dm. tall: leaf-blades elliptic to elliptic-lanceolate, or sometimes linear-elliptic, 1–3 cm. long: sepals orbicular or obovate to elliptic-ovate, 2.5–4 mm. long: petals bright-yellow, about 5 mm. long: capsule ovoid, 5–6 mm. long.—Low pinelands, Coastal Plain, Fla. to La., and S. C.—Sum.

10. **H. cistifolium** Lam. Plant woody, 3–9 dm. tall: leaf-blades linear-elliptic to linear-lanceolate, or sometimes narrowly elliptic, 1.5–8 cm. long: sepals ovate to lanceolate, 3–4 mm. long: petals cuneate to obovate-cuneate, 5–8 mm. long, bright-yellow: capsule globose or globose-ovoid, 4–6 mm. long. [*H. sphaerocarpum* Michx.]—River-banks, and rocky-slopes, various provinces, Ala. to Miss., Kans., Ia., and Ohio.—Sum.

11. **H. nudiflorum** Michx. Plant woody, 3–10 dm. tall: leaf-blades elliptic to elliptic-lanceolate, 1.5–6 cm. long: sepals elliptic to elliptic-oblanceolate, 3–3.5 mm. long: petals bright-yellow, 7–8 mm. long: capsule conic-ovoid.—Sandy soil, Coastal Plain and rarely adj. provinces, Fla. to Ala. and N. C.—Sum.

12. **H. apocynifolium** Small. Plant 4–7 dm. tall: leaf-blades elliptic or nearly so, 2–4 cm. long: sepals spatulate, elliptic or oval, 4–5 mm. long: petals elliptic, 7–8 mm. long, yellow; capsule ellipsoid-conic.—Swamps, Coastal Plain, Fla. to Tex., Ark., and Ga.—Sum.

13. **H. adpressum** Bart. Plant 2–6 dm. tall: leaf-blades narrowly elliptic to lanceolate, 2–6 cm. long, conspicuously veined: sepals lanceolate to ovate-lanceolate, 4–6 mm. long: petals cuneate, 6–8 mm. long, bright-yellow: capsule ovoid, the body 5–6 mm. long.—(CREEPING ST. JOHN'S-WORT.)—Swamps and pond-margins, various provinces, Ga. to La., Tenn., and Mass.—Sum.

14. **H. glomeratum** Small. Shrub 3–10 dm. tall: leaf-blades narrowly elliptic to linear-elliptic or nearly linear, 2–4 cm. long, sessile: sepals rather foliaceous, narrowly elliptic to linear-elliptic, 5–6 mm. long: petals bright-yellow, cuneate-spatulate, fully 1 cm. long: capsules densely clustered, ellipsoid-ovoid, 5–6 mm. high.—Rocky woods, Grandfather Mtn. and Table Rock, in the Blue Ridge of N. C.—Sum.

15. **H. ambiguum** Ell. Shrub 0.5–1.5 m. tall, evergreen: leaf-blades linear-elliptic to spatulate, 1–2.5 cm. long: sepals linear or slightly broadened upward, 3–5 mm. long: petals obliquely obovate or cuneate, almost laterally apiculate, 5–7 mm. long, bright-yellow: capsule almost conic, 5–6 mm. high. [*H. galioides pallidum* C. Mohr.]—River swamps and stream-banks, Coastal Plain, Fla. to Miss. and S.C.—Spr.-sum.

16. H. galioides Lam. Shrub 3–18 dm. high or taller, evergreen: leaf-blades narrowly linear or slightly broadened upward, 0.5–1.5 cm. long: sepals linear or linear-spatulate, 3–4 mm. long: petals cuneately narrowed, obliquely or almost laterally pointed, 4–7 mm. long, bright-yellow: capsule conic, 5–6 mm. long, acute.—Low pinelands and swamps, Coastal Plain and rarely adj. provinces, Fla. to Miss., Tenn., and N. C. (or Del.?).—Sum.–fall.

17. H. fasciculatum Lam. Shrub 9–45 dm. tall, evergreen: leaves numerous, a bunch usually clustered in the axils of the larger ones; blades leathery, linear-filiform, 1–2 cm. long, or shorter in the clusters: sepals linear, 3–4 mm. long, about 1 mm. wide: petals bright-yellow, obliquely apiculate, 7–8 mm. long: capsule ovoid or conic-ovoid, 4–5 mm. long. —(SAND-WEED.)—Ponds and low pinelands, Coastal Plain, Fla. to Tex. and N. C.—Spr.–fall.—A growth of this shrub in a pond indicates a hard sand bottom, hence the common name. It often reaches tree-like form in swamps near the gulf coast.

18. H. aspalathoides Willd. Shrub 2–8 dm tall, evergreen: leaves very numerous, with clusters of small ones borne in the axils of the large ones; blades linear-subulate to subulate, 5–8 mm. long, or shorter in the clusters: sepals linear or nearly so, 2–3 mm. long: petals 6–7 mm. long, intense orange-yellow: capsule 4 mm. long.—Pinelands and prairies, Coastal Plain, Fla. to La. and N. C.—Spr.–sum.—The flowers of some of the St. John's-worts are of such a bright yellow that they seem to irritate the eye. Those of this species come in that class, particularly when the plants are in open sunny places.

19. H. myrtifolium Lam. Shrub 3–10 dm. tall, evergreen: leaf-blades ovate to elliptic-ovate, or ovate-lanceolate or rarely nearly elliptic, 1–3 cm. long: sepals foliaceous, ovate, 5–8 mm. long: petals obovate, 12–15 mm. long, bright-yellow: capsule pyramidal-ovoid, incompletely 3-celled or rarely 4-celled, 5–6 mm. high.—Low pinelands and ponds, Coastal Plain, Fla. to Miss. and S. C. —Spr.–sum.

20. H. aureum Bartr. Shrub 6–12 dm. tall: leaf-blades elliptic to ovate-elliptic, 2.5–7 cm. long, glaucous beneath: flowers very showy, usually solitary, sometimes 3 in terminal or axillary cymes: sepals very unequal, broadened upward: petals quite oblique, 15–23 mm. long, golden-yellow: capsule conic, 1.3–2 cm. high, acuminate at the apex. (GOLDEN ST. JOHN'S-WORT.)—Bluffs and stream-banks, often in calcareous soil, various provinces, rarely Coastal Plain, Ga. to Tex., Tenn., and S. C.—Sum.

21. H. splendens Small. Shrub 0.5–1.5 m. tall: leaf-blades elliptic, 1.5–2.5 cm. long, glaucous, especially beneath: flowers very showy, several or many in terminal or axillary cymes: sepals unequal, elliptic, firm, apiculate, the outer about 8 mm. long, the inner 5 mm. long: petals golden-yellow, cuneate, oblique, 1.5–2 cm. long: capsules often crowded, conic, 1.5 cm. high, acuminate at the apex.—Granite rocks, Stone Mt. on the Piedmont of Ga.—Sum.

22. H. subpetiolatum Bicknell. Plant bright-green, heavy-scented, 2–8 dm. tall: leaf-blades thin or thinnish, elliptic, varying to elliptic-obovate or elliptic-ovate, 3–6 cm. long, narrowed, often gradually so, at the base, short-petioled: sepals becoming 3–4 mm. long, the narrower ones linear, the broader elliptic-lanceolate, all mostly acute: petals dull-yellow, 5–7 mm. long, sparingly black-streaked: capsule ovoid or globose-ovoid, 4–6 mm. long.—Woods and thickets, various provinces, Ga. to Miss. and Me.—Sum.

23. H. punctatum Lam. Plant dark-green, not heavy-scented, 2–9 dm. tall: leaf-blades thick, elliptic, varying to elliptic-obovate to elliptic ovate, 1–7 cm. long, obtuse or retuse at the apex, abruptly narrowed or subcordate, and often partly clasping at the base: sepals becoming 3.5–4.5 mm. long, narrower ones elliptic, the broader elliptic-lanceolate or elliptic-ovate, all acute, sometimes abruptly pointed: petals deep-yellow, 5-7 mm. long, copiously black-streaked: capsule ovoid, 3-5 mm. long. [*H. maculatum* Walt.]— (SPOTTED ST. JOHN'S-WORT.)—Dry soils or hillsides, various provinces, Fla. to Tex., Kans., Ont., and Que.—Sum.

24. H. pseudomaculatum Bush. Plant bright-green, not heavy-scented 4-9 dm. tall: leaf-blades ovate to lanceolate or nearly elliptic, 1.5-4.5 cm. long, acutish or obtuse, often revolute, sessile and clasping by the broad cordate base: sepals becoming 5-6 mm. long, the narrower ones lanceolate, the broader ovate-lanceolate or ovate, all acuminate, glandular-margined: petals copper-yellow, 11-15 mm. long, black-streaked: capsule ovoid, 4-5 mm. long.— Woods and dry soil, various provinces, Fla. to Tex., Mo., Ill., and S. C.— Spr.-sum.

25. H. perforatum L. Plant 4-7 dm. tall: leaf-blades linear-elliptic, 0.5-2 cm. long, glandular-punctate, those of the main stem usually subtending leafy branches: sepals linear-lanceolate, 3-4 mm. long, acute, glandular-punctate: corolla deep-yellow, 19-24 mm. wide; petals toothed on one side from the middle to the apex, bearing black glands near the teeth: capsule ovoid, oblique, 6-8 mm. high.—(ST. JOHN'S-WEED.)—Dry fields and waste-places, various provinces, nearly throughout U. S. and S Can. Nat. of Eu.—Sum.

26. H. graveolens Buckl. Plant erect or decumbent, 2-9 dm. tall: leaf-blades ovate to elliptic, often broader or subcordate at the base: sepals lanceolate to linear-lanceolate, 6-8 mm. long, acuminate: corolla copper-yellow, about 3 cm. broad; petals decidedly obliquely narrowed below the middle, faintly streaked with brown on one side: capsule conic-ovoid, 10-12 mm. long.—Moist woods and open slopes, Blue Ridge, N. C. and Tenn.—Sum.—Most abundant at about 6,000 feet alt.

27. H. Mitchellianum Rydb. Plant similar to *H. graveolens*: leaf-blades thickish, elliptic or ovate-elliptic, 2-6 cm. long, obtuse, mostly rounded at the base: sepals ovate to lanceolate, 5-6 mm. long, acute: corolla copper-yellow, 1.5-2 cm. broad; petals delicate, decidedly spotted with brown on one side: capsule ovoid, 8-10 mm. long.—(BLUE RIDGE ST. JOHN'S-WORT.)—Moist mtn. slopes, Blue Ridge, N. C. and Tenn. to Va.—Sum.—Most abundant at 4,000-5,000 feet alt.

28. H. Buckleyi M. A. Curtis. Plant 1-3 dm. tall, decumbent or ascending, often diffusely matted: leaf-blades obovate, elliptic-obovate, or elliptic, 0.5-2 cm. long, rounded at the apex or retuse: sepals obovate or spatulate, 4-5 mm. long, obtuse: corolla yellow, 2-2.5 cm. broad: petals rather delicate, about twice as long as the sepals: capsule conic, 6-10 mm. long, 3-celled.—(MOUNTAIN ST. JOHN'S-WORT.)—Cliffs and rocky mtn. summits, Blue Ridge and adj provinces, Ga. to N. C.—Sum.

29. H. prolificum L. Shrub 3-12 dm. tall, the branches narrowly 2-winged leaf-blades narrowly elliptic or rarely lanceolate, 2-8 cm. long, short-petioled: cymes few-flowered, short-peduncled, in cylindric panicles: sepals mostly obovate, 4-6 mm. long: corolla deep-yellow, 2-2.5 cm. broad: capsule conic or narrowly ovoid, 8-10 mm. long, acute.—(BROOM-BRUSH. SHRUBBY ST. JOHN'S-WORT.)—Rocky and sandy woods and stream-banks, often in calcareous soil, various provinces, rarely Coastal Plain, Ga. to Miss., Ark., Minn., and N. Y. —Sum.

30. H. densiflorum Pursh. Shrub 6-24 dm. tall: leaf-blades linear, linear-oblanceolate, or linear-elliptic, 1-5 cm. long, acute: sepals unequal, elliptic to elliptic-lanceolate, 2-2.5 mm. long: corolla bright-yellow, 1-1.5 cm. broad; petals obliquely pointed: capsule ovoid, 4-6 mm. long, slightly 3-lobed, completely 3-celled.—(BUSHY ST. JOHN'S-WORT.)—Acid swamps and marshes, various provinces, Fla. to Tex., Mo., and N. J.—Sum.

31. H. lobocarpum Gattinger.   Shrub 1–2 m. tall: leaf-blades narrowly elliptic or oblanceolate, 2–7 cm. long: flowers numerous: sepals elliptic to obovate-elliptic, 2.5–3.5 mm. long, rather obtuse: corolla yellow, 1–1.5 cm. broad: petals rather cuneate: capsule 5-celled, 5-lobed, 5–7 cm. long, separating into 5 carpels at maturity.—Swamps and low grounds, Coastal Plain, Tenn. and Blue Ridge, N. C.—Spr.–sum.

4. SAROTHRA L. Wiry scaly-leaved annual herbs. Sepals 5, equal or nearly so. Stamens grouped. Styles relatively long. Capsule exserted.—Two species, of eastern North America.

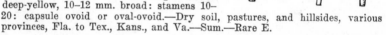

Flowers sessile or nearly so: sepals much shorter than the conic capsules.
                                                1. *S. gentianoides.*
Flowers pedicelled: sepals and ovoid or oval-ovoid capsule about
    equal in length, or sepals slightly shorter.   2. *S. Drummondii.*

1. S. gentianoides L. Stem 1–5 dm. tall: leaves scale-like, appressed, much shorter than the internodes, often subulate or those on the lower part of the stem sometimes linear or narrowly elliptic: sepals linear or linear-lanceolate, 2–3 mm. long: corolla yellow or orange, 4–8 mm. broad: stamens 5–10: capsule conic, 4–5 mm. long.—(PINEWEED. ORANGE-GRASS.)—Sandy and rocky soil in fields, pastures, and on roadsides, various provinces, Fla. to Tex., Ont., and Me.—Sum.–fall.—Sometimes used medicinally.

2. S. Drummondii Grev. & Hook. Stem 1–6 dm. tall: leaves scale-like, but longer than the internodes, narrowly linear or linear-subulate, erect or strongly ascending: sepals linear-lanceolate, 3–4 mm. long: corolla deep-yellow, 10–12 mm. broad: stamens 10–20: capsule ovoid or oval-ovoid.—Dry soil, pastures, and hillsides, various provinces, Fla. to Tex., Kans., and Va.—Sum.—Rare E.

5. SANIDOPHYLLUM Small. Biennial or perennial herbs. Leaves minutely pustulate, rather succulent: blades very narrow, those of the flowering stem erect or appressed. Sepals unequal, 2–4-ribbed. Corolla yellow: petals with the midnerve nearly lateral and an oblique blade on one side. Stamens grouped in 4's. Styles filiform. Capsule invested by the persistent perianth at the base, the 3 valves distinct.—One species.

1. S. cumulicola Small. Flowering stems few or many together, wiry, 2–7 cm. tall, with the leafy shoots on the caudex-like base: leaves linear-subulate, 1–6 mm. long: sepals broadly linear to ovate, 1–1.5 mm. long: petals yellow, 3–4 mm. long: capsule 5–6 mm. long, subulate-tipped, brown.— Scrub S pen. Fla.—All year.—The plants grow only in the white sand of the scrub and resembles some species of yellow-flax (*Cathartolinum*) in habit as well as the color and size of the flowers.

5. TRIADENUM Raf. Leafy perennial herbs, resembling species of *Hypericum.* Corolla pink, sometimes tinged with green or purple. Sepals 5, equal. Stamens mostly 9, grouped in 3's, the filaments of each group well united. Styles relatively long. Capsule exserted. Three species, of eastern North America.—Sum.—MARSH ST. JOHN'S-WORTS.

Filaments united near the base.   1. *T. virginicum.*
Filaments united to above the middle.
   Leaf-blades sessile, truncate or subcordate at the base.   2. *T. longifolium.*
   Leaf-blades petioled, narrowed at the base.   3. *T. petiolatum.*

1. T. virginicum (L.) Raf. Stem 2–6 dm. tall: leaf-blades elliptic or ovate, 2–10 cm. long, obtuse, clasping: sepals lanceolate to elliptic, 5–6 mm. long, acute: petals obovate to oblanceolate or nearly elliptic, 8–10 mm. long, acute, delicately nerved: capsule ellipsoid, 8–10 mm. long.—Acid bogs and sandy swamps, various provinces, Fla. to La., Man., and Lab.

2. T. longifolium Small. Stem 3–6 dm. tall: leaf-blades oblanceolate to elliptic: sepals lanceolate or linear-lanceolate, 3–4 mm. long, acuminate: petals broadened upward, 4–5 mm. long: capsule ellipsoid, about 1 cm. long.—Swamps and low grounds, Coastal Plain, Ga. to Ala. and Ky.

3. T. petiolatum (Walt.) Britton. Stem 3–10 dm. tall: leaf-blades elliptic or narrowly elliptic, 2–15 cm. long: sepals elliptic or nearly so 2.5–3.5 mm. long, obtuse: petals elliptic-obovate, 4–6.5 mm. long: capsule ellipsoid, prismatic 8–10 mm. long.—Swamps and borders of ponds, Coastal Plain, Fla. to La., Mo., and N. J.

FAMILY 6. **THEACEAE** — CAMELLIA FAMILY

Shrubs, trees, or vines. Leaves alternate. Flowers perfect and showy. Calyx of 5, or rarely 4–7, imbricate sepals. Corolla of 5, or rarely of 4–7, petals. Androecium of numerous, or rarely few, stamens. Gynoecium of 3–5 partly or wholly united carpels. Fruit mostly capsular, sometimes indehiscent.—Sixteen genera and about 160 species, natives of tropical and temperate regions.

Sepals slightly unequal: ovules 2, ascending: seeds lenticular, sometimes margined.
  Sepals ovate, united at the base: filaments united at the
    base: styles united: capsule not beaked: seeds margin-
    less.   1. STUARTIA.
  Sepals narrowly oblong, distinct: filaments distinct:
    styles distinct: capsule long-beaked: seeds margined.   2. MALACHODENDRON.
Sepals very unequal: ovules 4–8, pendulous: seeds strongly
  angled or winged.
  Leaf-blades membranous, deciduous: flowers nearly ses-
    sile: filaments distinct: capsule globose: seeds angled.   3. FRANKLINIA.
  Leaf-blades leathery, persistent: flowers long-pedicelled:
    filaments united into a thick tube: capsule ovoid:
    seeds winged.   4. GORDONIA.

1. STUARTIA L. Shrubs. Leaf-blades usually toothed. Sepals mostly 5, relatively broad. Petals mostly 5, white. Style columnar. Stigma radiate.

Capsule globular or depressed.—Four species, American and Japanese.

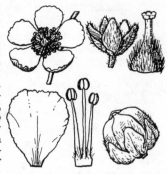

1. S. Malachodendron L. Shrub 1–5 m. tall: leaf-blades oval, elliptic, or sometimes ovate or obovate, 5–11 cm. long: sepals about 1 cm. long: petals obovate, 3–5 cm. long: capsule depressed-globular, 12–17 mm. in diameter.—(SILKY CAMELLIA. VIRGINIAN-STUARTIA.)—Wooded banks and hillsides, Coastal Plain and adj. provinces, W Fla. to La., Tenn., and Va.—Spr.—In Florida only in the Knox Hill country, where it grows in company with *Illicium floridanum* and *Magnolia Ashei*.—The stamens are usually purple.

2. MALACHODENDRON Cav. Shrubs resembling *Stuartia*. Sepals mostly 6, relatively narrow. Petals mostly 5, white. Styles 5, subulate. Stigmas introrse. Capsule slightly elongate.—One species.

1. M. pentagynum (L'Her.) Small. Shrub 1–5 m. tall: leaf-blades ovate, oval, or elliptic, 6–12 cm. long: sepals 1–1.5 cm. long: petals obovate, 3–3.5 cm. long: capsule ovoid, 1.5–2 cm. long. [*Stuartia pentagyna* L'Her.]—(MOUNTAIN CAMELLIA. MOUNTAIN-STUARTIA.)—Along streams and rich woods, Blue Ridge to Appalachian Plateau and adj. Piedmont, Ga. to Ala., Ky., and Va.—Spr.–early sum.—Contrary to *Stuartia* which seeks the lower provinces, this genus inhabits the higher ones, apparently entering the Coastal Plain only in SE Va.

3. FRANKLINIA Marsh. Trees. Leaves deciduous. Flowers nearly sessile. Sepals 5. Petals 5, unequal, white. Stamens distinct, adnate to the bases of the petals. Style ridged. Capsule loculidical from the top and septicidal from the bottom.—One species.

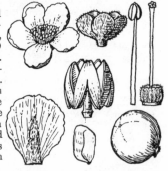

1. F. Alatamaha Marsh. Shrub or small tree with smooth black bark: leaf-blades oblanceolate to oblong-obovate, 6–15 cm. long, serrate: sepals 12–14 mm. long: corolla 7–9 cm. broad: capsule subglobose, 1.5–2 cm. in diameter: seeds 12–14 mm. long. [*Gordonia pubescens* L'Her.]—(LOST CAMELLIA. FRANKLIN-TREE.)—Moist acid sandy soil in swamps N or E of Ft. Barrington, on the Altamaha River, S W of Townsend, in the Coastal Plain of Ga.—Sum.—Associated with *Pinckneya pubens*. Discovered by John and William Bartram in 1765. Not seen in its native place since 1790, but preserved in cultivation.

4. GORDONIA Ellis. Trees. Leaves persistent. Flowers long-pedicelled. Sepals and petals, 5, concave. Stamens borne on a 5-lobed disk.

Style terete. Capsule loculicidal.—About 16 species, American and Asiatic.

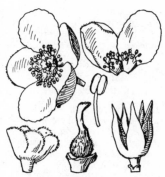

1. **G. Lasianthus** (L.) Ellis. Large trees with firm furrowed gray bark: leaf-blades narrowly elliptic or oblanceolate, 5–15 cm. long, appressed-serrate: sepals 8–10 mm. in diameter: corolla 5–7 cm. broad, white: capsule ovoid, 15–18 mm. long.—(LOBLOLLY-BAY. TAN-BAY. RED-BAY. BLACK-LAUREL.) —Non-alluvial swamps and bays, often in acid soil, Coastal Plain, Fla. to La. and N. C. (or S Va.?).—Sum.—The southern extremity of the range is about the latitude of Lake Okeechobee in Florida. The bark is some times used for tanning. The red heart-wood, close-grained but light and soft, is locally used for cabinet-work.

FAMILY 7. **TURNERACEAE** — TURNERA FAMILY

Herbs or shrubs. Leaves alternate: blades entire, toothed, or pinnatifid, pinnately veined. Flowers mostly perfect. Calyx of 5 imbricate sepals. Corolla of 5 convolute delicate petals. Androecium of 5 distinct stamens. Gynoecium of 3 united carpels. Ovary 1-celled, with 3 parietal placentae opposite the styles. Fruit a 3-valved capsule.—Six genera and about 180 species, tropical and subtropical.

Ovary seated in a receptacle with a crown-like edge: plant herbaceous. 1. PIRIQUETA.
Ovary seated in a receptacle without a crown: plant partially woody. 2. TURNERA.

1. **PIRIQUETA** Aubl. Herbs. Sepals slightly united. Stigmas lobed. —About 20 species, mostly in tropical and subtropical America.—Spr.–fall or all year southward.

Foliage glabrous, at least to the inflorescence.
  Pedicel and calyx glabrous: bracts leaf-like.   1. *P. viridis.*
  Pedicel and calyx pubescent: bracts scale-like.   2. *P. glabrescens.*
Foliage tomentose or hirsute throughout.
  Stem tomentose.   3. *P. tomentosa.*
  Stem hirsute as well as tomentose.   4. *P. caroliniana.*

1. **P. glabrescens** Small. Plants glabrous up to the inflorescence, 4–6 dm. tall: leaf-blades narrowly linear, 1–5 cm. long, entire: corolla light-yellow: capsule about 5 mm. long.—Everglades and swamps, Fla.

2. **P. viridis** Small. Plants glabrous, 1–5 dm. tall: leaf-blades linear-spatulate to linear, 3–8 cm. long, repand: calyx-lobes lanceolate: corolla yellow: capsule 7–8 mm. in diameter.—Pinelands, Fla.

3. **P. tomentosa** H.B.K. Plants stellate-tomentose, 2–4 dm. tall: leaf-blades oval, elliptic, or rarely narrowly elliptic-lanceolate, 1–4 cm. long, crenate-serrate: corolla bright-yellow: capsule 5–6 mm. in diameter. —Pinelands, S pen. Fla. and the Keys.— The stems are sometimes hirsute near the base.

4. P. caroliniana (Walt.) Urban. Plants fulvous-hirsute, 1–4 dm. tall: leaf-blades obovate, elliptic, cuneate, lanceolate, or rarely oval, 1–7 cm. long, repand or crenate-serrate: corolla deep-yellow: capsule 5–7 mm. long.—Pinelands and sand-dunes, Coastal Plain, Fla. to N. C.

2. **TURNERA** L. Shrubs or partly woody plants. Flowers usually solitary and axillary. Corolla yellow. Stigmas 3, brush-like.—About 75 species, mostly American.

1. **T. ulmifolia** L. Shrub 2 m. tall or less, with appressed-pubescent branchlets: leaf-blades ovate, varying to elliptic or spatulate, mostly 3–9 cm. long, serrate or crenate-serrate, 2-glandular at the base, short-petioled: calyx 14–17 mm. long; lobes lanceolate to ovate-lanceolate, acuminate: petals yellow, 2.5–3 cm. long: capsule globular to ovoid, 8–10 mm. long.—Hammocks and waste-places, Coastal Plain, Fla. to La. Nat. of trop. Am.—(*W. I., Mex., C. A., S. A.*)—All year.—Used medicinally. This plant naturalized on Key West many years ago. The washing and scouring of storms and the clearing and building operations covering most of the island have not eliminated it from the flora.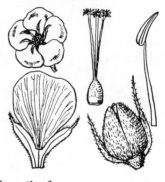

FAMILY 8. **CISTACEAE** — ROCK-ROSE FAMILY

Shrubs or partially woody plants. Leaves alternate or opposite: blades simple. Flowers generally perfect. Calyx of 3–5 persistent sepals. Corolla of 5 or 3 often fugacious petals, or wanting. Androecium of 6 or more stamens. Gynoecium of usually 3 united carpels. Fruit a capsule.—Nine genera and about 160 species, natives of the Northern Hemisphere.

Petals 5, yellow, fugacious or wanting.
    Leaves with flat blades; style short.   1. CROCANTHEMUM.
    Leaves scale-like or subulate; style elongate.   2. HUDSONIA.
Petals 3, greenish or purplish, withering-persistent.   3. LECHEA.

1. **CROCANTHEMUM** Spach.[1] Erect plants. Leaf-blades flat, but often narrowly revolute-margined. Flowers of two kinds, the earliest complete, showy with yellow petals and many stamens, some or all of the later ones apetalous, inconspicuous, and with few stamens. Ovules pendulous. Capsules of the petaliferous flowers larger than those of the apetalous ones. [*Helianthemum* (Fl. SE. U. S.)]—About 25 species, American.—ROCK-ROSES. SUN-ROSES. FROST-WEEDS.

Flowers few, in a simple raceme-like leafy-bracted inflorescence.   I. CAROLINIANA.
Flowers, at least the apetalous ones, clustered.
    Petaliferous and apetalous flowers in the same clusters.   II. CORYMBOSA.
    Petaliferous flowers solitary or few; apetalous flowers
      numerous, clustered, later in the season.   III. CANADENSIA.

I. CAROLINIANA
Leaves mostly in a basal rosette.   1. *C. carolinianum.*

II. CORYMBOSA
Flowers in a dense terminal cyme.   2. *C. corymbosum.*
Flowers in scattered or panicled clusters.
    Flower-clusters scattered or solitary.

[1] Contributed by John Hendley Barnhart.

Sepals becoming 6–8 mm. long; lateral nerves of leaves not prominent beneath.

Sepals becoming 4–6 mm. long: lateral nerves of leaves prominent beneath.   3. *C. arenicola.*

Flower-clusters in more or less elongate thyrsoid panicles.   4. *C. georgianum.*

Sepals of the apetalous flowers fully 2 mm. long at maturity.

Sepals canescent-puberulent.   5. *C. Nashii.*

Sepals hirsute.   6. *C. thyrsoideum.*

Sepals of the apetalous flowers less than 2 mm. long.   7. *C. rosmarinifolium.*

III. CANADENSIA

Petaliferous flowers 1 or 2, their capsules far overtopped by the apetalous inflorescence.   8. *C. canadense.*

Petaliferous flowers 5–12, the apetalous inflorescence on short lateral branches.   9. *C. Bicknellii.*

1. C. carolinianum (Walt.) Spach. Stem hirsute, 0.5–2.5 dm. tall: leaves mostly in a basal rosette; blades oblanceolate to elliptic, 2–4 cm. long: flowers few, in a raceme-like, leafy-bracted inflorescence: petaliferous flowers with 25–35 stamens and 80 ovules, the apetalous with 5 stamens and 50–60 ovules: inner sepals becoming 10–15 mm. long, acuminate: corolla yellow, 2.5–3 cm. broad: capsule subspheric, 8–10 mm. in diameter. [*H. carolinianum* (Walt.) Michx.]—Dry pinelands, Coastal Plain, N Fla. to E Tex. and N. C.—Spr.

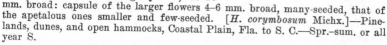

2. C. corymbosum (Michx.) Britton. Stem finely and densely canescent, 1.5–2 dm. high: leaf-blades elliptic, or the lowest obovate, 1.5–3 cm. long, pale beneath, dark-green above: corolla bright-yellow, 16–20 mm. broad: capsule of the larger flowers 4–6 mm. broad, many-seeded, that of the apetalous ones smaller and few-seeded. [*H. corymbosum* Michx.]—Pinelands, dunes, and open hammocks, Coastal Plain, Fla. to S. C.—Spr.–sum. or all year S.

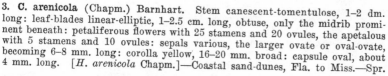

3. C. arenicola (Chapm.) Barnhart. Stem canescent-tomentulose, 1–2 dm. long: leaf-blades linear-elliptic, 1–2.5 cm. long, obtuse, only the midrib prominent beneath: petaliferous flowers with 25 stamens and 20 ovules, the apetalous with 5 stamens and 10 ovules: sepals various, the larger ovate or oval-ovate, becoming 6–8 mm. long: corolla yellow, 16–20 mm. broad: capsule oval, about 4 mm. long. [*H. arenicola* Chapm.]—Coastal sand-dunes, Fla. to Miss.—Spr.

4. C. georgianum (Chapm.) Barnhart. Stem 1.5–3 dm. long: leaf-blades elliptic or slightly narrower below the middle, 1–2.5 cm. long, the lateral nerves as well as the midrib prominent beneath: petaliferous flowers with 15–30 stamens and 35 ovules, the apetalous with 8 stamens and about 17 ovules: sepals various, the larger ovate or oval, becoming 4–6 mm. long, acute or slightly acuminate: corolla yellow, 15–18 mm. broad: capsule ovoid-globose, about 4 mm. long, apiculate. [*H. georgianum* Chapm.]—Sandy woods, pinelands, dunes, and fields, Coastal Plain, N Fla. to E Tex. and Va.—Spr.

5. C. Nashii (Britton) Barnhart. Stem 1.5–4 dm. long: leaf-blades elliptic or linear-elliptic, 1–3 cm. long, the midrib very prominent beneath: petaliferous flowers with 15 stamens and 8–10 ovules, the apetalous with 5 stamens and 3–6 ovules: sepals various, the inner oval or oval-elliptic, becoming 4–5 mm. long: corolla yellow, 16–20 mm. broad: petals broadly cuneate, slightly eroded: capsule broadly ovoid, 3–3.5 mm. long, blunt. [*H. Nashii* Britton]—Scrub, pen. Fla.—Spr.

6. C. thyrsoideum Barnhart. Plant similar to *C. Nashii* in habit, but the inflorescence less widely branched, and the sepals densely hirsute. [*H. thyrsoideum* Barnh.]—Dry sandy soil, Pinellas Co., Fla.—Spr.

7. C. rosmarinifolium (Pursh) Barnhart. Stem 1.5–4 dm. tall: leaf-blades linear or narrowly linear-oblanceolate, or those on basal shoots broader, 1–3 cm. long: petaliferous flowers few, with 12–30 stamens and 8 ovules, their sepals ovate, 2–3 mm. long, the corollas 12–15 mm. broad, their capsules 2–3 cm. long: apetalous flowers in dense clusters, with 3 stamens and 3 ovules, the capsule short-pedicelled, about 1 mm. broad. [*H. rosmarinifolium* Pursh]— Pinelands, sandy fields, and roadsides, Coastal Plain, N Fla. to E Tex. and S. C.—Sum.

8. C. canadense (L.) Britton. Stem 1–6 dm. tall: leaf-blades elliptic, linear-elliptic, or oblanceolate, nearly sessile, 1.2–3 cm. long, rough and dark-green above, paler and canescent beneath: petaliferous flowers with 30 stamens and 30–60 ovules, their corollas 1.8–3 cm. wide, the capsule ovoid or obovoid and 6–8 mm. long: apetalous flowers appearing later, axillary, nearly sessile, with 4 stamens and 6–20 ovules, the capsule about 4 mm. in diameter: seed papillose. [*H. canadense* (L.) Michx.]—(FROST-WEED.)—Acid sandy or rocky soil, often in woods, various provinces, N. C. to Miss., Wis., and Me.—Spr.–fall.

9. C. Bicknellii (Fernald) Barnhart. Stem 3–6 dm. tall: leaf-blades elliptic-lanceolate or oblanceolate, acute or obtuse, 1.5–3.5 cm. long, stellate-canescent beneath, darker above, short-petioled: petaliferous flowers with 30 stamens and 30–60 ovules, their sepals densely canescent, the outer nearly as long as the inner, their corollas 1.5–2.5 cm. broad, light-yellow, the capsule ovoid, 3–4 mm. long: apetalous flowers appearing later, with 4 stamens and 6–20 ovules: seed evenly reticulate. [*H. majus* (Fl. SE. U. S.) *H. Bicknellii* Fernald]—(HOARY FROST-WEED.)—Dry soil, often in open woods or old fields, various provinces, S. C. to Tex., Colo., and N. S.—Spr.–fall.

2. HUDSONIA L. Diffuse-spreading tufted or matted shrubs. Leaf-blades subulate or scale-like. Flowers complete. Corolla bright-yellow. Ovules erect. Capsules all alike.—Three species, of eastern North America.—BEACH-HEATHERS. FALSE-HEATHERS.

Flowers sessile or nearly so: leaves scale-like: ovary glabrous.   1. *H. tomentosa.*
Flowers slender-pedicelled: leaves subulate: ovary pubescent.
    Ovary pubescent all over: one sepal, at least, with a linear-
      subulate lobe.   2. *H. montana.*
    Ovary pubescent at the top: one sepal, at least, with a tooth
      near the apex.   3. *H. ericoides.*

1. H. tomentosa Nutt. Densely tufted and intricately branched, matted hoary-pubescent, pale, 1–2 dm. high, the branches stout, ascending: leaves 2 mm. long, oval or elliptic, densely imbricate and appressed: sepals obtuse: capsule ovoid, glabrous. — (BEACH-HEATHER.) — Sands of the seashore and in pinelands, Coastal Plain and New England Coast, N. C. to N. B.; and on lake and river shores, Great Lakes Lowland, Ind. to Man.—Spr.–early sum.

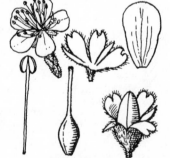

2. H. montana Nutt. Bushy, somewhat villous throughout, the branches tufted, 1–1.5 dm. long: leaves commonly erect, sometimes spreading in age, 3–6 mm. long, approximate: pedicels 8–10 mm. long: flowers several: sepals 5–6 mm. long, acuminate, densely pubescent: corolla yellow, 9–11 mm.

broad: capsule oval-ellipsoid or broadly ellipsoid, 3–4 mm. long, sparingly pubescent.—Dry, stony summit of Table Rock and adj. peaks, in the Blue Ridge of N. C.—Sum.—Now localized on a few mountain peaks, but doubtless once of wider distribution, and perhaps the ancestor of the following species.

3. H. ericoides L. Bushy, softly-pubescent, 1–2 dm. high, the principal branches slender, ascending: leaves 6–8 mm. long, somewhat spreading, densely imbricate on the younger branches, more scattered on the older ones: pedicels 10–15 mm. long: flowers numerous: corolla about 8 mm. broad: sepals 4–6 mm. long, obtuse, or acutish: capsule ellipsoid, slightly pubescent.—(GOLD-HEATHER.)—Dry sandy or rocky soil, especially in pinelands near the coast, Coastal Plain and New England Coast, N. C. to N. S.—Spr.

3. LECHEA Kalm. Erect plants with many very leafy shoots at the base of the stem in the fall. Leaf-blades narrow, or those of the leaves on the shoots often broad and short. Flowers complete, minute. Corolla purplish or greenish. Ovules erect. Capsules all alike.—Sum.—PINWEEDS.— Some species are used medicinally.

Plants with annual flowering stems from the base of which rosettes of leafy shoots spring.
Flowers, and fruits, relatively long-pedicelled, in long-peduncled lax clusters.
Flowers and fruits not drooping.
Calyx with the outer (narrow) sepals longer than the inner. — I. LONGISEPALAE.
Calyx with the outer (narrow) sepals shorter than the inner. — II. BREVISEPALAE.
Flowers and fruits drooping. — III. CERNUAE.
Flowers, and fruits, very short-pedicelled, in short-peduncled close or dense clusters. — IV. DIVARICATAE.
Plants largely woody, much branched, with copiously leafy branches which later develop panicles at the tip. — V. MYRIOPHYLLAE.

I. LONGISEPALAE
Blades of the cauline leaves of an oval or elliptic type.
Capsule oval or obovoid-oval: outer sepals much longer than the inner: basal shoots, stem, and branches appressed-pubescent. — 1. *L. minor.*
Capsule subglobose: outer sepals slightly longer than the inner: basal shoots, stem, and branches with lax or spreading hairs. — 2. *L. villosa.*
Blades of the cauline leaves of a linear or subulate type.
Capsule subglobose ellipsoid, or oval, not angled.
Outer sepals slightly longer than the inner: capsule slightly exserted from the calyx, longer than wide. — 3. *L. patula.*
Outer sepals much longer than the inner: capsule included, about as wide as long. — 4. *L. tenuifolia.*
Capsule ellipsoid-prismatic, decidedly 3-angled, fully 1.5 mm. long. — 5. *L. prismatica.*

II. BREVISEPALAE
Capsule ellipsoid: — 6. *L. racemulosa.*
Capsule oval or subglobose:
Capsule oval:
Capsule narrowly oval, much exserted: sepals sparingly pubescent. — 7. *L. exserta.*
Capsule broadly oval, scarcely exserted: sepals copiously pubescent. — 8. *L. Leggettii.*
Capsule subglobose.
Blades of the cauline leaves linear-subulate: inner sepals about 1.5 mm. long. — 9. *L. Torreyi.*
Blades of the cauline leaves linear to narrowly elliptic: inner sepals about 2 mm. long. — 10. *L. maritima.*

III. CERNUAE
Plant with several inconspicuously-pubescent flowering stems and several very stout copiously silvery pubescent branched and copiously leafy basal shoots. — 11. *L. cernua.*

IV. DIVARICATAE

Plant more or less diffuse, the branches with numerous relatively short branches: the whole plant loosely graypubescent.   12. *L. divaricata.*

V. MYRIOPHYLLAE

Leaf-blades subulate to elliptic-subulate: capsule depressedglobose.   13. *L. Deckertii.*

Leaf-blades elliptic, sometimes narrowly so: capsule globose.   14. *L. myriophylla.*

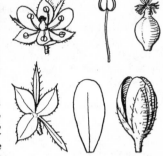

1. L. minor L. Stem 1.5–6 dm. tall, the often numerous branches rather short, erect or strongly ascending, which terminate in open clusters: blades of the cauline leaves oval or elliptic, 0.8–1.5 cm. long: basal shoots with strigose branches and suborbicular or oval leaf-blades: calyx in fruit obovoid; inner sepals 1.5 mm. long at maturity; outer sepals decidedly longer than the inner: capsule oval or obovoid-oval, about 1.5 mm. long, included.—Dry woods and banks, various provinces, Fla. to La., Mich., and Mass.—Sum.

2. L. villosa Ell. Stem 3–8 dm. tall, with short or long ascending branches above, which terminate in dense flower, or fruit, clusters: foliage loosely, sometimes copiously pubescent with gray hairs: blades of the cauline leaves elliptic, 1.5–2.5 cm. long: basal shoots slender with numerous leaves with elliptic, oval, or ovate blades much smaller than those of the cauline-leaves: calyx in fruit globose-turbinate and angular: inner sepals about 1.5 mm. long at maturity, outer sepals slightly longer than the inner: capsule subglobose, bluntly 3-angled, fully 1.5 mm. long, slightly exserted.—Dry woods, pinelands, sandhills, and prairies, various provinces, Fla. to Tex., Nebr., S Ont., and Mass.—Sum.

3. L. patula Leggett. Stem 1.5–4.5 dm. tall, with loosely spreading or divergent branches: blades of the cauline leaves linear or nearly so, 4–9 mm. long: basal shoots with linear-elliptic or somewhat spatulate leaf-blades: calyx in fruit obovoid; inner sepals 1–1.5 mm. long at maturity; outer sepals slightly longer than the inner: capsule oval, often broadly so, 1.5 mm. long or more, exserted at the tip.—Dry pinelands, sand-dunes, and hammocks, Coastal Plain, Fla. to S. C.—Sum.–fall or all year S.

4. L. tenuifolia Michx. Stem 1–3 dm. tall, laxly much-branched: foliage finely strigose: blades of the cauline leaves narrowly linear or linear-subulate, 0.4–1.5 cm. long: basal shoots with leaves nearly or quite similar to those of the stem: calyx in fruit subglobose or oval; inner sepals about 2 mm. long at maturity; outer sepals much exceeding the inner: capsule subglobose or globose-obovoid, 1.5 mm. long or less, included.—Dry, often rocky or sandy woods, plains, and prairies, various provinces, Fla. to Tex., Kans., Wis., and Mass.—Spr.–fall.

5. L. prismatica Small. Stem 1–3 dm. tall, loosely-branched, the branches loosely ascending or spreading: foliage rather coarsely strigose: blades of the cauline leaves narrowly linear or linear-subulate, about 1 cm. long: basal shoots with narrowly linear-elliptic to linear-spatulate leaf-blades: calyx in fruit narrowly turbinate; inner sepals about 1.5 mm. long at maturity; outer sepals much longer than the inner: capsule ellipsoid-prismatic, about 2 mm. long, 3-angled, exserted at the tip.—Scrub, S end of Lake Region, Fla.—Sum.–fall.

6. **L. racemulosa** Michx. Stem simple or branched at the base, the branches erect or ascending, 1–5 dm. tall, copiously branched above, the branchlets slender, mostly ascending, rather inconspicuously strigillose: blades of the cauline leaves elliptic-spatulate to elliptic, or linear-elliptic, mostly 1–2 cm. long, strigillose or glabrate: basal shoots with narrowly elliptic leaf-blades: calyx in fruit narrowly pyriform; inner sepals about 1.5 mm. long at maturity; outer sepals much shorter than the inner: capsule ellipsoid, fully 1.5 mm. long, slightly exserted.—Dry woods, often in sandy or rocky soil, various provinces, Fla. to Ala., Ind., and E Mass.—Sum.

7. **L. exserta** Small. Stem usually branched at the base, the branches erect, 3–6 dm. tall, fastigiately much-branched above, inconspicuously pubescent: blades of the cauline leaves linear-elliptic to almost linear, glabrous or nearly so: basal shoots not seen: panicles many-flowered: bracts linear-elliptic to subulate: calyx in fruit campanulate; inner sepals 1–1.2 mm. long, at maturity; outer sepals slightly shorter than the inner: capsule narrowly oval, about 1.5 mm. long, much-exserted.—Dry pinelands, S pen. Fla.—Spr.–fall or all year S.

8. **L. Leggettii** Britt. and Hollick. Stem branched at the base, the branches erect or nearly so, loosely branched above, the branches long and slender, inconspicuously strigillose: blades of the cauline leaves linear-spatulate to linear, 1–2.5 cm. long, sparingly strigillose or glabrous: basal shoots with linear-elliptic leaf-blades: calyx in fruit broadly pyriform; inner sepals about 1.5 mm. long, at maturity; outer sepals much shorter than the inner: capsule oval, about 1.5 mm. long, scarcely exserted.—Dry woods, pinelands, old fields, and sand-dunes, various provinces, Fla. to La., Ind., and E. Mass.—Sum.–fall.

9. **L. Torreyi** Leggett. Stem usually branched at the base, the branches 1.5–5 dm. tall, the branchlets rather long and slender, pale-strigose: blades of the cauline leaves linear-subulate, mostly 1–1.5 cm. long, acute, strigillose: basal shoots with leaves nearly similar to those of the stem or slightly wider: calyx in fruit globose-obovoid; inner sepals about 1.5 mm. long at maturity; outer sepals much shorter than the inner: capsule subglobose, about 1.5 mm. long, not exserted.—Pinelands, Coastal Plain, Fla. to S. C.—Spr.–fall or all year S.

10. **L. maritima** Leggett. Stem often branched at the base, the branches 1.5–3.5 m. tall, much-branched above, the branchlets rather short, gray-strigillose: blades of the cauline leaves linear to narrowly-elliptic, mostly 1–2 cm. long, whitish-strigose: basal shoots with narrowly elliptic leaf-blades: bracts similar to the cauline leaves, but much smaller: calyx in fruit globose-obovoid: inner sepals about 2 mm. long at maturity; outer sepals much shorter than the inner: capsule subglobose, about 1.5 mm. long, not exserted.—Sandy seashores and pinelands, Coastal Plain and New England Coast, Ga. to Me.—Sum.–fall.

11. **L. cernua** Small. Stem usually branched at the base, the branches 3–6 dm. tall, often numerous, widely often much-branched above, the branchlets rather finely strigose: blades of the cauline leaves elliptic or ovate-elliptic, about 1 cm. long or less, strigose, several-ribbed: basal shoots with ovate to suborbicular densely pale-hairy leaf-blades: calyx in fruit turbinate; inner sepals about 2 mm. long at maturity; outer sepals minute: capsule obovoid, about 2 mm. long, slightly exserted.—Scrub, on sand-dunes, Lake Region and eastern coast, Fla.—Sum.–fall.

12. **L. divaricata** Shuttlw. Stem often branched at the base, the branches erect, ascending, or spreading, copiously pubescent with lax or spreading hairs;

the branchlets usually divaricate, relatively short, ending in compact flower-
or fruit-clusters: blades of the numerous cauline and branch-leaves, elliptic,
often narrowly so, or oval, 4–8 mm. long, acute: calyx in fruit obovoid; inner
sepals about 1.5 mm. long, loosely pubescent; outer sepals slightly shorter than
the inner: capsule subglobose or globose-obovoid, 2 mm. long, exserted.—Dry
sandy soil, pen Fla., also reported from Tex.—Sum.–fall.

13. **L. Deckertii** Small. Stem branched at the woody base, the branches
forming tufts, very leafy, usually minutely and sparingly pubescent, sooner
or later developing terminal panicles: leaves numerous; blades elliptic-subulate
to subulate, 1.5–2.5 mm. long, acutish, glabrous or nearly so: panicles few–
several-flowered, with minute bracts: calyx in fruit lax, not enveloping the
capsule; inner sepals about 1.5 mm. long at maturity; outer sepals fully one-
half as long as the inner: capsule depressed-globose, 1.2–1.4 mm. long, much
exserted.—Scrub, Coastal Plain, pen. Fla. to S Ga.—Sum.–fall.

14. **L. myriophylla** Small. Stem branched at the woody base, the branches
forming tufts, very leafy, more or less pubescent, sooner or later developing
panicles at their tips: leaves numerous; blades elliptic, sometimes narrowly so,
3–5 mm. long, acute, somewhat loosely strigose or glabrous: panicles many-
flowered, with the bracts much smaller than the leaves: calyx in fruit, lax,
not enveloping the capsule; inner sepals nearly 1.5 mm. long at maturity;
outer sepals about half as long as the inner: capsule globose, about 1.5 mm.
long, much-exserted.—Scrub, S part of Lake Region, pen. Fla.—Sum.–fall.

FAMILY 9.   **VIOLACEAE** — VIOLET FAMILY

Herbs, or in tropical regions occasionally shrubs or trees, with simple
alternate or opposite stipulate leaves, and perfect irregular solitary or
clustered flowers. Sepals and petals 5, the latter hypogynous, imbricate
in the bud, the lowermost often spurred. Stamens 5, the anthers erect,
syngenesious or connivent. Gynoecium 3-carpellary. Ovary 1-celled, enclosing numerous ovules on the 3 parietal placentae and becoming in fruit
a loculicidal capsule. Seeds anatropous.—Fifteen genera and about 300
species, widely distributed.

Sepals auriculate at base.   1. VIOLA.
Sepals not auriculate at base.   2. CUBELIUM.

1. **VIOLA** L.[1] Herbs, either leafy stemmed and rather low or stemless; petaliferous flowers mostly in early spring on one-flowered peduncles:
succeeded throughout the season by cleistogamous flowers that bear abundant
seed; stamens 5 in the petaliferous flower, the two lowest with appendages
that project into the sac or spur of the odd petal; these two stamens alone
developed in the cleistogamous flower.—Allied species freely hybridize when
growing together; the hybrids commonly display characters more or less intermediate to those of the parent species, and show marked vegetative vigor but
impaired fertility; their offspring are often much unlike the mother plant and
unlike each other, reverting variously to the characters of the two original
species.—About 200 species, of wide geographic distribution.—VIOLETS.—
Some species are used medicinally; others for ornamental gardening.

Plant stemless: leaves and scapes from a rootstock or a runner.
  Flowers scentless or with a faint pungent fragrance: plants indigenous.
    Corolla violet or purple (white in albino forms): plant without stolons.
      All petals beardless: apetalous flowers wanting.   I. PEDATAE.

[1] Contributed by the late Ezra Brainerd for Flora of the Southeastern
United States (Ed. 2), and adapted with slight changes, for the present work,
by Edward Johnston Alexander.

Lateral petals bearded: apetalous flowers present.			II. PALMATAE.
Corolla white or yellow, the petals often with dark lines:
plant stoloniferous.								III. BLANDAE.
Flowers very fragrant: corolla violet or white: plant intro-
duced.										IV. ODORATAE.
Plant with leafy stems: flowers axillary.
Style scarcely enlarged at the tip or merely capitate.
Style capitate, beakless: spur of the corolla short:
stipules nearly entire, soon scarious.					V. HASTATAE.
Style not capitate, slender and bent at the tip: spur of
the corolla at least twice its width: stipules bristly
toothed, somewhat herbaceous.						VI. ROSTRATAE.
Style stout, much enlarged upward into globular hollow
summit: stipules large, leaf-like, lactinate at the base.		VII. ARVENSES.

I. PEDATAE

Leaf-blades pedately finely divided: petals lilac, or the two
upper ones dark-violet.								1. V. pedata.

II. PALMATAE

Cleistogamous flowers ovoid, on short prostrate peduncles,
their capsules usually brown.
Leaf-blades all palmately 5–11-lobed or -parted, or
rarely the first leaf of spring uncut: seed brown.
Plant villous-pubescent.							2. V. palmata.
Plant nearly or quite glabrous.						3. V. Egglestonii.
Earliest and later leaf-blades usually uncut, others
pedately 3–7-lobed, -parted, or -divided: seed gen-
erally buff.
Plants villous-pubescent.
Cut leaf-blades mostly 3-lobed, with broadly open
sinus.									4. V. triloba.
Cut leaf-blades mostly 5–7-parted, with narrow
sinus.									4a. V. triloba dilatata.
Plants obscurely pubescent and glabrate: corolla
deep-violet: inhabitant of shady uplands.			5. V. Lovelliana.
Plants glabrous: corolla pale-violet: inhabitant of
wet woods.								6. V. esculenta.
Leaf-blades all uncut.
Plant nearly or quite glabrous.
Flowers violet or purple (except in albinos).
Flowers violet-purple: seed brown.				7. V. papilionacea.
Flowers rose-purple: seed buff.				8. V. rosacea.
Flowers pale-violet or whitish.
Petals uniformly pale violet, with only a
few darker veins at the base: seeds buff:
leaf-blades reniform-hastate.				9. V. floridana.
Petals grayish, the basal veins so numerous
as to make large blotches of brilliant violet-
blue: seeds brown: leaf-blades cordate.		10. V. Priceana.
Plant villous-pubescent, especially on petiole and
lower leaf-surface: seed dark-brown.				11. V. sororia.
Plant hirsutulous on upper leaf-surface, elsewhere
glabrous: seed buff.						12. V. hirsutula.
Cleistogamous flowers on long ascending peduncles, their
capsules more or less brown.
Leaf-blades at vernal flowering narrowly cordate-
acuminate: seed buff.
Auricles of sepals short appressed.				13. V. affinis.
Auricles of sepals 2 mm. long, spreading.			14. V. Langloisii.
Leaf-blades at vernal flowering subcordate, 3-lobed:
seed bronze.							15. V. chalcosperma.
Cleistogamous flowers subulate or sagittate, on erect
peduncles, their capsules green.
Spurred petal glabrous, the lateral ones with clavate
beard: leaves glabrous; blades uncut, cordate-ovate.	16. V. cucullata.
Spurred petal villous at base, the lateral ones with
capillary beard.
Foliage finely pubescent.
Leaf-blades ovate-elliptic, acute.				17. V. fimbriatula.
Leaf-blades ovate to orbicular, obtuse.			18. V. villosa.
Foliage nearly or quite glabrous.
Leaf-blades elliptic-lanceolate, incised at base.		19. V. sagittata.
Leaf-blades deltoid to broadly ovate, coarsely
toothed at base.						20. V. emarginata.
Leaf-blades uncut or pedately 3–9-lobed.			21. V. septemloba.

III. BLANDAE

Corolla white.
  Cleistogamous flowers on prostrate peduncles, their
    capsules ovoid, commonly reddish-brown: plants
    of cold ravines and low rich woods.
      Lateral petals bearded: seed obtuse at base.   22. *V. incognita.*
      Lateral petals beardless: seed acute at base.   23. *V. blanda.*
  Cleistogamous flowers on erect peduncles, their capsules
    ellipsoid, green: plants of open bogs.
    Leaf-blades broadly elliptic to cordate-ovate.
      Leaf-blades broadly cordate-ovate.   24. *V. pallens.*
      Leaf-blades ovate or elliptic.
        Leaf-blades rugose, cordate-tapering at the
          base.   25. *V. rugosa.*
        Leaf-blades smooth, not rugose, sub-cordate
          or tapering at the base.   26. *V. primulifolia.*
    Leaf-blades narrowly elliptic to linear.
      Leaf-blades lanceolate or elliptic, 10–15 mm.
        wide: petals usually rounded at the tip.   27. *V. lanceolata.*
      Leaf-blades narrowly lanceolate or linear, 4–10
        mm. wide: petals usually acute or acutish.   28. *V. vittata.*
                                         29. *V. rotundifolia.*
Corolla yellow.

IV. ODORATAE

Plants producing leafy stolons and fragrant flowers: style
  terminating in a sharp hook.   30. *V. odorata.*

V. HASTATAE

Petals yellow.
  Rootstock long, thick, whitish, bearing crisp, capillary
    roots.   31. *V. hastata.*
  Rootstock short, woody, brown, bearing coarse, fibrous
    roots.
    Petals tinged outside with violet.
      Leaf-blades 3-lobed to 3-divided.   32. *V. tripartita.*
      Leaf-blades uncut, ovate or rhombic-ovate.   32a. *V. tripartita*
                                                 glaberrima.

    Petals yellow outside.
      Sparingly pubescent, root-leaves usually 1–3.   33. *V. eriocarpa.*
      Markedly pubescent, root-leaves usually wanting.   34. *V. pubescens.*
  Petals white inside, usually violet outside.   35. *V. canadensis.*

VI. ROSTRATAE

Corolla-spur less than 8 mm. long: lateral petals bearded.
  Petals white or cream-colored.   36. *V. striata.*
  Petals violet-blue.
    Stem ascending: later leaf-blades subacuminate.   37. *V. conspersa.*
    Stem soon prostrate: leaf-blades obtuse, usually
      mottled.   38. *V. Walteri.*
Corolla-spur 10–12 mm. long, slender: lateral petals beard-
  less.   39. *V. rostrata.*

VII. ARVENSES

Upper leaf-blades entire, or obscurely crenulate: petals
  twice the length of sepals.   40. *V. Rafinesquii.*
Upper leaf-blades plainly crenate: petals usually shorter
  than the sepals.   41. *V. arvensis.*

1. **V. pedata** L. Plant nearly glabrous: rootstock short, erect: leaf-blades 3-divided, the lateral divisions pedately 3–5-parted or -cleft, the segments linear

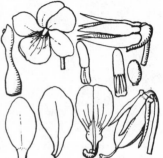

to spatulate, often 2–4-toothed or -cleft near
the apex; the leaf-blades of early spring
and of late autumn often smaller and less
deeply dissected: corolla 2–3 cm. broad, the
upper petals dark violet, the three lower
lilac-purple, all beardless (all petals lilac-
purple in *V. pedata lineariloba*): the orange
tips of the stamens large and conspicuous at
the center of the flower: capsule green, glabrous: seed copper-colored: apetalous flowers wanting, but petaliferous frequent in
late summer and autumn.—(BIRD'S-FOOT
VIOLET. CROWFOOT-VIOLET. PANSY-VIOLET.
JOHNNY-JUMP-UP.)—Open woods and dry
fields, often in acid soil, various provinces,

Fla. to La., Minn., and Mass.—Shows marked variations in leaf-form and coloration of petals; the color-form with the upper two petals dark-violet is more common in the east-central part of its range.

2. **V. palmata** L. Plant villous: leaf-blades palmately 5–11-lobed or -parted, the segments variously toothed or cleft, the middle segment usually widest; petioles, and veins of the lower leaf-surface, villous, the upper surface often glabrous: sepals ovate-lanceolate, rather blunt: corolla violet-purple, 2–3 cm. broad: cleistogamous flowers on prostrate peduncles, their capsules ovoid, mottled with brown, 8–12 mm. long: seeds brown.—Wooded hillsides in dry rich soil, various provinces, Fla. to Miss., Minn., and Mass.

3. **V. Egglestonii** Brainerd. Plant glabrous, of spreading habit especially in spring: leaf-blades truncate at base, often flabellately decurrent, rarely subcordate; early leaf-blades simply 3–5 lobed, the later ones 3-parted, with the middle or all three primary segments 2–3-cleft, the subdivisions oblanceolate or linear, crenately serrate towards the summit and bearing a few long narrow acute teeth below: corolla violet-purple, the lateral petals bearded at the throat; spurred petal somewhat villous: cleistogamous flowers and fruits on short underground peduncles till seeds ripen: capsule green turning pale-yellow, broadly ellipsoid, 13 mm. long, with lanceolate sepals one third as long, their auricles short, appressed: seed brown, 2.5 mm. long.—Barrens, Interior Low Plateaus, Tenn. and Ky.

4. **V. triloba** Schwein. Plant villous: earliest leaf-blades, and those put forth in late summer, broadly cordate-ovate, usually uncut, sparsely pubescent or glabrate; those unfolding at petaliferous flowering, densely villous beneath like the petioles, 3-lobed or rarely 3-parted, the middle segment broad, the lateral lunate, divaricate, often coarsely toothed or pedately cleft, the upper subdivision narrow, with more and deeper incisions, and the middle primary segment ovate, elliptic or rhombic-lanceolate in *V. triloba dilatata;* blades 10–15 cm. wide when mature: peduncles mostly glabrous, shorter than the leaves: petals deep-violet: outer sepals ovate-lanceolate, somewhat obtuse, slightly ciliate: cleistogamous capsules ovoid, purplish: seeds buff or brown.—Dry woodlands, various provinces, Ga. to Tex., Mo., and Mass.

5. **V. Lovelliana** Brainerd. Plant often minutely hoary-pubescent on the upper part of the petiole and the adjacent lower surface of the blade, elsewhere obscurely pubescent: leaf-blades cordate at base, earliest often uncut, later ones hastately 3-lobed, the middle lobe much the longest, lanceolate, sometimes contracted at the base and undulately serrate, the lateral lobes divaricate, either lunate or variously 2–3-cleft; leaf-blades at petaliferous flowering 2–5 cm. long, those of later summer twice as long, glabrate, often less deeply cut, or uncut: flowers on stalks often exceeding the leaves: sepals broadly lanceolate, acute, one third the length of capsule; the auricles short, appressed, rounded, sparsely ciliate: corolla violet-purple, the three lower petals villous at the throat and marked with dark-purple lines: cleistogamous flowers and immature fruit on prostrate peduncles: capsule purple-dotted, 14 mm. long: seed buff, 2 mm. long.—Sparsely wooded hillsides and knolls, Coastal Plain and adj. provinces, Miss. to La., Okla., and Ark.

6. **V. esculenta** Ell. Rootstock stout, ascending, sometimes with purple horizontal branches 5–7 cm. long; the foliage spreading, usually glabrous, becoming stiff and succulent: first leaf-blades usually uncut, broadly cordate-ovate, 2–3 cm. long, followed at flowering time by leaf-blades 3–5-lobed, successively larger and longer-petioled till blade may be 8 cm. in length and in breadth, the late summer ones with obscure lobes or none: flowers long-peduncled: sepals ovate-lanceolate with emarginate auricles: corolla pale-

violet or white, the spurred petal slightly villous: cleistogamous flowers ovoid-acuminate: mature capsule trigonous-cylindric, closely purple-dotted, 12–16 mm. long; their sepals one third as long: seed dark-brown or sometimes buff, 2 mm. long.—River swamps and borders of slow streams, Coastal Plain, Fla. to S. C.

7. V. papilionacea Pursh. Plant glabrous, commonly robust, from a stout horizontal branching rootstock: leaf-blades often 12 cm. broad, sometimes deltoid in outline above the cordate base, sometimes rounded and abruptly pointed; petioles often sparingly pubescent: outer sepals ovate-lanceolate: corolla deep-violet, white or greenish-yellow at the base, sometimes wholly white, the odd petal often narrow and boat-shaped, usually glabrous: cleistogamous flowers ovoid, on horizontal peduncles usually underground but lengthened and erect when the capsules ripen: capsule ellipsoid or cylindric, green or reddish-brown, 10–15 mm. long: seed 2 mm. long, dark-brown.— (WOOD-VIOLET.)—Moist meadows and woods, and frequently about dwellings, various provinces, Fla. to Tex., Minn., and Mass.

8. V. rosacea Brainerd. Plant nearly or quite glabrous: leaf-blades at vernal flowering narrowly cordate-ovate, acute or acuminate, crenate-serrate, 2–4 cm. long, sparsely hirtellous above; later leaf-blades much wider, sub-cordate, acuminate, glabrous, 5–7 cm. long: corolla rose-purple, about 2 cm. broad, the spurred petal glabrous or slightly villous: cleistogamous flowers ovoid on prostrate peduncles, their mature capsules ellipsoid, about 12 mm. long, purple-dotted, enclosed for over half their length in lanceolate sepals: seeds buff, 2 mm. long, about 50 in a capsule.—Dry open woods and well-drained bayou margins, Coastal Plain, Miss. and La.

9. V. floridana Brainerd. Leaf-blades at time of petaliferous flowering on spreading petioles, cordate, acute, finely crenate-serrate, often somewhat pu-berulent above, 2–3 cm. wide, 3–4 cm. long; leaves with blades twice as long and wide appearing soon after, on long erect petioles, glabrate, sometimes persisting through the winter: flowers on peduncles much surpassing the leaves: corolla whitish or pale-violet, the odd petal glabrous; apetalous flowers con-cealed under soil or dead leaves, narrowly ovoid-acuminate; their ripe capsules reddish-brown, about 16 mm. long, on decumbent peduncles: sepals broadly lanceolate, about one third the length of the capsule: seed 2 mm. long, salmon-colored or dark-brown, about 60 in a capsule.—Moist rich woodlands, C and N Fla.

10. V. Priceana Pollard. Plant glabrous, robust, from a stout, branching rootstock: leaf-blades glabrous, rather dark green, cordate-ovate in outline, the tip obtuse or abruptly acute: scapes equalling or exceeding the leaves: sepals lanceolate-acuminate: corolla 3 cm. broad, grayish, the petals heavily veined at the base with brilliant violet-blue, the veins extending well into the blades; the spurred petal somewhat smaller than the others, keel-shaped, glab-rous: cleistogamous flowers ovoid on horizontal peduncles: capsule broadly ellipsoid, purplish-green; seeds brown.—(CONFEDERATE VIOLET.)—Rich soil, in partially shaded situations, various provinces, Ga., Ark., Ken., N. C., and S. C. Brainerd regards this plant as an albino of *V. papilionacea*, but that species has flowers violet with white center, while this is reversed. This species also is very constant in its form and continually comes true from seed, never reverting to *V. papilionacea*.

11. V. sororia Willd. Leaf-blades broadly cordate-ovate, villous-pubescent especially on the under surface when young, and on the petioles, often 10 cm. wide when mature: vernal flowers on peduncles about the length of the leaves: outer sepals ovate-elliptic, commonly obtuse, all finely ciliate below the middle and on the short rounded auricles: corolla violet to lavender and occasionally white: cleistogamous capsule usually mottled with brown: seed dark-brown, 2 mm. long.—Moist meadows, shady ledges, and dooryards, various provinces, N. C. to Okla., Minn., and Que.

12. V. hirsutula Brainerd. Plant of small size: leaf-blades frequently appressed to the ground, 2–5 cm. wide, cordate-ovate to reniform, obtuse, purplish and glabrous beneath, silvery-pubescent above, often purple-veined and mottled with different shades of green: flowers on peduncles exceeding the leaves: corolla reddish-purple: apetalous flowers small, ovoid, on short prostrate peduncles, developing ovoid purplish capsules, 6–8 mm. long, bearing each 20–30 light-brown seeds.—Dry rich woods, various provinces, Ga. to Ala. and N. Y.

13. V. affinis LeConte. Plant nearly glabrous: leaf-blades that unfold at vernal flowering narrowly cordate-ovate and commonly attenuate toward the apex, becoming 4–6 cm. wide in summer, the margin noticeably crenate-serrate; petioles slender: corolla violet with the white base conspicuous, the spurred petal more or less villous: cleistogamous flowers small, ovoid, on rather long ascending peduncles: capsule ellipsoid, 5–8 mm. long, usually reddish-brown, sometimes green, either glabrous or clothed with minute dense pubescence: sepals half the length of the capsule, with small appressed auricles: seed normally buff.—Moist meadows, low woods, and shaded stream-banks, various provinces, Ga. to Ala., Wis., and Vt.

14. V. Langloisii Greene. Leaf-blades glabrous, cordate-ovate, attenuate, crenate-serrate (3–5-lobed in *V. Langloisii pedatiloba*); those that mature after flowering relatively wider, cordate-deltoid, about 6 cm. long: flowers on peduncles taller than the leaves: sepals lanceolate: corolla violet, 2–3 cm. broad, the lateral petals bearded, the spurred petal mostly glabrous: cleistogamous flowers on ascending peduncles, sagittate, their mature capsule narrowly ellipsoid, pale-yellow faintly dotted with purple, 10–12 mm. long, with lanceolate acuminate sepals one half as long, the auricles glabrous, dentate, 2 mm. long: seed buff, 1.5 mm. long.—Wet and shady borders of slow streams, Coastal Plain, Miss. to Tex.

15. V. chalcosperma Brainerd. Plant glabrous, heterophyllous: leaf-blades at the beginning and at the close of the season's growth uncut, the former cordate 2–3 cm. long, the latter truncate at base, broadly deltoid 4–5 cm. long; vernal leaf-blades cordate, 3-lobed, the middle lobe ovate, acute, the lateral ones more or less incised: flowers small, raised above the leaves on slender peduncles; corolla lilac-purple, the lateral petals bearded, the odd petal sparsely villous, all finely purple-veined: cleistogamous flowers sagittate, on ascending peduncles: ripe capsule pale-yellow tinged with purple at base, ellipsoid, about 11 mm. long, with sepals dark purple, lanceolate, 5 mm. long, the auricles 3–4 mm. long, the three outer sepals with one or more sharp teeth: seeds bronze-colored, 1.5 mm. long, about 50 in a capsule.—Wet soil in shaded ravines, near Jacksonville, Fla.

16. V. cucullata Ait. Plant glabrous: leaf-blades, except the earliest, cordate-ovate, acute or subacuminate, often 9 cm. wide when mature: peduncles commonly much exceeding the leaves: sepals narrowly lanceolate: corolla violet-blue, darker-colored at the throat, the lateral petals with strongly clavate beard, the spurred petal glabrous, generally somewhat shorter than the lateral ones: cleistogamous flowers long and slender, on erect often elongate peduncles: capsule ovoid-cylindric, green, 10–15 mm. long, but little exceeding the long-auricled sepals: seed nearly black, 1.5 mm. long.—(BLUE MARSH-VIOLET. MEADOW-VIOLET.)—Wet soil, various provinces, Coastal Plain only N, Ga. to Ont., Que., and Me.

17. **V. fimbriatula** J. E. Smith. Rootstock becoming long and stout, usually erect: earliest leaf-blades ovate, obtuse, the later ones ovate-elliptic, acute, finely pubescent, obscurely crenulate toward the apex, the basal lobes often sharply toothed, incised, or auriculate: scapes commonly exceeding the leaves: auricles of the sepals somewhat spreading and ciliate: corolla violet-purple: capsule green, ovoid, 6–10 mm. long; seed brown: cleistogamous flowers on erect peduncles.—Hillsides and dry fields, various provinces, Fla. to La., Wis., and N. S.

18. **V. villosa** Walt. Rootstock simple, often long and jagged; foliage spreading, minutely villous throughout: leaf-blades ovate, varying to elliptic-ovate and orbicular, obtuse, obscurely crenate, cordate with small narrow sinus, when mature sometimes 6 cm. long and on petioles 12 cm. long: flowers early: sepals ciliolate, elliptic-ovate with rather short auricles: corolla violet, the three lower petals bearded, the spur large globose: capsule green, ovoid-cylindric, 10 mm. long: seed dark brown, 1.8 mm. long. [*V. carolina* Greene]—Dry soil, open woods and roadsides, various provinces, Fla. to Miss., Tenn., and S W Va.; also W Ark., Tex., and E Okla.

19. **V. sagittata** Ait. Plant usually glabrous, except the often ciliate leaves, or finely pubescent throughout: leaf-blades lanceolate or elliptic-lanceolate, becoming 4–8 cm. long, hastately or sagittately toothed or cleft at the base; the earliest and those produced in late summer often deltoid-ovate, obtuse, merely crenate at the base: sepals narrowly lanceolate, acute, glabrous: corolla violet-purple: capsule 8–14 mm. long, containing 50–70 brown seeds.—(ARROW-LEAVED VIOLET.)—Moist banks and wet meadows, various provinces, Ga. to La., Minn., and Mass.

20. **V. emarginata** (Nutt.) LeConte. Plant glabrous: mature leaf-blades deltoid or broadly ovate, the base truncate or subcordate often decurrent, obscurely crenate-serrate above the middle, coarsely toothed or incised below: corolla violet-blue, the petals sometimes emarginate: cleistogamous capsule ellipsoid, 8–14 mm. long: peduncles erect, somewhat shorter than the leaves: seed brown.—Dry woods and hillsides, various provinces, N Ga. to Okla. and S E N. Y.

21. **V. septemloba** LeConte. Plant glabrous with a vertical rootstock: leaf-blades cordate-ovate; the first ones often, and sometimes all the leaves, uncut, the others primarily 3-lobed, 3-cleft or 3-parted with widely open sinuses, the middle segment uncut, relatively long and broad, usually narrowed at the base; the lateral segments sometimes uncut, but generally pedately cleft into 2–4 narrow divergent parts that become smaller towards the base of the leaf: flowers usually raised above the foliage: sepals narrowly lanceolate, with entire rounded auricles: corolla violet, the three lower petals villous at the base: cleistogamous flowers erect: capsule green, ovoid-cylindric, about 14 mm. long: seed dark-brown, 2 mm. long. [*V. vincialis* Greene]—Pinelands, Coastal Plain, Fla. to Miss. and Va.

22. **V. incognita** Brainerd. Peduncles, petioles and lower surface of leaf-blades pubescent with soft white hairs especially when young (nearly or quite glabrous in *V. incognita Forbesii*), the upper leaf-surface glabrous; aestival leaves large, the blades rugose, broadly cordate-ovate with open sinus, acute: petals white, the lateral bearded, the upper pair obovate: seed narrowly obovoid, obtuse at base, smooth, brown, 2 mm. long: plants flowering early, in summer producing numerous filiform runners.—Moist woods, Blue Ridge and more northern provinces, Tenn. to N. Dak. and Que.

23. **V. blanda** Willd. Leaf-blades cordate-ovate with narrow sinus, commonly acute, often acuminate, glabrous except for minute scattered hairs on the

upper surface; petioles, and scapes, usually tinged with red: lateral petals beardless, the upper pair often long, narrow, and strongly reflexed, sometimes twisted: cleistogamous capsules ovoid, dark-purple: seed dark-brown, minutely rugose, acute at base, 1.5 mm. long: plants freely producing in summer, slender leafy runners. [*V. LeConteana* G. Don]—(SWEET WHITE-VIOLET.)— Cool ravines and moist shaded slopes, often in humus, various provinces, on Coastal Plain only N, Ga. to Minn. and Que.

24. **V. pallens** (Banks) Brainerd. Leaf-blades broadly cordate-ovate, obtuse or rarely acute, glabrous on both sides; petioles and scapes often dotted with red in summer and more or less hirsutulous: lateral petals usually bearing a small tuft of hairs, the upper petals broadly obovate: seed 1 mm. long, almost black. [*V. blanda* of recent authors, not Willd.]—(WILD WHITE-VIOLET.)—Springy soil and banks of cool streams, various provinces, on Coastal Plain only N, S. C. to Ala., Tenn., Mich., and Lab.—Plants often grow in slow-flowing streams after the manner of water-lilies, the leaves and flowers only raised above the surface of the water. In most cases the plant sinks to the bottom in winter, retaining two or three leaves, and rises again in the spring to bloom.

25. **V. rugosa** Small. Leaf-blades ovate-elliptic, cordate at the base and in the larger leaves decurrent as wings down the petioles, 4–6 cm. long, rugose, sparsely pubescent on the veins, bright green, paler beneath; petioles about as long as the blades, copiously hirsutulous: scapes about as long as the leaves, hirsutulous, usually red: petals all about the same size; the lateral was a small tuft of hairs; the spurred petals veined at the base with brownish-purple: sepals lanceolate: cleistogamous capsule green, about 1 cm. long, on short erect peduncles, ellipsoid, seeds red-brown.—Edges of white-cedar swamps, Liberty Co., Fla.

26. **V. primulifolia** L. Plant often quite glabrous, but usually more or less pubescent especially toward the base of the petioles (with densely villous petioles and lower leaf-surfaces in *V. primulifolia villosa*): leaf-blades elliptic or ovate, the base slightly cordate, rounded or tapering, obscurely crenate-serrate; petioles often broadly winged above: flowers white: capsule green, the peduncle erect as in *V. lanceolata:* seed reddish-brown, 1.5 mm. long.— Marshes and swamps, various provinces, Fla. to Tex., W. Va., and N. B.

27. **V. lanceolata** L. Stolons leafy, often bearing apetalous flowers: leaves and scapes glabrous, 5–8 cm. high at time of vernal flowering; later leaves with lanceolate or elliptic blades, 10–15 mm. wide, 7–15 cm. long, obscurely crenulate, gradually tapering into margined, often reddish, petioles: sepals broadly lanceolate, acute: lateral petals usually beardless: cleistogamous capsules 6–12 mm. long, on erect peduncles but usually shorter than the leaves; seed dark-brown.— (BOG WHITE-VIOLET. LANCELEAF-VIOLET.)—Moist meadows, bogs, and marshes, various provinces, Fla. to Tex., Minn., and N. S.

28. **V. vittata** Greene. First leaf-blades narrowly lanceolate, obtuse, succeeded after flowering by linear leaves 4–10 mm. wide, 15–30 cm. long, the blades acute at the apex and gradually tapering at the base, mucronulately serrulate; petioles, peduncles, and lower leaf-surface usually more or less villous: flowers and capsules as in the preceding species: seed obovoid, brown, 1.3 mm. long. [*V. denticulosa* Pollard]—Marshes, bogs, and borders of hammocks, Coastal Plain, Fla. to Tex. and N. C.

29. **V. rotundifolia** Michx. Rootstock long and stout, jagged with the persistent bases of former leaves: runners short, usually without roots or leaves, bearing 1–4 cleistogamous flowers: leaf-blades oval or orbicular, cordate with

short and narrow sinus, repand-crenate, at vernal flowering sparsely hirtellous, 2–3 cm. wide, in midsummer mostly glabrate, 6–10 cm. wide, prostrate: corolla bright-yellow, the three lower petals with brown veins, the lateral ones bearded: style clavate, abruptly capitate, beakless: capsule ovoid, 6–8 mm. long, closely dotted with purple: seed nearly white.—(EARLY YELLOW-VIOLET.) —Cool woods, various provinces, coastal Plain only N, N Ga. to Ont. and Me.

30. **V. odorata** L.   Plant producing above ground leafy stolons rooting freely at the nodes: leaf-blades broadly cordate-ovate, finely pubescent: flowers violet or white, very fragrant: style hook-shaped: capsules from apetalous flowers broadly ovoid, angled, pubescent, purple: seed large, cream-colored. [*V. Thompsonae* Chapm.] — (SWEET-VIOLET. ENGLISH-VIOLET.) — Roadsides, fence-rows, and waste-places, locally established throughout U. S., as are some of its hybrids with other European species.

31. **V. hastata** Michx.   Plant slightly puberulent: stem slender, 1–2.5 dm. high, from a long white brittle horizontal rootstock: stem-leaves 2–4 near the summit; blades halberd-shaped with rounded basal lobes: radical leaves occasional; blades elliptic-lanceolate, more deeply cordate; all distantly serrulate: sepals linear-lanceolate, acute: corolla yellow, the upper petals often tinged outside with violet: capsule ovoid, glabrous, 8–10 mm. long: stipules ovate, small, often with a few bristly teeth.—Rich woods, various provinces, Fla. to Ala., Ohio, and Pa.

32. **V. tripartita** Ell.   Rootstock short and woody, with long coarse fibrous roots: stem erect, usually solitary, beginning to bear flowers when 1–2 dm. high, bearing foliage above the middle; the first two or three leaves with petioles 2–8 cm. long; blades commonly 3-lobed to 3-divided, ovate or rhombic-ovate merely toothed in *V. tripartita glaberrima* [*V. tenuipes*], the middle segment narrowly lanceolate to ovate, usually constricted at the base, remotely serrate toward the apex, the lateral segments falcate or lunate, coarsely toothed on the outer margin; upper leaves smaller, ovate-lanclate, mostly uncut; petioles and lower leaf-surface more or less pubescent when young, at length nearly glabrate: peduncles slender, 2–9 cm. long, axillary: sepals linear-lanceolate, ciliate: petals yellow, the upper usually tinged outside with violet, the three lower ones somewhat bearded: capsule trigonous-ovoid, glabrous: seed large, brown.—Rich woods, various provinces, N Fla. to Ala., Tenn., and N. C.

33. **V. eriocarpa** Schwein.   Plant glabrous except for minute pubescence along veins on lower leaf-surfaces and on upper parts of petioles and stem: stems ascending, commonly 2–4 from one rootstock: basal leaves 1–5; blades cordate-reniform, on long petioles; cauline leaves only on upper half of stem; blades broadly ovate, subcordate, acuminate, the uppermost smaller, truncate, nearly sessile; stipules ovate to lanceolate, nearly entire, glabrous, tardily scarious: sepals narrowly lanceolate: lateral petals bearded: capsule ovoid, woolly or sometimes glabrous: cleistogamous flowers on short peduncles from axils of upper leaves: seed brown, 2.5 mm. long. [*V. scabriuscula* Schwein.] —(YELLOW-VIOLET.)—Low open woods, various provinces, Coastal Plain only N, Ala. to Okla., Man., and N. S.—This and the following yellow-flowered violets are frequently called WILD-PANSY.

34. **V. pubescens** Ait.   Plant softly pubescent: stems 2–3 dm. high, often solitary: leaves, either cauline, 2–4, near the summit, or occasionally a long-petioled basal-leaf is present; blades broadly ovate, cordate or truncate-decurrent at the base, crenate-dentate, somewhat pointed; stipules large, ovate-elliptic: sepals narrowly lanceolate: lateral petals bearded: capsule ovoid, 10–12 mm. long, glabrous or sometimes woolly: seed brown, 2.5 mm. long.— (DOWNY VIOLET.)—Dry rich woods, various provinces, rarely Coastal Plain, Ala. to Miss., Mo., N. D., N. S., and N. C.

35. **V. canadensis** L. Stems usually 3–4 dm. high, minutely pubescent: leaf-blades cordate-ovate, pointed, serrate; stipules sharply lanceolate: sepals slender, acuminate, spreading: lateral petals bearded, the spurred petal yellow at the base and striped with fine dark lines: capsule subglobose, 6–10 mm. long, often downy or puberulent: seed brown.—(TALL WHITE-VIOLET. SUMMER-VIOLET.)—Rich woods, various provinces, N of Coastal Plain, S. C. to Ala., Sask., Ont., and N. B.

36. **V. striata** Ait. Stems several, ascending, 15–30 cm. long when in flower, in late summer often 6 dm. long, decumbent: leaves glabrous or nearly so; blades cordate-ovate, 2–4 cm. broad, usually acuminate, finely crenate-serrate: stipules large, elliptic-lanceolate: sepals ciliolate, narrow, attenuate: corolla white or cream-colored: style beaked: capsule ovoid, glabrous, 4–6 mm. long: seed light-brown.—(CREAM-VIOLET.)—Low woods and thickets, various provinces, rarely Coastal Plain, Ga. to Mo., Minn., and Conn.

37. **V. conspersa** Reichenb. Rootstock oblique, often much branched: stem, at time of vernal flowering, 8–16 cm. high: lower leaf-blades cordate-orbicular, obtuse, the upper ones cordate-ovate, crenate, subacuminate, becoming 2–4 cm. wide: flowers numerous, usually pale-violet, sometimes white, raised above the leaves on axillary peduncles 5–8 cm. long: cleistogamous flowers in summer on short peduncles from the same axils that bore vernal flowers, or from axils of later leaves of the lengthened stem: style bent downward at the tip and slightly hairy: seed light-brown.—(AMERICAN DOG-VIOLET.)—Low grounds and shaded banks, various provinces, Coastal Plain only N, Ga. to Minn., Que., and Me.

38. **V. Walteri** House. Plant finely puberulent: stems several, at first ascending, leafy, bearing in early spring small violet-blue flowers in the axils of basal leaves, later elongating, becoming prostrate, and bearing through the season apetalous flowers on long slender axillary peduncles: stems often surviving the winter and sending up in spring from their tips rosettes of leaves and petaliferous flowers, afterwards rooting and forming new plants: leaf-blades glabrous, cordate, orbicular to ovate, mostly obtuse, mottled with darker-green bordering the veins, 2–4 cm. wide: stipules bristly fimbriate, 6–10 mm. long: capsule purplish, ovoid-globose, 6 mm. long: seed brown. [*V. multicaulis* (T. & G.) Britton]—Dry woodlands and moist rocky ledges, various provinces, Fla. to Tex., Ky., and S. C.

39. **V. rostrata** Pursh. Stems often numerous, commonly 1–2 dm. high: leaf-blades orbicular to broadly ovate, cordate, nearly or quite glabrous, serrate, the upper acute or pointed: petaliferous flowers borne on long peduncles above the leaves: petals spotted with darker violet, all beardless, the spur slender, 10–12 mm. long: later cleistogamous flowers with minute or aborted petals and on short peduncles from the axils of the upper leaves: style straight, beakless, glabrous: capsule ovoid, 3–5 mm. long, glabrous: seed light-brown.—(BEAKED-VIOLET. LONG-SPURRED VIOLET.)—Shady hillsides and rich woods, various provinces, N of Coastal Plain, Ga. to Ala., Mich., Que., and Pa.

40. **V. Rafinesquii** Greene. Plant glabrous, annual, with the slender stem often branched from the base: leaf-blades small, the lowest 6–10 mm. wide, orbicular, on slender petioles, the upper obovate to linear-oblanceolate, sparsely crenulate, attenuate at the base; stipules pectinately cut, the upper segment elongate, narrowly spatulate, mostly entire; internodes usually exceeding the leaves: flowers small, but the obovate bluish-white to cream-colored petals nearly twice the length of the lanceolate sepals: seed light-brown, 1.2 mm. long.—(FIELD-PANSY.)—Open woods, exposed hillsides, and fields, various provinces, Ga. to Tex., Mich., and N. Y.—The roots have a wintergreen scent.

41. V. arvensis Murr. Similar to the next preceding, but stouter, often 3–4 dm. high, erect or branching and decumbent: leaf-blades ovate to lanceolate, noticeably crenate; stipules more coarsely pectinate, the upper lobe usually much enlarged, oblanceolate and sparsely crenate: petals usually shorter than the lanceolate acute sepals, pale-yellow, or sometimes the upper with violet tips, and the spurred petal deep-yellow at base: capsule globose: seed brown, narrowly obovoid, 1.7 mm. long.—(WILD-PANSY.)—Fields and roadsides, various provinces N of Coastal Plain, N. C. to Ont., and Newf.—Nat. of Eu.

2. **CUBELIUM** Raf. Perennial caulescent, rather tall herbs. Leaves alternate: blades entire or slightly toothed. Flowers borne in axillary clusters, inconspicuous. Sepals 5, nearly equal, not auricled. Petals 5, green, nearly equal in length, the lower one largest and gibbous near the base. Stamens 5, filaments united into a sheath around the pistil and bearing a gland on the lower side. Style hooked at the apex. Capsule longer than thick, slightly 3-lobed, 3-valved.—One species.

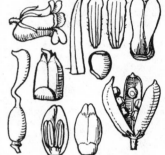

1. **C. concolor** (Forst.) Raf. Stem up to 1 m. tall, pubescent: leaf-blades elliptic or elliptic-obovate, 7–16 cm. long, acuminate or acute at the apex, tapering to a rather slender petiole-like base: sepals linear-subulate or linear-lanceolate, more than half as long as the corolla: lower petal 5–6 mm. long, notched at the apex: connective-tips ovate: capsule ellipsoid or nearly so: 1.5–2 cm. long: seed about 5 mm. in diameter.—(GREEN-VIOLET.)— Rich woods, ravines, and stream-banks, various provinces, rarely Coastal Plain, Ga. to Miss., Kans., Ont., and N. Y.—Spr.

ORDER **PASSIFLORALES** — PASSIFLORAL ORDER

Herbs, vines, or shrubby plants, or succulent tree-like plants with milky sap. Leaves alternate: blades entire, toothed, or lobed. Flowers perfect or dioecious. Calyx of 4 or 5 more or less united sepals. Corolla of 4 or 5 distinct or united petals, sometimes accompanied by a fringed crown, or rarely wanting. Androecium of 5 stamens, or of 10 stamens in 2 unequal rows. Gynoecium of 3–5 united carpels. Ovary superior. Fruit a berry or a capsule.

Corolla not accompanied by a crown: flowers mainly dioecious, the staminate and
   pistillate different.   Fam. 1. PAPAYACEAE.
Corolla accompanied by a crown: flowers perfect, all alike.   Fam. 2. PASSIFLORACEAE.

FAMILY 1. **PAPAYACEAE** — PAPAYA FAMILY

Shrubs or trees. Leaves with ample 7–9-lobed blades. Corolla salverform. Stamens 10: filaments adnate to the corolla-tube. Anthers erect. Fruit baccate, borne near the top of the stem.—Two genera and over 30 species tropical and subtropical.

1. **CARICA** L. Plants with milky juice, the stem rather tender, simple or branched, much-scarred above. Leaf-blades palmately or pinnately lobed.

Staminate flowers in long-peduncled cymes: pistillate flowers in short-peduncled cymes. Berries nearly sessile, many-seeded.—About 25 species, tropical American.—(PAPAYA. PAPAW. CUSTARD-APPLE. MELON-TREE.)— The flowers are sometimes polygamous.

1. **C. Papaya** L. Stem 3–6 m. tall, simple, leafy at the top: leaf-blades 3–6 dm. broad, on stout spreading petioles: corolla yellow or reddish, that of the pistillate flower the larger: berry ellipsoid to subglobose, 2–18 cm. long.—Hammocks, pinelands, and waste-places, pen. Fla. and the Keys. Nat. of Trop. Am.—(*W. I., Mex., C. A., S. A.*)—All year.—Frequently found in wild localities remote from human habitations, but doubtless sown there by birds who greatly relish the seeds. In cultivated forms the fruit is very large. The milky juice of unripe fruit has properties similar to those of pepsin.

FAMILY 2. **PASSIFLORACEAE** — PASSION-FLOWER FAMILY

Herbs, tendril-bearing vines, or shrubby plants. Leaves with entire or lobed, simple, or rarely compound blades. Corolla mostly rotate. Stamens 5: filaments usually monadelphous around the gynoecium. Fruit baccate. —Eighteen genera and about 350 species, most abundant in South America.

1. **PASSIFLORA** L. Perennial vines. Leaf-blades entire, lobed, or parted. Crown filamentous, single, double, or triple. Anthers versatile.— About 300 species, mostly of tropical America.—PASSION-FLOWERS. PASSION-VINES.—Some species are used medicinally; others in ornamental gardening.

Peduncle bearing an involucre of 3 bracts near the calyx.	I. INCARNATAE.
Peduncle without an involucre, or this obscure.	
Petioles without glands.	II. LUTEAE.
Petioles with glands at the middle or near the base of the leaf-blade.	
Peduncles single.	III. SUBEROSAE.
Peduncles clustered.	IV. MULTIFLORAE.

I. INCARNATAE

Leaf-lobes toothed: stipules minute: petiolar glands sessile.	1. *P. incarnata.*
Leaf-lobes entire: stipules foliaceous: petiolar glands stalked.	2. *P. pallens.*

II. LUTEAE

Cymes several-flowered: berry pubescent.	3. *P. sexflora.*
Cymes 1-flowered: berry glabrous.	4. *P. lutea.*

III. SUBEROSAE

Calyx or corolla 2.5–3 cm. wide: leaf-blades, or lobes, toothed.	5. *P. Warmingii.*
Calyx less than 2 cm. wide: leaf-blades, or lobes, not toothed.	6. *P. pallida.*

IV. MULTIFLORAE

Woody tomentose vine, with thick leaf-blades.	7. *P. multiflora.*

1. **P. incarnata** L. Twigs finely pubescent or glabrate: leaf-blades 8–12 cm. long, glabrous or sparingly pubescent, the lobes finely serrate: sepals 25–30

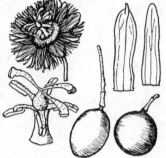

mm. long: petals pale-lavender: crown lavender and purple: berry ellipsoid or oval, 4–
10 cm. long, yellowish: seed 5–6 mm. long.—
(MAY-POP. APRICOT-VINE.)—Dry roadsides,
rocky slopes, and old fields, various provinces,
Fla. to Tex., Mo., and Va.—Spr.–sum.—The
fruit is edible.

2. **P. pallens** Poepp. Twigs glabrous, glaucous: leaf-blades nearly equally 3-lobed, 4–8
cm. long, the lobes ovate, the terminal one
usually slightly larger than the others: stipules foliaceous, ovate to reniform: sepals
lanceolate to linear-lanceolate, 20–30 cm.
long, white or greenish-white: corolla wanting: berry 4–5 cm. long, yellow.—Ham-
mocks, Everglade Keys and Cape Sable region, Fla.—(W. I.)—All year.

3. **P. sexflora** Juss. Twigs tomentulose: leaf-blades 6–14 cm. broad, pubescent: cymes several-flowered: sepals 9–11 mm. long: corolla greenish-white:
berry globular, 9–11 mm. in diameter, greenish-purple, pubescent: seed about
2.5 mm. long.—Hammocks, Everglade Keys, Fla.—(W. I.)—All year.

4. **P. lutea** L. Twigs finely pubescent or glabrous: leaf-blades 3–15 cm.
broad, mostly obtuse, glabrous: cymes 1-flowered: sepals 8–12 mm. long: corolla
greenish-yellow, about 2 cm. broad: berry 10–15 mm. in diameter, purple-black.
—(YELLOW PASSION-FLOWER.)—Rich woods and thickets, various provinces, Fla.
to Tex., Kans., and Pa.—Spr.–sum.

5. **P. Warmingii** Mast. Twigs sparingly fine-hirsute: leaf-blades 5–14 cm. in
diameter; lobes triangular or ovate, remotely toothed: sepals lanceolate, 18–21
mm. long: corolla pale-yellow, 2.5–3 cm. broad: berry globular, 25–30 mm.
long, white-hairy: seed 4.5–5 mm. long, wrinkled.—Thickets and woods, near
Clemson College, in the Piedmont of S. C.   Nat. of Brazil.—Spr.–sum.

6. **P. pallida** L. Twigs glabrous or minutely pubescent: leaf-blades entire to
3-lobed, mostly 2–10 cm. long: calyx greenish; sepals linear to lanceolate or
elliptic, 7–9 mm. long: corolla wanting: berry 6–10 mm. in diameter, purple-
black: seeds 2.5–3 mm. long. [*Passiflora suberosa* L. *P. minima* L. *P. angustifolia* Sw.]—(CORKY-STEMMED PASSION-FLOWER.)—Hammocks and pinelands, pen. Fla. and the Keys.—(W. I., C. A., S. A.)—The older stems frequently develop broad corky wings.

7. **P. multiflora** L. Twigs velvety: leaf-blades elliptic or nearly so, 5–12 cm.
long, entire, rugose beneath: sepals 5–6 mm. long, yellow-green: petals linear
or nearly so, white: berry subglobose, 6–8 mm. in diameter, purplish-black.—
Hammocks, S pen. Fla. and the Keys.—(W. I.)—The old stems are frequently
covered with a thick corky bark.

ORDER **OPUNTIALES** — OPUNTIAL ORDER

Succulent, typically spine-armed, herbs, shrubs, or trees, mainly leafless
or essentially so, or leafy rigid herbs, with more or less specialized hairs.
Flowers perfect. Hypanthium present. Calyx of 4 or 5, or many, sepals.
Corolla of 4 or 5, or many, stamens, in several series or groups, sometimes
partially reduced to staminodia. Gynoecium of 4, or 2–several, united
carpels. Ovary inferior. Fruit baccate or capsular.

Sepals and petals 4 or 5 each, very different: leaves with entire or dissected blades:
  erect or climbing plants, with rigid hairs.   Fam. 1. LOASACEAE.
Sepals and petals nearly alike, at least the latter numer-
  ous: leaves typically mere scales or wanting: succulent
  plants, usually armed with spines.   Fam. 2. OPUNTIACEAE.

FAMILY 1. **LOASACEAE** — LOASA FAMILY

Rigid herbs with barbed or stinging hairs. Leaves with entire lobed, pinnatifid, or dissected blades.—About 20 genera and 250 species, mostly American.

1. MENTZELIA [Plum.] L. Brittle-stemmed, mostly diffuse or reclining herbs. Leaf-blades relatively broad, sinuate or lobed. Androecium without staminodia. Seeds angled.—About 35 species, American.

1. M. floridana Nutt. Leaf-blades 2–9 cm. long, ovate to deltoid-ovate toothed and 3-lobed: sepals lanceolate, often very broad at the base: petals golden-yellow, 15–18 mm. long: capsule 1–1.5 cm. long.—(POOR-MAN'S PATCHES. STICK-LEAF. BLAZING-STAR.)— Hammocks, sand-dunes, and shell-mounds, pen. Fla. and the Keys.—(*W. I.*)—Spr.-fall or all year S.—The barbed hairs on the leaves cause them to adhere very closely to clothing. They are also very effective in cutting off the feet and legs of small insects that alight on them.

FAMILY 2. **OPUNTIACEAE** — CACTUS FAMILY

Shrubs or trees with more or less succulent tissues over a woody framework, the stem depressed or elongate, simple or branched, continuous or jointed, terete, fluted, or flattened, usually armed with spines which arise from cushions (areolae) of hairs or minute stiff bristles. Leaves rudimentary, obsolete, or wanting, or rarely well-developed. Flower solitary, often showy, diurnal or nocturnal. Calyx of several or numerous sepals. Corolla of few or many white or colored (except blue) petals. Androecium of numerous stamens in several series. Gynoecium of several united carpels. Ovary inferior, with the hypanthium often much produced beyond it, 1-celled, with several parietal placentae. Styles united. Stigmas clustered. Fruit a fleshy berry, either spiny or scaly, hairy or naked.—About 100 genera and over 1,200 species, American.—Many of the plants are used for foods and for ornamental gardening.

Plant copiously leafy, the leaves with broad blades, persistent.   I. PERESKIEAE.
Plants leafless, or leaves obsolete or rudimentary, mere suc-
  culent scale-like deciduous structures.
  Plants conspicuously jointed, sometimes loosely so, the
    internodes (joints) relatively short, more or less flat-
    tened: leaves mere thick deciduous scale-like structures:
    areolae with barbed bristles and often with single or
    clustered spines: hypanthium not prolonged beyond the
    ovary, deciduous from the ovary with a clean scar leav-
    ing a flat or more or less depressed umbilicus.   II. OPUNTIEAE.
  Plants inconspicuously jointed, the internodes (joints)
    terete, grooved, or angled: leaves none or obsolete:
    areolae without bristles, but spine-bearing: hypan-
    thium much prolonged beyond the ovary, persistent
    on the fruit or rotting off irregularly, or very short.

Flower rotate: hypanthium not prolonged: perianth of few sepals and petals. III. Rhipsalideae.

Flower funnelform, trumpet-shaped, or narrowly campanulate: hypanthium much prolonged: perianth of numerous sepals and petals. IV. Cereeae.

I. Pereskieae

Climbing or reclining plants with broad leaves and a pair of reflexed spines at each areola which is devoid of bristles: flowers stalked. 1. Pereskia.

II. Opuntieae

Plant prostrate or with erect diffusely branched stems, without a continuous terete trunk: seed glabrous. 2. Opuntia.

Plant with erect terete unjointed trunks: seed pubescent.

Trunk supporting dimorphous branches, the lateral ones terete, the succeeding ones flat: hypanthium short and terete: corolla with narrow, loosely spreading petals: berry subglobose. 3. Brasiliopuntia.

Trunk supporting all flat irregularly placed branches: hypanthium elongate, flattened, resembling a small joint: corolla with broad, short, closely imbricate petals: berry elongate. 4. Consolea.

III. Rhipsalideae

Pendent much-branched epiphyte with small white flowers. 5. Rhipsalis.

IV. Cereeae

Stem and branches unequally 3–5-angled, not terete: berry persistently scaly or spiny.

Hypanthium scaly and hairy, the scales subtending tufts of hairs. 6. Selenicereus.

Hypanthium scaly or spiny, but not hairy.

Hypanthium scaly: berry more or less clothed with broad scales: plant climbing with aerial roots. 7. Hylocereus.

Hypanthium spiny: berry armed with clusters of spines: plant erect, diffuse, or reclining. 8. Acanthocereus.

Stem and branches terete in outline, more or less fluted: berry neither persistently scaly or spiny.

Flower trumpet-shaped: hypanthium elongate, copiously scaly at the base: sepals and petals long and narrow: berry with stout scale-bases and often tufts of hair. 9. Harrisia.

Flower narrowly campanulate: hypanthium short, naked at the base: sepals and petals broad and short: berry naked and glabrous. 10. Cephalocereus.

1. PERESKIA Plum. Woody and partly succulent vines with reclining or clambering stems and branches with spines at the leaf-axils. Leaves alternate: blades broad, flat, entire, short-petioled. Flowers often panicled. Hypanthium depressed, smooth or scaly. Sepals narrow. Corolla rotate: petals relatively few and broad, white or colored, broader than the sepals. Stamens numerous. Berry pyriform to subglobose, translucent, sometimes scaly.—About 20 species, tropical American.

1. **P. Pereskia** (L.) Karst. Stems and branches reclining or clambering, elongate, glabrous: leaf-blades ovate to lanceolate-elliptic, 4–9 cm. long, often acute or abruptly pointed, coriaceous, short-petioled: flowers very fragrant: sepals lanceolate, 1–1.5 cm. long, recurved: corolla 3.5–4 cm. wide: petals ovate-lanceolate, elliptic, or elliptic-obovate, the outer green, the inner white or nearly so, or sometimes yellowish or pinkish: berry subglobose, yellowish, 1–1.5 cm. in diameter, smooth in age: seeds 3–4 mm. in diameter. [*P. aculeata* Mill.] —(West-Indian gooseberry. Lemon-vine. Barbados-gooseberry.)—Hammocks, thickets, and woods, S pen. Fla. Nat. of trop. Am.—Although frequently grown as an ornamental, the fruits are eaten raw or as a preserve and the leaves as a pot-herb.

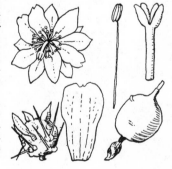

2. OPUNTIA [Tourn.] Mill. Shrubs or trees, the trunk of fused joints, more or less irregular, usually widely or diffusely branched, the branches (joints) flat, armed at the areolae with solitary or clustered spines which arise from among clusters of bristles, or spineless. Leaves small, fleshy, thick scales, deciduous. Flowers large, at least relatively so, solitary or several on a joint. Hypanthium broadened upward, with areolae like the joints. Sepals fleshy, mostly green. Petals broad, usually broadened upward. Berries longer than thick, enlarged upward, mostly fleshy. Seeds flattened, cochleate, with even edges and glabrous sides.—About 260 species, American.—PRICKLY-PEARS. DEVIL'S PINCUSHIONS. TUNAS. DEVIL'S-TONGUES.—The fruits of prickly-pears are edible. They formed an important food-supply for the aborigines, who also used the stems as food by roasting them. The fruits are much used for food in some countries to-day. In the following descriptions the color of the spine is first stated for the immature stage, followed by the mature stage when dry and the mature stage when wet.

Joints of the stem and of the branches loosely attached, readily separating when shocked or touched, or even when blown by the wind, at least in the case of the smaller plants: fruits early deciduous: plants of some species often propagating only by the easily separating joints.
    Spines acicular, gray or salmon-colored the first year, when dry.
      Longer spines of each areola solitary or paired, gray
        the first year, when dry.   I. CURASSAVICAE.
      Longer spines of each areola several, salmon-colored
        the first year, gray the second year, when dry.   II. PISCIFORMES.
    Spines subulate, ivory-white the first year, gray the
      second year, when dry.   III. TUNAE.
Joints of the stem and of the branches firmly attached:
    fruits persistent.
    Joints glabrous; spines acicular to elongate-subulate:
      very rigid, or wanting; hypanthium with few
      areolae.
      Plants with spine-armed joints.
        Mature spines gray when dry, at least in the
          second year.
          Mature plants prostrate or erect and diffuse,
            often bushy; spines gray, or white, or
            yellow the first year, becoming gray at
            maturity, when dry.
            Spines bright-yellow the first year, gray the
              second year.   IV. OCHROCENTRAE.
            Spines gray the first year or white the first
              year and gray the second.   V. TORTISPINAE.
          Mature plants erect, with the joints of the
            main stem fused into a subterete trunk
            which divides above into a few or many
            branches: spines red the first year, becoming
            gray at maturity, when dry.   VI. AMMOPHILAE.
        Mature spines yellow, red, or red-brown when dry,
          unchanged from year to year, uniform, discolored or banded.
          Mature spines yellow or slightly discolored,
           often stout and clustered, sometimes curved,
           rarely very short and then mostly hidden in
           the areolae, not closely spirally twisted.   VII. DILLENIANAE.
          Mature spines red or red-brown, banded in our
           species, closely spirally twisted.   VIII. ELATIORES.
      Plants with unarmed joints.
        Joints thin oh thinnish, with persistent bristles
         in the areolae: berries small, less than 5 cm.
         long.   V. TORTISPINAE.
        Joints thick and turgid, with deciduous or obsolete bristles in the areolae: berries large, over
         5 cm. long.   IX. FICUS-INDICAE.
Joints pubescent: spines setaceous, pliable: hypanthium
    with numerous areolae.   X. LEUCOTRICHAE.

I. Curassavicae

Larger joints broad, obovate, oval, suborbicular, or sub-globose: spines setaceous-acicular, exceptionally long and slender: berry urceolate, tuberculate. — 1. *O. abjecta.*

Larger joints elliptic, linear-elliptic, spatulate, or subcylindric: spines acicular-subulate: berry of a turbinate, obovoid or clavate type.

Joints mostly subcylindric, only slightly flattened, repand-tuberculate: berry narrowly turbinate or clavate-turbinate. — 2. *O. Tracyi.*

Joints decidedly flattened, although often quite turgid, not repand: berry obovoid to obconic-turbinate or clavate.

Corolla lemon-yellow: joints deep-green: spines dark-gray: berry narrowly obovoid to obconic-turbinate, less than twice as long as thick. — 3. *O. Drummondii.*

Corolla bright-yellow: joints pale-green: spines light-gray: berry clavate, over twice as long as thick. — 4. *O. impedita.*

II. Pisciformes

Plants in dense colonies with turgid very spiny narrow, deep-green joints, the spines conspicuously long and slender, salmon-colored in the first year, gray in the second: flowers numerous, bright-yellow: berry turbinate-obovoid, 4 cm. long or less. — 5. *O. pisciformis.*

III. Tunae

Plants in depressed colonies with conspicuously spiny broad pale-green joints, the spines conspicuously short and stout, white in the first year, gray in the second: flowers few, clear-yellow: berry obovoid, 2 cm. long or less. — 6. *O. eburnispina.*

IV. Ochrocentrae

Plants erect and diffusely branched, with rather narrow light-green joints: spines stout, bright-yellow in the first year, gray in the second. — 7. *O. ochrocentra.*

V. Tortispinae

Plants prostrate, the stem and branches often forming depressed mats or colonies of joints.

Plants not armed with spines.

Joints narrow, much longer than wide, thick or turgid: berry 4–6 cm. long. — 8. *O. macrarthra.*

Joints broad, little longer than wide, usually thinnish:

Joints deep-green: berry clavate-obovoid or narrowly obconic. — 9. *O. Opuntia.*

Joints bluish-green: berry obovoid: — 10. *O. Pollardi.*

Plants spine-armed, the spines mostly solitary in an areola.

Mature joints broad, not much longer than wide.

Joints dull, deep-green or bluish-green: inner sepals not reniform: corolla 6 cm. wide or more: mature spines gray in the first and second years: inner petals longer than wide.

Joints deep-green: berry clavate-obovoid or narrowly obconic: spines dark-gray, slender. — 9. *O. Opuntia.*

Joints bluish-green: berry obovoid: spines pale-gray, stout. — 10. *O. Pollardi.*

Joints shining: inner sepals reniform: corolla 5 cm. wide or less: mature spines ivory-white in the first year, gray in the second: inner petals nearly or quite as wide as long. — 11. *O. atrocapensis.*

Mature joints narrow, often elongate.

Intermediate sepals ovate; inner sepals merely acute: berry obconic-obovoid: seed usually less than 5 mm. in diameter. — 8. *O. macrarthra.*

Intermediate sepals lanceolate; inner sepals abruptly acuminate: berry clavate, constricted at the base: seed usually over 5 mm. in diameter. — 12. *O. lata.*

Plants erect, often diffusely branched, sometimes forming thickets.

Plants not armed with spines.

Hypanthium elongate: leaves spreading and recurved: berry broadly obovoid, nearly or quite as wide as long: seeds about 4 mm. in diameter.   13. *O. turgida.*

Hypanthium about as wide as long: leaves ascending: berry ellipsoid-obovoid, much longer than wide: seeds about 6 mm. in diameter.   14. *O. polycarpa.*

Plants armed with single or clustered spines at the areolae.

Mature spines (first year) gray, darker gray the second year.

Young spines mainly pale-yellow: berry rounded at the base: seeds 6 mm. in diameter.   14. *O. polycarpa.*

Young spines brown: berry narrowed, often constricted at the base: seeds 4 mm. in diameter.   15. *O. nitens.*

Mature spines (first year) white, becoming gray the second year.

Corolla 6–7 cm. wide: spines 2–4 cm. long: berry narrowly obovoid, 2.5–3.5 cm. long.   16. *O. austrina.*

Corolla 8–10 cm. wide: spines 5–7 cm. long: berry broadly obovoid, 4–5 cm. long.   17. *O. cumulicola.*

VI. AMMOPHILAE

Plants tree-like, the stout or stocky trunk divided above into few or many divergent branching joints, sometimes semaphore-like: joints gray-green, usually copiously armed.   18. *O. ammophila.*

VII. DILLENIANAE

Spines subulate to acicular, rigid, spreading.

Areolae bearing 4–13 short-subulate spines which seldom exceed the bristles, the joints thus apparently unarmed: corolla campanulate or cupulate.   19. *O. keyensis.*

Areolae bearing 2–6 long spines which much exceed the bristles, the joints thus conspicuously armed (individually sometimes unarmed): corolla rotate, except in *O. tenuiflora.*

Corolla campanulate: hypanthium and berry contracted into a long slender base, thus decidedly clavate.   20. *O. tenuiflora.*

Corolla rotate: hypanthium and berry not contracted into a long slender base.

Berry decidedly longer than thick, the umbilicus depressed.

Hypanthium long-turbinate or obconic-turbinate, much longer than its greatest diameter.

All the areolae armed with a cluster of spines.

Intermediate and inner sepals acute: berry more or less constricted at the base: seeds large, 5–6 mm. in diameter.   21. *O. Dillenii.*

Intermediate and inner sepals truncate or emarginate: berry not constricted at the base: seeds small, 3–4 mm. in diameter.   22. *O. Lindheimeri.*

Some of the areolae armed with 1, 2, or 3 spines.   23. *O. stricta.*

Hypanthium short-turbinate or obovoid-turbinate, slightly longer than the greatest diameter.

Outer sepals of a deltoid type; intermediate sepals reniform or rhombic-reniform, rounded and minutely pointed.   24. *O. Bentonii.*

Outer sepals of a reniform type: intermediate sepals papilionaceous, emarginate.   25. *O. tunoidea.*

Berry globose-turbinate, nearly or quite as thick as long, the umbilicus convex.   26. *O. turbinata.*

Spines acicular-setaceous, weak and pliable, sparse, reflexed or recurved.

Joints short, orbicular to orbicular-obovate, the larger ones 1–1.5 cm. long: leaves subulate, recurved-spreading.   27. *O. cantabrigiensis.*

Joints elongate, elliptic, oval or narrowly obovate, the larger ones 3–5 dm. long: leaves loosely ascending.   28. *O. magnifica.*

VIII. ELATIORES

Plants erect, but diffusely branched: spines banded: hypanthium broadly turbinate: berry broadly obovoid, not
constricted at the base.   29. *O. zebrina.*

IX. FICUS-INDICAE

Plants very robust, more or less tree-like, the thick joints
supported on the subterete trunk, mostly about 3 dm.
long: corolla large, mostly 8–10 cm. wide: berry red or
orange, said to be sometimes yellow.   30. *O. Ficus-Indica.*

X. LEUCOTRICHAE

Plants erect, often with the joints of the main stem fused
into a trunk, the older parts especially, clothed with
white hair-like bristles: joints with numerous, rather
close-set areolae: hypanthium with numerous areolae:
berry aromatic.   31. *O. leucotricha.*

1. O. abjecta Small.   Plant prostrate, often growing in large irregular patches
on almost bare limestone or where some sand and humus has collected, very
irregularly branched, often with small tuber-
ous roots: joints suborbicular, sometimes
nearly subglobose, oval or broadly obovate,
mostly 4–8 cm. long, very thick, frequently
very turgid, light-green, often much-
branched, loosely attached to each other:
leaves ovoid to conic-ovoid, 2–3 mm. long,
ascending and slightly curved upward, green
or purplish, accompanied by fine bristles, but
without spines: areolae not very conspicuous: spines acicular, mostly solitary, brown,
mottled light and dark, becoming chalky-
gray when dry, reddish-purple, except the
paler and more or less mottled distal part
when wet, the larger ones 2–6 cm. long:
flowers usually solitary on a joint: hypanthium turbinate: sepals green, the outer
subulate-lanceolate, 5–8 mm. long, acute: corolla light-yellow, 2.5–3.5 cm. wide;
petals few, obovate, usually minutely pointed: berry urceolate, 2–2.5 cm. long,
somewhat tuberculate, red or purple-red, rounded at the base, the umbilicus
relatively very broad, concave: seeds few, flattish, about 4 mm. wide.—Hammock, S end of Big Pine Key, Fla.—Although the plants of this species flower
and fruit in their native haunts, they have thus far failed to flower in cultivation.

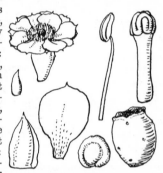

2. O. Tracyi Britton.   Plant similar to that of *O. Drummondii,* but usually
more diminutive; joints narrowly ellipsoid to narrowly cylindric, more or less
flattened, 2.5–8 cm. long or longer and worm-like, bright-green, very loosely
attached to each other: leaves green, ovoid, sometimes narrowly so, sometimes
accompanied by the young spines: areolae small but conspicuous, usually all
of them armed: spines solitary or 2–4 together, pink, at maturity light-gray
when dry, brown or purple-brown when wet, slightly flattened: flowers 1 or 2
on a joint: hypanthium turbinate-obconic: sepals sometimes purple-tinged,
the outer subulate, the intermediate triangular, the inner rhombic-ovate: corolla
bright-yellow, nearly similar to that of *O. Drummondii:* berry narrowly turbinate to clavate-turbinate, 3–4 cm. long, purple, the umbilicus depressed: seeds
few, 5–5.5 mm. in diameter, flattish.—Sand-dunes and sandy woods near the
coast, N E Fla. and S E Ga. to Miss.

3. O. Drummondii Graham.   Plant prostrate, diminutive and scattered in the
sand, or diffusely sprawling, sometimes forming depressed mats by the copious
branching and hanging together by the armament, tuberous: joints ellipsoid,

usually narrowly so, or slightly broadest above the middle or below it, thick or turgid and sometimes globular, 2–12 cm. long, light-green or pale-green, loosely attached to each other: leaves stout-subulate or ovoid-subulate, 3–6 mm. long, ascending and slightly recurved, green, unaccompanied by prominent bristles or spines: areolae inconspicuous, the upper ones, at least, armed: spines slender-subulate, solitary or 2, 3, or 4 together, pink, reddish, or red, at maturity gray, often dark-gray, except the sometimes darker tip, when dry, purple-black when wet, nearly terete: flowers usually solitary on a joint: hypanthium obconic: sepals green, the outer linear-subulate to lanceolate, 5–9 mm. long, acute or acuminate, the intermediate triangular-ovate to rhombic-ovate, acuminate, the inner orbicular-ovate above the broad claw-like base, about 2 cm. long, abruptly pointed: corolla lemon-yellow, 5–6 cm. wide: petals few, broadly obovate, truncate and emarginate at the apex and mucronate: anthers fully 2 mm. long: berry narrowly obovoid to obconic-turbinate, 2.5–3.5 cm. long, reddish purple, the umbilicus concave: seeds few, turgid, about 5 mm. in diameter. [*O. frustulenta* Gibbes. *O. Pes-Corvi* LeConte]—Sand-dunes and pinelands, outer part of Coastal Plain, Fla. to Miss. and N. C.— This and the next preceding species are so thoroughly disguised in connection with their habitats that the loosely articulated joints are frequently to be found adhering to one's clothing before they are noticed on the ground.

4. **O. impedita** Small. Plants closely prostrate, ultimately copiously branched, the joints often piled several layers deep and forming viciously armed mats, elliptic or nearly so, mostly 7–15 cm. long, rather thick, light-green: leaves stout-subulate, 4–6 mm. long, erect or ascending, slightly curved upward, dark-green, unaccompanied by exserted bristles or spines: spines stoutish, usually numerous, solitary or 2 together, pale-gray, except the brown at the tip when dry, salmon-colored and faintly banded when wet: flowers often several on a joint, numerous: hypanthium obconic, nearly terete and even: sepals green, the outer lanceolate to ovate, 4–8 mm. long, acuminate, the inner much larger, with the shoulders of the very broad body narrowed into the stoutish tip: corolla bright-yellow, 4.5–5.5 cm. wide; petals several, about 12, about 2.5–3 cm. long, broadly obovate to cuneate-obovate, broadly rounded at the apex, mostly mucronate; anthers nearly 2 mm. long: berry clavate, about 3 cm. long, rounded at the base, the umbilicus rather small, somewhat concave: seeds rather few, 4–4.5 mm. in diameter. [By error first published as *O. impedata*.]—Sand-dunes, Coastal Plain, N E Fla. to N. C.

5. **O. pisciformis** Small. Plant prostrate, copiously branched forming dense mats often 1–3 m. in diameter, with the joints piled several layers deep, with sparingly tuberous-thickened roots: joints narrowly elliptic, linear-elliptic, or spatulate, mostly 1–3 dm. long, very thick, deep-green: leaves stout-subulate, 2–4 mm. long, incurved, acute: areolae rather prominent, mostly armed: spines solitary or 2 or 3 together, cream-colored, becoming salmon-colored and gray with a dark tip when dry, salmon when wet, the longer ones 5–6 cm. long: flowers numerous: hypanthium turbinate, angular and tuberculate: sepals green, the outer lanceolate to triangular-lanceolate, 9–12 mm. long, acuminate, the inner much larger, the broad ovate or suborbicular base broadly tapering into the very stout tip: corolla bright-yellow, 6–7.5 cm. wide: petals several, about 12, 3–4 cm. long, broadly cuneate, mostly truncate or emarginate at the apex, mucronate: anthers nearly 2 mm. long: berry broadly turbinate-obovoid, 3.5–4 cm. long, purple, narrowed at the base, the umbilicus deeply concave: seeds rather numerous, 5–5.5 mm. in diameter.—Sand-dunes, estuary of the Saint Johns River, Fla.—This and the next preceding species are vigorous growers and loose-jointed. This combination causes plants to form disorderly masses of joints often a foot high.

6. **O. eburnispina** Small. Plant prostrate, widely branched and forming mats on the dune sands, with tuberous roots: joints oval or suborbicular, varying

to broadest above the middle, thickish, 6–13 cm. long, light-green, somewhat shining, especially when young: leaves ovoid-subulate, 4–5 mm. long, pale green, recurved-spreading: spines relatively stout, 2–4 together or sometimes solitary, 1–2 cm. long, ivory-white with yellowish tips when young, becoming dark-gray, not spirally twisted, greenish when wet: flowers few: hypanthium obconic: sepals triangular, green, 5–7 mm. long: corolla yellow, 4–5 cm. wide; petals few, narrowly cuneate, often minutely pointed: anthers nearly 1.5 mm. long: berry obovoid, about 2 cm. long, red, the umbilicus depressed: seed few, 3–3.5 mm. in diameter, flattish.—Coastal sands, Romano Island, Fla.—The numerous ivory-white spines contrasted against the green joints render patches of the plants very conspicuous.

7. O. ochrocentra Small. Plant erect, 1 m. tall or less, much-branched, sometimes more or less diffuse, with coarse fibrous or somewhat swollen roots: joints elliptic to oval, varying to broadest above the middle, 1–3 dm. long, thickish, bright-green: leaves ovoid or subulate-ovoid, 2–4 mm. long, often pink or purplish, acute, erect or slightly spreading: areolae rather prominent, armed: spines 5–6 together or sometimes fewer on new joints, yellow, becoming gray when dry, yellowish-green when wet, straight, the longer ones 4.5–5 cm. long: flowers rather few: hypanthium turbinate or obovoid-turbinate: sepals often purple tinged, deltoid to rhombic-orbicular or rhombic-reniform, acute: corolla bright lemon-yellow, 7–8.5 cm. wide, usually rotate: petals few, cuneate to obovate, notched at the apex or with a minute tip: anthers about 2 mm. long: berry obovoid-pyriform, 2–3.5 cm. long, red to red-purple, sometimes slightly constricted at the base: seeds numerous, 2.5–3 mm. long.—On edge of hammock, S E end of Big Pine Key and Cape Romano, Fla.

8. O. macrarthra Gibbes. Plant prostrate, the young growth sometimes ascending, rather sparingly branched, but seldom forming mats, conspicuous on account of its long, thick, smooth joints, with fibrous roots: joints elliptic to broadly linear, sometimes broadened upward, mostly 15–35 cm. long, very thick, shining, light-green: leaves ovoid-subulate, green, 5–8 mm. long, nearly straight: areolae few and distant, mostly unarmed: spines, when present, solitary, slender-subulate, brown, except the pale tip, becoming gray when dry, straw-colored when wet, 1.5–3.5 cm. long: flowers few, rarely several on a joint: hypanthium obconic, 4–4.5 cm. long: sepals mostly green, the outer subulate to lanceolate, 7–14 cm. long, acute, the intermediate triangular-lanceolate to deltoid, the inner ovate to rhombic-ovate, acute: corolla rotate, bright-yellow, 6–7 cm. wide; petals broadly cuneate-obovate to obovate, 3–3.5 cm. long, rounded at the apex, mucronate, broad at the base: anthers about 3 mm. long: berry narrowly obovoid or clavate-obovoid, 4–6 cm. long, red or red-purple, the umbilicus concave: seeds relatively few, 4–4.5 mm. in diameter, flattish.—Sand-dunes, coast of S. C. and N. C.

9. O. Opuntia (L.) Karst. Plant prostrate, the new growth sometimes ascending, with fibrous roots, often forming extensive bright-green mats: joints obovate, varying to suborbicular or elliptic, 5–18 cm. long, deep-green, often somewhat shining: leaves stout-subulate, 5–7 mm. long, often purple-tinged, ascending, nearly straight, usually unaccompanied by spines: areolae inconspicuous: spines when present pinkish, becoming dark-gray when dry, dark brown when wet: hypanthium obconic, somewhat angled: sepals mostly green, the outer subulate to lanceolate, 4–9 mm. long, acute, or abruptly sharp-tipped, the intermediate ovate-lanceolate, acuminate, the inner rhombic-obovate, abruptly pointed: corolla rotate, bright-yellow or sometimes reddish at the center, 5–8 cm. wide: petals few, 8–10, broadly obovate to broadly cuneate-obovate, about 3–4 cm. long, rounded or emarginate and erose at the apex, mucronate; anthers 2.5–3 mm. long: berry narrowly obovoid to clavate-obovoid, 2.5–5 cm. long, red or purple-red, the umbilicus concave: seeds 4–5 mm. in diameter.—(ATLANTIC PRICKLY-PEAR.)—Sandy or rocky places, various provinces, Coastal Plain only N, Ga. to Ala., N. Y. and Mass. Has been confused with *O. vulgaris* Mill., a South American plant.

10. **O. Pollardi** Britton & Rose. Plant prostrate, forming irregular mats, somewhat tuberous: joints suborbicular or oval, varying to broadly obovate, usually quite thick, 10–15 cm. long, or sometimes smaller, deep-green beneath the more or less glaucous surface, dull: leaves ovoid, 3–4 mm. long, erect or appressed, slightly incurved, deep-green, unaccompanied by bristles or spines: areolae rather conspicuous, much scattered, some of the upper ones, at least, usually armed: spines stout, usually solitary, yellowish or pinkish, becoming pale-gray at maturity when dry, cinnamon-brown when wet: hypanthium obovoid or obconic-obovoid, uneven: sepals green, the outer ovate to deltoid, 2–12 mm. long, acute, the inner cuneate-obovate, abruptly pointed or mucronate: corolla 5–7 cm. wide, bright-yellow: petals few, 7–10, cuneate, sometimes broadly so, 2.5–3 cm. long, notched and often mucronulate at the apex: anthers about 1.5–2 mm. long: berry obovoid, 2.5–3 cm. long, purple, the umbilicus concave: seeds sometimes rather numerous, 5–6 mm. in diameter, turgid.—Pinelands, sand-dunes, and rarely oak woods, Coastal Plain, Fla. to Miss. and Del.

11. **O. atrocapensis** Small. Plant diffusely prostrate, sometimes assurgent at the tip, much-branched, the decumbent branches with fibrous (?) roots: joints obovate, elliptic, or broadly oval, 0.5–1 dm. long, deep-green, sometimes shining, not glaucous: leaves stout-subulate, 2–4 mm. long: areolae small, often armed: spines usually solitary, light-yellow, becoming white or finally gray when dry, straw-colored and often brown-mottled when wet, the longer ones 2–3.5 cm. long: hypanthium obconic, 2–2.5 cm. long, nearly even, blunt at the base: sepals green, the outer ovoid to triangular-lanceolate, 3–7 mm. long, acute, the inner deltoid, about 1 cm. long, acute: corolla pale-yellow, 4.5–5 cm. wide: petals few, 8–10, oval to suborbicular, 2–3 cm. long, rounded or notched at the apex, crisped, somewhat mucronate, rounded or truncate at the base: anthers nearly 2 mm. long: berry narrowly obovoid, 3–3.5 cm. long, reddish-purple, many-seeded, the umbilicus depressed: seeds 3–3.5 mm. in diameter, flat.—Sand-dunes, Cape Sable, Fla.

12. **O. lata** Small. Plant prostrate, often radially branched, sometimes forming mats nearly a meter across, the tips of the branches sometimes assurgent, with elongate cord-like roots: joints elliptic to narrowly obovate, often narrowly so, thick, 0.4–1.5 dm. long, deep-green, sometimes glaucous, especially when young: leaves subulate, 6–11 mm. long, green or purple-tinged: areolae scattered, often conspicuous, sometimes very prominent and densely bristly, the marginal ones, at least, armed: spines slender, solitary or 2 together, pink, turning red or red-banded, at maturity gray or nearly white when dry, pale stramineous when wet: hypanthium obconic to clavate: sepals green, the outer subulate to lanceolate, acute, the intermediate lanceolate to triangular-lanceolate, acuminate, the inner rhombic, abruptly acuminate: corolla yellow, 7–9 cm. wide; petals rather numerous, the outer broadly cuneate-flabellate, the inner ones broadly obovate to flabellate or suborbicular, erose at the broad minutely mucronate apex: anthers about 3 mm. long: berry clavate, 5–6.5 cm. long, red or red-purple, many-seeded, the umbilicus concave: seeds about 5–6 mm. in diameter.—Pinelands, lime-sink region, Fla.

13. **O. turgida** Small. Plant erect, more or less diffusely branched, 0.5 m. tall or less, with fibrous roots: joints elliptic to elliptic-obovate, 5–12 cm. long, thickish, deep-green, sometimes slightly glaucous when young: leaves subulate, 6–10 mm. long, spreading and more or less recurved, green, sometimes accompanied by fine bristles, but without spines: areolae scattered, often

prominent and densely bristly on the older joints: spines (as far as known) wanting: flowers often several on a joint: hypanthium obovoid or obconic-obovoid, 2–2.5 cm. long, slightly tubercled: sepals green or purple-tinged, the outer subulate to lanceolate, 4–10 mm. long, acute, the inner rhombic-ovate, fully 1.5 cm. long, stout-pointed: corolla bright-yellow, 5.5–6.5 cm. wide: petals 10–12, about 3 cm. long, broadly cuneate, abruptly narrowed, rounded or subtruncate at the apex, mucronate: anthers 2 mm. long: berry obovoid, 2–2.5 cm. long, greenish-purple, even, broadly rounded at the base, the umbilicus flat or a little depressed at the middle: seeds rather numerous, about 4 mm. in diameter, somewhat turgid.—Hammocks on the mainland along the Halifax River to the St. Mary's River, Fla.

14. O. polycarpa Small. Plant erect, 1 m. tall or less, copiously and diffusely branched, often in large colonies or patches: joints elliptic, narrowly rhombic-elliptic or sometimes broadly so, more or less twisted, mostly 1–4 dm. long, bright-green: leaves subulate, 3–7 mm. long, or sometimes longer, ascending and more or less curved upward, often purple-tinged, accompanied by very fine bristles, with or without spines: areolae scattered, often prominently bristly: spines, when present, solitary or 2 or 3 together, rather slender, pale-yellow or marked with darker-yellow or salmon below, gray except the brown tip when dry, brown or reddish when wet, the longer ones 2–3 cm. long: hypanthium narrowly obconic, 3–3.5 cm. long with very few areolae, the scales erect or ascending: sepals mostly green, the outer subulate to narrowly lanceo-late, 6–15 mm. long, acute, the intermediate lanceolate, the inner nearly or quite as wide as long, more or less rhombic, sometimes broadly shouldered and narrowed into a short tip: corolla bright-yellow, 6.5–7.5 cm. wide; petals about 12, 2.5–3 cm. long, flabellate or cuneate-flabellate, broadly rounded or truncate at the apex, mucronate: anthers 2.5–3 mm. long: berry ellipsoid-obovoid, 4–5 cm. long, purple or reddish-purple, even, rounded or slightly narrowed at the base, the umbilicus flattish and shallowly pitted at the center: seeds, numerous, about 6 mm. in diameter, rather wide-margined, somewhat turgid.—Coastal sand-dunes from the mouth of the Saint John's River to the Halifax River and on dunes, islands of the Cape Romano region, also locally in the interior, Fla.

15. O. nitens Small. Plant 1 m. tall or less, more or less diffusely spreading, with long fibrous roots: joints mostly obovate, 6–15 cm. long, thickish, green, not glaucous, shining, sometimes slightly twisted: leaves short-subulate, 3–5 mm. long, ascending: areolae often prominent on account of the exserted coarse bristles, mostly armed: spines solitary or 2–4 together, brown with a light tip, becoming dark-gray with a brown tip when dry, most of the longer ones 2–3 cm. long: flowers usually several to a joint: hypanthium obconic, about 3 cm. long: sepals green, the outer subulate or lanceolate to triangular-lanceolate, 6–16 mm. long, the inner rhombic-ovate to broadly rhombic-cuneate, 1.5–2 cm. long, all acute: corolla light-yellow, rotate, 5.5–6.5 cm. wide; petals broadly cuneate-obovate, 2.5–3 cm. long, rounded or truncate at the apex, mucronate, rather broad at the base: anthers about 2.5 mm. long: berry clavate-obovoid, about 4 cm. long, purple, the stipe-like base much shorter than the body, the umbilicus concave: seeds numerous, about 4 mm. in diam-eter, very turgid.—Hammocks, on shell-mounds along the western side of the Halifax River, Fla.

16. O. austrina Small. Plant erect, 1 m. tall or less, irregularly branched, tuberous: joints broad, oval or suborbicular, varying to obovate, or nearly elliptic, thinnish, 5–10 cm. long or rarely longer, deep-green or bright-green: leaves stout-subulate, 4–7 mm. long, ascending, usually accompanied by spines; green or purple-tinged: areolae rather prominent, the marginal and upper ones usually armed: spines slender-acicular, yellowish or reddish, at maturity white or light-gray when dry, pale-brown when wet, solitary or 2 together: hypanthium obovoid-turbinate, 2.5–3 cm. long: sepals green, the outer subulate to lanceolate, 7–14 mm. long, acute, the intermediate lanceolate to ovate, somewhat acuminate, the inner rhombic-ovate, broadly acuminate: corolla 6–7 cm. broad, light-yellow, or sometimes very pale; petals few, the outer cuneate, emarginate and abruptly-pointed, the inner obovate, rounded and minutely pointed at the apex: anthers about 2 mm. long: berry narrowly obovoid, 2.5–3.5 cm. long, purple: seeds numerous, 2.5–4.5 mm. in diameter, very turgid.—Pinelands, S pen. Fla.

17. O. cumulicola Small. Plant similar to that of *O. austrina*, but more robust and larger throughout: joints elliptic, obovate, or suborbicular, 9–30 cm. long, thick, bright-green: leaves subulate, 5–11 mm. long, more or less spreading: areolae prominent, mostly marginal, nearly all often armed: spines stout-acicular, usually solitary, if 2, the additional one very small, light-yellow, becoming light-gray or whitish when dry, light-brown when wet: corolla mostly 8–11 cm. broad, deep-yellow; petals rather many, the outer cuneate-flabellate, truncate or slightly emarginate and pointed, the inner flabellate and broadly rounded at the apex: anthers about 2.5 mm. long: berry obovoid, 4–5 cm. long, purple, the umbilicus concave: seeds numerous, 4.5–5 mm. in diameter, very turgid.—Coastal sand-dunes, S pen. Fla.

18. O. ammophila Small. Plant erect, more or less branched throughout, or ultimately with a stem 1–2 m. tall or more, becoming 1–2.5 dm. in diameter, bearing several spreading branches at the top, thus tree-like, the roots tuberous: joints various, those of the main stem elongate, ultimately fused at the nodes and subcylindric, those of the branches typically obovate or cuneate, varying to elliptic or oval, thickish, 0.5–1.7 dm. long, becoming gray-green: leaves stout-subulate, 6–10 mm. long, spreading or ascending, sometimes purple-tinged: areolae relatively numerous, conspicuous on account of the densely crowded long bristles, especially on the older joints, the marginal ones, at least, armed: spines very slender, solitary or two together, reddish or red, at maturity gray, mostly 2–6 cm. long, nearly terete, scarcely spirally twisted: flowers usually several on a joint, the buds sharp-pointed: hypanthium turbinate, 3–3.5 cm. long, more or less tuberculate-ridged, with several areolae, the scales lax or spreading: sepals green or purple-tinged, the outer lanceolate, 8–16 mm. long, acute, the intermediate ovate-lanceolate to ovate, short-acuminate, the inner rhombic to broadly rhombic-cuneate, abruptly pointed: corolla bright-yellow, 5–8 cm. wide; petals broadly cuneate, cuneate-obovate or obovate, truncate or notched at the apex, prominently mucronate, even or obscurely erose: anthers 3–3.5 mm. long: berry obovoid, 2–3 cm. long or rarely somewhat larger, flushed with red-purple, tuberculate, somewhat juicy, the umbilicus concave: seeds numerous, about 4 mm. in diameter, narrowly margined, very turgid.—(SCRUB PRICKLY-PEAR.)—Scrub, pen. Fla.—This plant reaches its maximum development in the Lake George region of Florida. Bartram observed it there in his travels. However, in recording it in his narrative he confused the vegetative parts of this plant and the large fruits of the prickly-pear of the coastwise kitchenmiddens.

19. O. keyensis Britton. Plant erect, much-branched, sometimes forming clumps 3 m. tall, with long fibrous roots: joints elliptic, oval, obovate, or spatulate, thick, 1–3 dm. long, bright-green: leaves conic-subulate or narrowly ovoid, 2–4 mm. long, ascending, straight or nearly so, green, accompanied by inconspicuous bristles, but without spines: areolae rather conspicuous, often relatively large and prominent, apparently unarmed: spines stout, 4–13 together, very short, mostly hidden in the bristles, pink, at maturity salmon-colored, sometimes protruding from the areolae as tufts of very coarse bristles, slightly flattened: buds short-pointed: flowers solitary or 2 or 3 on a joint: sepals green, the outer deltoid to subreniform, acute or acutish, or abruptly pointed, intermediate ones somewhat reniform, the inner rhombic-reniform, abruptly pointed: corolla salmon-colored, cup-like or short-campanulate, 3–3.5 cm. wide; petals rather few, the outer broadly cuneate, the inner broadly obovate or orbicular-obovate, undulate, scarcely, if at all, mucronate: anthers about 2 mm. long: berry obovoid, 4–6 cm. long, purple, slightly constricted at the base, the umbilicus flattish around the edge, depressed in the middle: seeds numerous, about 5 mm. in diameter.—Hammocks and coastal sand-dunes, Florida Keys and Cape Sable region to Cape Romano region, Fla.

20. O. tenuiflora Small. Plant partly erect, 1 m. tall or less, usually much-branched and decumbent and diffuse, with coarse fibrous roots: joints spatulate to elliptic-spatulate, or narrowly elliptic, mostly 1.5–4 dm. long, thickish, deep-green and often sparingly glaucous: leaves ovoid or ovoid-subulate, 3–3.5 mm. long, spreading or ascending, accompanied by short spines: areolae not very conspicuous, mostly armed: spines mostly 3–6 together, pale-yellow, becoming sordid-yellow when dry, pale-brown or yellow tinged with brown when wet, curved, the longer ones 2–5 cm. long: flowers few: hypanthium clavate, 4–4.5 cm. long, prominently ridged and tuberculate, with a slender stipe-like base: sepals green, the outer deltoid, to broadly reniform and with lateral wings or shoulders, 5–8 mm. long, acute, the inner rhombic-reniform to rhombic-obovate, 1–1.5 cm. long, abruptly pointed, winged: corolla deep-salmon colored, campanulate, about 3 cm. wide; petals few, narrowly obovate to cuneate-obovate, 2–2.5 cm. long, rounded or truncate at the apex, mucronate, slightly narrowed at the base: anthers about 2.5 mm. long: berry stout-clavate, 6–7 cm. long, purple, the stipe-like base nearly or quite as long as the body, the umbilicus concave: seeds numerous, 3–3.5 mm. long.—Hammocks, upper Florida Keys.

21. O. Dillenii (Ker) Haw. Plant erect, rather strict and sparingly branched or much-branched and sometimes diffuse, or sometimes 2 m. tall and often somewhat tree-like, with stout fibrous roots: joints elliptic to obovate or oval, thickish, 1–3 dm. long, light-green, often glaucous: leaves conic-subulate, 2–5 mm. long, ascending, straight or nearly so, usually green, accompanied by bristles but without spines: areolae remote but conspicuous, mostly armed: spines stoutish, clustered, usually 3–6 together, flattened, often curved, pale-yellow, at maturity deeper yellow and often sordid when dry, paler yellow when wet: flowers several on a joint: hypanthium narrowly obconic, 4.5–5.5 cm. long, slightly ridged, not stipitate at the base: sepals green, the outer ovate to triangular or deltoid, 3–9 mm. long, wingless or obscurely winged, acute; the inner orbicular-reniform to rhombic-reniform, 1.5–2 cm. long, abruptly pointed: corolla yellow, salmon, or reddish, rotate, 6–8 cm. wide; petals rather few, broadly obovate to cuneate-flabellate, 3.5–4.5 cm. long, erose and usually notched at the apex, decidedly narrowed at the base: anthers about 2 mm. long: berry pyriform, 5–8 cm. long, or sometimes smaller, purple, narrowed to the base, the umbilicus flattish with a depressed center: seeds numerous, 5–6 mm. in diameter, turgid.—Hammocks, along or near the coast, tidal hammocks, and coastal sand-dunes, pen. Fla., adj. islands and Florida Keys.—(*W. I., Mex.*)

22. O. Lindheimeri Engelm. Plant robust, 3 m. tall or less, often widely branched throughout, thus forming a large shrub with coarse fibrous roots: joints obovate or elliptic-obovate to oval, more or less twisted, 2–3.5 dm. long, thickish, light-green or somewhat glaucous: areolae often prominent, conspicuous on account of the numerous long bristles, armed: spines stout, 5–13 together or fewer, flattened, light-yellow, becoming dingy-yellow or salmon when dry, stramineous when wet, curved, the larger ones 2–4 cm. long: flowers numerous: hypanthium obconic-turbinate, about 6 cm. long: outer sepals broadly reniform, 5–6 cm. long, mucronulate, dark-green near the center; inner sepals cuneate-flabellate, mucronate, thin-edged: corolla rotate, clear-yellow; petals about 10, the outer broadly obovate, 4–5 cm. long, the inner scarcely as broad as the outer, all notched and mucronulate, rather thin-edged and crisped, contracted at the base: anthers 2.5–3 mm. long: berry pyriform, varying to obovoid or nearly ellipsoid, 4–5.5 cm. long, purple, the umbilicus somewhat depressed: seeds numerous, 3–4 mm. in diameter, very turgid.—Pinelands, especially about old settlements and homesteads, pen. Fla. Nat. of Tex. and Mex.

23. **O. stricta** Haw. Plant erect, but ultimately diffusely much-branched, 1–2 m. tall: joints spatulate, elliptic, oval, or obovate, rather thick, mostly 1–3.5 dm. long, somewhat glaucous: leaves subulate, mostly 5–7 mm. long, ascending or spreading, sometimes accompanied by young spines: areolae widely separated, but evenly scattered, some of them usually armed: spines solitary or 2 or 3 together, pink or salmon, at maturity yellowish when dry, red-brown or orange-brown when wet; flowers showy, often several on a joint: hypanthium elongate-turbinate, 5–6.5 cm. long: sepals green, the outer with a very broad abruptly pointed body, the intermediate somewhat reniform, abruptly pointed, the inner cuneate-flabellate, truncate and mucronate: corolla light-yellow, up to 1 dm. wide; petals mostly 8–10, the outer cuneate-obovate, the inner obovate, obscurely pointed: anthers about 2.5 mm. long: berry pyriform or obovoid-clavate, 5–7.5 cm. long, purple, the umbilicus depressed: seeds rather numerous, 4.5–5 cm. in diameter, flattish.—Shell mounds, kitchenmiddens, and aboriginal village sites, Fla. and S E Ga.—(*W. I.*)—This and the next following species are two of the prickly-pears the early Spanish records tell us the aborigines feasted on for three months of each year and also cured, like figs, for food when out of season.

24. **O. Bentonii** Griffiths. Plants erect, but ultimately diffusely or widely branched, mostly less than 1 m. tall, not tuberous: joints broadly spatulate, obovate, elliptic, or oval, thinnish, or quite thick at the base of the plant, mostly 1–3 dm. long, bright-green: leaves stout-subulate, 4–6 mm. long, or rarely longer, spreading, straight or slightly recurved, not accompanied by spines and only obscurely bristly at the base: areolae rather evenly scattered or more numerous along the edges than on the faces of the joints, few of the upper marginal ones armed: or joints individually unarmed: spines slender, solitary, or 2 or 3 together and sometimes with several shorter ones, pale-yellow, at maturity deeper-yellow when dry, pale yellow when wet, nearly terete, obscurely spirally twisted: flowers showy, mostly few on a joint: hypanthium obovoid to short turbinate, 4–4.5 cm. long, glaucous: sepals green, darker near the center and the tips, the outer broadly ovate to deltoid, 5–10 mm. long, acute, the intermediate reniform or rhombic-reniform, the inner flabellate-reniform, rounded and minutely pointed: corolla yellow, 8–9 cm. wide; petals 12–15, the outer cuneate, often broadly so, the inner obovate to orbicular-obovate, deep-yellow within, often finely crisped and mucronulate: anthers about 3 mm. long: berry obovoid, sometimes slightly pyriform, 3.5–5 cm. long, purple, the umbilicus depressed in the middle: seeds numerous, 4–5 mm. in diameter, slightly turgid, unevenly thick-margined.—Pinelands and sand-dunes, mostly near the coast, N Fla. to Tex.

25. **O. tunoidea** Gibbes. Plant erect, but ultimately diffusely and widely branched, 2 m. tall or less, the roots not tuberous: joints broadly spatulate, obovate, elliptic or oval, mostly 1–3 dm. long, thick or sometimes thinnish, bright-green and more or less glaucous: leaves stout-subulate, 4–6 mm. long or rarely longer, spreading, straight or slightly recurved, not accompanied by spines, and only obscurely bristly at the base, green or purplish-green: areolae rather evenly placed, more numerous along the edges than on the faces of the joints, few of the upper marginal ones armed or all armed, or joints individually unarmed: spines solitary or clustered, 2–4 together or more, pale-yellow, becoming dingy-yellow at maturity when dry, pale yellow when wet, the longer ones 1–3 cm. long, straight or slightly curved: flowers solitary or few on a joint, showy: hypanthium short-turbinate or obovoid-turbinate: sepals green, the outer

reniform, 4–8 mm. long, abruptly pointed, the intermediate papilionaceous, the inner flabellate-cuneate, emarginate and mucronate: corolla bright-yellow, 6.5–8 cm. wide, rotate; petals few, the outer flabellate-cuneate, the inner broadly cuneate-obovate, all toothed, emarginate, mucronate: anthers 2.5–3 mm. long: berry globose-obovoid, 4.5–6 cm. long, purple, the umbilicus shallowly concave: seeds numerous, 5–6 mm. in diameter, turgid, thick-margined.—Coastwise sand-dunes, Ga. (N E Fla.?) to N. C.

26. O. turbinata Small. Plant erect, but diffuse, less than 1 mm. tall, much-branched, with stout fibrous roots: joints oval, suborbicular or obovate, 1–1.5 dm. long, light-green and glaucous, very thick: leaves ovoid, about 3 mm. long, areolae rather prominent, mostly armed: spines solitary or 2–5 together, pale-yellow to bright-yellow, becoming sordid-brown when dry, dark-brown when wet, the longer ones 2–3 cm. long: hypanthium turbinate: sepals green, the outer deltoid-ovate, acute, the intermediate orbicular-ovate, the inner somewhat reniform and broadly pointed: corolla light-yellow, 4.5–5.5 cm. wide; petals cuneate to obovate, minutely pointed: berry globose-turbinate, 3.5–4.5 cm. long, purple, the umbilicus convex: seeds numerous, about 4.5–5 mm. in diameter, very inequilateral.—Coastal sand-dunes, N E Fla. to Ga.

27. O. cantabrigiensis Lynch. Plant erect, 1 m. tall or less, diffusely branched, but with no definite main stem, with fibrous, sometimes stout roots: joints orbicular to orbicular-obovate, mostly 1–1.5 dm. long, thickish, bright-green, somewhat glaucous when young: leaves subulate, 5–11 mm. long: areolae small, nearly all armed and with long white hairs: spines solitary or 2–4 together, acicular, cream-colored when young, at maturity pale-yellow, except the dark tip when dry, light yellow-brown when wet, the longer ones 2–3 cm. long: hypanthium obovoid, green: corolla yellow, or sometimes red in the center, rotate, mostly 5–6 cm. wide: berry globose-obovoid or globular, 3.5–4.5 cm. long, purple: seeds numerous, 3–4 mm. long, somewhat turgid.—Coastal sand-dunes about Beaufort, N. C.   Nat. of Mex.

28. O. magnifica Small. Plant 2 m. tall or less, more or less widely branched and diffuse, with thick fibrous roots: joints elliptic, oval, or narrowly obovate, 2–5 dm. long or more, relatively thin, more or less twisted, bright-green and glaucous: leaves subulate, 6–8 mm. long, usually loosely ascending: areolae rather inconspicuous, feebly armed: spines very slender, even weak, solitary or 2 or 3 together, pale-yellow, becoming sordid and minutely banded when dry, pale yellow when wet, the longer ones 1.5 cm. long: flowers not very numerous, usually several to a joint: hypanthium obconic, 5.5–7 cm. long, green or sometimes purple-tinged: sepals mostly green, the outer subulate to triangular-lanceolate, 8–20 mm. long, the inner rhombic-ovate or rhombic-obovate, 2.5–3 cm. long, all acute or somewhat acuminate: corolla deep-yellow, rotate, 9–12 cm. wide; petals 12 or fewer, broadly-obovate to orbicular-obovate, 4–6 cm. long, rounded at the apex, mucronate, slightly narrowed at the broad base: anthers linear, 4–5 mm. long: berry obconic-turbinate, 8.5–9.5 cm. long, purple, the umbilicus flat or nearly so: seeds about 3 mm. in diameter, very numerous. —Pinewoods and bluffs, Amelia Island, Fla.

29. O. zebrina Small. Plant erect, more or less branched throughout, fully 1 m. tall, or less, the roots fibrous: joints oval or obovate, thickish, mostly 1–2 dm. long, deep-green, sometimes obscurely glaucous, not twisted: leaves conic-ovoid, 4–6 mm. long, or rarely smaller, erect or appressed, often slightly curved upward, bright-green, unaccompanied by bristles or spines: areolae scattered, some of them, usually the lower ones, unarmed, the upper ones irregularly armed: spines slender, solitary or 2, 3, or 4 together, red-brown and finely banded when dry, paler or salmon-pink and less conspicuously banded when wet, nearly terete, closely spirally twisted: flowers few, sometimes several on a joint: hypanthium obovoid or turbinate-obovoid, about 4 cm. long: sepals green, the outer lanceolate to deltoid, acute, the intermediate rhombic-obovate, acuminate, the inner rhombic-ovate or broadly cuneate, abruptly pointed: corolla rich-yellow, rotate, 6–8 cm. wide; petals about 8, the outer obovate-cuneate, the inner broadly obovate, all undulate, emarginate or notched at the apex and mucronate: anthers 2–2.5 mm. long: berry broadly obovoid, not constricted at the base, mostly 5–6 cm. long, red-purple, the umbilicus very broad, raised about the edges and somewhat depressed in the middle: seeds numerous, 5–6 mm. in diameter or rarely larger.—Coastal sand-dunes and hammocks, lower Florida Keys, Cape Sable, and Ten Thousand Islands, Fla.

30. O. Ficus-Indica (L.) Mill. Plant erect, often tree-like, 4 m. tall or less, the early joints somewhat fusing to form a thick trunk which supports irregularly spreading heavy branches: joints elliptic, varying to slightly broadest above the middle or below it, thick, mostly 3–4 dm. long, often slightly glaucous: areolae small, with yellowish bristles and white wool: spines wanting, or occasionally and irregularly developed, and mostly solitary, pale, at maturity turning white, nearly terete: flowers usually several on a joint: corolla yellow, 8–10 cm. wide: berries obovoid, red or orange (said to be sometimes yellow), 5–9 cm. long: seeds 3.5–4.5 mm. in diameter.—Old fields, roadsides, and wasteplaces, Fla. Naturalized from cultivated plants. The original home is not known.

31. O. leucotricha DC. Plant stout, 5 m. tall or less, widely branched above, with stout fibrous roots: joints elliptic, oval, or suborbicular, mostly 1–2 dm. long, often thickened and narrowed in the main stems, thinnish, minutely pubescent, gray-green: areolae numerous, closely set, armed: spines 3–5 together when young, later developing as many as 19, very unequal, becoming white or gray when dry, nearly white when wet, straight or nearly so, partly deflexed, the longer ones 2.5–3 cm. long: flowers few: hypanthium turbinate or obovoid-turbinate, 2.5–3.5 cm. long, with many close-set areolae bearing clusters of small spines: sepals green, the outer lanceolate, 8–14 mm. long, with curved acuminate tips, the intermediate rhombic-obovate, slender-acuminate, the inner with obovate, oval, or orbicular-obovate bodies which are abruptly narrowed into curved tips: corolla yellow, 7.5–9 cm. wide; petals broadly cuneate or cuneate-obovate, 3–4 cm. long, rounded at the apex and mucronate: anthers fully 2 mm. long: berry short-obovoid or globose-obovoid, 4–6 cm. long, yellow, or sometimes paler or red, finely pubescent, the hair-like spines fugaceous.—(DURASNILLA. AARON'S-BEARD CACTUS.)—Hammocks, W side of Saint Lucie Sound, Fla. Nat. of Mex.—Naturalized in the hammock south of Ft. Pierce from plants taken there by the pioneers during Seminole War times.

3. BRASILIOPUNTIA Small. Trees, more or less shrub-like in the early stages, with terete trunks and dimorphic branches, the lateral often horizontal ones terete like the trunk, spiny, supporting flat, dilated, leaf-like, relatively thin branchlets. Leaves small, stout, early deciduous. Spines various, clustered on the trunk and branches, often solitary on the branchlets. Flowers relatively small, sometimes numerous. Hypanthium stout, with bristly areolae. Sepals broad. Petals relatively narrow, often spatulate. Berry globose to clavate, juicy. Seeds few or solitary, relatively large, woolly.—Three species, South American.—Interpreted under this generic name as a subgenus, by Schumann.

1. B. brasiliensis (Willd.) Haw. Plant erect, tree-like, 5 m. tall or more, or often much smaller, with a terete upwardly tapering trunk which in mature plants supports terete spreading branches, these in turn divide into joints: leaves flat, oblong, elliptic, or obovate, mostly 1–3 mm. long, clear-green or light-green, nearly straight, unaccompanied by bristles or spines, deciduous; areolae small, minutely white-woolly, those of the stem, branches, and edges of the joints armed: spines slender, usually solitary on the flat branchlets, terete, mostly 1–3 cm. long, pale with reddish or brown tips, ultimately gray: flowers usually several on the terminal joints: sepals ovate, the inner ones broadly so: corolla lemon-yellow, mostly 3–4 cm. wide: berry subglobose to oval, 2.5–4 cm.

long, light-yellow, the areolae conspicuous on account of the tufted brown bristles, the umbilicus slightly concave in the middle: seeds 7–9 mm. in diameter. [*Opuntia brasiliensis* Haw.]—Hammocks, mostly on shell-mounds, or occasionally in waste-places, pen. Fla. and the Keys. Nat. of E S. A.

4. CONSOLEA Lemaire. Shrubs or small trees, the main stems or trunk ultimately a continuous terete or flattened shaft more or less copiously armed with acicular, clustered, often greatly elongate reflexed spines, the branches flat, inequilateral, thin, mostly spiny joints more or less irregularly spreading. Leaves usually very small deciduous scales. Flowers relatively small, commonly several on a joint. Hypanthium somewhat elongate, more or less flattened, usually with spiny, often numerous areoles. Sepals broad. Petals broad, often of an obovate type. Berry more or less elongate, enlarged upward, fleshy. Seeds flattened with cristate edges and hairy sides.—Eight species, West Indian and the following.

1. C. corallicola Small. Plants tree-like, 2 m. tall or less, or ultimately larger, light-green: stem (trunk) erect, arising from coarse fibrous roots, strict, copiously and bristly armed, elliptic or oval in cross-section: aerolae numerous, each with a cluster of 5–9 spines: spines salmon-colored when young, light-gray when mature and dry, darker when wet, acicular, one of each areola much longer than the others, often 7–12 cm. long: joints arising from the top or near the top of the stem or trunk, elliptic or broader above the middle or below it, inequilateral, more or less curved, relatively thin, the larger ones 2–3 cm. long, all copiously armed, the spines similar to those of the trunk, but smaller: flowers rather numerous: sepals green, the outer ones deltoid, 3–4 mm. long, very thick, the inner more or less reniform, thinner, abruptly pointed: petals bright-red, obovate to orbicular-obo-

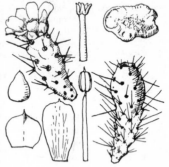

vate, 1 cm. long or less: style with an obovoid base: berry obovoid or clavate-obovoid, 2.5–5 cm. long, yellow, with spreading spines, the umbilicus deeply concave: seeds few, irregular, 7–9 mm. in diameter.—Hammocks, Key Largo and Big Pine Key, Fla. All year.—This plant has several unusual characteristics. The flat branches are inclined to grow in one plane from the trunk, hence the name semaphore-cactus; the unfertilized flower reverts to a vegetative branch; the berries are frequently proliferous.

5. **RHIPSALIS** Gaertn. Succulent pendent shrubs, sometimes with aerial fibrous roots. Main stem woody, the branchlets terete, but heteromorphic, very succulent. Leaves obsolete or minute scales. Areolae scattered. Flowers small for the family, diurnal and nocturnal. Hypanthium short-campanulate or hemispheric, naked, not produced beyond the ovary. Sepals very broad. Petals few, broad, white in our species. Stamens few. Style erect: stigmas 3, stout. Berry white, as thick as long or nearly so, smooth.—About 50 species, mostly tropical American.

1. **R. Cassutha** Gaertn. Plants in much-branched clusters a meter or more in length, the branches often very slender (1 mm. in diameter), becoming stouter (4–8 mm.), two together or 4–8 in a cluster, the areolae with 5–9 deciduous bristles: flowers sessile: sepals reniform to ovate-reniform, about 1 mm. long or less: petals white, oval or elliptic, varying to ovate or obovate, about 3 mm. long: stamens 1–2 mm. long: berry globose or oval varying to ovoid or obovoid, 4–5 mm. in diameter. — (PENCIL-CACTUS. MISTLETOE-CACTUS.) — Hammocks, Everglade Keys, pen. Fla.—(*W. I., Mex., C. A., S. A.*)—Nat. in the O. W.—All year.

6. **SELENICEREUS** Britton & Rose. Succulent shrubs with angled or ridged, trailing, sometimes creeping, clambering, or climbing stems and branches, the angles or ridges supporting separated areolae, each of which has a tuft of wool and single or clustered spines. Leaves obsolete. Flowers nocturnal, showy, arising from an areola. Hypanthium clavate, scaly and hairy. Sepals colored, often green or yellow, very narrow. Petals white, broader than the sepals. Berry oval, varying to ovoid or obovoid, or sub-globose, armed with clusters of deciduous spines.—About 18 species, tropical American.—Spr.—SNAKE-CACTI.

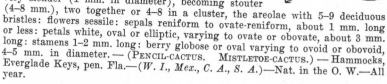

Branches armed with short conic inconspicuous spines: hypanthium about 15 cm. long, funnelform at the top. 1. *S. pteranthus.*
Branches armed with long slender-subulate spines: hypanthium about 10 cm. long, scarcely dilated at the top. 2. *S. coniflorus.*

1. **S. pteranthus** (Link & Otto) Britton & Rose. Vine, the stem and branches clambering, extensively rooting, dull green: old stems subterete, the branches obtusely usually 4-angled, the branchlets sharply 4–5-angled or ridged, altogether forming serpent-like masses over objects: areolae small, the hairs white, very short, the spines conic, usually 2–4 together: flowers lateral, starting as short conic buds which soon greatly elongate; basal part of the hypanthium subglobose, covered with close-set subulate scales which subtend tufts of long stiff white hairs and clusters of long slender spines; tubular part of the hypanthium about 15 cm. long, dilated into a funnelform throat, bearing widely scattered scales with tufts of long hairs and usually a long and a short spine in their axils: sepals narrowly elongate-linear, 9–12 cm. long, except the very outer ones, light-green,

acuminate: petals white, linear-spatulate to spatulate, the narrow ones acuminate, the broader somewhat erose and mucronate: anthers 4.5–5 mm. long; berry globose, 6–8 cm. in diameter, red.—Hammocks on high sand-dunes, S pen. Fla.—Nat. of Mex.—Introduced into the hammock south of Ft. Pierce by the pioneers during Seminole War times.

2. S. coniflorus (Weingart.) Britton & Rose. Vine, the stem and branches diffusely clambering and climbing by copious roots, deep-green, the older portions stout and turgid, the younger parts more slender, mostly rather sharply 5-angled: areolae small, the hairs pale or nearly white, often about 1 cm. apart, the spines acicular, 5–7 together, gray, the larger ones 1–1.5 cm. long: flowers lateral, starting as conic buds which soon elongate: basal part of the hypanthium ovoid, covered with close-set stiff subulate scales which subtend tufts of short white hairs and clusters of short spines; tubular part of the hypanthium about 10 cm. long, scarcely dilated at the top, bearing rather closely scattered scales with tufts of relatively short hairs and clusters of spines in their axils: sepals very narrowly elongate-linear, 3–9 cm. long, except the outermost ones, bright-green, attenuate: petals white: berry subglobose, 5–7 cm. in diameter.—Pinelands near the Everglades, west of Halendale, and fence-rows in pen. Fla.—Nat. of Mex.

7. HYLOCEREUS Britton & Rose. Coarse vines with 3-angled or 3-winged stems and branches, climbing by aerial roots, the areolae remote on the ridges, each with a tuft of short hairs and a cluster of spines. Leaves obsolete. Flowers nocturnal, very large and showy. Hypanthium trumpet-shaped, with foliaceous scales. Sepals various, the outer ones resembling the hypanthium scales, the inner resembling the petals. Petals white, narrow. Berry ovoid to globose, with broad scales.—About 18 species, tropical American.

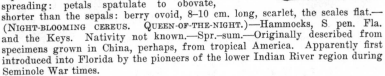

1. H. undatus (Haw.) Britton & Rose. Stem and branches stout, 8–12 cm. thick, light-green, commonly high-climbing, often formed in dense or compact masses: areolae usually with 3–5, relatively stout, dark spines 2–4 mm. long in the stem-sinuses: hypanthium relatively very stout, copiously scaly, shorter than the diameter of the calyx: sepals linear-lanceolate to linear, loosely spreading: petals spatulate to obovate, shorter than the sepals: berry ovoid, 8–10 cm. long, scarlet, the scales flat.—(NIGHT-BLOOMING CEREUS. QUEEN-OF-THE-NIGHT.)—Hammocks, S pen. Fla. and the Keys. Nativity not known.—Spr.–sum.—Originally described from specimens grown in China, perhaps, from tropical America. Apparently first introduced into Florida by the pioneers of the lower Indian River region during Seminole War times.

8. ACANTHOCEREUS Britton & Rose. Coarse shrubs with 3–6-angled, erect, diffuse, or reclining, often greatly elongate, stems and branches, the areolae remote on the ridges, each with a tuft of short hairs and a cluster of spines. Leaves obsolete. Flowers nocturnal, relatively large. Hypanthium trumpet-shaped, armed with spines. Sepals various, the outer short, the inner long and narrow. Petals white, linear to spatulate. Berry ovoid or oval, spine-armed.—About 8 species, of continental tropical America.

1. A. floridanus Small. Stems and branches diffusely spreading or reclining, 3–10 m. long, stout, starting as a several-ribbed plant about as thick as a lead-pencil, the successive joints thicker and prominently 3–5-angled, the mature branches mostly 3-angled, dark-green, often forming impenetrable thickets: areolae remote, with mostly 4–7 slender or subulate spines, the central one often 1–2 cm. long, or more: hypanthium stout-trumpet-shaped, 8–10 cm. long, with few large separated tubercled areolae at the base, the areolae at the base of the hypanthium bearing mostly 3–5 diverging spines, those on the tubular part usually with one spine each: calyx green or purple-tinged; sepals deltoid to triangular-lanceolate, lanceolate-subulate and almost linear, the longer ones 3.5–4 cm. long, acuminate: corolla 8–11 cm. wide, white;

petals broadly linear, 3.5–4.5 cm. long, about six times as long as wide, broadly acuminate: filaments adnate more than half way up from the base of the hypanthium: anthers less than 2.5 mm. long: berry ovoid, 4–6.5 cm. long, scarlet, shining. [*A. pentagonus* (Fl. SE. U. S.)]—(DILDOE. BARBED-WIRE CACTUS.)—Hammocks, along or near the coast, S pen. Fla., and the Keys.—Sum.

9. HARRISIA Britton. Succulent shrubs, with fluted stems and branches, the ridges supporting areolae, each of which supports a tuft of spines, the spines of each areola arising below the tuft of wool and varying greatly in length. Leaves obsolete. Flowers nocturnal, showy, arising from the upper side of an areola. Hypanthium narrowly funnelform or clavate, scaly. Sepals colored. Petals white, narrow. Berry globose or ovoid-globose, with few scale-bases, often with tufts of hairs. Seeds very numerous.—About 18 species, distributed from Florida to Argentina.—Spr.—PRICKLY-APPLES.

Flower-buds brown-hairy: scales of the hypanthium with tufts of brown hairs in their axils: berry yellow.   1. *H. Aboriginum.*
Flower-buds white-hairy: scales of the hypanthium with tufts of white hairs in their axils: berry red.
    Hypanthium prominently ridged, the scales turgid at the base: berry depressed-globose.   2. *H. Simpsonii.*
    Hypanthium even or scarcely ridged, the scales flat or nearly so: berry obovoid.   3. *H. fragrans.*

1. H. Aboriginum Small. Plants 6 m. tall or less, usually forming dense thickets, terrestrial, the stems erect or more or less reclining, simple or some of them usually branched, 9–11-ridged: spines 7–9 in each areola, very slender, the longer ones mostly 1 cm. long or less, or sometimes longer near the ends of the branches, all pink when young, becoming gray with brown near the tips: young buds clothed with brown hairs: hypanthium longer than the flower-limb, long-funnelform, the swollen base partly covered with lanceolate scales which are very small below, but larger above, all of them more or less separated, with stiff long brown hairs protruding from beneath them: scales on the tubular part of the hypanthium, distant, lanceolate, turgid, each with short brown

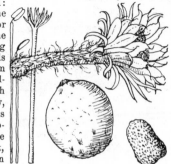

hairs protruding from beneath: flowers faintly scented: longer inner sepals narrowly linear, acuminate: petals white, most of them exceeded by the longer sepals, oblanceolate, erose near the apex, broadly acuminate and minutely slender-tipped: stamens erect: berry globular, 6.5–7.5 cm. in diameter, dull yellow, the scar at the apex about 1 cm. in diameter: seeds 3 mm. long.—Shore hammocks and shell-mounds, Tampa Bay region, Fla., to the Ten Thousand Islands.

2. **H. Simpsonii** Small. Plants 4 m. tall or less, scattered or in colonies, terrestrial or often epiphytic, the stems sometimes vine-like, simple or individually branched, 9- or 10-ridged: spines mostly 7–9 in each areola, slender, the longer ones of each cluster 1–2.5 cm. long: young buds clothed with white hairs: hypanthium longer than the flower-limb, long-funnelform, prominently and coarsely ridged, the swollen base clothed with broadly lanceolate, closely set or imbricate scales, with white hairs protruding from beneath them: scales of the tubular part of the hypanthium rather numerous and close-set, very turgid, lanceolate, each with white hairs protruding from beneath: flowers inodorous: longer inner sepals linear, 4.5–5.5 cm. long, acuminate: petals white, narrowly spatulate or narrowly cuneate-spatulate, erose near the apex, each abruptly narrowed into a short tip: stamens nearly erect: berry depressed-globose, about 6 cm. in diameter, dull-red, usually with partly persistent scales, the scar at the apex less than 1 cm. in diameter: seeds fully 3 mm. long. [*H. Brookii* (Fl. SE. U. S.)]—Hammocks and mangrove swamps, terrestrial or epiphytic, Cape Sable to Ten Thousand Islands and Madeira Bay region, Fla. and Florida Keys.

3. **H. fragrans** Small. Plants 5 m. tall or less, growing singly, sometimes approximate, but not in colonies, the stems erect, reclining, or clambering, prominently 10–12-ridged, the ridges more or less depressed between the areolae, the grooves rather deep and sharp: areolae about 2 cm. apart, each with a dense tuft of very short hairs on the upper side: spines acicular, 9–13 in each areola, mostly grayish and yellowish at the tip, one of each areola longer than the others, mostly 2–4 cm. long: young buds copiously white-hairy: buds about to expand fully 15 cm. long (18–20 cm. long): hypanthium light-green, longer than the flower-limb, slender-funnelform, scarcely ridged, the swollen base bearing subulate or lanceolate-subulate separated scales, with long white hairs protruding from beneath them and very lax: scales of the tubular part of the hypanthium few and remote, subulate, slenderly acuminate, not turgid, with a tuft of long white hairs in each axil: sepals very narrowly linear, slenderly acuminate: petals white or pinkish, spatulate, caudate-tipped: ovary-cavity ovoid: berry obovoid, about 6 cm. in diameter, dull-red, with tufts of long hairs persistent with the scale-bases: seeds nearly 3.5 mm. long.—Hammocks on high sand-dunes, kitchenmiddens, and coquina ledges, from Mosquito Inlet to Saint Lucie Sound, Fla.

10. **CEPHALOCEREUS** Pfeiff. Succulent shrubs or trees with fluted stems and branches, the ridges supporting areolae, each of which supports a tuft of spines, the spines of each areola arising from all parts of the tuft of wool and varying greatly in length. The bark at length scaly. Leaves obsolete. Flowers diurnal, inconspicuous, arising from the center of an areola. Hypanthium campanulate, naked or scaly above. Sepals colored. Petals white or pale, broad. Berry more or less depressed, naked. Seeds numerous.—About 40 species, tropical American.—Wint.–spr.—TREE-CACTI.—The two following species have a definite geologic distribution. *C. Deeringii* inhabits the Key Largo limestone, *C. keyensis* the Key West oölite. Where these two limestones meet on Big Pine Key the ranges of the two species come together.

Sepals and petals obtuse, rounded or emarginate: spines of the areolae mostly more than 25 (25–31). 1. *C. Deeringii.*

Sepals and petals acute, abruptly pointed or acuminate: spines of the areolae mostly fewer than 15 (9–15). 2. *C. keyensis.*

1. C. Deeringii Small. Shrub or small tree becoming 10 m. tall, the stem erect, simple or with few erect elongate fastigiate branches forming a very narrow head, the branches deep-green, usually 10-ribbed: areolae copiously hairy, the hairs rather persistent; spines 25–31, the longer ones 1 cm. long or more: flowers about 6 cm. long, narrowly campanulate: sepals obovate, obtuse or emarginate: petals 9–11 mm. long, clawless, oval, obtuse, scarcely narrowed at the base: anthers less than 2 mm. long: berry much depressed, 3–5 cm. in diameter, dark-red.—Rocky hammocks, upper Florida Keys, from the S front of Big Pine Key to Upper Matecumbe Key.

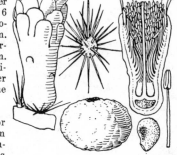

2. C. keyensis Britton & Rose. Shrub or small tree, becoming 5 or 6 m. tall, the stem erect, ultimately much-branched, often forming a compact narrow head, the branches light-green or somewhat glaucous, 9- or 10-ribbed: areolae copiously short-hairy, the hairs mostly deciduous; spines 9–15, the longer ones mostly less than 1 cm. long: flowers about 5 cm. long, campanulate: sepals ovate, acute: petals 14–16 mm. long, the outer ones clawed, with ovate or elliptic blades, the inner clawless, oblanceolate to almost broadly linear, all acute, erose: anthers over 2 mm. long: berry depressed, about 3.5 cm. in diameter, reddish.—Rocky hammocks, lower Florida Keys, from Key West to Big Pine Key.

Order BEGONIALES — Begonial Order

Succulent herbs, shrubby plants or vines. Leaves alternate: blades commonly inequilateral, toothed or lobed. Flowers monoecious, usually somewhat irregular, cymose: staminate flowers with 2 or more sepals, 5 minute petals and many stamens, whose anthers open by pores or valves. Pistillate flowers with a calyx, a corolla and a gynoecium of 2–5 united carpels. Ovary inferior, 2–several-celled, the placentae entire or lobed. Stigmas curved, twisted or coiled. Ovules numerous. Fruit capsular, winged.

Family 1. BEGONIACEAE — Begonia Family

Unusual looking plants with odd-shaped leaves and conspicuous inflorescence, the staminate and pistillate flowers usually borne in the same clusters. Capsule many-seeded.—About 4 genera and over 400 species, widely distributed in tropical regions.

1. BEGONIA L. Succulent plants sometimes woody below. Leaf-blades oblique. Staminate flowers with 2 unequal pairs of petals. Pistillate flowers with 5 somewhat unequal petals. Gynoecium with a short style, spiral stigmas and 2-lobed placentae. Capsule unequally 3-winged.—About 400 species, widely distributed.—ELEPHANT'S-EARS. BEGONIAS.—Many species with showy leaves and highly colored wax-like flowers are widely cultivated.

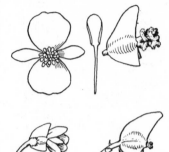

1. **B. semperflorens** Link & Otto. Plants 3–10 dm. tall: leaf-blades 4–7 cm. broad, the teeth apiculate: bracts ciliate-fimbriate: corolla white; larger petals of the staminate flowers 6–14 mm. long, the smaller ones spatulate: capsules drooping.—(PERPETUAL-BEGONIA)—Swamps and low grounds, pen. Fla. Nat. of S. A.

ORDER **PROTEALES** — PROTEAL ORDER

Perennial herbs, or shrubs or trees. Leaves alternate or rarely opposite: blades simple or compound. Flowers perfect, or occasionally polygamous or dioecious. Perianth of 4 valvate distinct or partially united sepals. Androecium of 4 stamens, one borne on each sepal. Gynoecium a single carpel. Ovary superior, often oblique. Fruit indehiscent, or often follicular or capsular.

FAMILY 1. **PROTEACEAE** — PROTEA FAMILY

Leaf-blades simple, entire, toothed, or divided. Flowers borne in spikes, racemes, or panicles, which are commonly congested. Calyx, androecium, and gynoecium, various, often very irregular.—Fifty genera and about 1,000 species, mostly of Asia, Africa, and Australia.

1. **GREVILLEA** R. Br. Shrubs or trees. Leaf-blades often pinnately parted. Flowers borne in racemes or panicles, sometimes irregular. Ovary stipitate. Style often protruding from the cleft of the calyx. Fruit follicular or 1- or 2-valved. Seeds flat, often winged.—About 175 species, most abundant in Australia.

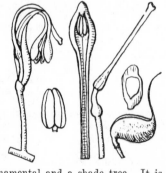

1. **G. robusta** A. Cunn. Tree becoming 20 m. tall: leaf-blades 2–4 dm. long: panicle showy, orange or red: the racemes 1–2 dm. long, many-flowered: sepals 9–11 mm. long: follicles recurved, the bodies 1.5–2 cm. long, slender-beaked.—(SILK–OAK.)—Roadsides, waste-places, and cult. grounds, Fla. Nat. of Australia.—(W. I.)—Spr.—This tree, wholly different from our native trees in both foliage and inflorescence, was introduced into Florida many years ago as an ornamental and a shade tree. It is unusual among our trees in that it bears the flower clusters along the trunk and the main branches.

Order THYMELEALES — Thymeleal Order

Shrubs or trees, or partially herbaceous plants. Leaves opposite or alternate, the blades simple, rarely mere scales, or obsolete. Flowers perfect, polygamous, or dioecious, regular or nearly so. Calyx of 6 or fewer sepals. Corolla wanting (in our species). Androecium of as many stamens as there are sepals or of twice as many. Anthers opening by slits or hinged valves. Gynoecium a single carpel. Ovary inferior. Ovules mostly solitary. Fruit usually baccate or drupaceous.

Anthers opening by slits.
  Ovule and seed pendulous: leaves green, sometimes merely pubescent.
                                            Fam. 1. Daphnaceae.
  Ovule and seed erect: leaves silvery-scurfy.   Fam. 2. Elaeagnaceae.
Anthers opening by hinged valves.
  Leafy shrubs or trees: fruit seated on the hypanthium. Fam. 3. Lauraceae.
  Leafless, twining, parasitic vines: fruit enclosed in
    the accrescent hypanthium.
                                      Fam. 4. Cassythaceae.

Family 1. DAPHNACEAE — Mezereon Family

Shrubs or trees, or rarely herbs, often pubescent. Leaves opposite or alternate: blades entire. Calyx of 4 or 5 sepals, sometimes with 4 or 5 scales within. Androecium of as many stamens as there are sepals or twice as many. Gynoecium seated in the bottom of the hypanthium. Style usually eccentric.—Forty genera and about 425 species, most abundant in Australia and southern Africa.

1. **DIRCA** L. Shrubs. Leaves alternate. Flowers appearing before the leaves. Sepals usually shorter than the hypanthium. Filaments slender. Ovary 1-celled: style filiform. Drupe slightly elongate.—Two species, North American.

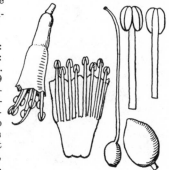

1. **D. palustris** L. Shrub 0.5–2 m. tall: leaf-blades oval or obovate, 4–8 cm. long: flowers lemon-yellow: hypanthium 7–8 mm. long: sepals very short: drupe oval, 7–9 mm. long, red.—(Leatherwood. Swampwood. Moose-wood. Leather-bark.) — Rich woods, bluffs, and stream-banks, various provinces, rarely Coastal Plain, Fla. to La., Ont., and N. B.—Spr.—The bark has been used medicinally. The wood is soft and brittle but the bark is unusually tough, and was used by the aborigines for thongs.

Family 2. ELAEAGNACEAE — Oleaster Family

Shrubs or trees, scaly or stellate-pubescent. Leaf-blades entire. Calyx of 4, or rarely of 2, sepals. Androecium of 4 or 8 stamens. Gynoecium closely invested by the hypanthium which is thickened and often ridged within. Style usually axial.—Three genera and about 25 species, widely distributed.

1. **ELAEAGNUS** L. Shrubs or rarely trees, pubescent with silvery scales. Leaves alternate. Flowers white or yellow within, silvery without. Sepals

shorter than the hypanthium. Stamens 4: filaments very short or wanting. Ovary 1-celled: style elongate. Drupe somewhat elongated.—SILVER-BERRIES.— About 20 species, Eurasian, Australian, and North American.—Some species are used in horticulture. The fruits of some species are edible.

Leaf-blades beneath, and hypanthium, not brown-scaly: sepals less than ½ as long
    as the prolonged portion of the hypanthium.   1. *E. umbellatus.*
Leaf-blades beneath, and hypanthium, brown-scaly: sepals over
    ½ as long as the prolonged portion of the hypanthium.   2. *E. multiflorus.*

1. **E. umbellatus** Thunb. Shrub, 1–3 m. tall. Leaves numerous; blades elliptic, 2–4 cm. long, mainly obtuse, green above, silvery beneath, short-petioled:

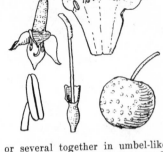

flowers few, in umbel-like clusters, short-pedicelled: hypanthium narrowly funnel-form, 4–6 mm. long during anthesis: sepals ovate, 2.5–3 mm. long, silvery scaly without like the hypanthium: anthers less than 1.5 mm. long: fruit globose to oval, 6–8 mm. long. — (AUTUMN-ELAEAGNUS.) — Thickets, banks, and cult. grounds, near Augusta, in the Piedmont of Ga. Nat. of Japan.—Sum.–fall.

2. **E. multiflorus** Thunb. Shrub, mostly 1–2.5 m. tall. Leaves rather numerous; blades elliptic or somewhat obovate to oval, 3–6.5 cm. long, rounded or abruptly blunt-tipped at the apex, bright green above, silvery beneath, short-petioled: flowers few or several together in umbel-like clusters, rather long-pedicelled: hypanthium stout, slightly dilated upward, 5.5–7 mm. long during anthesis: sepals orbicular-ovate to reniform, 3–4 mm. long, copiously scaly without, like the hypanthium: anthers over 1.5 mm. long: fruit oval, 7–10 mm. long.—(JAPANESE CHERRY.)—Roadsides and fields, Coastal Plain, Miss. and La. Nat. of Japan.—Sum.

FAMILY 3. **LAURACEAE** — LAUREL FAMILY.

Aromatic shrubs or trees. Leaves alternate or opposite: blades entire or lobed. Flowers in open or congested cymes. Calyx of 5 (or rarely 4–10) sepals in 2 series. Corolla wanting. Androecium of usually more stamens than there are sepals, in 2–4 series, those of the third series usually glandular-appendaged, those of the fourth series mostly mere staminodia. Gynoecium a single carpel. Ovary 1-celled. Fruit drupaceous.—Forty genera and about 1,000 species, most abundant in tropical regions.—Some of the species are of great economic value.

Anthers 4-celled, 4-valved.
    Anther-sacs of outer stamen-series extrorse.   Tribe   I. CINNAMOMEAE.
    Anther sacs introrse.   Tribe II. LITSEAE.
Anthers 2-celled, 2-valved.
    Mature hypanthium large, succulent: inflorescence
      of erect panicles: anther-sacs extrorse.   Tribe III. ACRODICLIDIEAE.
    Mature hypanthium minute, dry: inflorescence of
      umbel-like clusters: anther-sacs introrse.   Tribe IV. LAUREAE.

I. CINNAMOMEAE

Staminodia present, large, often sagittate.
    Sepals deciduous.
      Calyx falling away as separate sepals: leaf blades ribbed.   1. CAMPHORA.
      Calyx falling away with the sepals united: leaf-blades
      pinnate-veined.   2. PERSEA.

Sepals persistent under the fruit.   3. TAMALA.
Staminodia small, subulate, or wanting.   4. NECTANDRA.

II. LITSEAE

Sepals persistent on the cup-like hypanthium.   5. SASSAFRAS.
Sepals deciduous from the cylindric hypanthium.   6. GLABRARIA.

III. ACRODICLIDIEAE

Large trees with whitish flowers: leaf-blades coriaceous.   7. MISANTECA.

IV. LAUREAE

Shrubs with yellow flowers: leaf-blades membranous.   8. BENZOIN.

1. CAMPHORA [Gronov.] L. Trees or shrubs. Leaves alternate or opposite, persistent: blades entire. Flowers in panicled axillary cymes, mainly white or greenish. Style slender. Stigma minute. Drupe equilateral, as broad as long, or nearly so.—Few species, natives of eastern Asia.

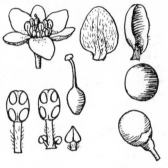

1. C. Camphora (L.) Karst. Small tree or shrub: leaf-blades elliptic to ovate, 4–12 cm. long, short-acuminate, pale beneath, long-petioled: panicles slender-peduncled: sepals 1–1.5 mm. long: drupes globose to oval-globose, 6–9 mm. in diameter.—(CAMPHOR-TREE.) — Pinelands and hammocks, pen. Fla. to Tex. Nat. of E Asia and cult.—Spr.—The wood yields the camphor of commerce.

2. PERSEA [Plum.] Gaertn. Trees. Leaves alternate, persistent: blades entire. Flowers in terminal panicled cymes, greenish. Sepals 6, nearly equal, united at the base. Style subulate: stigma minute. Drupe inequilateral.—One species, in many cult. forms.

1. P. Persea (L.) Cockerell. Large tree: leaf-blades elliptic or oval or nearly so, 8–15 cm. long, short-petioled (relatively small and with long and slender petioles in *P. Persea mexicana*): inner sepal 4–5 mm. long, somewhat surpassing the outer: fruits slightly elongate, often pyriform, 8–18 cm. long, the flesh butter-like.—(AVOCADO. ALLIGATOR-PEAR.)—Hammocks and pinelands, S pen. Fla. and the Keys.—Grown in many varieties for its edible fruit. Nat. of trop. Am. and cult.—(*W. I., Mex., C. A., S. A.*)—Spr.

3. TAMALA Raf. Shrubs or trees. Leaves alternate, persistent: blades entire. Flowers in axillary peduncled cymes, greenish. Sepals 6, dissimilar. Style long-columnar: stigma capitate. Drupe equilateral. Few species, American.—Spr. or all year S.

Peduncles, pedicels and petioles glabrous or appressed-pubescent: fruit over 1 cm. thick.
Leaf-blades glabrous or nearly so, except sometimes the nerves beneath.

Leaf-blades finely reticulated beneath, mainly over thrice
as long as wide. .... 1. *T. Borbonia.*
Leaf-blades not reticulated beneath, mainly about twice as
long as wide. .... 2. *T. littoralis.*
Leaf-blades lustrous-pubescent beneath. .... 3. *T. humilis.*
Peduncles, pedicels and petioles tomentose: fruit less than 1 cm.
thick. .... 4. *T. pubescens.*

1. T. Borbonia (L.) Raf. A large tree with bark broken into flat ridges:
leaf-blades elliptic or nearly so, 5–15 cm. long, often acuminate at both ends,
bright-green and lustrous above, glaucescent and finely
reticulate beneath: sepals ascending, the inner ovate,
2–3 times longer than the outer, acutish: drupe obovoid or globose-obovoid, 1–1.5 cm. long, dark-blue or
nearly black, lustrous. [*Persea Borbonia* (L.) Pax]
—(RED-BAY. SWEET-BAY. FLORIDA-MAHOGANY. TISS-
WOOD. LAUREL-TREE.) — Hammocks and swamps,
Coastal Plain, Fla. to Tex. and Va.—The bright-red
heart-wood, close-grained, heavy, and strong, is used
for cabinet-work and construction.

2. T. littoralis Small. Shrub or tree: leaf-blades
elliptic, 2–5.5 cm. long, mostly obtuse at the apex,
bright-green and lustrous above, pale and glabrous beneath, not reticulate,
the lateral veins inconspicuous: drupe globular, 12–14 mm. long, purple-black
under the bloom. [*Persea littoralis* Small]—(SHORE-BAY.)—Coastal hammocks, pen. Fla.

3. T. humilis (Nash) Small. Shrub or small tree, the twigs, lower leaf-
surfaces and the inflorescence silky-pubescent: leaf-blades elliptic, 4–10 cm.
long, more or less revolute, glabrous and shining above, lustrous beneath:
sepals erect, obtuse, the inner oblong, 5 mm. long: drupe globular, about 1.5
cm. long, purplish-black under the bloom. [*Persea humilis* Nash]—(SILK-
BAY.)—Scrub, C pen. Fla.

4. T. pubescens (Pursh) Small. Shrub or small tree, the twigs, lower leaf-
surfaces and inflorescence tomentose: leaf-blades narrowly elliptic or elliptic-
lanceolate, or rarely oval, 5–20 cm. long, usually obtuse, often acuminate at
the apex, slightly revolute: sepals erect, acutish, the inner elliptic-obovate,
about twice as long as the outer: drupe oval, 8–11 mm. long, dark-blue with a
thin bloom. [*Persea pubescens* (Pursh) Sarg.]—(SWAMP-BAY. SWAMP RED-
BAY.)—Swamps and low hammocks, Coastal Plain and rarely adj. provinces,
Fla. to Tex. and N. C. (or Va.?).—The orange-colored and brown-streaked
heart-wood, close-grained and heavy, is used like that of *T. Borbonia.*

4. NECTANDRA Roland. Shrubs or trees. Leaves alternate, persistent:
blades entire. Flowers in panicled cymes, white, fragrant. Sepals 6, nearly
similar, somewhat elongate, spreading. Style cylin-
dric: stigma capitate. Drupe somewhat elongate,
seated in the cup-like hypanthium from which the
calyx has fallen away.—About 300 species, mostly
tropical American.

1. N. coriacea (Sw.) Griseb. Shrub or small tree:
leaf-blades narrowly elliptic or elliptic-lanceolate, 5–
12 cm. long, lustrous above: calyx creamy-white, 8–9
mm. broad; sepals obtuse: drupe subglobose or oval,
10–15 mm. long, dark-blue or black, seated in the red
or yellow hypanthium. [*Ocotea Catesbyana* (Michx.) Sarg.]—(LANCEWOOD.)

Hammocks, pen. Fla. and the Keys.—(*W. I.*)—Spr.—The dark-brown heart-wood, hard, and heavy, is used locally for cabinet-work.

5. **SASSAFRAS** Nees. Trees or shrubs. Leaves alternate, deciduous: blades lobed or partly entire. Flowers in axillary clustered cymes. Style columnar: stigma depressed. Drupe some-what elongate.—Two species, the following and one Asiatic.

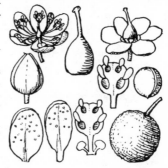

1. **S. Sassafras** (L.) Karst. Tree or shrub, with ridged bark: leaf-blades 3-lobed, or rarely entire or 2-lobed: flowers greenish-yellow, fragrant: sepals 6, narrowly elliptic, 2.5–3 mm. long: drupe oval, 8–10 long, dark-blue. — (SASSAFRAS. S A S S A F R A X. AGUE-TREE.)—Woods, fields, and roadsides, various provinces, N Fla. to Tex., Ia., and Me.—Spr.—Used medicinally and as a flavoring agent. The orange-brown heart-wood, coarse-grained, brittle, and weak, is used in boat-construction, cooperage, and for articles requiring lightness.

6. **GLABRARIA** L. Shrubs or trees. Leaves alternate (ours decidu-ous): blades entire. Flowers in clustered umbel-like involucrate cymes. Style subulate. Drupe (ours) subglobose. [*Mala-poena* Adans.]—About 100 species, widely distributed in tropical and warm regions.

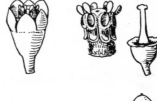

1. **G. geniculata** (Walt.) Britton. Spread-ing shrub 2–3 m. tall, with zigzag branches: leaf-blades elliptic, 1.5–6 cm. long: flowers 2–4 together: calyx yellow: sepals yellow, 2–3 mm. long: drupe 5–6 mm. in diameter, red.—(POND-SPICE. POND-BUSH.)—Swamps and ponds, Coastal Plain and rarely adj. provinces, Fla. to La., Tenn., and Va.—Wint.–spr.—One of our rarer shrubs of somewhat uncertain relationship. Its closest relatives are tropical.

7. **MISANTECA** Cham. & Schlecht. Shrubs or trees. Leaves alternate, persistent: blades entire. Flowers inconspicuous, in panicled cymes. Sepals 6, nearly similar, short, erect, about as long as the enlarged portion of the hypanthium. Style columnar: stigma minute, surrounded by the 3 erect stamens. Drupe slightly elongate, seated in the cup-like hypanthium which is bordered by the persistent calyx.— Four species, tropical American.

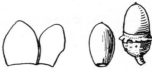

1. **M. triandra** (Sw.) Mez. Tree with somewhat flaky bark: leaf-blades elliptic or oval, 4.5–11 cm. long, abruptly acuminate, but often blunt, lustrous above: calyx white, 2–2.5 mm. broad; sepals obtuse: fruits

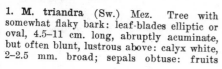

acorn-like, the drupe ovoid or ellipsoid-ovoid, 2–2.5 cm. long, green, the hypanthium reddish.—(MISANTECA.)—Hammocks, Everglade Keys, pen. Fla.—(W. I.)—Sum.—Known definitely only from the Brickell hammock, Miami, and now probably destroyed as a result of the real estate developments there.

8. **BENZOIN** Fabr. Shrubs or trees, strong-scented. Leaves alternate, deciduous: blades entire. Flowers yellow, in sessile cluster-like or umbel-like cymes. Style slender-columnar. Drupe somewhat elongate.—Seven species, North American and Asiatic.—Spr.—SPICE-BUSHES. BENJAMIN-BUSHES. SPICE-WOODS.

Leaf-blades tapering at the base: petioles slender and rather long.
　　　　　　　　　　　　　　　　　　　　　　　　　　　1. *B. aestivale.*
Leaf-blades rounded or cordate at the base: petioles stout and rather short.
　　　　　　　　　　　　　　　　　　　　　　　　　　　2. *B. melissaefolium.*

1. **B. aestivale** (L.) Nees. Shrub 1–3 m. tall, the branches often glabrous: leaf-blades obovate, oval, or elliptic, 5–12 cm. long, thin, obtuse or usually short-acuminate and acute at the apex, often slightly ciliate, acute or acuminate at the base, deep-green and glabrous above, pale or glaucescent and glabrous or sparingly pubescent beneath: flowers in dense clusters appearing before the leaves, 6–8 mm. broad: pedicels 3–5 cm. long: sepals thin, obovate or elliptic, obtuse, truncate or retuse at the apex: drupe oval, about 1 cm. long. [*Lindera Benzoin* (L.) Blume]—(SPICE-BUSH. BENJAMIN-BUSH.)—Wet woods, swamps, and stream-banks, various provinces, Fla. to La., Kans., Ont., and Me.—The bark and twigs are used medicinally and the fruit as a condiment.

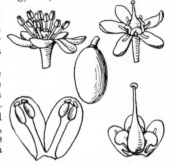

2. **B. melissaefolium** (Walt.) Nees. Shrub 3–10 dm. tall, the branches pubescent: leaf-blades quite firm, elliptic-ovate or elliptic-lanceolate, 3–12 cm. long, acutish, usually short-acuminate, more or less densely pubescent on both sides, rounded or cordate at the base: flowers in dense lateral clusters, appearing before the leaves: pedicels equalling the sepals or longer: sepals thin, 1–1.5 mm. long: drupe obovoid, nearly 1 cm. long.—(JOVE'S-FRUIT.)—Swamps and pond-margins, Coastal Plain and adj. provinces, Fla. to La., Mo., Ill., and N. C.—Bushes make a brilliant show in early spring.

FAMILY 4. **CASSYTHACEAE** — CASSYTHA FAMILY

Parasitic vines. Leaves mere scales, or wanting. Flowers perfect, in heads. spikes, or racemes. Calyx of 6 sepals in 2 unequal series, surmounting the accrescent hypanthium. Androecium of 9 stamens with 2-celled anthers, and 3 staminodia. Gynoecium of a single carpel. Drupe included.—One genus and about 15 species, tropical.

1. **CASSYTHA** [Osbeck] L. Vines with yellow or pale-green stems and branches, clinging to herbs and shrubs.—The flowers and fruits of *Cassytha*, although of quite different structure, resemble those of species of *Rhipsalis*. The drupe of our *Cassytha* resembles the berry of our species of *Rhipsalis* (page 913) in size, shape and color.

1. C. filiformis L. Stems matted, yellowish-green: flowers 3–6 in a spike: inner sepals triangular-ovate, 2–3 times larger than the outer: drupe globose, 5–7 mm. in diameter or rarely larger.—(Love-vine. Woe-vine.) —Coastal sand-dunes, hammocks, scrub, and pinelands, pen. Fla. and the Keys.—(*W. I.*) —This parasite appears to nearly all new acquaintances as a dodder (*Cuscuta*) which it resembles in habit and in color. Besides the technical characters closely associating it with the Lauraceae, it has the spicy fragrance of members of that family. The plants thrive on both herbaceous and woody hosts.

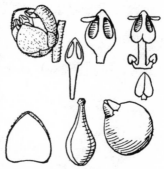

Order **MYRTALES** — Myrtal Order

Herbs, shrubs, or trees, sometimes aquatic or amphibious. Leaves alternate or opposite. Flowers regular or irregular, complete or much reduced. Hypanthium merely enclosing the ovary or adnate to it. Androecium of few or many stamens: anthers opening by slits or pores. Gynoecium 1–several-carpellary. Fruit capsular, baccate, or achene-like.

Style present, simple or compound: stigma terminal.
 Anthers opening by pores.   Fam. 1. Melastomaceae.
 Anthers opening by longitudinal valves.
  Hypanthium merely enclosing the ovary.   Fam. 2. Lythraceae.
  Hypanthium adnate to the ovary or mainly so.
   Cotyledons spirally convolute in the embryo.
    Ovary several-celled: ovules numerous, not
     pendulous.   Fam. 3. Punicaceae.
    Ovary 1-celled: ovules 2–5, pendulous.   Fam. 4. Terminaliaceae.
   Cotyledons not spirally convolute.
    Sepals imbricated, or united and the calyx
     falling away as a cap.   Fam. 5. Myrtaceae.
    Sepals valvate.
     Leaves stipulate: sepals leathery.   Fam. 6. Rhizophoraceae.
     Leaves not stipulate: sepals mem-
      branous or herbaceous.   Fam. 7. Epilobiaceae.
Styles wanting: stigmas sessile.   Fam. 8. Gunneraceae.

Family 1. **MELASTOMACEAE** — Meadow-beauty Family

Herbs, shrubs, or trees. Leaves opposite: blades with 3–several ribs. Flowers perfect. Calyx of 3–6 sepals surmounting the hypanthium. Corolla of 3–6 oblique petals. Androecium of 6–12 stamens, those opposite the petals sometimes abortive. Gynoecium of 3–5 united carpels. Ovary enclosed in or adnate to the hypanthium. Fruit baccate or capsular.—One hundred and fifty genera and about 2,500 species, most abundant in tropical South America.

Herbs: fruit a capsule.   1. Rhexia.
Shrubs or trees: fruit a berry.   2. Tetrazygia.

1. RHEXIA L. Perennial herbs with rootstocks. Leaf-blades usually 3–5-ribbed. Hypanthium urceolate, prolonged beyond the ovary. Sepals 4. Petals 4, deciduous. Ovary 4-celled, free. Capsule included, 4-valved.— About 15 species, natives of eastern North America and Cuba.—Maid-marian. Meadow-beauties.—Most of the species grow in highly acid soils.

Anthers relatively short, elliptic, not spurred at the base. 1. ELLIPTICAE.
Anthers elongate, linear, spurred at the base. 2. LINEARES.

I. ELLIPTICAE

Corolla yellow. 1. *R. lutea.*
Corolla purple or rarely white.
  Hypanthium glandular-pubescent: upper surface of the leaf-
  blades glabrous. 2. *R. serrulata.*
  Hypanthium glabrous: upper surface of the leaf-blades
  bristly. 3. *R. ciliosa.*

II. LINEARES

Neck of the mature hypanthium as long as the body or longer.
  Leaf-blades narrowly linear, the midrib only prominent and
  conspicuous. 4. *R. cubensis.*
  Leaf-blades not linear, the 3 nerves prominent and con-
  spicuous.
    Stems rather sparingly pubescent with delicate hairs:
    leaf-blades nearly glabrous. 5. *R. mariana.*
    Stems densely pubescent with coarse yellow hairs: leaf-
    blades shaggy-pubescent with hairs like those on the
    stem. 6. *R. Nashii.*
Neck of the mature hypanthium much shorter than the body.
  Stems and branches terete or nearly so.
    Hypanthium glabrous or with a few scattered hairs.
      Leaf-blades linear to lanceolate. 7. *R. lanceolata.*
      Leaf-blades oval, elliptic, or oblong-ovate, very thin. 8. *R. delicatula.*
    Hypanthium densely glandular-pubescent. 9. *R. Alifanus.*
  Stems sharply angled or narrowly 4-winged.
    Corolla over 2 cm. broad, colored.
      Sepals less than ½ as long as the hypanthium at
      maturity.
        Stems with pubescent internodes: hypanthium
        pubescent at maturity. 10. *R. virginica.*
        Stems with glabrous internodes: hypanthium
        glabrous at maturity. 11. *R. stricta.*
      Sepals fully ½ as long as the hypanthium at maturity. 12. *R. aristosa.*
    Corolla less than 2 cm. broad, white. 13. *R. parviflora.*

1. **R. lutea** Walt. Stems 1–3 dm. tall: leaf-blades cuneate to elliptic or elliptic-linear, 1–2.5 cm. long: petals yellow, 9–13 mm. long: capsule about 4 mm.
long.—Moist pinelands, Coastal Plain, Fla.
to La. and N. C.—Spr.–sum.

2. **R. serrulata** Nutt. Stems 5–30 cm. tall:
leaf-blades ovate, oval, or suborbicular, 0.5–1
cm. long: petals purple, about 10 mm. long:
capsule about 4 mm. long, subglobose.—
Low pinelands and open hammocks, Coastal
Plain, Fla. to Miss. and Ga.—Spr.–sum.

3. **R. ciliosa** Michx. Stems 2–6 dm. tall:
leaf-blades broadly ovate to ovate-lanceolate
or elliptic, 1–2 cm. long: petals violet-
purple or deep-pink, 9–15 cm. long: capsule
4–5 mm. long.—Moist pinelands and sandhill bogs, Coastal Plain, C Fla. to La. and
Md.—Spr.–sum.

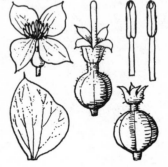

4. **R. cubensis** Griseb. Stems 2–5 dm. tall, glandular-hirsute: leaf-blades
linear or nearly so, 1.5–4 cm. long: sepals lanceolate or triangular-lanceolate:
petals purple, 11–17 mm. long: capsule 6–7 mm. long. [*R. floridana* Nash]—
Sandy and clayey swamps, Coastal Plain, Fla. to Miss. and Ga.—Sum. or all
year S.

5. **R. mariana** L. Stems 2–8 dm. tall, villous-hirsute: leaf-blades narrowly
elliptic, lanceolate, or elliptic-lanceolate, 1.5–8 cm. long: sepals ovate to triangular: petals pale-purple or deep-purple, 14–28 mm. long: capsule 6–7 mm.
long.—(PALE MEADOW-BEAUTY.)—Swamps, marshes, and ditches, various provinces, Fla. to Tex., Mo., and N. Y.—Spr.–fall.

6. R. Nashii Small. Stems 3–6 dm. tall, densely hirsute: leaf-blades narrowly elliptic-lanceolate, 2–5 cm. long: sepals triangular: petals purple, 14–17 mm. long: capsule 5–6 mm. long.—Swamps, Coastal Plain, Fla. to La.—Sum.

7. R. lanceolata Walt. Stems 1–4 dm. tall, villous-hirsute: leaf-blades oblanceolate, elliptic-oblanceolate, or linear-lanceolate, 1–2.5 cm. long: sepals lanceolate: petals white to pale-purple, 12–17 mm. long: capsule 6–7 mm. long. [*R. filiformis* Small.]—Marshes and swamps, Coastal Plain, Fla. to La., Tenn., and N. C.—Spr.-sum.

8. R. delicatula Small. Stems 1–4 dm. tall, sparingly pubescent: leaf-blades elliptic to ovate, 1–2.5 cm. long: sepals triangular: petals pale-purple, 10–15 mm. long: capsule 4–5 mm. long.—Stream-banks, in the Blue Ridge of Ga. —Sum.

9. R. Alifanus Walt. Stems 3–10 dm. tall, glabrous: leaf-blades lanceolate to linear-lanceolate, 3–8 cm. long: sepals triangular: petals bright-purple, 17–22 mm. long: capsule 6–7 mm. long. [*R. glabella* Michx.]—Moist pinelands, Coastal Plain, N Fla. to La. and N. C.—Spr.-sum.

10. R. virginica L. Stems 2–10 dm. tall: leaf-blades elliptic, oval, lanceolate, or ovate-lanceolate, 2–10 cm. long: sepals lanceolate or triangular-lanceolate: petals bright-purple, 11–17 mm. long: capsule 5–6 mm. long.—(DEER-GRASS. MEADOW-BEAUTY. HANDSOME-HARRY.)—Sandy swamps and damp meadows, various provinces, Fla. to La., Mo., and Me.—Spr.-fall.—The entire plant is sometimes red.

11. R. stricta Pursh. Stems 6–13 dm. tall: leaf-blades lanceolate to elliptic-lanceolate, 2–1 cm. long: sepals triangular: petals purple, 12–16 mm. long: capsule 6–7 mm. long.—Moist pinelands and ponds, Coastal Plain, Ga. to Miss. and N. C.—Sum.

12. R. aristosa Britton. Stems 2–6 dm. tall, glabrous: leaf-blades linear to linear-lanceolate or sometimes linear-elliptic, 1–3 cm. long: sepals linear to linear-lanceolate: petals magenta-red, 12–20 mm. long: capsule about 6 mm. long.—Sandy swamps and damp pinelands, Coastal Plain, Ga. to N. J.—Sum.

13. R. parviflora Chapm. Stems 1–3 dm. tall, pubescent: leaf-blades elliptic or nearly oval, 1–2 cm. long: sepals triangular-lanceolate: petals white, less than 10 mm. long: capsule about 3 mm. long.—Shallow ponds, near Apalachicola, Fla.—Sum.

2. TETRAZYGIA L. C. Rich. Shrubs or trees. Leaf-blades 3–5-ribbed, mostly scurfy or tomentose beneath. Sepals, and petals, 4–6. Ovary 4- or 5-celled. Berry included, the hypanthium-neck short.—About 16 species, West Indian.

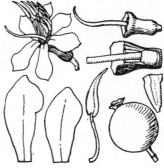

1. T. bicolor (Mill.) Cogn. Shrub or small tree with scaly bark: leaf-blades lanceolate to elliptic-lanceolate, 8–20 cm. long, silvery beneath, stout-petioled: panicle 1–2 dm. long: calyx about 1 mm. long: petals white, 7–8 mm. long, cuneate: anthers lanceolate, 5–6 mm. long: berry purple or black, the body 8–10 mm. long.—(TETRAZYGIA.)— Hammocks and pinelands, Everglade Keys, Fla.—(W. I.)—Sum.—This is one of the conspicuously tropical West Indian plants which are so numerous on the Everglade Keys that, floristically these limestone islands may be considered a part of the West Indies. In hammocks *Tetrazygia* is usually a small tree; in pinelands it is usually a shrub.

FAMILY 2. **LYTHRACEAE** — LOOSESTRIFE FAMILY

Herbs, shrubs, or trees. Leaves mostly opposite: blades usually entire. Flowers perfect. Calyx of 4 or 5 sepals, commonly accompanied by accessory teeth. Corolla of 4 or 5 petals, or wanting. Androecium of few or many stamens: anthers versatile. Gynoecium of mostly 2–6 united carpels. Ovary 2–6-celled, or rarely 1-celled, free from the hypanthium. Fruit a capsule, included in the hypanthium.—Twenty-one genera and about 400 species, widely distributed.

Flowers regular or nearly so: hypanthium symmetrical.   Tribe I. LYTHREAE.
Flowers irregular: hypanthium oblique.   Tribe II. PARSONSIEAE.

I. LYTHREAE

Hypanthium campanulate or turbinate, becoming hemispheric
   or globose.
  Herbs.
    Petals wanting: capsules indehiscent.   1. DIDIPLIS.
    Petals 4, except in *Ammannia latifolia*: capsules de-
      hiscent, sometimes irregularly so.
      Capsules bursting irregularly.   2. AMMANNIA.
      Capsules septicidally dehiscent.   3. ROTALA.
  Shrubs or trees.
    Flowers in axillary cymes: aquatic shrubs.   4. DECODON.
    Flowers in terminal panicles: terrestrial shrubs or
      trees.   5. LAGERSTROEMIA.
Hypanthium elongate, cylindric or tubular.   6. LYTHRUM.

II. PARSONSIEAE

Hypanthium enlarged or spurred on one side: petals unequal.   7. PARSONSIA.

1. **DIDIPLIS** Raf. Flaccid herbs, resembing *Callitriche*. Leaf-blades narrow, entire, pellucid. Flowers solitary in the axils. Sepals 4, without accessory teeth. Petals wanting. Stamens 2–4. Style very short: stigma 2-lobed. Embryo with narrow cotyledons. — One species.

1. **D. diandra** (Nutt.) Wood. Stem 1–3 dm. long: emersed leaves with linear to linear-spatulate blades, thicker than the submersed ones, 1–2 cm. long: capsule urceolate, about 1 mm. in diameter.—(WATER-PURSLANE.) — Ponds and wet shores, various provinces, Fla. to Tex., Minn., and N. C.— (*Mex.*)—Sum.

2. **AMMANNIA** L. Leathery-succulent herbs. Leaf-blades, narrow, often auricled at the base. Flowers in axillary, sometimes 1-flowered, cymes, greenish, or sometimes tinged with red. Sepals 4, often accompanied with small teeth. Petals 4, early deciduous, or wanting. Stamens 4–8. Style filiform, sometimes short: stigma capitate. Embryo with auricled cotyledons.— About 20 species, most abundant in warm regions.

Corolla present.
  Leaves broadest below the middle: capsule 3–4 mm. in diameter.   1. *A. coccinea.*
  Leaves broadest above the middle: capsule 5–6 mm. in diameter.   2. *A. Koehnei.*
Corolla wanting.   3. *A. latifolia.*

1. A. coccinea Rottb. Plant 1–5 dm. tall: leaf-blades linear to linear-lanceolate, 2–6 cm. long, partly clasping: petals broadly obovate: capsule 3–4 mm. in diameter.—Swamps and low grounds, various provinces, Fla. to Tex., S. D., and N. J.—(*W. I., Mex., C. A., S. A.*)—Sum.-fall.

2. A. Koehnei Britton. Plant 1–6 dm. tall: leaf-blades spatulate, oblanceolate or elliptic, 2–8 cm. long, those of the lower ones merely sessile: petals spatulate: stamens and short style included: capsule 5–6 mm. in diameter.—(Tooth-cups.)—Swamps and along streams, Coastal Plain and adj. provinces, Fla. to N. J.—Sum.-fall.

3. A. latifolia L. Plant 2–11 dm. tall: leaf-blades linear-elliptic to linear-lanceolate, mostly 3–7 cm. long, slightly auricled and clasping at the base: corolla wanting; capsule 4–5 mm. in diameter.—Low hammocks, lime-sinks, and swamps, S pen. Fla. and the Keys.—(*W. I., Mex., C. A., S. A.*)—All year.

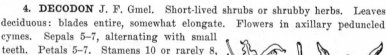

3. ROTALA L. Herbs resembling *Ammannia*. Leaf-blades narrow, entire. Flowers greenish, usually solitary in the axils. Sepals 4, accompanied by appendages in the sinuses. Petals usually 4. Stamens 4. Style very short. —About 30 species, most abundant in warm and tropical regions.

1. R. ramosior (L.) Koehn. Stem 0.5–4 dm. long: leaf-blades elliptic to linear or spatulate, 1–3 cm. long: sepals acute: petals obovate or cuneate, as long as the sepals or longer: capsule 2.5–3.5 mm. in diameter.— Hammocks, wet, sandy places, and swamps, various provinces, Fla. to Tex., Minn., and Mass.—(*W. I., Mex., C. A., S. A.*)—Sum.-fall.

4. DECODON J. F. Gmel. Short-lived shrubs or shrubby herbs. Leaves deciduous: blades entire, somewhat elongate. Flowers in axillary peduncled cymes. Sepals 5–7, alternating with small teeth. Petals 5–7. Stamens 10 or rarely 8, alternating short and long, the longer exserted. Capsule loculicidally 3–6-valved. One species.

1. D. verticillatus (L.) Ell. Stem arching, mostly 4–16 dm. long: leaf-blades lanceolate or elliptic-lanceolate, 3–20 cm. long: sepals acuminate: petals purple-pink, lanceolate to ovate, 7–9 mm. long: capsule about 5 mm. in diameter.—(Swamp-loosestrife. Willow-herb. Water-oleander. Peat-weed.)— Swamps and ponds, various provinces, Fla. to La., Minn., and Me.—Sum.

5. LAGERSTROEMIA L. Shrubs or trees. Leaves persistent: blades short. Flowers in terminal panicles. Sepals 5–7. Petals 5–7, the blades crisped. Stamens numerous. Capsule loculicidally 3–6-valved.—About 25 species, in Asia, Africa, and Australia.

1. L. indica L. Small tree or shrub with fluted trunk: leaf-blades obovate or oval, 1–2.5 cm. long, entire: sepals shorter than the hypanthium: petals purple, pink, or white, or rarely red, the blades crisped: capsule oval-globose, 8–9 mm. long.— (CRAPE - MYRTLE. LADIES' - STREAMER.) — Waste-places, cult. ground, old fields, and about gardens, various provinces, Fla. to Tex. and Va. (or Md.?). Nat. of Asia and cult.—Spr.–fall.—Trees are long-lived. They suggest premature age, but are very showy when in flower. They frequently indicate the position of residences or settlements that have long ago disappeared. The thin bark peels off the trunk leaving a smooth clean surface which gives the tree a pale ghostly appearance at night.

6. LYTHRUM L. Herbs or shrubs. Leaf-blades entire. Flowers axillary or in terminal spikes or racemes, rose-purple or white. Sepals 4–6, not involute, alternating with spreading appendages. Petals 4–6, nearly equal.— About 30 species of wide geographical distribution. Spr.–fall or all year S.— LOOSESTRIFES.

Leaves mostly alternate.
    Leaf-blades rounded or cordate at the base.   1. *L. alatum.*
    Leaf-blades narrowed at the base.
        Leaf-blades thick, those of the branches numerous, approximate, mostly less than 1.5 cm. long: hypanthium 6–8 mm. long.   2. *L. lanceolatum.*
        Leaf-blades thin, those of the branches few, mostly over 1.5 cm. long: hypanthium 3–5 mm. long.   3. *L. Curtissii.*
Leaves mostly opposite.
    Leaf-blades linear or nearly so, those on the flowering branches much reduced.   4. *L. lineare.*
    Leaf-blades elliptic to orbicular or rarely cuneate, those on the flowering branches not much reduced.   5. *L. flagellare.*

1. L. alatum Pursh. Stem 3–13 dm. tall: leaf-blades lanceolate, elliptic, or ovate-lanceolate, 1–5 cm. long: mature hypanthium 5–8 mm. long, the appendages slender-subulate, much longer than the triangular sepals: petals obovate or cuneate-obovate, 5–6 mm. long: capsule 4.5– 5 mm. long.—(WINGED-LOOSESTRIFE.)—Low grounds, swamps, and ditches, various provinces, Ga. to La., Colo., Minn., Ont., and Mass.—*L. cordifolium* Nieuwl. is based on an aberrant specimen of *L. alatum* from Florida.

2. L. lanceolatum Ell. Stem 6–16 dm. tall: leaf-blades elliptic to linear-elliptic, 1–6 cm. long: mature hypanthium 5–6 mm. long, the appendages subulate, much longer than the triangular sepals: petals obovate to cuneate-obovate, 6–7.5 mm. long: capsule

4.5–5 mm. long.—Ditches, stream-banks, and swamps, Coastal Plain and adj. provinces, Fla. to Tex., Okla., and S. C.

3. L. Curtissii Fernald. Similar to *L. lanceolatum* in habit: leaf-blades thin, oval, elliptic, or elliptic-lanceolate, 2–5.5 mm. long: mature hypanthium 3–4 mm. long, the appendages slender-subulate, longer than the minute sepals: petals elliptic to obovate-elliptic, 2.5–3.5 mm. long: capsule about 4 mm. long. —Muddy, often calcareous swamps, Coastal Plain, N Fla. and adj. Ga.

4. L. lineare L. Stem 3–12 dm. tall: leaf-blades linear, 1–4 cm. long: mature hypanthium about 4 mm. long, the appendages triangular, about as long as the deltoid sepals: petals cuneate or cuneate-elliptic, 4–5 mm. long: capsule barely 4 mm. long.—Coastal sand-dunes and open hammocks, Coastal Plain, Fla. to Tex. and N. J.

5. L. flagellare Shuttlw. Stem creeping: leaf-blades elliptic to orbicular or rarely cuneate, 0.5–1 cm. long: mature hypanthium 6–8 mm. long or longer, the appendages subulate, several times longer than the glabrous sepals: petals purple, cuneate-obovate, 4–5 mm. long: capsule 3–4 mm. long or shorter. [*L. Vulneraria* (Fl. SE. U. S.)]—Low grounds and swamps, S pen. Fla.

7. PARSONSIA P. Br. Herbs or woody plants, mostly clammy-pubescent. Leaf-blades entire. Flowers axillary, or in terminal spikes or racemes. Sepals 6, alternating with small teeth. Petals 6, unequal. Stamens adnate to near the top of the hypanthium. Embryo with orbicular cotyledons. [*Cuphea* P. Br.]—About 200 species, American.

Calyx-limb prominently 2-lipped: posterior pair of stamens not reduced.
  Style pubescent: stamens 12; anthers not woolly.
                                             1. *P. petiolata.*
  Style glabrous: stamens 11; anthers of the longer pair densely woolly.
                                             2. *P. procumbens.*
Calyx-limb with 5 equal lobes: posterior pair of stamens often much reduced.
  Plant perennial: hypanthium with glandular hairs all over; calyx more or less spreading: petals 1.5–2 mm. long.
                                             3. *P. lythroides.*
  Plant annual: hypanthium with few simple hairs on the ribs: calyx erect: petals 5–6 mm. long.
                                           4. *P. Balsamona.*

1. P. petiolata (L.) Rusby. Plant annual, 1–7 dm. tall: leaf-blades lanceolate to ovate-lanceolate, 1–1.5 cm. long: hypanthium and calyx 8–10 mm. long: flowers rose-purple: upper lip of the calyx much broader than long: upper petals 4.5–5.5 mm. long: capsule 6–8 mm. long.— (WAX-WEED. TAR-WEED. WAX-BUSH. CLAMMY-WEED.)—Dry rocky soil, hillsides, and old fields, various provinces, Ga. to La., Kans., and N. H.—Sum.–fall.

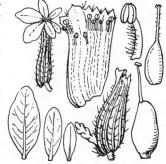

2. P. procumbens (Cav.) Small. Plant perennial, 10–12 dm. tall: leaf-blades lanceolate or ovate-lanceolate, 2–6 cm. long: hypanthium and calyx 18–22 mm. long: flowers purple or reddish: upper lip of the calyx about as long as broad: upper petals 12–14 mm. long: capsule 9–10 mm. long.—Wasteplaces and thickets, Blue Ridge, N. C. Nat. of Mex. and cult.—Sum.–fall.

3. **P. lythroides** Small. Plant perennial, 2–6 dm. tall: leaf-blades elliptic, 1–2 cm. long: hypanthium and calyx 8–10 mm. long: flowers lavender or white: calyx-lobes deltoid: petals spatulate, 5–6 mm. long, or the upper ones 7–8 mm. long: capsule 3.5–4.5 mm. long.—Low pinelands, M and W Fla.—Spr.–sum.

4. **P. Balsamona** (C. & S.) Standley. Plant annual, 2–9 dm. tall: leaf-blades elliptic to oval, or somewhat obovate, 2–6 cm. long, usually rugose in age: hypanthium and calyx 5.5–6.8 mm. long: flowers bluish: calyx-lobes broadly deltoid: petals elliptic or nearly so 1.5–2 mm, long: capsule 4–5 mm. long.—Low hammocks, lake region, pen. Fla.—(*Mex., C. A., S. A.*)—Spr.–fall.

FAMILY 3. PUNICACEAE — POMEGRANATE FAMILY

Shrubs or trees. Leaves opposite or nearly so, persistent: blades simple. Flowers perfect, solitary or in short-peduncled axillary clusters. Hypanthium leathery. Calyx of 5–7 sepals. Corolla of 5–7 wrinkled petals. Androecium of numerous stamens in several series: anthers versatile. Gynoecium of several united carpels. Ovary inferior. Fruit a several-celled berry crowned with the calyx, the seeds in a watery pulp.—One genus and 2 species, mostly in the Old World tropics.

1. **PUNICA** [Tourn.] L. Leaf-blades entire. Flowers showy. Sepals persistent on the fruit. Petals deciduous. Berry pendulous.

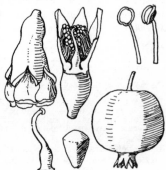

1. **P. Granatum** L. Small tree or shrub: leaf-blades oval, elliptic, or elliptic-lanceolate, varying to broadest above or below the middle, 1–8 cm. long: sepals triangular to triangular-lanceolate: petals scarlet, 1.5–2.5 cm. long: berry subglobose or depressed, 5–10 cm. in diameter.—(POMEGRANATE.)—Old-fields, woods, and waste-grounds, Fla. Nat. of the Orient and cult.—(*W. I.*)—Persistent on old settlement sites and homesteads long after the habitations have disappeared.—This plant in cultivation from prehistoric times has developed into a variety of habits and flower-color, vermilion, yellow, white, and variegated.

FAMILY 4. TERMINALIACEAE — WHITE-MANGROVE FAMILY

Shrubs or trees, or woody vines. Leaves alternate or opposite: blades simple, leathery. Flowers often apetalous, regular, perfect or polygamous, racemose or capitate. Calyx of 4–5 valvate deciduous or rarely persistent sepals. Corolla of 4–5 petals, or wanting. Androecium of twice, or rarely thrice, as many stamens as the sepals. Filaments distinct. Gynoecium a single carpel. Ovary 1-celled. Style terminal. Stigma entire or nearly so. Fruit drupaceous or berry-like, indehiscent, often crowned with the accrescent calyx.—Fifteen genera and 275 species, mostly tropical.

Sepals deciduous: corolla wanting.
  Flowers in heads: hypanthium flattened: fruit small, in a
    cone-like head.   1. CONOCARPUS.
  Flowers in spikes: hypanthium terete: fruit separate, large.   2. TERMINALIA.
Sepals persistent.
  Corolla wanting: leaves alternate.   3. BUCIDA.
  Corolla present: leaves opposite.   4. LAGUNCULARIA.

1. **CONOCARPUS** L. Shrubs or trees, evergreen. Leaves alternate. Flowers perfect, in spicate or panicled heads. Hypanthium not ribbed. Stamens 5. Fruit capitate.—One species.

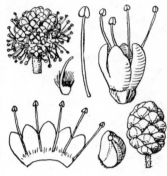

1. **C. erecta** L. Shrub, or tree sometimes 20 m. tall, with glabrous or fine-silky foliage: leaf-blades elliptic or oval, 2–5 cm. long, entire: heads 9–14 mm. in diameter at maturity: flowers greenish: drupe 2-winged, 4–7 mm. long.—(BUTTONWOOD.)—Coastal hammocks and sandy shores, pen. Fla., Everglade Keys, and Florida Keys.—(*W. I., Mex., C. A., S. A.*)—All year.—The bark is used medicinally and for tanning. The yellow-brown heart-wood, close-grained, very heavy, and hard, is used, in southern Florida for making charcoal.—A silvery pubescent variety occurs on the Florida Keys and on both coasts of the peninsula.

2. **TERMINALIA** L. Shrubs or trees, deciduous. Leaves clustered near the ends of the branches. Flowers in simple or branched spikes. Hypanthium not ribbed. Stamens 10.—About 100 species, of the Old World tropics.

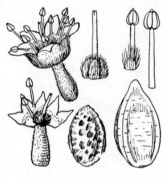

1. **T. Catappa** L. Shrub, or tree sometimes 17 m. tall: leaf-blades cuneate to oblanceolate: spikes 5–15 cm. long: flowers green or whitish: hypanthium and calyx 8–11 mm. long: drupe elliptic or nearly so, glabrous. —(INDIAN-ALMOND. WEST-INDIAN ALMOND.) Pinelands and old fields, S pen. Fla. and the Keys. Nat. of the E. Indies and Oceanica; escaped from cult.—(*W. I.*)—All year.— The seeds are edible. Although a native of the tropics where storms are usual, this tree never developed a wood or foliage capable of resisting the force of a hurricane. A severe storm will often tear a tree to pieces.

3. **BUCIDA** L. Shrubs or trees, evergreen. Leaves relatively small, clustered at the ends of the branches. Flowers in simple or branched spikes, often crowded. Hypanthium terete. Stamens 10. Fruit in short spikes.—Two species, West Indian.

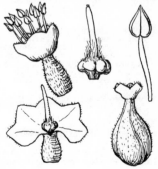

1. **B. Buceras** L. A tree sometimes 15 m. tall: leaf-blades spatulate to obovate, oval, or elliptic: spikes 2–10 cm. long: flowers greenish: hypanthium and calyx 4–5 mm. long: calyx-lobes shorter than the tube: drupe ovoid-conic or flask-shaped, pubescent. —(BLACK-OLIVE.)—Hammocks, upper Florida Keys.—(*W. I., C. A.*)—The light yellow-brown heart-wood is close-grained, very heavy, and hard. Great numbers of trees are used as shade-trees and ornamentals in Florida.

2. **LAGUNCULARIA** Gaertn.   Shrubs or trees, evergreen.   Leaves
opposite. Flowers polygamous, in simple or branched spikes. Hypanthium
ribbed.   Petals mostly shorter than the
sepals.   Stamens 10.   Fruit spicate or
paniculate.—One species.

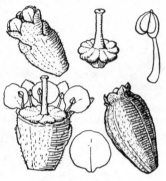

1. **L. racemosa** Gaertn. f. Shrub, or tree
sometimes 20 m. tall: leaf-blades oblong,
varying to oval or obovate, 2–5 cm. long,
entire, alike or nearly so on both sides:
spikes 3–6 cm. long: drupe elliptic-obovoid,
2 cm. long.—(WHITE-MANGROVE.   WHITE-
BUTTONWOOD.)—Rocky and sandy shores and
coastal hammocks, pen. Fla. and the Keys.
—(*W. I., Mex., C. A., S. A.*)—Spr.—The
white flowers are very fragrant. The dark
yellow-brown heart-wood is close-grained,
heavy, and hard. The bark is rich in tannic
acid.

FAMILY 5. **MYRTACEAE** — MYRTLE FAMILY

Shrubs or trees, or rarely herbs, abounding in pungent and aromatic
volatile oil, evergreen. Leaves opposite, or rarely alternate or whorled:
blades often simple, pellucid-punctate, flat or often very thick, often
with nerves parallel with the margins. Flowers perfect, regular. Calyx
of 4 or 5, or many, valvate or imbricate, persistent sepals, or cap-like and
deciduous. Petals borne on the margin of a hypanthium or wanting.
Androecium of numerous stamens, or very rarely of as many as the sepals.
Gynoecium compound. Ovary inferior or partly so, 1–many-celled.
Styles united. Fruit sometimes dehiscent, often crowned with the calyx.—
Sixty genera and about 1,750 species, widely distributed in the tropics.

Fruit fleshy, baccate : leaf-blades pinnately veined.
   Calyx of several persistent or tardily deciduous, val-
      vate sepals, not lid-like : petals present : disk
      annular : fruit a berry crowned with the persis-
      tent calyx or a capsule with an annular ring.
      Calyx of regularly separating sepals.   Tribe   I. EUGENIEAE.
      Calyx of irregularly separating sepals.   Tribe II. MYRTEAE.
   Calyx lid-like, early deciduous : petals wanting : disk
      cup-like : fruit crowned with the cup-like disk and
      hypanthium.   Tribe III. MYRCIEAE.
Fruit dry, capsular : leaf-blades parallel-veined.   Tribe IV. MELALEUCEAE.

I. EUGENIEAE

Inflorescence centripetal : flowers in raceme-like, umbel-like, or
   contracted clusters : persistent calyx inconspicuous.   1. EUGENIA.
Inflorescence centrifugal : flowers in sessile or peduncled
   dichotomous cymes : persistent calyx conspicuous.
   Cymes markedly peduncled, the terminal flowers sessile :
      disk contracted at maturity, the sepals crowded and con-
      verging on the top of the fruit : seeds one or two.   2. ANAMOMIS.
   Cymes sessile or nearly so, the terminal flowers stalked :
      disk expanded, the sepals lax, more or less spreading on
      the top of the fruit : seeds several to many.   3. MOSIERA.

II. MYRTEAE

Leaf-blades prominently ribbed : cymes 1–few-flowered, axillary.   4. PSIDIUM.

III. MYRCIEAE

Leaf-blades obscurely ribbed : cymes several–many-flowered.   5. CALYPTRANTHES.

IV. MELALEUCEAE

Tree with thick peeling bark in many papery layers: leaves very numerous: inflorescence conspicuously copiously flowered.   6. MELALEUCA.

1. **EUGENIA** [Mich.] L.   Shrubs or trees.   Leaf-blades thickish, neither prominently ribbed nor veiny, persistent.   Cymes cluster-like, sessile or short-peduncled.   Flowers white.   Sepals broad, not accrescent.   Petals much larger than the sepals.   Stamens numerous, borne on the annular disk.   Style filiform or subulate-filiform.   Berry minutely crowned in the calyx.   Seeds 1–4.—About 600 species, mostly of tropical regions.—STOPPERS.

Pedicels short and stout, usually shorter than the flowers and much shorter than
 the fruits.
  Fruit oval or ellipsoid-oval.   1. *E. buxifolia.*
  Fruit subglobose, sometimes depressed.
   Leaf-blades of a rhombic type, more or less constricted at
    the base and the tip: fruit depressed, 10–12 mm. in
    diameter.   2. *E. axillaris.*
   Leaf-blades of an oval or elliptic type, obtuse: fruit sub-
    globose, 6–8 mm. in diameter.   3. *E. anthera.*
Pedicels relatively long and slender, longer than the flowers and
 usually longer than the fruits.
  Leaf-blades bluntly acuminate, dull above: fruits depressed,
   9–16 mm. in diameter.   4. *E. rhombea.*
  Leaf-blades slenderly acuminate, shining above: fruits sub-
   globose or globose-obovoid, 5–8 mm. in diameter. 5. *E. confusa.*

1. **E. buxifolia** (Sw.) Willd.   Shrub or small tree, the bark scaly: leaf-blades cuneate to nearly elliptic, 2–4 cm. long, much paler beneath than above: corolla 4–5 mm. broad; petals longer than wide: fruit oval or ellipsoid-oval, 6–7 mm. broad, black.—(SPANISH-STOPPER.)—Coastal hammocks, S pen. Fla. and the Keys.—(*W. I.*)—The dark-brown heart-wood, close-grained, heavy, and very hard, is used locally in cabinet work.

2. **E. axillaris** (Sw.) Willd.   Shrub or small tree, the bark scaly: leaf-blades elliptic-ovate to nearly elliptic, 3–5 cm. long, slightly paler beneath than above: corolla 5–6 mm. broad; petals mostly wider than long: fruit depressed,   10–12   mm.   broad,   black. — (WHITE-STOPPER.)—Coastal hammocks, S pen. Fla. and the Keys.—(*W. I.*)—The brown heart-wood, close-grained, heavy, and hard, is used locally for cabinet work.

3. **E. anthera** Small.   Shrub or small tree, the bark pale, rather smooth: leaf-blades oval to elliptic or nearly so, 2–5.5 cm. long, slightly paler beneath than above: corolla 5–6 mm. broad; petals slightly longer than wide: fruit subglobose, 6–7 mm. in diameter, dark red to black.—Hammocks along or near the coast, S pen. Fla.—The brown heart-wood is close-grained and hard.

4. **E. rhombea** (Berg) Urban.   Tree, the bark smooth: leaf-blades ovate to elliptic, 3–6 cm. long, slightly acuminate: corolla about 10 mm. broad; petals slightly longer than the sepals: fruit depressed, 9–16 mm. broad, orange tinged with red, or black at maturity.—(RED-STOPPER.)—Hammocks, lower Florida Keys.—(*W. I.*)—The light-brown heart-wood, close-grained, heavy, and hard, is used locally for cabinet work.

5. E. confusa DC. Tree, the bark scaly: leaf-blades ovate, oval-ovate, or elliptic-ovate, 3–5 cm. long, markedly acuminate: corolla 4–6 mm. broad; petals about twice as long as the sepals: fruit subglobose or globose-obovoid, 5–8 mm. broad, scarlet. [*E. Garberi* Sarg.]—(IRONWOOD.)—Hammocks, Everglade Keys, Fla. and the Keys.—(*W. I.*)—The red-brown heart-wood, close-grained, heavy, and very hard, is used locally for cabinet work.

2. ANAMOMIS Griseb. Shrubs or trees. Leaf-blades thickish, not ribbed, with rather faint lateral veins. Cymes decidedly peduncled, 1–many-flowered, the branches shorter than the peduncle. Flowers fragrant. Sepals ciliate, one pair much larger than the other. Petals paired, white. Stamens numerous, borne on the small annular disk. Style filiform. Berry crowned with the persistent calyx, red or reddish. Seeds solitary or 2.—About 8 species, West Indian and Floridian.—Spr.—NAKEDWOODS.

Corolla over 1 cm. wide: petals 4.5–6 mm. long: stamens mostly 60–70: cymes several-flowered.   1. *A. Simpsonii.*
Corolla less than 1 cm. wide: petals 2.5–3.5 mm. long: stamens mostly 30–40: cymes few-flowered.   2. *A. dicrana.*

1. A. Simpsonii Small. Tree becoming 20 m. tall, the trunk with pale-tan bark, strongly buttressed at the base: leaf-blades narrowly obovate, elliptic-obovate, or nearly elliptic, 2.5–6.5 cm. long, acutish, obtuse or notched, much paler beneath than above, rather long-petioled: cymes long-petioled in anthesis, 7–14 flowered, the primary bracts small, but leaf-like: calyx 6–7 mm. wide; larger sepals about 3 mm. long: berry ellipsoid, often broadly so, 8–10 mm. long, red.—Hammocks, lower E coast and Everglade Keys, Fla.—The foliage contains a volatile oil, somewhat resembling that of nutmeg in flavor.

2. A. dicrana (Berg) Britton. Shrub or small tree becoming 8 m. tall, the trunk with a light-red or red-brown bark, not buttressed: leaf-blades cuneate, elliptic-cuneate, or narrowly elliptic, 1–4 cm. long, acute or obtuse, slightly paler beneath than above, short-petioled: cymes short-petioled in anthesis, 3–flowered, the primary bracts minute: calyx 4–5 mm. wide; larger sepals about 2 mm. long: berry globose or ellipsoid, 6–7 mm. long, reddish-brown. [*A. dichotoma* (Fl. SE. U. S.)]—Hammocks, E coast, M pen., Caloosahatchee region to Cape Romano, and Key West, Fla.

3. MOSIERA Small. Shrubs or small trees. Leaf-blades thick, obscurely veined, but finely reticulate. Cymes sessile or nearly so, 1–3-flowered, the branches longer than the peduncle. Flowers fragrant. Sepals eciliate, not decidedly paired. Petals nearly equal, white. Stamens numerous, borne on the large annular disk. Style slender-columnar. Berry globular, crowned with the persistent conspicuous calyx, black. Seeds several or many.—Few species, tropical.—STOPPERS.

Calyx less than 1 cm. wide: petals more than twice as long as the sepals: shrub with many prostrate-diffuse branches.   1. *M. longipes.*
Calyx over 1 cm. wide: petals less than twice as long as the sepals: shrub with erect branches or small tree.   2. *M. bahamensis.*

1. **M. longipes** (Berg) Small. Shrub with many wiry often decumbent branches 1–9 dm. long from a short woody base: leaf-blades ovate or oval, mostly 1–3 cm. long, finely reticulate: sepals about 2 mm. long: corolla mostly 10–12 mm. wide: berry globose or obovoid-globose, 6–9 mm. in diameter, black. [*Eugenia longipes* Berg.]—Pinelands, Everglade Keys, pen. Fla. and Florida Keys.—(*W. I.*)

2. **M. bahamensis** (Kiaersk.) Small. Shrub with erect branches or small tree: leaf-blades orbicular, oval, or elliptic, or somewhat ovate, mostly 2–5 cm. long, often decidedly shining above, minutely reticulate beneath: sepals about 3 mm. long: corolla mostly 1.5 cm. wide: berry subglobose, about 1 cm. in diameter, black (?). [*Eugenia bahamensis* Kiaersk.]—Hammocks and pinelands near hammocks, Everglade Keys, pen. Fla. and Florida Keys.—(*W. I.*)

4. **PSIDIUM** L. Shrubs or trees. Leaf-blades thickish, prominently many-ribbed. Cymes 1–few-flowered. Sepals separating irregularly. Petals 4 or 5, much larger than the sepals, white. Stamens very numerous, borne on the disk. Style subulate-filiform. Berry fleshy, crowned with the calyx. Seeds very numerous.— About 11 species, mostly tropical.

1. **P. Guajava** Raddi. Tree sometimes 8 m. tall, with roughish bark, or a shrub with smooth-bark; leaf-blades elliptic or nearly so, 4–8 cm. long, pubescent beneath: sepals 9–15 mm. long: petals 15–20 mm. long: berry globular or pyriform, 3–6 cm. in diameter.—(GUAVA.)—Hammocks, roadsides, pinelands, and old fields, especially in pen. Fla. and the Keys. Nat. of trop. Am. and cult.—(*W. I., Mex., C. A., S. A.*)—Grown extensively in several varieties for its fruit, which is eaten raw or made into a jelly or a preserve.

5. **CALYPTRANTHES** Sw. Shrubs or trees. Leaf-blades thick, faintly veined. Cymes panicle-like. Flowers several or numerous. Hypanthium produced beyond the ovary. Calyx cap-like, deciduous, white. Petals wanting. Stamens numerous, borne on the edge of the cup-like disk. Style slender. Berry conspicuously crowned. Seeds 1, 2, or 3. [*Chytraculia* P. Br.] —About 75 species, of tropical and subtropical America.

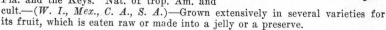

Calyx-lid not mammillate, hypanthium pubescent: leaf-blades manifestly petioled.
                                                                    1. *C. pallens.*
Calyx-lid mammillate: hypanthium glabrous: leaf-blades sessile or nearly so.
                                                                    2. *C. Zuzygium.*

1. **C. pallens** (Poir.) Griseb. Shrub, or tree becoming 9 m. tall, the bark light-gray or nearly white, smooth or ultimately scaly, the branchlets 2-edged:

leaf-blades elliptic or oval, varying to
broader above or below the middle, 3–5 cm.
long, or rarely larger, mostly short acuminate, pubescent beneath, at least when
young, manifestly petioled: inflorescence
pubescent: hypanthium about 2 mm. wide
during anthesis: calyx pubescent, less than
2 mm. in diameter: berry subglobose or oval,
5–7 mm. in diameter, pubescent: seed about
4 mm. long. [*Chytraculia chytraculia* (Fl.
SE. U. S.)]—(SPICEWOOD.)—Hammocks,
coast of S pen. Fla:, Everglade Keys, and
Florida Keys.—(*W. I.*)—The brown heart-
wood is close grained, heavy, and hard.

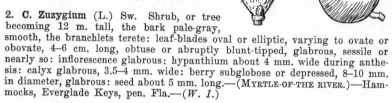

2. **C. Zuzygium** (L.) Sw. Shrub, or tree
becoming 12 m. tall, the bark pale-gray,
smooth, the branchlets terete: leaf-blades oval or elliptic, varying to ovate or
obovate, 4–6 cm. long, obtuse or abruptly blunt-tipped, glabrous, sessile or
nearly so: inflorescence glabrous: hypanthium about 4 mm. wide during anthesis: calyx glabrous, 3.5–4 mm. wide: berry subglobose or depressed, 8–10 mm.
in diameter, glabrous: seed about 5 mm. long.—(MYRTLE-OF-THE RIVER.)—Hammocks, Everglade Keys, pen. Fla.—(*W. I.*)

6. **MELALEUCA** L. Shrubs or trees with much branched stems. Leaf-
blades coriaceous, narrow, parallel-veined, persistent. Spikes dense, on woody
branchlets, the rachis growing into a leafy shoot after anthesis. Sepals very
broad, deciduous. Petals much longer than the sepals. Stamens numerous,
borne in five bundles opposite the petals, the free parts of the filaments greatly
elongate. Style elongate, nearly filiform. Capsule woody, with an annular
orifice. Seeds numerous.—More than 100
species, Australian, many of them cultivated.

1. **M. Leucadendra** L. Tree with irregular,
often drooping branches, the bark thick and
spongy, whitish: leaf-blades elliptic, often
narrowly so, 4–12 cm. long, acute, bright-
green, with short petiole-like bases: spikes
many-flowered, conspicuous: sepals ovate-
deltoid or orbicular-ovate, about 2 mm. long,
obtuse: petals white, obovate, 3–4 mm. long,
firm: filaments 1–1.5 cm. long: capsule short-
cylindric to nearly hemispheric, 3.5–4.5 mm.
long.—(CAJUPUT-TREE. PUNK-TREE. BOT-
TLE-BRUSH.)—Low grounds, hammocks, and
cypress swamps, S Fla. Nat. of Australia.—All year.—Another Australian
tree, *Callistemon lanceolatus*, with leaves resembling those of the above species,
but with bright-red stamens which are distinct, is cultivated in southern Florida
and often spontaneous on old homesteads.

FAMILY 6. **RHIZOPHORACEAE** — MANGROVE FAMILY

Maritime shrubs or trees. Leaves usually opposite: blades entire or
toothed. Flowers perfect, solitary or variously clustered. Calyx of 3
or 4 valvate sepals. Corolla of 3 or 4 petals. Androecium of twice, or

thrice as many stamens as sepals, or of 4 times as many. Gynoecium of 2–5 united carpels. Ovary inferior, at least partly so. Styles united. Fruit a leathery berry crowned with or surrounded by the calyx.—Fifteen genera and about 50 species, of tropical and subtropical regions.

1. **RHIZOPHORA** L. Evergreen trees with aerial roots arising from the trunk and branches, which branch and interlace about the base of the plant. Leaf-blades leathery, entire, persistent. Flowers 2–several in peduncled clusters, nodding. Sepals 4, leathery. Petals 4, leathery. Stamens 4–12. Ovary 2-celled, provided with a fleshy cone at maturity. Fruit pendulous, the seed germinating and sending out a long radicle before the fruits fall.— Three species, natives of tropical regions.

1. **R. Mangle** L. Shrub, or tree becoming 20 m. tall, with pale ultimately furrowed bark, forming impenetrable thickets on salt and brackish shores: leaf-blades elliptic to elliptic-obovate, 5–15 cm. long: sepals lanceolate, about 10 mm. long: petals pale-yellow, linear or nearly so: fruits 2–3 cm. long, the radicle becoming several dm. long.—(MANGROVE. RED-MANGROVE.)—Coasts of pen. Fla., and on the shores of creeks and rivers mostly to the limit of salt or brackish water, and on the Florida Keys.—(W. I., Mex., C. A., S. A.) —Grows most extensively in salt water; rarely in fresh water; but reaches its greatest size in brackish water. The bark is used in dyeing and tanning. The reddish-brown and streaked heart-wood, close-grained, heavy, and hard, is used for cabinet work. The clavate precocious embryo when it falls into the water floats in a perpendicular position. When stranded on the muddy bottom it strikes root.

FAMILY 7. **EPILOBIACEAE** — EVENING-PRIMROSE FAMILY

Herbs or rarely shrubs. Leaves alternate or opposite: blades simple. Flowers typically perfect. Hypanthium often elongate. Calyx of 2–6, usually 4, sepals. Corolla of 2–9, usually 4, petals, or rarely wanting. Androecium of as many stamens as the sepals or twice as many. Gynoecium of several, usually 4, united carpels. Ovary 1–6-celled, usually 4-celled, inferior. Fruit capsular or nut-like.—Forty genera and about 350 species, widely distributed, but most abundant in America.

Floral whorls of 4 parts, or more.
  Fruit a capsule, opening by valves or pores, or by the breaking down of the
    walls.   Tribe I. OENOTHEREAE.
  Fruit dry and indehiscent, nut-like.   Tribe II. GAUREAE.
Floral whorls of 2 parts.   Tribe III. CIRCAEAE.

I. OENOTHEREAE

Hypanthium not prolonged beyond the ovary.
  Seeds naked, *i.e.*, without a tuft of hairs.
    Stamens 4, in 1 row.
      Leaves opposite: stems prostrate, creeping or float-
        ing: flowers sessile or on peduncles longer
        than the leaves.
        Flowers sessile: petals wanting or very small:
          leaf-blades petioled: capsules sessile, short,
          flat at the apex.   1. ISNARDIA.

Flowers long-peduncled: petals conspicuous: leaf-blades sessile: capsule long-peduncled, elongate, curved, with a prominent 4-lobed stylopodium at the apex.   2. LUDWIGIANTHA.
Leaves alternate: stems erect or ascending: flowers sessile, the hypanthium and ovary sometimes narrowed into a pedicel-like base.   3. LUDWIGIA.
Stamens 8–12 in 2 rows.   4. JUSSIAEA.
Seeds furnished with a tuft of silky hairs.   5. CHAMAENERION.
Hypanthium prolonged beyond the ovary.
Seeds with a tuft of silky hairs.   6. EPILOBIUM.
Seeds naked or merely tuberculate.
Flowers with all the stamens equal in length: capsule subcylindric or somewhat tetragonal and tapering to the apex.
Ovules and seeds horizontal, borne in 2 or rarely more rows, prismatic-angled.   7. OENOTHERA.
Ovules and seeds ascending, not angled.   8. RAIMANNIA.
Flowers with the alternate stamens longer: capsule obovoid to clavate, tetragonal, short.
Ovules and seeds numerous, not tuberculate, clustered on slender funiculi.
Corolla yellow: capsules depressed at the apex.
Style terminating in an obscurely lobed stigma: capsule 4-winged.   9. KNEIFFIA.
Style terminating in 4 narrow stigmas: capsule 4-angled.   10. PENIOPHYLLUM.
Corolla red, purple, or white: capsules pointed.   11. HARTMANNIA.
Ovules and seeds few, sessile in 1 or 2 rows.   12. LAVAUXIA.

II. GAUREAE

Herbs with entire, toothed, or pinnatifid leaf-blades: hypanthium dilated upward in anthesis: achene angled.   13. GAURA.

III. CIRCAEAE

Tender herbs with toothed leaf-blades: petals 2-lobed: fruits clavate to pyriform.   14. CIRCAEA.

1. ISNARDIA L. Perennial succulent herbs. Leaf-blades relatively wide. Flowers axillary. Sepals 4, broad. Petals minute, reddish or greenish, or wanting. Filaments very short. Ovary short. Style wanting or nearly so. Capsule obovoid or turbinate.—About 4 species, North American.—MARSH-PURSLANES. WATER-PURSLANES.

Capsule 2.5–6 mm. long; corolla usually wanting.
Plant glabrous: capsule not turgid and not constricted at the top.
Capsule 2.5–3 mm. long: sepals acute.   1. *I. palustris.*
Capsule 5–6 mm. long: sepals acuminate.   2. *I. intermedia.*
Plant pubescent: capsule turgid and constricted at the top.   3. *I. spathulata.*
Capsule 6–7 mm. long: corolla usually present.   4. *I. repens.*

1. **I. palustris** L. Leaf-blades spatulate to oval or ovate, 1.5–2.5 cm. long: hypanthium glabrous: buds acute: sepals triangular; green or reddish: petals wanting or minute and reddish: capsule 2.5–3 mm. long, short-turbinate.—Ditches, wet shores, and swamps, various provinces, Fla. to Calif., Ore., Man., and N. S.—(Mex., C. A., S. A., O. W.)—Spr.–fall.

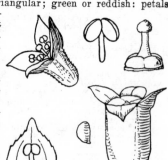

2. **I. intermedia** Small & Alexander. Plant similar to *I. palustris* in habit, but the flower-buds mostly acuminate: capsule 5–6 mm. long, long-turbinate or subcylindric.—Hammocks, wet shores, and stream-banks, pen. Fla.—All year.

3. **I. spathulata** (T. & G.) Small. Leaf-blades spatulate to oval, 2–2.5 cm. long: hypanthium pubescent: sepals broader than

long, or as broad as long, green: capsule globose-obovoid or obovoid, 2.5–3 mm. long.—Pineland ponds, M Fla.—Sum.

4. I. repens (Sw.) DC. Leaf-blades ovate, elliptic, or oval, 1–3 cm. long: hypanthium obpyramidal: sepals ovate-lanceolate: petals as long as the sepals or wanting: capsule obpyramidal. [*I. natans* (Ell.) Small]—Lime-sinks in hammocks, streams and marshes, Coastal Plain, and rarely adj. provinces, Fla. to Tenn. and N. C.—(*Mex.*)—Spr.–fall.

2. LUDWIGIANTHA Small. Perennial fleshy depressed herbs. Leaves numerous: blades narrow, entire. Flowers axillary. Sepals 4, narrow. Petals yellow, conspicuous. Filaments elongate. Ovary long. Style filiform. Capsule clavate.—One or 2 species, of the eastern United States.

1. L. arcuata (Walt.) Small. Stem creeping: leaf-blades oblanceolate, to almost linear, 7–25 mm. long, obtuse or acute: peduncles slender, elongate, longer than the leaves: sepals linear-lanceolate, 7–10 mm. long, acuminate: corolla 2–2.5 cm. wide; petals spreading, obovate, slightly clawed: stamens much shorter than the petals: capsule curved, 7–10 mm. long, as long as the persistent sepals or longer.—Swamps, marshes, springy places, and pond-margins, Coastal Plain, Fla. to Va.—Spr.–sum.—A related species, *L. brevipes* Long, from N. J. might occur on the southern Atlantic seaboard.

3. LUDWIGIA L. Annual or perennial erect or matted herbs. Leaf-blades entire or rarely shallowly toothed. Flowers axillary or terminal. Sepals generally persistent, green or reddish. Petals usually 4, yellow. Ovary usually 4-celled. Capsule cylindric or prismatic to subglobose.—About 25 species, most abundant in North America.

Corolla conspicuous; flowers peduncled: capsule opening by a terminal pore. I. ALTERNIFOLIAE.
Corolla inconspicuous, obsolete, or wanting: valves of the capsule separating from the disk-like top. II. MICROCARPEAE.

I. ALTERNIFOLIAE

Foliage, sepals, and capsule glabrous, puberulent or minutely appressed-pubescent.
  Stem-leaves with short-petioled blades: petals about as long as the sepals: pedicel shorter than the capsule. 1. *L. alternifolia.*
  Stem-leaves with closely sessile blades: petals about twice as long as the sepals: pedicel longer than the capsule.
    Sepals thrice as long as the hypanthium in anthesis: style longer than the sepals. 2. *L. virgata.*
    Sepals twice as long as the hypanthium in anthesis: style shorter than the sepals. 3. *L. maritima.*
Foliage, sepals, and capsule hirsute. 4. *L. hirtella.*

II. MICROCARPEAE

Petals wanting or minute, shorter than the sepals.
  Capsule 1–3 mm. long; stem-leaves of a spatulate type.
    Leaf-blades entire.
    Leaf-blades toothed near the apex. 5. *L. microcarpa.*
      Leaf-blades broadly spatulate: sepals much shorter than the hypanthium. 6. *L. Simpsonii.*

Leaf-blades narrowly spatulate: sepals about as
    long as the hypanthium.   7. *L. Curtissii.*
  Capsule 3–8 mm. long.
    Blades of the stem-leaves spatulate.   8. *L. spathulifolia.*
    Blades of the stem-leaves not spatulate.
      Capsule about as thick as long, not cylindric.
        Foliage and fruit glabrous or merely appressed-
          puberulent.
          Flowers in a terminal head or congested
            panicle.   9. *L. suffruticosa.*
          Flowers in elongate interrupted spikes or
            axillary.
            Capsule turbinate, cubic-turbinate, or
              obpyramidal.
              Capsule slightly longer than broad,
                the angles rounded or merely
                square.
                Capsule glabrous, the angles
                  rounded: bractlets adnate to
                  the hypanthium.   10. *L. polycarpa.*
                Capsule puberulent, the angles
                  square: bractlets not adnate to
                    the hypanthium.   11. *L. simulata.*
              Capsule slightly broader than long,
                the angles winged or margined.
                Sepals nearly as broad as long,
                almost as long as the capsule:
                seeds oval.   12. *L. alata.*
                Sepals broader than long, ½ as
                  long as the capsule: seeds
                  cylindric.   13. *L. lanceolata.*
            Capsule globular.   14. *L. sphaerocarpa.*
        Foliage and fruit copiously pilose-tomentose.   15. *L. pilosa.*
      Capsule cylindric.   16. *L. glandulosa.*
  Petals as long as or longer than the sepals.
    Capsule cylindric, terete or nearly so.   17. *L. linifolia.*
    Capsule narrowly obpyramidal.   18. *L. linearis.*

1. L. alternifolia L. Plant 6–12 dm. tall: leaf-blades lanceolate, 6–12 cm.
long: sepals ovate: petals about equalling the sepals: capsule slightly winged
on the angles, 5–7 mm. long.—(SEEDBOX.)—
Swamps and wet places, various provinces,
Fla. to Tex., Kans., Ont., and N. H.—Spr.–
fall.

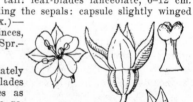

2. L. virgata Michx. Plant fastigiately
branched, glabrous or nearly so; leaf-blades
linear to lanceolate: sepals 3–4 times as
long as the hypanthium, permanently reflexed: style longer than the sepals: capsule
very slightly winged on the angles.—Pinelands, Coastal Plain, Fla. to Miss. and N. C.
—Spr.–fall.

3. L. maritima Harper. Plant fastigiately
branched, glabrous or nearly so: leaf-blades
linear to lanceolate: sepals twice as long
as the hypanthium, permanently reflexed: capsule very slightly winged on
angles, 2 mm. long.—Ditches and low pinelands, pen. Fla.—Spr.–fall.

4. L. hirtella Raf. Plant 3–6 dm. tall: leaf-blades elliptic-lanceolate or
ovate-lanceolate, 2.5–3 cm. long: sepals ovate-lanceolate: petals longer than the
sepals: capsule cubic above the rounded base, about 5 mm. long.—Moist sand,
mainly in acid pinelands, Coastal Plain and adj. provinces, Fla. to Tex., Tenn.,
and N. J.—Spr.–fall.

5. L. microcarpa Michx. Plant low or depressed: leaf-blades spatulate or
obovate-spatulate, 0.5–3 cm. long: sepals triangular: petals wanting: capsule
broadly obpyramidal, 1.5–2 mm. long.—Hammocks, limesinks, and marshes,
Coastal Plain, Fla. to Miss. and N. C.—Spr.–fall.

6. **L. Simpsonii** Chapm. Plant weak, often decumbent: leaf-blades 1–2.5 cm. long: sepals triangular: petals wanting: capsule broadly turbinate, about 2 mm. long.—Hammocks, ditches, and low pinelands, pen. Fla.—Spr.–fall.

7. **L. Curtissii** Chapm. Plant erect or ascending: leaf-blades 1–2 cm. long: sepals lanceolate or triangular-lanceolate: petals wanting: capsule turbinate, 2–3 mm. long.—Everglades, ponds, and ditches, pen. Fla.—Spr.–fall.

8. **L. spathulifolia** Small. Plant 1.5–8 dm. tall, the stem narrowly ridged: leaf-blades spatulate, 1–2.5 cm. long, those of the basal shoots somewhat broader than those of the stem: sepals deltoid: petals wanting: capsule broadly obpyramidal, about 4 mm. long, the angles blunt.—Wet ground, Everglades, Fla.—All year.

9. **L. suffruticosa** Walt. Plant 3–10 dm. tall: leaf-blades narrowly elliptic to narrowly lanceolate or linear, 2–10 cm. long: sepals broadly ovate or triangular-ovate: petals minute or wanting: capsule broadly obpyramidal, 4–5 mm. long. [*L. capitata* Michx.]—Wet pinelands, and shores of ponds, Coastal Plain, Fla. to N. C.—Spr.–fall.

10. **L. polycarpa** Short & Peter. Plant 3–9 dm. tall, the stem winged: leaf-blades narrowly lanceolate, 5–10 cm. long: sepals triangular-lanceolate: petals minute, greenish: capsule 4-sided, the angles rounded, 5 mm. long.—(FALSE-LOOSESTRIFE.)—Swamps, various provinces, Tenn. to Nebr., Minn., Ont., and Mass.—Spr.–fall.

11. **L. simulata** Small. Plant 4–9 dm. tall, the stem nearly terete: leaf-blades narrowly elliptic to almost linear, 1.5–5.5 cm. long: sepals triangular to ovate-triangular: petals minute: capsule obpyramidal, about 4 mm. long.—Swamps, Coastal Plain, Fla. to N. C.—Spr.–fall.

12. **L. alata** Ell. Plant 3–9 dm. tall, the stem winged: leaf-blades linear-oblanceolate, to linear-lanceolate, or nearly linear, 2.5–10 cm. long: petals wanting: capsule 3–4 mm. long, the angles winged.—Marshes, Coastal Plain and adj. provinces, Fla. to La., Mo., and N. C.—Spr.–fall.

13. **L. lanceolata** Ell. Plant 3–9 dm. tall, the stem angled or sometimes winged: leaf-blades linear-oblanceolate to linear-lanceolate or linear, 2–10 cm. long: sepals very broad, acute: petals wanting: capsule 4–5 mm. long, the angles margined.—Everglades, swamps, and marshes, Coastal Plain, Fla. to N. C.—Sum.–fall.

14. **L. sphaerocarpa** Ell. Plant 6–9 dm. tall, the stem leaf-blades lanceolate, 5–10 cm. long: sepals triangular: petals commonly wanting: capsule about 4 mm. long.—Swamps, often in acid soil, Coastal Plain and adj. provinces, Fla. to La. and Mass.; and Great Lake Lowland, Ind.—Sum.–fall.

15. **L. pilosa** Walt. Plant 6–12 dm. tall, the stem nearly terete: leaf-blades lanceolate, elliptic, or linear-elliptic, 1–6 cm. long: sepals triangular-ovate: petals minute or wanting: capsule cubic-globose, 4–6 mm. in diameter, hoary.—Swamps and ponds, Coastal Plain, Fla. to La. and N. C.—Sum.–fall.

16. **L. glandulosa** Walt. Plant 3–9 dm. tall, the stem nearly terete: leaf-blades elliptic-lanceolate, 5–10 cm. long: sepals triangular-ovate, acute: petals wanting: capsules cylindrical, 6–8 mm. long.—Swamps, and marshes, Coastal Plain and adj. provinces, Fla. to Tex., Kans., Ill., and S. C.—Sum. & fall.

17. **L. linifolia** Poir. Plant 1–5 dm. tall, the stem 4-angled: leaf-blades linear-oblanceolate to linear, 2–6 cm. long: sepals lanceolate or ovate-lanceolate,

acuminate: petals about as long as the sepals: capsule about 10 mm. long.—
Pineland swamps, Coastal Plain, Fla. to Miss. and N. C.—Spr.–fall.

18. L. linearis Walt.   Plant 3–7.5 dm. tall: leaf-blades narrowly linear,
2.5–5 cm. long: sepals triangular-ovate: petals slightly longer than the sepals:
capsule 6–8 mm. long.—Swamps, often in acid soil, Coastal Plain, Fla. to La.
(Tex.?), Tenn., and N. J.—Sum.–fall.

4. JUSSIAEA L.   Perennial herbs or partially woody plants, erect or diffuse and creeping. Leaf-blades usually entire. Flowers axillary. Sepals 4–6,
persistent. Petals 4–6, white or yellow, or rarely none. Stamens 8–12. Ovary
4–6-celled. Capsule linear, ellipsoid, or clavate.—About 50 species, mostly of
the American tropics.—Spr.–fall or all year S.

Plant diffuse, the stems and branches creeping (rooting) or floating.   I. Diffusae.
Plant erect, the stem more or less branched.   II. Erectae.

I. Diffusae

Corolla 2–3 cm. broad: leaf-blades long-petioled.   1. *J. diffusa.*
Corolla 4–5 cm. broad: leaf-blades short-petioled.   2. *J. grandiflora.*

II. Erectae

Capsule long-clavate, the body narrowly cylindric, more than 3
  cm. long.
  Calyx of 5 sepals.   3. *J. leptocarpa.*
  Calyx of 4 sepals.
    Leaf-blades narrow: 4. *J. angustifolia.*
    Leaf-blades broad: 5. *J. scabra.*
Capsule short-clavate, the body obconic or cylindric-obovoid,
  mostly less than 2 cm. long.
  Leaf-blades sessile, decurrent as wings on the angles of the
    stem: fruit winged.   6. *J. decurrens.*
  Leaf-blades short-petioled: fruit not winged.
    Corolla about 1 cm. broad.   7. *J. erecta.*
    Corolla 4–6 cm. broad.
      Blades of the upper leaves long and narrow. 8. *J. neglecta.*
      Blades of the upper leaves broad and short. 9. *J. peruviana.*

1. J. diffusa Forskl.   Stem glabrous: blades of the upper leaves elliptic to
lanceolate, 2.5–10 cm. long: sepals 5–8 mm. long: petals 1–1.5 cm. long: capsule-
body 2.5–4 cm. long.—Ponds, Coastal Plain
and adj. provinces, Fla. to Tex., Kans., and
Ky.—(*W. I.*)

2. J. grandiflora Michx.   Stem villous or
hirsute: blades of the upper leaves narrowly
elliptic or lanceolate, 3–12 cm. long: sepals
about 12 mm. long: petals fully 2 cm. long:
capsule body 1–2 cm. long.—Ponds and
streams, Coastal Plain, Fla. to La. and N. C.

3. J. leptocarpa Nutt.   Stem hirsute, 6–20
dm. tall: leaf-blades narrowly elliptic or
lanceolate, 3–20 cm. long: hypanthium hirsute: sepals lanceolate: corolla about 15 mm.
broad: capsule 3.5–6 cm. long.—Ditches and
low grounds, Coastal Plain, Fla. to Tex., Ark., and Ga.—Glabrous forms with
very narrow leaf-blades and four-merous flowers occur in S Fla.

4. J. angustifolia Lam.   Stem mostly 1–2 m. tall, glabrous or sparingly
pubescent: leaf-blades elliptic to almost linear, varying to broadest above the
middle or below it, 2–11 cm. long, usually glabrous or nearly so: hypanthium

longer than the calyx in bud, minutely pubescent in anthesis: sepals ovate, mostly less than 1 cm. long: corolla less than 4 cm. wide: capsule 4–6 cm. long, much longer than the pedicel-like base.—Swamps, stream-banks, and low grounds, Coastal Plain, Fla. to Tex.—(*W. I., Mex., C. A., S. A.*)—Spr.-fall or all year S.

5. **J. scabra** Willd. Stem hirsute, 6–14 dm. tall: leaf-blades ovate to obovate, 2–6 cm. long: hypanthium hirsute: sepals ovate: corolla 2–2.5 cm. broad: capsule 3–5 cm. long.—Moist soil, Fla.—(*W. I.*)

6. **J. decurrens** (Walt.) DC. Stem 3–6 dm. tall, glabrous: leaf-blades lanceolate, 2.5–10 cm. long: sepals ovate-lanceolate: corolla 8–12 mm. broad: capsule-body 2–2.5 cm. long.—Ditches and low grounds, Coastal Plain and adj. provinces, Fla. to Tex., Ark., Ill., and Md.

7. **J. erecta** L. Stem 9–20 dm. tall, glabrous: leaf-blades lanceolate to linear-lanceolate, 5–12 cm. long: hypanthium short-pubescent or glabrate: sepals lanceolate, about 5 mm. long: petals about 5 mm. long; capsule-body cylindric, much longer than the base, 1.5 cm. long.—Hammocks, near Manatee, Fla.—(*W. I., C. A.*)

8. **J. neglecta** Small. Stem mostly less than 1 m. tall, or taller in age, copiously pubescent: leaf-blades elliptic, varying to elliptic-oblanceolate or elliptic-lanceolate, especially on the lower part of the stem, to elliptic-linear or narrowly linear above, mostly 4–15 cm. long, pubescent on both sides: hypanthium shorter than the calyx in bud, copiously pubescent with short and long hairs, in anthesis: sepals broadly ovate, mostly over 1.5 cm. long: corolla over 5 cm. wide: capsule 1–2 cm. long.—Waste-places and river-banks, about seaports, Coastal Plain, Fla. to La. and N. C.—Referred to *J. suffruticosa* in Fl. SE U. S., in error.

9. **J. peruviana** L. Stem 1–4 m. tall, hirsute: leaf-blades ovate, oval, lanceolate, or oblong-lanceolate, 4–10 cm. long, or more: hypanthium hirsute: sepals lanceolate to ovate-lanceolate, 10–15 mm. long: petals 2–3 cm. long: capsule-body ellipsoid-obovoid, slightly longer than the base.—Everglades, swamps, and banks of streams, pen. Fla.; and adv. elsewhere along the Gulf Coast.—(*W. I., Mex., C. A., S. A.*)

5. **CHAMAENERION** Adans. Perennial herbs. Leaf-blades entire or nearly so. Flowers irregular, in showy racemes. Sepals 4, deciduous. Petals 4, entire. Stamens 8, declined. Stigmas 4. Capsule elongate, obtusely angled. Seeds comose.—Four species, of the north temperate zone.

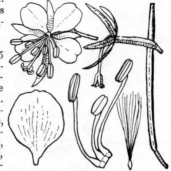

1. **C. angustifolium** (L.) Scop. Plant 5–25 dm. tall, often clustered: leaf-blades lanceolate, 5–15 cm. long: corolla purple or sometimes white; petals 1–1.5 cm. long: capsule 5–7.5 cm. long: coma of seeds about 10 mm. long. — (FIRE-WEED. SALLY-BLOOM. WILLOW-HERB. WILLOW-WEED.) — Open woods, thickets, and especially clearings and recently burned areas, various provinces, Coastal Plain only N N. C. to N. M., Calif., Alas., Ont., and Lab.—Sum.-fall.—Its abundance in burned over areas has given it the name of fireweed.

6. EPILOBIUM L. Perennial herbs or somewhat woody plants. Leaf-blades entire or toothed. Flowers solitary, spicate, or racemose. Sepals 4, short, deciduous. Petals 4, pink or white, often notched. Stamens 8. Stigmas 4, or united and clavate. Capsule elongate, 4-sided. Seeds comose.—About 75 species, chiefly northern.—Sum.-fall.—WILLOW-HERBS. COTTON-WEEDS.

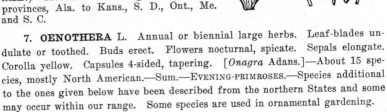

1. E. coloratum Muhl. Plant 3–9 dm. tall: leaf-blades lanceolate, 5–15 cm. long: flowers generally nodding: sepals 2.5–3.5 mm. long: petals 3–4 mm. long, shallowly notched: capsule 4.5–6 cm. long.—(BRONZE WILLOW-HERB.)—Meadows and low grounds, various provinces, Ala. to Kans., S. D., Ont., Me. and S. C.

7. OENOTHERA L. Annual or biennial large herbs. Leaf-blades undulate or toothed. Buds erect. Flowers nocturnal, spicate. Sepals elongate. Corolla yellow. Capsules 4-sided, tapering. [*Onagra* Adans.]—About 15 species, mostly North American.—Sum.—EVENING-PRIMROSES.—Species additional to the ones given below have been described from the northern States and some may occur within our range. Some species are used in ornamental gardening.

Sepals less than 3 cm. long, the free tips subulate, less than 4 mm. long: corolla 2–5 cm. wide.   1. *O. biennis.*
Sepals over 3 cm. long, the free tips filiform, over 5 mm. long: corolla 8–12 cm. wide.   2. *O. grandiflora.*

1. O. biennis L. Stem 13–25 dm. tall, hirsute: leaf-blades elliptic to lanceolate, 2.5–15 cm. long, repand-denticulate: petals bright-yellow, 1–2.5 cm. long: capsule narrowly oblong-conic, 18–25 mm. long, nearly terete.—(WEEDY EVENING-PRIMROSE.)—Fields, roadsides, and thickets, various provinces, Fla. to Tex., Minn., and Lab.—Sum.-fall.

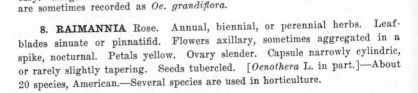

2. O. grandiflora Ait. Similar to *O. biennis*, but larger throughout sometimes 3 m. tall: petals 4–6 cm. long, golden-yellow: capsule linear-conic, 3–4 cm. long, 4-sided.—Woods and river-banks, and roadsides, Coastal Plain, Ala.—Sum.-fall.—This species seems to be known in the wild state only in the type region in Alabama where Bartram discovered it late in the eighteenth century. Large flowered forms of *Oe. biennis* are sometimes recorded as *Oe. grandiflora*.

8. RAIMANNIA Rose. Annual, biennial, or perennial herbs. Leaf-blades sinuate or pinnatifid. Flowers axillary, sometimes aggregated in a spike, nocturnal. Petals yellow. Ovary slender. Capsule narrowly cylindric, or rarely slightly tapering. Seeds tubercled. [*Oenothera* L. in part.]—About 20 species, American.—Several species are used in horticulture.

Flowers axillary: stem and branches decumbent or prostrate.   I. HUMIFUSAE.
Flowers in a terminal bracted spike.   II. HETEROPHYLLAE.

I. HUMIFUSAE

Corolla less than 5 cm. wide.
  Leaf-blades entire or sinuate: capsule densely pubescent.
    Stem and capsule with appressed silky pubescence:
      plant appearing grayish.   1. *R. humifusa.*
    Stem and capsule with loose, spreading pubescence:
      plant appearing green.   2. *R. mollissima.*
  Leaf-blades mostly pinnatifid: capsule not densely pubescent.   3. *R. laciniata.*
Corolla over 6 cm. wide.   4. *R. Drummondii.*

II. HETEROPHYLLAE

Plant relatively slender: blades of the lower leaves slender-
petioled, pinnatifid, those of the upper ones sessile or nearly
so, entire or obscurely toothed: capsules in a virgate spike.   5. *R. Curtissii.*

1. R. humifusa (Nutt.) Rose. Stem branched below, the branches spreading or decumbent, 2-5 dm. long, silky-canescent: leaves various, the basal with oblong-spatulate pinnatifid blades, the cauline with oblanceolate to lanceolate acute, undulate repand or toothed blades, 2-3.5 cm. long: flowers axillary: hypanthium 2-3 cm. long: sepals about ½ as long as the hypanthium: corolla 2-3 cm. broad: capsule narrowly cylindric, 2-3 cm. long, somewhat curved upward: seed 1.5-2 mm. long, striate. — (SEASIDE EVENING-PRIMROSE.)—Sea-beaches and sand-dunes, Coastal Plain, Fla. to Miss. and N. J.—(*W. I.*)—All year S.

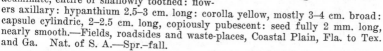

2. R. mollissima (L.) Sprague and Riley. Stem branched, the branches ascending or decumbent, softly hirsute: leaf-blades elliptic or ovate-elliptic to lanceolate or linear-lanceolate, mostly 2-5 cm. long, acute or acuminate, entire or shallowly toothed: flowers axillary: hypanthium 2.5-3 cm. long: corolla yellow, mostly 3-4 cm. broad: capsule cylindric, 2-2.5 cm. long, copiously pubescent: seed fully 2 mm. long, nearly smooth.—Fields, roadsides and waste-places, Coastal Plain, Fla. to Tex. and Ga. Nat. of S. A.—Spr.-fall.

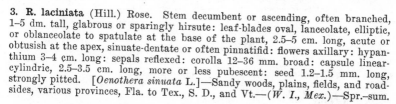

3. R. laciniata (Hill.) Rose. Stem decumbent or ascending, often branched, 1-5 dm. tall, glabrous or sparingly hirsute: leaf-blades oval, lanceolate, elliptic, or oblanceolate to spatulate at the base of the plant, 2.5-5 cm. long, acute or obtusish at the apex, sinuate-dentate or often pinnatifid: flowers axillary: hypanthium 3-4 cm. long: sepals reflexed: corolla 12-36 mm. broad: capsule linear-cylindric, 2.5-3.5 cm. long, more or less pubescent: seed 1.2-1.5 mm. long, strongly pitted. [*Oenothera sinuata* L.]—Sandy woods, plains, fields, and roadsides, various provinces, Fla. to Tex., S. D., and Vt.—(*W. I., Mex.*)—Spr.-sum.

4. R. Drummondii (Hook.) Rose. Stem branched, the branches decumbent, 2-7 cm. long, pubescent with appressed stiff-silky hairs: leaves various; blades spatulate to lanceolate, or sometimes ovate or obovate towards the ends of the branches, 1-4 cm. long, entire or distantly toothed: flowers axillary: hypanthium stout, 2-4 cm. long: sepals nearly linear, more than ¾ as long as the hypanthium: corolla 7-9 cm. broad: capsule cylindric, 2.5-4 cm. long, spreading, curved upward: seed nearly 1.5 mm. long, pitted.—Sand-dunes, pinelands, and roadsides, Coastal Plain, Fla. to Tex. and N. C. Native only in Tex.—All year S.

5. R. Curtissii Rose. Stem slender, 1 m. tall or less, sparingly appressed-pubescent: leaf-blades lanceolate to almost linear and entire or obscurely

toothed, or oblanceolate at the base of the stem and coarsely toothed or pinnatifid, all narrowed at the base: sepals mostly 9–11 mm. long, with very short
free tips, glabrous or with few long hairs: corolla about 3 cm. wide: petals
obovate, about 1.5 cm. long: capsule stout-subulate, 12–16 mm. long, decidedly
tapering to the apex, curved, appressed-pubescent: seed about 1.5 mm. long.—
Dry sand, pinelands, edges of hammocks, and river-banks, Coastal Plain, Fla.
and adj. Ga.—Sum.–fall.—Formerly included in *Oenothera heterophylla,* a
western species which does not occur in our range.

9. KNEIFFIA Spach. Perennial small herbs. Leaf-blades spatulate
to linear or ovate, entire or shallowly toothed. Buds mostly erect. Flowers
spicate, diurnal. Petals yellow. Ovary clavate or stout. Capsule erect, clavate or with an ellipsoid body, 4-winged, opening in wet weather. Seed not
tubercled. [*Oenothera* L. in part.]—About 12 species, mostly of temperate
North America.—Sum.—SUNDROPS.

Inflorescence and buds erect: flowers relatively large, the petals of the earlier ones
 15–25 mm. long.   I. FRUTICOSAE.
Inflorescence, at the tip, and buds nodding: flowers relatively
 small, the petals of the earlier ones 5–10 mm. long.   II. PUMILAE.

I. FRUTICOSAE

Capsule linear-clavate, not stipitate.   1. *K. pratensis.*
Capsule with a clavate or ellipsoid stipitate body.
  Capsule-body decidedly clavate at maturity, pubescent
    with incurved glandless hairs, or with inter-
    spersed gland-tipped hairs in *K. semiglandulosa.*
    Capsule-body about as wide as long, usually much
      shorter than the stipe: blades of the basal
      leaves narrow.
      Capsule with minute appressed hairs: leaves
        strigillose or glabrous, the basal narrowly
        oblanceolate: blades of the cauline leaves
        linear.   2. *K. subglobosa.*
      Capsule hirsute-strigose: leaves densely silvery-
        silky: blades linear-lanceolate.   3. *K. arenicola.*
    Capsule-body decidedly longer than wide, longer
      than the stipe or about equalling it: blades
      of the basal leaves broad.
      Capsule-body and stipe both pubescent with
        glandless hairs: stipe frequently about
        equalling the capsule-body.
        Stipe of capsule equalling or somewhat ex-
          ceeding the permanently pubescent body.   4. *K. fruticosa.*
        Stipe of capsule shorter than the body, which
          tends to become glabrate.
          Capsule-body pubescent with minute
            hairs: leaves of the main stem 7–9 cm.
            long, glabrate.   5. *K. riparia.*
          Capsule-body pubescent with coarse hairs:
            leaves of the main stem 3–6 cm. long,
            densely pubescent.   6. *K. brevistipata.*
      Capsule-body pubescent with glandless hairs:
        stipe with glandular hairs: stipe shorter than
        the capsule-body.   7. *K. semiglandulosa.*
  Capsule-body ellipsoid or nearly so, pubescent with
    short straight gland-tipped hairs, sometimes
    glabrate.
    Leaves of the main stem with linear-lanceolate,
      lanceolate, or lanceolate-ovate blades, not glau-
      cous: stem pubescent or rarely glabrous:
      petals of the earlier flowers 1–2.5 cm. long.   8. *K. hybrida.*
      Stem pubescent with long lax or spreading hairs.
      Stem pubescent with short crisped hairs.
        Capsule-body gradually narrowed into the
          stipe: corolla 2–4 cm. wide.   9. *K. tetragona.*
        Capsule-body abruptly narrowed into the
          stipe: corolla 4–5 cm. wide.   10. *K. latifolia.*
    Leaves of the main stem with ovate to lanceolate-
      ovate blades, glaucous beneath: stem glabrous or

rarely pubescent: petals of the earlier flowers
2.5–3 cm. long.

II. PUMILAE

Plants with assurgent often gregarious flower-stems and
thickish leaf-blades.

11. *K. glauca.*

12. *K. perennis.*

1. K. pratensis Small. Stem 5–11 dm. tall: leaf-blades narrowly elliptic
to elliptic-lanceolate, 3–11 cm. long, undu-
late or sinuate, acute, thin, hirsute, flat:
hypanthium more or less hirsute: sepals 17–
22 mm. long, the free tips 2.5–4 mm. long:
petals 2–3.5 cm. long: capsule-body clavate,
17–21 mm. long, hirsute.—(MEADOW-SUN-
DROPS.)—Low grounds, woods and prairies,
various provinces, N of Coastal Plain, Tenn.
to Ark., Ia., Wis., and Ohio. Introd. in
more E States.—Sum.–fall.

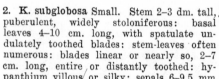

2. K. subglobosa Small. Stem 2–3 dm. tall,
puberulent, widely stoloniferous: basal
leaves 4–10 cm. long, with spatulate undulately toothed blades: stem-leaves often
numerous: blades linear or nearly so, 2–7
cm. long, entire or distantly toothed: hy-
panthium villous or silky: sepals 6–9.5 mm. long: petals 1.5 to almost 2 cm.
long: capsule-body globose-obovoid, 6–7 mm. long.—Sandy soil and rocky
places, Piedmont, Ga. and Ala.—Sum.–fall.

3. K. arenicola Small. Stem 1.5–4.5 dm. tall, strigillose: leaf-blades linear
or nearly so, or some of them narrowly elliptic, 1.5–5 cm. long, entire or essentially so: hypanthium somewhat hirsute: sepals 5.5–8 mm. long: petals 16–23
mm. long: capsule-body globular or obovoid-globose, about 4 mm. long.—Sandhills or dry pinelands, Coastal Plain, Ga. to Miss., Ark., and N. C.—Sum.–fall.

4. K. fruticosa (L.) Raimann. Stem 1–6.5 dm. tall, pubescent with short,
usually incurved hairs: basal leaves with oval, elliptic or spatulate blades
commonly 2–8 cm. long: stem-leaves not crowded; blades spatulate to linear
or linear-lanceolate, undulate or shallowly toothed: sepals 1–1.8 cm. long,
finely pubescent: petals 1.5–2.5 cm. long: capsule-body narrowly obovoid to
ellipsoid-clavate, 6–14 mm. long. [*O. fruticosa* L. *K. linearis* Spach *K.
longipedicellata* Small]—(SUNDROPS.)—Open sandy places or barrens, various
provinces, Fla. to Tex., Mo., and N. Y.—Spr.–sum.

5. K. riparia (Nutt.) Small. Stem 5–12 dm. tall: basal leaves with spatulate blades commonly over 10 cm. long: stem-leaves often numerous; blades
linear to linear-lanceolate, 5–13 cm. long, or shorter on the branches, entire or
undulate denticulate: sepals about 2 cm. long, finely pubescent: petals over 2
cm. long: capsule-body clavate, pubescent all over, with minute hairs, mostly
over 2 cm. long.—River banks and swamps, Coastal Plain, Ga. to N. C.—
Spr.–sum.

6. K. brevistipata Pennell. Stem 2–4 dm. tall, pubescent, leaves 3–6
cm. long: blades linear, lanceolate, acutish, densely strigose: sepals 7–9 mm.
long: petals 12–15 mm. long: capsule-body clavate-ellipsoid, 5–6 mm. long,
winged, pubescent with coarse hairs, but becoming glabrate.—Dry pine ridges,
Coastal Plain, N Fla. to La.—Sum.

7. K. semiglandulosa Pennell. Stem 3–6 dm. tall, finely pubescent, becoming glandular above, purple-red: leaves 5–9 cm. long; blades lanceolate-
linear, acutish, finely pubescent or glabrate: sepals 10–13 mm. long, acuminate:
petals 15–25 cm. long: capsule-body clavate, 8–10 mm. long, the wings exceed-

ing the ridges, finely pubescent with gland-tipped and glandless hairs, often nearly glabrous, the stipe-like base shorter than the body.—Pinelands, Coastal Plain, W Fla. to Miss.; introd. in E N. C.—Spr.–sum.

8. **K. hybrida** (Michx.) Small. Stem 3–10 dm. tall, hirsute, sometimes thinly so: leaf-blades oblanceolate to elliptic or lanceolate, 2.5–11 cm. long, entire, undulate, or denticulate: sepals 10–15 mm. long, the free tip usually about 2 mm. long: petals 14–21 mm. long: capsule-body obovoid-ellipsoid, 4.5–10 mm. long, sharply angled below, winged at the apex, very short-stipitate.—Woods, meadows, and roadsides, various provinces, N. C. to Tenn. and N. S.—Sum.

9. **K. tetragona** (Roth.) Pennell. Stem 3–9 dm. tall, purple throughout or green above: leaf-blades narrowly elliptic to lanceolate or linear, 2.5–10 cm. long, entire or denticulate: sepals 9–14 mm. long, the free tips about 1 mm. long: petals 10–18 mm. long: capsule-body ellipsoid, 6–12 mm. long, sharply angled and usually winged above, short-stipitate.—Dry soil, barren places, rocky river-banks, and swampy grounds, various provinces, Ga. to Ala., Mo., Mich., and N. Y.—Sum.–fall.

10. **K. latifolia** Rydb. Stem 3–6 dm. tall, pubescent, purplish or brownish below: leaf-blades elliptic, often narrowly so, to elliptic-lanceolate or ovate-lanceolate, 3–9 cm. long, entire or undulate-denticulate: sepals 12–18 mm. long, the free tips about 1 mm. long: petals 18–22 mm. long: capsule-body ellipsoid 7–9 mm. long, prominently sharply angled below, winged above, usually very short-stipitate.—Woods, Blue Ridge, N. C. and Tenn.—Sum.

11. **K. glauca** (Michx.) Spach. Stem glaucous, 4–9 dm. high: leaf-blades oval, ovate, or lanceolate-ovate, 5–14 cm. long: sepals 20–25 mm. long: petals 2.5–3 cm. long: capsule-body ellipsoid, 11–13 mm. long, broadly 4-winged. [*K. fruticosa* (Fl. SE. U. S.)]—(BLUE-LEAF SUNDROPS.)—Dry woods, usually on mt. slopes, Blue Ridge to Appalachian Plateau, Ga. to Ky. and Va.—Spr.–fall.

12. **K. perennis** (L.) Pennell. Stem puberulent, 2–6 dm. tall: basal leaves mostly with oblanceolate or spatulate blades: stem-leaves few or many; blades elliptic to linear, 2–8 cm. long, entire or very nearly so: sepals 5–7 mm. long: petals 6–9 mm. long: capsule-body obovoid or ellipsoid-obovoid, 6–12 mm. long, glabrous or nearly so. [*O. pumila* L. *K. pumila* Spach]—Open woods and moist sandy grounds, Blue Ridge and more northern provinces, N. C. to Minn., Ont., and N. S.—Spr.–sum.

10. **PENIOPHYLLUM** Pennell. Annual or biennial slender-stemmed herbs. Leaves of two forms, the basal with broad blades, the cauline linear-filiform to filiform, entire. Flowers in terminal spikes. Petals triangular. Stigma capitate, the four lobes scarcely or not distinguishable. Capsule ellipsoid, sharply 4-angled, not stipitate. Seeds angled, irregularly clustered.—One species.

1. **P. linifolium** (Nutt.) Pennell. Stem 1.5–4.5 dm. tall; basal leaves clustered, with oblanceolate or spatulate blades about 2–5 cm. long: sepals 2–3.5 mm. long: corolla yellow, 6–8 mm. broad: capsule-body ellipsoid, 4–6 mm. long: seed about 1 mm. long, brown. [*Oenothera linifolia* Nutt. *Kneiffia linifolia* (Nutt.) Spach]—Dry rocky hills and prairies, Coastal Plain and adj. provinces, Ga. to Tex., Kans., and Ill.—Spr.–sum.

11. HARTMANNIA Spach. Annual or perennial caulescent herbs. Leaf-blades commonly pinnatifid or lyrate. Buds drooping. Flowers spicate, diurnal. Hypanthium funnelform. Petals white, pink or purple. Capsule-body ellipsoid to subglobose, 4-winged, narrowed to a stipe-like base. Seeds not tubercled. About 10 species, American.—Spr.–fall.—PRIMROSES.

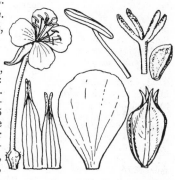

1. H. speciosa (Nutt.) Small. Plant 2–7 dm. tall: blades of the basal leaves oblanceolate to spatulate in outline, lyrate-pinnatifid: sepals 2–4 cm. long: petals 2.5–5 cm. long: capsules 1–2 cm. long. [*Oenothera speciosa* Nutt.]—Dry soil, fields and roadsides, various provinces, La. to Ariz., Kans., and Mo.; also abundantly naturalized from Miss. to Fla., Ill., and N. C.—(*Mex.*)—Spr.–fall.—Commonly grown in gardens whence it escapes.

12. LAVAUXIA Spach. Perennial or annual usually acaulescent herbs. Leaf-blades pinnatifid. Flowers few. Petals white, pink, or pale-yellow. Hypanthium tubular, slender. Ovary short. Capsule short and stout, often winged above. seeds granular, few.—About 6 species, North American.—Spr.–sum.—PRIMROSES.

1. L. triloba (Nutt.) Spach. Perennial, nearly glabrous throughout: leaves basal: blades oblong-lanceolate in outline, 7–30 cm. long, runcinate-pinnatifid or sinuate, sometimes ciliate: corolla white or pink, 4–6.5 cm. broad: petals often 3-lobed: capsule ovoid, 20–30 mm. long, manifestly longer than broad, 4-winged above, reticulate-veined. [*Oenothera triloba* Nutt.] — Dry, often calcareous soil, various provinces, Miss to Calif., Wyo., and Ky.—(*Mex.*)

13. GAURA L. Annual, biennial, or perennial herbs. Leaf-blades entire, toothed, or pinnatifid. Flowers spicate or racemose. Hypanthium narrow, somewhat prolonged beyond the ovary. Petals unequal, with clawed blades. Stamens 8, declined. Style declined. Stigma 4-lobed, surrounded by a cup-like border. Fruit ribbed or angled.—About 18 species, North American.

Anthers linear to narrowly elliptic, attached near the base.   I. BIENNES.
Anthers oval, attached near the middle.   II. PARVIFLORAE.

I. BIENNES
Fruit not stipitate, sometimes with a stout stipe-like base.
  Fruit 6–8 mm. long: flower-buds less than 2 cm. long.
    Fruit with rounded or obtuse angles.
    Fruit with sharp angles.   1. *G. biennis.*
      Fruit pubescent: flower-buds pubescent.
        Stem simple or with few ascending branches
          above: species ranging from South Carolina to
          Florida and Alabama.   2. *G. angustifolia.*

Stem diffusely much branched: species of the
   lower Mississippi valley.   3. *G. filiformis.*
Fruit glabrous: flower-buds glabrous.
   Stem, leaves, and inflorescence-rachis pubescent: 4. *G. simulans.*
   Stem, leaves, and inflorescence-rachis glabrous, at
      least at maturity: 5. *G. Eatonii.*
                                   6. *G. longiflora.*
  Fruit 3–4 mm. long: flower-buds over 2 cm. long.
Fruit contracted into a slender stipe which resembles a pedicel. 7. *G. Michauxii.*

II. PARVIFLORAE

Rather coarse herb, with slender elongate spikes of inconspicuous flowers.   8. *G. parviflora.*

1. **G. biennis** L. Stem 6–15 dm. tall, villous-hirsute: leaf-blades lanceolate,
elliptic-lanceolate, or elliptic, 3–10 cm. long, remotely denticulate or merely
undulate: buds pubescent: base of the hy-
panthium villous: sepals 8–9.5 mm. long:
petals white, sometimes turning pink, 7–11
mm. long: fruit elliptic to oval-elliptic, 6–10
mm. long, more or less hirsute.—(MORNING-
HONEYSUCKLE.)—Dry soil and stream-banks,
various provinces, Ga. to Miss., Minn., and
Que.—Sum.-fall.

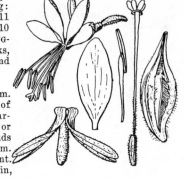

2. **G. angustifolia** Michx. Stem 7–12 dm.
tall, finely appressed-pubescent: blades of
the stem-leaves spatulate to linear or linear-
lanceolate, 1–6 cm. long, acute, sinuate or
nearly entire, sparingly pubescent: buds
pubescent: petals white or pink, 5–6.5 mm.
long: fruit elliptic, 5–9 mm. long, pubescent.
—Dry woods and sandy fields, Coastal Plain,
Fla. to Miss. and N. C.—Spr.-fall.

3. **G. filiformis** Small. Stem 1–2.5 m. tall, canescent-puberulent: leaf-
blades linear to narrowly linear-lanceolate, 2–10 cm. long, sharply, but finely
toothed, or entire above: buds puberulent, less than 1.5 cm. long: sepals 9–10
mm. long: petals pink-purple, 7–8 mm. long: fruit narrowly elliptic, 6–7 mm.
long, canescent.—Sandy soil, Coastal Plain, Miss. to Tex. and Ark.—Sum.-fall.

4. **G. simulans** Small. Stem 9–20 dm. tall, loosely pubescent below: blades
of the stem-leaves oblanceolate or narrowly spatulate to lanceolate or linear-
lanceolate, 2–12 cm. long, pinnatifid to sharply toothed: sepals broadly linear,
rather obtuse: petals pinkish, 4.5–5 mm. long: fruit 8–10 mm. long, glabrous.
—Coastal sand-dunes and pinelands, S Fla.—Sum.-fall.

5. **G. Eatonii** Small. Stem 3–11 dm. tall, glabrous or with scattered hairs:
leaf-blades nearly similar to those of the two preceding species: buds glabrous:
sepals narrowly linear, rather acute: petals pinkish, 5–6.5 mm. long: fruit
glabrous, the body ellipsoid-ovoid, 7–10 mm. long, 4-angled, contracted into a
very short stipe-like base.—Sand-dunes, Punta Rassa, Fla.—Spr.

6. **G. longiflora** Spach. Similar to *G. angustifolia* in habit: leaf-blades linear,
narrowly so above, remotely and inconspicuously toothed or entire, somewhat
revolute: buds canescent-puberulent, over 2 cm. long: sepals 11–13 mm. long:
petals pink, 9–10 mm. long: fruit oval-elliptic, about 4 mm. long, canescent.—
Sandy soil, Coastal Plain, Miss. (or Ala.?), La. and Tex.—Spr.-sum.

7. **G. Michauxii** Spach. Stem 6–18 dm. tall, puberulent, leaf-blades linear
or linear-elliptic, 2.5–8 cm. long, sinuate or remotely dentate: buds canescent:
petals white, turning reddish, 4–6 mm. long: sepals 4–6 mm. long: fruit nar-

rowly ovoid, puberulent, the body 3–4 mm. long, sharply 4-angled above, narrowed to a pedicel-like base, longer than the body.—Dry woods and fields, various provinces, Fla. to La., Kans., and N. C. (or Va.?).—Sum.–fall.

8. G. parviflora Dougl. Stem 6–35 dm. tall, villous-hirsute: leaf-blades lanceolate, ovate-lanceolate or elliptic, 3.5–10 cm. long, repand-dentate, softly pubescent: buds glabrous or nearly so: sepals 2–3 mm. long: petals 1.5–4 mm. long: fruit fusiform, 6–8 mm. long, 4-nerved, obtuse between the angles.—Dry soil, fields, and roadsides, various provinces, Ala. to Calif., Ore., and S. Dak.—(*Mex.*)—Spr.–sum.

14. CIRCAEA [Tourn.] L. Perennial herbs. Leaves opposite: blades mostly toothed, petioled. Flowers racemose. Sepals 2. Petals 2, white, notched. Stamens 2, alternate with the petals. Ovary 1–2-celled. Fruit obovoid, usually bristly with hooked hairs—About 8 species, natives of the Northern Hemisphere.

Plant herbaceous: leaf-blades ovate: bracts obsolete: fruit over 3 mm. long. 2-celled.   1. *C. latifolia.*
Plant succulent: leaf-blades cordate: bracts minute: fruit less than 3 mm. long, 1-celled.   2. *C. alpina.*

1. C. latifolia Hill. Plant 3–6 dm. tall: leaf-blades ovate, 5–10 cm. long, remotely denticulate: pedicels 4–8 mm. long: corolla about 3 mm. broad: fruit broadly obovoid, about 4 mm. long, with stiff hairs. [*C. lutetiana* (Fl. SE. U. S.)] — (ENCHANTER'S-NIGHTSHADE.) — Rich woods and thickets, various provinces, Ga. to La., Kans., S. D., Ont., and N. S.—Sum. —*C. intermedia* Ehrh. with saliently toothed leaf-blades, the upper ones more or less cordate, and minute bracts, has been reported from Texas and may occur in our range.

2. C. alpina L. Plant 0.5–2 dm. tall: leaf-blades ovate, 2.5–5 cm. long, coarsely dentate: pedicels 3–4 mm. long: corolla about 2 mm. broad: fruit narrowly obovoid, about 2 mm. long, with soft hairs.—Cold woods, Blue Ridge and more northern provinces, Ga. to Ind., S. Dak., Alas., and Lab.—(*Eurasia.*)—Sum.–fall.

FAMILY 9. **GUNNERACEAE** — WATER-MILFOIL FAMILY

Perennial, or rarely annual, aquatic or amphibious herbs. Leaves alternate to whorled: blades entire to dissected, often 2 kinds on the same plant. Flowers perfect or monoecious. Calyx of 2–4 sepals. Corolla of 2–5 small petals, or wanting. Androecium of 1–8 relatively large stamens. Gynoecium of 1 or of 2–4, sometimes united, carpels. Ovary inferior. Stigmas 1–4.—Eight genera and about 100 species, widely distributed.

Gynoecium 3-carpellary: stamens 3: flowers perfect.   1. PROSERPINACA.
Gynoecium 4-carpellary: stamens 4 or 8: flowers monoecious or polygamous.   2. MYRIOPHYLLUM.

1. PROSERPINACA L. Herbs with stems decumbent or creeping at base. Leaves alternate: blades toothed or pectinate, sometimes both kinds on one plant. Flowers perfect, with the perianth in 3's, apetalous. Sepals broad, often deltoid, green or sometimes whitish. Stamens 3. Stigmas 3, erect. Fruit 3-carpellary. Four species, North American.—MERMAID-WEEDS.

Leaves all nearly alike and pectinate; blades of those subtending the flowers or
flower-clusters finely pectinate: stigmas stout.   1. *P. pectinata.*
Leaves all nearly alike and toothed; blades of those subtending
  the flowers or flower-clusters serrate or serrulate, or the
  submersed ones pectinate, in aquatic forms all pectinate or
  pinnatifid-pectinate: stigmas slender.
  Fruit not auricled; nutlets with even or uneven angles.
    Fruit ovate or suborbicular in outline, with obtuse or
    rounded angles, and turgid faces.   2. *P. amblygona.*
    Fruit deltoid or rhombic in outline, with acute or margined
    angles, and concave faces.   3. *P. palustris.*
  Fruit auricled; nutlets with prominently appendaged angles.   4. *P. platycarpa.*

1. **P. pectinata** Lam. Leaf-blades elliptic to ovate in outline, 1–3 cm. long, one-half as wide or nearly so, the segments slender or filiform-subulate, about as wide as the rachis: fruit ovoid or globose-ovoid, 3–3.5 mm. long, tuberculate-rugose, thick-angled.—Ponds, ditches, and sluggish streams, various provinces, Fla. to La. and Me.—Spr.–fall.—This species is less widely distributed than the two following, and is more decidedly restricted to coastal regions.

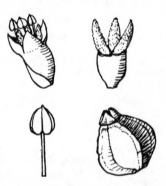

2. **P. amblygona** (Fernald) Small. Leaf-blades linear, elliptic, lanceolate, or spatulate, 1.5–5 cm. long, less than one-half as wide as long, serrate or the submerged ones pinnatifid or pectinate, the segments coarse or slender, but mostly narrower than the rachis: fruit ovoid or subglobose, 3–3.5 mm. long, tuberculate-roughened, thick-angled.—Ponds, swamps, and ditches, various provinces, Ga. to Tex., Mo., and Ont.—Spr.–fall.—Specimens of this species from Georgia have been erroneously referred to *P. intermedia* Mackenzie.

3. **P. palustris** L. Leaf-blades elliptic, linear, linear-lanceolate or broadened upward, mostly 2–6 cm. long, serrate or serrulate, or the submersed ones pinnatifid or pectinate, the segments slender: fruit pyramidal or rhomboidal, 4–5 mm. long, thin-angled, tuberculate-roughened.—(MERMAID-WEED.)—Moist soil, ponds, ditches, and swamps, various provinces, Fla. to La. (or Tex.?), Minn., and N. S.—Spr.–fall.

4. **P. platycarpa** Small. Leaf-blades elliptic varying to oblanceolate or obovate, 1–3 cm. long, serrate, or those of the submersed ones, or in aquatic forms all pectinate: fruit broad, mostly obreniform by the auricled angles, the faces sparingly rugose.—Pools, lime-sinks, and cypress swamps, pen. Fla.; perhaps further N along the Atlantic coast.—(*W. I.*)—All year.

2. **MYRIOPHYLLUM** L. Herbs with mostly submersed stems, or sometimes creeping in the mud. Leaves alternate to whorled: blades of the emersed (floral) ones entire, toothed, or pectinate; those of the submersed ones larger and with finer divisions than the others. Flowers monoecious or polygamous, with the perianth in 4's and the staminate ones petaliferous, green, red, or purplish. Sepals mostly narrow. Stamens 4 or 8. Stigmas 4, recurved. Fruit 4-carpellary.—About 20 species, widely distributed.—WATER-MILFOILS.

Sepals broad and short: plants monoecious or polygamous.
  Stamens 4: corolla persistent.
    Floral leaves with entire or serrate blades: anthers acuminate: petals broadly
    ovate.   1. *M. heterophyllum.*
    Floral leaves with incised-pinnatifid blades: anthers
    obtuse: petals elliptic.   2. *M. pinnatum.*
  Stamens 8: corolla deciduous.   3. *M. laxum.*
Sepals long and slender: plants dioecious.   4. *M. proserpinacoides.*

1. M. heterophyllum Michx. Leaves in 4's to 6's; blades of the usually crowded submersed ones with 6–10 pairs of linear-filiform or capillary segments; those of the floral ones elliptic, ovate, linear, or broadened upward, serrate: petals broadly ovate, 2–2.5 mm. long, abruptly pointed: anthers narrowly elliptic, 1.5–2 mm. long: fruit globose-ovoid, 2–2.5 mm. long; carpels with 2 dorsal ridges, tuberculate-roughened.—Ponds and sluggish streams, various provinces, Fla. to Tex., Minn., Ont., and N. J.—(*Mex.*)—Sum.—Forms of *M. heterophyllum* have often been erroneously referred to *M. verticillatum* in our range.

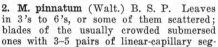
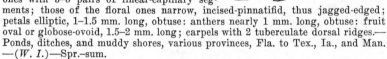

2. M. pinnatum (Walt.) B. S. P. Leaves in 3's to 6's, or some of them scattered; blades of the usually crowded submersed ones with 3–5 pairs of linear-capillary segments; those of the floral ones narrow, incised-pinnatifid, thus jagged-edged; petals elliptic, 1–1.5 mm. long, obtuse: anthers nearly 1 mm. long, obtuse: fruit oval or globose-ovoid, 1.5–2 mm. long; carpels with 2 tuberculate dorsal ridges.—Ponds, ditches, and muddy shores, various provinces, Fla. to Tex., Ia., and Man. —(*W. I.*)—Spr.–sum.

3. M. laxum Shuttlw. Leaves in 4's; blades of the approximate submersed ones with 3–7 pairs of capillary segments; those of the floral ones spatulate: petals elliptic, 2.5–3 mm. long: anthers linear to narrowly elliptic, about as long as the filaments: fruit ovoid-globose, about 1.5 mm. long; carpels minutely warty.—Ponds and lakes, Coastal Plain, N Fla., S Ga. and S Ala.—Sum.

4. M. proserpinacoides Gill. Leaves in 4's and 5's, feather-like; blades of the submersed and floral ones nearly or quite similar, all rather remote, with mostly 10–15 pairs of linear-subulate or rarely linear-spatulate segments: hypanthium subtended by minute or subulate bracts: sepals very slender.— (WATER-FEATHER. PARROT'S-FEATHER.)—Pools, and ditches, Coastal Plain, Fla. to Tex.; also locally as far N as N. Y.—Native of S. Am.—Spr.–fall.

ORDER AMMIALES

Herbs, shrubs, trees, or vines. Leaves alternate or opposite: blades simple or compound. Flowers perfect, polygamous, or dioecious, often borne in umbels. Calyx of typically 5 small sepals surmounting the hypanthium. Corolla typically of 5 petals, or wanting. Androecium of as many stamens as the sepals. Gynoecium 2-carpellary or rarely several–1-carpellary. Ovary inferior. Fruit drupaceous or baccate, or dry and then a cremocarp.

Fruit drupaceous or baccate: gynoecium 1–several-carpellary, if 2-carpellary, stigmas
  introrse.
    Styles single or united: ovule with a dorsal raphe: leaves mostly opposite; blades
    entire or merely toothed.   Fam. 1. NYSSACEAE.

Styles distinct : ovule with a ventral raphe : leaves mostly
alternate ; blades lobed or compound.　　　　　　Fam. 2. HEDERACEAE.
Fruit dry, a cremocarp : gynoecium 2-carpellary : stigmas
terminal.　　　　　　　　　　　　　　　　　　　　　Fam. 3. AMMIACEAE.

FAMILY 1.　**NYSSACEAE** — DOGWOOD FAMILY

Shrubs or trees, or rarely partly herbaceous plants.　Leaves opposite
or alternate : blades usually entire.　Flowers perfect or unisexual, borne
in naked or involucrate open or congested cymes.　Calyx of mostly 4 or 5
sepals.　Corolla of 4 or 5, or rarely more, petals, or wanting.　Androecium
of usually as many stamens as the sepals.　Gynoecium of 1 or of 2–4
united carpels.　Styles united.　Fruit mostly a drupe.—Sixteen genera
and about 90 species, most abundant in the northern hemisphere.

Flowers dioecious or polygamo-dioecious ; stigmas lateral : drupe
1-celled.　　　　　　　　　　　　　　　　　　　　　　　1. NYSSA.
Flowers perfect : stigmas terminal : drupe 2-celled, 2-seeded.
　Flowers in open cymes, not subtended by an involucre : fruit
　surmounted by the style, globular, not red.　　　　　2. SVIDA.
　Flowers in a head, subtended by a large involucre : fruit sur-
　mounted by the calyx, elongate, red.　　　　　　　　3. CYNOXYLON.

1. NYSSA L.　Shrubs or trees, with terete branches.　Leaves alternate, deciduous.　Flowers polygamo-dioecious, green, the staminate with 5–several sepals and 5–many stamens, the pistillate with 5 sepals and a 1-celled pistil.
Drupe somewhat elongate.—About 8 species, North American and Asiatic.—Spr.

Pistillate flowers 2 or more together : drupe small (1–1.5 cm.), black, beneath a
bloom ; stone smooth or bluntly ridged.　　　　　　I. MULTIFLORAE.
Pistillate flowers solitary : drupe large (3–4 cm.), purple to red ;
stone winged or sharply ridged.　　　　　　　　　　II. UNIFLORAE.

I.　MULTIFLORAE
Leaf-blades obovate to ovate : stone nearly ribless.　　　1. N. sylvatica.
Leaf-blades spatulate, oblanceolate or elliptic : stone ribbed.
　Drupe oval to ellipsoid : leaf-blades mostly 8–12 cm. long.　2. N. biflora.
　Drupe globular : leaf-blades mostly 2.5–7 cm. long.　　　3. N. ursina.

II.　UNIFLORAE
Pistillate flowers short-pedicelled : drupe red ; stone winged.
　Leaf-blades narrow, acuminate : shrub with underground stems
　and erect branches.　　　　　　　　　　　　　　　4. N. acuminata.
　Leaf-blades broad, obtuse or abruptly pointed : tree with spread-
　ing branches.　　　　　　　　　　　　　　　　　　5. N. Ogeche.
Pistillate flowers long-pedicelled : drupe purple or blue ; stone
sharp-ridged.　　　　　　　　　　　　　　　　　　6. N. aquatica.

1. N. sylvatica Marsh.　Tree becoming 50 m. tall, with angular-checked
bark : leaf-blades oval or obovate, sometimes pubescent beneath, 5–15 cm. long :
drupe oval, 10–15 mm. long ; stone oval or
ellipsoid, rarely broadened upward and
slightly curved. — (BLACK-GUM.　SOUR-GUM.
PEPPERIDGE.)—Rich soil, wet places or dry
hillsides, various provinces, Fla. to Tex.,
Mo., Mich., and Me.—The wood of this and
the next following species is used for making various utensils.　It is light-yellow or
nearly white and soft, but tough.

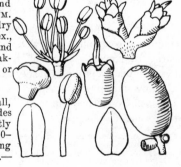

2. N. biflora Walt.　Tree becoming 40 m. tall,
with longitudinally ridged bark : leaf-blades
oblanceolate, spatulate, or elliptic, mostly
2–12 cm. long : drupe oval or ellipsoid, 10–
13 mm. long ; stone ellipsoid, 8–10 mm. long
or sometimes longer, or rarely smaller.—

(WATER-GUM. WATER-TUPELO. BLACK-GUM.)—Swamps and pond-margins, Coastal Plain and adj. provinces, Fla. to Tex. and Del. (or N. J.).—A form with rather small blunt leaves and roundish drupes 6–7 mm. in diameter from the coastal regions from South Carolina to Virginia may represent an additional species.

3. **N. ursina** Small. Shrub with copiously branched stems or a small much-branched tree: leaf-blades elliptic, often narrowly so, to spatulate, 2.5–7 cm. long, coriaceous, mostly rounded at the apex: drupe globular, 9–12 mm. in diameter, very fleshy; stone oval, 8–10 mm. long.—(BEAR-GUM.)—Pineland swamps, Apalachicola River delta, Fla.—A much-branched shrub with the habit of *Cliftonia* and *Cyrilla*, with which it grows, conspicuous by its numerous small leaves and in flower or fruit, by the very numerous flower clusters or fruits, respectively. The juicy drupes, although intensely bitter, are a favorite food of the bears of the region.

4. **N. acuminata** Small. Shrub becoming 3 m. tall, usually with numerous erect branches: leaf-blades narrowly elliptic or oblanceolate, 4–16 cm. long, acuminate: drupe ellipsoid, about 2 cm. long.—Pineland swamps near the coast, Ga.

5. **N. Ogeche** Marsh. Tree becoming 20 m. tall, the stem crooked; leaf-blades elliptic, varying to oblanceolate or lanceolate, or rarely oval, 5–20 cm. long, usually entire: petioles about 1 cm. long: drupe 3–4 cm. long, red, longer than the pedicel; stone papery-winged. — (OGEECHE-LIME. OGEECHEE-PLUM. TUPELO-GUM.)—Wet swamps, Coastal Plain, Fla. to S. C.—The fruits are used to make an acid drink and for a preserve. The wood is white, light, soft and tough.

6. **N. aquatica** L. Tree becoming 35 m. tall, the stem erect: leaf-blades ovate to elliptic, 9–30 cm. long, often sinuate or coarsely toothed; petioles 2.5 cm. long: drupe nearly 3 cm. long, dark-purple, shorter than the pedicel; stone sharp-ridged.—(TUPELO-GUM. COTTON-GUM.)—River-swamps, Coastal Plain and rarely adj. provinces, Fla. to Tex., Ill., and Va.—The wood is used for making various utensils. It is light-brown or nearly white, soft, but tough.

2. **SVIDA** Opiz. Shrubs or trees. Leaves opposite or rarely alternate. Flowers in naked corymb-like cymes. Sepals 4, minute. Petals 4, white, spreading. Stamens 4. Drupe globular or depressed. [*Cornus* L. in part.]— About 15 species, North American.—Spr.—CORNELS.—Some species are used medicinally.

Leaves alternate, approximate at the end of the branches: drupe deep-blue or blue-black.	1. *S. alternifolia.*
Leaves opposite, remote: drupe white or pale-blue or light-blue.	
Lower leaf-surfaces glabrous.	
Twigs gray: drupe white: stone broader than long.	2. *S. femina.*
Twigs reddish-brown: drupe pale-blue: stone mostly longer than broad.	3. *S. stricta.*
Lower leaf-surfaces with straight or curled hairs.	
Stones longer than broad: drupe 3–4 mm. in diameter.	
Leaf-blades membranous, those below a peduncle elliptic or oval.	4. *S. microcarpa*
Leaf-blades leathery, those below a peduncle ovate to ovate-lanceolate.	5. *S. Priceae.*
Stones broader than long: drupe 6–8 mm. in diameter.	
Sepals much shorter than the hypanthium: drupe white: stone sharply 4-angled.	6. *S. asperifolia.*
Sepals about as long as the hypanthium: drupe pale-blue: stone slightly angled.	7. *S. Amomum.*

1. **S. alternifolia** (L. f.) Small. Shrub, or tree sometimes 9 m. tall: leaf-blades elliptic or oval, varying to ovate or obovate, 5–15 cm. long, whitish be-

neath, prominently ribbed: petals oblong-
ovate: drupe depressed-globose, 8–10 mm. in
diameter, blue-black.—(Pagoda-cornel. Um-
brella-cornel.)—Bluffs, woods and thickets, various provinces, Fla. to Ala., Minn.,
and N. B.—The brown heart-wood is close-
grained and hard.

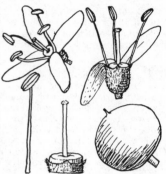

2. **S. femina** (Mill.) Small. Shrub with
gray twigs: leaf-blades elliptic or lanceolate, 4–15 cm. long: sepals triangular: petals
oblong to oblong-lanceolate: drupe subglobose, 4–5 mm. in diameter. [*S. candidissima*
(Marsh.) Small]—River-banks, thickets, and
roadsides, various provinces, Ga. to Nebr.,
Minn., and Me.

3. **S. stricta** (Lam.) Small. Shrub, or small tree with smoothish bark: leaf-
blades elliptic, oval, or ovate, 4–12 cm. long: petals linear-oblong to linear-
lanceolate: drupe 5–6 mm. in diameter, pale-blue.—Swamps, Coastal Plain,
Fla. to Tex., Mo., Ind., and Va.

4. **S. microcarpa** (Nash) Small. Shrub with brownish twigs: leaf-blades
oval or elliptic, 3–9 cm. long: petals ovate-lanceolate to lanceolate: drupe about
4 mm. in diameter, light-blue.—Low woods, Coastal Plain, Fla. and Ga.

5. **S. Priceae** Small. Shrub with red twigs: leaf-blades elliptic, ovate-elliptic,
ovate or ovate-lanceolate, 5–12 cm. long: petals narrowly lanceolate: drupe
about 3 mm. in diameter, white.—Bluffs and river banks, Interior Low Plateaus, Tenn. and Ky.

6. **S. asperifolia** (Michx.) Small. Shrub with brownish twigs: leaf-blades
ovate to elliptic or oval, 4–15 cm. long: drupe 5–6 mm. in diameter, white.—
(Rough-leaf cornel.)—Low grounds or moist banks, various provinces W of
Blue Ridge, Ala. to Tex., Minn., and Ont.

7. **S. Amomum** (Mill.) Small. Shrub with purple twigs: leaf-blades lanceolate to broadly ovate, 3–13 cm. long, silky and often somewhat rusty beneath:
drupe 6–8 mm. in diameter, pale-blue.—Common, in moist thickets and along
streams.—(Kinnikinnik. Silky-cornel.)—Wet places and stream-banks,
various provinces, Fla. to Tex., N. D., and Newf.

3. **CYNOXYLON** Raf. Trees. Leaves opposite. Flowers perfect, borne
in involucrate heads. Sepals 4, broadly ovate to oblong. Petals 4, greenish
or yellow-green, recurving. Stamens 4.
Drupe elongate. Two species, North American.

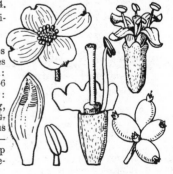

1. **C. floridum** (L.) Raf. Tree sometimes
15 m. tall, with rough black bark, leaf-blades
elliptic to oval, 5–18 cm. long, pale beneath:
involucral bracts white or pink, obovate, 4–6
cm. long: petals linear, 3–4.5 mm. long:
drupe ellipsoid to oval, about 15 mm. long,
red. [*Cornus florida* L.]—(Flowering dog-
wood.)—Hammocks and rich woods, various
provinces, Fla. to Tex., Minn., and Me.—
There is always a black crumple at the tip
of each involucral bract. The very close-

grained wood is sometimes used as a substitute for boxwood, in wood engraving and for a variety of articles.

FAMILY 2. **HEDERACEAE** — IVY FAMILY

Herbs, shrubs, trees, or vines. Leaves alternate: blades simple or compound. Flowers perfect or polygamous, often umbellate. Calyx of 5 sepals, or obsolete. Corolla of 5 or 10 petals. Gynoecium of 2–5 united carpels. Styles often distinct. Fruit a berry or a drupe.—Fifty-two genera and about 475 species, natives of the north temperate zone.

Vines: leaf-blades simple.
Herbs, shrubs or trees: leaf-blades compound.   1. HEDERA.
   Umbel simple: plant scapose, the bracts whorled: styles 2 or 3.   2. PANAX.
   Umbel compound: plant caulescent, the leaves alternate: styles 5.   3. ARALIA.

1. HEDERA L. Vines. Leaf-blades leathery, entire or lobed. Flowers polygamous, in panicled umbels. Sepals 5, or obsolete. Petals 5. Stamens 5. Ovary 5-celled. Styles united. Fruit angled.

—One species, in many cult. varieties.

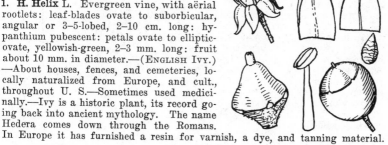

1. H. Helix L. Evergreen vine, with aërial rootlets: leaf-blades ovate to suborbicular, angular or 3–5-lobed, 2–10 cm. long: hypanthium pubescent: petals ovate to ellipticovate, yellowish-green, 2–3 mm. long: fruit about 10 mm. in diameter.—(ENGLISH IVY.) —About houses, fences, and cemeteries, locally naturalized from Europe, and cult., throughout U. S.—Sometimes used medicinally.—Ivy is a historic plant, its record going back into ancient mythology. The name Hedera comes down through the Romans. In Europe it has furnished a resin for varnish, a dye, and tanning material.

2. PANAX L. Perennial herbs. Leaf-blades palmately compound. Scape topped with a whorl of bracts quite similar to the leaves. Umbel simple. Ovary mostly 2- or 3-celled. Styles distinct. Fruit red, yellowish, or yellow.— Seven species, North American and Asiatic.

Rootstock globular: leaflets sessile, obtuse: berry yellow.   1. *P. trifolium.*
Rootstock fusiform: leaflets stalked, acuminate: berry red.   2. *P. quinquefolium.*

1. P. trifolium L. Plant 1–2 dm. tall: bracts 3: leaflets 3, the blades elliptic, 1–8 cm. long: petals white: berry 4–5 mm. broad.—(DWARF-GINSENG. GROUND-NUT.)—Damp places in woods, various provinces, Coastal Plain only N, Ga. to Ill., Minn., and N. S.—Spr.

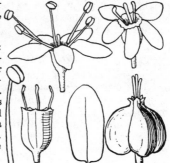

2. P. quinquefolium L. Plant 2–4 dm. tall: bracts 3 or 5: leaflets 5–7, the blades obovate, or those of the basal leaflets oval or suborbicular, 2–12 cm. long: petals greenish: berry 8–10 mm. broad.—(GINSENG. SANG.)—Cool places in rich woods, various provinces, Fla. to La., Nebr., Minn., and Que.—Sum.—The root is exported to China where it is used in superstitious practices. The natural supply being much depleted, the plant is now extensively cultivated.

3. **ARALIA** [Tourn.] L. Perennial herbs, shrubs, or trees, sometimes prickle-armed or spiny. Leaves alternate: blades pinnately or ternately compound. Umbel compound. Flowers white or greenish. Ovary mostly 5-celled. Styles distinct or united at the base. Fruit black. About 30 species, North American and Asiatic.—SPIKENARDS. SARSAPARILLAS.—Several of the species are used in medicine.

Umbels few, in terminal corymbs or few-rayed umbels.
   Plant with elongate rootstock, a peduncle or a leaf, or both, arising together at
      intervals from the rootstock.   1. *A. nudicaulis.*
   Plant with leafy branches arising from the rootstock.   2. *A. hispida.*
Umbels numerous, in terminal or axillary racemes or panicles.
   Large unarmed herb: leaflets membranous: hypanthium cam-
      panulate: anthers globular.   3. *A. racemosa.*
   Shrub or small tree, with prickle-armed stems: leaflets leathery:
      hypanthium broadly turbinate: anthers ellipsoid.   4. *A. spinosa.*

1. **A. nudicaulis** L. Plant 2–3.5 dm. tall, sparingly soft-pubescent or glabrous: leaf usually solitary: inflorescence overtopped by the leaf: berry 6–8 mm. in diameter: seed 4.5–5 mm. long, very flat.—(WILD SARSAPARILLA.)—Woods and rocky hillsides, various provinces, Ga. to Mo., Man., and Newf.—Spring–sum.

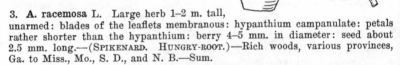

2. **A. hispida** Vent. Plant 2–9 dm. tall, bristly pubescent: leaves several or many: inflorescence overtopping the leaves: berry rather smaller than those of *A. nudicaulis*: seed 2.5–3 mm. long, swollen.—(WILD-ELDER. BRISTLY-SARSAPARILLA.)—Sandy thickets and rocky woods, various provinces, Coastal Plain only N, N. C. to Ind., Minn., Ont., and Lab.—Sum.

3. **A. racemosa** L. Large herb 1–2 m. tall, unarmed: blades of the leaflets membranous: hypanthium campanulate: petals rather shorter than the hypanthium: berry 4–5 mm. in diameter: seed about 2.5 mm. long.—(SPIKENARD. HUNGRY-ROOT.)—Rich woods, various provinces, Ga. to Miss., Mo., S. D., and N. B.—Sum.

4. **A. spinosa** L. Shrub or small tree, prickle-armed: blades of the leaflets leathery: hypanthium broad-turbinate: petals longer than the hypanthium: berry 6–7 mm. in diameter: seed about 4 mm. long.—(PRICKLY-ASH. TOOTH-ACHE-TREE. HERCULES-CLUB. PRICKLY-ELDER. DEVIL'S-WALKINGSTICK.).— Low grounds and woods, various provinces, Fla., to Tex., Mo., and N. Y.— Sum.—Sometimes cultivated for ornament. The bark and fruits are occasionally used in medicine. The brown heart-wood is streaked with yellow, close-grained but light and soft.

FAMILY 3. **AMMIACEAE** — CARROT FAMILY

Herbs with hollow stems. Leaves typically alternate: blades dissected, or sometimes merely toothed, or entire. Flowers perfect or polygamous, umbellate. Calyx of 5 tooth-like sepals, or obsolete. Corolla of 5 petals. Androecium of 5 stamens. Gynoecium of 2 united carpels, often with a stylopodium. Fruit dry, a cremocarp, the ribbed or winged carpels separating at maturity.—About 250 genera and more than 2,000 species, widely distributed, but most abundant in the tropics.

Flowers densely capitate: fruit scaly, ribless.   Tribe I. ERYNGIEAE.
Flowers evidently umbelled, the umbels sometimes compact:
  fruit ribbed, or if ribless, not scaly.
    Fruit ribless, covered with hooked prickles or stellate
      hairs.
      Fruit with hooked prickles, pointed at the apex, the
        carpels broadly united: leaf-blades pinnately or pal-
        mately 3-7-foliolate.
      Fruit with stellate hairs, broadly rounded at the   II. SANICULEAE.
        apex, the carpels nearly distinct: leaf-blades
        lobed.
    Fruit ribbed, at least on the beak.   IIa. BOWLESIEAE.
     • Secondary ribs of the carpels more prominent than
        the primary, armed with prickles, the primary
        ribs bristly.   III. CAUCALIEAE.
     Secondary ribs wanting, the primary ones evident or
        prominent.
      Fruit narrow, linear or linear-clavate, several
        times longer than wide.   IV. OSMORRHIZEAE.
      Fruit short, ellipsoid to globose, less than twice
        as long as wide.
        Fruit terete in cross-section or compressed
          laterally.
          Umbels simple, rarely proliferous: leaves
            with blades.   V. HYDROCOTYLEAE.
          Umbels compound, if simple the leaves
            mere hollow phyllodia.   VI. AMMINEAE.
        Fruit much flattened dorsally, with the lat-
          eral ribs more or less strongly winged.   VII. ANGELICEAE.

I. ERYNGIEAE

Erect or prostrate herbs, often with bristly or spiny leaves
and bracts, the inflorescence frequently highly colored.   1. ERYNGIUM.

II. SANICULEAE

Erect herbs with palmate leaf-blades and irregular umbels,
the flowers perfect and staminate.   2. SANICULA.

IIa. BOWLESIEAE

Weak-stemmed herbs, with slender-petioled leaf-blades and
short-peduncled, few-flowered axillary umbels.   2a. BOWLESIA.

III. CAUCALIEAE

Sepals obsolete: fruit dorsally flattened.   3. DAUCUS.
Sepals prominent: fruit laterally flattened.   4. TORILIS.

IV. OSMORRHIZEAE

Fruit bristly.
  Fruit with an elongate beak longer than the body, not
    narrowed at the base.   5. SCANDIX.
  Fruit beakless, narrowed at the base.   6. OSMORRHIZA.
Fruit not bristly.
  Fruit beaked, the beak shorter than the body: oil-tubes
    wanting.   7. CEREFOLIUM.
  Fruit beakless or slightly beaked: oil-tubes present.
    Seed-face concave: leaf-blades decompound: annual
      plants.   8. CHAEROPHYLLUM.
    Seed-face flat: leaf-blades 3-foliolate: perennial
      plants.   9. DERINGA.

V. HYDROCOTYLEAE

Fruit without secondary ribs or reticulations: involucre
  wanting.   10. HYDROCOTYLE.
Fruit with secondary ribs and reticulations: involucre
  present.   11. CENTELLA.

VI. AMMINEAE

Corolla white, greenish, or pinkish.
  Fruit terete or nearly so.
    Umbel compound: leaves much-divided.
      Ribs of the carpels all corky thickened.   12. CYNOSCIADIUM.

Ribs of the carpels slender, the lateral sometimes
corky.
    Fruit subglobose.   13. CORIANDRUM.
    Fruit ellipsoid.   14. LIGUSTICUM.
Umbel simple : leaves philodia-like, linear or spatulate.   15. LILAEOPSIS.
Fruit laterally flattened.
    Fruit tubercled.   16. SPERMOLEPIS.
    Fruit smooth.
       Carpels strongly flattened laterally, the fruit
        nearly orbicular.   17. ERIGENIA.
       Carpels nearly terete, or only slightly flattened.
        Carpels without oil-tubes.
           Involucre present : carpel-ribs wavy-mar-
             gined.   18. CONIUM.
           Involucre wanting.   19. AEGOPODIUM.
        Carpels with oil-tubes.
           Seed-face concave : oil-tubes more than one
             in the intervals.   20. EULOPHUS.
           Seed-face flat or nearly so : oil-tubes usu-
             ally solitary in the intervals.
             Umbels terminal or axillary.
               Stylopodium depressed.
                 Carpels with the lateral ribs
                  largest : leaf-blades bipinnate,
                  the segments lanceolate.   21. CICUTA.
                 Carpel-ribs nearly equal : leaf-
                  blades pinnate or finely
                  dissected with linear or
                  filiform segments.
                    Carpel-ribs winged : leaf-
                    blades pinnate.   22. SIUM.
                    Carpel-ribs not winged : leaf-
                    blades finely dissected into
                  linear or filiform segments. 23. AMMI.
               Stylopodium conic.
                 Carpel-ribs, at least the lateral,
                 corky-thickened.
                   Fruit narrow; 8–10 mm.
                    long, umbel rays 5 or less. 24. TREPOCARPUS.
                   Fruit broad ; 1.5–4 mm. long,
                    umbel rays numerous.   25. PTILIMNIUM.
                                      26. HARPERELLA.
                 Carpel-ribs not corky-thickened.
            Umbels, at least the lower ones, oppo-
             site the leaves.
               Carpel-ribs slender winged, stylo-
               podium prominent on the mature
               fruit.   27. CELERI.
               Carpel-ribs corky-thickened, stylo-
               podium not prominent on the ma-
               ture fruit.   28. CYCLOSPERMUM.
Corolla yellow or greenish-yellow, sometimes purple in
  Thaspium.
    Leaf-blades simple, perfoliate : carpels without oil-tubes.   29. BUPLEURUM.
    Leaf-blades compound : carpels with oil-tubes.   30. THASPIUM.
       Fruit not flattened : carpel-ribs winged.
       Fruit flattened laterally : carpel-ribs not winged.   31. TAENIDIA.
         Leaf-segments entire.
         Leaf-segments toothed, incised, or lobed.   32. ZIZIA.
            Stylopodium wanting.
            Stylopodium present.
              Involucre of 2–4 linear bracts : stylopo-
              dium depressed.   33. APIUM.
              Involucre wanting : stylopodium conic.   34. FOENICULUM.

VII. ANGELICEAE

Corolla yellow : stylopodium depressed.
  Fruit with thick corky lateral ribs and obsolete dorsal
    ribs : oil-tubes several in the intervals.   35. PLEIOTAENIA.
  Fruit with thin-margined lateral ribs and evident dorsal
    ribs : oil-tubes solitary in the intervals.
      Leaf-segments very narrow.   36. ANETHUM.
      Leaf-segments broad.   37. PASTINACA.

Corolla white: stylopodium conic (except in *Angelica*).
  Oil-tubes more than one in the intervals.
    Leaf-blades 2-3 pinnately decompound, the segments
      narrow.   38. CONIOSELINUM.
    Leaf-blades 1-2 ternately divided, the segments
      broad.   39. ANGELICA.
  Oil-tubes solitary in the intervals.
    Fruit notched at the apex, the carpels very flat.   40. HERACLEUM.
    Fruit not notched at the apex, the carpels not very
      flat.   41. OXYPOLIS.

1. **ERYNGIUM** Tourn. L. Biennial or perennial herbs. Leaf-blades spiny-toothed, lobed or incised, or rarely entire. Bracts of the involucre often colored, otherwise often resembling the leaves. Sepals acute or spine-like. Petals 5, blue, white, or greenish, each prolonged into an inflexed tip. Carpels with obsolete ribs and 5 oil-tubes. About 175 species, of tropical and temperate regions.—ERYNGOS. BUTTON-SNAKEROOTS.—Some species are accredited with medicinal properties.

Leaf-blades parallel-veined.   I. AQUATICA.
Leaf-blades not parallel-veined.
  Blades of the basal-leaves lobed or parted, the segments
    spine-tipped.
    Heads subglobose, spiny-bristly: bracts and bractlets
      3-5-pronged.   II. AROMATICA.
    Heads ovoid to ellipsoid, not bristly: bracts and bract-
      lets not 3-pronged.   III. DIVARICATA.
  Blades of the basal leaves entire or merely toothed.
    Stem and branches filiform or very slender, prostrate:
      plants biennial.   IV. PROSTRATA.
    Stem relatively stout, erect or ascending: plants peren-
      nial, or, perhaps rarely biennial.   V. INTEGRIFOLIA.

I. AQUATICA

Petals ovate, acuminate: bristles on the leaf-margin solitary.   1. *E. aquaticum.*
Petals suborbicular, mucronate: bristles on the leaf-margin
  mostly 2-4 together.   2. *E. synchaetum.*

II. AROMATICA

Diffuse plant, the branches from the top of the root decumbent: inflorescence near the tip of the branches widely
  branched.   3. *E. aromaticum.*
Plant erect, the stem corymbosely branched at the top: leaf-
  blades with 3-5 apical prong-like teeth.   3a. *E. cuneifolium.*

III. DIVARICATA

Prostrate plant, the heads mostly axillary, much longer than
  wide.   4. *E. divaricatum.*

IV. PROSTRATA

Bractlets longer than the flowers: stem-leaves with narrow
  blades or segments: fruit strongly tuberculate.   5. *E. Baldwinii.*
Bractlets shorter than the flowers: stem-leaves with broad
  blades or segments: fruit not strongly tuberculate.   6. *E. prostratum.*

V. INTEGRIFOLIA

Lower leaves with elongated hollow petioles and long blades.
  Bractlets entire.   7. *E. floridanum.*
  Bractlets 3-pronged.
    Teeth of the bractlets unequal, the lateral teeth
      smaller.   8. *E. virginianum.*
    Teeth of the bractlets about equal.   9. *E. Ravenelii.*
Lower leaves with short petioles and blades.
  Leaf-blades ovate, elliptic or lanceolate, serrate or cre-
    nate: heads mostly over 7 mm. high.   10. *E. integrifolium.*
  Leaf-blades linear or linear-spatulate, laciniately toothed,
    at least near the base: heads mostly less than 7 mm.
    high.   11. *E. ludovicianum.*

1. **E. aquaticum** L. Plant 3-18 dm. tall: blades of the lower leaves broadly linear, mostly 2-9 dm. long, stiff: sepals ovate to elliptic-ovate, about 2.5 mm.

long: petals over 2 mm. long: fruit 3.5–4
mm. long.—(CORN-SNAKEROOT. RATTLE-
SNAKE-MASTER.)—Low woods, swamps, and
acid meadows, various provinces, Fla. to
Tex., Minn., and Conn.—Spr.–fall.—The spe-
cific name is somewhat of a misnomer, as
the plant often grows in rather dry soil.

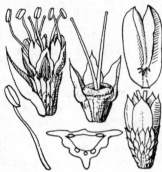

2. **E. synchaetum** (A. Gray) Rose. Plant
3–9 dm. tall: blades of the lower leaves narrowly linear, usually pliable: sepals broadly
ovate to deltoid-ovate, 1.5–1.8 mm. long:
petals less than 2 mm. long: fruit 2–2.5
mm. long.—Pinelands and prairies, Coastal
Plain, Fla. to Tex., Ark., and Ga.—Spr.–
fall.—A decoction made from the roots con-
stitutes the ceremonial ''black-drink'' of the Seminoles.

3. **E. aromaticum** Baldw. Plant ultimately diffuse, the branches 1–6 dm.
long: blades of the lower leaves spatulate in outline, pinnatifid or pinnately
parted, 3–4 cm. long, pale-margined: heads becoming 8–10 mm. long: sepals
lanceolate, 2–2.3 mm. long, acuminate: petals fully 1.5 mm. long: fruit granular, 1.5–2 mm. long, or rarely smaller.—Dry pinelands, Coastal Plain, Fla. and
adj. Ga.—Spr.—Sometimes erroneously accredited to Ala.

3a. **E. cuneifolium** Small. Plant erect, 2–5 dm. tall: blades of the numerous
basal leaves cuneate, long-petioled, the 3–5 apical teeth callous-margined spine-
tipped: heads becoming 5–8 mm. in diameter: sepals lanceolate, 1.5–2 mm.
long, acuminate: petals about 1.5 mm. long: fruit scarcely 1.5 mm. long.—
Scrub, S part of Lake Region, Fla.—Sum.–fall.

4. **E. divaricatum** H. & A. Plant prostrate: blades of the lower leaves bipinnatifid, those of the upper ones pinnatifid, the segments linear to lanceolate,
minutely spine-tipped: heads ovoid, becoming ellipsoid, 1 cm. long or less:
bracts of the involucre linear-subulate, spreading: fruit less than 1 mm. long,
bristly.—Low grounds and waste-places, around sea-ports, Fla. to N. C. Nat.
of Argentina.—Spr.–fall or all year S.

5. **E. Baldwinii** Spreng. Plant prostrate: blades of the basal leaves elliptic,
varying to broadest above or below the middle, 2–9 cm. long: heads ovoid to
cylindric: bracts of the involucre subulate.—Swamps and wet sandy soil,
Coastal Plain, Fla. to La. and Ga.—Spr.–fall.

6. **E. prostratum** Nutt. Plant prostrate: blades of the basal leaves elliptic or
ovate, 2–4 cm. long: heads ellipsoid: bracts of the involucre linear-lanceolate
to linear-spatulate.—Low grounds and wet places, Coastal Plain and adj. provinces, Fla. to Tex., Mo., Ky., and Ga.—Sum.

7. **E. floridanum** Coult. & Rose. Stem 6–9 dm. tall: blades of the lower leaves
narrowly elliptic to linear-lanceolate, 3–11 cm. long, entire or nearly so: heads
becoming about 1 cm. long: sepals ovate, about 2 mm. long: petals about 1 mm.
long: fruit about 2 mm. long.—Brackish marshes, Fla.—Spr.–fall.

8. **E. virginianum** Lam. Stem 3–9 dm. tall: blades of the lower leaves linear
to oblanceolate, 15–40 cm. long, undulate or toothed, often coarsely so: heads
becoming about 1.5 cm. long: sepals lanceolate, about 2.5 mm. long, slender-
tipped: petals 1–1.5 mm. long: fruit about 1.5 mm. long. [*E. praealtum*
A. Gray]—Low grounds and swamps, Coastal Plain, Fla. to Tex. and N. J.—
Spr.–fall.

9. E. Ravenelii A. Gray. Stem 5–10 dm. tall: blades of the lower leaves narrowly elongate-linear, 25–50 cm. long, undulate or slightly toothed: heads becoming 1–1.5 cm. long: sepals ovate or ovate-lanceolate, 2–3 mm. long, short-acuminate: petals 1.5–2 mm. long: fruit about 2–2.5 mm. long. [*E. Mettaueri* Wood]—Swampy pinelands, Coastal Plain, Fla. to S. C.—Sum.–fall.

10. E. integrifolium Walt. Stem 4–9 dm. tall: blades of the lower leaves ovate to elliptic, 5–8 cm. long, serrate-crenate: heads becoming about 1 cm. long: sepals ovate, about 1.5 mm. long, acute: petals 1–1.3 mm. long: fruit 1.5–2 mm. long. [*E. virgatum* Lam.]—Sandy bogs, Coastal Plain and rarely adj. provinces, Fla. to Tex., Tenn., and N. C.—Sum.–fall.

11. E. Ludovicianum Morong. Stem more slender than in *E. integrifolium*: blades of the lower leaves linear-spatulate, 3–7 cm. long, laciniately toothed: heads depressed, less than 1 cm. long at maturity: sepals ovate, 1–1.5 mm. long, abruptly pointed: petals 1–1.5 mm. long: fruit about 1 mm. long.—Low pinelands, Coastal Plain, Ga. to Tex.—Sum.–fall.

2. SANICULA [Tourn.] L. Biennial or perennial, glabrous or nearly glabrous herbs. Leaves alternate: blades pinnatifid or palmately 3–7-foliolate: leaflets toothed or incised. Umbels irregular, compound, few-rayed. Bracts of the involucres resembling the leaves. Sepals 5, persistent. Petals white, yellowish, or purple. Fruit subglobose or ellipsoid, somewhat dorsally flattened, armed with hooked bristles: carpels ribless: oil-tubes usually 5.—About 25 species, of wide geographic distribution.—Spr.–fall.—SNAKE-ROOTS. BLACK SNAKE-ROOTS SANICLES.—Some species are used in medicine.

Perennial plants: stamens and style exserted.
　Roots slender: leaf-blades 5-divided or 5-foliolate: stamens and styles exserted.
　　Petals and anthers greenish-white: sepals linear-subulate:
　　　fruit about 6 mm. long. .... 1. *S. marylandica.*
　　Petals and anthers yellow: sepals ovate: fruit about 3
　　　mm. long. .... 2. *S. gregaria.*
　Roots tuberous thickened: leaf-blades 3-divided or 3-foliolate:
　　stamens and style short-exserted. .... 3. *S. Smallii.*
Biennial plants: stamens and style included.
　Pedicels of the staminate flowers 3–4 times the length of the
　　hypanthium and calyx: seed with 2 large oil tubes. .... 4. *S. trifoliata.*
　Pedicels of the staminate flowers 1–2 times the length of the
　　hypanthium and calyx: seed with 5 large oil-tubes.
　　Leaf-blades becoming 8–15 cm. broad: leaflets or leaf-
　　　segments thin, the teeth weakly aculeate. .... 5. *S. canadensis.*
　　Leaf-blades mostly less than 6 cm. broad: leaflets or leaf-
　　　segments thickish, the teeth spinulose-cuspidate. .... 6. *S. floridana.*

1. S. marylandica L. Stem 4.5–13 dm. tall, mostly simple below the inflorescence: leaves bluish-green: involucels of scale-like bractlets: petals slightly longer than the sepals: fruit obovoid, not stipitate.—(BLACK-SNAKEROOT.)—Rich woods and thickets, various provinces, Ga. to Miss., Colo., Alb., Ont., and Newf.

2. S. gregaria Bicknell. Stem 3–9 dm. tall, widely branched: leaves bright-green: involucels of foliaceous bractlets: petals much longer than the sepals: fruit broadly obovoid, stipitate.—Moist woods and thickets, various provinces, rarely Coastal Plain, Fla. to Kans., Nebr., Wis., and Vt.

3. S. Smallii Bicknell. Stem 2.5–6 dm. tall, widely branched: leaves pale-green: involucels of very small bractlets: petals not longer than the sepals, greenish: fruit ovoid.—Rich soil or rocky woods, various provinces, Fla. to Miss., Mo., and N. C.

4. S. trifoliata Bicknell. Stem 3–8 dm. tall: divisions of the leaf ovate or rhombic: involucre of foliaceous bracts: petals greenish: fruits ellipsoid or broader, 7 mm. long at maturity.—Rich woods, various provinces N of Coastal Plain, Tenn. to Ind., Ont., Vt., and Me.

5. S. canadensis L. Stem 3–13 dm. tall: divisions of the leaf-blade cuneate-obovate to narrowly elliptic: involucre of minute bracts: petals greenish: fruit subglobose, 3–5 mm. long, very short-stipitate.—Rich woods and thickets, various provinces, Fla. to Tex., Nebr., Minn., and N. H.—Apparently not in Canada as the name implies.

6. S. floridana Bicknell. Similar to *S. canadensis* in habit, but smaller throughout: divisions of the leaf-blades abruptly cuneate with concave sides: involucre of very small or minute bracts: petals green: fruit smaller than that of *S. canadensis.*—Sandy soil, Coastal Plain, Fla. to Miss. and S. C.

2a. **BOWLESIA** R. & P. Annual caulescent herbs, with stellate pubescence. Leaves opposite: blades merely lobed. Flowers in simple, few-flowered umbels which terminate axillary peduncles. Sepals 5, prominent. Corolla white. Disk rather flat. Fruit turgid, smooth, stellate-pubescent: carpels ribless, becoming depressed on the back, nearly distinct: oil-tubes wanting or obsolete. Seed dorsally flattened, the face essentially flat.— About a dozen species, mostly South American.

1. **B. septentrionalis** Coult. & Rose. Stems weak, reclining or decumbent, 0.5–6 dm. long, dichotomously branched: leaf-blades reniform to ovate-cordate, 1.5–3 cm. broad, thin, 3–5-lobed, slender-petioled: umbels short-peduncled, 1–4-flowered; fruit about 2 mm. long, sessile or nearly so.—Rich soil, marshes, swamps, and woods, various provinces, La. to Calif.—Spr.

3. **DAUCUS** [Tourn.] L. Annual or biennial herbs. Leaf-blades pinnately decompound. Umbels compound. Involucres and involucels various, or wanting. Sepals minute or obsolete. Petals white or rarely colored, often unequal, broadest above the middle, inflexed at the apex. Fruit longer than broad: carpels with 5 low primary ribs and 4 winged secondary ribs which are also armed with a row of barbed bristles: oil-tubes solitary under the secondary ribs and 2 on the inner face.—About 25 species, widely distributed.—CARROTS.

Carpels broadest at the middle; wings divided into 12 or more bristle-like prickles.
                                                                                    1. *D. Carota.*
Carpels broadest below the middle; wings parted into 1–8 flat
    prickles.   2. *D. pusillus.*

1. **D. Carota** L. Stem bristly-hispid, erect, 4–12 dm. tall, often branched, channeled: leaf-segments acute or cuspidate, cleft or toothed: rays of the com-

pound umbel numerous: corolla white or rarely pink, a few in each umbel larger than the rest, the central one often purple: petals very unequal, suborbicular, unequally cleft, crisped: fruit 3–4 mm. long, the carpels broadest at the middle, the wings divided into 12 or more bristle-like prickles. — (WILD-CARROT. QUEEN - ANNE'S LACE. DEVIL'S PLAGUE.)—In fields and waste-places, nearly throughout N. A.; except the extreme N and S. Nat. of Eurasia.— (*W. I.*)—Spr.-fall. The root of the cultivated plant is esculent.

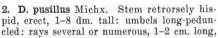

2. **D. pusillus** Michx. Stem retrorsely hispid, erect, 1–8 dm. tall: umbels long-peduncled: rays several or numerous, 1–2 cm. long, nearly equal: corolla white, or the central one larger and purple: fruit ovoid-ellipsoid, 3–4 mm. long, the wings parted into 1–8 flat prickles. Fields and waste-places, various provinces, Fla. to Tex., Calif., B. C., and Mo.—Spr.-fall.

4. **TORILIS** Adans. Annual herbs. Leaf-blades pinnately decompound. Umbels capitate or spreading. Involucres of few bracts or wanting. Involucels of several or many narrow bracts. Sepals acute. Petals white, unequal. Carpels short, with 5 primary ribs and 4 winged secondary ribs. Oil-tubes solitary under the ribs and 2 in the inner face.—About 20 species, natives of the Northern Hemisphere.

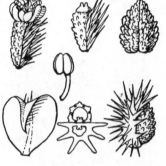

1. **T. nodosa** (L.) Gaertn. Plant diffuse, the branches hispid, 1–4 dm. long: fruit ovoid or elliptic-ovoid, about 3 mm. long, the outer ones spine-armed.—(HEDGE-PARSLEY.)—Waste-places, various provinces, Fla. to Tex., Ia., and Pa., also in Calif. Nat. of Eu. and Afr.—Spr.-sum.

5. **SCANDIX** [Tourn.] L. Annual herbs. Leaf-blades pinnately dissected; umbel compound. Involucre wanting or nearly so. Involucel of several entire lobed or dissected bractlets. Sepals minute or obsolete. Petals white, unequal. Fruit narrow, much elongate, the body prolonged into a long slender beak, the primary ribs prominent, the secondary ones wanting: oil tubes solitary or wanting.— About 10 species, natives of the Old World.

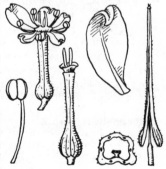

1. **S. Pecten-Veneris** L. Stem 1–5 dm. tall, pubescent, commonly branched at the base: leaf-blades 2 or 3 pinnately dissected, the lobes acute: umbels usually paired or in threes: fruit needle-like, erect, the body narrow grooved, the beak 4–6 cm. long,

ciliate.—(VENUS'-COMB. LADY'S-COMB. CROW-NEEDLES.)—Waste-places, Atlantic sea-ports, Ga. northward; locally to the Pacific Coast. Native of Eurasia.—(S. A.) Sum.–fall.—The shoots are used as salad.

6. **OSMORRHIZA** Raf. Perennial herbs. Leaf-blades ternately compound, the segments broad. Umbels loose, compound. Involucres and involucels of few bracts or bractlets, or wanting. Sepals obsolete. Petals white, inflexed at the apex. Fruits elongate: carpels 5-angled, with barely equal ribs: oil-tubes obsolete or wanting. [*Washingtonia* Raf.]—About 15 species, American and Asiatic.—Spr.—SWEET-CICELIES.

Rachis of the leaf-blades with villous hairs: stylopodium and styles about 1 mm. long.   1. *O. Claytonii.*
Rachis of the leaf-blades glabrous or with short hairs: stylopodium and styles fully 3 mm. long.   2. *O. longistylis.*

1. **O. Claytonii** (Michx.) DC. Roots slightly if at all aromatic: foliage villous-hirsute: stem erect or ascending, 3–9 dm. tall, usually branched: leaf-segments 4–8 cm. long, acute or acuminate, coarsely toothed, cleft, incised, or divided: umbel-rays 4–6, 2–5 cm. long: bracts of the involucres and bractlets, linear to oblong-linear, acute: corolla white, about 4 mm. broad: fruit narrowly oblong, 18–20 mm. long, the body longer than the slender strigose base. — (SWEET-JARVIL.) — Rich woods and thickets, various provinces, rarely Coastal Plain, Ala. to Kans., S. D., Ont., N. S., and N. C.

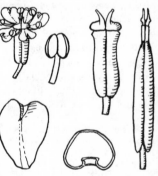

2. **O. longistylis** (Torr.) DC. Root sweet-aromatic: foliage glabrous or finely pubescent: leaf-segments mainly ovate or oblong-ovate, 5–10 cm. long, acute or short-acuminate, coarsely serrate or incised, or even divided: umbel-rays usually 3–6, ascending: corolla white, 4–5 mm. broad: fruit narrowly oblong, 15–18 mm. long: the body longer than the slender very strigose base.—(ANISE-ROOT.)—Rich woods, various provinces, Ala. to Colo., Assina., N. S., and N. C.

7. **CEREFOLIUM** [Rivin.] Haller. Annual herbs, resembling *Chaerophyllum.* Leaf-blades ternately decompound, the segments small. Umbels compound, regular or nearly so. Involucre of toothed or compound bracts. Involucels of narrow, mostly entire, bractlets. Sepals obsolete. Petals white, usually nearly or quite equal, inflexed at the apex. Fruit elongate. Carpels more or less angled, but not ribbed: oil-tubes wanting. [*Anthriscus* Bernh.]—Few species, in the warm and temperate parts of the Old World.

1. **C. Cerefolium** (L.) Britton. Plants 1 m. tall or less, often weak-stemmed: leaf-blades broad, the segments rather numerous, thin: umbels long-peduncled, the rays few, 2–4

mm. long: petals white, obovate, 1.5–2 mm. long: fruit linear-subulate, 8–10
mm. long, shining, slender-beaked.—(CHERVIL.)—Waste places and roadsides,
various provinces, La. to Tenn., Ont., and Pa.—Nat. of Eu.—Spr.

8. CHAEROPHYLLUM [Tourn.] L. Annual herbs. Leaf-blades ternately decompound, the segments narrow. Umbels irregular, compound. Involucres of 1 or 2 bracts, or usually wanting. Involucels of several small
bracts. Sepals obsolete. Petals white, usually unequal, inflexed at the apex.
Fruit elongate: carpels 5-angled, the angles equally ribbed: oil-tubes solitary
in the intervals and 2 in the inner face. About 40 species, natives, mostly, of
the warmer parts of the north temperate zone. Spr.—CHERVILS.

Fruit sometimes contracted below the apex, but beakless : plants glabrous.
   Fruit less than 2 mm. broad, constricted below the apex.   1. *C. procumbens.*
   Fruit fully 2 mm. broad, not constricted below the apex.   2. *C. Shortii.*
Fruit beaked or narrowed to the apex : plants more or less
   pubescent.
   Fruit with the ribs narrower than the intervals.
      Fruit pubescent.   3. *C. dasycarpum.*
      Fruit glabrous.   4. *C. floridanum.*
   Fruit with the ribs broader than the intervals.   5. *C. Teinturieri.*

1. C. procumbens (L.) Crantz. Stem weak, decumbent or spreading, 1–5 dm.
long, simple or sparingly branched: umbels few-rayed, peduncled or nearly sessile: pedicels sometimes 8 mm. long, lax and
spreading: fruit narrow, about 8 mm. long,
glabrous, contracted below the apex, the
ribs narrower than the intervals.—(WILD-
CHERVIL.)—Open woods and damp thickets,
various provinces, Ala. to Ark., Kans., Mich.,
and N. Y.

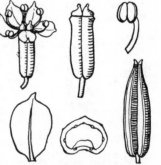

2. C. Shortii (T. & G.) Bush. Stem 2–5
dm. long, spreading or decumbent, often
branched: umbels few-rayed, sessile or
peduncled: fruit oblong, 5–6 mm. long, not
contracted below the apex, the ribs narrower
than the intervals.—Thickets and fields,
various provinces, Tenn. to Va. and Pa.

3. C. dasycarpum Nutt. Stem erect, 2–6 dm. tall, branching: umbels sessile
or short-peduncled, the rays ascending or spreading, 3–5 cm. long: fruit narrow, 5–6 mm. long, pubescent, beaked, the ribs prominent, narrower than the
intervals.—Hillsides and thickets, Coastal Plain, Ala. to Tex.

4. C. floridanum (Coult. & Rose) Bush. Stems erect, 2–6 dm. tall, glabrous
or somewhat pubescent: umbels peduncled, the rays 2–5 cm. long: fruit narrow, 7 mm. long, glabrous, the beak one-fourth or one-fifth as long as the body.
—Woods, Coastal Plain, Fla. to S. C.; (also in Mo.?).

5. C. Teinturièri Hook. Stem erect, 2–7 dm. tall, more or less branched:
umbels sessile or short-peduncled: rays 2–3, 2–5 cm. long: fruit narrow, 6–7
mm. long, beaked, glabrous or nearly so, the ribs prominent, broader than the
intervals.—Thickets, cedar-glades, waste-places, and roadsides, various provinces, Fla. to Tex., Ky., and Va.

9. DERINGA Adans. Perennial herbs with fibrous roots. Leaf-blades
3-foliolate. Umbels irregular, compound. Involucres and involucels wanting.

Sepals obsolete. Petals white. Fruit elongate: carpels with 5 low ribs, and an oil-tube beneath each rib and in each interval.—One species.

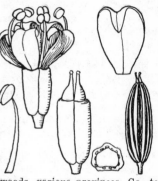

1. D. canadensis (L.) Kuntze. Plant glabrous or nearly so: stem 3–10 dm. tall, finally widely branched: leaf-blades 3-foliolate: leaflets ovate, oval, or elliptic, 4–10 cm. long, acute or abruptly pointed, doubly serrate with sharp teeth, the lateral ones often lobed: umbels peduncled: rays few, slender, unequal in length: pedicels 2–25 mm. long: corolla white, 2–3 mm. broad: fruit oblong 4–6 mm. long, straight, or curved at full maturity.—(HONEWORT.)—Thickets and rich woods, various provinces, Ga. to Tex., S. D., Ont., and N. B.—Spr.–sum.

10. HYDROCOTYLE [Tourn.] L. Perennial amphibious herbs. Leaves solitary at each node. Umbels simple or proliferous. Sepals manifest. Petals valvate, white. Carpels with distinct ribs, and oil-bearing tissues beneath the epidermis.—About 75 species, widely distributed.—Sum. or all year S.—MARSH-PENNYWORTS. WATER-PENNYWORTS. NAVELWORTS.—Some species are used medicinally.

Leaf-blades suborbicular to transversely elliptic, peltate.
  Fruit notched at the base and the apex at maturity: intermediate ribs corky.
    Umbels not proliferous, at least not normally so.   1. *H. umbellata.*
    Umbels or most of them proliferous.
      Peduncle produced beyond the first umbel as a single
        rachis, bearing one or more umbels beyond it.   2. *H. Canbyi.*
      Peduncle produced beyond the first umbel branching
        and bearing several more or less proliferous
        umbels.   3. *H. bonariensis.*
  Fruit rounded at the base and the apex or cuneate at the
    base: intermediate ribs not corky, very slender.
    Fruit rounded or truncate at the base, not cuneate.   4. *H. verticillata.*
    Fruit cuneate at the base.   5. *H. australis.*
Leaf-blades reniform to suborbicular, not peltate.
  Umbel long-peduncled: leaf-blades deeply lobed.   6. *H. ranunculoides.*
  Umbel nearly sessile: leaf-blades shallowly lobed.   7. *H. americana.*

1. H. umbellata L. Leaf-blades suborbicular, 2–5 cm. wide, crenate or crenate-lobed: pedicels slender, 4–12 mm. long: fruit about 3 mm. wide, with corky-thickened ribs.—Swamps, meadows, ditches, and low pinelands, various provinces, Fla. to Tex., Minn., and Mass.—(*W. I., Mex., C. A., S. A., O. W.*)

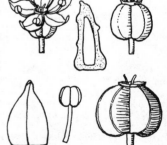

2. H. Canbyi Coult. & Rose. Leaf-blades 1.5–4 cm. wide, shallowly crenate-lobed: pedicels 1–4 mm. long: fruit between 3 and 4 mm. wide.—Damp places, usually sandy soil, Coastal Plain, Fla. to Miss. and N. J.

3. H. bonariensis Lam. Leaf-blades depressed, orbicular to orbicular-reniform, 3.5–9.5 cm. wide, shallowly lobed, the lobes crenate: fruit about 3 mm. wide.—Waste-places, ponds and ditches, Coastal Plain, Fla. to Tex., Tenn., and N. C.—(*W. I., Mex., C. A., S. A.*)—Often grows very large and forms floating masses.

4. H. verticillata Thunb. Leaf-blades suborbicular to oval, 1–6 cm. wide, shallowly crenate: pedicels very short or wanting: fruit 3–4 mm. wide, with slender ribs.—Low grounds, swamps, and ponds, Coastal Plain and adj. provinces, Fla. to Tex., Ark. and Mass.

5. H. australis Coult. & Rose. Similar to *H. Canbyi* in habit: fruit slightly broader than long.—Low grounds, Coastal Plain, Fla. to Tex. and Va.— (*W. I.*)

6. H. ranunculoides L. f. Leaf-blades reniform to orbicular-reniform, 2–5 cm. wide, deeply lobed: petals over 1 mm. long: fruit 2.5–3 mm. wide, obscurely ribbed, oblong in cross-section.—Swamps, ditches, shallow ponds, and muddy shores, various provinces, Fla. to Tex., Ark., and Pa.; also Pacific Coast.— (*W. I., C. A., S. A., O. W.*)

7. H. americana L. Leaf-blades reniform, 2–5 cm. wide, crenate-lobed; petals less than 1 mm. long: fruit 1–1.5 mm. wide, sharply ribbed, oval in cross-section.—(MARSH-PENNYWORT.)—Moist thickets, wet banks, and swamps, various provinces, Coastal Plain only N, N. C. to Tenn., Minn., and N. S.

11. CENTELLA L. Perennial amphibious plants. Leaves clustered at the nodes. Umbels capitate. Sepals obsolete. Petals imbricate, white. Carpels without large oil-tubes, the prominent ribs anastomosing.—About 20 species, most abundant in Southern Africa.

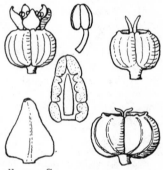

1. C. repanda (Pers.) Small. Leaves clustered; petioles erect, 9–30 cm. long (about 2.5 cm. long, and with larger fruit, in *C. repanda floridana*); blades thickish, ovate, 2–6 cm. long, repand, cordate or nearly truncate at the base: peduncles usually several together, mostly shorter than the petioles: umbels 2–4-flowered: fruit 4–5 mm. wide. [*Hydrocotyle repanda* Pers.]— Moist pinelands, lake-shores, and shallow ponds, Coastal Plain, Fla. to Tex., and Md. —(*W. I., Mex., C. A., S. A.*)—Spr.–fall, or all year S.

12. CYNOSCIADIUM DC. Annual herbs. Leaf-blades pinnately or palmately divided into narrow segments, or the basal leaves with entire blades: umbels compound. Involucres and involucels of persistent or deciduous narrow bracts. Sepals persistent. Petals white, broadest above the middle. Fruit elongate: carpels with strong ribs, the lateral ribs more prominent: oil-tubes solitary in each interval or two in the inner face.—About 10 species, natives of the north temperate zone.

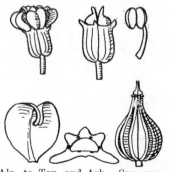

1. C. digitatum DC. Plant 2–6 dm. tall: leaf-blades, or segments, linear to linear-lanceolate: umbel-rays 3–8, 1–3.5 cm. long: pedicels 2–8 mm. long: fruit beaked.—Wet grounds, Coastal Plain and adj. provinces, Ala. to Tex. and Ark.—Spr.–sum.

13. CORIANDRUM [Tourn.] L. Annual slender herbs. Leaf-blades pinnately dissected. Umbels compound. Involucres wanting. Sepals acute, unequal. Petals white, often unequal, broadest above the middle. Fruit sub-globose, not constricted at the commissure: carpels with 5 delicate ribs: oil-tubes solitary under the secondary ribs.—Two species, natives of the Old World.

1. C. sativum L. Stem 2–6 dm. tall: blades of the lower cauline and basal leaves with coarse-toothed, incised, or lobed segments, those of the upper leaves with narrowly linear segments: umbel-rays 4–8, 12–21 mm. long: pedicels 1–3 mm. long: fruit subglobose or ovoid-globose, 3–3.5 mm. long: carpels slightly ribbed.—(CORIANDER.)—Waste-places and cult. grounds, in and about towns and cities, nearly throughout U. S. Nat. of Eurasia.—Sum.—The fruit is used medicinally and as a condiment.

14. LIGUSTICUM L. Perennial herbs with large roots. Leaf-blades ternately compound. Umbels compound. Involucres of a few narrow bracts. Involucres of a few narrow bracts. Involucels of numerous narrow bractlets. Sepals obsolete. Petals white, broadened upward. Fruit more or less elongate: carpels with sharp prominent ribs and 2–6 oil-tubes in each interval.—About 20 species, natives of the Northern Hemisphere.

1. L. canadense (L.) Britton. Stem 5–20 dm. tall: leaflets elliptic, elliptic-oval, or ovate, 3–8 cm. long, coarsely toothed: fruit ellipsoid, oval, or ovate, 4–6 mm. long, the ribs narrow-winged. — (ANGELICO. NONDO. LOVAGE.)—Dry or rich woods, various provinces, rarely Coastal Plain, Ga. to Miss., Mo., and Pa.—Sum.—The root is aromatic.

15. LILAEOPSIS Greene. Perennial herbs, with creeping stems. Leaves clustered, reduced to terete clavate, separate organs, sometimes dilated above. Bracts of the involucre several. Umbels several-flowered, simple. Sepals acute. Petals white, concave. Fruit subglobose, or lenticular: carpels with thick corky lateral ribs and filiform dorsal and intermediate ribs or all sometimes corky, with oil-tubes solitary in the intervals. [*Crantzia* Nutt.]—About 10 species.—Sum.

Peduncles surpassing the leaves: fruit pinched at the base; lateral ribs only corky.
    1. *L. lineata.*
Peduncles shorter than the leaves: fruit not pinched at the base; all ribs corky.
    2. *L. carolinensis.*

1. L. lineata (Michx.) Greene. Stem creeping in the mud: leaves 2–5 cm. long; petioles dilated upward, usually linear-spatulate, barely broadened into

blades, conspicuously cross-partitioned: peduncles 3–7 cm. long, surpassing the leaves:
fruit orbicular-ovoid, pinched near the base,
about 2 mm. long, the lateral ribs corky, the
dorsal not at all corky. [*Crantzia lineata*
Nutt.]—Salt or brackish marshes and low
grounds, Coastal Plain and New England
Coast, Fla. to Miss. and Mass.

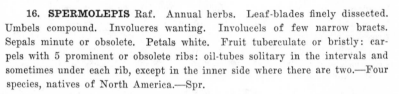

2. L. carolinensis Coult. & Rose. Stem
creeping in the mud: leaves 5–25 cm. long;
petioles elongate; blades oblong or spatulate, shorter than the petioles: peduncles
1–1.5 cm. long, shorter than the leaves: fruit
suborbicular or oval-orbicular, about 3 mm.
long, not pinched near the base; all the ribs corky.—Low grounds, Coastal
Plain, Fla. to N. C.

16. SPERMOLEPIS Raf. Annual herbs. Leaf-blades finely dissected.
Umbels compound. Involucres wanting. Involucels of few narrow bracts.
Sepals minute or obsolete. Petals white. Fruit tuberculate or bristly: carpels with 5 prominent or obsolete ribs: oil-tubes solitary in the intervals and
sometimes under each rib, except in the inner side where there are two.—Four
species, natives of North America.—Spr.

Fruit tubercled.
  Umbel-rays divaricate, the primary ones mostly 3 or 4.   1. *S. divaricata.*
  Umbel-rays erect or nearly so, the primary ones mostly 6–8. 2. *S. patens.*
Fruit covered with short bristly hooked hairs.   3. *S. echinata.*

1. S. divaricata (Walt.) Raf. Stem 1–6 dm. tall, often widely branched,
sometimes diffusely so, the branches very slender or nearly filiform: leaf-blades
2–8 cm. long, twice or thrice pinnately
parted; segments narrowly linear or filiform: corolla white, about 1 mm. broad:
fruit broadest about the middle, about 1
mm. long, tuberculate, prominently ribbed.
—Dry or sandy soil, various provinces, Fla.
to N. M., Kans., and N. C.

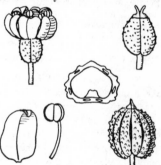

2. S. patens (Nutt.) B. L. Robinson.
Stem 2–6 dm. tall: leaf-segments filiform:
fruit ovoid, about 1 mm. long, granular.—
Dry soil, various provinces, Tenn. to Tex.,
Nebr., and Ind.

3. S. echinata (Nutt.) Heller. Stem 1–5
dm. tall, more of less diffusely branched:
leaf-blades 1–6 cm. long; twice or thrice pinnately parted; segments narrowly
linear or filiform: umbels slender-peduncled, 1.5–4 cm. broad: rays slender,
more or less variable in length: corolla white, less than 1 mm. broad: fruit
broadest below the middle, 2 mm. long, covered with hooked bristles, the ribs
obsolete.—Dry soil, various provinces, Ala. to Tex., Calif., and Mo.—(*Mex.*)

17. ERIGENIA Nutt. Perennial herbs with tuberous roots. Leaf-blades
ternately decompound. Umbels few-rayed, compound. Involucres usually of a

single bract. Sepals obsolete. Petals white, broadest above the middle, flat. Fruit broader than high, laterally flattened: carpels with 5 delicate ribs: oil-tubes 2–3 in each interval.—One species.

1. E. bulbosa (Michx.) Nutt. Plant 5–20 cm. tall from a depressed tuber: leaf-segments of an elliptic type: fruit about 2 mm. high, 3–4 mm. broad.—(HARBINGER-OF-SPRING. PEPPER-AND-SALT.)—Rich open woods and thickets, various provinces, rarely Coastal Plain, Ala. to Miss., Kans., Minn., Ont., and Md.—Spr.

18. CONIUM L. Biennial large herbs with spotted stems. Leaf-blades broad, pinnately decompound. Umbels compound, the rays unequal. Involucres and involucels inconspicuous, of entire, scarious-margined bracts or bractlets. Sepals minute or obsolete. Petals white, somewhat unequal, broadest above the middle, inflexed at the apex. Fruit short and thick: carpels with prominent wavy ribs: oil-tubes wanting.—One species.

1. C. maculatum L. Plant 1–2 m. tall, the stem usually much branched: leaf-blades broad, the segments very numerous; umbels rather long-peduncled; rays 2–4 cm. long: petals white, obovate or cuneate, mostly about 1 mm. long: fruit ovoid, 2.5–3 mm. long. — (POISON-HEMLOCK.) — Waste-places, cult-grounds, and roadsides, various provinces, Ala. to Tex., Mich., Ont., and Del.; also on Pacific Coast. Nat. of Eu.—(*W. I., Mex., C. A., S. A.*)—Sum. —The fruit is used medicinally.

19. AEGOPODIUM L. Perennial caulescent herbs. Leaf-blades ternate, the leaflets or segments large, toothed. Umbel compound, the rays equal or nearly so. Involucres and involucels of narrow bracts and bractlets, or wanting. Sepals minute or obsolete. Petals white, equal or nearly so, broadest above the middle, inflexed at the apex. Fruit short, but longer than thick; carpels turgid, the angles margined: oil-tubes wanting.—One species.

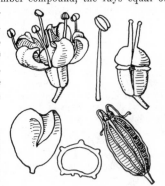

1. A. Podagraria L. Plant 3–11 dm. tall, simple or sparingly branched: leaflets elliptic to ovate, 2.5–9 cm. long, serrate, incised or lobed: umbels long-peduncled; rays 2–4 cm. long: petals white, obovate or orbicular-obovate, 1–1.5 mm. long: fruit conic-ovoid, about 4 mm. long.—(GOUTWEED.) —Waste-places, roadsides and thickets, N. C. to Pa. and Mass.—Nat. of Eu.— Sum.—A form with variegated leaves is used in gardening.

20. EULOPHUS Nutt. Perennial herbs with tuberous roots. Leaf-blades ternately compound. Umbels compound. Involucre wanting or of 1 bract. Involucels usually of 2 bracts. Sepals promi- 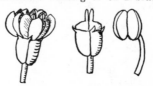 nent. Petals white or pink, broadest above the middle, inflexed at the tip. Fruit some- what elongate, laterally flattened: carpels delicately ribbed: oil-tubes 2–5 in the inter- vals.—About 8 species, North American.

1. E. americanus Nutt. Plant 8–15 dm.  tall: segments of the upper leaves much narrower than those of the lower ones: fruit elliptic or elliptic-ovoid, 4–6 mm. long.—Low grounds, various provinces, Tenn. to Ark., Kans. and Ohio.—Sum.

21. CICUTA L. Perennial herbs with tuberous roots. Leaf-blades pin- nately compound or decompound. Umbels compound. Involucres of few bracts or wanting. Involucels of several small bractlets. Sepals acute. Petals white. Fruit short: carpels with 5 corky ribs, and one oil-tube in each interval and 2 in the inner face.—About 8 species, of the North-temperate zone.— Sum.–fall—WATER-HEMLOCKS.—The roots are poisonous.

Fruit ridged at the commissure, typically oval or ovoid.   1. *C. maculata.*
Fruit grooved at the commissure, typically subglobose or reniform-
  globose.   2. *C. Curtissii.*

1. C. maculata L. Plant stout, 1–2 m. tall: leaf-blades 1–6 dm. long, the veins ending in the notches of the segments: fruit with lateral ribs manifestly much larger than the others and wedge- 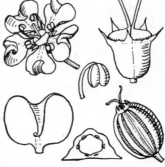 shaped in section, and contiguous. (SPOT- TED-COWBANE. MUSQUASH-ROOT.)—Swamps, low-grounds, and river-banks, various prov- inces, Miss. to Tex., Man., Ont., N. B., and N. C.

2. C. Curtissii Coult. & Rose. Plant re- sembling *C. maculata,* but with thicker and more reticulate leaf-segments: fruit with apparently equal ribs, the lateral ones neither wedge-shaped nor contiguous.— Swamps and low grounds, Coastal Plain and adj. provinces, Fla. to La., Tenn., (Ky. ?), and Va., also represented by sporadic sta- tions as far North as Nova Scotia.

22. SIUM [Tourn.] L. Perennial herbs. Leaf-blades pinnately com- pound. Umbels compound. Involucres and involucels of narrow bracts and bractlets. Sepals small, acute. Petals white. Fruit stout, somewhat laterally flattened: carpels ribbed, the intervals with 1–3 oil-tubes. Seed 5-angled.—About 8 species, natives of the north temperate zone.

Blades of the leaflets saliently sharp-serrate or incised: larger petals about 1 mm. long: umbels large, the terminal ones at least 5 cm. or more wide in anthesis.   1. *S. cicutaefolium.*

Blades of the leaflets appressed-serrate: larger petals much less than 1 mm. long: umbels small, the terminal ones, at least, 4 cm. wide or less.   2. *S. floridanum.*

1. **S. cicutaefolium** Schrank. Plant 6–19 dm. tall, glabrous: stem stout, sparingly branched: stipular expansion at base of the petiole auriculate at the top: leaflets 7–17; blades linear to linear-lanceolate, or rarely wider, finely, or usually coarsely and saliently, toothed, or those of the submerged ones coarsely or finely pinnatifid: umbel-rays slender: larger corollas fully 2 mm. wide: fruit oval, 3–3.5 mm. long, prominently 10-ribbed.—(WATER-PARSLEY.)—Swamps, marshes, and ponds, various provinces, N. C. to La., Calif., and S Can.—Sum.–fall.

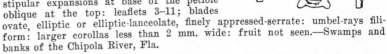

2. **S. floridanum** Small. Plant smaller and more slender than that of *S. cicutaefolium*, the stem slender, the branches very slender: stipular expansions at base of the petiole oblique at the top: leaflets 3–11; blades ovate, elliptic or elliptic-lanceolate, finely appressed-serrate: umbel-rays filiform: larger corollas less than 2 mm. wide: fruit not seen.—Swamps and banks of the Chipola River, Fla.

23. **AMMI** L. Herbs resembling *Daucus* in habit and inflorescence. Leaf-blades finely divided or dissected. Flowers perfect, very numerous in compound umbels. Involucres and involucels present, the bracts of the former, at least, divided. Sepals obsolete. Petals white, very unequal, cleft at the apex. Fruit short: carpels 5-angled, with prominent ribs and an oil-tube in each interval.—Seven species, natives of the Old World.—(BISHOP'S-WEEDS.)

Leaf-segments numerous, very narrowly linear or filiform and entire: umbel-rays concreted into a disk-like structure at the base.   1. *A. Visnaga.*

Leaf-segments few, at least in the lower leaves slightly broadened and toothed: umbel-rays not concreted at the base.   2. *A. majus.*

1. **A. Visnaga** (L.) Lam. Stem 5–12 dm. tall: mature umbels and umbellets contracted, the concreted bases of the rays of the latter 3–4 mm. broad: fruit 2–2.5 mm. long.—Waste-places, Fla. and Gulf State seaports to N. C. Nat. of Eu.—Spr.

2. **A. majus** L. Stem 3–15 dm. tall: mature umbels and umbellets open, the concreted bases of the rays of the latter barely 2 mm. broad: fruit 1.5–2 mm. long.—Waste-places, Coastal Plain, Ala. to Tex. Nat. of Eu. and cult.—The plants of these species of *Ammi*, like those of very many species of other genera of this family, especially those of the Old World, have been used as medicinal remedies, real or reputed, by both the aborigines and medical men, in all countries.

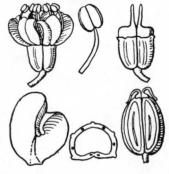

24. TREPOCARPUS Nutt. Annual herbs. Leaf-blades pinnately decompound. Umbels compound. Involucre usually present. Sepals unequal. Petals white, broad. Fruit elongate: carpels with 4 secondary ribs, the primary ribs wanting: oil tubes solitary under the secondary ribs.—One species.

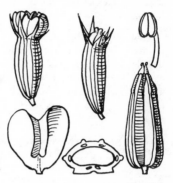

1. T. Aethusae Nutt. Stem 1–10 dm. tall, branched: leaf-blades 5–10 cm. long, finely dissected, the lower ones with petioles about equal to them in length, the upper short-petioled, the segments narrowly linear, entire or incised: umbels commonly long-peduncled: rays 2–5, becoming 1–2 cm. long: flowers few in each umbellet: fruit oblong, 8–10 mm. long, sharply ribbed.—Dry soil, Coastal Plain and adj. provinces, Ala. to Tex., Okla., and Ark.—Spr.–sum.

25. PTILIMNIUM Raf. Annual, faintly-scented, slender herbs. Leaf-blades 1–3-pinnately or -ternately divided, the ultimate segments entire or nearly so. Umbels compound. Involucres and involucels of several very slender, entire or pinnate bracts, and bractlets. Sepals small, broad or narrow. Petals white, each with a broad body and a short entire inflexed apex. Stylopodium depressed or elongate. Fruit short, as wide as long or nearly so: carpels with prominent separated dorsal and intermediate ribs and thick corky lateral ribs; oil-tubes small between each rib. Seed terete-angled, the inner face convex.—Following are the only known species.—Mock Bishop's-weeds.

Sepals deltoid, often broadly so.   1. *P. capillaceum.*
Sepals subulate to narrowly lanceolate.
  Styles long, much longer than the stylopodium: stylopodium ovoid, together with the styles over 1 mm. long: leaf-blades rather long-petioled.   2. *P. costatum.*
  Styles short, about as long as the stylopodium: stylopodium depressed, together with the styles, less than 1 mm. long: leaf-blades short-petioled.   3. *P. Nuttallii.*

1. P. capillaceum (Michx.) Raf. Plant 2–8 dm. tall: leaf-segments relatively few and lax: umbel-rays few–several, less than 2.5 cm. long at maturity: bracts lobed: fruit ovoid, about 2 mm. long, acute. —Wet soil, marshes, swamps, and ditches, various provinces, Fla. to Tex., Kans., and Mass.

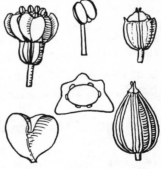

2. P. costatum (Ell.) C. & R. Plant 8–16 dm. tall: leaf-segments narrowly linear, numerous, but not crowded: umbel-rays stout, over 3 cm. long at maturity: bracts entire or lobed: petals fully 1 mm. long: fruit ovoid, 3–4 mm. long or rarely longer, not constricted at the apex.—Swamps, Coastal Plain, Ga. to N. C.—Sum.–fall.

3. P. Nuttallii (DC.) Britton. Plant 3–7 dm. tall: leaf-segments almost capillary, not very numerous, lax: umbel-rays slender, mostly over 3 cm. long at maturity: bracts entire: petals less than 1 mm. long: fruit ovoid, 1.5 mm. long or less, barely constricted at the apex.—Swamps and damp hillsides, various provinces, Ala. to Tex., Kans. and Ill.—Spr.-fall.

26. **HARPERELLA** Rose. Perennial aquatic caulescent herbs. Leaves alternate, reduced to terete jointed phyllodia. Flowers perfect, in compound umbels. Involucres and involucels inconspicuous. Sepals acute, slightly unequal. Petals white, broad. Stylopodium short. Fruit oval, flattened laterally: carpels rather prominently 5-angled: oil-tubes solitary in the intervals and 2 in the inner side.—Three species, natives of the southeastern United States.

Basal and lower cauline leaves mostly over 2 dm. long: corolla 3–3.5 mm. wide: fruit about 1.5 mm. wide.   1. *H. nodosa*.
Basal and lower cauline leaves mostly less than 1.5 cm. long: corolla 1–1.5 mm. wide: fruit about 1 mm. wide.   2. *H. fluviatilis*.

1. **H. nodosa** Rose. Plant stout, stiff, 3–13 dm. tall, rather freely branched, the stem fluted: basal and lower cauline leaves mostly 2–4.5 dm. long, without bulblets in the axils: peduncles elongate, mostly 2–4 cm. long: umbel-rays 5–15, becoming 1–2.5 cm. long: corolla 3–3.5 mm. wide: anthers barely 0.5 mm. long: fruit about 1.5 mm. wide.—Shallow ponds, Coastal Plain, S W Ga.—Spr.–sum.

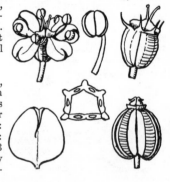

2. **H. fluviatilis** Rose. Plant slender, weak, 1–3 dm. tall, sparingly branched, the stem angled: basal and lower cauline leaves mostly 1–1.5 dm. long, with bulblets in their axils: peduncles short, mostly 1–2 cm. long: umbel-rays 2–5, becoming 5–8 mm. long: corolla 1–1.5 mm. wide: anthers barely 0.3 mm. long: fruit about 1 mm. wide.—Rocky beds of streams, in the Appalachian provinces in Ala.—Sum.–fall.

27. **CELERI** Adans. Annual or perennial herbs. Leaf-blades pinnate or ternately decompound. Umbels compound. Involucres present or wanting. Sepals obsolete or minute. Petals white, broad. Fruit somewhat smooth or tuberculate: carpels 5-angled or 5-ribbed, with 1 oil-tube in each interval or 2 in the inner face.—About 5 species, widely distributed.

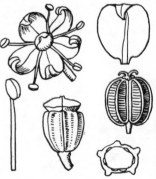

1. **C. graveolens** (L.) Britton. Stem 2–9 dm. tall: leaf-segments cuneate to suborbicular, incised and toothed: petals 0.5–1 mm. long: fruit ovoid, about 1.5 mm. long. [*Apium graveolens* L.]—(CELERY.)—Wasteplaces and fields, near the coast, various provinces, Fla. to N. M., Calif. and Va.— Nat. of Eu.—Spr.–sum.—Used in medicine. The blanched leaves are esculent.

28. CYCLOSPERMUM Lag. Annual or perennial herbs. Leaf-blades pinnately or ternately decompound. Umbels compound. Involucre present or wanting. Sepals obsolete or minute. Petals white, broad. Fruit somewhat smooth or tuberculate: carpels 5-angled or ribbed with 1 oil-tube in each interval or two in the inner face. [*Apium* L. in part]—About 6 species, natives of the Old World.—Spr.–sum.

Leaf-blades ternate; segments linear-filiform to filiform.   1. *C. Ammi.*
Leaf-blades pinnate; segments ovate, oval, or elliptic.   2. *C. nodiflorum.*

1. C. Ammi (L.) Britton. Stem erect, 1–6 dm. tall, more or less branched: leaf-blades ternately divided; segments filiform or narrowly linear, acute: corolla white, less than 1 mm. broad: fruit oval or ovoid-oval, 1.5–2 mm. long, prominently ribbed. [*A. leptophyllum* (DC.) F. Muell.]—(MARSH-PARSLEY.)—Roadsides and waste-places, various provinces, Fla. to Tex., Mo. and N. Y.—(*W. I., Mex., C. A., S. A.*)

2. C. nodiflorum (L.) Koch. Stem prostrate, often creeping, 3–7 dm. long, sparingly branched: leaf-blades pinnately compound, 5–10 cm. long; leaflets oblong, ovate-lanceolate or lanceolate, serrate, mostly acute: umbels opposite the leaves 1.5–3 cm. broad, short-peduncled: bractlets of the involucels 5–6: corolla white, about 1 mm. broad: fruit oval or orbicular-oval, about 2 mm. long.— Ditches and waste-places, near Charleston, S. C., and other seaport towns. Nat. of Eu.

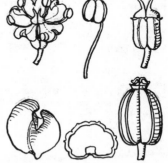

29. BUPLEURUM [Tourn.] L. Annual or perennial herbs. Leaf-blades entire. Umbels compound. Involucre wanting (in our species). Involucels conspicuous, of entire bractlets. Sepals obsolete. Petals broad, yellow or greenish. Fruit elliptic or oval: carpels with slender ribs and no oil-tubes in our species.—About 65 species, widely distributed.

1. B. rotundifolium L. Plant 3–10 dm. tall: leaf-blades ovate or elliptic, 2–8 cm. long, perfoliate: corolla yellow: fruit 3–3.5 mm. long, about 2.5 mm. broad.—(HARE'S-EAR. THOROUGH-WAX.) — Roadsides, fields, and waste-places, various provinces N of Coastal Plain, Ala. to Ariz., S. D., N. H., and N. C. Nat. of Eu.

30. THASPIUM Nutt. Perennial herbs. Leaf-blades 3-foliolate or ternately compound, or those of the basal leaves sometimes simple. Umbels compound. Involucre of few bracts. Involucels of many bracts. Sepals present.

Petals yellow or rarely purple. Fruit longer than wide: carpels with winged ribs and oil-tubes solitary in the intervals.—Only the following species known.—Sum.—MEADOW-PARSNIPS.

Petal-blades less than 1 mm. long: leaves with ternate blades: leaflets relatively thick, crenate.   1. *T. trifoliatum.*
Petal-blades over 1 mm. long: leaves with biternate blades:
  leaflets relatively thin, incised or lobed.
  Peduncles and umbel-rays glabrous, except at the nodes, or merely puberulent: fruits, between the wings, glabrous, 5-6 mm. long: leaves 1-2-ternate.   2. *T. barbinode.*
  Peduncle and umbel-rays scabrous-pubescent: fruits, between the wings, permanently pubescent, 4-5 mm. long: leaves 2-3-ternate.
    Blades of the leaflets coarsely divided, the ultimate segments or teeth of an ovate type: styles about 2 mm. long: petals about 1.5 mm. long.   3. *T. Chapmanii.*
    Blades of the leaflets finely divided, the ultimate segments or teeth of a lanceolate type: styles about 1 mm. long: petals about 1 mm. long.   4. *T. pinnatifidum.*

1. **T. trifoliatum** (L.) A. Gray. Stem 2-7 dm. tall, sparingly branched, often zigzag: leaf-blades various, those of the basal or lower stem-leaves ovate and undivided or 3-foliolate; segments ovate to lanceolate, serrate; petioles slender, often longer than the blades: upper stem-leaves similar to the divided basal leaves; petioles shorter than the blades, winged: umbels peduncled, 2-5 cm. broad: rays variable in length: corolla dark-purple (or yellow in *T. trifoliatum aureum*): fruit oval, 4 mm. long, the ribs prominently winged.—(PURPLE MEADOW-PARSNIP.)—Woods, bluffs, stream-banks, and sunny slopes, various provinces, Fla. to Miss., Wyo., Ill., and R. I.—Sum.

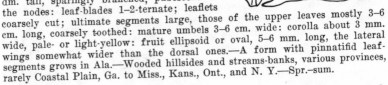

2. **T. barbinode** (Michx.) Nutt. Stem 3-12 dm. tall, sparingly branched, pubescent at the nodes: leaf-blades 1-2-ternate; leaflets coarsely cut; ultimate segments large, those of the upper leaves mostly 3-6 cm. long, coarsely toothed: mature umbels 3-6 cm. wide: corolla about 3 mm. wide, pale- or light-yellow: fruit ellipsoid or oval, 5-6 mm. long, the lateral wings somewhat wider than the dorsal ones.—A form with pinnatifid leaf-segments grows in Ala.—Wooded hillsides and streams-banks, various provinces, rarely Coastal Plain, Ga. to Miss., Kans., Ont., and N. Y.—Spr.-sum.

3. **T. Chapmanii** (C. & R.) Small. Stem 8-15 dm. tall, often much-branched, pubescent at the nodes and sometimes sparingly so along the internodes: leaf-blades 2-3-ternate; leaflets much cut; ultimate segments relatively small, those of the upper leaves mostly 1-2.5 cm. long, incised-toothed or pinnatifid: mature umbels 2.5-7 cm. wide: corolla light yellow, fruit elliptic or oval, 4-5 mm. long, the lateral wings much wider than the dorsal ones.—River-bluffs, woods and hillsides, Coastal Plain and Piedmont, Fla. and Ga.—Spr.-sum.

4. **T. pinnatifidum** (Buckl.) A. Gray. Stem 5-12 dm. tall, finely pubescent about the nodes and sometimes also along the internodes: leaf-blades usually 3-ternate; leaflets finely cut and with narrow divisions; ultimate segments small, those of the upper leaves pinnatifid, the lobes usually lanceolate: mature umbels 3-4 cm. wide: corolla light yellow: fruit ellipsoid, 3-4 mm. long, all the ribs narrowly winged.—Woods, hillsides and river-banks, Blue Ridge to Interior Low Plateaus, Ala. to Ky. and N. C.—Spr.-sum.

31. TAENIDIA Drude. Perennial herbs with fibrous roots. Leaf-blades pinnate or ternately compound. Umbels compound. Involucres and involucels wanting: sepals obsolete or minute. Petals 5, their tips inflexed. Fruit oblong: carpels 5-angled, with slender ribs and 3 oil-tubes in the intervals. Seeds nearly terete except the flat face.—One species.

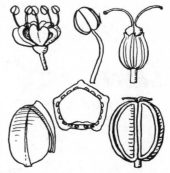

1. T. integerrima (L.) Drude. Plant 3–9 dm. tall, from a tough root: leaflets ovate to elliptic or elliptic-lanceolate, 1–3 cm. long, entire: umbel-rays 10–20, elongate: corolla yellow: fruit broadly ellipsoid, 3.5–4 mm. long.— (YELLOW-PIMPERNEL.)—Rocky hillsides and sandy woods, various provinces, rarely Coastal Plain, Ga. to La., Minn. and Que.—Spr.

32. ZIZIA Koch. Perennial erect herbs. Leaf-blades 3-foliolate or ternately compound, or the basal ones sometimes simple. Umbels compound, the central umbellet sessile. Involucres wanting. Involucels of a few bractlets. Sepals prominent. Petals yellow. Fruit somewhat elongate, laterally flattened: carpels with 5 slender wingless ribs and an oil tube in each interval and sometimes under each rib.—Following are the only known species.—Spr.–sum.—MEADOW-PARSNIPS.

Blades of the basal leaves merely toothed cordate.   1. *Z. cordata.*
Blades of the basal leaves ternately compound.
  Blades of the basal leaves 2-ternate.   2. *Z. aurea.*
  Blades of the basal leaves 1-ternate.
    Blade of the terminal leaflet much longer than wide, with few or relatively few blunt teeth.
      Fruit ovoid or ellipsoid, 4–4.5 mm. long: longer umbel-rays 2.5–5 cm. long at maturity.   3. *Z. arenicola.*
      Fruit suborbicular or broader than high, to ovoid-orbicular, 3–3.5 mm. long: longer umbel-rays 6–11 cm. long at maturity.   4. *Z. Bebbii.*
    Blade of the terminal leaflet about as wide as long or wider, with many sharp salient teeth.   5. *Z. latifolia.*

1. Z. cordata (Walt.) DC. Stem 4–10 dm. tall, pale-green: leaf-blades various, those of the basal leaves ovate or suborbicular, 3–10 cm. long, crenate, deeply cordate, long-petioled, those of the cauline leaves mostly 3-foliolate or sometimes 5-foliolate; segments crenate or serrate-crenate: umbels 2–6 cm. broad; rays 7–16, ascending, 1–5 cm. long: corolla yellow, about 2 mm. broad: fruit oval or ovate-oval, 3–4 mm. long, 10-ribbed.—(GOLDEN-PARSNIP.)—Woods, thickets, and prairies, various provinces, rarely Coastal Plain, Ga. to Mo., Ore., Alb., and Conn.

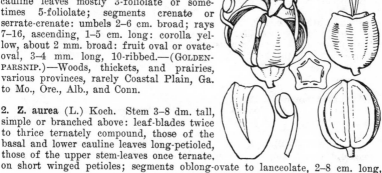

2. Z. aurea (L.) Koch. Stem 3–8 dm. tall, simple or branched above: leaf-blades twice to thrice ternately compound, those of the basal and lower cauline leaves long-petioled, those of the upper stem-leaves once ternate, on short winged petioles; segments oblong-ovate to lanceolate, 2–8 cm. long, sharply serrate: umbel 3–6 cm. broad: rays 9–25, stiff, ascending, unequal, 2–5 cm. long: corolla yellow, 3–3.5 mm. broad: fruit ellipsoid, 4–4.5 mm. long.— (GOLDEN-ALEXANDERS.)—Meadows, woods, and swamps, various provinces, rarely Coastal Plain, Ga. to Tex., Sask., Ont., and N. B.

3. **Z. arenicola** Rose. Stem 4–7 dm. tall, sparingly branched above: leaf-blades once ternately compound; leaflets 1–6 cm. long, the blades oval or ovate to lanceolate, often rounded at the apex, coarsely toothed: umbels long-peduncled; rays few, slender, nearly equal, 1.5–2.5 cm. long, erect or ascending: fruit ovoid to ellipsoid, 4–4.5 mm. long, prominently ribbed.—Dry woods, Coastal Plain, N Fla. and adj. Ga.

4. **Z. Bebbii** (Coult. & Rose) Britton. Stem often tufted, 1–8 dm. tall, simple or branching, dark-green: leaf-blades once ternately compound, the lower ones long-petioled, the upper with winged petioles: leaflets 1–7.5 cm. long, the blades thickish, oval, elliptic, or lanceolate, serrate or crenate: umbels slender-peduncled, straggling; rays 2–12, filiform, unequal, 2–11 mm. long, unequally spreading: fruit suborbicular or broader than high, to ovoid-orbicular, 3–3.5 mm. long or rarely smaller.—Woods, Blue Ridge to Appalachian Plateau, N. C. to Tenn., W. Va., and Va.

5. **Z. latifolia** Small. Stem mostly 4–6 dm. tall, sometimes sparingly branched, pubescent at the nodes: leaf-blades 3-foliolate, long-petioled, except the uppermost; leaflets 3–6.5 cm. long, the blades ovate, suborbicular or orbicular-reniform, irregularly and sharply toothed, except at the broadly cuneate or truncate base: umbels stout-peduncled; rays stoutish, usually 6–12, mostly ascending, unequal, some usually twice as long as the others, the longer becoming 2–3 cm. long: fruit ellipsoid, 3–3.5 mm. long, ribbed.—Borders of fields, near Bristol, Fla.

33. **APIUM** [Tourn.] L. Annual or biennial herbs. Leaves alternate: blades 1–3-pinnate, the leaflets toothed, incised or lobed. Umbels compound. Sepals minute or obsolete. Petals small, yellow, very broad, excepting the bent tip. Fruit slightly flattened laterally: carpels with 5 slender ribs, with a single oil-tube in each interval and 2 in the inner face.— About 5 species, European.

1. **A. Petroselinum** L. Stem 2–5 dm. tall: leaf-segments linear or linear-filiform, or those of the basal leaves cuneate: petals mostly less than 1 mm. long: fruit ovoid, 3.5–4 mm. long. — (PARSLEY. ACHE.) — Waste-places and cult. grounds, various provinces, N. C. to Tex., Ark., and Ont. Nat. of Eu.—Sum.—Used medicinally. The leaves are used in culinary practices.

Aethusa cynapium L. (FOOL'S-PARSLEY), has been found as fugitive on ballast at Mobile, Ala. It differs from the preceding genus by the globose-ovoid fruit which is not flattened either way, and the white flowers.

34. **FOENICULUM** Adans. Biennial or perennial herbs. Leaf-blades pinnately decompound, the segments often very slender. Umbels compound.

Involucre and involucels wanting. Sepals
obsolete. Petals yellow or yellowish. Fruit
elongate: carpels 5-ribbed: oil-tubes solitary
in the intervals and 2 on the inner side.—
Four species, natives of the Old World.

1. F. Foeniculum (L.) Karst. Stem 5–15
dm. tall: leaf-segments filiform or linear-
filiform: umbel-rays 5–6: fruits ellipsoid,
about 5 mm. long. — (FENNEL.) — Waste-
places, roadsides, and fields, various provinces, Fla. to Tex., Tenn. and N. J.—Nat.
of Eu.—(*W. I.*)—Sum.-fall.—Used medicinally and as a culinary herb.

35. PLEIOTAENIA Coult. & Rose. Perennial caulescent herbs. Leaf-
blades pinnately decompound. Umbels compound. Involucres and involucels
of few narrow bracts or the former want-
ing. Sepals triangular. Petals yellow,
broadest above the middle. Fruit broad:
carpels with the dorsal and contiguous ribs
corky but obscure and thick, broadly winged
lateral ribs with a nerve near the margin:
oil-tubes numerous, 12–18, accompanied by
smaller ones irregularly disposed. — One
species.

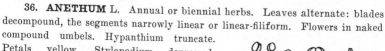

1. P. Nuttallii (DC.) C. & R. Stem 2–9 dm.
tall, slightly scabrous: leaf-segments narrowly cuneate: umbel-rays 2–3 cm. long or
a few conspicuously short: fruit broadly
elliptic, 6–10 mm. long (obovate and thin-winged in *P. Nuttallii texana*).
[*Polytaenia Nuttallii* DC.]—Dry soil, prairies, and barrens, various provinces,
Ala. to Tex., Ia. and Mich.—Spr.

36. ANETHUM L. Annual or biennial herbs. Leaves alternate: blades
decompound, the segments narrowly linear or linear-filiform. Flowers in naked
compound umbels. Hypanthium truncate.
Petals yellow. Stylopodium depressed.
Styles short. Fruit slightly elongate, flattened dorsally: carpels ribbed and with
narrow lateral wings.—Two species, natives
of Eurasia.

1. A. graveolens L. Plant 1 m. tall or less,
glaucous: leaf-segments numerous: umbels
many-flowered, the rays unequal: sepals
minute: petals ovate to orbicular, 1 mm.
long or less: fruits ellipsoid to oval-ellipsoid, 4.5–5 mm. long, glaucous.—(DILL.
DILLWEED.) — Hammocks and cultivated
grounds, S pen. Fla. and the Keys. Nat.
of Eu.—(*W. I.*)—The aromatic fruit is used as a condiment.

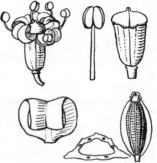

37. PASTINACA L. Annual or biennial herbs. Leaf-blades pinnately compound. Umbels compound. Involucres and involucels usually wanting.

Sepals obsolete. Petals yellow. Fruit some-what longer than broad, much dorsally flat-tened: carpels with the dorsal and con-tiguous ribs slender, and thin lateral wings: oil-tubes solitary in the intervals and 2–4 in the inner side.—About 7 species, natives of Eurasia.

1. P. sativa L. Plant coarse, strong-scented, 6–20 dm. tall: leaf-segments ovate or elliptic, crenate-serrate, incised or lobed: fruit obovate, oval, or orbicular-oval, 5–6 mm. long. — (WILD-PARSNIP.) — Roadsides, fields, thickets, and waste-places, nearly throughout U. S. and S. Can. Nat. of Eurasia.—Sum.—The root is esculent.

38. CONIOSELINUM Hoffm. Perennial herbs. Leaf-blades 2–3-pin-nately decompound, the alternate segments narrow, incised or lobed. Umbels compound. Involucres and involucels of several narrow bracts, or the former want-ing. Sepals obsolete. Petals white. Fruit longer than broad: carpels with the dorsal and contiguous ribs prominent and the lateral ones winged: oil-tubes solitary in the dorsal intervals, 1–several in the lateral, and 4–8 in the inner face.—About 10 spe-cies, natives of the north temperate zone.

1. C. chinense (L.) B. S. P. Plant 5–15 dm. tall: leaf-segments incised: umbel-rays 2–4 cm. long: fruit oval or ellipsoid-oval, 4–5 mm. long.—(HEMLOCK-PARSLEY.)—Swamps and wet cliffs, Blue Ridge and more northern provinces, N. C. to Ind., Minn., Lab. and Pa.—Sum.-fall.

39. ANGELICA L. Perennial caulescent herbs. Leaf-blades pinnate or decompound. Umbels compound. Involucres and involucels present or want-ing. Sepals small or obsolete. Petals white or greenish, broadest above the middle. Fruit longer than broad: carpels with the dorsal and contiguous ribs prominent, and broadly winged lateral ribs: oil-tubes solitary or several in the intervals and 2–10, or more, in the inner face.—About 40 species, mostly in the northern hemisphere.—Sum.-fall.—(ANGELICAS.)—The roots and fruits of some species are used medicinally.

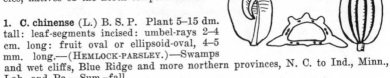

Peduncles and rays pubescent.	1. *A. villosa.*
Peduncles and rays glabrous.	
Leaflets thin; lobes ascending: oil-tubes 1–3 in each interval.	2. *A. Curtisii.*
Leaflets leathery; lobes spreading: oil-tubes about 20, contigu-ous and continuous.	3. *A. dentata.*

1. **A. villosa** (Walt.) B. S. P. Plant 6–18 dm. tall: leaflets 2–5 cm. long, the blades thickish, elliptic, elliptic-lanceolate, or oval, 2–5 cm. long, serrate: umbel-rays 2–5 cm. long: pedicels 3–4 mm. long: corolla white: fruit orbicular or orbicular-obovate, 4.5–5 mm. long, pubescent.—(ANGELICO. HAIRY-ANGELICA.)—Dry thickets and woods, various provinces, Fla. to Miss., Ark., Minn., and Conn.—The leaves are used to discourage the use of tobacco.

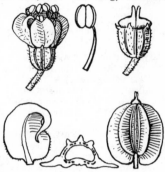

2. **A. Curtisii** Buckl. Plant 6–18 dm. tall: leaflets with ovate or lanceolate, sharply serrate or incised, acuminate: umbel-rays 12–25: pedicels 6–12 mm. long: corolla greenish: fruit ellipsoid or oval, 4–6 mm. long, glabrous. — (FILMY ANGELICA.) — Woods, mt. slopes and summits, Blue Ridge to Appalachian Plateau, N. C. to Pa.

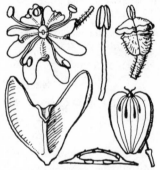

3. **A. dentata** (Chapm.) Coult. & Rose. Plant 5–10 dm. tall: leaflets with elliptic to lanceolate, incised or incised-serrate blades, acute: umbel-rays 5–12; corolla white: fruit oval, 5–6 mm. long.—Dry pinelands, Coastal Plain, M Fla. and adj. Ga.

40. HERACLEUM L. Perennial herbs. Leaf-blades ternately compound. Umbels compound. Involucres and involucels of few, often deciduous, bracts and bractlets or the former wanting. Sepals minute or obsolete. Petals white, broadest above the middle, those of the outer and inner flowers different in shape. Fruit usually longer than broad, strongly dorsally flattened: carpels with the dorsal and contiguous ribs slender, and broadly winged lateral ribs, the latter nerved near the outer edge: oil-tubes solitary in each interval, and 2–4 in the outer face, rarely extending beyond the middle of the carpel.—About 60 species, natives of the Northern Hemisphere.

1. **H. lanatum** Michx. Plant course and heavy-scented, 6–25 dm. tall: leaf-blades 1–4 dm. long, the segments sharply toothed: umbel-rays 8–30, stout, 3–15 cm. long: fruit oval to obovate-oval, 8–12 mm. long.—(COW-PARSNIP.)— Thickets, fence-rows, fields, and waste-places, various provinces, Ga. to Calif., Alas., Ont., and Newf.—Sum.—The roots and fruits are mechanical.

41. OXYPOLIS Raf. Perennial herbs. Leaf-blades pinnate or ternate, or rarely reduced to hollow septate phyllodia. Umbels compound. Involucres and involucels present. Sepals acute. Petals white. Fruit longer than broad, dorsally flattened: carpels with the dorsal and contiguous ribs thin, and winged lateral ribs, the latter nerved near the inner part of the wing: oil-tubes solitary in the intervals and 2–6 in the inner face. [*Tiedemannia* DC.]—Five species, North American.—Sum.-fall or all year S.—DROPWORTS.

Leaves reduced to hollow, terete, transversely-jointed petioles (phyllodia).
  1. *O. filiformis.*
Leaves with simple, pinnate or palmate blades.
  Leaf-blades simple, or of 3 palmately disposed leaflets at the
    end of an elongate petiole. 2. *O. ternata.*
  Leaf-blades pinnately divided.
    Fruit thinnish, the wings papery. 3. *O. rigidior.*
    Fruit turgid, the wings corky. 4. *O. turgida.*

1. O. filiformis (Walt.) Britton. Plant 5–18 dm. tall: phyllodia 3–60 cm. long: fruit elliptic-oval or oval obovate, 5–6 mm. long, broadly winged.— (WATER-DROPWORT.) — Low pinelands and shallow ponds, swamps, Coastal Plain, Fla. to La. and S. C.—Erroneously, apparently, reported from further N.

2. O. ternata (Nutt.) Heller. Plant 5–9 dm. tall: leaf-blades, or leaf-segments, linear or filiform: fruit elliptic, 4–5 mm. long.— Low pinelands, Coastal Plain, Fla. to N. C.

3. O. rigidior (L.) Raf. Plant 5–18 dm. tall: leaves with relatively short, often broad segments, the blades entire or saliently toothed, pale beneath: umbel usually many-rayed: fruit elliptic, 4–5 mm. long, thin-winged. — (PIG-POTATO. WATER-DROP-WORT. COW-BANE.)—Wet woods, swamps, and cliffs, various provinces, Fla. to La., Minn., and N. Y.—*O. longifolia* seems to be an extreme form of this species with very narrow leaf-segments.

4. O. turgida Small. Plant 4–12 dm. tall: leaves and umbels similar to those of *O. rigidior*: fruit elliptic-oval or elliptic-obovate, 2.5–3 mm. long, thick-winged.—Swamps, Blue Ridge and adj. provinces, S. C. to Va., and Coastal Plain, S E N. Y.

SERIES 2. **GAMOPETALAE**

Petals more or less united, or occasionally distinct, or very rarely wanting.

ORDER **ERICALES** — ERICAL ORDER

Herbs, undershrubs, shrubs, or trees, sometimes humus-plants or saprophytes. Leaves alternate, often evergreen: blades simple. Flowers mainly perfect and complete. Calyx of 2–8, usually 5, partially united sepals. Corolla of 2–8, usually 5, mostly united petals. Androecium of as many or twice as many stamens as petals, sometimes partially reduced to staminodia: filaments mostly free. Gynoecium of several united carpels. Fruit capsular, baccate, or drupaceous.

Stamens with free and distinct filaments.
  Ovary superior: fruit exposed or enclosed in the calyx.
    Gynoecium 3-carpellary: pollen-grains simple. Fam. 1. CLETHRACEAE.
    Gynoecium 4–7-carpellary, but the ovary rarely
      1-celled: pollen-grains simple or compound.
      Herbaceous root-parasites or saprophytes, with
        scale-like leaves: plants devoid of chloro-
        phyl: pollen-grains simple. Fam. 2. MONOTROPACEAE.
      Herbs, undershrubs, shrubs, or trees: plants
        with chlorophyl: pollen-grains compound.

Herbaceous or partly woody plants with
  rootstocks.   Fam. 3. PYROLACEAE.
  Shrubs or trees with erect or diffuse stems.   Fam. 4. ERICACEAE.
Ovary wholly or partly inferior.   Fam. 5. VACCINIACEAE.
Stamens with the filaments wholly or partly adnate to
  the corolla.
  Androecium without staminodia: caulescent plants.   Fam. 6. DIAPENSIACEAE.
  Androecium with staminodia: acaulescent plants.   Fam. 7. GALACACEAE.

FAMILY 1. CLETHRACEAE — WHITE-ALDER FAMILY

Shrubs or trees, the pubescence of branched hairs. Leaves deciduous: blades mostly toothed. Flowers in racemes or panicles. Calyx of 5 persistent sepals. Corolla white, of 5 distinct petals. Androecium of 10 stamens: filaments elongate: anthers inverted in anthesis. Gynoecium of 3 united carpels: stigmas 3. Fruit a 3-valved loculicidal capsule.—Only the following genus, and about 30 species, widely distributed, except in Europe and Africa.

1. **CLETHRA** [Gronov.] L. Erect shrubs or trees, with toothed leaf-blades and elongate racemes or panicles.—Sum.—PEPPERBUSHES. WHITE-ALDERS.

Filaments glabrous: style pubescent: racemes erect.
  Sepals acute: leaf-blades glabrous beneath, or nearly so.   1. *C. alnifolia.*
  Sepals obtuse: leaf-blades tomentose beneath.   2. *C. tomentosa.*
Filaments pubescent: style glabrous: racemes nodding.   3. *C. acuminata.*

1. C. alnifolia L. Shrub 1–3 m. tall, the twigs sparingly pubescent: leaf-blades obovate or cuneate, 3–8 cm. long: pedicels 1–3 mm. long: sepals elliptic to lanceolate, 2.5–3 mm. long: petals 5–6 mm. long: capsule subglobose, 2.5–3 mm. in diameter, erect.—(SUMMERSWEET. SWEET-PEPPERBUSH.)—Acid swamps, low sandy woods, and wet pinelands, Coastal Plain and adj. provinces, Fla. to La., Pa. and Me. The flowers are very fragrant. Pink-flowered forms are occasional.

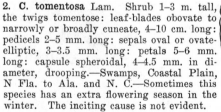
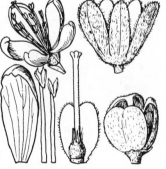

2. C. tomentosa Lam. Shrub 1–3 m. tall, the twigs tomentose: leaf-blades obovate to narrowly or broadly cuneate, 4–10 cm. long: pedicels 2–5 mm. long: sepals oval or ovate-elliptic, 3–3.5 mm. long: petals 5–6 mm. long: capsule spheroidal, 4–4.5 mm. in diameter, drooping.—Swamps, Coastal Plain, N Fla. to Ala. and N. C.—Sometimes this species has an extra flowering season in the winter. The inciting cause is not evident.

3. C. acuminata Michx. Shrub, or tree becoming 6 m. tall, the twigs tomentulose: leaf-blades oval or elliptic, 9–20 cm. long: racemes nodding: pedicels recurved: sepals ovate, 3.5–4 mm. long, acute: petals 6–7 mm. long: capsule ovoid, 4–5 mm. long, drooping.—Woods, ravines, and cliffs of non-calcareous rocks, inner Piedmont to Appalachian Plateau, Ga. to Tenn., W. Va., and Va.

FAMILY 2. MONOTROPACEAE — INDIAN-PIPE FAMILY

Saprophytic or humus herbs, with matted roots. Stems scape-like, simple. Leaves reduced to scales. Flowers in racemes, or solitary, nodding. Calyx of 2–6 deciduous sepals. Corolla white or colored, of 3–6 petals, or wanting. Androecium of 6–12 stamens: anthers with valves or pores. Gynoecium of 4–6 united carpels: stigma capitate, disc-like, or funnelform. Fruit a 4–6-valved loculicidal capsule.—About 9 genera and 16 species, most abundant in North America.

Corolla of several distinct petals, deciduous.
   Flowers solitary: plants white or pink (black in drying).   1. MONOTROPA.
   Flowers several: plants yellowish or red.   2. HYPOPITYS.
Corolla gamopetalous, campanulate, persistent.   3. MONOTROPSIS.

1. **MONOTROPA** L. White or pale-pink wax-like herbs blackening in drying. Flowers colorless, pink, ochroleucous, or salmon-colored. Sepals 2–4, unequal. Petals 5 or 6, saccate at the base, dilated at the apex. Gynoecium glabrous.—About 3 species, in North America and Asia.—INDIAN-PIPES. CORPSE-PLANTS.

Flowers white or pale-pink: petals obscurely ciliate: filaments sparingly pubescent.
    1. *M. uniflora.*
Flowers ochroleucous or salmon-colored: petals copiously ciliate
  and densely pubescent within: filaments copiously pubescent.   2. *M. Brittonii.*

1. **M. uniflora** L. Stem 0.5–3 dm. tall, white: leaves lanceolate or elliptic-lanceolate, somewhat pointed: sepals and petals deeply saccate at the base, entire or eroded at the top: filaments slightly pubescent with short hairs: lobes of the disk slender, acute, projecting downward: capsule ovoid, 1–1.5 cm. long.—Woods and rich shaded banks, various provinces, N Fla. to Calif., Wash., and Newf.—Sum.—A pink-stemmed form flowering in fall, at higher altitudes in our range, may represent a distinct species.

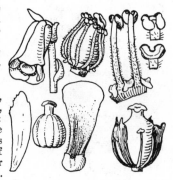

2. **M. Brittonii** Small. Stem 1–4 dm. tall, ochroleucous: leaves ovate or oblanceolate, or spatulate near the top of the stem, obtuse: sepals and petals shallowly saccate at the base, sometimes toothed at the top: filaments densely pubescent with long hairs: lobes of the disk stout, blunt, projecting outward or upward: capsule ellipsoid-ovoid, 1.5–2 cm. long.—Scrub, Coastal Plain, S pen. Fla. to SE N. C.—Wint.

2. **HYPOPITYS** Adans. Colored fragrant herbs. Flowers in a terminal raceme, deep-pink, yellow, red, or crimson. Sepals and petals 5 each in the earliest flower, or 4 in the later ones. Gynoecium pubescent.—About 7 species, in the north temperate zone.—Sum.-fall.—PINE-SAPS. FALSE BEECH-DROPS.

Stigma not retrorsely bearded: style sparingly pubescent: sepals and petals with
  short cilia.   1. *H. americana.*
Stigma retrorsely bearded: style copiously pubescent: sepals
  and petals with long cilia.   2. *H. lanuginosa.*

1. **H. americana** (DC.) Small. Plant tawny or yellow, finely pubescent or nearly glabrous, 1–3 dm. tall: sepals 7–10 mm. long: petals sparingly pubes-

cent: capsule oval or oblong-oval, 7–10 mm.
long.—Woods, Blue Ridge, N. C. and Tenn.
to Md., and various provinces, N. J. to
W. Va. and Ont.

2. H. lanuginosa (Michx.) Nutt. Plant
deep-pink and crimson, markedly or copiously
pubescent, 0.5–3.5 dm. tall: sepals 6–9 mm.
long: petals markedly pubescent: capsule
globular, 4–5 mm. long.—Woods and thickets, various provinces, Fla. to La., Ky., Que.,
and Newf.—A late-blooming and bright-red-
flowered species, with flowers and leaves
tipped with yellow, has been published as
H. insignata Bicknell, and may prove to be
only a form of the above species, or the
original plant of Michaux.

3. MONOTROPSIS Schwein.   Colored herbs.   Flowers in a raceme,
fragrant, white, pink, or purple.   Sepals 5, erose near the apex, persistent.
Petals partially united: tube 5-saccate at the base.—Three species, given below.
—Sweet pine-saps. Pygmy-pipes.

Corolla about as long as the calyx during anthesis or shorter, colored.
   Corolla-lobes much shorter than the tube: calyx and corolla
     about equal in length.   1. *M. odorata.*
   Corolla-lobes about as long as the tube: calyx about twice
     as long as the corolla.   2. *M. Lehmaniae.*
Corolla about twice as long as the calyx during anthesis, white. 3. *M. Reynoldsiae.*

1. M. odorata Ell.   Stems 5–11 cm. tall, purple or purplish-brown: flowers
violet-scented: sepals 7–10 mm. long: corolla 7–8 mm. long, the lobes much
shorter than the tube. [*Cryptophila pudica*
W. Wolf.] — (Carolina beech-drops.) —
Moist acid woods, various provinces, N Ga.
to Ala., Ky., and Md.—Early spr.—The
corolla is usually pink, but varies to almost
white and purplish.

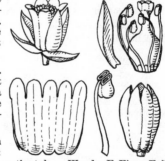

2. M. Lehmaniae Burnham. Stem 4–10 cm.
tall, mainly brownish-purple: flowers not
fragrant: sepals 7–8 mm. long: corolla
mainly pink, the lobes about as long as the
tube.—Woods, in Blue Ridge, W N. C.—
Fall.

3. M. Reynoldsiae (A. Gray) Heller. Stem
4–12 cm. tall, purple: sepals 2–4 mm. long:
corolla 6.5–8 mm. long, the lobes 1/3 as long as the tube.—Woods, E Fla.—Fall.

Family 3. **PYROLACEAE** — Wintergreen Family

Perennial mostly evergreen herbs, with elongate rootstocks. Leaves
alternate, mostly near the base of the stem: blades leathery. Flowers in
terminal racemes, corymbs. or umbel-like clusters, or solitary, sometimes
irregular. Calyx of 4 or 5 persistent sepals. Corolla white or pink, of
4 or 5 essentially distinct, wax-like petals. Androecium of twice as many
stamens as there are petals: anthers inverted in anthesis. Gynoecium of
4 or 5 united carpels: stigmas united. Fruit a 4- or 5-valved loculicidal
capsule.—Three genera and about 25 species, natives of the Northern
Hemisphere.

Style elongate: flowers racemose: filaments unappendaged: capsule opening from
base to top.   1. PYROLA.
Style very short: flowers corymbed or umbelled: filaments appendaged at the base: capsule opening from top to base.   2. CHIMAPHILA.

1. **PYROLA** [Tourn.] L. Leaves with broad blades. Flowers white,
greenish, or pink, in elongate racemes. Filaments unappendaged, glabrous.
Capsule nodding, the valve-margins cobwebby.—About 18 species, widely distributed in temperate and cool regions.—Sum.—WINTERGREENS. SHIN-LEAFS.

Leaf-blades suborbicular: calyx-lobes mainly longer than the tube: filaments less
than twice as long as the anthers.   1. *P. americana.*
Leaf-blades elliptic-oval or oblong: calyx-lobes mainly shorter
than the tube: filaments over twice as long as the anthers.   2. *P. elliptica.*

1. **P. americana** Sweet. Plant 2–3 dm. tall: leaf-blades thickish, 2–3 cm. long,
mostly shorter than the petiole: sepals elliptic or lanceolate, 2–3 mm. long:
petals obovate to orbicular-obovate, 7–9 mm. long:
capsule 6–7 mm. wide. [*P. rotundifolia* Michx. not
L.]—Woods, Blue Ridge, N. C. and Tenn., various
provinces, Va. to Wisc. and N. S.

2. **P. elliptica** Nutt. Plant 1–3 dm. tall: leaf-
blades thinnish, 3–9 cm. long, mostly longer than the
petiole: sepals triangular-ovate: petals oblong to
elliptic-obovate, 5.5–7 mm. long: capsule 5–6 mm.
wide.—Thickets and woods, Blue Ridge, Tenn., and
various provinces, Tenn. to N. M., B. C., Ont., and
Va.—The petals of both species are usually white,
but pink tinged corollas occur in occasional forms.

2. **CHIMAPHILA** Pursh. Leaves with relatively narrow blades. Flowers
white, in corymbs. Filaments with pubescent or erose-ciliate appendages at the
base. Capsule erect, the valve-margins glabrous.—About 7 species, distributed
from the equator to the Arctic regions.—Sum.—PIPSISSEWAS.

Sepals longer than wide: petals ciliolate all around: filament-appendages pubescent.
                                                                1. *C. maculata.*
Sepals wider than long: petals erose-ciliolate and jagged at the
apex; filament-appendages erose-ciliate.   2. *C. corymbosa.*

1. **C. maculata** (L.) Pursh. Plant 7–22 cm. tall: leaf-blades lanceolate or
sometimes broader, 2–5 cm. long, dark-green with whitish veins: inflorescence
usually 1–5-flowered: sepals rounded at the apex,
ciliolate: petals white, 10–12 mm. long: filament-
appendages narrow.—(SPOTTED-WINTERGREEN.) — Dry
woods, various provinces, Ga. to Ala., Minn., and Me.

2. **C. corymbosa** Pursh. Plant 9–32 cm. tall: leaf-
blades oblanceolate, cuneate, or obovate-cuneate, 2–10
cm. long, deep yellow-green, not variegated: inflorescence usually 3–10-flowered: sepals not rounded at
the apex, erose: petals 9–11 mm. long, white except
the pink base: filaments and broad appendages
purplish-pink. — (PRINCE'S-PINE.) — Dry acid woods,

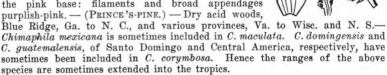

Blue Ridge, Ga. to N. C., and various provinces, Va. to Wisc. and N. S.—
Chimaphila mexicana is sometimes included in *C. maculata.* *C. domingensis* and
C. guatemalensis, of Santo Domingo and Central America, respectively, have
sometimes been included in *C. corymbosa.* Hence the ranges of the above
species are sometimes extended into the tropics.

Family 4. **ERICACEAE** — Heath Family

Shrubs, trees, or undershrubs. Leaves often persistent: blades commonly leathery. Flowers typically perfect. Calyx of 4–7 distinct or partially united sepals. Corolla of 4–7 distinct or partially united petals, sometimes slightly 2-lipped. Androecium of as many or twice as many stamens as there are petals: anthers opening by pores, chinks, or valves. Gynoecium of 2–7 united carpels. Fruit a capsule, or sometimes baccate or drupaceous.—About 60 genera and 1,100 species, widely distributed.

Calyx not accrescent: capsule exposed.
  Capsule septicidal.   Tribe I. Rhododendreae.
  Capsule loculicidal or marginicidal.
    Anther-sacs opening by apical pores or chinks above
      the middle: capsule loculicidal: erect shrubs, trees,
      or vines.   II. Andromedeae.
    Anther-sacs opening lengthwise: capsule marginicidal: prostrate shrub with creeping branches.   III. Epigaeae.
Calyx accrescent, enclosing the capsule and becoming fleshy.   IV. Gaultherieae.

I. Rhododendreae

Corolla of distinct petals.
  Anther-sacs opening by apical pores: petals 6 or 7.   1. Befaria.
  Anther-sacs opening lengthwise.
    Anthers sagittate: tall shrub with thin-membranous
      leaf-blades: petals long and narrow.   2. Elliottia.
    Anthers globular-didymous: low or depressed shrubs
      with leathery leaf-blades: petals short and broad.   3. Leiophyllum.
Corolla of partly united petals.   4. Azalea.
  Corolla decidedly 2-lipped, funnelform.
  Corolla not 2-lipped, campanulate or rotate-campanulate,
    urceolate or saucer-shaped.
    Flower-body, and usually leaf-buds, scaly-strobilaceous.
      Corolla campanulate or rotate-campanulate.
        Upper corolla-lobe interior: calyx-lobes small,
          but prominent: leaves persistent; blades
          leathery.   5. Rhododendron.
        Upper corolla-lobe exterior: calyx-lobes minute:
          leaves deciduous; blades membranous.   6. Biltia.
      Corolla urceolate.   7. Menziesia.
    Flower-buds, and leaf-buds, not scaly-strobilaceous.
      Calyx persistent: corolla-lobes rounded: capsule
      depressed.   8. Kalmia.
      Calyx deciduous: corolla-lobes acute: capsule
      ovoid.   9. Kalmiella.

II. Andromedeae

Calyx-lobes imbricate, at least in the bud.
  Capsule depressed: anther-sacs opening by apical pores
    or chinks.
    Capsule-wall double, the outer layer 5-valved.   10. Chamaedaphne.
    Capsule-wall single, 5-valved.
      Anthers awned: panicles terminal.   11. Eubotrys.
      Anthers awnless: panicles axillary.   12. Leucothoe.
  Capsule elongate: anther-sacs opening by chinks above
    the middle.   13. Oxydendron.
Calyx-lobes valvate or separated in the bud.
  Anther-sacs awned: capsule-sutures not thickened.
    Awns of the anther-sacs ascending: seeds smooth.   14. Zenobia.
    Awns of the anther-sacs deflexed: seeds reticulate or
      with a loose coat.
      Flowers in terminal compound panicles: filaments
      subulate, straight or nearly so.   15. Pieris.
      Flowers in axillary simple raceme-like panicles:
      filaments much-flattened, sigmoid-curved.   16. Ampelothamnus.
  Anther-sacs awnless: capsule-sutures thickened.
    Filaments appendaged: corolla about twice as long
      as the calyx.
      Style fusiform: corolla of an urceolate type: leaf-
      blades with intramarginal veins: sepals per-
      sistent.   17. Desmothamnus.
      Style columnar: corolla of a cylindraceous-
      campanulate type: leaf-blades without intra-
      marginal veins: sepals deciduous.   18. Neopieris.

Filaments unappendaged: corolla several times ex-
    ceeding the calyx.
Capsule longer than thick, prominently angled:
    lepidote shrubs with persistent leaves: flowers
    in axillary clusters.   19. XOLISMA.
Capsule depressed, not angled: pubescent shrubs
    with deciduous leaves: flowers in panicled
    racemes.   20. ARSENOCOCCUS.

III. EPIGAEAE

Plant with creeping stems and evergreen leaves: flowers in
    axillary clusters: corolla salverform: calyx-lobes dry.   21. EPIGAEA.

IV. GAULTHERIEAE

Stem erect from a horizontal rootstock: leaves evergreen:
    flowers solitary in the axils: corolla urceolate: calyx-lobes
    fleshy.   22. GAULTHERIA.

1. BEFARIA Mutis. Evergreen shrubs with erect branches. Leaves
alternate: blades thick.   Flowers large in long erect spike-like racemes.
Calyx-lobes 6 or 7.   Petals broadened upward, spreading.   Stamens 12 or 14:
anthers with terminal pores.   Ovary 6- or 7-celled.
Capsule subglobose.—About 15 species, mostly tropical American.—Sometimes spelled *Bejaria*.

1. B. racemosa Vent.   Shrub 1–2.5 m. tall, the
branches hirsute: leaf-blades mainly elliptic to oval,
2–5.5 cm. long, often somewhat hirsute: calyx-lobes
about 4 mm. long: petals white, sometimes pink-
tinged, spatulate to linear-spatulate, 2–3 cm. long,
glutinous: filaments pubescent: capsule depressed-
globose, 6–9 mm. in diameter.—(TAR-FLOWER, FLY-
CATCHER.)—Pinelands, Coastal Plain, Fla. to Ga.—
Spr.–fall.—This outlier of a typically Mexican-South American genus is a
striking plant when in flower.   Bouquets made of the inflorescence as it starts
to flower, will continue to bloom for nearly or quite a week.

2. ELLIOTTIA Muhl.   Deciduous shrubs, with more or less spreading
branches.   Leaves alternate: blades thinnish.   Flowers small, numerous, in
short panicles.   Calyx-lobes 3 or 4.   Petals not
broadened upward.   Stamens 4–10: anthers with longitudinal valves.   Ovary 3–5-celled.   Capsule subglobose.—One species.

1. E. racemosa Muhl.   Shrub 1–5 m. tall, the
branches glabrous: leaf-blades elliptic, oval, or elliptic-
oblanceolate, 4–12 cm. long: calyx-lobes about 1 mm.
long: petals white, linear-elliptic, 12–14 mm. long, not
glutinous: filaments glabrous: capsule ovoid-globose.
—(ELLIOTTIA.)—Oak ridges and sandhills, Coastal
Plain and adj. provinces, Ga. and S S. C.—Sum.—One
of the rarest of American shrubs, known to have been found at but 7 or 8
stations, and at some of these now exterminated.   At each station but a single
individual is represented, although this may often spread into a large patch
by its rootstocks.   Being sterile to its own pollen, seeds are only produced when
cross-fertilization from one clump to another is brought about.   Before the
coming of the white man, such plants must have grown close enough together for

insects to accomplish this crossing at times, but lumbering and agriculture have destroyed so many, that propagation by seeds seems to have ceased.

3. **LEIOPHYLLUM** Pers. Evergreen shrubs with erect, spreading, or prostrate branches. Leaves alternate or opposite, box-like: blades coriaceous, entire, often shining. Flowers in terminal umbel-like clusters. Calyx-lobes 5, longer than the tube. Petals 5, white or pink, spreading. Stamens 10: anthers opening lengthwise. Style straight. Capsule ovoid. [*Dendrium* Desv.]— Only the following species.—Spr.–sum.—SAND-MYRTLES.

Style slender, fully twice as long as the ovary in anthesis: disk minute: petals elliptic to ovate-elliptic: pedicels glabrous.   1. *L. buxifolium.*
Style stout, less than twice as long as the ovary: disk prominent:
  petals ovate to rhombic-ovate: pedicels pubescent.
  Leaves mostly opposite: capsule-valves sharp-tuberculate: depressed or diffuse shrub.   2. *L. Lyoni.*
  Leaves alternate: capsule-valves muricate or scabrous: erect shrub.   3. *L. Hugeri.*

1. **L. buxifolium** (Berg.) Ell. A much-branched shrub resembling a dwarf-box plant, 3 dm. tall or less: leaf-blades elliptic or slightly broadened upward, mostly 3–8 mm. long, shining above, paler and dull beneath: calyx-lobes elliptic-lanceolate or lanceolate, about 1 mm. long: petals elliptic to ovate-elliptic, 2–2.5 mm. long: capsule ovoid, about 3 mm. long, more than twice as long as the calyx. [*D. buxifolium* Desv.]—Sandy pine-barrens, Coastal Plain, N. C. to N. J.; recorded from as far south as Fla.

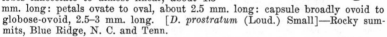
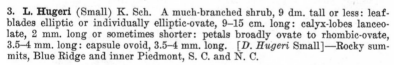

2. **L. Lyoni** Sweet. A low, diffuse or depressed shrub 2 dm. tall or less, the usually numerous branches often prostrate and matted: leaf-blades oval or broadly elliptic, 4–7 mm. long or sometimes smaller: calyx-lobes lanceolate to almost linear, about 1.5 mm. long: petals ovate to oval, about 2.5 mm. long: capsule broadly ovoid to globose-ovoid, 2.5–3 mm. long. [*D. prostratum* (Loud.) Small]—Rocky summits, Blue Ridge, N. C. and Tenn.

3. **L. Hugeri** (Small) K. Sch. A much-branched shrub, 9 dm. tall or less: leaf-blades elliptic or individually elliptic-ovate, 9–15 cm. long: calyx-lobes lanceolate, 2 mm. long or sometimes shorter: petals broadly ovate to rhombic-ovate, 3.5–4 mm. long: capsule ovoid, 3.5–4 mm. long. [*D. Hugeri* Small]—Rocky summits, Blue Ridge and inner Piedmont, S. C. and N. C.

4. **AZALEA** L. Erect deciduous-leaved shrubs, sometimes tardily deciduous at the extreme south. Leaves alternate: blades sometimes bristle-toothed. Calyx deciduous: lobes 5, conspicuously ciliate. Corolla variously colored, funnelform: tube elongate: limb 2-lipped. Stamens 5 or rarely 10, conspicuously exserted: anthers with terminal pores. Style declined. Capsule elongate, opening at the apex.—About 40 species, American and Asiatic.—WILD-HONEY-SUCKLES. AZALEAS.—Natural hybrids are to be expected.—Several of the species are much used in horticulture.

Flower-clusters appearing before the leaves or as the leaves unfold.
                                    I. NUDIFLORAE.
Flower-clusters appearing after the leaves.
  Twigs strigose: style usually pubescent.   II. VISCOSAE.

Twigs glabrous : style usually glabrous.
Corolla white or pinkish ; tube glandular pubescent
without. III. ARBORESCENTES.
Corolla crimson ; tube glabrous or nearly so without. IV, PRUNIFOLIAE.

I. NUDIFLORAE

Corolla red, orange, or yellow.
Flowers appearing as the leaves unfold : scales of the winter-buds glabrous on
the back.
Corolla-tube glandular without, as long as the lobes
or shorter ; limb yellow to orange or scarlet. 1. A. calendulacea.
Corolla-tube pubescent with glandless hairs without,
longer than the lobes ; limb scarlet or bright red. 2. A. speciosa.
Flowers appearing before the leaves unfold : scales of the
winter-buds pubescent on the back. 3. A. austrina.
Corolla white, pink, or carmine.
Shrubs with tap-roots and erect, usually much-branched
stems, mostly 1–2 m. tall : flower-buds without
prominent rows of stipitate glands at the apex.
Corolla pink.
Corolla-tube hirsute or strigose without. 4. A. nudiflora.
Corolla-tube more or less glandular-pubescent.
Leaf-blade thick, usually pubescent beneath
when mature : capsule softly pubescent
and hirsute : corolla-tube abruptly expanded into the limb.
Leaf-blade softly pubescent beneath when
mature, but green. 5. A. canescens.
Leaf-blade white or pale-tomentose beneath
when mature, not green. 6. A. candida.
Leaf-blade thin-membranaceous : capsule glandular-hirsute : corolla-tube gradually expanded
into the limb. 7. A. prinophylla.
Corolla white. 8. A. alabamensis.
Shrub with horizontal underground stem and low erect
simple or nearly simple branches, in small or large
colonies (stoloniferous) : flower-buds with conspicuous
rows of stipitate glands at the apex. 9. A. atlantica.

II. VISCOSAE

Twigs pale : scales of the winter-buds few (15 or less), obtuse or acutish, usually brown : leaves usually glabrous
beneath : northern plant. 10. A. viscosa.
Twigs red-brown : scales of the winter-buds many (15 or
more), aristate-mucronate, pale, except the dark margin :
leaves often pubescent beneath : southern plant. 11. A. serrulata.

III. ARBORESCENTES

Shrub or small tree, with glabrous yellowish-brown or
reddish-brown twigs : leaf-blades of an obovate type,
usually glaucous beneath. 12. A. arborescens.

IV. PRUNIFOLIAE

Shrub with dark purplish-red twigs : leaf-blades of an elliptic or elliptic-lanceolate type, light-green beneath. 13. A. prunifolia.

1. A. calendulacea Michx. Shrub 0.5–5 m. tall, the twigs strigillose : leaf-
blades oval, elliptic, or obovate, 3–8 cm. long, more or less canescent beneath :
calyx-lobes ovate to elliptic, 3–4 mm. long : corolla
yellow, orange, or scarlet, often somewhat variegated ;
tube 1.5–2 cm. long, glandular-pubescent ; upper lobe
with an orange blotch : capsule ovoid-ellipsoid, 1.5–2.5
cm. long, or sometimes shorter, hirsute. [*A. lutea* L.?]
—(FLAME-AZALEA. YELLOW-AZALEA.)—Acid humus,
in open woods, inner Piedmont to Appalachian Plateau, Ga. to Ala., Tenn., W. Va., and S N. Y.—Late
spr.—A red azalea native in the Cumberland mountains, with pedicel and calyx non-glandular and leaf-
blades glaucous beneath, flowering in late June and
July, may be distinct.

2. A. speciosa Willd. Shrub 0.5–2 m. tall, the twigs strigillose: leaf-blades obovate to elliptic, 3–6 cm. long, finely pubescent beneath and more or less strigillose on the midrib: calyx-lobes broadly ovate to elliptic, 0.5–3 mm. long, long-ciliate: corolla scarlet or bright-red; tube 2–2.5 cm. long; upper lobe with an orange blotch: capsule 2–3 cm. long, narrowly ovoid to elliptic-ovoid, strigose.—Woods and sandhills, Piedmont and adj. provinces, Ga. and S. C.—Spr.

3. A. austrina Small. Shrub mostly 3 m. tall or less, the twigs sparingly strigose and softly pubescent, and usually glandular: leaf-blades oval, obovate, elliptic, or elliptic-spatulate, 2.5–9 cm. long, rather firm in age, finely pubescent, usually permanently so: calyx-lobes deltoid to triangular-lanceolate, acute, glandular-ciliate: corolla yellow and orange; tube 1.8–2 cm. long, finely glandular-pubescent; lobes broad, acute or abruptly short-acuminate: capsule narrowly cylindric ellipsoid, slightly narrowed upward, 2–2.5 cm. long, finely glandular-pubescent.—Woods and stream-banks, in moderately acid sandy soils, N W Fla. —Spr.—The flowers are slightly fragrant.

4. A. nudiflora L. Shrub 3 m. tall or less, the twigs finely pubescent and more or less strigose: leaf-blades elliptic to obovate or elliptic-obovate, 3–10 cm. long, thick and firm in age, strigose on or near the veins beneath, or glabrous, except the margins: calyx-lobes ovate to half-orbicular, copiously ciliate: corolla pink (or deep-pink or carmine, the tube with some equal gland-tipped hairs in *A. nudiflora glandifera*); tube 2–3 cm. long, pilose or strigose; lobes rather broad, shorter than the tube: capsule ellipsoid, often narrowly so or somewhat narrowed upward, strigose or hirsute-strigose.—(PINXTER-FLOWER. HONEY-SUCKLE. EARLY-AZALEA.)—Woods and low grounds, various provinces, N. C. to Tenn., Ohio and Mass.—Spr.—The flowers are scarcely fragrant.

5. A. canescens Michx. Shrub up to 5 m. tall the twigs minutely soft-pubescent and usually also strigose: leaf-blades elliptic, elliptic-oblanceolate, oblanceolate, or narrowly obovate, thickish and firm at maturity, 4–10 cm. long, ciliate, with scattered hairs above or nearly glabrous, permanently tomentose-canescent beneath, (or glabrous, except the margins and the midrib in *A. canescens subglabra*): calyx-lobes deltoid to ovate or half-orbicular, usually about 1 mm. long, ciliate: corolla pink; tube 1.5–2.5 cm. long, or rarely somewhat longer, finely glandular-pubescent, abruptly dilated near the throat; lobes shorter than the tube: capsule cylindric-ellipsoid, narrowed upward, 1.5–2.5 mm. long, canescent and hirsute.—Stream-banks, in rather acid sandy soil, Coastal Plain and adj. provinces, Fla. to Tex., Ark., Tenn., and N. C.—Spr.— The flowers are slightly fragrant.

6. A. candida Small. Shrub 2 m. tall or less, the twigs tomentulose and often somewhat glandular: leaf-blades obovate, obovate-oblanceolate, cuneate, or elliptic, coriaceous at maturity, 1–7 cm. long, thinly fine-pubescent above, glaucous and white- or pale-tomentose beneath and sometimes reticulate-veiny: calyx-lobes deltoid, ciliate, obtuse: corolla white: capsule narrow, gradually narrowed upward, 2–2.5 cm. long, canescent, curved.—Hammocks, Coastal Plain, N Fla. to S Ga.—Spr.—The flowers are slightly fragrant.

7. A. prinophylla Small. Shrub up to 5 m. tall, the twigs finely loose-pubescent and somewhat strigose: leaf-blades oval or elliptic, varying to obovate, 2–8 cm. long, thinnish and not very firm at maturity, ciliate, canescent beneath or glabrate, especially in age: calyx-lobes half-orbicular to deltoid or ovate, sparingly ciliate, obtuse: corolla deep-pink, or sometimes pale; tube 1.5–2 cm. long, thinly villous-tomentose and glandular-pubescent; lobes as long as the tube or slightly shorter: capsule ellipsoid to ovoid-ellipsoid, 1.5–2 cm. long, or smaller, glandular-pubescent. [*A. canescens* (Fl. SE. U. S.) not Michx.]—Woods and rocky banks, various provinces N of Coastal Plain, Tenn. to Ark., Vt., and Va.—Spr.—The flowers are very fragrant.

8. A. alabamensis (Rehder) Small. Shrub up to 1 m. tall, the twigs pale-strigose: leaf-blades obovate to elliptic or elliptic-obovate, 3–6 cm. long, loosely short-pubescent beneath and strigillose on the midrib: calyx-lobes ovate, often broadly so, bristly pubescent: corolla white; tube 2–3 cm. long, usually glandular-pubescent without; lobes shorter than the tube: anthers 2–3 mm. long: capsule cylindric-ellipsoid, about 1.5 cm. long, loosely pubescent and more or less glandular-bristly. [*Rhododendron alabamense* Rehder.]—Dry woods, Coastal Plain and adj. provinces, Ala.—Spr.—The flowers are fragrant.

9. A. atlantica Ashe. Shrub with the more or less gregarious branches usually less than 0.5 m. tall, the twigs sparingly strigillose and sometimes glandular-hirsute: leaf-blades obovate, elliptic-obovate, or sometimes elliptic, 3–6 cm. long, mostly glabrous beneath, except the pubescent midrib, (finely pubescent on both sides and bluish-green in *A. atlantica luteo-alba*): calyx-lobes broadly ovate or elliptic-ovate, 2–4 mm. long, ciliate, often with gland-tipped hairs: corolla white or pink, (purplish-pink in *A. atlantica neglecta*); tube 2–2.5 cm. long or barely longer, glandular-pubescent without; lobes shorter than the tube: anthers 2–3 mm. long: capsule ovoid-ellipsoid, 1.5–2 cm. long, bristly with glandless or gland-tipped hairs.—Low pinelands, Coastal Plain, S. C. to Del.—Spr.—The flowers are very fragrant.—An azalea apparently referable to *A. atlantica luteo-alba* occurs in S Ala.

10. A. viscosa L. Shrub 0.5–5 mm. tall, the twigs loosely pubescent and strigillose (or decidedly hispid in *A. viscosa hispida*); the winter-buds typically glabrous (or densely pubescent, and the leaves up to 6 cm. long in *A. viscosa aemulans*, or silky-pubescent, and the leaves up to 4 cm. long in *A. viscosa montana*): leaf-blades cuneate to obovate or individually elliptic or elliptic-oblanceolate, 2–6 cm. long, thickish, ciliate, strigillose on the midrib beneath, (or finely and rather densely pubescent beneath in *A. viscosa tomentosa*), dull (or small and shining in *A. viscosa nitida*; glaucous on one or both sides in *A. viscosa glauca*): calyx-lobes ovate to semi-orbicular, pectinate-ciliate: corolla white or pink-tinged; tube 1.5–2.5 cm. long, rather abruptly dilated near the limb; lobes much shorter than the tube: capsule ellipsoid-ovoid, 1.5–2 cm. long, glandular-hirsute.—(Swamp-azalea.)—Acid swamps, various provinces, Fla. to Miss., Ohio, and Me.—Late Spr.-sum.—The flowers are very fragrant.

11. A. serrulata Small. Shrub 7 m. tall or less, the twigs red-brown, strigose, and usually also finely villous, the winter-buds with numerous glabrous scales, (or with few and densely gray-pubescent in *A. serrulata georgiana*): leaf-blades elliptic to obovate or obovate-elliptic, or individually elliptic-oblanceolate, 4–9 cm. long, serrulate-ciliate, shining, finely reticulate, glabrous, except for scattered hairs on the midrib beneath: calyx-lobes ovate or broader, long-ciliate, obtuse: corolla white; tube 3–3.5 cm. long, somewhat enlarged near the base, expanded near the limb, glandular-pubescent; lobes narrow, shorter than the tube: capsule ovoid-ellipsoid, 1–1.5 cm. long, glandular-setose.—Wet hammocks, Coastal Plain, Fla. to La. and S. C.—Spr.-sum.—The flowers are very fragrant.

12. A. arborescens Pursh. Shrub with tall stems, (or with low widely branched stems and small very glaucous leaves in *A. arborescens Richardsonii*), or tree becoming 6 m. tall, with the scales of the winter-buds short-mucronate: leaf-blades elliptic, oblanceolate, or cuneate, 4–10 cm. long, glabrous beneath except the midrib and more or less glaucous: calyx-lobes ovate to linear-elliptic, 3–6 mm. long: corolla white or pale-pink; tube 2.5–3 cm. long, densely glandular-hirsute without; lobes acuminate, much shorter than the tube: anthers about 3 mm. long: capsule ellipsoid-ovoid, 1–2 cm. long, stout, bristly-glandular, abruptly narrowed at the apex.—(Smooth-azalea.)—Stream-banks and rocky woods, in rather acid soil, various provinces, N of Coastal Plain, Ga. to Ala., Ky., and Pa.—The flowers are fragrant and have conspicuous red filaments. The dried leaves give off the fragrance of coumarin.—Late spr.-early sum.

13. A. prunifolia Small. Shrub 3 m. tall or less, with the scales of the winter-buds short-aristate: leaf-blades elliptic or elliptic-lanceolate, varying to some-what obovate, 2.5–13 cm. long, acute or slightly acuminate, deep-green above, light-green beneath, glabrous, except for scattered hairs on the midrib and on the veins beneath, and the ciliolate margins: calyx-lobes ovate or half-orbicular, about 1 mm. long, coarsely long-ciliate, obtuse: corolla crimson, 2–2.5 cm. long; tube glabrous or merely with scattered hairs, gradually dilated from the base to the limb; lobes broad, abruptly pointed: anthers 2.5–3 mm. long: capsule gradually narrowed upward, about 2 cm. long, strigose and puberulous.—Moist woods, Coastal Plain, Ga. and Ala.—Sum.

5. RHODODENDRON L. Evergreen shrubs or trees. Leaves alternate: blades leathery, not ciliate. Calyx persistent: lobes broad and short. Corolla variously colored, campanulate: tube very short: limb 2-lipped. Stamens usually 10, slightly exserted with terminal pores. Style declined. Capsule elongate, opening at the apex.—About 100 species, most abundant in Asia.—Rose-bays. Rhododendrons. Many species are used in horticulture.

Leaf-blades neither glandular-dotted nor scaly.	I. Maxima.
Leaf-blades glandular-dotted or scaly.	II. Minora.

I. Maxima

Calyx-lobes longer than wide: corolla mainly white or pink: pedicels viscid.	1. *R. maximum.*
Calyx-lobes wider than long: corolla rose-purple or lilac-purple: pedicels not viscid.	2. *R. catawbiense.*

II. Minora

Flower-clusters appearing after the leafy shoots of the season: leaf-blades acute or acuminate.	
Corolla 1.5–2 cm. long: calyx-lobes of a deltoid type.	3. *R. carolinianum.*
Corolla 2.5–3 cm. long: calyx-lobes of an ovate type.	4. *R. minus.*
Flower-clusters appearing before the leafy shoots of the season: leaf-blades obtuse or retuse.	5. *R. Chapmanii.*

1. R. maximum L. An evergreen shrub commonly 5 m. tall, or rarely a small tree, with scurfy-pubescent twigs: leaf-blades elliptic or elliptic-oblanceolate, 10–25 cm. long, acute or short-acuminate, glabrous, or somewhat scurfy beneath, bright-green above, pale-green beneath, abruptly narrowed at the base, the stout petioles tomentulose when young: calyx-lobes ovate to oblong, mostly longer than wide: corolla mainly white or pink, often somewhat greenish in the throat and with yellow or orange spots within, broadly campanulate, 2–3 cm. long; lobes not crisped: filaments slender, the longer ones about 2 cm. long: anthers about 2 mm. long: style elongate: capsule narrowly ellipsoid or cylindric-ellipsoid or slightly narrowed up-ward, 1–1.5 cm. long: seeds less than 2 mm. long. — (Great-laurel. Rose-bay.)—Acid 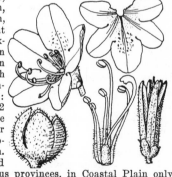 woods, mt. slopes, and stream-banks, various provinces, in Coastal Plain only N, Ga. to Ala., Ont., and N. S.—Sum..—The hard, close-grained brown heart-wood is used for tool handles. The root is used for making tobacco pipes.

2. R. catawbiense Michx. An evergreen shrub commonly 1–3 m. tall, or rarely a small tree, with finely pubescent twigs: leaf-blades elliptic, or nearly so, or oval, 7–16 cm. long, abruptly pointed at the apex, glabrous, dark-green above, pale-green beneath, mostly rounded or subcordate at the base, the stout petioles pubescent: calyx-lobes half-orbicular or broadly deltoid, much wider than long: corolla rose-purple or lilac-purple, broadly campanulate, 3.5–5 cm. long; lobes scarcely undulate: filaments slender, the longer ones about 3 cm. long; anthers about 3 mm. long: style elongate: capsule narrowly ellipsoid, or slightly enlarged at the base, 2–2.5 cm. long: seeds less than 3 mm. long.—(PURPLE-LAUREL. MOUNTAIN ROSE-BAY.)—Mt. slopes, summits, bluffs and cliffs, in acid soils, Piedmont to Appalachian Plateau, Ga. to Ala. and W. Va.—Spr.-early sum.—The form growing in the Piedmont is *R. catawbiense insulare.*

3. R. carolinianum Rehder. A much-branched shrub, with resinous-dotted foliage; leaf-blades elliptic or somewhat broadened upward, 8–13 cm. long, acute or acuminate at both ends, somewhat shining above, paler beneath and copiously resinous-dotted; petioles stout but relatively long, resinous-dotted and slightly pubescent above: calyx-lobes ovate, often broadly so: corolla rose-colored, often mottled, 1.5–2 cm. long, broadly funnel-form; tube short: longer filaments less than 2.5 cm. long; capsule ellipsoid-ovoid, 8–12 mm. long.—Woods and mountain summits, Blue Ridge, S. C. to Tenn. and N. C.—Spr.

4. R. minus Michx. A branching straggling shrub, with resinous-dotted foliage: leaf-blades elliptic or oval, 3–12 cm. long, acute or somewhat acuminate at both ends, deep-green above, paler and copiously resinous-dotted beneath; petioles stout, but relatively long, resinous and more or less pubescent at least when young: calyx-lobes deltoid, often broadly so or rarely deltoid-ovate: corolla clear rose-colored, 2.5–3 cm. long, funnelform-campanulate; tube rather long: longer filaments more than 2.5 cm. long: anthers about 2.5 mm. long: capsule ellipsoid or ellipsoid-ovoid, 8–12 mm. long. [*R. punctatum* Andr. *R. Cuthbertii* Small]—Sandy woods, inner Coastal Plain to lower Blue Ridge, Ga. to Ala. and N. C.—Spr.—Albinos of this as of other species occur.

5. R. Chapmanii A. Gray. An evergreen shrub 2 m. tall or less, with glandular-dotted foliage and erect rigid branches: leaf-blades elliptic or oval, 2–5 cm. long, obtuse or retuse at the apex, somewhat lustrous above, glandular-dotted beneath, revolute, abruptly narrowed at the base; petioles short, resinous-dotted, glabrous: calyx-lobes broadly deltoid or rounded, broader than long: corolla rose-colored, 2.5–3 cm. long, funnelform-campanulate; tube rather short and stout: longer filaments more than 2.5 cm. long: anthers less than 2.5 mm. long: capsule nearly 1 cm. long.—Low pinelands, W Fla.—Early Spr.

6. BILTIA Small. Deciduous-leaved shrubs. Leaves alternate: blades thinnish, ciliate. Calyx undulate. Corolla bright-colored, rotate-campanulate: tube short: lobes 5, the 2 lower ones overlapping the others, the middle lobe of the three upper ones exterior. Style declined. Capsule narrowed upward, opening only along the sides, the apex remaining closed. —One species.

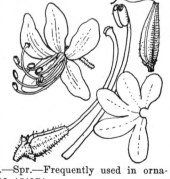

1. B. Vaseyi (A. Gray) Small. Shrub 1–5 m. tall, the twigs sparingly pubescent: leaf-blades elliptic, 6–15 cm. long: corolla rose-colored with yellow-orange or reddish-orange spots on the 3 upper spreading lobes: capsule ellipsoid-ovoid, about 10 mm. long. [*Rhododendron Vaseyi* A. Gray. *Azalea Vaseyi* Rehder]—Rocky mt. slopes and summits in rather acid soil, Blue Ridge, N. C.—Spr.—Frequently used in ornamental gardening, under the name PINK-SHELL AZALEA.

7. **MENZIESIA** J. E. Smith. Deciduous-leaved shrubs. Leaves alternate: blades entire. Calyx persistent: lobes 4 or 5, very broad. Corolla regular, white, pink, greenish, or reddish, campanulate or urceolate. Stamens 5, 8 or 10, inclined: anthers elongate. Capsule of an ovoid type.—About 7 species, North American and Japanese.

1. **M. pilosa** (Michx.) Pers. Shrub 0.5–2 m. tall, the twigs finely pubescent: leaf-blades elliptic to oval or elliptic-oblanceolate, 1.5–5 cm. long, ciliate, gland-tipped: calyx-lobes glandular-ciliate: corolla greenish to reddish, 6–7 mm. long; lobes rounded, much shorter than the tube: capsule ovoid, 5–6 mm. long.— (MINNIE-BUSH.)—Acid woods, Blue Ridge to Appalachian Plateau, Ga. to Tenn. and Pa.—Spr.

8. **KALMIA** L. Evergreen shrubs or trees. Leaves alternate, opposite, or whorled: blades entire. Calyx persistent: lobes 5, leathery. Corolla regular, white, pink, purple, or crimson, rotate, the lobes obtuse: tube short, with 10 sacs. Stamens 10: filaments elastically straightening at maturity: anthers short, attached near the top. Capsule spheroidal.—Six species, North American.—LAURELS.

Corymbs or flower-clusters terminal: corolla large, over 2 cm. wide.
I. LATIFOLIAE.
Corymbs or flower-clusters lateral: corolla small, 1.5 cm. wide or less.
II. ANGUSTIFOLIAE.

I. LATIFOLIAE

Shrub or rarely a tree: leaf-blades broad: flower-clusters clammy-pubescent: inflorescence compound: filaments short-pubescent, at least above the middle: capsule spheroidal: branchlets terete. 1. *K. latifolia.*

II. ANGUSTIFOLIAE

Corolla large, about 1.5 cm. wide: calyx glabrous: leaf-blades of a cuneate or spatulate type. 2. *K. cuneata.*
Corolla small, 5–10 mm. wide: calyx pubescent: leaf-blades of an oblong, oval, or lanceolate type.
Leaf-blades green, and dull above: pedicels and calyx usually glandular: corolla crimson or purplish. 3. *K. angustifolia.*
Leaf-blades glaucous above and shining: pedicels and calyx not glandular: corolla pink or white. 4. *K. carolina.*

1. **K. latifolia** L. Shrub, or tree becoming 12 m. tall, the twigs often fuzzy when young: leaf-blades elliptic to oval, 5–12 cm. long, glabrous, dark-green: calyx-lobes elliptic to elliptic-ovate, about 2 mm. long: corolla white or pink, filaments 20–25 mm. wide: filaments 10–12 mm. long: capsule 5–7 mm. wide.—(MOUNTAIN-LAUREL. IVY. CALICO-BUSH. SPOON-WOOD.)—Dry rocky woods, hillsides, and prairies, in rather acid soil, various provinces, W Fla. to La., Ont., and N. B. —Spr.—The hard root is used for making tobacco pipes. The hard, brown heart-wood is used for tool-handles.

2. **K. cuneata** Michx. Shrub 2–10 dm. tall, the twigs hispidulous: leaf-blades spatulate to cuneate, 1.5–5 cm. long, sparsely pubescent beneath: calyx-lobes elliptic, 3–3.5 mm. long: corolla mainly white or pinkish, 14–15 mm. wide: cap-

1000 ERICACEAE

sule 4–5 mm. wide.—(WHITE-WICKY.)—Acid swamps, Coastal Plain, S. C. and S N. C.—Spr.

3. K. angustifolia L. Shrub 2–12 dm. tall, the twigs glabrous or nearly so: leaf-blades elliptic to lanceolate, 2–6 cm. long, pale beneath: calyx-lobes ovate to elliptic-ovate, 1–1.5 mm. long: corolla purple to crimson, 6–10 mm. wide: filaments 3–4 mm. long: capsule 3–3.5 mm. wide.—(SHEEP-LAUREL. LAMBKILL. WICKY.)—Banks, hillsides, pastures and swamps, various provinces, Ga. to Ont. and Lab.—Sum.

4. K. carolina Small. Shrub similar to *K. angustifolia* in habit, but with copiously fine-pubescent foliage: leaf-blades oval to elliptic, 1.5–4.5 cm. long, canescent-tomentulose beneath: calyx-lobes elliptic-lanceolate, about 2 mm. long: corolla mainly rose-colored, 5–7 mm. wide: capsule 2.5–3.5 mm. wide.—(WICKY.)—Woods, inner margin of Coastal Plain to Blue Ridge, S. C. to S Va.—Sum.

9. KALMIELLA Small. Evergreen low shrubs. Leaves alternate: blades relatively small. Calyx deciduous: lobes 5, foliaceous. Corolla regular, pink or sometimes purplish, mainly similar to that of *Kalmia*, but lobes acute. Stamens 10: filaments elastic, anthers short, attached near the middle. Capsule of an ovoid type. —Three species, the following and two Cuban.

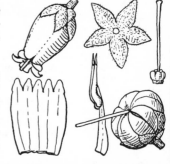

1. K. hirsuta (Walt.) Small. Shrub 1–6 dm. tall or often incumbent, the twigs hirsute: leaf-blades elliptic, lanceolate, or oval-orbicular, 4–10 mm. long: pedicels 4–10 mm. long, hirsute: calyx-lobes elliptic-lanceolate, 5–7 mm. long, acuminate: corolla 10–15 mm. wide: capsule about 3 mm. long.—(WICKY.) —Low pinelands and sandhills, Coastal Plain, Fla. to Miss. and S Va.—Spr–sum.

10. CHAMAEDAPHNE Moench. Evergreen shrubs. Leaves alternate: blades shallowly toothed. Flowers in terminal leafy-bracted racemes. Calyx-lobes 5, much longer than the tube. Corolla white, urceolate; lobes 5, shorter than the tube. Stamens 10, included: anthers awnless, tubular at the apex. Capsule depressed.—One species.

1. C. calyculata (L.) Moench. Shrub 1–12 dm. tall: leaf-blades elliptic, obovate, or oblanceolate, 1–5 cm. long: calyx-lobes triangular or triangular-ovate: corolla 6–7 mm. long; lobes oblong or oblong-ovate: capsule 3–4 mm. wide.—(LEATHER-LEAF.)— Bogs, various provinces, Ga. to Ill., B. C., Alas., Ont., and Newf.—Spr.

11. EUBOTRYS Nutt. Deciduous-leaved shrubs with rigid stems and branches. Leaves alternate: blades finely toothed. Flowers white, in terminal racemes. Calyx-lobes very short. Stamens 10, included: anthers awned. Capsule depressed.—Only the following species.—Spr.—FETTER-BUSHES.

Capsule not lobed; seeds wingless; panicles straight or nearly so.
  Calyx-lobes of an ovate type, less than one-half as long as
    the corolla; capsule exceeding the calyx.   1. *E. racemosa.*
  Calyx-lobes of a lanceolate type, one-half as long as the
    corolla or longer; capsule shorter than the calyx.   2. *E. elongata.*
Capsule lobed; seeds winged; panicles curved.   3. *E. recurva.*

1. E. racemosa (L.) Nutt. Shrub 1–4 m. tall, the twigs glabrous, at least
in age: leaf-blades elliptic, 2–7 cm. long: calyx-lobes triangular, becoming
triangular-lanceolate or deltoid-ovate: corolla 8–9 mm.
long: anthers much shorter than the filaments: capsule 4–5 mm. wide.—Acid swamps and bogs, Coastal
Plain, and occasionally other provinces, Fla. to La.,
Pa., and Mass.

2. E. elongata Small. Shrub 1–3 m. tall, the twigs
copiously pubescent: leaf-blades elliptic, or sometimes elliptic-lanceolate or elliptic-ovate, 2–5 cm.
long: calyx-lobes lanceolate, often narrowly so: corolla 7–8 mm. long: anthers slightly longer than the
filaments: capsule 3–4 mm. wide.—Acid swamps and
sandhill ponds, Coastal Plain, Fla. to La. and S Va.

3. E. recurva (Buckl.) Small. Shrub 1–4 m. tall, the twigs glabrous at least
in age: leaf-blades oval-elliptic or oval, 4–10 cm. long: calyx-lobes ovate or
elliptic-ovate: corolla 6–7 mm. long; lobes ovate: anthers nearly as long as the
filaments: capsule 5–6 mm. wide.—Rocky woods, in acid soil, Blue Ridge to
Appalachian Plateau, Ga. to Ala., Tenn. and Va.

12. LEUCOTHOË D. Don. Evergreen shrubs with weak stems and
branches. Leaves alternate: blades shallowly toothed, sometimes obscurely
so, or entire. Flowers in racemes from the axils of the persistent leaves.
Calyx-lobes longer than the tube; corolla white, ovoid or mostly urceolate:
lobes very short. Stamens 10, included: anthers awnless. Capsule depressed.
About 30 species, American and Asiatic.—Spr.—FETTER-BUSHES.

Filaments scabrous or short-pubescent, straight or nearly so: anthers prominently
    bimucronate.
  Calyx-lobes strongly imbricate in anthesis: leaf-blades
    abruptly pointed or short-acuminate.   1. *L. axillaris.*
  Calyx-lobes scarcely imbricate in anthesis: leaf-blades long-
    acuminate.   2. *L. Catesbaei.*
Filaments villous, sigmoid-curved above: anthers obscurely bi-
    mucronate: twigs pale: leaf-blades reticulate, acute or short-
    acuminate.   3. *L. acuminata.*

1. L. axillaris (Lam.) D. Don. Shrub 1–2 m. tall: leaf-blades elliptic to
elliptic-lanceolate, or rarely suborbicular to broadly elliptic, 4–15 cm. long:
larger calyx-lobes ovate: corolla 6–7 mm. long; lobes
ovate: capsule 6–7 mm. wide. [*L. platyphylla* Small]
—Damp woods, swampy thickets, and stream-banks
in rather acid soil, Coastal Plain, Fla. to Miss. and
S Va.

2. L. Catesbaei (Walt.) A. Gray. Shrub 1–2 m. tall:
leaf-blades lanceolate to narrowly elliptic, 6–15 cm.
long: larger calyx-lobes ovate: corolla 5.5–6.5 mm.
long; lobes ovate: capsule about 5 mm. wide.—(IVY.
SWITCH-IVY. DOG-HOBBLE.)—Wooded slopes, usually
along streams, Piedmont to Appalachian Plateau, Ga.
to Ala., Tenn., and Va.

3. L. acuminata (Ait.) D. Don. Shrub 1–4 m. tall: leaf-blades lanceolate to ovate-lanceolate, 3–10 cm. long: larger calyx-lobes broadly ovate, ciliolate: corolla 8–10 mm. long; lobes ovate: capsule about 5–6 mm. wide.—Swamps, ponds, and low hammocks, Coastal Plain, Fla. to S. C.

13. OXYDENDRUM DC. Deciduous-leaved shrubs or trees. Leaves alternate: blades serrate. Flowers drooping in horizontally expanded panicles. Calyx-lobes 5, persistent. Corolla white, ovoid or conic, 5-lobed. Filaments dilated, pubescent all over: anthers linear, awnless, narrower than the filaments. Stigma entire. Capsule ovoid, erect on a recurved pedicel, the valve-margins thickened.—One species.

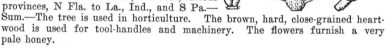

1. O. arboreum (L.) DC. Shrub or tree becoming 20 m. tall: leaf-blades elliptic or elliptic-lanceolate, 8–20 cm. long, acuminate: panicles 1–2 dm. long, the pedicels strongly curved at maturity: calyx-lobes ovate: corolla 6–7 mm. long, pubescent like the calyx: capsule 4–6 mm. long, pubescent.—(SOUR-WOOD. SORREL-TREE. TITI.)—Woods, various provinces, N Fla. to La., Ind., and S Pa.—Sum.—The tree is used in horticulture. The brown, hard, close-grained heartwood is used for tool-handles and machinery. The flowers furnish a very pale honey.

14. ZENOBIA D. Don. Deciduous-leaved shrubs. Leaves alternate: blades entire or shallowly toothed. Flowers in clusters from axillary buds. Calyx-lobes 5, longer than the tube. Corolla white or pink, often campanulate: lobes 5, very broad. Stamens 10, included: anthers slender-awned. Capsule depressed.—Only the following species.—Spr.

Pedicels and lower surfaces of the leaf-blades green: calyx less than 7 mm. wide.
　　　　　　　　　　　　　　　　　　　　　　　　　　1. *Z. cassinefolia.*
Pedicels and lower surface of the leaf-blades densely glaucous:
　　calyx over 7 mm. wide.
　　　　　　　　　　　　　　　　　　　　　　　　　　2. *Z. pulverulenta.*

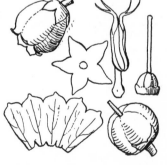

1. Z. cassinefolia (Vent.) Pollard. Shrub 1–2 m. tall, the foliage green: leaf-blades elliptic, varying to ovate or obovate, 2–6 cm. long, shallowly serrate: corolla 8–10 mm. long.—Pinelands, Coastal Plain, NE Fla. to N. C.

2. Z. pulverulenta (Willd.) Pollard. Shrub 1–2 m. tall, the foliage glaucous: leaf-blades elliptic to oval, 2–7 cm. long, entire or obscurely serrate: corolla 6–7 mm. long. —Pinelands, Coastal Plain, Ga. (or Fla.?) to N. C.—The two zenobias are distinctive among our heaths by the peculiar shades of their foliage. The one is a pale-green the other is glaucous.

15. PIERIS D. Don. Evergreen shrubs. Leaves alternate: blades distinctly toothed. Flowers in axillary and terminal racemes formed the year before they expand. Calyx-lobes 5, much longer than the tube. Corolla white, of an ovoid type, 5-lobed. Filaments unappendaged: anthers appendaged. Capsule globular, varying to spheroidal or ovoid.—About 6 species, North American and Asiatic.

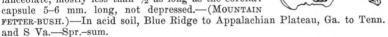

1. P. floribunda (Pursh) Benth. Shrub 3–18 dm. tall, with rigid branches and strigose twigs: leaf-blades elliptic or elliptic-lanceolate, 2–8 cm. long, serrulate all around: calyx-lobes lanceolate or ovate-lanceolate, mostly less than ½ as long as the corolla: capsule 5–6 mm. long, not depressed.—(MOUNTAIN FETTER-BUSH.)—In acid soil, Blue Ridge to Appalachian Plateau, Ga. to Tenn. and S Va.—Spr.–sum.

16. AMPELOTHAMNUS Small. Evergreen shrubs or woody vines, the branches nearly terete. Leaves alternate: blades leathery, more or less toothed above the middle. Panicles raceme-like, borne solitary in the leaf-axils. Calyx-lobes 5, appressed to the corolla, leathery. Corolla white, ovoid, the tube slightly, if at all angled: lobes very short, nearly erect. Filaments flat, broad, sigmoid-curved near the top, unappendaged: anthers appendaged. Capsule spheroidal.—One species.

1. A. phillyreifolius (Hook.) Small. Shrub with weak branches and puberulent twigs, or a vine ascending trees by creeping under their bark: leaf-blades elliptic or oval, or rarely elliptic-oblanceolate or obovate, 2–7 cm. long, serrate near the apex: calyx-lobes lanceolate or narrowly triangular-lanceolate, mostly ½ as long as the corolla: corolla 7–8.5 mm. long: capsule slightly depressed, 3–4 mm. long.—Moist pinelands and ponds, Coastal Plain, N Fla., to Ala. and Ga.—Wint.–spr.—Apparently the only climbing vine in this family in our range.

17. DESMOTHAMNUS Small. Evergreen shrubs with prominently angled branches and glabrous foliage. Leaves alternate: blades thick-leathery, entire, with intramarginal veins. Flower-clusters axillary to the leaves of the preceding year. Calyx-lobes 5, narrow, somewhat succulent, persistent. Corolla white, pink, or red, ovoid-conic, urceolate, nodding, constricted at the orifice. Filaments slender above the slightly dilated bases, glabrous, each with a pair of appendages near the top: anthers unappendaged. Style fusiform. Capsule globose or ovoid-globose, rounded at the apex, the sutures thickened.—One species.

1. D. lucidus (Lam.) Small. Shrub 1.5–2 m. tall: leaf-blades leathery, elliptic to oval or obovate, 2–8 cm. long, abruptly acuminate: flower-clusters axillary: calyx-lobes narrowly lanceolate, acuminate: corolla white or rose, 7–9 mm. long, fully twice as long as the calyx: capsule 3.5–4 mm. long. [*Pieris nitida* B. & H.]—(FETTER-BUSH.)—Moist pinelands, swamps, ponds, bays, and scrub, Coastal Plain, Fla. to La. and S Va.—Spr.–sum.

18. **NEOPIERIS** Britton. Deciduous-leaved shrubs with terete branches and sparingly pubescent or glabrate foliage. Leaves alternate: blades thin-leathery, entire, without intramarginal veins. Flower-clusters along the leafless branches of the previous year. Calyx-lobes 5, narrow, deciduous with the leaves. Corolla white or pink, cylindraceous-campanulate, nodding. Filaments flat, pubescent, each with a pair of appendages near the top: anthers unappendaged. Style columnar. Capsule of an ovoid type, truncate at the contracted apex, the sutures much thickened.—One species.

1. **N. mariana** (L.) Britton. Shrub 1–2 m. tall: leaf-blades membranous, elliptic to oval, or nearly so, 2–6 cm. long, obtuse or apiculate: flower-clusters lateral: calyx-lobes broadly lanceolate, acute: corolla white or pinkish, 10–12 mm. long, less than twice as long as the calyx: capsule 7–9 mm. long.— (STAGGER-BUSH.)—Pinelands and acid prairies, Coastal Plain, and occasionally other provinces, Fla. to Ark., W. Va. and R. I.—Spr.

19. **XOLISMA** Raf. Evergreen shrubs with lepidote foliage. Leaves alternate: blades leathery, entire or nearly so, often reticulate. Flower-clusters in the axils of the persistent leaves of the previous year. Calyx-lobes broad, short, persistent. Corolla white or pink, globular to urceolate, with short spreading or recurved lobes. Filaments tapering up to the anthers, unappendaged. Capsule somewhat elongate, often of an ovoid type, prominently angled.—About 35 species, North American.—Spr. or all year S.—STAGGER-BUSHES.

Leaves slightly reduced toward the ends of the branches; blades inconspicuously reticulate. 1. *X. ferruginea.*
Leaves much reduced toward the ends of the branches; blades prominently reticulate. 2. *X. fruticosa.*

1. **X. ferruginea** (Walt.) Heller. Evergreen tree sometimes 5 m. tall or shrub: leaves not much reduced in size at the ends of the branches; blades elliptic, oval, obovate, or oblanceolate, 2.5–7 cm. long, scarcely reticulate: corolla 2.5–3 mm. long, angled at the base: capsule 4.5–5 mm. long.—Hammocks with acid humus, sandhills and scrub, Coastal Plain, Fla. to S. C.

2. **X. fruticosa** (Michx.) Nash. Evergreen shrub 1–3 m. tall: leaves much reduced toward the ends of the branches; blades oval, obovate, or oblanceolate, reticulate: corolla 3.5–5 mm. long, rounded at the base: capsule 4–4.5 mm. long.—Hammocks and pinelands, Coastal Plain, Fla. to S. C.

20. **ARSENOCOCCUS** Small. Deciduous-leaved shrubs with more or less pubescent foliage. Leaves alternate: blades membranous or thickish. Flower-clusters in terminal panicled racemes. Calyx-lobes broad, short, persistent. Corolla white, urceolate, usually globular or depressed, with very short spreading or recurved lobes. Filaments thickened below the anthers, unappendaged. Capsule depressed, not angled.—Only the following species.—Spr.–sum.—MALE-BERRIES.

Racemes and panicles leafy-bracted.   1. *A. frondosus.*
Racemes and panicles naked or nearly so.   2. *A. ligustrinus.*

1. **A. frondosus** (Pursh) Small. Deciduous-leaved shrub 1–4 m. tall: leaf-blades elliptic to narrowly elliptic, or sometimes oval or obovate, 2–8 cm. long, serrulate: corolla mostly less than 3.5 mm. long, often depressed: capsule mainly 2.5–3 mm. wide. [*Andromeda paniculata foliosiflora* Michx.]—Swamps and low pinelands, Coastal Plain, Fla. to La. and S Va.

2. **A. ligustrinus** (L.) Small. Deciduous-leaved shrub 1–4 m. tall: leaf-blades elliptic or obovate, 3–7 cm. long, entire or indistinctly serrulate: corolla mostly 3.5 mm. long, not appressed: capsule globular, mainly 3–4 mm. wide.—Dry woods and thickets, hillsides, moist thickets, and acid swamps, various provinces, Fla. to Ark., W. Va., and Me.

21. **EPIGAEA** L. Evergreen creeping undershrubs, with woody roots, Leaves alternate: blades entire. Flowers perfect or dioecious, in axillary clusters. Calyx-lobes 5, persistent, but scarcely accrescent. Corolla white or pink, salverform, the limb 5-lobed. Filaments slender, with a tuft of hairs near the middle: anthers ellipsoid-ovoid, awnless. Stigma 5-lobed. Capsule depressed.—Two species, the following, and one in Japan.

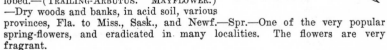

1. **E. repens** L. Stem and branches 5–30 cm. long, hirsute: leaf-blades elliptic to elliptic-ovate or suborbicular, 2–10 cm. long, finely reticulate: calyx-lobes lanceolate, acuminate: corolla about twice as long as the calyx; lobes ovate: capsule depressed, 5-lobed.—(TRAILING-ARBUTUS. MAYFLOWER.) —Dry woods and banks, in acid soil, various provinces, Fla. to Miss., Sask., and Newf.—Spr.—One of the very popular spring-flowers, and eradicated in many localities. The flowers are very fragrant.

22. **GAULTHERIA** L. Evergreen undershrubs, with rootstocks. Leaves alternate, approximate near the ends of the branches: blades shallowly toothed.

Flowers axillary. Calyx-lobes 5, persistent and accrescent. Corolla urceolate, 5-lobed. Filaments dilated near the base, pubescent: anthers awned. Capsule enclosed in the accrescent fleshy calyx.—About 100 species, American and Asiatic.

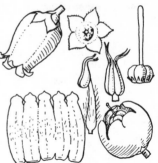

1. **G. procumbens** L. Plant 3–15 cm. tall: leaf-blades oval or elliptic, varying to ovate or obovate, 1.5–6 cm. long, serrate: calyx-lobes ovate: corolla white, 6–7 mm. long; lobes recurved: fruit globular, 7–11 mm. thick, red or white, spicy.—(WINTERGREEN. CREEPING-WINTERGREEN. CHECKERBERRY. WINTER-BERRY. TEABERRY.)—Woods and swamps, in acid humus, various provinces, in Coastal Plain only northward, Ga. to Ala., Mich., Man., and Newf.

FAMILY 5. **VACCINIACEAE** — HUCKLEBERRY FAMILY

Shrubs, in some cases with underground stems, or small trees, or rarely trailing or creeping plants. Leaves alternate, in some species evergreen: blades simple. Flowers perfect, regular, either solitary, in racemes, or in panicles, usually nodding. Calyx of 4 or 5 sepals. Corolla of 4 or 5 petals, in most genera partly united. Androecium of twice as many stamens as there are corolla-lobes. Anthers in most species bearing dorsal appendages and apical tubes. Gynoecium of 4 or 5 united carpels. Ovary inferior, or in one genus half-inferior. Styles united. Fruit a berry or drupe.—About 25 genera and 300 species, widely distributed.— Most species thrive best in sandy acid soil.

Ovary 10-celled: fruit a berry-like drupe with 10 nutlets. Tribe I. GAYLUSSACIEAE.
Ovary 4- or 5-celled: fruit a many-seeded berry or in one
    genus few-seeded berry.
    Ovary wholly inferior: anther-sacs with tubular tips:
        berry typically colored.
        Petals more or less united: berry variously colored,
          but when red not markedly acid.   II. VACCINIEAE.
        Petals distinct: berry red, very acid.   III. OXYCOCCEAE.
    Ovary one-half inferior or less: anther-sacs 2-pronged at
      the apex: berry white.   IV. CHIOGENEAE.

I. GAYLUSSACIEAE

Leaves deciduous; blades entire.
    Inflorescence with deciduous bracts: hypanthium and
      fruit glabrous.   1. DECACHAENA.
    Inflorescence with persistent bracts: hypanthium and
      fruit pubescent or glandular.   2. LASIOCOCCOS.
Leaves evergreen; blades toothed.   3. BUXELLA.

II. VACCINIEAE

Petals united nearly to their tips; corolla campanulate to
    globose, more or less urceolate: berry not red.
    Upright shrubs or trees.
      Corolla campanulate: anthers awned.
        Anthers included: hypanthium jointed to the
          pedicel, deep: berry black, rather dry.   4. BATODENDRON.
        Anthers exserted: hypanthium continuous with
          the pedicel, shallow: berry in some species
          pale, thick-skinned, and bitter, in others sweet,
          but insipid.   5. POLYCODIUM.
      Corolla urceolate, campanulate-urceolate, or cylin-
        draceous: anthers awnless: berry blue, black, or
        rarely whitish, juicy and sweet.   6. CYANOCOCCUS.

Trailing shrub.
Petals united only near the base, recurved: corolla rotate:
berry red or purplish.

III. OXYCOCCEAE

Slender plants with trailing and creeping stems, and small
pink or pinkish corollas: calyx-lobes meeting over the top
of the mature ovary.

IV. CHIOGENEAE

Aromatic creeping plant with inconspicuous flowers: calyx-
lobes not meeting over the top of the mature ovary.

7. HERPOTHAMNUS.

8. HUGERIA.

9. OXYCOCCUS.

10. CHIOGENES.

1. DECACHAENA T. & G. Resinous-dotted or resinous-coated shrubs,
with tap-roots, or with underground stems. Leaves deciduous: blades membranous, entire. Flowers in lax panicles from wood of previous season, the
bracts and bractlets small and minute, deciduous. Sepals broad, eciliate.
Corolla white, greenish, or red, urceolate to campanulate or conic-urceolate.
Filaments narrowed upward. Anthers with tubular tips. Drupe black or
blue, glabrous.—Represented by the following species.—HUCKLEBERRIES.—The
fruits are often gathered for the market along with blueberries.—This and
the two following genera are often included in *Gaylussacia* which, however, tech-
nically considered, forms a group of plants confined mostly to northern South
America.

Leaf-blades thick-membranous, obtuse or notched at the apex: sepals ovate to deltoid: filaments glabrous: anther-tubes long.   I. FRONDOSAE.
Leaf-blades thin-membranous, acute or acuminate: sepals broader
than long: filaments pubescent: anther-tubes short.   II. URSINAE.

I. FRONDOSAE

Corolla campanulate or globular-campanulate: drupe blue, glaucous.
 Corolla about 4 mm. long: sepals about one-third as long as the corolla-tube.
  Corolla-lobes about one-fifth as long as the tube: leaf-
   blades glaucous, and sometimes finely pubescent be-
   neath.   1. *D. frondosa.*
  Corolla-lobes about one-third as long as the tube: leaf-
   blades copiously pubescent beneath.   2. *D. tomentosa.*
 Corolla about 3 mm. long: sepals nearly one-half as long as
  the corolla-tube.   3. *D. nana.*
Corolla conic to cylindraceous: drupe black.   4. *D. baccata.*

II. URSINAE

Slenderly branched shrub: sepals broad, half-orbicular to reni-
form.   5. *D. ursina.*

1. D. frondosa (L.) T. & G. Stem widely branched, up to 3 m. tall, the young
foliage finely pubescent, or the twigs glabrous: leaf-blades elliptic to oval,
somewhat rhombic or broadened upward,
mostly 3–6.5 cm. long, thickish, permanently
fine-pubescent beneath or glabrous, finely
rugose: panicles scattered, the branches glabrous or with scattered hairs: hypanthium
and calyx glabrous: corolla white: stamens
about 3 mm. long: anthers slightly longer
than the filaments: drupes 8–10 mm. in diameter, dull, but bright-blue. [*Gaylussacia
frondosa* T. & G.]—(BLUE-TANGLE. DANGLE-
BERRY. TANGLEBERRY.)—Acid swamps and
moist woods, various provinces, Fla. to La.,
Ohio, and N. H.

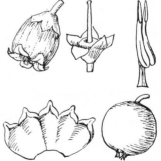

2. D. tomentosa (Pursh) Small. Stem
strict, up to 11 dm. tall, the twigs copiously

tomentose: leaf-blades elliptic to oval, or somewhat broadened upward, 2.5–7 cm. long, rugose, brownish-tomentose: panicles spreading, the branches pubescent: hypanthium and calyx resinous-dotted and often pubescent: corolla white or pinkish: stamens nearly 3.5 mm. long; anthers longer than the filaments: drupe 8–9 mm. in diameter, dull. [*Gaylussacia tomentosa* Small]—Moist pinelands, Coastal Plain, Fla. to Ala. and Ga.

3. **D. nana** (A. Gray) Small.   Stem strict, up to 6 dm. tall, the twigs finely pubescent: leaf-blades elliptic to narrowly obovate, 2–3 cm. long, rugose, glaucous: panicles rather numerous, the branches glaucous or resinous-dotted: hypanthium and calyx glabrous, glaucous: corolla white or greenish: stamens about 2.5 mm. long; anthers about as long as the filaments: drupe 6–7 mm. in diameter, dull. [*Gaylussacia nana* Small]—Dry to moist open woods and pinelands, Coastal Plain, Fla. to Ala. and Ga.

4. **D. baccata** (Wang.) Small.   Stem much-branched up to 12 dm. tall: leaf-blades elliptic to oval or somewhat obovate or ovate, 2–4.5 cm. long, sticky-resinous and finely pubescent; finely rugose at maturity: panicles spreading, the branches finely pubescent: hypanthium and calyx glabrous, but usually resinous-dotted: corolla pink or reddish: stamens 4 mm. long; anthers and filaments about equal in length: drupe shining, 6–10 mm. in diameter, without bloom (or blue and with bloom, in *D. baccata glaucocarpa*), sometimes shining, sweet. [*Gaylussacia resinosa* (Ait.) T. & G.]—(BLACK-HUCKLEBERRY.)—Rocky woods, thickets, and swamps, usually in acid soil, various provinces, Ga. to La., Sask., Ont., and Newf.

5. **D. ursina** (M. A. Curtis) Small.   Stem loosely branched, up to 1.5 m. tall, the twigs finely pubescent: leaf-blades varying from elliptic, to obovate and somewhat rhombic, 4–10 cm. long, thin, bright-green with scattered hairs, especially on the veins: panicles lax, the branches with scattered hairs: hypanthium and calyx glabrous, with resinous globules: corolla greenish, 4–5 mm. long: stamens 3.5–4 mm. long; anthers much shorter than the filaments: drupe 10–12 mm. in diameter, shining, insipid or sometimes sweet and of good flavor. [*Gaylussacia ursina* M. A. Curtis.]—(BEAR-HUCKLEBERRY.   BUCKBERRY.)—Wooded slopes and summits, often in acid humus, Blue Ridge and occasionally adj. provinces, Ga. to Tenn. and N. C.—Erroneously reported from Ky.

2. **LASIOCOCCUS** Small.   Glandular-pubescent shrubs, often with underground stems, the branches erect.   Leaves tardily deciduous: blades thick-membranous, veiny.   Flowers in lateral somewhat raceme-like panicles on previous year's wood, with large persistent bracts and bractlets.   Sepals glandular-ciliate.   Corolla campanulate, white or pinkish.   Stamens about equaling the corolla.   Anthers much longer than the filaments, with subulate tubular tips exceeding the sacs.   Drupe black, shining, pubescent.—Only the following species.—Spr.—GOPHERBERRIES.   DWARF-HUCKLEBERRIES.

Hypanthium glandular-puberulent: corolla globular-urceolate, wider than long.
                                                                1. *L. dumosus.*
Hypanthium   glandular-hirsute: corolla   campanulate-urceolate, longer than wide.
    Sepals deltoid, slightly acuminate: corolla-lobes broadly ovate, acute: hypanthium long-hirsute.   2. *L. Mosieri.*
    Sepals ovate-deltoid, obtuse: corolla-lobes reniform acutish: hypanthium short-hirsute.   3. *L. orocola.*

1. **L. dumosus** (Andr.) Small.   Stem 1–3 dm. tall or rarely more, the twigs puberulent: leaf-blades obovate to spatulate, or sometimes nearly elliptic or

oval, 2–4 cm. long, minutely pubescent, at least when young: hypanthium with granular very short glandular hairs: sepals ovate to deltoid-ovate, often unequal: corolla 5–7 mm. long, the lobes subreniform: stamens between 4 and 5 mm. long; anthers between 3 and 4 mm. long, the tubular appendages slightly longer than the sacs: drupe 6–8 mm. in diameter. [*Gaylussacia dumosa* (Andr.) T. & G.] — (DWARF-HUCKLEBERRY.)—Acid swamps, low pinelands, and scrub, various provinces, though most abundant in Coastal Plain, Fla. to La., W. Va., and Newf.

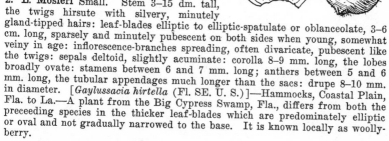

2. **L. Mosieri** Small. Stem 3–15 dm. tall, the twigs hirsute with silvery, minutely gland-tipped hairs: leaf-blades elliptic to elliptic-spatulate or oblanceolate, 3–6 cm. long, sparsely and minutely pubescent on both sides when young, somewhat veiny in age: inflorescence-branches spreading, often divaricate, pubescent like the twigs: sepals deltoid, slightly acuminate: corolla 8–9 mm. long, the lobes broadly ovate: stamens between 6 and 7 mm. long; anthers between 5 and 6 mm. long, the tubular appendages much longer than the sacs: drupe 8–10 mm. in diameter. [*Gaylussacia hirtella* (Fl. SE. U. S.)]—Hammocks, Coastal Plain, Fla. to La.—A plant from the Big Cypress Swamp, Fla., differs from both the preceeding species in the thicker leaf-blades which are predominately elliptic or oval and not gradually narrowed to the base. It is known locally as woolly-berry.

3. **L. orocola** Small. Stem up to 11 dm. tall, the twigs downy: leaf-blades elliptic or slightly broadened upward, 2–4 cm. long, with minute scattered hairs on both sides, at least when young: inflorescence-branches erect or ascending, softly glandular-pubescent: sepals ovate-deltoid, obtuse: corolla 8–9 mm. long, the lobes reniform: stamens about 6 mm. long; anthers about 5 mm. long, the tubular appendages very slender, much longer than the sacs.—Swamps, Blue Ridge, N. C.

3. **BUXELLA** Small. Nearly glabrous shrubs with extensive underground stems and branches, the branchlets erect or assurgent, sharply ridged. Leaves evergreen: blades coriaceous, toothed. Flowers in axillary congested raceme-like panicles with deciduous bracts. Hypanthium saucer-shaped. Sepals broad, glabrous. Corolla urceolate, pink. Stamens much shorter than the corolla. Anthers shorter than the broad filaments, with apical tubes shorter than the bodies. Drupe dark-blue, usually glaucous, or rarely white with a pink cheek.—One species.

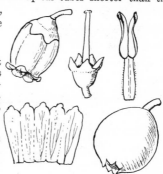

1. **B. brachycera** (Michx.) Small. Plant forming extensive ''colonies,'' the branchlets mostly 2–5 dm. tall, the twigs often puberulent: leaf-blades elliptic to ovate, 1.5–2.5 cm. long, shining above, shallowly crenate-serrate, each tooth with a deciduous stipitate gland: sepals ovate to triangular, acute or obtuse: corolla angled, 5–7 mm. long, the lobes as broad as long or broader, much shorter than the tube: drupe subglobose to pyriform, 7–12 mm. long. [*Vaccinium brachycerum* Michx.

Gaylussacia brachycera A. Gray]—(Box-huckleberry. Jerusalem-huckleberry. Juniper.)—Wooded slopes, mostly facing north, in acid soil, various provinces, E Tenn., E Ky., and S border of Va. to Pa., Md., and Del.; best developed in SE W. Va., and occurring elsewhere only in isolated patches, each representing a single plant.—Spr.—Where abundant the berries are made into a preserve.

4. BATODENDRON Nutt. Shrubs or small trees, with much-branched stems. Leaves somewhat persistent: blades thin-coriaceous, often glandular denticulate. Flowers in leafy-bracted panicles. Sepals acute. Corolla campanulate, white or pinkish. Stamens shorter than the corolla: anther-sacs longer than the filaments, shorter than the apical-tubes. Berry black, shining, many-seeded.—Two or three species, in the southern United States.

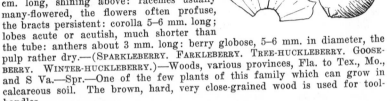

1. B. arboreum (Marsh.) Nutt. Stem and branches rigid, the twigs finely pubescent: leaf-blades oval, elliptic, or obovate, 2.5–5 cm. long, shining above: racemes usually many-flowered, the flowers often profuse, the bracts persistent: corolla 5–6 mm. long; lobes acute or acutish, much shorter than the tube: anthers about 3 mm. long: berry globose, 5–6 mm. in diameter, the pulp rather dry.—(Sparkleberry. Farkleberry. Tree-huckleberry. Gooseberry. Winter-huckleberry.)—Woods, various provinces, Fla. to Tex., Mo., and S Va.—Spr.—One of the few plants of this family which can grow in calcareous soil. The brown, hard, very close-grained wood is used for tool-handles.

5. POLYCODIUM Raf. Shrubs with irregularly branched stems. Leaves deciduous: blades thick-membranous, often pubescent or glaucous, entire. Flowers in leafy panicles. Sepals rounded, acute, or acuminate. Corolla white or greenish, open-campanulate. Stamens longer than the corolla: anther-sacs shorter than the filaments, much shorter than the apical tubes. Berry green, yellow, blue, purple, or black, in many species glaucous, dull, few-seeded.—About 10 species, in eastern North America.—Spr.—Buckberries. Squaw-huckleberries. Deerberries. Gooseberries.

Racemes or panicles with bracts resembling the leaves of the branches and usually about as large: berry greenish or blue.
  Leaves and branchlets pubescent.   1. *P. floridanum.*
  Leaves and branchlets glabrous.   2. *P. Ashei.*
Racemes or panicles with bracts conspicuously smaller than the leaves.
  Leaves and branchlets glabrous.   3. *P. neglectum.*
  Leaves and branchlets pubescent.
    Sepals deltoid to ovate-deltoid, not exceeding the corolla-sinuses: corolla-lobes usually shorter than the tube.
      Hypanthium and calyx glabrous, except the ciliolate sepals, green or glaucous: berry green, yellowish, or glaucous.
        Leaf-blades rather pale-green beneath: berry green or yellowish.   4. *P. stamineum.*
        Leaf-blades glaucous, sometimes chalky-white beneath; berry glaucous.   5. *P. candicans.*

Hypanthium and calyx pubescent: berry plum-
    purple or nearly black.
  Sepals acuminate: plants erect up to 1.5 m.
    tall.
    Corolla about thrice as long as the calyx:
      sepals about 1 mm. long in anthesis:
      stamens 7–8 mm. long.   6. *P. melanocarpum.*
    Corolla scarcely twice as long as the calyx:
      sepals about 2 mm. long in anthesis:
      stamens 3.5–4.5 mm. long.   7. *P. macilentum.*
  Sepals obtuse or merely acute: plants de-
    pressed.   8. *P. depressum.*
Sepals lanceolate, exceeding the corolla-sinuses:
  corolla-lobes longer than the tube.   9. *P. leptosepalum.*

1. P. floridanum (Nutt.) Greene. Stem up to 1.5 m. tall, the branchlets loosely
fine-pubescent: leaf-blades oval to ovate or obovate, or a few suborbicular, 1.5–4
cm. long, finely pubescent, especially on the
whitish lower surface, abruptly narrowed at
the base, rounded or even subcordate, closely
reticulate-veined: pedicels pubescent: sepals
bearded at the apex: stamens 4–5 mm. long:
berry subglobose to pyriform, about 10 mm.
in diameter. [*P. caesium* Greene]—Pinelands, scrub, and hammocks, Coastal Plain,
Fla. to S. C.

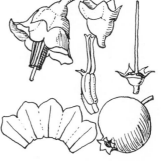

2. P. Ashei Harbison. Stem up to usu-
usually 1 m. tall, the branchlets glabrous:
leaf-blades elliptic to oval, varying to somewhat ovate or obovate, 2.5–5.5 cm. long,
glaucous, especially beneath, obtuse or
rounded at the base, rather sparingly reticulate-veined: pedicels glaucous: sepals glab-
rous: stamens mostly 5–6 mm. long: berry subglobose, 9–12 mm. in diameter,
with copious bloom.—Pinelands and barren ridges, Coastal Plain and rarely
adj. provinces, Ga. to S. C.

3. P. neglectum Small. Stem up to 2 m. tall, with glabrous branchlets: leaf-
blades elliptic to oval, elliptic-lanceolate, or cuneate, glabrous: hypanthium
glabrous: sepals glabrous: stamens mostly 5–6 mm. long: berry subglobose to
globose-obovoid, 5–8 mm. in diameter, green or yellow.—Open woods and thickets, various provinces, Fla. to La., Kans., and S Va.

4. P. stamineum (L.) Greene. Stem up to 2 m. tall, with pubescent branchlets:
leaf-blades oval to elliptic, varying to somewhat ovate or obovate, 3–7 cm. long,
rounded or abruptly narrowed at the base, usually pale beneath: hypanthium
glabrous: sepals very broad, sometimes ciliolate: stamens about 7 mm. long:
berry globular, about 10 mm. in diameter, green.—Hillsides and open woods, in
rather acid soil, various provinces, Ga. to La., Minn., Sask., and Me.

5. P. candicans Small. Stem up to 2 m. tall, with softly pale-pubescent
branchlets: leaf-blades elliptic, sometimes narrowly so, varying to somewhat
ovate or obovate, 3–10.5 cm. long, acute or somewhat acuminate, light-green
above, white beneath and more or less finely pubescent: pedicels minutely
pubescent: hypanthium glaucous: sepals sparingly pubescent or ciliate with
simple hairs, and sometimes with slender gland-tipped hairs in addition: stamens 5–6 mm. long: berry globular, about 10–11 mm. in diameter, glaucous.—
Acid woods, Piedmont to Appalachian Plateau, Ga. to Ala. and Pa.

6. P. melanocarpum (C. Mohr.) Small. Stem 1–1.5 m. tall, with copiously
pubescent branchlets: leaf-blades elliptic to elliptic-lanceolate, elliptic-oblanceo-

late, or a few ovate, 4–11 cm. long, acute or somewhat acuminate, permanently pubescent, at least beneath: pedicels pubescent and sometimes glandular: hypanthium pubescent: sepals pubescent, ciliate and sometimes with large sessile glands on the edges: corolla 6–7 mm. long: stamens 7–8 mm. long: berry globose, about 10 mm. in diameter, pubescent when young, glabrous at maturity.—Sandy woods and pinelands, Coastal Plain and adj. provinces, Ga. to Miss., Mo., and N. C.

7. **P. macilentum** Small. Stem about 1 m. tall, with closely fine-pubescent branchlets: leaf-blades elliptic, sometimes narrowly so, varying to somewhat ovate or obovate, 2.5–8 cm. long, finely pubescent, especially beneath, slightly veiny at maturity: pedicels closely pubescent with glandless hairs: hypanthium and calyx closely pubescent: sepals ciliate: corolla 2–3 mm. long: stamens 3.5–4.5 mm. long: berry not seen mature, but evidently much smaller than in the next preceding species.—Pinelands, in the Coastal Plain of Ala.

8. **P. depressum** Small. Stem 1–3 dm. tall, with finely pubescent branchlets: leaf-blades elliptic or nearly so, or individually broadly elliptic, 2–5.5 mm. long, closely pubescent: pedicels pubescent with curved hairs: hypanthium bristly-pubescent: sepals pubescent: corolla about 4 mm. long: stamens about 7 mm. long: berry not seen.—Pinelands, Coastal Plain, W Fla. to S La.

9. **P. leptosepalum** Small. Stem up to 1 m. tall, with minutely pubescent branchlets: leaf-blades elliptic or slightly broadened upward, 3–6.5 cm. long, somewhat acuminate, finely reticulate beneath, minutely pubescent on the veins on both sides: pedicels pubescent: hypanthium glabrous: sepals lanceolate, more or less pubescent, shaggy-ciliate: corolla about 4 mm. long, the lobes longer than the tube: stamens 5–6 mm. long: berry not seen.—Rich woods, Miss.

Note: Since the above matter was in type species additional to those described here have been proposed by William Willard Ashe in Jour. Elisha Mitchell Sci. Soc. 46: 196–213, 1931.

6. **CYANOCOCCUS** Rydb. Shrubs often with underground stems and erect branches, or small trees, the foliage glabrous or pubescent. Leaves evergreen or deciduous, sometimes tardily so: blades coriaceous or firm-membranous, entire or toothed. Flowers in bracted racemes or panicles, more or less fascicled. Sepals broad, persistent. Corolla urceolate, campanulate-urceolate, or cylindraceous, white to red. Stamens included: filaments pubescent: anthers awnless, with apical tubes. Berry blue or black and glaucous, or rarely red, many-seeded.—About 150 species, widely distributed.—Spr.–very early sum.—BLUEBERRIES. HUCKLEBERRIES.—Herbarium material is yet too meagre for a good interpretation of the species. The plants flowering and fruiting at widely different seasons usually results in the collection of incomplete specimens.—The berries of many species are gathered for the market. Several kinds are cultivated in order to supply the demand. The following species were heretofore included in *Vaccinium*.

Leaves evergreen: blades fleshy-coriaceous.   I. NITIDI.
Leaves deciduous, sometimes partly persistent, with the blades
  membranous or thin-coriaceous southward.
    Hypanthium and calyx glabrous, often glaucous.   II. CORYMBOSI.
    Hypanthium and calyx glandular-pubescent.   III. HIRSUTI.

I. NITIDI

Shrub with numerous small green or sometimes glaucous leaves, white or pink
  corollas, and black or sometimes glaucous fruits.   1. *C. Myrsinites.*

II. CORYMBOSI

Corolla cylindric or cylindraceous, approximately twice as
long as thick.
Leaf-blades more or less pubescent beneath, serrulate or
individually entire and ciliate.
Leaf-blades thin-coriaceous: corolla red or reddish. 2. *C. fuscatus.*
Leaf-blades membranous, but often firm in age: co-
rolla usually white or pinkish.
Low plant (2–3 dm. or rarely more): leaf-blades
decidedly broadened upward. 3. *C. tenellus.*
Taller plants: leaf-blades of an elliptic or oval
type, a few, or rarely many, broadened upward: plants widely branched.
Corolla 5–6 mm. long: leaf-blades not over 2.5
cm. long: the branches slender. 4. *C. Elliottii.*
Corolla 7–10 mm. long: leaf-blades usually
over 3–8 cm. long: the branches stout. 5. *C. amoenus.*
Leaf-blades glabrous, entire, eciliate. 6. *C. virgatus.*
Corolla urceolate or campanulate, mostly less than twice as
long as thick.
Leaf-surfaces pubescent, sometimes mainly or only on the
midrib above or beneath.
Tall shrubs, exceeding 1 m. tall: leaf-blades pre-
dominantly of an elliptic type.
Peduncle glabrous: juvenile leaf-blades more or
less pubescent, but not downy.
Leaf-blades ciliate or serrulate.
Leaf-blades ciliate.
Berry black: branches light-green. 7. *C. atrococcus.*
Berry blue: branches dark-green. 8. *C. corymbosus.*
Leaf-blades serrulate, the teeth often hair-
tipped.
Leaf-blades pale or glaucescent beneath
and finely pubescent: seeds about 1
mm. wide. 9. *C. simulatus.*
Leaf-blades green beneath, with scat-
tered spine-like hairs on the midrib
and veins: seeds about 0.5 mm. wide. 10. *C. Cuthbertii.*
Leaf-blades entire and eciliate, brownish-pubes-
cent beneath: leaves semi-persistent. 11. *C. holophyllus.*
Peduncle closely pubescent: juvenile leaves downy. 12. *C. Margarettae.*
Low shrubs, mostly less than 0.5 m. tall: leaf-blades
predominantly oval. 13. *C. vacillans.*
Leaf-blades glabrous on both sides or pubescent on the
midrib above.
Leaf-blades pubescent on the midrib above, glabrous
beneath.
Leaf-blades ciliate-serrulate: branchlets dark-green. 14. *C. pallidus.*
Leaf-blades entire: branchlets pale-green. 15. *C. liparus.*
Leaf-blades glabrous on both sides.
Leaf-blades narrowed at the base, often cuneate. 16. *C. tallapusae.*
Leaf-blades rounded to cordate at the base. 17. *C. subcordatus.*

III. HIRSUTI

Shrub with copiously pubescent foliage and flowers: bracts
somewhat foliaceous, persistent. 18. *C. hirsutus.*

1. C. Myrsinites (Lam.) Small. Stem 2–6 dm. tall, much-branched: leaf-blades
obovate, oblanceolate, oval, elliptic, or ovate, 6–20 mm. long with bristly and
glandular shallow teeth, green above, paler, veined,
and sparingly pubescent beneath (or glaucous and
essentially glabrous, and with glaucous berries in
Vaccinium Myrsinites glaucum): flowers in umbel-like
clusters: sepals broadly ovate to deltoid: corolla 6–7
mm. long or smaller: anthers about 5 mm. long: berry
globular, 5–8 mm. in diameter. [*V. nitidum* Andr.]—
Pinelands, scrub, prairies, and open woods, in acid
soil, Coastal Plain, Fla. to La. and N. C. (or Va.?).—
Recent collections indicate that *V. nitidum*, maintained
in Fl. SE. U. S., is not specifically distinct.

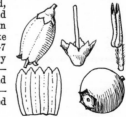

2. C. fuscatus (Ait.) Small. Stem 1–2.5 m. tall, irregularly branched, the
branchlets finely pubescent: leaf-blades ovate, oval, or elliptic, varying to

lanceolate or oblanceolate, 3–7 cm. long, or some 12 cm., firm in age, finely pubescent at least beneath, finely and shallowly toothed, or individually entire: sepals ovate to deltoid, or half-orbicular, obtuse: corolla red or reddish, 7–9 mm. long: stamens 6–8 mm. long: berry subglobose, 5–7 mm. in diameter.— Swamp margins, low pinelands, sandhills, and ancient dunes, Coastal Plain, Fla. to La., Ark., and Ga.—Characterized by its erratic branching and irregular leaves with subcoriaceous blades.

3. **C. tenellus** (Ait.) Small. Stem 2–3 dm. tall or rarely more, from underground main stems, the branchlets copiously pubescent: leaf-blades oblanceolate, obovate-oblanceolate, or spatulate, 1–2.5 cm. long, mostly obscurely toothed: sepals ovate to deltoid, corolla ellipsoid-conic, 5–7 mm. long: stamens about 5 mm. long: berry 6–8 mm. in diameter, black beneath the bloom.—Pinelands, open woods and acid swamp-margins, Coastal Plain and adj. provinces, Fla. to Miss., Tenn., and S Va. Often growing in large colonies. The flowers, usually pink or whitish, are sometimes tinged with green.

4. **C. Elliottii** (Chapm.) Small. Stem 1–2.5 m. tall, branched, the branchlets pubescent: leaf-blades ovate, oval, or elliptic, 1–2.5 cm. long, or rarely longer, often conspicuously uniform in size, acute or obtuse, serrulate-ciliate or crenulate, finely pubescent on both sides, or sometimes above only on the midribs: sepals ovate, deltoid, or wider than long, obtuse: corolla pink or pinkish, 5–6 mm. long: stamens 4.5–5.5 mm. long: berry subglobose, 7–8 mm. in diameter, black to bluish-black, but without bloom.—Low pinelands, acid swamps, streambanks, and thickets, Coastal Plain and adj. provinces, N Fla. to Tex., Ark., and Va.—The leaves often suggest those of cassena (*Ilex vomitoria.*)

5. **C. amoenus** (Ait.) Small. Stem 1–5 m. tall, the branches spreading, finely pubescent: leaf-blades variously elliptic, 3–8 cm. long, acute or sometimes short-acuminate, serrulate or serrulate-ciliate, more or less pubescent, especially beneath, usually only on the veins above, the pubescence becoming sparse with age: hypanthium and calyx usually glaucous: sepals deltoid-ovate, ovate or rarely reniform-ovate, usually about as broad as long, mostly acutish: corolla white to pinkish, 7–10 mm. long, cylindraceous-campanulate: stamens 6–9 mm. long: berry globular, 6–10 mm. in diameter, black with a bloom causing it to appear blue. [*V. corymbosum* in part (Fl. SE U. S.)]—Acid bogs, meadows, woods and thickets, various provinces, Fla. to Ark., Mich., and N. S.—Long confused with *C. corymbosus* from which it differs in its serrulate leaves, and its more narrow and differently shaped corolla. A form with non-glaucous hypanthium, calyx and fruit and with the leaf-blades broadest beyond the middle may be a distinct species. A form with glaucous foliage occurs in W Fla., where various forms are cultivated under the name rabbiteye blueberry. *Vaccinium Ashei* Read seems to belong here.

6. **C. virgatus** (Ait.) Small. Stem 1–3 m. tall, branched, with glabrous branchlets: leaf-blades elliptic or oval, or some slightly ovate or obovate, mostly 4–8 cm. long, deep-green above, more or less glaucous beneath, glabrous: sepals deltoid or nearly so, corolla white or whitish, 8–10 mm. long: stamens 8–9 mm. long: berry 7–9 mm. in diameter, glaucous. [*V. australe* Small.]—Rich woods near streams, swamps, and lake shores, Coastal Plain, Fla. to Ala. and S. C.— Flowering before the leaves appear or with their appearance, and characterized by the total absence of hairs on the foliage.

7. **C. atrococcus** (A. Gray) Small. Stem 1–2.5 m. tall, with irregular branches and sparingly pubescent branchlets: leaf-blades elliptic or oval, or slightly broadened upward, 3–7 cm. long, entire, mostly acute or short-acuminate, dark-green above, paler and more or less pubescent beneath: hypanthium and

calyx green: sepals broader than long, obtuse: corolla yellowish-white or pinkish, campanulate or somewhat ovoid, 7–8 mm. long (rarely 5 mm.): stamens 5–8 mm. long: berry globular, 6–10 mm. in diameter, not glaucous.—Swamps and woods, various provinces, Ga. to Ark., Ont., and N. B.—Flowering before the leaves expand, and also fruiting earlier than *C. corymbosus.*

8. C. corymbosus (L.) Rydb. Stem 1–4 m. tall, widely branched, the branchlets finely pubescent: leaf-blades elliptic, oval, or elliptic-lanceolate, 4–8 cm. long, mostly acute or short-acuminate, deep-green above, more or less pubescent, sparingly so in age, beneath, entire: hypanthium and calyx glaucous: sepals broader than long, obtuse or broadly rounded: corolla white to pinkish, 6–10 mm. long, ovoid to open-campanulate: stamens 6–9 mm. long: berry globular, 7–10 mm. in diameter, black, but very glaucous.—Acid bogs, meadows and moist and occasionally rocky woods, various provinces, Ga. to La., Minn., and Newf.—Flowering with the leaves half grown; also readily distinguishable from the next preceding species by the fruit.

9. C. simulatus Small. Stem 1–2 m. tall, with irregular branches and minutely pubescent branchlets: leaf-blades elliptic to oval, varying to elliptic-lanceolate or obovate, 2.5–7 cm. long, acuminate or merely acute, serrulate, bright-green above, glabrous or glabrate and pale or glaucescent beneath: hypanthium and calyx green or glaucescent: sepals reniform, often repand: corolla urceolate, 3.5–4.5 mm. long, white to pinkish-green: stamens 4–5 mm. long: berry globular, 5–7 mm. in diameter, somewhat glaucous.—Acid woods, Blue Ridge to Appalachian Plateau, Ga. to Ala. and S N. Y.—Flowering with the leaves partly grown.

10. C. Cuthbertii Small. Stem up to 2.5 m. tall, widely branched, the branchlets glabrous: leaf-blades elliptic-obovate to oval, 1.5–3.5 cm. long, acute, serrulate, nearly glabrous, with few scattered minute spine-like hairs on the veins ˙beneath, lightly reticulate-veiny beneath: hypanthium and calyx light-green: sepals half-orbicular to orbicular-reniform: corolla white to pink, about 5 mm. long, urceolate: stamens 3–4 mm. long, the filaments short and broad: berry globose, 4–6 mm. in diameter, black.—Swamps, Coastal Plain, Ga. to S. C.— Flowering with the appearance of the leaves.

11. C. holophyllus Small. Stem up to 1.5 m. tall, much-branched, the branchlets softly pubescent: leaf-blades oval to elliptic, or individually broadest above or below the middle, 1–3.5 cm. long, acute, entire, brownish-pubescent on both sides when young, softly and closely pubescent beneath: hypanthium and calyx somewhat glaucous: sepals triangular-ovate to half-orbicular, obtuse: corolla white or pinkish, 6–7 mm. long, cylindraceous: stamens 5–6 mm. long: berry globose, 4–6 mm. in diameter, glaucous.—About river-swamps, Coastal Plain, Fla. and Ga.—Flowering with the appearance of the leaves, which, however, are sometimes partly persistent. The entire leaf-blades are diagnostic.

12. C. Margarettae (Ashe) Small. Stem up to 2 m. tall, with spreading branches, the branchlets closely soft-pubescent: leaf-blades elliptic to oval or ovate, 2–3.5 cm. long, acute or slightly acuminate, entire, closely soft-pubescent beneath, acute or rounded at the base: hypanthium and calyx glaucous: sepals broadly ovate to reniform-ovate: corolla greenish-yellow, more or less striped with red, 5–6 mm. long, or rarely 7 mm., campanulate-urceolate: stamens 4.5–5.5 mm. long: berry globose, 5–6 mm. in diameter, black, shining.—Woods, Piedmont and Blue Ridge, Ga. to Ala. and S. C.—Flowering with the leaves half grown. Plants spread by underground stems.

13. C. vacillans (Kalm) Rydb. Stem less than 0.5 m. tall, widely branched, the branchlets glabrous, or with minute hairs when young: leaf-blades oval, varying to ovate or obovate, 2–3 cm. long, apiculate to acute, ciliate-serrulate to serrulate, light-green, glabrous or with scattered hairs and more or less glaucous beneath: hypanthium and calyx glaucous: sepals deltoid or deltoid-reniform, obtuse: corolla 4–6 mm. long, reddish-green: stamens 3–5 mm. long: berry globose, 4–7 mm. in diameter, very glaucous.—Woods, usually in dry and moderately acid soil, various provinces, Ga. to Miss., Ark., Mo., Mich., and Me.—Flowering while the leaves are appearing; grows in large patches from underground stems, often conspicuous by the numerous uniform leaves.

14. C. pallidus (Ait.) Small. Stems 1–2.5 m. tall, irregularly branched, the branchlets minutely pubescent: leaf-blades oval or elliptic, varying to ovate or obovate, 2.5–7 cm. long, mostly acute or slightly acuminate, glabrous except on the midrib above, and along the ciliate-serrulate margin, bright-green above, pale or glaucescent beneath: hypanthium and calyx glaucescent: sepals ovate, sometimes broadly so, to triangular: corolla greenish-pink, campanulate-urceolate, 4–5 mm. long: stamens 3.5–4.5 mm. long: berry subglobose, 8–12 mm. in diameter, very glaucous.—Acid woods, Blue Ridge to Appalachian Plateau, Ga. to Ala., Tenn., and Va.—Flowering with the leaves well developed. Most luxuriant and fruitful at high altitudes.—*V. carolinianum* Ashe, known only from scant material, seems to be a form of this species.

15. C. liparus Small. Stem up to 1 m. tall, irregularly branched, the branchlets glabrous or finely pubescent: leaf-blades narrowly obovate or elliptic, 3–7 cm. long, acute, sometimes abruptly pointed, glabrous, except on the midrib above, pale-green or glaucous beneath: hypanthium and calyx glaucous: sepals deltoid or wider than long, obtuse: corolla white to pink, 7–8 mm. long, campanulate-urceolate: stamens 6–7 mm. long: berry globose, 5–7 mm. long, glaucous.—Acid woods, and sometimes in pinelands, Appalachian and New England provinces, E Tenn. to S N. Y. and N. H.—Flowering with the leaves half developed; flowers much larger than those of *C. pallidus*.

16. C. tallapusae Coville. Stem 15–60 dm. tall, from a thick rootstock, glabrous, or the branches sparingly pubescent in lines: leaf-blades elliptic-lanceolate to ovate-lanceolate, 2–5 cm. long, acute, entire, glabrous or sometimes pubescent above along the midrib or even ciliolate at maturity: sepals oval, sometimes broadly so, obtuse or acutish, entire: corolla greenish-white, sometimes with a blush of pink, campanulate-urceolate, 5–5.5 mm. long: stamens 4.5–5 mm. long: berry globose, 7–10 mm. in diameter or rarely larger, blue.—Oak woods, Piedmont and adj. provinces, W .Ga., especially in the vicinity of Tallapoosa, and E Ala.—Flowering as the leaves appear.

17. C. subcordatus Small. Stem apparently less than 1 m. tall, widely branched, the branchlets glabrous or sometimes with few minute hairs: leaf-blades ovate or oval-ovate, 1–3 cm. long, mucronate or acute, bright-green above, glaucous beneath, glabrous, sparingly ciliate-serrulate, rounded to cordate at the base: hypanthium and calyx glaucous: sepals ovate to deltoid: corolla not seen: berry globose, 6–8 mm. in diameter, very glaucous.—Open woods, near Knoxville, Appalachian valley, Tenn.—Distinguished from our other blueberries by the more or less cordate leaf-blades.

18. C. hirsutus (Buckl.) Small. Stem up to 1 m. tall, irregularly branched, the branchlets copiously soft-pubescent: leaf-blades elliptic to ovate, 2–5 cm. long, mostly acute, entire, softly pubescent on both sides: bracts shaped like the leaves but much smaller: hypanthium and calyx copiously and softly glandular-pubescent: sepals ovate: corolla greenish-white to reddish, 8–9 mm. long, or rarely 7 mm.: filaments with long hairs: berry subglobose, 6–7 mm. in diameter, pubescent, purplish-black.—Open woods, in acid soil, Blue Ridge, N. C. and Tenn.—Distinguished from all our other blueberries by the pubescent fruits.

7. **HERPOTHAMNUS** Small. Shrubs with trailing, creeping stems and branches. Leaves evergreen: blades coriaceous, obscurely toothed. Flowers in cluster-like racemes with scale-like bracts. Hypanthium cup-shaped. Sepals very broad, acute. Corolla depressed-urceolate, 5-lobed. Stamens included. Filaments longer than the anthers. Anthers awnless, with short apical tubes. Berry globose, black.—One species.

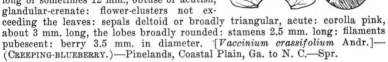

1. **H. crassifolius** (Andr.) Small. Stem and branches up to 1 m. long, glabrous: leaves numerous; blades oval or elliptic, or sometimes ovate or suborbicular, 3–10 mm. long or sometimes 12 mm., obtuse or acutish, glandular-crenate: flower-clusters not ex-

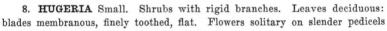

ceeding the leaves: sepals deltoid or broadly triangular, acute: corolla pink, about 3 mm. long, the lobes broadly rounded: stamens 2.5 mm. long: filaments pubescent: berry 3.5 mm. in diameter. '[*Vaccinium crassifolium* Andr.]— (CREEPING-BLUEBERRY.)—Pinelands, Coastal Plain, Ga. to N. C.—Spr.

8. **HUGERIA** Small. Shrubs with rigid branches. Leaves deciduous: blades membranous, finely toothed, flat. Flowers solitary on slender pedicels arising from a short peduncle and a pair of bracts. Hypanthium obconic. Sepals of a deltoid type. Corolla rotate, pink or white, with the 4 long lobes curled backward. Stamens conspicuously exserted. Anthers awnless, with very slender apical tubes. Berry globose, red, sometimes turning purple, insipid or sometimes sweet and pleasant tasting.—The following species and one or two others in eastern Asia.

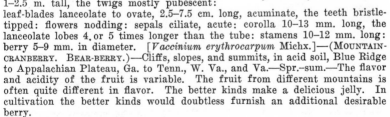

1. **H. erythrocarpa** (Michx.) Small. Stem 1–2.5 m. tall, the twigs mostly pubescent: leaf-blades lanceolate to ovate, 2.5–7.5 cm. long, acuminate, the teeth bristle-tipped: flowers nodding: sepals ciliate, acute: corolla 10–13 mm. long, the lanceolate lobes 4. or 5 times longer than the tube: stamens 10–12 mm. long: berry 5–9 mm. in diameter. [*Vaccinium erythrocarpum* Michx.]—(MOUNTAIN-CRANBERRY. BEAR-BERRY.)—Cliffs, slopes, and summits, in acid soil, Blue Ridge to Appalachian Plateau, Ga. to Tenn., W. Va., and Va.—Spr.-sum.—The flavor and acidity of the fruit is variable. The fruit from different mountains is often quite different in flavor. The better kinds make a delicious jelly. In cultivation the better kinds would doubtless furnish an additional desirable berry.

9. **OXYCOCCUS** Hill. Shrubs with slender trailing and creeping stems and branches. Leaves evergreen: blades coriaceous, entire, revolute. Flowers

terminating slender stalks with one or two small bractlets, 1–4 of which arise from terminal scaly buds. Hypanthium cup-shaped. Sepals 4, often of a deltoid type. Corolla white or pinkish, of 4 narrow petals with one or more curled back. Stamens conspicuously exserted. Anthers awnless, with long slender apical tubes. Berry globose or somewhat elongate, red, acid.—About 6 species, natives of the Northern Hemisphere.

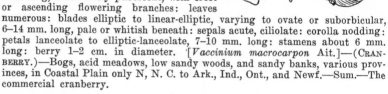

1. O. macrocarpus (Ait.) Pursh. Stem up to 1 m. long, often finely pubescent, with erect or ascending flowering branches: leaves numerous: blades elliptic to linear-elliptic, varying to ovate or suborbicular, 6–14 mm. long, pale or whitish beneath: sepals acute, ciliolate: corolla nodding: petals lanceolate to elliptic-lanceolate, 7–10 mm. long: stamens about 6 mm. long: berry 1–2 cm. in diameter. [*Vaccinium macrocarpon* Ait.]—(CRANBERRY.)—Bogs, acid meadows, low sandy woods, and sandy banks, various provinces, in Coastal Plain only N, N. C. to Ark., Ind., Ont., and Newf.—Sum.—The commercial cranberry.

10. CHIOGENES Salisb. Slightly woody plants with slender creeping stems and branches. Leaves evergreen: blades coriaceous, entire. Flowers solitary and sessile in a pair of bractlets terminating a very short axillary peduncle. Hypanthium saucer-shaped. Sepals 4, as wide as long. Corolla greenish-white, campanulate. Stamens included. Filaments and anthers about equal in length, the anther-sacs separate, awnless, each 2-horned at the apex. Berry globose, white.—One species.

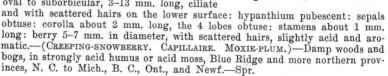

1. C. hispidula (L.) T. & G. Stem branched at the base, the branches often numerous, slightly woody: leaves numerous; blades oval to suborbicular, 3–13 mm. long, ciliate and with scattered hairs on the lower surface: hypanthium pubescent: sepals obtuse: corolla about 2 mm. long, the 4 lobes obtuse: stamens about 1 mm. long: berry 5–7 mm. in diameter, with scattered hairs, slightly acid and aromatic.—(CREEPING-SNOWBERRY. CAPILLAIRE. MOXIE-PLUM.)—Damp woods and bogs, in strongly acid humus or acid moss, Blue Ridge and more northern provinces, N. C. to Mich., B. C., Ont., and Newf.—Spr.

FAMILY 6. DIAPENSIACEAE — PYXIE FAMILY

Undershrubs. Leaves alternate, often numerous: blades entire, leathery. Flowers solitary. Calyx of 5 partly united persistent sepals. Corolla of 5 partly united petals. Androecium of 5 stamens, the filaments partly united to the corolla-tube. Gynoecium of 3 united carpels. Fruit a 3-valved capsule.—Two genera and about 6 species, natives of the Northern Hemisphere.

1. PYXIDANTHERA Michx. Evergreen plants with creeping stems and branches. Leaves numerous. Calyx-lobes broad and imbricate. Corolla white, persistent: lobes 5, rounded, spreading. Anthers in the sinuses of the corolla. Capsule subglobose.—Two species.—Spr.—PYXIE. FLOWERING-MOSS.

Leaves bright-green: calyx-lobes obscurely ciliolate: corolla-lobes with suborbicular tips.
1. *P. barbulata.*

Leaves lanate, hence hoary: calyx-lobes ciliate: corolla-lobes cuneate.
2. *P. brevifolia.*

1. P. barbulata Michx. Plant forming a mat: leaf-blades linear, linear-ob-lanceolate, linear-elliptic, or linear-lanceolate, 5–8 mm. long, pubescent and ciliate at the base: bracts ciliate: calyx-lobes 3.5–4 mm. long, green or pink at the tip, ciliolate: corolla 6–7 mm. wide; lobes with suborbicular blades: capsule about 2.5 mm. in diameter.—Pinelands, Coastal Plain, S. C. to N. J.

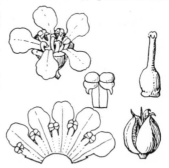

2. P. brevifolia Wells. Similar to *P. bar-bulata* in habit, but with the hoary clusters of leaves smaller: leaf-blades linear-elliptic, linear, or linear-lanceolate, 2–4 mm. long, lanate: bracts copiously lanate: calyx-lobes about 3 mm. long, pink, ciliate: corolla 5–6 mm. wide; lobes with cuneate blades: capsule slightly smaller than that of *P. barbu-lata.*—Sandhills, interior Coastal Plain, N. C.

FAMILY 7. **GALACACEAE** — GALAXY FAMILY

Perennial, evergreen, scapose herbs. Leaves alternate, but few and all basal: blades leathery, toothed. Flowers solitary or in a raceme. Calyx of 5 partly united persistent sepals. Corolla of 5 partly united petals. Androecium of 5 stamens alternating with 5 staminodia, all some-times partly united into a tube. Gynoecium of 3 united carpels. Fruit a 3-valved capsule.—Four genera, North American and Asiatic.

Flowers large, solitary: anthers surpassing the staminodia.
1. SHERWOODIA.

Flowers small, in a long raceme: anthers surpassed by the staminodia.
2. GALAX.

1. SHERWOODIA House. Herbs with short caudices bearing few leaves, with broad long-petioled blades. Flower-stalks bearing few scales and a single flower. Staminodia very short. Style elongate. [*Shortia* T. & G. not Raf.]—Two species, the following and one Asiatic.

1. S. galacifolia (T. & G.) House. Plant gregarious: leaf-blades oval or suborbicular, 2–7 cm. long, crenate-dentate with mucro-nate teeth, truncate or subcordate at the base: flower-stalk 5–15 cm. tall: calyx-lobes 7–10 mm. long: corolla white, 2–3 cm. wide: capsule 5–6 mm. long, shorter than the calyx. [*Shortia galacifolia* T. & G.]—(SHORTIA. OCONEE-BELLS. ONE-FLOWER COLTSFOOT.)— Ravines and stream-banks, in acid humus, inner Piedmont and Blue Ridge, S. C. and N. C.—Rare.—Spr.

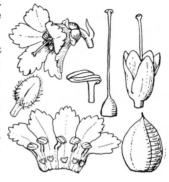

2. GALAX L. Herbs with a short caudex bearing few leaves with broad long-petioled blades. Flowers in an elongate spike-like raceme. Staminodia exceeding the anthers. Style very short.— One species.

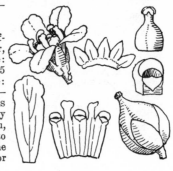

1. G. aphylla L. Plant gregarious: leaf-blades suborbicular, 4–10 cm. in diameter, crenate, with apiculate teeth, deeply cordate: flower-stalk 2–7 dm. tall: calyx-lobes 1.5 mm. long: corolla white, 4–5 mm. wide: capsule about twice as long as the calyx.— (GALAX. GALAXY. WAND-FLOWER. COLT'S FOOT. BEETLE-WEED.)—Open woods, in dry acid soil, Piedmont to Appalachian Plateau, Ga. to Ala. and W. Va., extending into Coastal Plain in N. C. and Va.—Sum.—The leaves are gathered in great quantities for use by florists.

ORDER PRIMULALES—PRIMULAL ORDER

Herbs, shrubs, trees, or vines. Leaves alternate or opposite, sometimes all basal. Flowers perfect or polygamo-dioecious, variously disposed. Calyx of 2–several partially united sepals. Corolla of 2–several distinct or partially united petals. Androecium of as many stamens as there are sepals or petals, and sometimes accompanied by staminodia. Gynoecium of 4–6 united carpels, or rarely more. Fruit capsular or drupaceous, or rarely an achene or a utricle.

Styles and stigmas distinct, slender: fruit an achene or an utricle: ovule solitary. Fam. 1. ARMERIACEAE.
Styles united: fruit capsular or drupe-like: ovules several.
  Herbs: ovules and seeds not immersed: fruit capsular. Fam. 2. PRIMULACEAE.
  Shrubs or trees: ovules and seeds immersed: fruit drupe-like.
    Staminodia at the sinuses of the corolla: fruit containing few to many seeds. Fam. 3. THEOPHRASTACEAE.
    Staminodia wanting: fruit containing a single seed. Fam. 4. ARDISIACEAE.

FAMILY 1. ARMERIACEAE — LEADWORT FAMILY

Perennial or rarely annual, often partly woody plants with leafy stems or with caudices. Leaves alternate: blades entire. Flowers perfect, in heads, spikes, panicles, or cymes. Calyx of 4 or 5 partly united sepals, the tube ribbed, the limb sometimes corolloid. Corolla of 4 or 5 petals, with the claws nearly distinct or united into a tube. Androecium of 4 or 5 stamens opposite the petals. Gynoecium of 4 or 5 carpels with the bodies at least united. Stigmas distinct. Fruit an achene or utricle, wholly or partly included in the persistent calyx.—Ten genera and 350 species, widely distributed.

Acaulescent plants with a leafy caudex, the leaves basal: petals with the claws nearly distinct; filaments partly adnate to the petals; anthers broad: styles distinct. 1. LIMONIUM.
Caulescent plants with alternate leaves: petals with the claws united into a slender tube: filaments free: anthers narrow: styles united. 2. PLUMBAGO.

1. LIMONIUM [Tourn.] Hill. Perennial seaside herbs with woody roots and a short leafy caudex which supports several leaves with thick entire blades. Flower-stem erect, nearly naked, branched. Flowers violet or lavender, solitary or 2 or 3 together subtended by several scale-like bracts. Calyx funnelform or trumpet-shaped, persistent, 5-lobed, with teeth in the sinuses. Corolla 5-lobed, the tube very short. Utricle exserted from the calyx. [*Statice* Willd. not L.]—About 120 species, widely distributed.—Spr.–sum. or all year S.—SEA-LAVENDERS. MARSH-ROSEMARYS. CANKER-ROOTS.

Calyx-tube pubescent, at least at the base.
  Calyx 6–6.8 mm. long; lobes ovate-lanceolate, acuminate: panicle much-branched.
  Calyx 4–4.7 mm. long; lobes deltoid-ovate, obtuse: panicle   1. *L. Nashii.*
    sparingly branched.
Calyx-tube glabrous, or rarely with 1 or 2 hairs.   2. *L. obtusilobum.*
  Calyx-lobes broadly ovate-deltoid, obtuse: innermost bract-
    let obtuse.
  Calyx-lobes ovate-lanceolate to deltoid, acute: innermost   3. *L. carolinianum.*
    bractlet acute.
   4. *L. angustatum.*

1. L. Nashii Small. Flowering stem 2–8.5 dm. tall, usually branched from near the middle, the branches slightly zigzag: leaf-blades elliptic, elliptic-spatulate, or obovate, 5–18 cm. long, obtuse to retuse: panicle-branches ascending-spreading: outermost bractlet 2 mm. long or nearly so: calyx pubescent at the base and often on 1 or 2 of the ribs up to the middle, the teeth between the lobes deltoid, entire, lobed, or obsolete: corolla violet: capsule about 4 mm. long.—Beaches and coastal salt-marshes, Fla. to Tex. and S. C.—(*Mex.*)

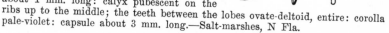
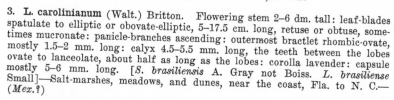

2. L. obtusilobum Blake. Flowering stem about 3 dm. tall, mostly branched near the top: leaf-blades oblanceolate-spatulate, 3.5–4.5 cm. long, mucronate and acute: panicle-branches ascending: outermost bractlet about 1 mm. long: calyx pubescent on the ribs up to the middle; the teeth between the lobes ovate-deltoid, entire: corolla pale-violet: capsule about 3 mm. long.—Salt-marshes, N Fla.

3. L. carolinianum (Walt.) Britton. Flowering stem 2–6 dm. tall: leaf-blades spatulate to elliptic or obovate-elliptic, 5–17.5 cm. long, retuse or obtuse, sometimes mucronate: panicle-branches ascending: outermost bractlet rhombic-ovate, mostly 1.5–2 mm. long: calyx 4.5–5.5 mm. long, the teeth between the lobes ovate to lanceolate, about half as long as the lobes: corolla lavender: capsule mostly 5–6 mm. long. [*S. brasiliensis* A. Gray not Boiss. *L. brasiliense* Small]—Salt-marshes, meadows, and dunes, near the coast, Fla. to N. C.—(*Mex.?*)

4. L. angustatum (A. Gray) Small. Flowering stem 2–6 dm. tall: leaf-blades linear, narrowly spatulate to narrowly elliptic, 5–8.5 cm. long, obtuse or sometimes cuspidate: panicle-branches ascending: outermost bractlet ovate: calyx 5.5–6.5 mm. long, the teeth between the lobes minute: corolla lavender: capsule about 7 mm. long. [*S. brasiliensis* (Chapm. Fl.)]—Salt-marshes along the coast, Fla. to Tex. and N. C.

2. PLUMBAGO L. Perennial caulescent hammock herbs with somewhat woody, often greatly elongate stems and alternate leaves. Flowers in terminal spike-like panicles. Calyx tubular, with stalked glands, unevenly 5-lobed, with merely hyaline sinuses. Corolla salverform: tube elongate: lobes broad: capsule included.—LEADWORTS.—About 12 species, widely distributed in warm regions.

Corolla white; tube less than twice as long as the calyx: calyx merely glandular all over.   1. *P. scandens.*
Corolla blue; tube over twice as long as the calyx: calyx finely pubescent and glandular except near the base.   2. *P. capensis.*

1. **P. scandens** L. Stem erect, decumbent, or climbing, somewhat woody: leaf-blades elliptic, elliptic-lanceolate, or ovate, 2–10 cm. long, acute or short-acuminate: panicles elongate, interrupted: bracts acuminate: calyx scarcely 1 cm. long in anthesis, more than one third the length of the corolla: corolla mostly 3–4 cm. long: capsule linear-prismatic, about 7 mm. long, beaked.—Hammocks, S Fla. and kitchen-middens N along the coasts.—(*W. I., Mex., C. A., S. A.*)—All year.

2. **P. capensis** Thumb. Stem erect, often diffusely branched or bushy: leaf-blades elliptic, varying to elliptic-spatulate or elliptic-ovate, 3–9 cm. long, obtuse or acutish: panicles compact, short: bracts mucronate: calyx fully 1 cm. long in anthesis, less than one-third the length of the corolla: corolla mostly 4–5 cm. long.—Roadsides and waste-places, S Fla. Nat. of S Afr. and cult.—(*W. I., Mex., C. A., S. A.*)—All year.

FAMILY 2. **PRIMULACEAE** — PRIMROSE FAMILY

Herbs, various in habit. Leaves alternate, opposite, or whorled, sometimes all basal: blades entire, toothed, or rarely dissected. Flowers perfect. Calyx of 4–9 partially united sepals, commonly persistent. Corolla of 4–9 partially united petals, or rarely wanting. Androecium of as many stamens as there are sepals and alternate with them, sometimes with staminodia. Gynoecium a single pistil, with a central placenta: style single. Fruit a 1-celled, 2–8-valved capsule.—Twenty-eight genera and 400 species, widely distributed in the Northern Hemisphere.

Ovary superior.
    Lobes of the corolla imbricate: ovules attached at the base: leaf-blades dissected.   Tribe I. HOTTONIEAE.
    Lobes of the corolla valvate or convolute: ovules attached
        at the middle: leaf-blades entire or toothed.   II. PRIMULEAE.
Ovary half-inferior.   III. SAMOLEAE.

I. HOTTONIEAE

Aquatic, rooting, and floating herb: stems and peduncles swollen and inflated: corolla salverform.   1. HOTTONIA.

II. PRIMULEAE

Corolla-lobes erect or merely spreading: anthers not sagittate.
    Capsule opening lengthwise.
        Filaments united below the middle: anthers ovoid.   2. LYSIMACHIA.
        Filaments distinct or essentially so: anthers linear.   3. STEIRONEMA.
    Capsule circumscissile.

Corolla longer than the calyx: style longer than the
    ovary.   4. ANAGALLIS.
Corolla shorter than the calyx: style shorter than the
    ovary.
    Corolla-tube very short: filaments united at the base.   5. MICROPYXIS.
    Corolla-tube globular, about as long as the lobes:
        filaments united to above the middle.   6. CENTUNCULUS.
Corolla-lobes reflexed: anthers sagittate.   7. DODECATHEON.

III. SAMOLEAE

Staminodia present: corolla-lobes longer than the tube.   8. SAMOLUS.
Staminodia wanting: corolla-lobes shorter than the tube.   9. SAMODIA.

1. **HOTTONIA** L. Aquatic herbs. Leaves crowded: blades pinnately dissected: petioles inflated. Flowers whorled. Calyx-lobes 5, narrow, persistent. Corolla white, salverform: lobes shorter than the tube. Filaments adnate to the lower part of the corolla-tube. Capsule subglobose.—Two species, the following and an Eurasian.

1. **H. inflata** Ell. Stem 2–6 dm. long, fistulous: leaf-blades ovate to elliptic in outline, the segments filiform. Calyx-lobes linear, 3–3.5 mm. long, or longer at maturity, glandular-ciliate below: corolla about 3 mm. long: capsule 3 mm. in diameter.—(FEATHERFOIL.)—Ponds, pools, and ditches, Coastal Plain and New England Coast, Fla. to La., Mo., and Me.; and Great Lake Lowland, Ohio and Ind.—Rare.—Spr.–sum.

2. **LYSIMACHIA** [Tourn.] L. Perennial or rarely annual herbs, the foliage glandular-punctate. Leaves opposite or apparently whorled. Corolla yellow, rotate or nearly so: lobes entire, acute or obtuse. Filaments partially united. Staminodia wanting. Anthers ovoid.—About 70 species, mostly natives of the Northern Hemisphere.—Sum.—LOOSESTRIFES.

Calyx-lobes ovate: stem and branches creeping.   1. *L. Nummularia.*
Calyx-lobes lanceolate, elliptic-lanceolate or linear: stems
    erect.
    Flowers in a terminal raceme, the raceme sometimes leafy-
        bracted: corolla streaked.
        Inflorescence extending nearly the length of the plant:
            flowers axillary to leaf-like bracts.   2. *L. quadrifolia.*
        Inflorescence a terminal virgate raceme: flowers axil-
            lary to small bracts.
            Staminodia manifest, but minute.
                Pedicels shorter than the bracts: corolla-lobes
                    6–7 mm. long.   3. *L. producta.*
                Pedicels longer than the bracts: corolla-lobes
                    8–9 mm. long.   4. *L. terrestris.*
            Staminodia wanting.
                Corolla-lobes 5–6 mm. long: pedicels longer
                    than the bracts.   5. *L. Loomisii.*
                Corolla-lobes 10–11 mm. long: pedicels shorter
                    than the bracts.   6. *L. asperulaefolia.*
    Flowers in a terminal panicle: corolla without dots or
        streaks.   7. *L. Fraseri.*

1. **L. Nummularia** L. Stem and branches 1–7 dm. long: leaf-blades suborbicular, 0.8–3 cm. long: calyx-lobes ovate, 8–9 mm. long, cordate at the base:

corolla-lobes 11–14 mm. long, obovate to ovate: capsule about 4 mm. thick.—(MONEY-WORT.)—Moist banks and about gardens, various provinces, Ga. to Mich. and Newf.—Nat. of Eu. and cult.

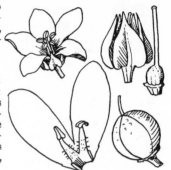

2. **L. quadrifolia** L.   Stem 2–9 dm. tall: leaf-blades lanceolate to oval, 1.5–9 cm. long: pedicels shorter than the bracts: calyx-lobes lanceolate, 5–6 mm. long, acuminate: corolla-lobes elliptic to ovate-elliptic, exceeding the calyx: capsule 2.5–3 mm. thick.—(CROSS-WORT.   WHORLED-LOOSESTRIFE.) — Thickets and woods, various provinces, Ga., to Ala., Ont., and N. B.

3. **L. producta** (A. Gray) Fernald.   Stem 3–6 dm. tall: blades lanceolate or elliptic-lanceolate, 2–8 cm. long: pedicels shorter than the bracts: calyx-lobes narrowly elliptic-lanceolate, 3 mm. long, acute or acutish: corolla-lobes ovate to elliptic-ovate, more or less notched at the apex: capsule subglobose, about 2 mm. thick. [*L. foliosa* Small]—Damp woods and stream-banks, various provinces, N. C. to Mich. and Me.

4. **L. terrestris** (L.) B. S. P.   Stem 5–8 dm. tall: leaf-blades lanceolate, elliptic-lanceolate, or narrowly elliptic, 2–6 cm. long, abruptly smaller near the inflorescence: pedicels longer than the bracts: calyx-lobes elliptic-lanceolate, about 2 mm. long: corolla-lobes elliptic-lanceolate: capsule about 2 mm. thick.—(SWAMP-CANDLES.)—Wet, sandy soil and swamps, various provinces, Ga. to Ark., Man., and Newf.

5. **L. Loomisii** Torr.   Stem 3–8 dm. tall: leaf-blades linear, 1–3 cm. long, blunt: pedicels longer than the bracts: calyx-lobes lanceolate, 2.5–3 mm. long: corolla-lobes elliptic to ovate-elliptic, eciliate; capsule about 2.5 mm. thick.   [*L. angustifolia* Michx. not Lam.]—Low grounds, Coastal Plain and Piedmont, Ga. to N. C.

6. **L. asperulaefolia** Poir.   Stem 2–6 dm. long: leaf-blades lanceolate, 2–5 cm. long, acute or acuminate: pedicels shorter than the bracts: calyx-lobes lanceolate, 4–5 mm. long: corolla-lobes lanceolate to elliptic-lanceolate, ciliolate: capsule 3.5–4.5 mm. thick.—Pinelands, Coastal Plain, Ga. to N. C.

7. **L. Fraseri** Duby.   Stem 8–20 dm. tall, glandular near the nodes: leaf-blades lanceolate, narrowly elliptic or oblanceolate, or sometimes ovate-lanceolate, 6–15 cm. long: panicle broad: calyx-lobes lanceolate, about 5 mm. long: corolla-lobes elliptic to ovate, 7–8 mm. long: capsule 3–4 mm. thick.—Woods and slopes, over non-calcareous rocks, Blue Ridge to Appalachian Plateau, Ga. (and Ala.?) to Tenn. and S. C.

3. **STEIRONEMA** Raf.   Perennial herbs, the foliage not glandular-punctate.   Leaves opposite.   Corolla yellow, rotate: lobes erose or erose-ciliate, mucronate.   Filaments distinct or nearly so, alternating with manifest staminodia.   Anthers linear.   Six species, North American.—Sum.—LOOSESTRIFES.

Bracts with ovate or broadly lanceolate blades.
    Calyx-lobes less than 5 mm. long: corolla 8–10 mm. wide.   1. *S. radicans*.
    Calyx-lobes over 5 mm. long: corolla 15–25 mm. wide.
        Staminodia ovate: corolla-lobes 7–8 mm. long.   2. *S. tonsum*.

Staminodia subulate: corolla-lobes 10–12 mm. long.
Bracts with linear, elliptic or narrowly lanceolate blades.
Staminodia ovate: capsule 2.5–3 mm. thick.
Staminodia lanceolate to subulate: capsule 3.5–4.5 mm.
  thick.
Cauline leaves not narrowed into petioles, the blades
  of the upper ones mostly narrower than those of the
  lower.
Cauline leaves narrowed into petioles, the blades of
  the upper ones not much narrower than those of the
  lower.

3. *S. ciliatum.*

4. *S. lanceolatum.*

5. *S. heterophyllum.*

6. *S. hybridum.*

1. S. radicans (Hook.) A. Gray. Stem 3–8 dm. long, ultimately reclining or creeping: leaf-blades ovate to lanceolate, 2–8 cm. long: calyx-lobes lanceolate, 3.5–4 mm. long: corolla-lobes obovate or orbicular-obovate, 4.5–5.5 mm. long, truncate or emarginate at the apex: capsule about 3 mm. thick.—Swamps and wet river banks, Coastal Plain and occasionally other provinces, Miss. to Tex., Mo., and Va.—Sum.

2. S. tonsum (Wood) Bicknell. Stem 2–7 dm. tall: leaf-blades ovate to ovate-lanceolate, 1.5–8 cm. long, like the petioles eciliate: calyx-lobes broadly lanceolate, 5.5–6 mm. long: corolla-lobes suborbicular, erose-lacerate: capsule about 4 mm. thick. [*S. tonsum simplex* Kearney]—Dry woods, cliffs, and bluffs, various provinces, rarely Coastal Plain, Ga. to Ark., Tenn., and Va.—Spr.-sum.

3. S. ciliatum (L.) Raf. Stem 2–15 dm. tall: leaf-blades ovate, elliptic-ovate, or broadly lanceolate, 4–12 cm. long, like the petioles ciliate: calyx-lobes narrowly lanceolate, 6–7 mm. long: corolla-lobes ovate or obovate, erose-ciliate: capsule about 5 mm. thick.—Stream-banks and damp thickets, various provinces, Fla. to Tex., Ariz., B. C., Ont., and N. S.—Spr.-sum.

4. S. lanceolatum (Walt.) A. Gray. Stem 2–6 dm. tall: lower cauline leaves with elliptic or lanceolate blades; upper cauline leaves much longer than the lower ones, the blades mainly linear, 3–10 cm. long, the petiole-like bases only or mainly ciliate near the stem: calyx-lobes 4–5 mm. long: corolla-lobes 5–8 mm. long: staminodia ovate: capsule 2.5–3 mm. thick.—Thickets, borders of woods, and low grounds, various provinces, Ga., to Miss., Ont., and Me.—Sum.

5. S. heterophyllum (Michx.) Raf. Stem 0.5–5 dm. tall: lower cauline leaves with oval, obovate, or spatulate blades; upper cauline leaves conspicuously longer than the lower ones: blades narrowly elliptic to linear, 4–15 cm. long, not narrowed to petioles: calyx-lobes 5–6 mm. long: corolla-lobes 5–8 mm. long: staminodia lanceolate to subulate: capsule 3.5–4 mm. thick.—Woods, meadows, and shaded banks, Coastal Plain and adj. provinces, Fla. to Miss., Ark., and Va.—Spr.-fall.

6. S. hybridum (Michx.) Raf. Stem 1–9 dm. tall: leaf-blades lanceolate to linear-lanceolate, or sometimes broader near the base of the stem, 3–7.5 cm. long, each more or less abruptly narrowed into a copiously ciliate petiole: calyx-lobes 6–7 mm. long: corolla-lobes 6–9 mm. long: staminodia lanceolate to subulate: capsule 4–4.5 mm. thick.—Thickets and moist soil, various provinces, Fla. to Tex., Ariz., Minn., and Me.—Spr.-sum.

4. ANAGALLIS [Tourn.] L. Annual or rarely perennial herbs of cultivated or waste-places. Leaves mostly opposite: blades thinnish. Corolla rotate, longer than the calyx; lobes dilated. Filaments pubescent: anthers ellipsoid.— About 15 species, mostly natives of the Old World.

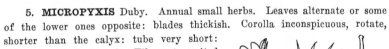

1. A. arvensis L. Stem and branches 5–30 cm. long: leaf-blades ovate, or oval, 5–20 mm. long, entire, sessile: calyx-lobes lanceolate, about 2 mm. long: corolla scarlet or rarely white (blue in *A. arvensis coerulea*), 5–7 mm. wide; lobes glandular-ciliate: capsules about 4 mm. in diameter, on recurved pedicels. — (POOR-MAN'S WEATHER-GLASS. SHEPHERD'S WEATHER-GLASS. PIMPERNEL.) —Waste-places, fields, and roadsides, various provinces, Fla. to Tex., Minn., and Newf.; also Pacif. States. Nat. of Eurasia.—Spr.–sum.

5. MICROPYXIS Duby. Annual small herbs. Leaves alternate or some of the lower ones opposite: blades thickish. Corolla inconspicuous, rotate, shorter than the calyx: tube very short: lobes narrowed upward. Filaments united only at the base. Anthers didymous.—One species.

1. M. pumila (Sw.) Duby. Stem 5–20 cm. tall: leaf-blades oval to suborbicular, 3–10 mm. long, apiculate: flowers slender-pedicelled: calyx-lobes elliptic-ovate, abruptly pointed: corolla white or greenish: capsule less than 2 mm. in diameter. [*Centunculus pentandrus* R Br.]—(FALSE-PIMPERNEL.)— Low grounds, pen. Fla.—(*W. I., Mex., C. A., S. A., O. W.*)—Spr.–fall.

6. CENTUNCULUS L. Annual small herbs of low grounds. Leaves alternate, or some of the lower ones opposite: blades thickish. Corolla inconspicuous, not exceeding the calyx, with a globular tube and 5 narrow spreading lobes. Filaments united above the middle. Anthers didymous.—Two species, widely distributed.

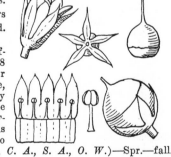

1. C. minimus L. Stem 2–15 cm. tall: leaf-blades spatulate, elliptic, or obovate, 3–8 mm. long, acute or obtuse: flowers sessile or nearly so: calyx-lobes narrowly lanceolate, 2–2.5 mm. long: corolla pink or nearly white; lobes lanceolate, acuminate: capsule usually fully 2 mm. in diameter.—(CHAFFWEED. FALSE-PIMPERNEL.)—Low grounds and moist soil, various provinces, Fla. to Tex., B. C., Minn., and Ill.—*W. I., Mex., C. A., S. A., O. W.*)—Spr.—fall.

7. DODECATHEON L. Perennial scapose herbs with erect flower-stalks. Leaves on a short caudex: blades entire to coarsely toothed. Flowers showy, in a terminal umbel, nodding. Calyx-lobes reflexed in anthesis. Corolla with a very short tube and reflexed elongate lobes. Stamens erect.—About 30 species, North American and Asiatic.—MEDIAS. SHOOTING-STARS. AMERICAN-COWSLIPS.

Anthers slender (mostly over 7 mm. long) ; connective-body broader than the anthersacs : capsule elongate, much exceeding the calyx.
　Connective-body lanceolate : corolla typically pink-purple.　1. *D. Meadia.*
　Connective-body ovate : corolla typically white.　2. *D. Hugeri.*
Anthers stout (mostly less than 7 mm. long) ; connective-body narrower than the anther-sacs : capsule short, about equaling the calyx.　3. *D. brachycarpa.*

1. D. Meadia L. Leaf-blades spatulate to elliptic, 5–20 cm. long, entire to coarsely crenate: scapes overtopping the leaves: calyx-lobes linear to linear-lanceolate, much longer than the tube: corolla pink-purple; lobes 1–1.5 cm. long: capsule ellipsoid-cylindric, 1.2–1.5 cm. long; much longer than the calyx.—Gravelly fields, open woods, bluffs, cliffs, and rocky river-banks, often in rich or calcareous soil, various provinces, rarely Coastal Plain, Ga. to Tex., Wis., and Pa.—Spr.–sum.—Sometimes cultivated in gardens.

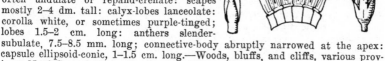

2. D. Hugeri Small. Leaf-blades spatulate, elliptic, or elliptic-lanceolate, 5–40 cm. long, often undulate or repand-crenate: scapes mostly 2–4 dm. tall: calyx-lobes lanceolate: corolla white, or sometimes purple-tinged; lobes 1.5–2 cm. long: anthers slender-subulate, 7.5–8.5 mm. long; connective-body abruptly narrowed at the apex: capsule ellipsoid-conic, 1–1.5 cm. long.—Woods, bluffs, and cliffs, various provinces N of Coastal Plain, Ga. to Ala., Ohio, and Md.—Spr.

3. D. brachycarpa Small. Leaf-blades spatulate or elliptic, entire or undulate: scapes 2–4 dm. tall: calyx-lobes lanceolate to triangular-lanceolate: corolla pink-purple; lobes linear or nearly so, 1–1.5 cm. long: anthers stout-subulate, 5.5–6.5 mm. long; connective-body lanceolate: ovary-apex flattened: capsule ovoid, less than 1 cm. long.—Plains and prairies, various provinces, Ala. to Ark.—Spr.–sum.

8. SAMOLUS [Tourn.] L. Caulescent herbs. Leaves alternate: blades entire. Flowers in simple or branched, sessile or nearly sessile racemes. Calyx perigynous: lobes 5. Corolla perigynous: lobes 5, with staminodia at the sinuses. Stamens 5: filaments very short, adnate to the base of the very short corolla-tube. Ovary and capsule ½ inferior.—About 4 species, widely distributed.

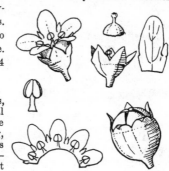

1. S. floribundus H.B.K. Plant glabrous, 1–6 dm. tall: leaf-blades spatulate to oval or ovate, mainly 3–15 cm. long: sepals ovate or triangular-ovate, barely 1 mm. long, acute: corolla white, 3 mm. wide; lobes elliptic: capsule 2.5–3 mm. in diameter.—(WATER-PIMPERNEL. BROOK-WEED.) — Wet soil, swamps, and streams, various provinces, Fla. to Tex., Calif., B. C., Ont., and Newf.—(*W. I., Mex., C. A., S. A.*)—Spr.-sum.

9. **SAMODIA** Baudo. Caulescent herbs, of low grounds. Leaves alternate: blades entire. Flowers in simple or branched long-peduncled racemes. Calyx perigynous: lobes 5. Corolla white or pink, perigynous, without staminodia: lobes 5. Stamens 5: filaments adnate to above the middle of the relatively long corolla-tube. Ovary and capsules ½ inferior.—About 6 species, widely distributed.

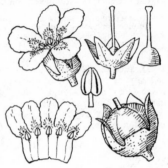

1. **S. ebracteata** (H.B.K.) Baudo. Plant 1–3 dm. tall: leaf-blades spatulate or obovate, 3–10 cm. long, obtuse or apiculate: corolla 6–7 mm. wide; lobes more or less retuse at the apex. [*Samolus ebracteatus* H.B.K.]—Low pinelands, swamps, prairies and edges of salt marshes, Coastal Plain, Fla. to Texas.—(*W. I., Mex.*)

FAMILY 3. **THEOPHRASTACEAE** — JOE-WOOD FAMILY

Shrubs or trees. Leaves opposite, persistent: blades leathery, entire. Flowers perfect, in racemes, corymbs, or panicles. Calyx of 5 imbricate sepals. Corolla campanulate or rotate-salverform, of 5 partly united petals. Androecium of 5 stamens partly adnate to the corolla-tube, and 5 staminodia. Gynoecium of 5 united carpels. Fruit a drupe-like berry. —Five genera and about 50 species, of tropical distribution.

1. **JACQUINIA** L. Leaves usually numerous: blades entire, thick and very brittle. Flowers erect. Calyx persistent. Corolla deciduous. Anthers extrorse. Staminodia very broad. Berry erect.—About 25 species, tropical American.

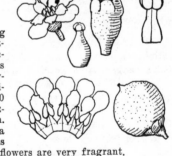

1. **J. keyensis** Mez. Shrub, or tree becoming 5 m. tall, the bark pale, the twigs very brittle: leaf-blades cuneate-spatulate or elliptic-obovate, 1–5 cm. long, shining: calyx-lobes 2–3 mm. long, orbicular-ovate: corolla straw-colored; lobes longer than the tube: staminodia elliptic, erose: berry subglobose, 8–10 mm. in diameter.—(JOE-WOOD. CUDJOE-WOOD.)—Hammocks along the coast, S pen. Fla., Everglade Keys, Fla. and Florida Keys.—(*W. I.*)—All year.—The wood is brown, hard, and very close-grained. The flowers are very fragrant.

FAMILY 4. **ARDISIACEAE** — MYRSINE FAMILY

Shrubs or trees. Leaves mostly alternate, ours persistent: blades leathery, entire. Flowers perfect or polygamo-dioecious, in racemes, corymbs, or cymes, sometimes clustered on scaly spurs. Calyx of usually

4–6 sepals. Corolla of usually 4–6 partly united petals, short-salverform or rotate, often streaked or dotted. Androecium of mostly 4–6 stamens, partly adnate to the corolla-tube. Gynoecium of mostly 4–6 united carpels. Fruit a drupe-like berry.—Twenty genera and 450 species, mostly of tropical distribution.

Flowers on scattered spurs: corolla-lobes not reflexed: stigma lobed.   1. RAPANEA.
Flowers in terminal panicles: corolla-lobes reflexed: stigma entire.   2. ICACOREA.

1. **RAPANEA** Aubl. Shrubs or small trees. Flowers inconspicuous, clustered on scaly spurs, stout-pedicelled. Corolla white or nearly so: lobes ascending or spreading. Stamens with ascending or spreading anthers. Style very short: stigma lobed.—More than 80 species, mostly tropical.

1. **R. guayanensis** Aubl. Shrub or small tree, with grayish bark: leaves mostly near the ends of the branchlets: blades obovate-elliptic or nearly elliptic, 4–10 cm. long: flower-clusters scattered along the branchlets: sepals broadly ovate: corolla-lobes elliptic, unequal: berry about 4 mm. in diameter. *[Myrsine Rapanea* R. & S.]— (MYRSINE.)—Coastal hammocks, pen. Fla., hammock islands in the Everglades, and Everglade Keys, and Florida Keys.—(*W. I., C. A., S. A.*)—All year.

Ardisia polycephala Wall., native of the East Indies, is an evergreen shrub up to six or eight feet tall, with oblanceolate spatulate or somewhat elliptic coriaceous leaf-blades: flowers in axillary cluster-like cymes: corolla white or pinkish, with ovate or elliptic-ovate pointed lobes: stamens erect, yellowish: berry depressed-globose, about 1 cm. in diameter, purple-black or almost black, shining.— Hammocks and old homesteads, pen. Fla.—*Ardisia* differs from *Rapanea* in the contorted corolla-lobes and the slender-tipped anthers.

2. **ICACOREA** Aubl. Shrubs or trees. Flowers conspicuous, in panicles, cymes, or clusters, slender-pedicelled. Corolla white or pink, and often purple-streaked: lobes recurved. Stamens with converging anthers. Style elongate: stigma minute, entire.—More than 200 species, of tropical and subtropical regions.

I. **paniculata** (Nutt.) Sudw. Shrub or small tree, with white or whitish bark: leaves scattered; blades oblanceolate to elliptic, 4–18 cm. long: panicles terminal: calyx-lobes ovate to obovate: corolla-lobes elliptic: berry 7–8 mm. in diameter. *[Ardisia Pickeringia* T. & G.]—(MARLBERRY. CHERRY.)—Coastal hammocks, pen. Fla., pinelands, and hammocks, Everglade Keys, Fla. and Florida Keys.—(*W. I., Mex.*)—All year.

Order **EBENALES**—Ebenal Order

Shrubs or trees. Leaves alternate, opposite, or whorled: blades simple. Flowers perfect, monoecious, or dioecious. Calyx of 3–12 partly united sepals. Corolla of 3–12 partly united petals. Androecium of as many stamens as there are corolla-lobes or twice as many or more, sometimes accompanied by staminodia. Gynoecium of 3–several united carpels. Fruit capsular or baccate.

Styles or stigmas distinct: flowers mostly monoecious or dioecious.	Fam. 1. EBENACEAE.

Styles and stigmas united: flowers mostly perfect.
    Stamens as many as the corolla-lobes, at least in our
    representatives.
	Fam. 2. SAPOTACEAE.

Stamens twice as many as the corolla-lobes or more.
        Stamens in several series.
        Stamens in 1 series.
	Fam. 3. SYMPLOCACEAE.
	Fam. 4. STYRACACEAE.

Family 1. **EBENACEAE** — Ebony Family

Shrubs or trees. Leaves mostly alternate: blades entire. Flowers solitary or in cymes. Calyx of 3–7 partly united sepals, persistent, accrescent. Corolla of 3–7 partially united petals, often urceolate. Androecium of 3 or 4 times as many stamens as there are corolla-lobes. Gynoecium of 3–several united carpels. Fruit a berry or sometimes capsular.—Six genera and about 275 species, mostly of tropical regions.

1. **DIOSPYROS** L. Shrubs or trees. Leaves scattered: blades entire. Calyx 3–7 lobed. Corolla urceolate, white. Stamens with pubescent filaments: anthers opening lengthwise. Berry spheroidal or elongate. Seeds oblique. —About 160 species, mostly Asiatic.—PERSIMMONS. DATE-PLUMS. SIMMONS. POSSUMWOODS.—Spr.

Larger anthers slender-subulate, 6–7 mm. long: seeds much longer than wide.	1. *D. virginiana.*
Larger anthers stout-subulate, 4–5 mm. long: seeds slightly longer than wide.	2. *D. Mosieri.*

1. **D. virginiana** L. Tree becoming 35 m. tall, with dark furrowed bark, or sometimes a shrub: leaf-blades ovate, oval, or elliptic, 8–20 cm. long, acute or acuminate, glabrous or sometimes pubescent, especially beneath: staminate flower with lanceolate or triangular-lanceolate calyx-lobes and a corolla 9–11 mm. long: berry subglobose, varying to depressed or elongate, 3–4 cm. in diameter, thin-skinned: seed flat, elliptic.—Woods, fields, road-sides, oak-ridges, and hammocks, various provinces, Fla. to Tex., Ia., and Conn.—The dark-brown or nearly black heart-wood is used for various tools and utensils. The fruit is edible when ripe.

2. **D. Mosieri** Small. Tree nearly similar to that of *D. virginiana*, but usually smaller, or a shrub: staminate flower with ovate or deltoid-ovate calyx-lobes and a corolla 6–8 mm. long: berry depressed-

globose, 2.5–3.5 cm. in diameter, thick-skinned: seed turgid, oval and some-what rhombic.—Hammocks and pinelands, pen. Fla.

FAMILY 2. **SAPOTACEAE** — SAPODILLA FAMILY

Shrubs or trees, with milky sap, sometimes thorny. Leaves mostly alternate: blades entire. Flowers perfect or rarely polygamous, clustered. Calyx of 4–12 slightly united sepals. Corolla of 4–12 partially united petals, with or without appendages at the sinuses of the lobes. Androe-cium of usually as many stamens as there are corolla-lobes, commonly accompanied by staminodia. Gynoecium of several united carpels. Fruit a several-celled berry, or by suppression 1-celled.—About 35 genera and 425 species, most abundant in the tropics.

Corolla-lobes without dorsal appendages.
   Staminodia wanting.   Tribe I. CHRYSOPHYLLEAE.
   Staminodia present.   Tribe II. SIDEROXYLEAE.
Corolla-lobes with dorsal appendages.   Tribe III. MIMUSOPEAE.

I. CHRYSOPHYLLEAE

Shrubs or trees with leaves green above and copiously pubescent with golden, copper-colored or silvery hairs beneath.   1. CHRYSOPHYLLUM.

II. SIDEROXYLEAE

Ovary 10–12-celled: staminodia broad, petal-like.   2. SAPOTA.
Ovary 2–5-celled.
  Corolla-lobes entire: staminodia scale-like or filament-like.
    Seeds with endosperm: staminodia scale-like.   3. SIDEROXYLON.
    Seeds without endosperm: staminodia filament-like.   4. LUCUMA.
  Corolla-lobes with a large median lobe and 2 smaller lat-
    eral lobes: staminodia petal-like.
    Ovary glabrous: endosperm copious.   5. DIPHOLIS.
    Ovary pubescent: endosperm wanting or scant.   6. BUMELIA.

III. MIMUSOPEAE

Shrubs or trees with broad many-veined leaf-blades: the
  young fruits conspicuously tipped with the style.   7. MIMUSOPS.

1. CHRYSOPHYLLUM L. Shrubs or trees. Leaf-blades commonly lus-trous-pubescent beneath. Calyx-lobes mostly 5. Corolla, like the calyx, often pubescent: lobes mostly 5, entire. Anthers emarginate and apiculate. Style wanting: stigma lobed.—More than 60 species, mostly tropical American.

1. C. olivaeforme L. Evergreen shrub, or tree becoming 10 m. tall, the twigs pubes-cent: leaf-blades coriaceous, elliptic or oval, 3–10 cm. long, shining above, lustrous-pubes-cent beneath: calyx-lobes suborbicular, 1.5 mm. long: corolla white, about 5 mm. wide; lobes suborbicular: berry oval, about 2 cm. long, dark-purple. [*C. monopyrenum* Sw.]— (SATINLEAF.)—Hammocks, S pen. Fla.; pinelands and hammocks, Everglade Keys, Fla. and Florida Keys.—(*W. I.*)— All year.—The light-brown, hard, and close-grained heart-wood is used locally in cabinet-work.

2. SAPOTA Mill. Trees. Leaf-blades glabrous. Calyx-lobes 6, or rarely 5, pubescent. Corolla glabrous: lobes 6, or rarely 5, toothed. Anthers blunt.

Staminodia nearly as long as the corolla-
lobes. Style elongate: stigma minute. Berry
spheroidal, rough.—One species.

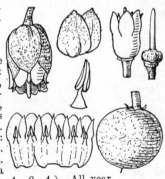

1. **S. Achras** Mill. Tree with rusty-tomentose
twigs: leaves and flowers approximately at
the ends of the branchlets; blades elliptic,
varying to broadest above or below the middle, 5–12 cm. long: pedicels rusty-tomentose,
about as long· as the petioles: calyx-lobes
8–10 mm. long: corolla white, 8–10 mm.
long; lobes about ½ as long as the tube:
berry 4–8 cm. in diameter.—(SAPODILLA.
DILLY.)—Hammocks, old fields, and cult.
grounds, Everglade Keys, Fla. and Florida
Keys.—Nat. of W. I., and cult.—(*Mex., C. A., S. A.*)—All year.

3. **SIDEROXYLON** [Dill.] L. Shrubs or trees. Leaf-blades not lustrous-
pubescent. Calyx-lobes 5 or 6. Corolla glabrous: lobes 5 or 6, entire. Anthers
notched. Staminodia much shorter than the
corolla-lobes. Style columnar: stigma truncate.—About 75 species, of warm and tropical regions.

1. **S. foetidissimum** Jacq. Evergreen tree
becoming 25 m. tall: leaf-blades thin-coriaceous, elliptic to oval or rarely ovate, 4–15
cm. long, glabrous at maturity: calyx-lobes
suborbicular, about 2 mm. long: corolla
light-yellow, 6–7 mm. wide; lobes elliptic to
ovate-elliptic: staminodia lanceolate: berry
oval or globose, 2–2.5 cm. long, yellow. [*S.
mastichodendron* Jacq.]—(MASTIC. WILD-
OLIVE.)—Hammocks, S pen. Fla. and the
Keys.—(*W. I.*)—Spr.–sum. or all year.—The orange-colored, heavy, and strong
heart-wood is used locally for cabinet-work and boat-building.

4. **LUCUMA** Juss. Trees. Leaf-blades more or less elongate, usually broadened upward. Calyx-lobes 5, in 1 or 2 series. Corolla white or pale: lobes 5,
entire or nearly so. Staminodia slender,
shorter than the corolla-lobes. Ovary 5-
celled, or sometimes 4–6-celled: style columnar: stigma slightly dilated. Berry globular, or slightly elongate, smooth.—Fifty
species or more, mostly of tropical America.

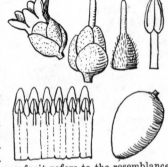

1. **L. nervosa** A. DC. Leaf-blades elliptic,
10–20 cm. long, acute or acutish: calyx-lobes
5, the inner ones rounded at the apex:
corolla 7–9 mm. long; lobes ovate: staminodia subulate: berry globose-ovoid, 5–7
cm. long, smooth, usually 2- or 3-seeded.—
(EGG-FRUIT.)—Hammocks, Florida Keys.
Nat. of S. A. and cult.—(*W. I.*)—The name egg-fruit refers to the resemblance
of the flesh of the fruit to the yolk of a hard-boiled egg.

5. DIPHOLIS A. DC. Shrubs or small trees. Leaf-blades mostly glabrous. Calyx-lobes 5, pubescent. Corolla-lobes 5, each 3-lobed, shorter than the tube. Staminodia petaloid. Endosperm copious.— About 10 species, West Indian.

1. D. salicifolia (L.) A. DC. Evergreen shrub, or tree becoming 16 m. tall: leaf-blades elliptic or elliptic-oblanceolate, 5–12 cm. long: calyx-lobes ovate to elliptic, 1.5 mm. long: corolla white, 4 mm. wide; lobes elliptic or oval: staminodia ovate to ovate-lanceolate, laciniate-toothed: berry oval or subglobose, about 8 mm. in diameter, black. —(BUSTIC. CASSADA.) — Hammocks and pinelands, Everglade Keys, Fla., and Florida Keys.—(*W. I., Mex.*)—All year.—Flowers very fragrant.—The red or dark-brown, very heavy heart-wood is used in cabinet-work.

6. BUMELIA Sw. Shrubs or trees, usually with thorny branches. Leaf-blades often pubescent beneath. Calyx-lobes 5. Corolla white: lobes 5, each 3-lobed, the middle lobe suborbicular, longer than the tube. Staminodia petaloid. Endosperm wanting or very scant.—About 35 species, American.— BUCKTHORNS.

Leaf-blades glabrous, or merely with scattered hairs or slight cobwebby beneath.
  Fruit ellipsoid-cylindric.   1. *B. angustifolia.*
  Fruit subglobose or oval.
      Leaf-blades of an obovate or spatulate type, mainly
        broadest above the middle.
        Twigs copiously pubescent with deep-red hairs.   2. *B. rufotomentosa.*
        Twigs glabrous or soon becoming so.
          Fruit less than 8 mm. long.
            Corolla-lobes about 1.5 mm. long: leaf-blades
              blunt: fruit 5 mm. long.   3. *B. microcarpa.*
            Corolla-lobes about 2 mm. long: leaf-blades
              retuse: fruit 6–7 mm. long.   4. *B. reclinata.*
          Fruit over 9 mm. long.   5. *B. megacocca.*
      Leaf-blades of an elliptic type broadest at the middle. 6. *B. lycioides.*
  Leaf-blades manifestly or copiously pubescent beneath.
    Pubescence woolly, not at all lustrous.   7. *B. lanuginosa.*
    Pubescence lustrous, white, becoming tawny or coppery.
      Pedicel longer than the berry, slender: calyx-lobes of a
        suborbicular type.   8. *B. tenax.*
      Pedicel shorter than the berry, stout: calyx-lobes of an
        ovate type.   9. *B. lacuum.*

1. B. angustifolia Nutt. Evergreen shrub, or tree becoming 8 m. tall, the twigs glabrous: leaves relatively few and not crowded; blades oblanceolate to oblanceolate-spatulate, 2–4 cm. long, smooth and glabrous: calyx-lobes ovate, 2 mm. long: corolla about 4 mm. wide; lateral divisions of the lobes narrowly lanceolate, irregularly toothed: staminodia 2.5 mm. long, lacerate: berry 17–20 mm. long.— (SAFFRON-PLUM. ANTS-WOOD. DOWNWARD-PLUM.)—Coastal hammocks, S pen. Fla., hammocks, Everglade Keys, Fla., and Florida Keys.—(*W. I.*)—All year.—The light-brown, hard, heart-wood is used for cabinet-work. The flowers are fragrant.

2. B. rufotomentosa Small. Evergreen shrub, the twigs red-tomentose: leaf-blades

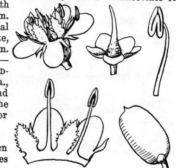

obovate or oval, 1.5–2 cm. long, reticulate and sparingly pubescent beneath with red hairs: calyx-lobes suborbicular, nearly 1.5 mm. long: corolla about 3 mm. wide: lateral divisions of the lobes ovate or ovate-lanceolate, acutish; staminodia slightly over 1 mm. long: berry about 5 mm. in diameter.—Pinelands, pen. Fla.—Spr.–sum.

3. B. microcarpa Small. Evergreen shrub, the twigs becoming glabrous: leaf-blades spatulate, oblanceolate, or rarely oblong-obovate, 1–3.5 cm. long, cobwebby pubescent beneath: calyx-lobes suborbicular, about 1.5 mm. long: corolla about 2.5 mm. wide; lateral divisions of the lobes ovate-lanceolate, almost 1 mm. long: staminodia 1.5 mm. long, erose: berry subglobose, 5 mm. in diameter.—Sandy woods, pen. Fla.—Spr.–sum.

4. B. reclinata Vent. Evergreen erect, diffuse, or depressed, shrub, the twigs glabrous: leaf-blades thinnish, oblanceolate, varying to spatulate, obovate, or ovate, 2–5 cm. long, somewhat reticulate and glabrous beneath: calyx-lobes broadly ovate or orbicular-ovate, 1.8 mm. long: corolla about 4 mm. wide; lateral divisions of the lobes broadly lanceolate, fully 1.5 cm. long: staminodia ovate, 2 mm. long, erose: berry oval, 6–7 mm. long.—Pinelands, hammocks, and sandhills, Coastal Plain, Fla. to La. and Ga.—Spr.–sum. or all year S.

5. B. megacocca Small. Evergreen shrub, the twigs glabrous: leaf-blades thick, obovate to elliptic-oblanceolate, 1–3.5 cm. long, reticulate and glabrous beneath: flowers not seen: berry globose to broadly oval, 11–13 mm. long.—Sandy woods, pen. Fla.—Spr.–sum.

6. B. lycioides (L.) Gaertn. Deciduous-leaved or partly evergreen shrub or small tree, the twigs glabrous: leaf-blades elliptic or rarely oblanceolate, 4–12 cm. long, dull and prominently reticulate on both sides: calyx-lobes oval or orbicular-ovate, 2 mm. long: corolla about 5 mm. wide; lateral divisions of the lobes lanceolate or broadly lanceolate, 1.5 mm. long, entire: staminodia ovate, 2–2.5 mm. long, entire: berry oval, fully 10 mm. long.—(BUCKTHORN. MOCK-ORANGE. IRONWOOD. SHITTIMWOOD.)—Rich open woods and riverbanks, various provinces, rarely Blue Ridge, Fla. to Tex., Ark., Ill., and S. Va.—Spr.—The yellow or light-brown heart-wood is close-grained, heavy, and hard.

7. B. lanuginosa (Michx.) Pers. Evergreen (or deciduous-leaved northward) shrub, or tree becoming 20 m. tall, the twigs dull-tomentose: leaf-blades elliptic-oblanceolate, elliptic-obovate, or elliptic, 3–8 cm. long, dull-tomentose beneath: calyx-lobes suborbicular or orbicular-ovate, about 3 mm. long: corolla about 5 mm. wide; lateral divisions of the lobes lanceolate, fully 1.5 mm. long: undulate: staminodia ovate, 2 mm. long, acute or acutish: berry oval or obovoid-ellipsoid, 10–15 mm. long.—(GUM-ELASTIC. BLACK-HAW. SHITTIMWOOD.)—Rocky, gravelly, and sandy woods, Coastal Plain and occasionally other provinces, Fla., to Tex., Kans., Ill., and Ga.—Sum.—The yellow or light-brown heart-wood is close-grained, but rather soft.

8. B. tenax (L.) Willd. Evergreen (or deciduous-leaved northward) shrub, or tree becoming 9 m. tall, the twigs lustrous-silky, the hairs white, becoming tawny or copper-colored: leaf-blades oblanceolate, obovate-spatulate, or obovate, 2–7 cm. long, lustrous-silky beneath: calyx-lobes suborbicular to orbicular-ovate, about 2 mm. long at maturity: corolla about 5 mm. wide; lateral divisions of the lobes ovate or ovate, fully 1.5 mm. long, undulate: staminodia ovate-deltoid, 2 mm. long, obtuse: berry obovoid or ellipsoid-obovoid, 11–14 mm. long.—(TOUGH-BUCKTHORN. IRONWOOD. BLACK-HAW.)—Sandy woods and hammocks, Coastal Plain, Fla. to N. C.—Spr.—The light-brown and white-streaked heart-wood is hard and close-grained.

9. B. lacuum Small. Evergreen shrub, 0.5–3 m. tall, the twigs copper-colored or dark-tawny: leaf-blades cuneate to spatulate, 1–2.5 cm. long, or larger on shoots, lustrous-silky beneath, often becoming brown: calyx-lobes elliptic-ovate to ovate, about 2 mm. long at maturity: corolla about 4 mm. wide; lateral divisions of each lobe lanceolate, about 1.5 mm. long, toothed at the apex: staminodia ovate, about 1.5 mm. long, obtuse: berry oval, 8–10 mm. long.— (SANDHILL-BUCKTHORN.)—Sandhills, usually in scrub, C. pen. Fla.—Spr.

7. **MIMUSOPS** L. Shrubs or trees. Leaf-blades leathery, finely many-veined. Calyx-lobes 6 or 8, the outer ones valvate. Corolla with dorsal appendages; lobes 6 or 8, each with 2 very small lateral lobes. Staminodia petaloid.— About 40 species, mostly of tropical regions.

1. **M. emarginata** (L.) Britton. Evergreen shrub or small tree: leaves clustered at the ends of the branchlets; blades elliptic, 3–10 cm. long: calyx, like the pedicels, red-tomentose; lobes lanceolate to ovate-lanceolate: corolla light-yellow, 1.5–2 cm. wide: staminodia triangular: berry spheroidal, nearly 3 cm. thick. [*M. Sieberi* A. DC.]— (WILD-DILLY. WILD-SAPODILLA.) — Hammocks, Florida Keys.—(*W. I.*)—Wint.-spr. The dark-brown heart-wood is close-grained.

FAMILY 3. **SYMPLOCACEAE**—SWEETLEAF FAMILY

Shrubs or trees, the hairs, when present, simple. Leaves alternate: blades usually leathery, entire or toothed. Flowers polygamo-dioecious or perfect, in close or open clusters. Calyx of 5 partly united sepals. Corolla of 5 more or less united petals. Androecium of numerous stamens in several series, partly adnate to the corolla-tube. Gynoecium of 2–5 carpels, the ovary superior. Fruit baccate or drupaceous.—Consists of the following genus and 200 species, most abundant in South America.

1. **SYMPLOCOS** Jacq. Leaves often persistent: blades thick. Inflorescence congested or open. Calyx often persistent. Corolla deciduous, yellow or yellowish. Stamens conspicuous. Style columnar. Fruits, often crowned with the calyx, drupe-like or nut-like.

1. **S. tinctoria** (L.) L'Her. Evergreen or partly evergreen shrub or small tree: leaf-blades elliptic or elliptic-oblanceolate, 4–15 cm. long, undulate or shallowly toothed, tomentose beneath: flowers densely clustered: calyx 2–2.5 mm. long; lobes shorter than the tube: corolla yellowish; lobes obovate or obovate-spatulate, 6–8 mm. long: stamens exserted: drupe 10–14 mm. long. — (SWEETLEAF. HORSE-SUGAR. WILD-LAUREL. YELLOW-WOOD.)—Hammocks, bluffs, cliffs, and rock outcrops, Coastal Plain to Blue Ridge, Fla. to La., Ark., and Del.— Spr.—The brown or red heart-wood is close-grained, but light and soft. The sweet leaves are eaten by horses and cattle, and, like the bark, yield a yellow dye.—Further study may show the coastal and mountain plants to represent two species instead of one.

FAMILY 4. STYRACACEAE — STYRAX FAMILY

Shrubs or trees, the hairs when present branched or scurfy. Leaves alternate: blades entire or shallowly toothed. Flowers perfect, in racemes, panicles, cymes, or clusters. Calyx of 5, or 4–8, partly united sepals. Corolla of 5, or 4–8, distinct or partly united petals. Androecium of 8–16 stamens in one series, partly adnate to the corolla. Gynoecium of 2–5 carpels, the ovary sometimes inferior. Fruit drupaceous or capsular.— Seven genera and about 75 species, mostly of tropical regions, but most abundant in South America.

Ovary inferior: fruits nut-like, elongate, winged.   1. HALESIA.
Ovary superior: fruits drupaceous, subglobose.   2. STYRAX.

1. **HALESIA** Ellis. Shrubs or trees. Leaves with thinnish blades, deciduous. Inflorescence not leafy-bracted. Calyx with relatively large lobes. Corolla white, with nearly erect lobes. Anthers elliptic. Ovules 4 in each cavity, 1 pair ascending, 1 pair drooping. [*Mohrodendron* Britton.]—Three species, as follows.—Spr.—SILVERBELL-TREES. BELL-TREES.

Corolla-lobes shorter than the tube: fruit 4-winged.
    Fruit ellipsoid or somewhat obovoid: corolla 1–2.5 cm. long.   1. *H. carolina.*
    Fruit clavate: corolla less than 1 cm. long.   2. *H. parviflora.*
Corolla-lobes longer than the tube: fruit 2-winged.   3. *H. diptera.*

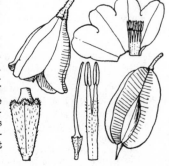

1. **H. carolina** L. Small tree with a reddish-brown, ridged and scaly bark, or shrub, the winter-buds acute: leaf-blades oval, elliptic, or obovate, 7–15 cm. long, or longer on shoots, serrate: calyx 5–6 mm. long; corolla 15–20 mm. long: filaments and style glabrous: fruit ellipsoid to ellipsoid-obovoid, 3.5–4.5 cm. long, 4-winged, short-beaked. [*H. tetraptera* L. *M. carolinum* Britton]—(WILD-OLIVE TREE. OPOSSUM-WOOD. RATTLEBOX. CALICOWOOD. TISSWOOD.)—Woods and stream-banks, various provinces, Fla. to Tex., Ill., and S W Va.—Spr.—The plant of the Blue Ridge and the Appalachian Highlands, with usually larger corollas, has been described as *H. monticola* (Rehder) Sarg.—The light-brown heart-wood is close-grained, but light and soft.

2. **H. parviflora** Michx. Small tree with dark-brown or nearly black bark, or a shrub, the winter-buds obtuse: leaf-blades elliptic, elliptic-ovate, or slightly obovate, 3–7 cm. long, finely serrate: calyx 2.5–3 mm. long, pubescent: corolla 10–12 mm. long: fruit clavate, mostly 1.5–3 cm. long, narrowly winged. [*M. parviflorum* Britton]—Woods and hillsides, Coastal Plain and adj. provinces, N Fla. to Miss., Okla., and S Ga.—Early spr.

3. **H. diptera** Ellis. Small tree with brown, fissured and scaly bark, the winter-buds obtuse, or a shrub: leaf-blades oval, elliptic, or obovate, or sometimes ovate, 4–15 cm. long, rather coarsely toothed: calyx 3–4 mm. long, pubescent: corolla about 2.5 cm. long, copiously pubescent without: filaments and style pubescent: fruit narrowly ellipsoid, 4–5 cm. long, 2-winged, scarcely beaked. [*M. dipterum* Britton.]—(SNOWDROP-TREE. COW-LICKS.)—Hammocks and stream-banks, Coastal Plain and adj. provinces, N Fla. to Tex., Ark., and S. C.—Spr.—The wood is similar to that of *H. carolina.*

2. STYRAX [Tourn.] L. Shrubs or trees. Leaves with thickish blades, but deciduous. Inflorescence leafy-bracted. Calyx with minute lobes. Corolla white, with recurved petals or lobes. Anthers linear. Ovules several, ascending. —About 75 species, American and Eurasian.—Spr.—STORAXES.

Corolla-lobes valvate in the bud.   1. *S. americana.*
Corolla-lobes manifestly imbricate or convolute in the bud.
   Bracts of the inflorescence mostly leaf-like: leaf-blades
   slightly pubescent beneath.   2. *S. pulverulenta.*
   Bracts of the inflorescence only leaf-like at the base of the
   panicle or raceme: leaf-blades densely pubescent beneath.   3. *S. grandifolia.*

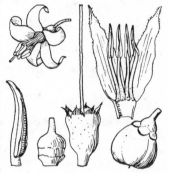

1. S. americana Lam. Shrub with sparingly stellate twigs: leaf-blades oval or elliptic, varying to ovate or obovate, 2–10 cm. long, entire or distinctly and shallowly toothed: pedicels glabrous or nearly so: calyx much shorter than the pedicel: corolla-lobes elliptic or lanceolate-elliptic, acute: drupe 6–8 mm. in diameter. —Swamps and stream-banks, Coastal Plain and adj. provinces, Fla. to La., Ill., and S Va.—The flowers are fragrant.

2. S. pulverulenta Michx. Shrub with densely stellate twigs: leaf-blades ovate, oval, or obovate, 2–8 cm. long, sharply serrate or undulate: pedicels canescent or hoary: calyx about as long as the pedicel: corolla-lobes elliptic or elliptic-lanceolate, rather obtuse: drupe 7–9 mm. in diameter. —Wet pinelands about swamps and streams, Coastal Plain, Fla. to Tex., Ark., and S Va.

3. S. grandifolia Ait. Shrub or small tree, with densely stellate twigs: leaf-blades ovate, oval, or sometimes elliptic, 9–20 cm. long, coarsely toothed or nearly entire: pedicels canescent: corolla-lobes elliptic: drupes 8–10 mm. in diameter.—Woods, sandy river-banks, and hammocks, Coastal Plain and adj. provinces, Fla. to La. and S Va.

ORDER OLEALES—OLEAL ORDER

Shrubs, trees, undershrubs, or partially herbaceous plants. Leaves opposite, or rarely alternate or whorled: blades simple or compound. Flowers perfect, polygamous, or dioecious. Calyx of 4 or more partially united sepals, or wanting. Corolla of 2–6 distinct or partially united petals, or wanting. Androecium of 2–4 stamens partially adnate to the corolla when it is present. Gynoecium of 2 united carpels, the ovary superior. Fruit a capsule, a samara, or a berry, usually 1-celled by suppression.

FAMILY 1. OLEACEAE — OLIVE FAMILY

Woody or partially woody plants with erect or climbing stems. Leaves predominantly opposite: blades simple and entire or toothed, or pinnately compound.—About 22 genera and 525 species, widely distributed in temperate and tropical regions.

Shrubs or trees: fruits not didymous.
 Fruit dry, an indehiscent or dehiscent capsule.
  Fruit a loculicidal capsule: leaf-blades simple.   Tribe I. SYRINGEAE.
  Fruit indehiscent, a samara: leaf-blades pinnate.   Tribe II. FRAXINEAE.
 Fruit fleshy, a drupe or a berry.   Tribe III. OLEAE.
Woody vines, with compound leaf-blades: fruits didymous.   Tribe IV. JASMINEAE.

I. SYRINGEAE

Shrubs: flowers conspicuous, numerous in ovoid or pyramidal
 thyrsoid panicles.   1. SYRINGA.

II. FRAXINEAE

Shrubs or trees: flowers mostly inconspicuous, apetalous, in
 dense racemes or panicles from the axils of last year's leaves.   2. FRAXINUS.

III. OLEAE

Flowers apetalous or sometimes with 1 or 2 small petals, mainly
 polygamo-dioecious: styles slender.   3. FORESTIERA.
Flowers with a corolla, perfect or polygamous: styles short or
 stout.
  Corolla rotate, with elongate strap-like nearly distinct
   petals: leaves deciduous.   4. CHIONANTHUS.
  Corolla funnelform or salverform, with short lobes: leaves
   mostly persistent.
    Corolla funnelform, white; lobes induplicate-valvate.   5. LIGUSTRUM.
    Corolla salverform, greenish; lobes imbricate.   6. AMAROLEA.

IV. JASMINEAE

Leaf-blades pinnate, sometimes 1-foliolate: calyx-lobes and
 corolla-lobes 5 or more.   7. JASMINUM.

1. SYRINGA L. Shrubs. Leaves opposite: blades broad, entire. Flowers in terminal panicles. Calyx-lobes broad, shorter than the tube. Corolla white or purple: tube longer than the lobes. Stigma 2-lobed. Capsule longer than wide. —Twelve species, Eurasian.

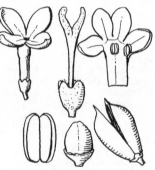

1. S. vulgaris L. Stems commonly 2–3 m. tall, usually clustered: leaf-blades ovate, 4–10 cm. long, acuminate: panicles 1–3 dm. long: calyx 2–2.5 mm. long; lobes ovate or triangular: corolla 9–11 mm. long; lobes ovate to obovate: capsule ellipsoid, 14–16 mm. long. — (LILAC. COMMON-LILAC.)— Waste-places, thickets, and gardens, various provinces, E U. S. Nat. of Eu. and cult. —Spr.

2. FRAXINUS [Tourn.] L. Shrubs or trees. Leaves opposite: blades unequally pinnate. Flowers polygamous, dioecious, or rarely perfect, in clusters or panicles. Calyx unequally 4-lobed or obsolete. Corolla greenish, of 2–4 petals, or wanting. Stamens 2 or rarely 3 or 4. Stigma 2-lobed. Samara winged at the tip or all around.—About 50 species, mostly of the north temperate zone.—Spr.—ASHES.

Body of the samara flat, the wing extending to its base or around it.
 Leaflets 7–11: twigs 4-sided: samara rounded or obtuse
  at the base.   1. F. quadrangulata.
 Leaflets 5–7: twigs terete: samara narrowed or acute
  at the base.
   Samara spatulate or elliptic-spatulate.   2. F. pauciflora.
   Samara elliptic to ovate or obovate.   3. F. caroliniana.
Body of the samara terete or slightly compressed, the wing
 terminal or slightly decurrent.

Wing of the samara decurrent on the sides of the body.
　Samara-wing linear, sometimes elongate-linear.　　　　4. *F. Darlingtonii.*
　Samara-wing spatulate to elliptic.
　　Samara-body terete.
　　　Body of the samara narrow.
　　　　Samara broadly spatulate : blades of the
　　　　　leaflets thick, entire.　　　　　　　　　　5. *F. Michauxii.*
　　　　Samara narrowly linear : blades of the
　　　　　leaflets thin, serrate.　　　　　　　　　　6. *F. pennsylvanica.*
　　　Body of the samara stout, ellipsoid.　　　　　7. *F. Smallii.*
　　Samara-body compressed.　　　　　　　　　　　8. *F. profunda.*
Wing of the samara terminal or nearly so.
　Twigs and leaves glabrous or nearly so.　　　　　9. *F. americana.*
　Twigs and leaves densely pubescent.　　　　　　10. *F. biltmoreana.*

1. F. quadrangulata Michx. Tree, rarely becoming 36 m. tall, the twigs glabrous: leaflets 7–11; blades of the lateral ones lanceolate, elliptic, or ovate, 5–15 cm. long, serrate, short-petioluled: samaras 3–4 cm. long, the wing linear-elliptic or elliptic-cuneate.—(BLUE-ASH.)—Rich woods, often in calcareous soil, various provinces, rarely Coastal Plain, Ala. to Miss., Ark., Minn., Ont., and Ohio.—The light-yellow and brown-streaked heart-wood is used in construction and wagon-building. The inner bark yields a blue dye.

2. F. pauciflora Nutt. Tree becoming 10 m. tall or shrub, the twigs glabrous: leaflets 5–7; blades of the lateral ones lanceolate, elliptic, or some of them ovate, 4–15 cm. long, undulate or repand: samaras 4–6 cm. long, the wing elliptic to spatulate, longitudinally veined.—(SWAMP-ASH.)—Swamps, Coastal Plain, Fla. to La., and Ga.—The wood is nearly similar to that of the next following species.

3. F. caroliniana Mill. Tree sometimes 12 m. tall or shrub, the twigs often pubescent: leaflets 5–9, usually 5–7; blades of the lateral ones elliptic-lanceolate, 4–12 cm. long, shallowly serrate or nearly entire: samaras 4–5 cm. long, the wings elliptic, or nearly so, varying to ovate or obovate, pinnately veined.—(WATER-ASH. POP-ASH.)—Swamps, and low grounds, Coastal Plain and adj. provinces, Fla. to Tex., Mo., and S Va.—The white or yellow-tinged heart-wood is close-grained but soft and weak.

4. F. Darlingtonii Britton. Tree up to 20 m. tall, the twigs glabrous, or pubescent in more northern forms: leaflets 5–7; blades thin, lanceolate to oblong-lanceolate or ovate-elliptic, 11 cm. long or less, usually acuminate, entire, bright green, often pubescent beneath: samaras 5–7.5 cm. long, each with a narrowly elongate-linear wing which is decurrent on the upper part of the slender fruit-body.—Swamps, woods, and stream-banks, various provinces, Ala. to La., Kans., Ill., Pa., N. Y., Mass., and N. C.

5. F. Michauxii Britton. Tree up to 12 m. tall, the twigs velvety or glabrous: leaflets 5–7; blades thick, ovate, oval, ovate-lanceolate, or elliptic-lanceolate, 15 cm. long or less, usually acuminate, entire, deep-green above, paler and pubescent beneath: samaras 3.5–5 cm. long, each with a spatulate, usually broadly spatulate wing which is decurrent on the stoutish fruit-body.—Swamps, meadows, and stream-banks, various provinces, La. to Md., N. Y., and N. J.

6. F. pennsylvanica Marsh. Tree sometimes 20 m. tall, the twigs velvety pubescent (or glabrous in *F. pennsylvanica lanceolata*): leaflets 5–7; blades of the lateral ones lanceolate or sometimes elliptic, 5–20 cm. long, entire, or serrate, especially near the apex: samaras 3.5–6 cm. long, the wing spatulate, decurrent to the middle of the linear body or near it.—(RED-ASH. GREEN-ASH.)— Low woods and stream-banks, various provinces, N. C. to Ala., Kans., S. Dak., and N. B.; reported also from Miss.—The light-brown, coarse-grained heartwood, hard and heavy, is used in a variety of ways.

7. **F. Smallii** Britton. Tree becoming 16 m. tall, the twigs glabrous: leaflets 5–7; blades thinnish, elliptic-lanceolate, ovate-lanceolate, ovate, or elliptic-ovate, 15 cm. long or less, acuminate, entire or nearly so, bright-green above, pale and more or less pubescent beneath, slender-petioled: samaras 3–5 cm. long, each with an elliptic or linear-elliptic, usually acute wing which is decurrent on the upper half of the stout seed-body.—River-banks, bottoms, and swamps, Coastal Plain and adj. provinces, N Fla., to La., Mo., and N. C.

8. **F. profunda** Bush. Tree sometimes 35 m. tall, the twigs pubescent: leaflets 7–9; blades of the lateral ones lanceolate-ovate or elliptic, 6–12 cm. long, entire or undulate: samaras 4–5 cm. long, the wing linear-elliptic or elliptic-spatulate.—(PUMPKIN-ASH.)—Swamps and river-banks, various provinces N of Coastal Plain, Ga. to Ala., Mo., and W N. Y.—A plant closely related to *F. profunda*, but with thinner and relatively broader leaflets and smaller fruits (3–3.5 cm.) has been described as *F. catawbiensis* Ashe. It occurs in the Piedmont of Ga. and the Carolinas.

9. **F. americana** L. Tree becoming 40 m. tall, the twigs glabrous: leaflets 5–9; blades of the lateral ones lanceolate or elliptic, 5–15 cm. long, relatively thin, entire or shallowly toothed: samaras 2.5–3.5 cm. long, (less than 2 cm. long and seedless in *F. americana Curtissii*), the wing linear-spatulate or elliptic-spatulate, terminal or nearly so on the ellipsoid-cylindric body.—(WHITE-ASH.)—Rich or moist woods, various provinces, Fla. to Tex., Minn., and N. S.— The brown heart-wood, close-grained, tough and strong, is used in a great variety of ways. Our most valuable ash.

10. **F. biltmoreana** Beadle. Tree becoming 18 m. tall, the twigs densely soft-pubescent: leaflets 7–9; blades of the lateral ones ovate to elliptic-lanceolate, 7–14 cm. long, relatively thick, entire or obscurely toothed: samaras 3.5–5 cm. long, the wing linear or nearly so, terminal or nearly so on the stout elliptic body.—Woods on river-banks, Blue Ridge to Appalachian Plateau, Ga. to Ala. and Pa.

3. **FORESTIERA** Poir. Shrubs or trees. Leaves opposite: blades simple. Flowers mostly polygamo-dioecious, in lateral clusters, green or whitish. Calyx minute, 4–6-lobed, or obsolete. Corolla wanting, or rarely of 1–2 deciduous petals. Stamens 2–4. Stigma 2-lobed. Drupe ellipsoid to globular. [*Adelia* P. Br.]—About 15 species, American.

Leaf-blades acuminate at both ends: drupe much longer than thick, narrowly
   ellipsoid.   1. *F. acuminata.*
Leaf-blades obtuse: drupe as thick as long or slightly longer
   than thick, globose to oval.
     Leaves deciduous; blades toothed, membranous, not punctate.
       Leaf-blades pubescent on the veins beneath and often
         with scattered hairs between: pistillate flowers and
         drupes very short-pedicelled or sessile.   2. *F. ligustrina.*
       Leaf-blades copiously pubescent beneath: pistillate flow-
         ers and drupes markedly pedicelled.   3. *F. pubescens.*
     Leaves persistent; blades entire, coriaceous, punctate.
       Drupe oval or ovoid.
         Leaf-blades elliptic or elliptic-spatulate.   4. *F. porulosa.*
         Leaf-blades linear, linear-elliptic, or oblanceolate.   5. *F. pinetorum.*
       Drupe globular.   6. *F. globularis.*

1. F. acuminata (Michx.) Poir. Tree sometimes 10 m. tall or shrub, the twigs glabrous: leaf-blades 3–10 cm. long, elliptic-oval to ovate-elliptic, slightly serrate: bracts rhombic, 5–6 cm. long: drupe narrowly ellipsoid, 12–15 mm. long; stone tapering to the apex.—(FORESTIERA.) —River-swamps, stream-banks, and ponds, various provinces, Fla. to Tex., Ill., and S. C.—Spr.

2. F. ligustrina (Michx.) Poir. Shrub 1–3 m. tall, the twigs usually brown or purplish, glabrous or nearly so: leaf-blades 1–4 cm. long, elliptic oval or approaching obovate, finely serrate: bracts ovate or rhombic, about 2.5 mm. long, eciliate: drupe broadly globose-oval, 7–8 mm. long; stone oval.— Sandy or rocky soil and river-banks, various provinces, Fla. to Tenn. and Ga.—Sum.

3. F. pubescens Nutt. Shrub mainly 1–2 m. tall, the twigs yellowish, pubescent: leaf-blades 1–4 cm. long, elliptic-oval or elliptic-obovate, somewhat serrate: bracts obovate, 2–2.5 mm. long, or rarely longer, ciliate: drupe ellipsoid, 6–7 mm. long; stone narrowly ellipsoid.—River-banks, Coastal Plain, Fla. to Tex. and Ark.—Spr.

4. F. porulosa (Michx.) Poir. Small tree or shrub 1–3 m. tall, the twigs glabrous or nearly so: leaf-blades 1.5–5 cm. long, elliptic to elliptic-spatulate, mostly 2.5–6 cm. long, entire: bracts oval or sub-orbicular, about 1.5 mm. long, ciliate: drupe ellipsoid, 7–8 mm. long. [*Adelia segregata* (Fl. SE. U. S.)]— (FLORIDA-PRIVET.)—Hammocks and sand-dunes, S Fla.—Spr.

5. F. pinetorum Small. Shrub with short rigid, sometimes virgate branches 0.2–1 m. tall, the twigs puberulent, gray: leaf-blades 1–2.5 cm. long, linear-elliptic or oblanceolate, entire, thin-coriaceous: bracts obovate to orbicular-cuneate, 1.5–2 mm. long, ciliate: drupe oval, 5–7 mm. long, equilateral, black: stone ellipsoid.—(WILD-OLIVE.)—Pinelands, S pen. Fla.—Fall–Spr.

6. F. globularis Small. Shrub with intricately branched stems, 1–3 m. tall, the twigs pale-gray and striate, glabrous: leaf-blades elliptic or slightly broadened upward, coriaceous-fleshy, mainly 1–2 cm. long, paler beneath than above: flowers few, nearly sessile: bracts oval to suborbicular, 2–2.5 mm. long, ciliate: drupe globular, 7–9 mm. in diameter, blue; stone globose or oval-globose.— Dune-hammocks, E Fla.—Spr.

4. CHIONANTHUS L. Shrubs or trees. Leaves opposite, deciduous: blades simple. Flowers perfect or polygamous, in drooping festoon-like panicles. Calyx deeply 4-lobed. Corolla white: lobes narrow, many times longer than the tube. Stamens 2: filaments adnate to the corolla-tube. Stigma notched or 2-lobed. Drupe oval to subglobose.—Two species, American.—FRINGE-TREES. OLD-MAN'S BEARDS. FLOWERING-ASHES. GRANDSIR-GRAYBEARDS.—Spr.

Corolla-lobes 2–3 cm. long: anthers acuminate: drupe 1–1.5 cm. long.
 1. *C. virginica.*

Corolla-lobes about 1 cm. long: anthers abruptly blunt-tipped: drupe 2–2.5 cm. long.
 2. *C. pygmaea.*

1. C. virginica L. Tree up to 10 m. tall or a tall shrub with a taproot: leaf-blades oval to elliptic, varying to obovate, mostly 8–18 cm. long, becoming thick-membranous, rather long-petioled: panicles with persistent bracts which are often 2–4 cm. long: anthers fully 2 mm. long: drupe ellipsoid.—Swampy woods, rocky bluffs, and stream-banks, often in acid soil, various provinces, Fla. to Tex., Mo., and N. J.—The light-brown heart-wood is close-grained and hard.

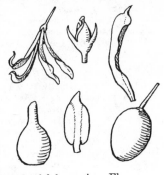

2. C. pygmaea Small. Shrub with underground stems, the branches 2–4 dm. tall, simple below, sparingly branched throughout: leaf-blades elliptic or nearly so, 3–9 cm. long, becoming thin-coriaceous, short-petioled: panicles with very small deciduous bracts: anthers less than 2 mm. long: drupe oval.—Scrub, inland sandhills, S end of lake region, Fla.

5. LIGUSTRUM [Tourn.] L. Shrubs or trees. Leaves opposite: blades simple, entire. Flowers perfect, in erect panicles. Calyx shallowly 4-lobed or nearly truncate. Corolla white or greenish, funnelform: lobes broad, about as long as the tube or much shorter. Stamens 2: filaments adnate to the corolla-tube. Stigma 2-lobed. Drupe mostly subglobose.—About 35 species, natives of the Old World.

Corolla-lobes as long as the tube or nearly so: anthers oval.　　1. *L. vulgare.*
Corolla-lobes much shorter than the tube: anthers linear.　　2. *L. ovalifolium.*

1. L. vulgare L. Shrub becoming 3 m. tall: leaves tardily deciduous; blades elliptic, elliptic-lanceolate, lanceolate, or individually broadest above the middle, 1–5 cm. long, or rarely larger, obtuse or acutish, slender-petioled: panicles many-flowered, compact: bracts somewhat persistent: calyx-lobes minute, acute: corolla 5–6 mm. long; lobes broadly ovate: anthers less than 2 mm. long: drupes subglobose, 6–8 mm. in diameter, black.—(PRIVET. PRIM.)—Roadsides, old-fields, and thickets, various provinces, N. C. to Tex., Ont. and Me. Nat. of O. W., and cult.—Spr.–sum.

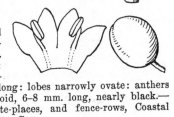

2. L. ovalifolium Hassk. Shrub or small tree: leaves very tardily deciduous or evergreen; blades ovate, elliptic or oval, 3–7 cm. long, mostly acute or acutish; stout-petioled: panicle many-flowered, open: bracts caducous: calyx-lobes obsolete: corolla 7–8 mm. long: lobes narrowly ovate: anthers over 2 mm. long: drupes mostly oval to ovoid, 6–8 mm. long, nearly black.—(CALIFORNIA PRIVET.)—Cult. grounds, waste-places, and fence-rows, Coastal Plain, Fla. to Tex. Nat. of Japan, and cult.—Sum.

Ligustrum sinense Lour. A shrub differing from *L. vulgare* in the densely pubescent young branches and inflorescence, and with the midrib of the leaves pubescent beneath and the stamens much longer than the corolla-lobes, occurs as an escape in S La.

Ligustrum lucidum Ait., a shrub or small tree, with large, ovate or ovate-lanceolate leaf-blades, often 6–12 cm. long, large erect panicles of sessile flowers, and drooping clusters of bluish-black fruits, is widely cultivated in southern coastal regions. It is a native of China and Japan, and is occasionally spontaneous about towns where it is grown on the coasts of North Carolina and Louisiana.

6. **AMAROLEA** Small. Shrubs or small trees. Leaves opposite, persistent: blades simple, entire. Flowers polygamous, in small axillary scaly-bracted panicles. Calyx prominently 4-lobed. Corolla funnelform, greenish-white or white: lobes broad, nearly as long as the tube. Stamens 2: filaments partly adnate to the corolla-tube: anthers notched. Stigma capitate. Drupe oval or globose, very bitter.—Only the following 2 species.—Spr.—WILD-OLIVES. DEVIL-WOODS.—Differs from *Osmanthus* by the coralloid inflorescence, the subsessile flowers, the introrse anthers, and the capitate stigma.

Drupe oval or ellipsoid, 1 cm. in diameter or less: stone acute at both ends. (See note.)   1. *A. americana.*
Drupe globose, 2-2.5 cm. in diameter: stone acute at the base.   2. *A. megacarpa.*

1. **A. americana** (L.) Small. Tree becoming 15 m. tall or shrub, the bark pale: leaf-blades narrowly elliptic, varying to oblanceolate or lanceolate, 5-15 cm. long, entire, lustrous above: inflorescence-branches and calyx usually finely pubescent: corolla 3-4 mm. long: drupe 10-15 mm. long, dark-purple; stone ellipsoid, less than 1 cm. in diameter. [*Osmanthus americana* B. & H.] —Hammocks, wooded bluffs, and swamps, Coastal Plain, Fla. to La. and N. C.—The dark-brown heart-wood is close-grained and hard.—*Osmanthus floridana* Chapm. is said to differ from this species in its yellowish-green fruit.—A plant of the coastal region of NE Florida with a small globose drupe, about a centimeter in diameter and a stone scarcely pointed at the base, may represent another species.

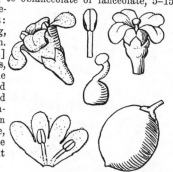

2. **A. megacarpa** Small. Shrub or small tree with a trunk-diameter usually less than 1 dm., the bark pale-green: leaf-blades elliptic or slightly broader above the middle, mostly 9-15 cm. long, very coriaceous: drupe globose, 2-2.5 cm. long, dull-purple; stone globose-obovoid, more than 1 cm. in diameter. [*Osmanthus megacarpa* Small.]—Scrub, S end of the lake region, pen. Fla.

7. **JASMINUM** [Tourn.] L. Shrubs or woody vines. Leaf-blades 3–7-foliolate or sometimes 1-foliolate. Flowers mostly in terminal compound cymes. Calyx with 4–9 short or elongate, often narrow, lobes. Corolla salverform, the limb 4–12-lobed. Filaments adnate to the corolla-tube. Fruit didymous.— About 100 species, natives of the Old World.

Leaves with 3 or more leaflets, usually 5–7-foliolate: anthers slender, long-tipped.   1. *J. grandiflorum.*
Leaves reduced to a single leaflet, thus 1-foliolate: anthers stout, short-tipped.
  Calyx much less than half the length of the corolla-tube: corolla-lobes narrowly elliptic, acute or short-acuminate.   2. *J. undulatum.*
  Calyx about half the length of the corolla-tube or more: corolla-lobes oval, ovate, or orbicular, obtuse.   3. *J. Sambac.*

1. **J. grandiflorum** L. Plant partly erect or diffusely reclining, glabrous or nearly so: leaflets mostly 5–7; blades ovate to oval, mucronate, except the

usually ovate-lanceolate or narrowly ovate, acute or acuminate terminal one: calyx 4–8 mm. long; lobes subulate, often unequal: corolla white; tube 17–21 mm. long; lobes mostly elliptic to oval, obtuse.—(ITALIAN-JESSAMINE. CATALONIA-JESSAMINE. ROYAL-JESSAMINE. SPANISH-JESSAMINE.) — Pinelands, thickets, and waste-places, S pen. Fla. Nat. of E. I., and cult.—(*W. I., Mex., C. A., S. A.*)—All year.

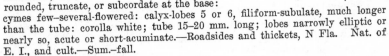

2. **J. undulatum** Ker. Plant climbing, the stems and branches closely fine-pubescent: leaflets 2–8 cm. long; blades ovate to ovate-lanceolate, acute or acuminate at the apex, rounded, truncate, or subcordate at the base: cymes few–several-flowered: calyx-lobes 5 or 6, filiform-subulate, much longer than the tube: corolla white; tube 15–20 mm. long; lobes narrowly elliptic or nearly so, acute or short-acuminate.—Roadsides and thickets, N Fla. Nat. of E. I., and cult.—Sum.–fall.

3. **J. Sambac** (L.) Soland. Plant climbing, the stems and branches finely pubescent: leaflets 4–13 cm. long; blades oval to ovate or elliptic, mostly acute at the apex, obtuse or rounded at the base: cymes few–several-flowered: calyx-lobes 7–many, longer than the tube, very narrowly linear: corolla white; tube 10–15 mm. long; lobes oval, ovate, or orbicular, mostly obtuse.—(ARABIAN-JESSAMINE. NASSAU-JESSAMINE.)—Woods and thickets, S pen. Fla. Nat. of E. I., and cult.—(*W. I.*)—All year.

ORDER **GENTIANALES** — GENTIANAL ORDER

Herbs, shrubs, or trees, sometimes aquatic or humus plants or vines. Leaves mainly opposite: blades simple. Flowers mostly perfect, solitary or in cymes. Calyx of 5 partially united sepals, or fewer. Corolla of 5 partially united petals, or fewer. Androecium of as many stamens as there are corolla-lobes: filaments often partially adnate to the corolla-tube. Gynoecium of 2 more or less united carpels. Fruit capsular, baccate or drupaceous.

Ovary 2-celled: leaves stipulate or with stipular lines.	Fam. 1. SPIGELIACEAE.
Ovary 1-celled: leaves not stipulate.	
Corolla-lobes convolute or imbricated in the bud.	Fam. 2. GENTIANACEAE.
Corolla-lobes induplicate-valvate in the bud.	Fam. 3. MENYANTHACEAE.

FAMILY 1. **SPIGELIACEAE** — LOGANIA FAMILY

Herbs, vines, or woody plants. Leaves typically opposite. Flowers in open or compact clusters. Calyx of 4 or 5 partially united sepals. Corolla of 4 or 5 partially united petals. Androecium of 4 or 5 stamens. Gynoecium of 2 united carpels, or rarely more: ovary 2-celled or rarely 4-celled. Fruit capsular and 2-valved, or baccate or drupaceous.—Thirty genera and about 400 species, most abundant in warm and tropical regions.

Woody vines: stigmas 4: corolla yellow.	Tribe I. GELSEMIEAE.
Herbs or erect shrubs: stigma entire or slightly 2-lobed: corolla not yellow, at least without.	II. SPIGELIEAE.

I. GELSEMIEAE

Stem diffusely twining: leaves persistent.	1. GELSEMIUM.

II. Spigelieae

Corolla-lobes valvate.
  Corolla funnelform or salverform : styles permanently united.
    Flowers in the forks of leafy branches : style jointed near
      the middle.   2. Coelostylis.
    Flowers in terminal spikes or spike-like racemes : style
      jointed near the base.   3. Spigelia.
  Corolla urn-shaped : styles soon distinct.   4. Cynoctonum.
Corolla-lobes imbricate.
  Annual herb : sepals nearly distinct : capsule loculicidal.   5. Polypremum.
  Shrubs, or partly woody herbs : sepals chiefly united : cap-
    sule septicidal.   6. Adenoplea.

1. **GELSEMIUM** Juss. Evergreen vines. Flowers dimorphous, in axillary cymes, or solitary. Calyx 5-lobed. Corolla funnelform, straight. Filaments with the free portion much longer than the adnate portion. Stigmas 4. Capsule flattened contrary to the septum, septicidal. Seeds winged.—Three species, the following and 1 Asiatic.—Wint.-spr.—Yellow-jessamine. Evening Trumpet-flower.

Leaf-blades narrowed at the base : calyx-lobes obtuse : anthers elliptic-ovate : capsule short-beaked : seed winged.   1. *G. sempervirens.*
Leaf-blades rounded at the base : calyx-lobes acuminate :
  anthers lanceolate : capsule long-beaked : seed wingless.   2. *G. Rankinii.*

1. **G. sempervirens** (L.) Ait. f. Stem and branches often tangled and matted, the flowering shoots reddish-brown : leaf-blades lanceolate to elliptic-lanceolate, 1.5–7 cm. long, entire : pedicels scaly throughout : calyx-lobes 3–4 mm. long, elliptic to ovate-elliptic : bud blunt : corolla deep-yellow, 3–4 cm. long ; tube gradually dilated : capsule-body veiny, 19–22 mm. long, the beak 1–1.5 mm. long : seed 8–9 mm. long, the body about as long as the wing.—Hammocks, thickets, bluffs, and swamps, Coastal Plain and adj. provinces, Fla. to Tex., Ark., and Va.—Wint.-spr.—The flowers are very fragrant.

2. **G. Rankinii** Small. Plant with the same habit as *G. sempervirens*, the flowering shoots green : leaf-blades lanceolate to ovate, 1.5–7 cm. long, entire : pedicels scaly at the base : calyx-lobes about 4 mm. long, lanceolate : bud acute : corolla deep-yellow, 2.5–3 cm. long ; tube abruptly dilated : capsule-body veinless, 10–11 mm. long, the beak 3–4 mm. long : seed 3–4 mm. long.—Swamps and river banks, Coastal Plain, N Fla. to La. and N. C.—Wint.-spr.—The flowers are not fragrant.

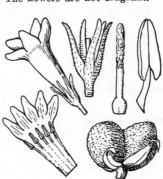

2. **COELOSTYLIS** T. & G. Annual erect herbs. Flowers in the forks of leafy branches, or in the leaf axils. Calyx-lobes narrow. Corolla white or whitish, narrowly funnelform, plicate in the bud. Filaments adnate to about the middle of the corolla-tube.—Two species, North American.

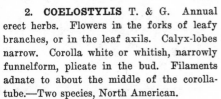

1. **C. loganioides** T. & G. Plant 1–3 dm. tall, glabrous : leaf-blades oval to elliptic or lanceolate, 1.5–3.5 cm. long : calyx-lobes narrowly linear, about ⅓ as long as the corolla, denticulate : corolla-lobes lanceolate : capsule about 6 mm. wide.—Pinelands, E Fla.

3. SPIGELIA L. Erect herbs. Flowers in solitary or clustered spikes or spike-like racemes. Calyx-lobes narrow. Corolla colored, rarely pale, tubular-funnelform, scarcely if at all plicate in the bud. Filaments adnate to above the middle of the corolla-tube or to near the top.—About 35 species, American.

Plant perennial: inflorescence not subtended by a whorl of bracts.
    Corolla scarlet without, 4–5 cm. long: anthers exserted.   1. *S. marylandica.*
    Corolla purplish without, 1.5–2.5 cm. long: anthers included.   2. *S. gentianoides.*
Plant annual: inflorescence subtended by a whorl of bracts.   3. *S. Anthelmia.*

1. S. marylandica L. Plant 2–6 dm. tall: leaf-blades ovate to lanceolate, or sometimes elliptic, 3–10 cm. long: calyx-lobes 10–11 mm. long: corolla red without, yellow within; lobes lanceolate: capsule about 9 mm. wide.—(INDIAN-PINK. CAROLINA-PINK. PINK-ROOT. WORM-GRASS.)— Rich woods and hillsides, Fla. to Tex., Ind. and Md. (or N. J.)—Spr.

2. S. gentianoides Chapm. Plant 2–3 dm. tall: leaf-blades ovate, or sometimes oval-lanceolate near the base of the stem or almost orbicular, 1.5–5 cm. long: calyx-lobes 7–9 mm. long: corolla pink; lobes deltoid or ovate-deltoid.—Dry soil, W Fla.—Spr.

3. S. Anthelmia L. Plant 1–4 dm. tall: leaf-blades lanceolate, 3–12 cm. long: inflorescence subtended by a whorl of large bracts: calyx-lobes 1.5–2 mm. long: corolla 6–10 mm. long, purplish, often pale: capsule 5–6 mm. wide, tuberculate.—(WEST-INDIAN PINK-ROOT. WORM-GRASS.)— Hammocks and cult. grounds, Florida Keys.—(*W. I., Mex., C. A., S. A.*)

4. CYNOCTONUM J. F. Gmel. Annual (ours) erect herbs. Flowers in terminal cymes, secund. Calyx usually 5-lobed. Corolla white or pink, urceolate, somewhat longer than the calyx. Filaments almost completely adnate to the corolla-tube. Styles united by their tips in anthesis, ultimately distinct. Capsule miter-shaped.—About 5 species, of warm regions.—MITERWORTS.

Leaf-blades narrowed into petiole-like bases: inflorescence lax.   1. *C. Mitreola.*
Leaf-blades sessile: inflorescence dense.
    Leaf-blades ovate to orbicular: corolla-lobes ovate.   2. *C. sessilifolium.*
    Leaf-blades narrowly elliptic to almost linear: corolla-lobes
      lanceolate to linear-lanceolate.   3. *C. angustifolium.*

1. C. Mitreola (L.) Britton. Stem 1–7 dm. tall: leaf-blades thin, elliptic, lanceolate, or ovate, or sometimes narrower, 1.5–8 cm. long, acute or acuminate: corolla-lobes ovate to elliptic-lanceolate: capsule 2–2.5 mm. long.—Damp soil, muddy banks, low pinelands and lime-sinks, Coastal Plain, and rarely adj. provinces, Fla. to Tex., Ark., and S Va.—(*W. I., Mex., C. A., S. A.*) —Sum, or all year S.

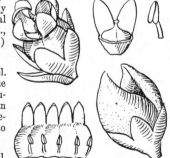

2. C. sessilifolium (Walt.) J. F. Gmel. Stem 1–5 dm. tall: leaf-blades thick, ovate to orbicular, 1–5 cm. long, obtuse or apiculate: corolla-lobes ovate, mainly shorter than the tube: capsule about 4 mm. long.—Pinelands and wet places, Coastal Plain, Fla. to La.—Sum.

3. C. angustifolium (T. & G.) Small.

Stem 2–6 dm. tall: leaf-blades thick, narrowly elliptic to lanceolate or nearly linear, 2–4 cm. long, obtuse or acutish: corolla-lobes lanceolate or linear-lanceolate, mainly longer than the tube: capsule about 4 mm. long.—Wet places, Coastal Plain, Fla. and S Ga.

5. **POLYPREMUM** L. Annual diffuse herbs. Flowers solitary in the forks of the branches and in the leaf-axils. Calyx-lobes 4 or 5, narrow. Corolla white, campanulate, shorter than the calyx. Filaments adnate to the corolla-tube for about ½ their length. Styles very short, permanently united. Capsule obovoid or subglobose.—One species.

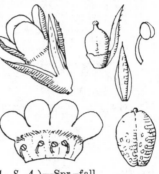

1. **P. procumbens** L. Stem and branches 1–3 dm. long: leaf-blades narrowly linear to subulate, scabrous-margined: calyx-lobes narrowly lanceolate, about 3 mm. long: corolla-lobes suborbicular, slightly shorter than the tube: capsule about 2 mm. long.— Waste-places, roadsides, fields, and pond-margins, Coastal Plain and adj. provinces, Fla. to Tex., Mo., and Pa.—(*W. I., Mex., C. A., S. A.*)—Spr.–fall.

6. **ADENOPLEA** Radlk. Shrubs or partly woody plants. Flowers in lax or dense cymes borne in racemes or panicles. Calyx-lobes 4, shorter than the tube. Corolla trumpet-shaped, curved. Filaments adnate to below the middle of the corolla-tube. Capsule thick, septicidal.—Few species, of tropical regions.

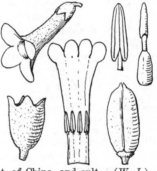

1. **A. Lindleyana** (Fort.) Small. Stem diffusely branched, 1–2 m. tall, the branches angled: leaf-blades ovate to lanceolate, 3–9 cm. long, entire, glabrous: panicles 1–3 dm. long, often partly drooping: calyx about 2.5 mm. long: corolla purplish, violet, or reddish, 12–16 mm. long, the tube curved: capsule 4–5 mm. long. [*Buddleia Lindleyana* Fort.]—Roadsides, cult. grounds, and waste-places, Coastal Plain, Fla. to Tex. and Ga. Nat. of China, and cult.—(*W. I.*)— Sum.–fall.

FAMILY 2. **GENTIANACEAE** — GENTIAN FAMILY

Annual or perennial caulescent herbs or rarely shrubs. Leaves typically opposite: blades entire, sometimes connate. Flowers perfect, solitary or variously clustered. Calyx of 2, 4 or 5, or more, partially united sepals, persistent. Corolla of 4 or 5 or more, partially united petals, varying from rotate to tubular. Androecium of as many stamens as there are corolla-lobes, the filaments partially adnate to the corolla-tube. Gynoecium of two united carpels. Fruit a capsule.—Seventy genera and 700 species, most abundant in temperate regions.

Corolla-lobes convolute in the bud: leaves not scale-like.	Tribe I. GENTIANEAE.
Corolla-lobes imbricate in the bud: leaves mere scales.	
Stigmas 2, distinct: plant green or purple-tinged.	Tribe II. OBOLARIEAE.
Stigmas united, dilated: plant white, not green.	Tribe III. LEIPHAIMEAE.

I. GENTIANEAE

Style filiform, mostly deciduous : anthers recurving or twisting at maturity.
Stigmas roundish, much shorter than the style.
    Corolla-tube surpassing the calyx.   1. CENTAURIUM.
    Corolla-tube much shorter than the calyx.   2. EUSTOMA.
Stigmas linear or nearly so, about as long as the style.
    Flowers pedicelled, when more than one, paniculate : an-
      thers coiled.   3. SABBATIA.
    Flowers sessile, when more than one, capitate : anthers
      curved.   4. LAPITHEA.
Style stout, short or wanting : anthers straight at maturity.
Corolla not furnished with nectariferous structures.
    Corolla without plaits in the sinuses of the lobes : calyx
      without an interior membrane.
      Sepals unequal, the inner much broader than the
        outer and thin-margined : corolla-lobes fimbriate or
        erose.   5. ANTHOPOGON.
      Sepals essentially equal, or if unequal the inner nar-
        rower than the outer : corolla-lobes entire or
        merely toothed.   6. GENTIANELLA.
    Corolla with plaits in the sinuses of the lobes : calyx
      with an interior membrane.   7. DASYSTEPHANA.
Corolla furnished with nectariferous pits, glands, or scales,
    1 or 2 for each lobe.   8. FRASERA.

II. OBOLARIEAE

Calyx-lobes 4, narrowed upward : petals slightly united.   9. BARTONIA.
Calyx-lobes 2, broadened upward : petals well united.   10. OBOLARIA.

III. LEIPHAIMEAE

Humus plant with slender stems and small, colored flowers.   11. LEIPHAIMOS.

1. CENTAURIUM Hill. Annual, biennial, or sometimes perennial, relatively small herbs. Flowers in terminal
cymes. Calyx-lobes 4 or 5, keeled. Corolla
white, or commonly deep-pink or rose-purple,
salverform : lobes 4 or 5, shorter than the
tube, often strongly involute, acuminate.—
About 25 species, widely distributed.

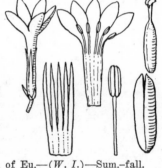

1. C. pulchellum (Sw.) Druce. Stem 3–25
cm. tall: blades of the upper leaves elliptic
to ovate, 5–20 mm. long, obtuse: calyx 6–8
mm. long: corolla 9–10 mm. long; lobes
elliptic-ovate, obtuse: capsule 7.5–8 mm. long.
[*Erythraea pulchella* (Sw.) Fries.]—(CEN-
TAURY.)—Fields and waste-places, various
provinces, Miss. to La., Ill., and N. Y. Nat. of Eu.—(*W. I.*)—Sum.–fall.

2. EUSTOMA Salisb. Annual relatively large herbs. Flowers solitary or in
open panicles. Calyx-lobes 5 or 6, narrow.
Corolla white, pink, violet, or purple, campanulate-funnelform : lobes 5 or 6, usually
erose-denticulate, longer than the tube.—
Five species, North American.

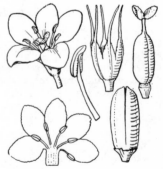

1. E. exaltatum (L.) Griseb. Stem 1–9 dm.
tall: blades of the upper leaves elliptic to
elliptic-lanceolate, 1.5–7 cm. long: calyx-
lobes 10–12 mm. long: corolla rose-purple;
lobes elliptic or oval, 17–20 mm. long: capsule 2–2.5 cm. long.—Pinelands, coastal
sand-dunes, and hammocks, pen. Fla. and
Florida Keys.—(*W. I.*)—All year.—Albino
forms occur.

3. SABBATIA Adans. Annual or biennial, relatively slender herbs. Flowers solitary or in cymes. Calyx-lobes 4–12, narrow. Corolla white, or pink to lilac, or magenta, often with a distinct eye, rotate: lobes entire, longer than the tube.—About 20 species, North American.

Calyx-lobes and corolla-lobes usually 4 or 5.
Calyx-lobes and corolla-lobes 8–12.

I. ANGULARES.
II. DODECANDRES.

I. ANGULARES

Upper part of the stem with opposite branches.
  Stem and branches terete.
    Calyx-lobes shorter than the tube, erect: style and stigmas about equal in length.
    Calyx-lobes longer than the tube, recurved: style much shorter than the stigmas.
  Stem and branches 4-ridged or 4-winged.
    Corolla-lobes elliptic to spatulate: upper leaves with narrow blades.
      Corolla white.
        Leaf-blades rounded at the base.
        Leaf-blades truncate and somewhat auricled at the base.
      Corolla rose.
    Corolla-lobes oval to obovate: upper leaves with broad blades.
Upper part of the stem with alternate branches.
  Corolla-lobes of a spatulate or oblanceolate type.
    Calyx-lobes foliaceous, mostly broadened upward.
    Calyx-lobes not foliaceous, narrowed upward.
  Corolla-lobes of an elliptic or oval type.
    Calyx-lobes typically about as long as the corolla-lobes: corolla mainly less than 3 cm. broad.
    Calyx-lobes typically much shorter than the corolla-lobes: corolla mainly over 3.5 cm. broad.

1. *S. macrophylla.*

2. *S. recurvans.*

3. *S. difformis.*

4. *S. paniculata.*
5. *S. brachiata.*

6. *S. angularis.*

7. *S. calycina.*
8. *S. Elliottii.*

9. *S. campanulata.*

10. *S. grandiflora.*

II. DODECANDRES

Corolla-lobes elliptic-spatulate to oblanceolate, less than 25 mm. long, usually acutish at the tip.
  Calyx-lobes much shorter than the corolla.
    Calyx-lobes linear or slightly narrowed upward.
    Calyx-lobes linear-spatulate.
  Calyx-lobes as long as the corolla or nearly so.
Corolla-lobes obovate-spatulate, over 25 mm. long, usually rounded at the tip.

11. *S. dodecandra.*
12. *S. Harperi.*
13. *S. foliosa.*

14. *S. decandra.*

1. S. macrophylla Hook. Stem 6–10 dm. tall: blades of the upper leaves elliptic to elliptic-lanceolate or ovate-lanceolate, 2–6 cm. long, acute: calyx 2–3 mm. long; lobes shorter than the tube: corolla white; lobes 6–8 mm. long: capsule 3–4 mm. long.—Wet pinelands or acid bogs, Coastal Plain, Fla. to La. and Ga.—Sum.

2. S. recurvans Small. Similar to *S. macrophylla* in habit: calyx 4–5 mm. long; lobes longer than the tube: corolla white; lobes 5–6.5 mm. long: capsule 3.5–4.5 mm. long.—Low or moist pinelands, Coastal Plain, Fla. and Ga.—Sum.

3. S. difformis (L.) Druce. Stem 4–9 dm. tall: blades of the upper leaves ovate to lanceolate or linear-lanceolate, 1–4 cm. long, apiculate or acute: calyx 7–9.5 mm. long; lobes much longer than the tube: corolla white, drying yellowish; lobes 12–18 mm. long: capsule 5–6 mm. long. [*S. lanceolata* (Walt.) T. & G.]—Wet pinelands, and acid bogs, Coastal Plain, Fla. to Tenn. and N. J.—Spr.–sum.

4. S. paniculata (Michx.) Pursh. Stem 1–4 dm. tall: blades of the upper leaves elliptic to elliptic-lanceolate or nearly linear, 1–3 cm. long: calyx 6.5–7.5 mm. long; lobes somewhat longer than the tube: corolla white; lobes 10–14 mm. long; capsule 7–9 mm. long.—Acid meadows and pinelands, Coastal Plain, Fla. to Ala. and S Va.—Spr.–sum.

5. S. brachiata Ell. Stem 1–4 dm. tall: blades of the upper leaves elliptic to linear-lanceolate, 1.2–3.5 cm. long: calyx 7–8 mm. long; lobes much longer than the tube: corolla rose to white; lobes 11–15 mm. long: capsule 5–7 mm. long. '[*S. angustifolia* (Michx.) Britton]—Moist soil, often in pinelands, Coastal Plain, and adj. provinces, Fla. to La., Mo., and N. C.—Spr.–sum.

6. S. angularis (L.) Pursh. Stem 3–8 dm. tall: blades of the upper leaves ovate to ovate-lanceolate, 1.5–3 cm. long: flowers fragrant; calyx 7–8 mm. long; lobes much longer than the tube: corolla typically deep-pink; lobes 10–18 mm. long: capsule 4.5–5.5 mm. long.—(ROSE-PINK. BITTER-BLOOM.)—Sterile woods, thickets, and meadows, various provinces, Fla. to La., Okla., Ont., and N. J.—Sum.

7. S. calycina (Lam.) Heller. Stem 1–4 dm. tall: blades of the upper leaves elliptic to elliptic-lanceolate, 2–6 cm. long: calyx 15–25 mm. long; lobes linear-oblanceolate or some of them merely linear, much longer than the tube: corolla rose or nearly white; lobes spatulate to elliptic-spatulate, mostly shorter than the calyx lobes: capsule 7–8 mm. long.—River-swamps and low hammocks, Coastal Plain, Fla. to Tex., Ark. and Va.—Spr.–sum.

8. S. Elliottii Steud. Stem 2–7 dm. tall: blades of the upper leaves elliptic to linear, 0.5–2 cm. long: calyx 7–8 mm. long; lobes about twice as long as the tube: corolla white or cream; lobes spatulate to oblanceolate, 10–13 mm. long, much longer than the calyx-lobes: capsule 4–5 mm. long.—Pinelands, Coastal Plain, Fla. to Ala., and Va.—Sum.–fall.

9. S. campanulata (L.) Torr. Stem 1–4 dm. tall: blades of the upper leaves narrow, but typically broader than the diameter of the stem or branches: calyx with filiform or nearly filiform lobes, typically about as long as the corolla: corolla deep-rose or magenta, with a yellow eye; lobes elliptic to spatulate-elliptic: capsule 6–8 mm. long.—Pinelands, sandy places. swamps, and meadows, various provinces, Fla., to La., Tenn., and Mass.—Sum.–fall.—A foliose variety with the blades of the lower leaves obovate to spatulate and of the upper leaves lance-elliptic varying to linear and with calyx lobes much shorter than the corolla occurs at various localities in the Coastal Plain from Fla. to La. and S N. C. This has sometimes been included in *S. stellaris* Pursh.

10. S. grandiflora (A. Gray) Small. Stem 8–12 dm. tall: blades of the upper leaves typically stout-filiform or nearly so, mainly narrower than the diameter of the stem and the branches, 3–10 cm. long: calyx with filiform or very narrow lobes much shorter than the corolla: corolla deep-rose or magenta, the eye yellow; lobes oval or elliptic-oval to rhombic-obovate: capsule 8–10 mm. long.—Everglades, low pinelands, and prairies, pen. Fla.—All year.

11. S. dodecandra (L.) B. S. P. Stem 2–4 dm. tall: blades of the upper leaves narrowly lanceolate to linear, 2–4 cm. long: calyx-lobes linear or nearly so: corolla rose-purple or white, the eye yellow; lobes spatulate to elliptic-spatulate, 2–2.5 cm. long: capsule 8–9 mm. long.—Pinelands, Coastal Plain, Fla. to La. and S N. Y.—Sum.–fall.

12. S. Harperi Small. Stem 2–6 dm. tall: blades of the upper leaves elliptic-lanceolate to lanceolate, 1.5–3.5 cm. long: calyx-lobes linear-spatulate: corolla bright-pink or whitish, the eye yellow; lobes spatulate to elliptic-spatulate, much longer than the calyx-lobes: capsule 5–7.5 mm. long.—Swamps or pond-margins in pinelands, Coastal Plain, N Fla. and Ala. to S. C.—Spr.

13. S. foliosa Fernald. Stem 1–5 dm. tall: blades of the upper leaves linear-elliptic to linear-lanceolate or almost linear, 2–6.5 cm. long: calyx-lobes linear: corolla rose, the eye yellow; lobes oblanceolate to elliptic-spatulate, about as long as the calyx-lobes: capsule 5–7 mm. long.—Low grounds, Coastal Plain, Fla. and Ala.—Spr.–fall.

14. S. decandra (Walt.) Harper. Stem 6–9 dm. tall: blades of the upper leaves linear-subulate, 3–10 cm. long, lower leaves spatulate: calyx-lobes subulate: corolla deep-rose to white, the eye yellow: lobes obovate-spatulate, 2.5–3.5 cm. long: capsule about 10 mm. long.—Shallow pineland ponds, Coastal Plain, Fla. to Ala. and S. C.—Sum.–fall.

4. LAPITHEA Griseb. Annual or biennial herbs. Flowers solitary or in a congested cyme. Calyx-lobes mostly 7–10, narrow, unequal. Corolla red, purple, or pink, rotate: lobes mostly 7–10, longer than the tube.—Only the following species:

Blades of the cauline leaves above the lower part of the stem elliptic to elliptic-lanceolate: bracts of the involucre linear-elliptic to lanceolate. 1. *L. capitata.*
Blades of the cauline leaves above the lower part of the stem narrowly lanceolate: bracts of the involucre narrowly linear-attenuate.
2. *L. gentianoides.*

1. L. capitata (Raf.) Small. Stem 2–4 dm. tall: blades of the upper leaves elliptic to elliptic-lanceolate, 1.5–4 cm. long: bracts oval or elliptic: calyx-lobes linear or linear-lanceolate: corolla pink or whitish; lobes broadly spatulate, 15–20 mm. long. [*Pleienta capitata* Raf. *Sabbatia Boykinii* A. Gray *L. Boykinii* Small]—Rich woods, Blue Ridge to Appalachian Plateau, Ga. and Ala.—Sum.–fall.

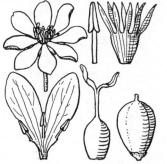

2. L. gentianoides (Ell.) Griseb. Stem 2–7 dm. tall: blades of the upper leaves linear, 3–10 cm. long: bracts linear: calyx-lobes linear-subulate: corolla reddish, lilac or pink-purple; lobes spatulate or elliptic-spatulate, 20–25 mm. long. [*Sabbatia gentianoides* Ell.]—Low pinelands, Coastal Plain, Fla. to Tex. and Ga.—Sum.

5. ANTHOPOGON Neck. Annual, biennial, or rarely perennial herbs. Flowers solitary at the ends of the stem and its branches, the whorls mostly of 4 parts each. Calyx relatively large: lobes keeled, unequal, the inner ones broader than the outer and hyaline or scarious-margined. Corolla salverform to funnelform: lobes shorter than the tube, without plaits in the sinuses. Stigmas very broad.—About 50 species, widely distributed.

1. A. crinitum (Froel.) Raf. Stem 2–5 dm. tall, mostly branched: leaf-blades ovate to lanceolate, mainly 2–5 cm. long, partly clasping: calyx 25–30 mm. long: corolla sky-blue, 4–5 cm. long lobes fimbriate; capsule about 3 cm. long. [*Gentiana crinata* Froel.]—(FRINGED-GENTIAN.)—Swamps, moist thickets, and meadows, various provinces, Coastal Plain only N, Ga. to N. D. and Que.—Fall.

6. GENTIANELLA Moench. Annual, biennial, or perennial herbs. Flowers solitary or in open or contracted cymes, the whorls of 4 parts each, or sometimes of 5 parts. Calyx relatively small: lobes essentially equal or the outer ones broader than the inner. Corolla blue or pale bluish-purple, funnelform or salverform: lobes shorter than the tube, with plaits in the sinuses, but often filamentose at the base.—Numerous species of wide geographic distribution.

Calyx-lobes shorter than the tube: corolla-lobes ovate.   1. *G. quinquefolia.*
Calyx-lobes longer than the tube: corolla-lobes lanceolate.   2. *G. occidentalis.*

1. G. quinquefolia (L.) Small. Stem 1–11 dm. tall, mostly branched, 4-winged; leaf-blades ovate to lanceolate, 2–3 cm. long, partly clasping; calyx-lobes spatulate, 2–3 mm. long: corolla blue or purplish-blue, 18–20 mm. long: capsule about 14 mm. long. [*Gentiana quinqueflora* Lam.] — (AGUE-WEED. STIFF-GENTIAN.) — Rich woods or moist calcareous soil, various provinces, rarely Coastal Plain, Fla. to Mo., Mich., Ont., and Me.—Sum. & fall.

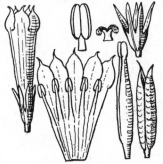

2. G. occidentalis (A. Gray) Small. Similar to the preceding species in habit: flowers larger: calyx-lobes linear or linear-lanceolate, 8–11 mm. long: corolla 22–24 mm. long, pale-blue: capsule fully 15 mm. long. —Moist soil, various provinces, Miss. to La., Minn., and Ohio.—Sum.–fall.

7. DASYSTEPHANA Adans. Annual, biennial, or perennial herbs. Flowers in a compact terminal cyme and axillary cymes or solitary, the whorls mainly of 5 parts each. Calyx persistent: lobes minute or foliaceous, more or less unequal. Corolla funnelform or clavate, with neither glands at the base of the tube nor filaments at the base of the lobes: lobes much shorter than the tube, with plaits at the sinuses. Stigmas narrow. Capsule stipitate.—About 75 species, natives of the north temperate zone.—Fall.—GENTIANS.

Flowers sessile, clustered: corolla-lobes shorter than the plaits in their sinuses or
  decidedly longer, erect, ascending, or converging.   I. LATIFOLIAE.
Flowers pedicelled, solitary: corolla-lobes much longer than the
  plaits, spreading, or reflexed.   II. ANGUSTIFOLIAE.

I. LATIFOLIAE

Corolla open funnelform: anthers separate.   1. *D. puberula.*
Corolla campanulate-funnelform to clavate: anthers cohering in
  a tube or a ring.
    Corolla blue.
      Corolla-lobes larger and longer (only slightly so in *D.*
        Saponaria) than the plaits.
        Corolla-lobes decidedly longer than the plaits: stem
          pubescent.
          Calyx-tube glabrous.
            Leaf-blades rounded or subcordate at the base:
              corolla-plaits with 2 unequal fimbriate lobes.   2. *D. parvifolia.*
            Leaf-blades narrowed at the base: corolla-
              plaits with 2 equal, nearly entire lobes.   3. *D. latifolia.*
                                    4. *D. decora.*
          Calyx-tube pubescent.
        Corolla-lobes slightly longer than the plaits: stem
          glabrous.   5. *D. Saponaria.*
      Corolla-lobes very small, mostly smaller and shorter
        than the plaits.   6. *D. Andrewsii.*

Corolla white, more or less tinged with green or yellow, or
greenish-white or purplish-green.
   Calyx-lobes shorter than the tube: leaf-blades broad at
     the base and more or less clasping: seeds winged.   7. *D. flavida.*
   Calyx-lobes longer than the tube: leaf-blades narrowed
     at the base: seeds wingless.   8. *D. villosa.*

II. ANGUSTIFOLIAE

Corolla-limb deep-blue: free portions of the filaments lanceolate.   9. *D. Porphyrio.*
Corolla-limb white: free portions of the filaments subulate.   10. *D. tenuifolia.*

1. **D. puberula** (Michx.) Small. Plant 2–4.5 dm. tall, finely pubescent or
puberulent: blades of the upper leaves lanceolate or elliptic-lanceolate: calyx
18–26 mm. long; lobes linear to narrowly
linear-lanceolate, about as long as the tube:
corolla rose-purple, 3.5–5 cm. long; lobes
broadly ovate, ascending; plaits cleft and
laciniate, much shorter than the lobes:
capsule-body about 2 cm. long.—Dry prairies
and stony soil, various provinces N of
Coastal Plain, Ga. to Kans., S. Dak., and
Md.—Differs from our other blue-flowered
species in the widely open corolla-throat and
large ascending lobes which conspicuously
exceed the narrow deeply-lobed plaits.

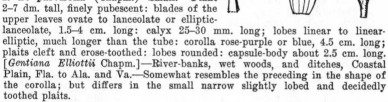

2. **D. parvifolia** (Chapm.) Small. Plant
2–7 dm. tall, finely pubescent: blades of the
upper leaves ovate to lanceolate or elliptic-
lanceolate, 1.5–4 cm. long: calyx 25–30 mm. long; lobes linear to linear-
elliptic, much longer than the tube: corolla rose-purple or blue, 4.5 cm. long;
plaits cleft and erose-toothed: lobes rounded: capsule-body about 2.5 cm. long.
[*Gentiana Elliottii* Chapm.]—River-banks, wet woods, and ditches, Coastal
Plain, Fla. to Ala. and Va.—Somewhat resembles the preceding in the shape of
the corolla; but differs in the small narrow slightly lobed and decidedly
toothed plaits.

3. **D. latifolia** (Chapm.) Small. Plant 3–8 dm. tall, finely pubescent: blades
of the upper leaves elliptic to broadly elliptic or sometimes nearly linear, 2–8
cm. long: calyx 15–25 mm. long; lobes linear to linear-lanceolate, commonly
shorter than the tube or fully as long: corolla rose-purple, 4–5 cm. long; lobes
acute; plaits cleft and somewhat erose: capsule-body nearly 2.5 cm. long.
[*Gentiana Elliottii latifolia* Chapm.]—Moist soil, Coastal Plain, Fla. to Ala.
and S Va.—Larger than the next preceding, with more typically elliptic leaf-
blades, and with larger scarcely toothed corolla-plaits.

4. **D. decora** (Pollard) Small. Plant similar to that of *D. latifolia* in habit:
leaf-blades thinner, more decidedly acuminate: calyx less than 15 mm. long;
lobes subulate to linear-subulate or lanceolate, shorter than the tube: corolla
purple, 2.5–3 cm. long; lobes longer than the plaits: plaits very broad, rather
truncate and erose: capsule-body about 2 cm. long.—Moist mt. woods, Blue
Ridge, Ga. to Va.—Differs from all the preceding species and from the next
following in the small calyx-lobes and from all related species in the small
corolla-lobes which are separated by wide broadly 2-lobed erose plaits.

5. **D. Saponaria** (L.) Small. Plant 3–8 dm. tall, glabrous: blades of the upper leaves lanceolate to ovate-lanceolate or elliptic, 2.5–7.5 cm. long: calyx 15–
22 mm. long; lobes spatulate to linear-spatulate, as long as the tube or shorter:
corolla blue or purplish-blue, 3.5–4 cm. long; lobes mainly shorter than the
plaits: plaits narrow, cleft and incised-laciniate: capsule-body fully 1.5 cm.
long. [*Gentiana Saponaria* L.]—(SOAPWORT-GENTIAN.)—Moist shaded banks

and woods, often in acid soil, various provinces, Ga. (or Fla.?), to La., Minn., Ont., and Conn.—Readily distinguished from related species by the large lobed and somewhat laciniate corolla-plaits which about equal the corolla-lobes.

6. **D. Andrewsii** (Griseb.) Small. Plants 3–10 dm. tall, glabrous; blades of the upper leaves lanceolate, elliptic-lanceolate, ovate-lanceolate or ovate, mainly 4–9 cm. long: calyx mostly 11–19 mm. long; lobes elliptic, oval, or ovate, shorter than the tube, rather loosely spreading: corolla blue or purplish-blue or exceptionally white, 2.5–4 cm. long; lobes inconspicuous, very short, much broader than long, abruptly pointed, much exceeded by the broad, somewhat truncate unequally 2-lobed and erose toothed plaits: capsule-body 2–2.5 cm. long. [*Gentiana Andrewsii* Griseb.]—Moist woods, meadows, prairies and swampy thickets, often in calcareous soil, various provinces, in Coastal Plain only northward, Ga. to Ark. (Kans.?), N. Dak., and Me.—Easily distinguished from all our other species by the small inconspicuous corolla-lobes which are much exceeded by the large broad-topped plaits.

7. **D. flavida** (A. Gray) Britton. Plants 2–9 dm. tall, glabrous: blades of the upper leaves lanceolate to ovate, not of an obovate type, 5–11 cm. long: calyx 11–20 mm. long; lobes ovate to orbicular-ovate, shorter than the tube, reflexed-spreading: corolla white, or sometimes tinged with yellow, 3–4 cm. long; lobes deltoid-ovate to reniform-ovate, longer than the coarsely and irregularly few-toothed plaits: capsule-body about 2 cm. long.—Woods, prairies, moist banks and somewhat acid meadows, various provinces N of Coastal Plain, N. C. to Ark., Mo., Ont., and W Pa.—May be distinguished from our other species by the white or yellow-tinged corolla and the short and broad calyx-lobes.

8. **D. villosa** (L.) Small. Plant 1–6 dm. tall, glabrous: blades of the upper leaves elliptic, oval, cuneate-obovate, or obovate, not of an ovate type, 2–8 cm. long: calyx 25–40 mm. long; lobes linear to linear-spatulate, longer than the tube, erect or nearly so: corolla greenish-white or purplish-green, 4–5 cm. long; lobes ovate to deltoid-ovate, much longer than the entire or merely 2-lobed plaits: capsule-body 2.5–3 cm. long. [*Gentiana ochroleuca* Froel.]—Grassy thickets, acid open woods, and pinelands, various provinces, Fla. to La., Tenn., and N. J.—Differs from our other species in the mainly greenish-white corolla and narrow calyx-lobes.

9. **D. Porphyrio** (J. F. Gmel.) Small. Plant mostly 2–4.5 dm. tall, the stem simple or rarely branched: leaf-blades narrow, those of the lower leaves spatulate, those of the upper linear-spatulate to linear: calyx-lobes linear-subulate: corolla deeply colored, the limb deep-blue; lobes ovate, entire or obscurely erose: plaits rather sparingly laciniate: capsule-body 1.5–2 cm. long.—Pinelands, and margins of acid pools, Coastal Plain, S. C. to N. J.—This and the following species differ from all the preceding in the funnelform corolla and laciniate plaits.

10. **D. tenuifolia** (Raf.) Pennell. Plant mostly 1–2 dm. tall, the stem usually simple: leaf-blades very narrow, those of the lower leaves linear-spatulate, those of the upper narrowly linear: calyx-lobes linear-subulate: corolla white or greenish-white, the limb white; lobes ovate, evidently erose-toothed: plaits rather copiously laciniate: capsule-body about 1.5 cm. long.—Low pinelands, M Fla.—Most readily separated from the next preceding species by its low stature and white or greenish-white corolla-limb.

8. **FRASERA** Walt. Biennial or perennial herbs, usually coarse and with hollow stems. Flowers in panicled cymes. Calyx-lobes 4, narrow. Corolla

white, yellowish, or bluish, rotate: lobes 4, longer than the tube, each with 1 or 2 glands.—Five species, North American.

1. F. carolinensis Walt. Stem 1–2.5 m. tall: leaves usually in whorls of 4; blades spatulate to elliptic or elliptic-lanceolate, 1–3 dm. long: calyx-lobes linear to linear-lanceolate, acuminate: corolla ochroleucous and purple-dotted; lobes broadly elliptic to oval, 13–16 mm. long, each with a fringed gland below the middle: capsule ovoid, about 2 cm. long. —Rich woods, and dry, calcareous slopes, various provinces, Ga. to La., Ont., and W N. Y.—Spr.–sum.—This plant is usually triennial, blooming the second year after the seed germinates, and dying as soon as the new seed is perfected.

9. BARTONIA Muhl. Annual or biennial, slender wiry herbs. Leaves mere narrow scales. Flowers in racemose or panicled cymes, or solitary, each subtended by a narrow bract. Calyx-lobes 4, keeled, narrowed upward. Corolla white or yellowish, rotate: lobes 4, longer than the tube.—Four species, of eastern North America.—Sum.–fall.

Corolla 6 mm. long or more; lobes spatulate to obovate-spatulate.	1. *B. verna.*
Corolla 5 mm. long or less; lobes lanceolate to elliptic.	
Corolla-lobes elliptic, more or less erose, abruptly pointed:	
branches and pedicels stiff.	2. *B. virginica.*
Corolla-lobes lanceolate, entire, acute or acuminate: branches	
and pedicels lax.	3. *B. lanceolata.*

1. B. verna (Michx.) Muhl. Plant 0.5–3 dm. tall: leaves (scales) opposite, 1–2 mm. long: calyx-lobes linear-lanceolate: corolla white: lobes 7–10 mm. long: capsule 5–6 mm. long.—Moist pinelands, prairies, and lake shores, Coastal Plain, Fla. to La. and Va.—Wint.–spr.

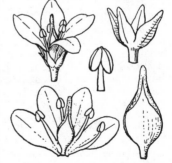

2. B. virginica (L.) B. S. P. Plant 1–4 dm. tall: leaves (scales) opposite, or alternate on small plants: calyx-lobes subulate or lanceolate-subulate: corolla yellowish-white; lobes mostly 2–2.5 mm. long: capsule 3–5 mm. long.—Open woods, swamps, and grassy banks, in acid soil, various provinces, Fla. to La., Minn., and Newf.

3. B. lanceolata Small. Plant 2–6 dm. tall: leaves (scales) opposite or alternate: calyx-lobes similar to those of *B. virginica*: corolla greenish-white; lobes mostly 2.5–3 mm. long: capsule 4–5 mm. long.— Wet pinelands and swamps, Coastal Plain and rarely adj. provinces, Fla. to Ark. and N. Y.—In this and the next preceding species the plants are often yellowish, containing little chlorophyl and apparently living, at least in part, as saprophytes in decaying organic matter.

10. OBOLARIA L. Perennial small, but stout succulent herbs. Leaves mere dilated scales. Flowers in spike-like cymes, each subtended by a dilated

bract. Calyx-lobes 2, dilated upward.
Corolla white, pinkish, or purplish, broadly
funnelform: lobes 4, about as long as the
tube.—One species.

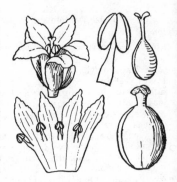

1. **O. virginica** L. Plant purplish-green,
5–20 cm. tall: leaves (scales) 5–10 mm. long,
the upper ones broadened upward, longer
than the lower ones: calyx-lobes spatulate or
elliptic-spatulate: corolla 7–10 mm. long:
lobes nearly as long as the tube, acute:
capsule 5–6 mm. long.—(PENNYWORT.)—
Moist thickets and rich woods, various
provinces, Fla. to Tex., Ill., and N. J.—Spr.

11. **LEIPHAIMOS** Schlecht. & Cham. Annual or perennial humus-plants.
Leaves mere scales. Flowers solitary or in cymes. Calyx-lobes 4 or 5, narrow,
commonly about as long as the tube. Corolla
white or variously colored, salverform: lobes
4 or 5, much shorter than the tube.—About
20 species, mostly tropical American.

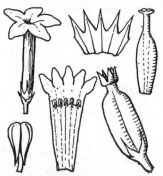

1. **L. parasitica** Schlecht. & Cham. Plant
pale, 1–4 dm. tall: leaves (scales) opposite,
3–5 mm. long: calyx-lobes lanceolate, acute:
corolla white or pink, 6–8 mm. long, about
twice as long as the calyx; lobes triangular
to lanceolate: capsule 5–6 mm. long. [*Voyria
mexicana* Griseb.]—Hammocks, Everglade
Keys, Fla. and Florida Keys.—(*W. I.*)—All
year.

FAMILY 3. **MENYANTHACEAE** — BOGBEAN FAMILY

Perennial aquatic or bog herbs. Leaves alternate; blades simple or
3-foliolate. Flowers perfect, solitary, or in clusters or racemes. Calyx
of 5 partly united sepals. Corolla white or colored, rotate or funnelform.
Androecium of 5 stamens, with the filaments partly adnate to the corolla-
tube. Gynoecium of 2 united carpels. Style very short. Fruit a capsule, sometimes indehiscent.—Five genera and about 35 species, widely
distributed.

1. **NYMPHOIDES** [Tourn.] Hill. Aquatic herbs. Leaves with elongate
petioles and broad blades with a deep basal sinus. Flower-clusters sometimes
tuber-bearing, borne on a petiole-like stalk. Calyx-lobes narrow. Corolla
rotate. Filaments adnate to near the middle of the corolla-tube or above it.
Capsule ellipsoid to ovoid. [*Limnanthemum* J. F. Gmel.]—About 20 species,
widely distributed in temperate and tropical regions.—FLOATING-HEARTS.

Leaf-blades relatively small: corolla about twice as long as the calyx: capsule
   slightly longer than the calyx: seed smooth.   1. *N. lacunosum.*
Leaf-blades relatively large: corolla about thrice as long as the
   calyx: capsule about twice as long as the calyx: seed tuberculate.   2. *N. aquaticum.*

1. **N. lacunosum** (Vent.) Kuntze. Leaf-blades ovate or orbicular-ovate, 2–4.5 cm. long: flower-clusters usually with tubers: corolla white: filaments adnate to above the middle of the corolla-tube, the free portion longer than the anther: capsule about 4 mm. long. [*L. lacunosum* Griseb.] —Shallow water, various provinces, Fla. to La., Minn., Ont., and Me.—Spr.–fall.

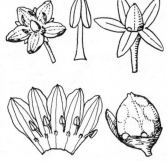

2. **N. aquaticum** (Walt.) Kuntze. Leaf-blades suborbicular to reniform, 5–15 cm. in diameter: flower-clusters usually without tubers: corolla white: filaments adnate to below the middle of the corolla-tube, the free portion shorter than the anther: capsule about 6 mm. long. [*L. trachyspermum* A. Gray]—Ponds and slow streams, Coastal Plain, Fla. to Tex. and N. J.—Spr.–sum.

ORDER ASCLEPIADALES—ASCLEPIADAL ORDER

Herbs, shrubs or trees, commonly with a milky juice. Leaves alternate or opposite: blades entire. Inflorescence cymose, sometimes umbellate. Calyx of usually 5, partially united, sepals. Corolla of usually 5 partially united petals. Androecium of 5 distinct or monadelphous stamens. Pollen granular, or in waxy masses. Gynoecium of usually 2 carpels sometimes only united at the apex. Stigma terminal. Fruit a pair of follicles, or drupaceous.

Styles united: stamens distinct: pollen loosely granular. Fam. 1. APOCYNACEAE.
Styles distinct: stamens monadelphous: pollen united into
 waxy masses. Fam. 2. ASCLEPIADACEAE.

FAMILY 1. APOCYNACEAE — DOGBANE FAMILY

Perennial herbs, vines, shrubs or trees, mostly with a milky acrid juice. Leaf-blades simple. Androecium of 5 stamens with the anthers converging around the stigma or partly adhering to it. Filaments partially adnate to the corolla-tube. Pollen-grains simple. Gynoecium of 2 distinct carpels or 2 united carpels. Styles united. Stigmas simple. Fruit usually of 2 follicles or drupes. Seed often appendaged.—About 130 genera and 1,100 species, widely distributed but mostly tropical.

Carpels distinct: fruit a pair of follicles or drupes, sometimes single by abortion.
 Anthers unappendaged at the base, not connected with the stigma: corolla-lobes
  sinistrorsely convolute. I. VINCEAE.
 Anthers appendaged at the base, converging around the
  stigma and partially adherent to it: corolla-lobes dex-
  trorsely convolute. II. ECHITIDEAE.
Carpels united: fruit a 1-celled capsule. III. ALLAMANDAE.

I. VINCEAE

Fruit drupaceous: shrubs or trees.
 Corolla salverform, relatively small; lobes equilateral,
  shorter than the tube. 1. VALLESIA.
 Corolla funnelform, relatively large; lobes inequilateral,
  longer than the tube. 2. CERBERA.
Fruit a pair of follicles: herbs, sometimes partially shrubby.
 Flower without a disk: leaves alternate. 3. AMSONIA.
 Flower with a 2-lobed disk: leaves opposite.

Anther with a foliaceous connective: carpels 6–8-
ovuled: stigma glabrous: corolla funnelform.   4. VINCA.
Anther with an inconspicuous connective: carpels
several-ovuled: stigma pubescent: corolla salverform.   5. CATHARANTHUS.

II. ECHITIDEAE

Shrubs or trees.   6. NERIUM.
Herbs or vines.
  Corolla appendaged within: calyx-tube partially at-
  tached to the gynoecium by the thick disk: upright
  herbs.   7. APOCYNUM.
  Corolla unappendaged: calyx-tube wholly free: vines.
    Stigmas appendaged with a reversed cup or 5 lobes.
      Corolla funnelform, the throat widened upward.
        Calyx-lobes relatively long and narrow: scale-
        like glands borne at the base of the calyx
        within.   8. URECHITES.
        Calyx-lobes relatively broad and short: scale-
        like glands wanting.   9. RHABDADENIA.
      Corolla salverform, the throat narrowed upward.   10. ECHITES.
    Stigma merely thickened.   11. TRACHELOSPERMUM

III. ALLAMANDAE

Shrub with opposite, sometimes whorled leaves, yellow funnelform corollas, and echinate capsules.   12. ALLAMANDA.

1. VALLESIA R. & P. Shrubs. Leaves alternate: blades relatively broad. Calyx-lobes short. Corolla salverform, the throat contracted at the mouth: lobes shorter than the tube, equilateral. Stamens adnate up to the throat of the corolla: anthers cordate: disk wanting. Carpels 2. Drupe narrow. Seeds clavate, unappendaged.—Two species tropical American.

1. V. glabra Cav. Shrub 3 m. tall or less, the branches sometimes elongate and vine-like: leaves remote; blades elliptic to elliptic-lanceolate, 4–7 cm. long: calyx-lobes deltoid to ovate-deltoid, less than 1 cm. long: corolla white; tube 5–6 mm. long; lobes linear-elliptic, 3–4 mm. long; drupe 10–14 mm. long.—Hammocks, Florida Keys.—(W. I.) Mex., C. A., S. A.—Spr.–fall.

2. CERBERA L. Shrubs or trees. Leaves alternate: blades relatively narrow. Calyx-lobes long. Corolla funnelform, the throat not constricted at the mouth. Drupe broad. Seeds angular. [Thevetia L.]—About 7 species, tropical American.

1. C. Thevetia L. Shrub: leaves approximate; blades narrowly linear, 8–16 cm. long: calyx-lobes lanceolate, 5–7 mm. long: corolla saffron-colored or rarely yellow or white; tube 2–2.5 cm. long; lobes very broad, 3–4 cm. long: drupe depressed, 3–4 cm. broad.— (TRUMPET-FLOWER. YELLOW-OLEANDER.)— Pinelands, cult. grounds, and waste-places, S. pen. Fla. and Florida Keys. Nat. of Trop. Am.—(W. I., Mex., C. A., S. A.)—All year. —Known as lucky-nut in the West Indies and in southern Florida.

3. **AMSONIA** Walt. Herbs. Leaves alternate: blades various. Calyx-lobes deltoid to lanceolate. Corolla mainly salverform, blue or purple-blue; lobes narrow.—About 8 species, North American and Asiatic.—BLUE–DOGBANES. BLUE-STARS.

Corolla pubescent without.
  Leaf-blades glabrous or nearly so, at least at maturity: follicles glabrous.
    Leaf-blades broad, ovate, oval, or broadly elliptic-lanceolate.   1. *A. Amsonia.*
    Leaf-blades narrow, elliptic, elliptic-lanceolate, lanceolate, or linear-lanceolate.   2. *A. salicifolia.*
    Leaf-blades tomentose beneath, permanently pubescent beneath: follicles pubescent, at least on the upper part.   3. *A. ludoviciana.*
Corolla glabrous without.
  Leaves elongate; blades elliptic-lanceolate, linear-lanceolate, linear, or linear-filiform, those of the upper ones at least sessile.   4. *A. ciliata.*
  Leaves short; blades elliptic, oval, or ovate, distinctly petioled.   5. *A. rigida.*

1. **A. Amsonia** (L.) Britton. Plant 6–13 dm. tall, glabrous or nearly so: leaves relatively few; blades relatively broad, oval to broadly elliptic-lanceolate, 6.5–13 cm. long: corolla purplish-blue; tube 6–8 mm. long; lobes shorter than the tube; follicles 9–12 cm. long. [*A. Tabernaemontana* Walt.]—(TEXAS-STAR.)—River banks and rich woods, various provinces, Fla. to Tex., Kans., and S. C., naturalized as far N as Mass.—Spr.–sum.

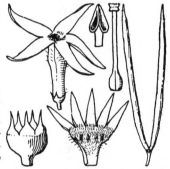

2. **A. salicifolia** Pursh. Plant 6–12 dm. tall, glabrous: leaf-blades relatively narrow, lanceolate to linear-lanceolate, 7–16 cm. long; corolla purplish-blue; lobes as long as the tube or longer; follicles 8–12 cm. long.— Low grounds and thickets, in somewhat acid soil, various provinces, Fla. to Tex., Kans., and Va.—Spr.–sum.

3. **A. ludoviciana** Vail. Plant 5–11 dm. tall, pubescent at least when young: leaves relatively few; blades broadly elliptic to oval-elliptic, 6–9 cm. long, white-tomentose beneath: corolla bluish; tube 6–7 mm. long; lobes about as long as the tube: follicles 8–10 cm. long.—Moist grounds, often in open woods, Coastal Plain and adj. provinces, Miss. to La. and Ark.—Spr.—The flowers are very fragrant.

4. **A. ciliata** Walt. Plant 2–8 dm. tall, often much-branched, pubescent: leaves numerous; blades linear to linear-filiform on the upper part of the plant (almost filiform in *A. ciliata filifolia*), 4–7 cm. long: corolla purplish-blue, tube 6–8 mm. long, the lobes ovate to elliptic-ovate, mostly shorter than the tube: follicles 8–16 cm. long.—Dry pinelands, Coastal Plain, and adj. Piedmont, Fla. to Tex., Ark., and N. C.—Spr.–sum.

5. **A. rigida** Shuttlw. Plant 8–13 dm. tall, glabrous: leaves very numerous; blades elliptic, oval, or ovate, 2.5–5 cm. long: calyx-lobes about 1 mm. long: corolla purplish-blue; tube 4–6 mm. long; lobes as long as the tube or longer: follicles 7–12 cm. long.—Moist pinelands and shallow ponds, Coastal Plain, Fla. and Ga.—Spr.–sum.

4. **VINCA** L. Trailing or creeping herbs. Leaves opposite. Corolla blue, or rarely white: tube dilated at the mouth.—About 12 species, natives of the Old World.—Spr.–sum.—PERIWINKLES. MYRTLES.

Leaf-blades elliptic to elliptic-ovate, eciliate: calyx-lobes eciliate: follicles beakless 1. *V. minor*.

Leaf-blades ovate to deltoid-ovate, ciliate: calyx-lobes ciliate: follicles beaked. 2. *V. major*.

1. V. minor L. Leaf-blades subcoriaceous, 1–5 cm. long, narrowed to a short petiole: calyx-lobes lanceolate, 3–4 mm. long, glabrous: corolla 1.5–2 cm. wide: follicle 2.5 cm. long or less.—Roadsides, shaded banks, and cult. grounds, various provinces, Ga. to Ark. and Ont.—Nat. of Eu.

2. V. major L. Leaf-blades membranous, 4–7 cm. long, manifestly petioled: calyx-lobes subulate, 9–15 mm. long, bearded at the tip: corolla 4–5 cm. wide: follicle 3 cm. long or more.—Woods and roadsides, Coastal Plain, Ga. and S. C.—Nat. of Eu.—These periwinkles were brought to America from Europe by the early settlers in the eastern United States. By means of the creeping stems, plants soon spread from gardens to roadsides and even into woodlands.

5. CATHARANTHUS G. Don. Erect herbs. Leaves opposite. Corolla variously colored or white: tube with a contracted mouth. Follicle narrow.— Three species, the following and two in the Old World tropics.

1. C. roseus (L.) G. Don. Stems 2–7 dm. tall: leaf-blades oblong to oblong-cuneate, 4–8 cm. long: calyx-lobes linear-subulate, 3–4 mm. long: corolla white, pink, or rose-purple, with an eye; tube 27–34 mm. long: lobes abruptly pointed: follicle 2–3 cm. long. [*Vinca rosea* L. *Ammocallis rosea* Small]—(PERIWINKLE. OLD-MAID.)—Pinelands, hammocks, waste-places, roadsides, and cult. grounds, pen. Fla. and the Keys. Nat. of Madagascar (?).—(*W. I., Mex., C. A., S. A.*)—This showy plant has taken possession of acres of scrub land in southern peninsular Florida.

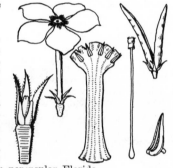

6. NERIUM [Tourn.] L. Shrubs or trees. Leaves opposite: blades relatively narrow. Corolla salverform, the throat campanulate, with toothed scales at the mouth: the lobes spreading, broad. Follicles elongate.—Three species, Eurasian.

1. N. Oleander L. Tree becoming 10 m. tall, or shrub: leaf-blades narrowly elliptic to linear-elliptic, 6–15 cm. long, many-veined: calyx-lobes lanceolate, 4.5–6 mm. long: corolla white to rose-purple or crimson; limb 3–4.5 cm. wide, the lobes obliquely apiculate: follicles 1–2 dm. long.—(OLEANDER.)—Roadsides, fields, and edges of woods, Coastal Plain, Fla. to La. Nat. of the Levants and cult.—(*W. I.*)—All year.—The sap is exceedingly poisonous. In some varieties the leaves contain a good percentage of rubber, in others practically none.

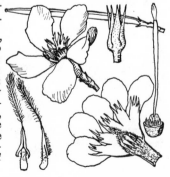

7. APOCYNUM [Tourn.] L. Upright herbs. Leaves opposite: blades relatively broad. Corolla campanulate to urceolate, with entire appendages near the base, the lobes erect or recurved, narrow.—About 12 species, in the north temperate zone.—Sum.—DOGBANES. INDIAN-HEMPS.

Corolla white, or pink within, 5–9 mm. long.
    Corolla-lobes revolute: flowers nodding: corolla pink
      within: leaves spreading.   1. *A. androsaemifolium.*
    Corolla-lobes spreading: flowers slightly or not at all
      nodding: corolla usually white: leaves erect.   2. *A. medium.*
Corolla white or greenish, 2.5–4 mm. long: lobes usually
    erect: leaves and branches erect.   3. *A. cannabinum.*

1. A. androsaemifolium L. Plant 3–15 dm. tall: leaf-blades ovate, elliptic, or oval, 4–11 cm. long: cymes rather long: calyx-lobes ovate to ovate-lanceolate, 2–2.5 mm. long: corolla-lobes nearly as long as the tube: follicles 10–17 cm. long.— Thickets, fields, and fence-rows, various provinces, in Coastal Plain only northward, Ga. to Tex., B. C., Ont., and N. B.

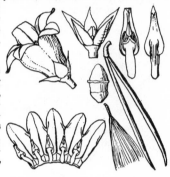

2. A. medium Greene. Plant intermediate between the preceding and the following species: leaf-blades elliptic to ovate-elliptic, 4–9 cm. long: cymes somewhat dense: calyx-lobes lanceolate, 2–2.5 mm. long: corolla-lobes nearly as long as the tube: follicles 8–13 cm. long.—Thickets, fields, fencerows, and low grounds, various provinces, in Coastal Plain only northward, N. C. to Mo., Minn., and Newf.

3. A. cannabinum L. Plant 8–18 dm. tall: leaf-blades elliptic to elliptic-ovate or elliptic-lanceolate, 5–12 cm. long: cymes rather dense: calyx-lobes lanceolate, 2.5–3 mm. long: corolla-lobes about half as long as the tube: follicles 12–20 cm. long.—Thickets, open woods, and stream-banks, various provinces, Fla. to Tex., B. C., Ont., and N. B.—The several proposed segregates of this species do not prove to be definitely distinct, all variations being found between the several segregates.

8. URECHITES Muell.-Arg. Vines, or erect woody plants. Leaves opposite: blades flat, entire. Calyx-lobes 5, relatively long and narrow. Corolla showy, large, the short tube dilated into a longer campanulate throat, the limb prominently lobed. Anthers sagittate, longer than the filaments, each usually with a much elongate narrow apical appendage. Follicles elongate, very slender, more or less incurved. Seeds numerous, slender-beaked.—About 6 species, tropical American.

Calyx permanently copiously pubescent: corolla pubescent without: basal lobes of
    the anther over 1 cm. long.   1. *U. pinetorum.*
Calyx glabrous, at least ultimately so: corolla glabrous without:
    basal lobes of the anther less than 1 cm. long.   2. *U. lutea.*

1. U. pinetorum Small. Plant gray-green, the stem underground, the branches erect, or when more elongate reclining, simple or nearly so, copiously fine-pubescent: leaf-blades obovate, oval, or elliptic, 3–7.5 cm. long, dull above, copiously fine-pubescent beneath: cymes usually solitary, 1–few-flowered, with very narrow bracts: calyx-lobes lanceolate-subulate, 8–10 mm. long, acuminate: corolla deep-yellow, mostly 6–9 cm. wide: anthers about 6 mm. long, the basal lobes slender:

follicles 9–19 cm. long. — (WILD-ALLA-MANDA.)—Pinelands, Everglade Keys, Fla. —Spr.–sum.

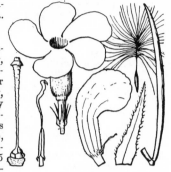

2. **U. lutea** (L.) Britton. Plant bright-green, the stem and branches high-twining, glabrous or inconspicuously pubescent: leaf-blades obovate, elliptic, oval, or ovate, or sometimes suborbicular, mostly 4–7 cm. long, shining above, sometimes inconspicuously pubescent beneath: cymes several or numerous, several- to many-flowered, with foliaceous bracts: calyx-lobes subulate or lanceolate, 9–11 mm. long, acuminate: corolla bright-yellow, mostly 4–5 cm. wide: anthers 4–5 mm. long, the basal lobes stout: follicles 12–15 cm. long. [*Echites Andrewsii* Chapm.]—Hammocks, S pen. Florida and the Keys.—(*W. I.*)—All year.—An imperfect specimen collected many years ago and recorded as coming from Key West represents an extremely pubescent form of this plant, or another species. Several forms of this plant, or perhaps species occur in our range: In one the plant leaves and inflorescence are essentially glabrous; in another the leaf-blades are sparingly pubescent beneath and the inflorescence bristly pubescent; in a third form the leaf-blades are closely often velvety pubescent beneath and the inflorescence is softly fine-pubescent.

9. **RHABDADENIA** Muell.-Arg. Vines, sometimes nearly erect. Leaves opposite. Calyx-lobes relatively broad and short. Corolla-tube gradually dilated into the funnelform throat.—About 10 species, tropical American.

Corolla-limb white, 4.5–5 cm. wide: twining vine, the branches glabrous.   1. *R. biflora.*
Corolla-limb yellow, 2.5–3 cm. wide: erect herb, the branches pubescent.   2. *R. corallicola.*

1. **R. biflora** (Jacq.) Muell.-Arg. Stem greatly elongate: leaf-blades elliptic or elliptic-lanceolate, 4–9 cm. long, apiculate: calyx-lobes elliptic or nearly so, 4–5 mm. long: corolla 5–6 cm. long, white, except the yellow tube within; lobes 2.5–3 cm. wide: follicles 12–15 cm. long.—(RUB-BER-VINE.)—Coastal hammocks, S pen. Fla. and the Keys.—(*W. I.*)—All year.

2. **R. corallicola** Small. Stem 3–11 dm. long: leaf-blades elliptic or nearly so, 1–3 cm. long, more or less revolute: calyx-lobes deltoid ovate, 2–2.5 mm. long: corolla 2.5–3 cm. long, yellow; lobes 1–1.5 cm. wide: follicles 8–11 cm. long.—Pinelands, Everglade Keys and Big Cypress swamp region, Fla. and lower Florida Keys.—All year.—Fragmentary specimens apparently of a related species, *R. Sagraei*, of the Bahamas and Cuba, were collected on "Pine Key" many years ago by Dr. Blodgett. It differs from *R. corallicola* in the twining stem, the broader calyx-lobes, the shorter free portions of the filaments, and the stout-beaked seeds.

10. **ECHITES** P. Br. Vines. Leaves opposite. Flowers relatively large. Calyx with glands within. Corolla salverform, the throat narrowed to the

mouth.—About 40 species, tropical American.

1. E. Echites (L.) Britton. Stem from a tuber-like root, widely twining: leaf-blades ovate to oval, 4–9 cm. long: calyx-lobes triangular, 2.5–3.5 mm. long: corolla white or greenish-white; tube 5–6 cm. long; lobes 1.5–2.5 cm. long: follicles 15–20 cm. long. [*Echites umbellata* Jacq.]—(DEVIL'S-POTATO. RUBBER-VINE.)—Pinelands, Everglade Keys, Fla., and hammocks and pinelands, Florida Keys.—(*W. I.*)—All year. This vine, particularly in the pinelands, is often very vigorous. Its stems and numerous branches are intricately intertwined.

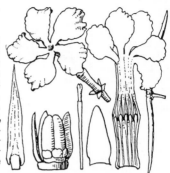

11. TRACHELOSPERMUM Lemaire. Vines with slender woody stems. Leaves opposite. Flowers relatively small. Calyx with glands within. Corolla funnelform.—About 6 species, North American and Asiatic.

1. T. difforme (Walt.) A. Gray. Stem extensively twining: leaf-blades ovate or oval to elliptic or lanceolate, 3–9 cm. long: calyx-lobes lanceolate-subulate, 3–4 cm. long; corolla greenish; tube 5–6 mm. long; lobes ovate, shorter than the tube: follicles 15–22 cm. long. [*Forsteronia difformis* A. DC.] —River-banks, low grounds, and swamps, Coastal Plain, and adj. provinces, Fla. to Tex., Ark., Ind., and Del.—(*Mex.*)—Spr.–sum. The true relationships of this vine are uncertain. It has no close relatives geographically. Its associates in the present genus are in eastern Asia; the species of *Secondatia*, a genus in which it is sometimes included are South American.

12. ALLAMANDA L. Shrubs, trees, or woody vines. Leaves opposite, sometimes whorled. Flowers large, often showy. Calyx-lobes rather narrow. Corolla funnelform, with a cylindric tube, a campanulate throat, and broad lobes. Capsule subglobose, more or less compressed, echinate.—About 12 species, tropical.

1. A. cathartica L. Shrub mostly 1–3 m. tall, the twigs finely pubescent: leaf-blades oblanceolate to elliptic, 5–12 cm. long, mostly abruptly short-acuminate, glabrous except the veins beneath: flowers short-pedicelled: calyx-lobes lanceolate to elliptic-lanceolate: corolla yellow, 7–10 cm. long, the tube and throat about equal in length: the limb 6–8 cm. wide: capsule 4–6 cm. in diameter,

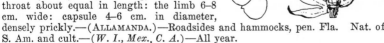

densely prickly.—(ALLAMANDA.)—Roadsides and hammocks, pen. Fla. Nat. of S. Am. and cult.—(*W. I., Mex., C. A.*)—All year.

FAMILY 2. **ASCLEPIADACEAE** — MILKWEED FAMILY

Perennial herbaceous or woody plants, with usually umbel-like cymes. Androecium of usually 5 stamens, with the anthers more adherent to the stigma than in *Apocynaceae,* the filament-appendages forming a crown with 5 lobes. Gynoecium of 2 carpels with the stigmas united; only one carpel usually maturing.—About 240 genera and 2,000 species, widely distributed.

Pollen granular, the grains grouped in 4's: caudicles spoon-shaped, without a corpuscle.   I. PERIPLOCEAE.
Pollen united in 2 waxy masses (pollinia) : caudicles united by a corpuscle.
   Pollinia pendulous: stigma not saucer-shaped nor cup-like: anthers tipped with a scarious membrane, the sacs lower than the top of the stigma.   II. ASCLEPIADEAE.
   Pollinia horizontal or nearly so: stigma saucer-shaped or cup-like: anthers scarcely or not at all tipped with a scarious membrane, the sacs on the margin of or close under the stigma.   III. VINCETOXICEAE.

I. PERIPLOCEAE

Corolla rotate: follicles long-subulate, nearly terete, erect: cymes several–many-flowered.   1. PERIPLOCA.
Corolla funnelform: follicles short and stout, irregularly angled, divergent: cymes few-flowered.   2. CRYPTOSTEGIA.

II. ASCLEPIADEAE

Crown double, the outer a shallow ring, the inner consisting of 5 fleshy hook-like scales.   3. FUNASTRUM.
Crown single.
  Erect, ascending, or spreading herbs.
    Corolla ellipsoid-campanulate: lobes erect.   4. PODOSTIGMA.
    Corolla rotate, the lobes spreading or reflexed in anthesis.
      Corolla-lobes reflexed during anthesis: hoods of the crown crestless or each with a horn-like process.
        Anther-wings corneous: pollinia longer than the caudicles.
          Hoods of the crown without horns or crests.   5. ACERATES.
          Hoods of the crown each with an internal projecting horn.
            Hoods scoop-like or trowel-like, with free edges, the horn free or partly adnate to the hood: flower-buds not flat-topped.   6. ASCLEPIAS.
            Hoods saccate or with the sides conduplicate and thus dorso-ventrally flattened, the tip of the horn protruding from the groove or slit on the inner side of the hood.
            Hoods subglobose, inflated, the horn protruding from the groove between the 2 sacs: flower-buds flat-topped.   7. BIVENTRARIA.
            Hoods elongate, dorso-ventrally flattened, the horn protruding from the slit between the conduplicate edges: flower-buds not flat-topped.   8. OXYPTERYX.
        Anther-wings membranous or papery: hoods of the crown ellipsoid-clavate, ascending and incurved over the anthers, each with a lamelliform crest within: pollinia shorter than the caudicles.   9. ANANTHERIX.
      Corolla-lobes erect-spreading during anthesis: hoods of the crown pendulous or saccate at the base, curved upwards, obtuse, crested within, at least in the upper part.
        Hoods of the crown involute, and hooded at the apex, crested above the middle: anthers rounded at the base.   10. ASCLEPIODORA.
        Hoods of the crown concave, open at the apex: anthers sagittate at the base.   11. ASCLEPIODELLA.

Twining vines.
    Petals slightly united at the base: column not elongate.
        Crown-lobes each with an entire or cleft terminal appendage.   12. GONOLOBUS.
        Crown-lobes entire or lobed.
            Corolla-lobes glabrous within: crown-lobes broad.
                Stigma flat: crown-lobes not notched.   13. AMPHISTELMA.
                Stigma conic: crown-lobes notched at the apex.   14. LYONIA.
            Corolla-lobes pubescent within: crown-lobes narrow.   15. METASTELMA.
    Petals united to about the middle: column elongate.   16. EPICION.

III. VINCETOXICEAE

Crown disk-like or saucer-shaped, obscurely, if at all ridged.
    Corolla reticulate: column distinct, appendaged at the base or ridged.   17. CYCLODON.
    Corolla not reticulate: column nearly obsolete, neither appendaged nor ridged.   18. VINCETOXICUM.
Crown cup-shaped or incurved at the tip, usually crested or appendaged on the inner side.
    Cymes long-peduncled, many-flowered: leaves large.   19. ODONTOSTEPHANA.
    Cymes sessile, 1–5-flowered: leaves small.   20. EDISONIA.

1. PERIPLOCA L. Slender twining, partly woody, vines. Leaf-blades broad, membranous. Cymes broad. Calyx-lobes spreading. Corolla rotate, inconspicuous, lobes pubescent within. Crown with lobed scales, each slender-appendaged, adnate to the corolla. Anthers merely connected at the apex, pubescent. Follicles slender.—About 12 species, Eurasian and African.

1. P. graeca L. Stem slender: leaf-blades elliptic to ovate, 6–10 cm. long, acuminate: calyx-lobes ovate to deltoid: corolla-lobes broadly linear, 9–11 mm. long, brownish-purple and green-margined within: crown-appendages nearly as long as the corolla-lobes: follicles curved: seed fusiform, 9–11 mm. long.—(SILK-VINE.)—Waste-places, fence-rows, and cult. grounds, various provinces, Fla. to Okla., Kans., and Mass. Nat. of Eu.—Sum.

2. CRYPTOSTEGIA R. Br. Stout woody sprawling vines. Leaf-blades broad, coriaceous. Cymes narrow. Calyx-lobes erect. Corolla funnelform, showy: lobes glabrous within. Crown with 5 entire or 2-lobed scales attached to the corolla. Anthers connate around the stigma, glabrous. Follicles stout.—Two species, in the Old World tropics.

1. C. grandiflora R.·Br. Stem stout: leaf-blades oval, elliptic, or ovate, 5–10 cm. long, blunt: calyx-lobes lanceolate to ovate, acuminate: corolla-lobes broad, often ovate, 2–3 cm. long, about as long as the throat, white, pink, or rose-purple: crown-appendages shorter than the corolla-throat: follicles straight, 10–15 cm. long: seeds bottle-shaped,

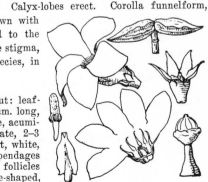

7-8 mm. long.—(PINK-ALLAMANDA. RUBBER-VINE.)—Hammocks, roadsides, and waste-places, S Fla. Nat. of Africa?—(*W. I.*)

3. **FUNASTRUM** Fourn. Vines with narrow or broad leaf-blades. Calyx 5-lobed. Corolla rotate: lobes broad, glabrous within. Anthers coherent. [*Philibertia* B. & H. not H.B.K. *Philibertella* Vail.]—About 30 species, of tropical and subtropical America.

1. **F. clausum** (Jacq.) Schlecht. Leaf-blades 3-8 cm. long, ovate-elliptic to elliptic-lanceolate, rounded or subcordate at the base: peduncles twice as long as the leaves or more: calyx-lobes elliptic-lanceolate: corolla white; lobes elliptic to ovate, 4-5 mm. long: follicles 5-7 cm. long: seeds about 3 mm. long. [*Philibertia viminalis* A. Gray *Philibertella clausa* Vail]—Coastal hammocks and lake regions, pen. Fla. and the Keys.—(*W. I., Mex., C. A., S. A.*)— All year.

4. **PODOSTIGMA** Ell. Erect herbs, with narrow leaf-blades. Calyx-lobes 5. Corolla campanulate. Hoods incurved; blades remote from the anthers which are elevated on a slender column.—One species.

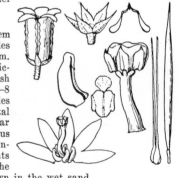

1. **P. pedicellata** (Walt.) Vail. Stem usually simple, 2-4 dm. tall; leaf-blades linear, lanceolate, or linear-elliptic, 2-6 cm. long: calyx-lobes lanceolate or elliptic-lanceolate, 2-2.5 mm. long: corolla yellowish or greenish-yellow; lobes linear-elliptic 7-8 mm. long: hoods 2.5-3 mm. long: follicles 11-15 cm. long.—Low pinelands, Coastal Plain, Fla. to N. C.—Spr.-fall.—A peculiar plant in our flora, the erect cylindraceous yellow or greenish-yellow corollas being unlike those of the other genera. The plants grow in pineland submerged parts of the year and send their elongate roots far down in the wet sand.

5. **ACERATES** Ell. Erect or spreading herbs, with narrow or relatively narrow leaf-blades. Calyx-lobes 5. Corolla rotate, green: lobes reflexed. Hoods approximate to the anthers, the column very short and stout, or slender, or wanting: follicles fusiform.—About 8 species, North American.—GREEN-MILKWEEDS.

Crown stalked; hoods oval or obovate: pollinia with short thick bases.
  Hoods with erect tips: pedicels with curved-appressed hairs.
    Crown ellipsoid: androecium much exceeding the crown.   1. *A. floridana.*
    Crown globose or depressed: androecium slightly exceeding
      the crown.   2. *A. delticola.*
  Hoods with spreading tips: pedicels with spreading hairs.   3. *A. hirtella.*
Crown not stalked; hoods elliptic to lanceolate: pollinia with
  slender stalk-like bases.   4. *A. viridiflora.*

1. **A. floridana** (Lam.) A. Hitchc. Plant 2–7 dm. tall, finely cinereous: leaf-blades narrowly linear, often elongate, to rarely narrowly linear-lanceolate: umbels usually slender-peduncled: pedicels strigillose: calyx-lobes triangular-ovate: corolla-lobes about 5 mm. long, or sometimes shorter, elliptic; crown about 2.5 mm. in diameter: follicles 9–11 cm. long: seed 10–11 mm. long. [*A. longifolia* Ell.]— Damp pinelands and prairies, Coastal Plain, and rarely adj. provinces, Fla. to Tex., Ark., and Del.—Spr.–sum. or all year S.

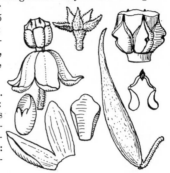

2. **A. delticola** Small. Plant similar to *A. floridana* in habit: leaf-blades lanceolate: umbels rather slender-peduncled: pedicels sparingly strigillose: calyx-lobes deltoid-ovate: corolla-lobes broader than in *A. floridana*: crown about 3.5 mm. in diameter: follicles not seen.—Low grounds, New Orleans, La.—Spr.–sum.

3. **A. hirtella** Pennell. Plant 6–10 dm. tall, densely cinereous: leaf-blades narrowly linear-lanceolate to linear, often numerous and elongate: umbels stout-peduncled: pedicels hirsutulous: calyx-lobes ovate-lanceolate: corolla-lobes fully twice the length of the calyx-lobes: crown somewhat more than half the length of the androecium: follicles 9–10 mm. long: seeds about 8 mm. long.—Prairies and roadsides, various provinces, Ala. to Okla., Ill., and Mich.—Sum.

4. **A. viridiflora** (Raf.) Eaton. Plant 2–6 dm. tall: leaf-blades lanceolate to ovate, elliptic, or oval, 4–12 cm. long: calyx-lobes lanceolate: corolla-lobes 5–6 mm. long: hoods 3–4 mm. long: anther-wings about 4 mm. long: follicles 8–12 cm. long: seed 7–8 mm. long.—Dry sterile soil, various provinces, Fla. to Tex., N. Mex., Sask., and Mass.—Spr.–sum.

6. **ASCLEPIAS** [Tourn.] L. Erect or spreading herbs, with narrow or broad leaf-blades. Calyx-lobes 5. Corolla rotate: lobes reflexed. Hoods of the crown trowel-like or scoop-like, erect or spreading, not adnate to the anther-column, the horn free, or partly adnate to the hood. Anther-wings salient at the base. Follicles ovoid or fusiform.—About 95 species, mostly American.—Sum.—MILKWEEDS. SILKWEEDS.

Crown longer than the androecium or slightly shorter; hoods rounded, obtuse, or truncate at the apex.
  Corolla bright-colored, rarely white: crown white, maroon, or bright-colored, not green.
    Follicles erect on deflexed pedicels.
      Follicles smooth, glabrous or pubescent.
        Leaves mostly scattered, not opposite: plant copiously pubescent.   I. TUBEROSAE.
        Leaves mostly opposite or whorled.
          Corolla orange-scarlet, red, or purple.   II. RUBRAE.
          Corolla white or greenish-red.
            Umbel solitary on an elongate terminal peduncle, or an accessory umbel sometimes present: hoods maroon.   III. AMPLEXICAULES.
            Umbels usually several, axillary and terminal: hoods pale.
              Stem prostrate: leaves vertical; blades sessile and cordate-clasping.   IV. HUMISTRATAE.
              Stem erect: leaves not vertical; blades petioled and tapering at the base.   V. EXALTATAE.

Follicles echinate-warty, sometimes only near the
tip.   VI. SYRIACAE.
Follicles erect on erect pedicels.
    Flowers scarlet and yellow.   VII. CURASSAVICAE.
    Flowers purplish, pink, or white.
        Leaves merely opposite, not whorled.   VIII. INCARNATAE.
        Leaves, at least at some of the nodes, whorled
        in 4's or 6's.   IX. QUADRIFOLIAE.
Corolla green: crown green, greenish-white or yellow-
tinged.
    Follicles erect on deflexed pedicels.   X. TOMENTOSAE.
    Follicles erect on erect pedicels.   XI. VERTICILLATAE.
Crown about half as long as the androecium: hoods deeply
sinuate by the projection of 2 acuminate lateral lobes:
column none.   XII. CINEREAE.

I. TUBEROSAE

Leaf-blades acute or acutish, lanceolate or lance-elliptic: horn very slender.
    Calyx-lobes 1/3 the length of the corolla-lobes or less:
    hood narrowly elliptic.   1. *A. decumbens.*
    Calyx-lobes nearly as long as the corolla-lobes: hoods obo-
    vate.   2. *A. tuberosa.*
Leaf-blades obtuse and broadly rounded, pandurate: horn
very stout.   3. *A. Rolfsii.*

II. RUBRAE

Corolla and crown orange-scarlet.   4. *A. lanceolata.*
Corolla and crown red or purple.
    Leaf-blades glabrate, or least beneath.
        Leaf-blades ovate, ovate-lanceolate, or elliptic-lanceo-
        late, acuminate, distinctly petioled.   5. *A. rubra.*
        Leaf-blades lanceolate to linear-lanceolate, attenuate,
        truncate or nearly cordate-clasping at the base.   6. *A. laurifolia.*
    Leaf-blades densely and softly pubescent beneath.   7. *A. purpurascens.*

III. AMPLEXICAULES

A stiffly erect plant with spreading glossy leaves, the blades
with crisped margins.   8. *A. amplexicaulis.*

IV. HUMISTRATAE

Plant with one or several prostrate stems, the vertically
placed leaves with white veins.   9. *A. humistrata.*

V. EXALTATAE

Umbel loosely flowered, the pedicels more or less nodding:
flowers greenish-red.   10. *A. exaltata.*

VI. SYRIACAE

Tall herb with broad spreading leaves and with many-flowered umbels in the axils of some of them.   11. *A. syriaca.*

VII. CURASSAVICAE

Tall plant with bright-green leaves and showy flowers, the
scarlet corolla and yellow crown very conspicuous. 12. *A. curassavica.*

VIII. INCARNATAE

Flowers pink or purplish: leaf-blades abruptly narrowed at
the base, short-petioled or nearly sessile.
    Plant nearly glabrous: leaf-blades narrow, lanceolate to
    lance-elliptic or nearly linear.   13. *A. incarnata.*
    Plant softly and copiously hirsute: leaf-blades rather
    broad, broadly lanceolate to elliptic or ovate-lanceolate. 14. *A. pulchra.*
Flowers white: leaf-blades tapering to a long petiole. 15. *A. perennis.*

IX. QUADRIFOLIAE

Slender plant with few leaves, the relatively few-flowered
umbels with very slender pedicels.   16. *A. quadrifolia.*

X. TOMENTOSAE

Hoods much exceeding the androecium, the projecting tip
slightly recurved: horn at about the middle of the hood. 17. *A. obovata.*
Hoods about equalling the androecium, turgid, truncate and
slightly fornicate; horn at the top of the hood.
    Horn with the triangular or triangular-lanceolate tip only
    slightly exserted.   18. *A. aceratoides.*
    Horn with the subulate tip much exserted.   19. *A. tomentosa.*

XI. VERTICILLATAE

Hoods nearly equalling the androecium, the much exserted
slender horns converging over its top: column about
1 mm. long.
Upper leaves predominantly opposite; blades flat.   20. *A. linearis.*
Upper leaves predominantly whorled in 3's to 6's; blades
revolute.   21. *A. verticillata.*
Hoods much exceeding the androecium, the horns not much
exserted, flattened: column scarcely 0.5 mm. long.
Umbels usually several in the upper leaf-axils: hoods
erect or nearly so.   22. *A. viridula.*
Umbels usually terminal and solitary: hoods somewhat
spreading.   23. *A. Michauxii.*

XII. CINEREAE

Slender-stemmed plant with few pairs of leaves and few-
flowered umbels: corolla-lobes tardily reflexed.   24. *A. cinerea.*

1. **A. decumbens** L.   Stem decumbent or procumbent, 3–6 dm. long, hirsute
or hispid: leaf-blades mainly elliptic to lanceolate with more or less hastate
base, 3–19 cm. long, acutish: corolla-lobes
6–7 mm. long: horn arising above the hood-
auricles, included only near the base: follicles mostly over 10 cm. long.—Dry fields,
various provinces, Fla. to Tex., Ill., and N.
Y., probably also further north.—Sum.—
Corolla orange or nearly so.

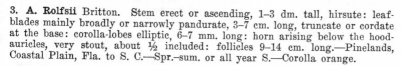

2. **A. tuberosa** L.   Stem mostly erect or
ascending, 3–6 dm. tall, hirsute: leaf-blades
usually lanceolate, varying to lanceolate-
elliptic to linear-lanceolate, 3–9 cm. long,
acute: corolla-lobes 5–6 mm. long: horn arising opposite the hood-auricles, about ⅓
included: follicles mostly less than 10 cm.
long.—(BUTTERFLY-WEED.   PLEURISY-ROOT.)
—Dry fields, various provinces, Fla. to Tex.,
Ariz., Minn., Ont., and Me.—Sum.-fall.—Corolla bright-orange or yellow.

3. **A. Rolfsii** Britton.   Stem erect or ascending, 1–3 dm. tall, hirsute: leaf-
blades mainly broadly or narrowly pandurate, 3–7 cm. long, truncate or cordate
at the base: corolla-lobes elliptic, 6–7 mm. long: horn arising below the hood-
auricles, very stout, about ½ included: follicles 9–14 cm. long.—Pinelands,
Coastal Plain, Fla. to S. C.—Spr.–sum. or all year S.—Corolla orange.

4. **A. lanceolata** Walt.   Stem 4–11 dm. tall, glabrous or nearly so: leaves few,
distant; blades elongate-linear, linear-lanceolate, or narrowly lanceolate, mostly
1–2.5 dm. long, tapering to the base: corolla-lobes elliptic, 8–9 mm. long, red:
hoods ovate, less than twice as long as the androecium, orange-red, rounded at
the apex: horn narrowly lanceolate, much shorter than the hood: follicles 7–10
cm. long.—In acid swamps, Coastal Plain, Fla. to Tex. and N. J.—Sum.

5. **A. rubra** L.   Stem 3–12 dm. tall, glabrous: leaf-blades ovate, ovate-lanceolate, or elliptic-lanceolate, 7–20 cm. long: corolla-lobes purple-red or rarely
purplish-green, 7–8 mm. long: hoods lanceolate, about 6 mm. long, orange-
tinged, about twice as long as the androecium: horn slender-subulate, nearly
as long as the hood: follicles 9–11 cm. long.—Acid swamps and moist grounds,
Coastal Plain and rarely inland provinces, Fla. to Tex., W. Va., and N. J.

6. **A. laurifolia** Michx.   Stem 8–11 dm. tall, almost glabrous: leaf-blades lanceolate to linear-lanceolate, mostly 1–3 dm. long: corolla- lobes reddish-purple,
9–10.5 mm. long: hoods 4–4.5 mm. long, purplish, much exceeding the androe-

cium, rounded at the apex; horn subulate, much shorter than the hood: follicles 8–11 cm. long.—Swamps and low pinelands, Coastal Plain, Fla. to Tex. and Ga.—Spr.–sum.

7. **A. purpurascens** L. Stem 3–12 dm. tall, pubescent in lines or becoming glabrous: leaf-blades mainly ovate or elliptic-ovate, 9–20 cm. long: corolla-lobes purple, 8–10 mm. long: hoods 4.5–5 mm. long, fully twice as long as the androecium, ovate at the entire apex; horn much shorter than the hood, with a horizontal subulate tip: follicles 10–12 cm. long.—(Purple-milkweed.)—Dry grounds, various provinces, N. C. to Okla., Kans., Minn., and N. H.; reported also from Miss.—Sum.

8. **A. amplexicaulis** J. E. Smith. Stem erect, 3–10 dm. tall, glaucous: leaf-blades horizontal, elliptic, 6–12 cm. long, sessile and clasping: corolla-lobes greenish-red or greenish-purple, 7–9.5 mm. long: hoods about 4 mm. long, maroon, exceeding the androecium, shallowly several lobed at the truncate apex; horn subulate, much exserted; follicles 8–16 cm. long. [*A. obtusifolia* Michx.] —In dry or sandy soil, various provinces, Fla. to Tex., Nebr., and N. H.

9. **A. humistrata** Walt. Stem prostrate, 3–9 dm. long, glaucous: leaf-blades vertical, alike on both sides, ovate, 5–13 cm. long, glaucous, white-veined: corolla-lobes gray or greenish-purple, 6–7 mm. long: hoods about 3.5 mm. long, white, much exceeding the androecium, broadly rounded; horn broad and flat, scarcely exserted: follicles 8–15 cm. long.—Pinelands, scrub and sandhills, Coastal Plain, Fla. to Miss. and N. C.—Spr.–sum.

10. **A. exaltata** (L.) Muhl. Stem 9–15 dm. tall, sometimes pubescent in lines above: leaf-blades ovate, oval, elliptic or elliptic-lanceolate, 1–2.5 cm. long: corolla-lobes greenish or greenish-purple, 7–10 mm. long: hoods 3.5–4 mm. long, white or flushed with pink, about equalling the androecium, truncate, the broad top irregularly lobed, the lateral lobes the longest; horn with a much exserted subulate incurved tip: follicles 10–16 cm. long.—(Poke-milkweed.)—In thickets and moist woods, various provinces, Ga. to Miss., Minn., and Me.

11. **A. syriaca** L. Stem 5–15 dm. tall, usually sparingly pubescent: leaf-blades elliptic or elliptic-ovate, 9–25 cm. long: corolla-lobes pinkish-purple, 6–8 mm. long: hoods usually white, sometimes pink-tinged, 3–4 mm. long, exceeding the androecium, obtuse; horn subulate, shorter than the hood: anther-wings much longer than wide; follicles 7–9 cm. long, echinate.—(Common-milkweed.)— Fields and waste-places, various provinces, Ga. to Kans., Sask., and N. B.

12. **A. curassavica** L. Stem 3–19 dm. tall, sometimes minutely pubescent above: leaf-blades elliptic to elliptic-lanceolate, 5–12 cm. long or more, glabrous or nearly so: corolla-lobes scarlet, 6–8 mm. long: column 1–1.5 mm. long: hoods ovate, 3.5–4 mm. long, yellow, exceeding the androecium; horn stout, incurved, exceeding the hood: follicles 6–10 cm. long.—In sandy soil, Coastal Plain, W Fla. and La.—All year.

13. **A. incarnata** L. Stem 6-11 dm. tall, glabrous or nearly so: leaf-blades mainly elliptic-lanceolate, lanceolate, or linear-lanceolate, 4–17 cm. long, glabrous or nearly so: corolla-lobes pink or rarely white, 4–6 mm. long: hoods ovate, purplish-pink, 2.5–3 mm. long, somewhat exceeding the androecium; horn slender, much longer than the hood: follicles 7–9 cm. long.—(Swamp-milkweed.)— Swamps, various provinces, N. C. to La., N W Terr., Ont., and N. B.—Sum.

14. **A. pulchra** Ehrh. Stem 5–15 dm. tall, closely pubescent: leaf-blades broadly lanceolate to elliptic, 6–12 cm. long, pubescent: corolla-lobes bright-pink to purple or rarely white, 5–6 mm. long: hoods ovate, deep-pink, about 2.5 mm. long, slightly exceeding the androecium; horn slender, much longer than the hood: follicles 5–8 cm. long.—In moist fields and swamps, various provinces, Ga. to Minn. and Me.—Sum.–fall.

15. A. perennis Walt. Stem 3–9 dm. tall, often branched, puberulent in lines above: leaves opposite; blades elliptic, elliptic-lanceolate, or lanceolate, 5–15 cm. long, glabrous or nearly so: umbels solitary or few in a terminal corymb, the pedicels glabrous: corolla-lobes mainly white, 2.5–3.5 mm. long: hoods about 2 mm. long, scarcely exceeding the androecium; horn very slender, much exceeding the hood: column nearly 1 mm. long: follicles 5–8 cm. long: seeds 9–12 mm. long.—Moist woods and swamps, often in clayey soil, Coastal Plain and adj. provinces, Fla. to Tex., Mo., and Ind.—Spr.–sum.

16. A. quadrifolia Jacq. Stem 3–6 dm. tall, simple, sometimes puberulent in lines: leaves opposite, or whorled in 3's or 4's at one or more nodes; blades ovate-elliptic or lanceolate, 4–10 cm. long: umbels solitary or 2 or 3, the pedicels mostly 1.5–2 cm. long: corolla-lobes pink or nearly white, 5–6 mm. long: hoods 3.5–4 mm. long, about twice as long as the androecium; horn slender, much shorter than the hood: follicles 10–12 cm. long: seeds 5–6 mm. long.— Dry soil, woods and thickets, various provinces, N. C. to N Ala., Ark., Minn., Ont., and Me.—Spr.

17. A. obovata Ell. Stem 4–11 dm. tall, softly pubescent: leaf-blades obovate to oval or elliptic, 3–10 cm. long, closely pubescent: umbels terminal and in the upper leaf-axils, the densely hairy pedicels up to 1 cm. long: corolla-lobes greenish-yellow, 9–10 mm. long: hoods 5–6 mm. long, nearly twice as long as the androecium; horn falcate or lanceolate, arising about the middle of the hood, horizontally spreading: anthers about 2.5 mm. long: follicles 8–12 cm. long.—Dry grounds, Coastal Plain, Fla. to Tex. and S. C.—Sum.

18. A. aceratoides M. A. Curtis. Stem 3–5 dm. tall, tomentulose: leaf-blades oblanceolate to elliptic or elliptic-ovate, 7–12 cm. long: umbels few-flowered, very lax: corolla-lobes greenish, 8–10 mm. long: hoods truncate, about 4 mm. long, scarcely equalling the androecium; horn very broad, horizontally incurved: follicles not seen.—Sandy pine woods, Coastal Plain, S. C. and N. C.—Spr.

19. A. tomentosa Ell. Stem 3–12 dm. tall, softly pubescent: leaf-blades mainly elliptic to ovate, 5–8 cm. long: umbels several–many-flowered, rather lax: corolla-lobes greenish, 9–11 mm. long: hoods about 4 mm. long, truncate, about equalling the androecium; horn broad, horizontal and slightly incurved: follicles 10–13 cm. long.—Dry sandy soil and high pinelands, Coastal Plain, Fla. and Ga.—Spr.–sum.

20. A. linearis Scheele. Stem solitary or few together, 2–8 dm. tall, minutely pubescent in lines: leaf-blades narrowly elongate-linear, 4–12 cm. long: umbels usually several in the upper leaf-axils, the pedicels about 1 cm. long: corolla-lobes greenish-white, elliptic, 3–3.5 mm. long: hoods nearly 1.5 mm. long, about equalling the androecium; horn about twice as long as the hood: column about 1 mm. long: follicles 7–9 cm. long. [*A. galioides* (Fl. SE. U. S.)]—In damp clay soil, Coastal Plain, Ala. to Tex.—Sum.–fall.

21. A. verticillata L. Stem 3–8 dm. tall, commonly pubescent in lines: leaf-blades very narrowly linear to linear-filiform, 2–6 cm. long: umbels few to several in the upper leaf-axils: corolla-lobes greenish-white, 3–4 mm. long: hoods about 1 mm. long, about equalling the androecium or shorter; horn slender, about twice as long as the hood: follicles 7–12 cm. long.—In dry and sterile soil, various provinces, Fla. to Tex., Nebr., Sask., Ont., and Mass.—Spr.–sum. or all year S.

22. A. viridula Chapm. Stems often solitary, 3–7 dm. tall, pubescent in lines, at least above: leaf-blades narrowly linear, 2.5–10 cm. long: umbels usually 3 or more in the upper axils, few-flowered, the pedicels up to 1 cm. long: corolla-lobes greenish, elliptic or obovate-elliptic, 3–4 mm. long: hoods 2.5–3 mm. long, exceeding the androecium; horn flat, equalling the hood: follicles 8–10 cm. long.—Wet pinelands, Appalachicola region, Fla.—Sum.–fall.

23. A. Michauxii Decne. Stems usually several together, 1–13 dm. tall, minutely pubescent: leaf-blades linear, often narrowly so, 4–9 dm. long: umbels many-flowered, the pedicels 1–1.5 cm. long: corolla-lobes greenish, elliptic, 5–6 mm. long: hoods 3–3.5 mm. long, exceeding the androecium; horn stoutish, shorter than the hood: column about 0.5 mm. long: follicles 8–14 cm. long.— Pinelands and sandhills, Coastal Plain, Fla. to Miss. and S. C.—Spr.

24. A. cinerea Walt. Stem 3–5 dm. tall, sometimes slightly pubescent in lines: leaf-blades narrowly linear or filiform, 3–9 cm. long: umbels usually paired at the top of the stem and additional ones often in the upper axils, the pedicels mostly 1.5–2 cm. long: corolla-lobes purplish, 5–7 mm. long: hoods about 3 mm. high, much shorter than the androecium, each with 2 lateral acute lobes which exceed the broad horn: anthers about 2 mm. long: follicles 8–10 cm. long:—Rather dry pinelands, Coastal Plain, Fla. to Miss. and S. C.—Spr.–sum.

7. BIVENTRARIA Small. Erect herbs with broad leaf-blades. Umbels solitary or paired, or sometimes 3 or 4 at the top of the stem. Calyx-lobes 5. Corolla rotate: lobes reflexed. Hoods erect, free, saccate, the two inflated sacs flat on the back, with a groove on the inner side from which the flat horn projects horizontally. Anther-wings curved upward from the base and salient just below the middle. Follicles fusiform. Seed with a coma.—One species.

1. B. variegata (L.) Small. Stem 3–9 dm. tall, glaucous, sometimes pubescent above: leaf-blades typically oval, varying to ovate or obovate, 6–14 cm. long: corolla-lobes white, 6–8 mm. long: hoods about 3 mm. long, inflated, at the broadly rounded apex, much exceeding the androecium; horn very broad, protruding horizontally: follicles 8–14 cm. long. [*Asclepias variegata* L.]—Dry shaded grounds, in rather acid soil, various provinces, Fla. to Tex., Ill., and Conn.—Spr.–sum.

8. OXYPTERYX Greene. Erect herbs with the habit of *Acerates*, the leaf-blades broad. Umbels mostly lateral. Calyx-lobes 5. Corolla rotate: lobes reflexed. Hoods erect, elongate, free, distinctly stalked, with the sides conduplicate, the body thus dorsiventrally flattened, the free tip of the horn which is adnate to the midrib of the hood up to the middle, horizontally protruding from the slit between the edges of the hood and curved upward near the apex. Anther wings deltoid, protruding between the hood-claws. Follicles erect, fusiform. Seed with a coma.—One species.

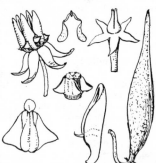

1. O. Curtissii (A. Gray) Small. Stem decumbent or ascending, 5–7 dm. long, minutely pubescent, sometimes widely branched: leaf-blades broadly elliptic to oval, varying to broadest above the middle or below it, 3–5 cm. long, glabrous or nearly so: umbels many-flowered, the pedicels slender, sparingly pubescent: corolla-lobes greenish-white, lanceolate, 5.5–6 mm. long: hood lanceolate, 4–4.5 mm. long, fully twice as long as the androecium: anthers about 1.5 mm. long: follicles 8–11 cm. long. [*Asclepias Curtissii* A. Gray *A. aceratoides* Nash *A. arenicola* Nash]—Sandhills and scrub, pen. Fla.—Spr.–fall.

9. **ANANTHERIX** Nutt. Upright herbs, with relatively narrow leaf-blades. Calyx-lobes 5. Corolla rotate: lobes reflexed. Hoods relatively long, the tips converging high over the stigma. Pollinia shorter than the caudicles. Follicles fusiform.—One species.

1. **A. connivens** (Baldw.) Feay. Plant 3–6 dm. tall: leaf-blades elliptic to lanceolate, 3–8 cm. long, fleshy: peduncles longer than the pedicels: umbels 2–6, borne along the naked or nearly naked upper part of the stem: corolla greenish; lobes 9–10.5 mm. long: hoods white, incurved, 8 mm. long: anthers 3.5 mm. long; follicles 8–9 cm. long.—Moist pinelands and bogs, Coastal Plain, Fla. to Miss. and Ga.—Sum.—The perpendicular root is deep-seated in wet sand.

10. **ASCLEPIODORA** A. Gray. Spreading herbs with alternate leaves. Calyx-lobes 4. Corolla rotate: lobes spreading. Hoods involute and hooded at the apex, with an internal ridge above the middle. Anthers equalling the gynostegium: wings rounded at the base.—About 6 species, North American.

1. **A. viridis** (Walt.) A. Gray. Stem 2–6 dm. long, stout: leaf-blades elliptic to lanceolate, 6–10 cm. long, rather thin: calyx-lobes about 4 mm. long, ciliolate: corolla-lobes greenish, 10–11 mm. long: hoods about 4.5 mm. long, purplish or violet: anther-wings 2.5 mm. long: follicles 6–11 cm. long.—Pinelands, open woods, and fields, various provinces, Fla. to Tex., Kans., Tenn., and S. C.—Spr.–sum.

11. **ASCLEPIODELLA** Small. Upright herbs, with opposite leaves. Calyx-lobes 5. Corolla rotate: lobes spreading. Hoods concave, open at the apex, ridged within mainly below the middle. Anthers curving over the top of the gynostegium: wings sagittate at the base.—One species.

1. **A. Feayi** (Chapm.) Small. Stem 2–4 dm. tall, slender: leaf-blades linear-filiform, 3–10 cm. long: calyx-lobes 1.5–2 mm. long: corolla-lobes white, 6–7 mm. long: hoods 2.5–3 mm. long, white: anther-wings barely 3 mm. long: follicles 3–4.5 cm. long. [*Asclepiodora Feayi* Chapm.] —Pinelands, Fla.—Spr.–fall.—This small milkweed is nowhere plentiful, but occurs as scattered plants in the open pinewoods. The slender stem and very slender leaves are out of proportion to the rather large pale flowers.

12. **GONOLOBUS** Michx. Vines, with broad leaf-blades. Calyx-lobes longer than the corolla-tube. Corolla campanulate: lobes spreading or reflexed at the tip. Crown borne near the base of the anthers: lobes each terminating in an entire or cleft appendage. Anther-wings salient at the base. Stigma with an elevated lobed top. Follicles wing-angled.—Three species, North American.

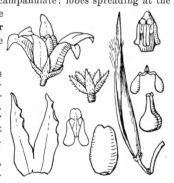

1. **G. laevis** Michx. Leaf-blades ovate, 4–15 cm. long, acuminate at the apex, cordate at the base: calyx-lobes 2–2.5 mm. long: corolla whitish; lobes 4–4.5 mm. long, linear-lanceolate: crown-lobes about 4 mm. long, the slender appendages quite as long as the body: anther-wings barely 1 mm. long: follicles 9–10 cm. long. [*Enslenia albida* Nutt.]—Thickets and river-banks, various provinces, Fla. to Tex., Kans., and Pa.—Sum.

13. **AMPHISTELMA** Griseb. Slender vines, with narrow leaf-blades. Calyx-lobes longer than the corolla-tube. Corolla rotate-campanulate: lobes glabrous within. Crown adnate to the column, sessile on the base of the corolla, cup-like: lobes very broad, surpassed by the androecium. Stigma flat.—About 25 species, tropical American.

1. **A. scoparia** (Nutt.) Small. Diffuse vine: leaf-blades narrowly linear, 2–5 cm. long: calyx-lobes about 1 mm. long, deltoid, corolla-lobes greenish, 1.5–2 mm. long: crown-lobes about 0.5 mm. long: follicles 3.5–4.5 cm. long.—Hammocks, Coastal Plain, Fla. to S. C.—Spr.–fall.—This plant is often quite leafy when young, but as it develops and makes myriad branches, the leaves fall off or fail to develop. The ultimate growth is sometimes sufficiently abundant to smother a host.

14. **LYONIA** Ell. Slender vines, with narrow leaf-blades. Calyx-lobes longer than the corolla-tube. Corolla rotate-campanulate: lobes spreading at the tip, glabrous within. Crown adnate to the short column: lobes naked at the apex, longer than the androecium. Stigma conic.—One species.

1. **L. palustris** (Pursh) Small. Leaf-blades linear, 2–7 cm. long, acute, pendent: calyx-lobes lanceolate, about 2.5 mm. long: corolla-lobes purplish or greenish-white, 3–4 mm. long: crown-lobes 1.5–2 mm. long, retuse or emarginate at the apex: anther-wings about 1 mm. long: follicles 4.5–5.5 cm. long. [*Seutera maritima* Decne. *S. palustris* Vail] —Hammocks and salt-marshes, Coastal Plain, Fla. to Tex. and N. C.—(*W. I.*)—Spr.–fall.

15. METASTELMA R. Br. Slender vines, with narrow leaf-blades. Calyx-lobes longer than the corolla-tube. Corolla rotate-campanulate: lobes pubescent within. Crown adnate to the base of the corolla-tube: lobes slender, curved over the anthers. Stigma flat.—About 25 species, mostly tropical American.

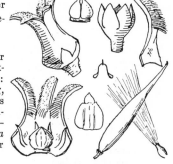

1. M. Blodgettii A. Gray. Leaf-blades linear or linear-lanceolate, 8–27 mm. long: calyx-lobes broadly ovate about 1 mm. long: corolla whitish; lobes 2–2.5 mm. long, penicillate-bearded within: crown-lobes subulate: follicles 4–5 cm. long.—Hammocks and sand-dunes, S Fla. and S Tex.—Spr.–fall.—As in the case of *Amphistelma* this plant often makes copious growth over bushes, but it generally holds its leaves.

16. EPICION Small. Slender vines, with relatively broad leaf-blades. Calyx-lobes shorter than the corolla-tube. Corolla campanulate: lobes pubescent within. Crown adnate to the top of the elongate column: lobes narrow. Stigma flat or depressed.—Three or four species, tropical American.

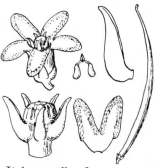

1. E. Northropiae (Schlecht.) Small. Leaf-blades elliptic to oval, 1.5–2.5 cm. long, slender-petioled: calyx-lobes ovate, 1.5 mm. long: corolla white; lobes 2.5–3 mm. long, longer than the tube, obtuse: crown-lobes 1.5 mm. long: follicles 5–6.5 cm. long. [*Metastelma Northropiae* Schlecht.]—Hammocks and pinelands, Everglade Keys, Fla. and Florida Keys.—(*W. I.*)—All year.— *E. bahamense*, formerly recorded for Florida, is confined to the Bahamas and Cuba. It has smaller flowers than *E. Northropiae*, with a short corolla-tube and a very short gynostegium.

17. CYCLODON Small. Stout twining vines. Leaf-blades broad, with an open basal sinus. Cymes few-flowered, short-peduncled. Calyx-lobes 5, longer than the corolla-tube. Corolla rotate, glabrous within: lobes relatively wide. Crown an irregularly 5-lobed disk, the lobes erose. Column distinct, with 5 horn-like appendages free or adnate at its base. Follicles armed.—Several species, mainly tropical.

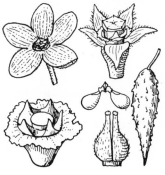

1. C. alabamense (Vail) Small. Stem short-pubescent: leaf-blades ovate to elliptic-ovate, 6–15 cm. long, the basal lobes not overlapping: calyx-lobes ovate, hirsute, the basal glands in pairs: corolla mainly greenish-yellow; lobes elliptic, 6–7 mm. long, pubescent without, reticulate: follicles stout-fusiform, about 9 cm. long, covered with fleshy spines: seeds nearly 1 cm. long. [*Vincetoxicum alabamense* Vail]—Hillsides and thickets, Coastal Plain, Ala.—Sum.–fall.

18. VINCETOXICUM Walt.[1] Stout twining, usually pubescent vines. Leaves with broad cordate blades. Cymes usually peduncled. Calyx-lobes 5, usually glabrous, longer than the corolla-tube. Corolla rotate, glabrous or puberulent within: lobes relatively narrow. Crown a fleshy disk at the base of the gynostegium, 5-lobed, with an obscure rib dividing each lobe, thus making it appear 10-lobed. Follicles unarmed, wing-ridged toward the apex, glabrous.—Several species, mainly North American.—ANGLE-PODS.—Spr.–sum.

Corolla-lobes glabrous within, more than twice as long as the calyx-lobes.   1. *V. gonocarpos.*
Corolla-lobes pubescent within, twice as long as the calyx-lobes or less.   2. *V. suberosum.*

1. V. gonocarpos Walt. Leaf-blades broadly ovate to ovate-elliptic, 7–18 cm. long, the basal sinus sometimes broad or with the lobes overlapping; petioles pubescent: flowered-buds long-conic: calyx-lobes glabrous, rarely ciliate near the tip, 2–4 mm. long: corolla greenish; lobes glabrous, lance-linear, 9–14 mm. long: follicles smooth, 8–10 cm. long. [*Gonolobus macrophyllus* Michx.]—River-banks and thickets, various provinces, Ga. to Tex., Mo., and Ky.

2. V. suberosum (L.) Britton. Leaf-blades elliptic-ovate to elliptic-oval, 6–12 cm. long, the basal sinus shallow, the lobes not overlapping: petioles glabrate: flower-buds broadly conic: calyx-lobes 3–4.5 mm. long: corolla brown-purple or yellowish with a dark center; lobes pubescent within, lanceolate, 6–9 mm. long: follicles smooth, 10–14 cm. long. [*Gonolobus suberosus* R. Br.]—Thickets and river-banks, Coastal Plain, Fla. to La. and Va.

Metalepis cubensis (A. Rich.) Griseb. of Cuba, a vine with ovate to hastate leaf-blades, a single crown in the flower and ovoid, oval, or obovoid melon-like fruits 1–2 dm. long, has been found in Brickell Hammock, Miami, Fla.

19. ODONTOSTEPHANA Alexander.[1] Stout twining vines resembling *Vincetoxicum*, the stems usually pubescent. Leaves with broad, usually large, cordate blades. Cymes dense, peduncled. Calyx-lobes 5, pubescent, longer than the corolla-tube. Corolla rotate, pubescent without: lobes relatively narrow. Crown cup-shaped, usually appearing 10-lobed, the longer lobes usually erect and toothed with the shorter lobes usually incurved, toothed or entire, and also crested or appendaged on the inside, the appendage as broad as the lobe. Follicles armed with fleshy spines. [*Vincetoxicum* Walt. in part.]—Several species, American—SPINY-PODS.—Sum. or spr. S.

Crown appearing 10-lobed, each lobe entire or 2-toothed.
    Corolla purple, brownish or reddish; crown thick-fleshy, the lower lobes entire.
       Narrower lobes of the crown prominently 2-toothed, markedly longer than the broader lobes.
          Corolla-lobes usually 10–15 mm. long, lance-linear: buds ellipsoid-ovoid to conic.   1. *O. decipiens.*

[1] Contributed by Edward Johnston Alexander.

Corolla-lobes usually 7–10 mm. long, narrowly ellip-
tic: buds short-ovoid.   2. *O. carolinensis.*
Narrower lobes of the crown truncate or emarginate, not
markedly longer than the broader lobes.
Crown undulate-lobed, the crest double.   3. *O. obliqua.*
Crown crenate-lobed, the crest if present, a narrow
fold or ridge.   4. *O. Shortii.*
Corolla white or yellowish: crown-thin, the lower lobes
2-toothed.
Lower lobes only cleft to above the middle, the teeth of
the slender lobes far surpassing them.   5. *O. Baldwiniana.*
Lower lobes cleft well below the middle, surpassed by the
broader bluntly toothed lobes.   6. *O. flavidula.*
Crown appearing 5-lobed, each lobe 4-toothed.   7. *O. floridana.*

1. O. decipiens Alexander. Leaf-blades ovate, 7–12 cm. long, the sinus narrow or closed: flower-buds ellipsoid-ovoid or conic: calyx-lobes about 3 mm.
long: corolla brown-purple; lobes lance-
linear, 10–15 mm. long: crown with the
longer lobes usually 2-toothed, the broader
lobes appendaged or crested; follicles 8–10
cm. long.—Woods and stream-banks, in
rather acid soil, Coastal Plain and occasionally adj. provinces, S. C. to Okla., Mo., and
Md.—The variability of the crown of this
and the following species is most confusing,
but the larger flowers and narrower corolla
lobes of this species easily separate it.

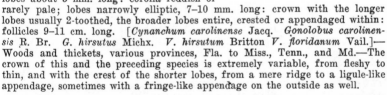

2. O. carolinensis (Jacq.) Alexander. Leaf-
blades ovate, 5–11 cm. long, the sinus open
or closed: flower-buds short-ovoid: calyx-
lobes about 3 mm. long: corolla reddish or
rarely pale; lobes narrowly elliptic, 7–10 mm. long: crown with the longer
lobes usually 2-toothed, the broader lobes entire, crested or appendaged within:
follicles 9–11 cm. long. [*Cynanchum carolinense* Jacq. *Gonolobus carolinensis* R. Br. *G. hirsutus* Michx. *V. hirsutum* Britton *V. floridanum* Vail.]—
Woods and thickets, various provinces, Fla. to Miss., Tenn., and Md.—The
crown of this and the preceding species is extremely variable, from fleshy to
thin, and with the crest of the shorter lobes, from a mere ridge to a ligule-like
appendage, sometimes with a fringe-like appendage on the outside as well.

3. O. obliqua (Jacq.) Alexander. Leaf-blades broadly ovate to orbicular-
ovate, 7–20 cm. long, the basal lobes mostly forming a closed sinus by the overlapping edges: calyx-lobes about 3 mm. long: corolla reddish-purple; lobes
lance-linear, 9–14 mm. long: crown with the longer lobes truncate or emarginate: follicles 7–9 cm. long: seeds about 7 mm. long. [*Gonolobus obliquus* R.
Br. *Vincetoxicum obliquum* Britton]—Woods, thickets, and river-banks, in
rich soil, various provinces, N of Coastal Plain, Tenn. to Ohio, Pa., and N. C.

4. O. Shortii (A. Gray) Alexander. Leaf-blades broadly ovate, 5–14 cm. long,
the basal lobes often forming a narrow sinus: calyx-lobes about 4 mm. long:
corolla greenish-purple; lobes lance-linear, 11–15 mm. long: crown with the
longer lobes truncate or emarginate: follicles 8–10 cm. long: seeds about 8
mm. long. [*Gonolobus Shortii* A. Gray *Vincetoxicum Shortii* Britton]—Dry
woods, Appalachian provinces, Ga. to Ky. and Pa.—The flowers are said to
have the scent of *Calycanthus* flowers.

5. O. Baldwiniana (Sweet) Alexander. Leaf-blades broadly ovate, 6–14 cm.
long, deeply and somewhat obliquely cordate at the base, the sinus open or the
basal lobes of the larger leaves overlapping: flower-buds long-conic: calyx-
lobes 2–3 mm. long: corolla white or yellowish: lobes thin, erect or barely
spreading: oblong-linear, 9–11 mm. long: crown very thin, with the longer
lobes divided into two very slender linear teeth fully double the length of the

rather quadrate shallowly toothed broader lobes: follicles about 8 cm. long: seeds about 9 mm. long. [*Gonolobus Baldwinianus* Sw. *Vincetoxicum Baldwinianum* Britton].—Thickets and open woods, various provinces, Ga. to Okla. and Mo.—Spr. and sum.

6. **O. flavidula** (Chapm.) Alexander. Leaf-blades broadly ovate, 9–16 cm. long, the basal lobes rarely overlapping: flower-buds ovoid: calyx-lobes about 3.5 mm. long: corolla greenish-yellow; lobes elliptic, 10–11 mm. long: crown with the longer lobes shallowly toothed: follicles 14–17 cm. long. [*Gonolobus flavidulus* Chapm. *Vincetoxicum flavidulum* Heller]—Rich soil, mostly in woods, Coastal Plain, Fla. to S. C.

7. **O. floridana** (Vail) Alexander. Leaf-blades ovate-cordate, 2–5 cm. long, the sinus open and somewhat oblique: calyx-lobes about 2 mm. long: flower-buds conic: corolla purplish or greenish-purple, about 5 mm. long, the lobes spreading, linear-lanceolate: crown with five broad lobes, each bidentate at the callous-thickened apex and with a smaller tooth on each side at about the middle: follicles not seen. [*Vincetoxicum floridanum* Vail].—Sandy soil, E Fla.—Sum.

20. **EDISONIA** Small. Slender prostrate vine-like herbs. Leaf-blades broad but small. Cymes sessile. Calyx-lobes 5, about as long as the corolla-tube. Corolla campanulate: lobes villous within, short. Crown 5-lobed, each lobe with an appendage which is decurrent on the inner side, each sinus folded as if to form another lobe. Column sunken in a cavity beneath the converging crown-lobes.—One species.

1. **E. pubiflora** (Decne.) Small. Leaf-blades broadly cordate or reniform, 2–4 cm. long, the sinus open: flower-buds oval or obovoid: calyx lobes 2–2.5 mm. long: corolla dull-purple; lobes about 2 mm. long: crown with 10 rounded undulations, each alternate one with an adnate beak or horn: follicle ovoid-fusiform, 4–5 cm. long. [*Chthamalia pubiflora* Decne. *Gonolobus pubiflorus* Engelm. *Vincetoxicum pubiflorum* Vail]—Sandhills and scrub, Coastal Plain, Fla. and Ga.—Spr.–sum.

Order **POLEMONIALES**—Polemonial Order

Herbs, sometimes parasitic, shrubs or trees. Flowers mainly perfect. Calyx of partially united sepals. Corolla, regular or irregular. Androecium of as many stamens as there are corolla-lobes, or fewer. Gynoecium 2–several carpellary. Ovary superior. Fruit a capsule, a berry or a drupe, or a group of nutlets or utricle-like.

Stamens 5, usually equal: corolla regular or nearly so.
   Gynoecium of 2 distinct carpels.   Fam. 1. DICHONDRACEAE.
   Gynoecium of 2 or more partially or wholly united
     carpels.
     Fruit capsular or baccate: ovary not 4-lobed.
       Styles or stigmas distinct.
         Ovary 1–2-celled, or 4-celled: stigmas 2.
           Ovary 2-celled or 4-celled.
             Corolla unappendaged within:
              plants with normal leaves, at
              least if vines.   Fam. 2. CONVOLVULACEAE.
             Corolla appendaged within: para-
              sitic vines: leaves scale-like.   Fam. 3. CUSCUTACEAE.

Ovary 1-celled (2-celled in *Nama*).	Fam. 4. HYDROLEACEAE.
Ovary 3-celled : stigmas 3.	
Calyx-lobes imbricated : corolla mostly plaited in the bud.	Fam. 2. CONVOLVULACEAE.
Calyx-lobes valvate : corolla merely convolute in the bud.	Fam. 5. POLEMONIACEAE.
Styles or stigmas wholly united.	Fam. 6. SOLANACEAE.

Fruit drupaceous, or of 2 or 4 nutlets.
Style or stigmas without a glandular ring.
  Fruit a group of 2 or 4 nutlets : style arising from between the lobes of the ovary. — Fam. 7. BORRAGINACEAE.
  Fruit drupaceous : style terminating the lobeless ovary. — Fam. 8. EHRETIACEAE.
Style or stigmas with a glandular ring. — Fam. 9. HELIOTROPIACEAE.
Stamens 4 and didynamous, or 1 or 2 : corolla usually irregular and bilabiate.
Carpels ripening into a group of 4 nutlets, an achene or a drupe.
Style apical on the lobeless ovary.
  Ovary 2-celled.
    Fruit dry or drupaceous, with 2 or 4 nutlets. — Fam. 10. VERBENACEAE.
    Fruit fleshy-capsular, with a solitary seed. — Fam. 11. AVICENNIACEAE.
  Ovary 1-celled. — Fam. 12. PHRYMACEAE.
Style arising between the 4 lobes of the ovary. — Fam. 13. LAMIACEAE.
Carpels ripening into a capsule.
Placentae of the ovary axile.
  Ovary 2-celled, or rarely 3–5-celled.
    Corolla-lobes imbricated : capsule not elastically dehiscent. — Fam. 14. RHINANTHACEAE.
    Corolla-lobes convolute : capsules elastically dehiscent.
  Ovary 1-celled. — Fam. 15. ACANTHACEAE.
Placentae of the ovary parietal. — Fam. 16. PINGUICULACEAE.
  Herbs parasitic on the roots of other plants : leaves scale-like : foliage not green. — Fam. 17. OROBANCHACEAE.
  Trees, shrubs or woody vines, or herbs, but not parasitic : leaves not scale-like : foliage green.
    Ovary and capsule 2-celled : trees, shrubs or woody vines : seeds winged. — Fam. 18. BIGNONIACEAE.
    Ovary and capsule 1-celled or spuriously 2- or 4-celled : herbs, seeds wingless.
      Anther-sacs parallel : fruit a columnar, crestless dry capsule. — Fam. 19. PEDALIACEAE.
      Anther-sacs divergent : fruit a ventricose, fleshy coated capsule. — Fam. 20. MARTYNIACEAE.

FAMILY 1. **DICHONDRACEAE** — DICHONDRA FAMILY

Annual or perennial creeping herbs. Leaves alternate: blades broad, entire, long-petioled. Flowers axillary, solitary. Calyx of 5 slightly united sepals. Corolla rotate to campanulate, 5-lobed. Androecium of 5 stamens shorter than the corolla. Gynoecium of 2 distinct carpels. Styles basal. Capsules utricle-like, 2 together.—Only the following genus and 5 species, widely distributed.

1. **DICHONDRA** Forst. Stems much-branched, often densely matted. Flowers erect, greenish white.

1. **D. carolinensis** Michx. Plant inconspicuously pubescent: leaf-blades reniform to suborbicular, 5–20 mm. wide, deeply cordate: calyx-lobes 2–3 mm. long: corolla-lobes obtuse. [*D. repens* (Chapm. Fl.)]— Hammocks, pinelands, roadsides, low grounds, and moist grassy banks, Coastal Plain, and adj. provinces, Fla. to Tex., Ark., and S. Va.—(*W. I.*)—This plant has two roles in southern latitudes: it may be a persistent weed in lawns or it may be a lawn plant itself, thriving where other lawn plants refuse to grow.

FAMILY 2. **CONVOLVULACEAE** — MORNING-GLORY FAMILY

Annual or perennial herbs, or vines, or rarely shrubs or trees. Leaves alternate, without stipules: blades various. Flowers perfect, regular, solitary or cymose. Calyx of 5, more or less united sepals, in one or two series. Corolla convolute in aestivation, its limb lobed or entire. Androecium of 5 stamens, partially adnate to the corolla-tube, alternate with the lobes. Gynoecium of 2 united carpels. Ovary 2–4-celled (rarely 5-celled, or 1-celled by the loss of the septum). Seeds 1 or 2 in each cavity, often pubescent.—Forty-five genera and 1,000 species, widely distributed.

Styles distinct or partly so.   I. EVOLVULEAE.
Styles united up to the stigmas.   II. CONVOLVULEAE.

I. EVOLVULEAE

Styles nearly distinct or partially united, entire: stigmas 2.
     Sepals leathery, 2 cm. long or longer: stems stout.   1. BONAMIA.
     Sepals herbaceous, 1 cm. long or less: stems slender.   2. STYLISMA.
Styles distinct, each 2-cleft: stigmas 4.   3. EVOLVULUS.

II. CONVOLVULEAE

Capsules dehiscent and valvular.
   Stigmas ovoid or subglobose.
     Calyx urn-shaped: stamens spirally twisted: corolla
      broadly campanulate-funnelform.   4. OPERCULINA.
     Calyx campanulate: stamens straight.
      Stamens and style included: corolla funnelform.
       Sepals herbaceous, elongate, usually pilose: ovary
        usually 3-celled.   5. PHARBITIS.
       Sepals coriaceous or membranous, not elongate:
        ovary 2- or 4-celled.   6. IPOMOEA.
      Stamens and style exserted: corolla usually salver-
      form.
       Corolla large, showy, 10–20 cm. long, white.   7. CALONYCTION.
       Corolla smaller, 3–6 cm. long or less, rarely white.
        Herbaceous vines: seeds smooth.   8. QUAMOCLIT.
        Woody vines: seeds woolly.   9. EXOGONIUM.
   Stigmas somewhat flattened or linear.
     Stigmas flattened.
      Inflorescence densely capitate.   10. THYELLA.
      Inflorescence solitary or paniculate.   11. JACQUEMONTIA.
     Stigmas filiform or oblong-cylindric.
      Calyx enclosed in 2 broad bracts which subtend it:
       stigmas long-cylindric or broadly ellipsoid.   12. CONVOLVULUS.
      Calyx naked, without bracts at the base: stigmas
       filiform or nearly so.   13. STROPHOCAULOS.
Capsules or fruit indehiscent, dry or berry-like.
   Carpels turbinate, 1-celled and usually 1-seeded by abor-
   tion: foliage glabrate.   14. TURBINA.
   Fruit berry-like: leaf-blades silvery beneath.   15. ARGYREIA.

1. **BONAMIA** Thouars. Spreading, herbaceous or woody vines. Leaf-blades rarely cordate, usually entire. Corolla funnelform, blue or white, hirsute without. Filaments glandular-villous at the base. Ovary 2-celled, 4-ovuled. Capsule chartaceous, 4-valved. Seeds smooth or pubescent. [*Breweria* R. Br.]—Four species, 2 in North America.

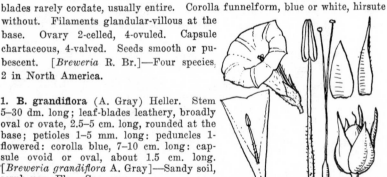

1. **B. grandiflora** (A. Gray) Heller. Stem 5–30 dm. long; leaf-blades leathery, broadly oval or ovate, 2.5–5 cm. long, rounded at the base; petioles 1–5 mm. long: peduncles 1-flowered: corolla blue, 7–10 cm. long: capsule ovoid or oval, about 1.5 cm. long. [*Breweria grandiflora* A. Gray]—Sandy soil, scrub pen. Fla.—Spr.–sum.

2. **STYLISMA** Raf. Herbaceous vines, often prostrate. Leaf-blades narrow or broad, not cordate. Flowers 1–3 on axillary peduncles. Sepals equal or nearly so, pointed. Corolla white or colored, rotate or subfunnelform. Capsule thin-walled. [*Breweria* (Chapm. Fl.) (Fl. SE. U. S.)]—Seven species, in the southeastern United States and Mexico.—Spr.–fall.

Sepals glabrous or merely ciliate, elliptic, acute.
Leaf-blades elliptic.   1. *S. humistrata.*
Leaf-blades narrowly linear.   2. *S. angustifolia.*
Sepals distinctly pubescent.
  Filaments densely pubescent.
    Foliage sparingly villous-tomentulose: peduncles 1–3 cm.
      long: corolla 1.5 cm. long.   3. *S. trichosanthes.*
    Foliage densely brown-tomentose: peduncles 4–6 cm.
      long: corolla 2 cm. long.   4. *S. villosa.*
  Filaments glabrous or nearly so.
    Bracts shorter than the flowers: leaf-blades elliptic to
      narrowly lanceolate.   5. *S. aquatica.*
    Bracts exceeding the flowers: leaf-blades linear.   6. *S. Pickeringii.*

1. **S. humistrata** (Walt.) Chapm. Stem and branches decumbent; leaf-blades elliptic and subcordate to elliptic-lanceolate, 2.5–5 cm. long, mucronate, sparingly pubescent; petioles 2–10 mm. long: peduncles 1–7-flowered: sepals 6–8 mm. long: corolla white, 15–18 mm. long: styles united at the base for about one-third their length. [*B. humistrata* A. Gray]—Pinelands, and dry sand, Coastal Plain, Fla. to La., Ark., and Va.

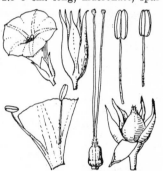

2. **S. angustifolia** (Nash) House. Stem and branches trailing, appressed-pubescent; leaf-blades 2.5–7 cm. long, pubescent or glabrate, acute; petioles 1–2 mm. long: peduncles 1-flowered: sepals ciliate, 7–10 mm. long: corolla white, 2 cm. long: styles distinct, nearly to the base. [*B. angustifolia* Nash]—High pinelands, pen. Fla.

3. **S. trichosanthes** (Michx.) House. Stem and branches decumbent; pubescent; leaf-blades elliptic or linear-lanceolate, 2.5–7 cm. long, apiculate, often somewhat viscid; petioles 1–3 mm. long: sepals strigillose, glabrate, elliptic or nearly so, 6–8 mm. long, bearded at the apex: corolla white, pubescent without, about 12 mm. broad. [*B. trichosanthes* Small]—Pinelands, Coastal Plain, Fla. to Ala. and N. C.

4. **S. villosa** (Nash) House. Stem and branches trailing, villous-pubescent; leaf-blades elliptic or elliptic-ovate, 2.5–7 cm. long, obtuse, apiculate, rounded at the base; petioles 2–8 mm. long: sepals ovate-lanceolate, 8–10 mm. long, acuminate, villous: corolla white, 15–20 mm. long: capsule 4–5 mm. in diameter, nearly as long as the calyx. [*B. villosa* Nash]—Dry sandy soil, pen. Fla.

5. **S. aquatica** (Walt.) Chapm. Stem and branches trailing, softly pubescent: leaf-blades 2.5–3 cm. long, obtuse: peduncles longer than the leaves, 1–3-flowered: sepals elliptic-lanceolate, acute, 4–6 cm. long: corolla rose-purple, 10–15 mm. long: capsule 6–8 mm. in diameter. [*B. aquatica* A. Gray]—Pinelands, and shallow ponds, Coastal Plain, and adj. provinces, Fla. to Tex., Mo., and S Va.

6. **S. Pickeringii** (M. A. Curtis) A. Gray. Stem and branches prostrate or trailing, minutely pubescent: leaf-blades acute at both ends, subsessile, 2–7 cm. long: peduncles rarely longer than the leaves: sepals ovate, obtuse, 4–5 mm. long, villous: corolla white, about 10 mm. long: capsule ovate-conoidal,

exceeding the calyx. [*B. Pickeringii* A. Gray]—Pinelands, in acid soil, various provinces, Fla. to Tex., Ia., and N. J.

3. EVOLVULUS L. Erect or diffuse herbs or partially woody plants. Leaf-blades entire. Flowers solitary and axillary or in terminal racemes or panicles. Calyx small: lobes nearly equal. Corolla white, pink, or blue, rotate or rotate-funnelform: limb 5-angled or 5-lobed. Capsule subglobose, 2–4-valved.—About 85 species, in warm and tropical regions.

Peduncles as long as the leaves or longer.
  Leaf-blades glabrous or nearly so at maturity.   1. *E. glaber.*
  Leaf-blades copiously pubescent.   2. *E. alsinoides.*
Peduncles wanting or very short: pedicels shorter than the leaves.
  Plant more or less pubescent.
    Leaf-blades glabrous above.   3. *E. sericeus.*
    Leaf-blades copiously pubescent on both sides.   4. *E. Wrightii.*
  Plant glabrous.   5. *E. macilentus.*

1. E. glaber Spreng. Stem and branches diffuse, prostrate, sometimes creeping, silky: leaf-blades oblong, oval, or obovate, mostly 1–1.5 cm. long, mucronate, glabrous at maturity: calyx-lobes oblong, oblong-lanceolate, or oblong-ovate, 3–4.5 mm. long, acute or slightly acuminate: corolla blue, pink, or white, about 1 cm. broad: capsule ovoid, 2.5–3.5 mm. in diameter. [*E. mucronatus* (Chapm. Fl., Fl. SE. U. S.)]—Hammocks and open sandy places, lower Florida Keys.—(*W. I., S. A.*)

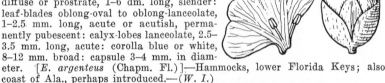

2. E. alsinoides L. Stem and branches diffuse or prostrate, 1–6 dm. long, slender: leaf-blades oblong-oval to oblong-lanceolate, 1–2.5 mm. long, acute or acutish, permanently pubescent: calyx-lobes lanceolate, 2.5–3.5 mm. long, acute: corolla blue or white, 8–12 mm. broad: capsule 3–4 mm. in diameter. [*E. argenteus* (Chapm. Fl.)]—Hammocks, lower Florida Keys; also coast of Ala., perhaps introduced.—(*W. I.*)

3. E. sericeus Sw. Plants silky, the branches ascending or decumbent, 1–3 dm. long: leaf-blades linear to oblong, 1–2.5 cm. long, acute at both ends: calyx-lobes 4–6 mm. long, acute or acuminate: corolla white or blue, 8–10 mm. wide.—Low grounds and wet woods, various provinces, Fla. to Tex., Ariz., and Ga.—(*W. I., Mex., C. A., S. A.*)

4. E. Wrightii House. Stem and branches tufted, mostly less than 1 dm. long, villous-hirsute with silvery hairs: leaf-blades suborbicular to ovate, 3–8 mm. long, acute or abruptly pointed: calyx-lobes linear-lanceolate, 4–5 mm. long, acuminate: corolla blue or white, 7–9 mm. broad.—Pinelands and open sandy places, lower Florida Keys.—(*W. I.*)

5. E. macilentus Small. Stem and branches wiry-filiform, glabrous, diffuse: leaf-blades linear to linear-subulate, 0.5–2 cm. long, acuminate, glabrous: calyx-lobes linear-lanceolate, 4–5 mm. long, acuminate: corolla pale-blue or white, nearly 1 cm. broad: capsule subglobose, 3–4 mm. in diameter.—Pinelands, lower Florida Keys.

4. OPERCULINA S. Manso. Twining vines. Leaf-blades entire, palmately lobed, or divided. Calyx large, pear-shaped, constricted above in flower: lobes closely imbricate, membranaceous or chartaceous. Corolla campanulate. Capsule globose, large, often operculate or irregularly dehiscent, sometimes valvate.—About 10 species, natives of tropical America and the East Indies.

Corolla yellow : sepals becoming 4–5 cm. long.   1. *O. tuberosa.*
Corolla white, purple throat : sepals becoming 1.5–2 cm. long.   2. *O. dissecta.*

1. O. tuberosa (L.) Meisn. Leaf-blades 5–7-lobed; lobes elliptic-lanceolate, acuminate, 4–6 cm. long: corolla 3.5–4 cm. long; limb 5–6 cm. wide: capsule 3–4 cm. in diameter: seeds 20 x 15 mm., black-velvety. — (YELLOW MORNING-GLORY.) Pinelands, hammocks and waste-places, Coastal Plain, Fla. and Tex. Nat. of the Tropics, and cultivated.—(*W. I.*)

2. O. dissecta (Jacq.) House. Leaf-blades 5–7-parted; segments oval to oblong or lanceolate, 3–10 cm. long, coarsely toothed: corolla 2–3 cm. long; limb 3–5 cm. broad: capsule about 1.5 cm. in diameter: seeds glabrous. [*Ipomoea dissecta* Jacq. *I. sinuata* Ort.]—Pinelands, Coastal Plain, Fla. to Tex., and Ga.—(*W. I.*)

5. PHARBITIS Choisy. Annual (ours), or perennial, climbing or trailing vines. Leaf-blades entire, lobed, or angled. Calyx-lobes equal or unequal, herbaceous, each with a pubescent base and a narrow tip. Corolla white, blue, pink, or purple, funnelform. Ovary 3–5-celled. Seeds smooth.—About 200 species, widely distributed.—Sum.–fall. —MORNING-GLORIES.

Calyx bristly pubescent, especially near the base.
    Tips of sepals merely acute or acuminate.   1. *P. purpurea.*
    Tips of sepals conspicuously elongate.
       Leaf-blades densely appressed silky-pubescent and ciliate, often entire.   2. *P. barbigera.*
       Leaf-blades hirsute-pubescent, lobed or angled.
          Bases of sepals conspicuously broadened : lobes of blades contracted below : corolla 2.5–4 cm. long.   3. *P. hederacea.*
          Sepals linear-lanceolate, not conspicuously broadened at the base: blades 3-lobed but the lobes rarely contracted below : corolla 4–6 cm. long.   4. *P. Nil.*
Calyx glabrous or nearly so, not bristly.   5. *P. cathartica.*

1. P. purpurea (L.) Voigt. Stem twining: leaf-blades ovate to orbicular-ovate, 6–18 cm. long, short-acuminate, cordate: calyx-lobes, 10–15 mm. long: corolla 5–7 cm. long; limb purple or sometimes pink, blue, white, or variegated, 4–6 cm. broad.—(COMMON MORNING-GLORY.)— Waste-places, various provinces, Fla. to Tex., Nebr., Ont., and N. S. Nat. of trop. Am., and cult.

2. P. barbigera (Sims) G. Don. Stem twining, several m. long: leaf-blades orbicular-ovate, 5–12 cm. long: peduncles shorter than the petioles: sepals 1.5–3 cm. long: corolla 3–3.5 cm. long; limb purple or partly so, 3–4 cm. broad.—(MORNING-GLORY.)— Thickets and cult. grounds, Coastal Plain and adj. provinces, Fla. to La. and Ga.

3. P. hederacea (L.) Choisy. Stem twining: leaf-blades 5–12 cm. long, deeply 3-lobed; lobes acuminate: peduncles usually shorter than the petioles: calyx-lobes 2–3 cm. long, the bases ovate or oval: corolla 2.5–4 cm. long, deep-blue, or the tube white; limb about 3 cm. broad.—Waste-places and cult. grounds, various provinces, Fla. to Tex., S. Dak., and Me.—(*W. I.*, *Mex.*,)—Nat. of trop. Am., and cult.

4. P. Nil (L.) Choisy. Stem hispid or hirsute: leaf-blades broadly ovate to suborbicular in outline, 6–16 cm. long, 3-angled or 3-lobed, the lobes acute: sepals 2.5–4 cm. long: corolla-limb deep-blue, 4–6 cm. wide.—Hammocks and cult. grounds, Fla. and La. Nat. of Africa, and cult.

5. P. cathartica (Poir.) Choisy. Stem minutely strigillose or glabrate: leaf-blades broadly ovate, 5–9 cm. long, entire or 3-lobed: sepals ovate-lanceolate, 1–2 cm. long, acuminate: corolla-limb purple to white, 6–8 cm. wide.—Hammocks and thickets, along or near the coast, pen. Fla. and the Keys.—(*W. I.*)

6. IPOMOEA L. Annual or perennial climbing or trailing vines, or rarely upright plants. Leaf-blades entire, angled or divided. Flowers solitary on axillary peduncles or in cymes. Calyx-lobes coriaceous or membranous, rarely fleshy. Corolla funnelform, the limb usually spreading. Capsule mostly septifragally 2- or 4-valved. Seeds often pubescent.—About 200 species, widely distributed.—Sum.–fall or all year S.—MORNING-GLORIES

Stems and branches prostrate and creeping or climbing.	I. PANDURATAE.
Stems and branches erect or diffuse.	II. FISTULOSAE.

I. PANDURATAE

Stem creeping, perennial, glabrous, fleshy or succulent.	
Corolla-limb white: leaf-blades elliptic to ovate in outline, mainly lobed.	1. *I. stolonifera.*
Corolla-limb purple: leaf-blades suborbicular, notched at the apex.	2. *I. Pes-Caprae.*
Stem twining or rarely trailing, never creeping.	
Leaf-blades entire or 3-lobed.	
Leaf-blades sagittate or denticulate-hastate at the base: inner sepals less than 1 cm. long.	
Leaf-blades denticulate-hastate at the base, linear or linear-lanceolate: corolla white.	3. *I. angustifolia.*
Leaf-blades sagittate, sometimes broadly so: corolla-limb purple.	
Sepals equal, 6 mm. long: corolla 3–4 cm. long.	4. *I. tenuissima.*
Sepals unequal, 7–9 mm. long: corolla 5–6 cm. long.	5. *I. sagittata.*
Leaf-blades never sagittate: inner sepals often over 1 cm. long.	
Sepals obtuse or mucronate.	
Leaf-blades cordate, of an ovate type.	
Pedicels thickened and fleshy, with the petioles and sepals densely setaceous.	6. *I. setosa.*
Pedicels not fleshy, not setaceous.	
Sepals tomentose: seeds with long wool all over.	7. *I. macrorhiza.*
Sepals glabrous: seeds with wool on the angles.	8. *I. pandurata.*
Sepals cuspidately pointed or acuminate.	
Corolla yellow: inflorescence umbellate.	9. *I. polyanthes.*
Corolla blue, purple, or white: inflorescence solitary or cymose.	
Perennial: calyx glabrous.	
Corolla 3 cm. long or less, pink or lilac-purple.	10. *I. trifida.*
Corolla 4 cm. long, or longer.	
Sepals 10–14 mm. long: stem usually glabrous and trailing.	11. *I. Batatas.*

Sepals 8–10 mm. long: stem usually
  pubescent and twining.   12. *I. tiliacea.*
Annual: calyx pubescent, at least the sepals
  ciliate.
    Corolla 3 cm. long, or longer.   13. *I. trichocarpa.*
    Corolla less than 3 cm. long.
      Peduncles shorter than the petioles:
        corolla-tube white.   14. *I. lacunosa.*
      Peduncles longer than the petioles:
        corolla-tube purple.   15. *I. triloba.*
Leaf-blades palmately 5–7-parted.
  Peduncles stout, short, 1–9-flowered.   16. *I. cairica.*
  Peduncles filiform, sometimes tendril-like, 1–2-flowered.   17. *I. heptaphylla.*

II. FISTULOSAE

Perennial plants; leaf-blades entire, ovate: corolla puberulent
  without: seeds shaggy-pubescent.   18. *I. fistulosa.*

1. **I. stolonifera** (Cyrill.) Poir. Leaf-blades 2–5 cm. long, the early ones ovate to elliptic, the later ones pandurate or more deeply lobed, mostly truncate or cordate at the base: sepals elliptic to oval, 1–1.5 cm. long, mucronate or acuminate: capsule subglobose, 1.5 cm. long. [*I. littoralis* (L.) Boiss. *I. acetosaefolia* R. & S.]—Coastal sand-dunes, Fla. to Tex., and S. C.—(*W. I., Mex., C. A., S. A.*)

2. **I. Pes-Caprae** (L.) Sweet. Leaf-blades 6–10 cm. long and as broad, rounded or cordate at the base: sepals oval or suborbicular, obtuse: corolla 4–5 cm. long: capsule globose-ovoid, 1.5 cm. long.—(RAILROAD-VINE.)—Coastal sand-dunes, Fla. to Tex. and Ga.—(*W. I.*)

3. **I. angustifolia** Jacq. Leaf-blades linear or linear-lanceolate, 3–5 cm. long, acute: peduncles 1–2-flowered, 1–3 cm. long: sepals unequal, ovate, acute, 6–8 mm. long: corolla 1–2 cm. long: capsule globose, 8 mm. in diameter: seeds smooth.—Banks, thickets, and waste-places, Coastal Plain, Brunswick, Ga., and at other southern ports. Nat. of Africa. —(*W. I.*).

4. **I. tenuissima** Choisy. Stems twining: leaf-blades lanceolate or linear-lanceolate, 2–5 cm. long, obtuse and mucronulate: sepals ovate-lanceolate, obtuse, ciliate: corolla purple, 3–4 cm. long: capsule globose.—Pinelands, Everglade Keys, Fla. and Florida Keys.—(*W. I.*)—All year.

5. **I. sagittata** Cav. Leaf-blades 3–10 cm. long, sagittate or hastate-sagittate, the segments linear or lanceolate, the basal ones about half as long as the terminal one: sepals 6–9 mm. long: corolla 5–6 cm. long. [*I. speciosa* Walt.] —Low prairies, swamps, and low hammocks, Coastal Plain and adj. provinces, Fla. to Tex. and N. C.

6. **I. setosa** Ker. Leaf-blades orbicular-ovate, deeply 3-lobed; petioles, pedicels, and calyces bristly with spreading purplish setae: peduncles 3–9-flowered; pedicels thickened: sepals elliptic, 10–14 mm. long, accrescent in fruit: corolla purple, 5–6 cm. long: capsule 4-celled: seeds hairy on the angles.—(BRAZILIAN MORNING-GLORY.)—Waste-places, Coastal Plain, Fla. to La. Nat. of Brazil.

7. **I. macrorhiza** Michx. Leaf-blades broadly ovate, 5–15 cm. long, erose-crenulate or lobed, truncate or subcordate at the base, tomentose beneath: sepals elliptic-lanceolate, obtuse, 1.5–2 cm. long: corolla white, 5–8 cm. long; limb 5–10 cm. broad: seeds with long silky-villous wool. [*I. jalapa* Pursh]— Sandy soil, on or near the coast, Fla. to Ala. and S. C.

8. I. pandurata (L.) G. F. W. Mey. Leaf-blades ovate, often fiddle-shaped, 3–10 cm. long: peduncles 5–10 cm. long, 1–5-flowered: calyx-lobes elliptic, 12–18 mm. long, obtuse, erect, imbricate and forming a tube: corolla 7–10 cm. broad; limb white, tube lavender within.—(WILD POTATO-VINE. MAN-OF-THE-EARTH.)—Dry soil, often in woods, various provinces, Fla. to Tex., Ont., and Conn.

9. I. polyanthes R. & S. Leaf-blades orbicular and cordate to oblong-lanceolate and cordate-sagittate, 5–10 cm. long; peduncles longer than the petioles, 5–many flowered in a dense umbel-like cyme: sepals oblong-lanceolate, 8–10 mm. long, glabrous, acute or acuminate: corolla bright yellow, 2–4 cm. long: seeds black, pubescent. [*I. umbellata* G. F. W. Mey. Not L.]—Florida Keys.—(*W. I.*)

10. I. trifida (H. B. K.) G. Don. Perennial, pubescent or glabrate, twining: leaf-blades 2–6 cm. long, lower ones often entire, upper 3-lobed, all cordate; peduncles 3–10-flowered; sepals glabrous, 10–12 mm. long, oblong to lanceolate or ovate-lanceolate, acuminate: corolla pink or lilac-purple, 2.5–4 cm. long; capsules more or less pubescent near the top.—Valleys and light soil, Coastal Plain, La. and Tex.—(*W. I., Mex., C. A., S. A.*) Represented in Florida by *I. trifida Torreyana* A. Gray, with glabrous stems and corolla 4 cm. long, a native of Tex.

11. I. Batatas (L.) Lam. Leaf-blades ovate, 5–11 cm. long, entire or angulately lobed, cordate: sepals unequal, ovate-lanceolate or lanceolate, acuminate: corolla 3–5 cm. long, white varying to shades of pink or purple.—(SWEET-POTATO.)—Pinelands, hammocks and waste-places, southern pen. Fla., and the Keys. Nat. of E. Indies, and cult.—(*W. I.*)

12. I. tiliacea (Willd.) Choisy. Leaf-blades ovate, cordate, acuminate, entire or 3–5-lobed: peduncles dichotomous at summit, several or many flowered: sepals elliptic-lanceolate, cuspidate-acuminate, unequal, the inner ones longest: corolla rose-purple or pink, 4–5 cm. long. [*I. fastigiata* (Roxb.) Sweet].—Sandy thickets, Florida Keys.

13. I. trichocarpa Ell. Leaf-blades ovate, entire or deeply 3-lobed, cordate: peduncles stout, 1–3-flowered: sepals hirsute, elliptic or elliptic-lanceolate, 9–12 mm. long: corolla pink or purple, 2.5–4 cm. long: capsule more or less pubescent: seeds glabrous. [*I. commutata* R. & S.]—Sandy soil, Coastal Plain, Fla. to Tex. and S. C.

14. I. lacunosa L. Leaf-blades ovate, entire or 3-lobed, 2–7 cm. long, deeply cordate: peduncles 1–3-flowered: calyx-lobes elliptic or ovate, 10–12 mm. long, acute or acuminate: corolla mainly white, 1.5–2 cm. long; limb often purple-margined.—River-banks, low grounds, and fields, various provinces, S. C. to Ala., Tex., Kans., and Pa.

15. I. triloba L. Leaf-blades ovate, 4–10 cm. long, entire or hastately 3-lobed, glabrate: sepals pubescent, oblong or suborbicular, 8–10 mm. long, acute or acuminate: corolla purple, 1.5 cm. long: capsule subglobose, 6–8 mm. in diameter, often pubescent: seeds glabrous.—Hammocks and sand-dunes, S pen. Fla. and the Keys.—(*W. I., Mex., C. A., S. A., O. W.*)

16. I. cairica (L.) Sweet. Segments of the leaf-blades elliptic-lanceolate, acute or acuminate, 4–9 cm. long: sepals 4–8 mm. long, obtuse: corolla purplish, 5–6 cm. long: capsule ovoid, 10–12 mm. long; seeds finely pubescent.—Roadsides and waste-places, Fla. Nat. of Africa.—(*W. I., Mex., S. A.*)

17. I. heptaphylla (Rottb. & Willd.) Voigt. Leaf-segments linear-lanceolate, 1–5 cm. long, acute or acuminate at the ends, entire or undulately toothed:

peduncles filiform, often spirally twisted and used in climbing: sepals ovate, 4–5 mm. long, becoming 6–7 mm. long: corolla pale-violet, 18–30 mm. long: capsules 10 mm. long or less.—Near New Orleans, La. Nat. of trop. regions.

18. I. fistulosa Mart. Leaf-blades ovate, 5–9 cm. long, acute, cordate: peduncles usually several-flowered: sepals suborbicular, 5–7.5 mm. long: corolla rose-colored, 6–8 cm. long: capsule ovoid, about 1.5 cm. long: seeds shaggy pubescent. [*I. texana* Coulter].—Waste-places, Coastal Plain, Pensacola, Fla., S Tex., and James Is., S. C. Nat. of S. A.

7. CALONYCTION Choisy. High-twining vines. Leaf-blades broad. Flowers showy. Calyx-lobes herbaceous, becoming leathery, the outer ones sometimes horned at the apex. Corolla white, expanding in the evening, salverform: tube elongate, not dilated at the throat. Capsule large, longer than broad.—Four species, in tropical America.—MOON-FLOWERS. MOON-VINES.

Sepals, at least the outer, long-appendaged: seeds glabrous or essentially so.	1. *C. aculeatum.*
Sepals unappendaged: seeds velvety and comose around the edges.	2. *C. Tuba.*

1. C. aculeatum (L.) House. Leaf-blades ovate to orbicular-ovate, 5–15 cm. long, entire or frequently hastately 3–5-lobed, thin-textured, rather slenderly acuminate, the lobes, when present acute or acuminate: appendaged calyx-lobes 2–3 cm. long: corolla very showy; tube slender, 9–14 cm. long; limb 10–14 cm. wide: capsule much-depressed, 3–3.5 cm. wide, enveloped by the accrescent inner calyx-lobes, before these become reflexed, the supporting pedicel much thickened under the calyx. [*Ipomoea Bona-Nox* L.]—Hammocks, S pen. Fla. and the Keys.—(*W. I., Mex., C. A., S. A., O. W.*) —All year.—This plant is a "fire-weed," *par excellence.* The growth of vines over burned areas, especially in hammocks, is prodigious.

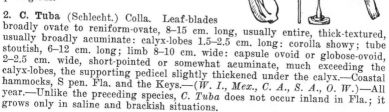

2. C. Tuba (Schlecht.) Colla. Leaf-blades broadly ovate to reniform-ovate, 8–15 cm. long, usually entire, thick-textured, usually broadly acuminate: calyx-lobes 1.5–2.5 cm. long: corolla showy; tube stoutish, 6–12 cm. long; limb 8–10 cm. wide: capsule ovoid or globose-ovoid, 2–2.5 cm. wide, short-pointed or somewhat acuminate, much exceeding the calyx-lobes, the supporting pedicel slightly thickened under the calyx.—Coastal hammocks, S pen. Fla. and the Keys.—(*W. I., Mex., C. A., S. A., O. W.*)—All year.—Unlike the preceding species, *C. Tuba* does not occur inland in Fla.; it grows only in saline and brackish situations.

8. QUAMOCLIT [Tourn.] Moench. Annual (ours) or perennial vines, with twining, glabrous stems. Blades entire, lobed, or divided. Flowers in axillary cymes or solitary. Calyx-lobes equal or nearly so. Corolla scarlet orange, yellow, or white, salverform: tube narrowly funnelform; limb spreading, shorter than the tube. Ovary 2- or falsely 4-celled. Capsule usually 4-celled and 4-seeded.—About 10 species, in warm and tropical regions.—Sum.– fall or all year S.

Leaf-blades pinnately parted, the segments narrow: calyx-lobes obtuse or mucronate.	1. *Q. Quamoclit.*
Leaf-blades entire: calyx-lobes acuminate.	2. *Q. coccinea.*

1. Q. Quamoclit (L.) Britton. Leaf-blades 2–10 cm. long; segments narrowly linear: pedicels clavate: calyx-lobes appressed to the corolla-tube: corolla-tube clavate, 2.5–3 cm. long; lobes ovate or triangular. [*Ipomoea Quamoclit* L.]—(CYPRESS-VINE.)—Waste-places and old fields, various provinces, Fla. to Tex., Kans., and Va. (Trop. Am.)

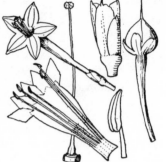

2. Q. coccinea (L.) Moench. Leaf-blades ovate, 3–10 cm. long, acuminate, angled or entire: peduncles usually stouter than the pedicels: calyx-lobes oblong: corolla scarlet or orange, rarely white; tube 2–4 cm. long; limb cup-like, 1.5–2 cm. broad. [*Ipomoea coccinea* L.]—In fields, and waste-places, various provinces, Fla. to Ariz., Mo., and Pa. Nat. of trop. Am. (Cent. Am.).

9. EXOGONIUM Choisy. Creeping, trailing or twining vines. Leaf-blades, entire, lobed, or divided, rarely cordate. Flowers in axillary cymes or solitary. Calyx-lobes leathery, unequal, obtuse. Corolla salverform, scarlet or white. Capsule thick-walled, 4-seeded.—About 25 species of tropical and subtropical America.

1. E. microdactylum (Griseb.) House. Leaf-blades elliptic, thickish, obtuse at base, entire or lobed, 3–8 cm. long: corolla crimson or scarlet; tube 4–5 cm. long: limb 4–5 cm. broad, slightly 5-lobed: capsule longer than the calyx. — (WILD-POTATO.) — Pinelands, Everglade Keys, Fla.—(W. I.)—This wild-potato, within our range, occurs only in the weathered surface of oölitic limestone. The roots, resembling sweet-potatoes, often fill the small erosion holes so completely that the rock must be broken in order to get them out.

10. THYELLA Raf. Annual or perennial twining vines. Leaf-blades entire or lobed. Flowers in dense capitate clusters interspersed with numerous enlarged foliaceous, pubescent or hirsute bracts. Sepals equal. Corolla blue, violet or white, funnelform. Ovary 2-celled. Styles united up to the 2 ovoid flattened stigmas. Capsule subglobose, 4-valved. Seeds minutely roughened.—About 10 species of warm and tropical America.

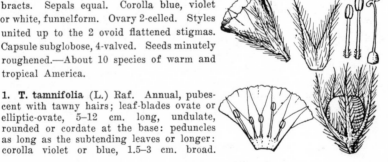

1. T. tamnifolia (L.) Raf. Annual, pubescent with tawny hairs; leaf-blades ovate or elliptic-ovate, 5–12 cm. long, undulate, rounded or cordate at the base: peduncles as long as the subtending leaves or longer: corolla violet or blue, 1.5–3 cm. broad.

[*Jacquemontia tamnifolia* (L.) Griseb.]—Fields and thickets, Coastal Plain, Fla. to Ark. and S. C.—(*W. I., Mex., C. A., S. A., O. W.*)

11. JACQUEMONTIA Choisy. Trailing or twining vines or upright shrubs or herbs. Leaf-blades entire or rarely toothed or lobed. Flowers in loose cymes without conspicuous bracts, or solitary. Calyx-lobes equal or unequal. Corolla white, or blue, limb plaited. Capsule subglobose, 4-valved or sub-8-valved.—About 30 species, in tropical and subtropical America.

Corolla white: plant perennial.
  Corolla over 2 cm. wide: capsule obtuse.
    Leaves fleshy: calyx becoming 2–3 mm. long.   1. *J. reclinata.*
    Leaves herbaceous: calyx becoming 4–5 mm. long.   2. *J. Curtissii.*
  Corolla less than 1.5 cm. wide: capsule acute.   3. *J. jamaicensis.*
Corolla blue: plant annual.   4. *J. pentantha.*

1. J. reclinata House. Stem tomentulose or glabrate, prostrate, reclining, or ascending, woody below, often 1–2.5 m. long: leaf-blades elliptic to ovate-orbicular, 1–3 cm. long, obtuse or retuse: peduncles usually shorter than the leaves: calyx-lobes ovate: corolla white, 2.5–3 cm. broad: capsule 4–5 mm. long. [*Convolvulus havanensis* (Chapm. Fl.)]—Coastal sand-dunes and coastal hammocks, eastern shores of S pen. Fla.—(*W. I.*)—All year.

2. J. Curtissii Peter. Stem woody, prostrate spreading or erect, glabrous or slightly cob-webby-pubescent, 2–9 dm. long: leaf-blades elliptic or elliptic-spatulate, 1–2 cm. long, obtuse or abruptly pointed, slightly revolute: calyx-lobes orbicular-ovate or oval: corolla white, 2.5–3 cm. broad: capsule 5–6 mm. long.—Pinelands and adj. Everglades, S pen. Fla.

3. J. jamaicensis (Jacq.) Hall. Stem erect or ascending, finely pulverulent-pilose: leaf-blades ovate to elliptic, 5–15 mm. long, obtuse at the base, apex rounded or obtuse, rigid, revolute: peduncles 1-flowered, 6–9 mm. long; sepals obovate, 1.5–2 mm. long: corolla white. [*Convolvulus nodiflorus* (Chapm. Fl.)]—Hammocks, Bahia Honda Key, Fla.—(*W. I.*)

4. J. pentantha (Jacq.) G. Don. Stem pubescent or glabrate, 3–10 dm. long; leaf-blades ovate or ovate-lanceolate, 2–5 cm. long, truncate or subcordate at the base: corolla about 2 cm. long, the slightly angular lobes acute. [*J. violacea* Chois.]—Hammocks, Florida Keys.—(*W. I.*)

12. CONVOLVULUS [Tourn.] L. Annual or (ours) perennial, erect, reclining, trailing, or twining vines. Leaf-blades usually hastate or cordate at the base. Flowers solitary, or clustered on axillary peduncles. Calyx subtended by bracts. Calyx-lobes equal or the outer longer. Corolla funnelform or campanulate. Ovary 1- or 2-celled. Ovules 4. Capsule globose or nearly so. Seeds glabrous.—About 150 species, in temperate and tropical regions.—Spr.–sum.—BINDWEEDS.

Stem trailing or climbing.
  Mature stem and leaves glabrous or glabrate: leaf-blades ovate or hastate.
    Leaf-blades with more or less angular spreading basal
      lobes.   1. *C. americanus.*
    Leaf-blades with rounded or scarcely angled basal lobes
      which are not spreading.   2. *C. sepium.*
  Mature stem and leaves copiously and softly pubescent:
    leaf-blades more or less sagittate.
    Leaf-blades elliptic, basal lobes rounded.
      Leaf-blades densely white-tomentulose beneath.   3. *C. sericatus.*
      Leaf-blades green, softly pubescent.   4. *C. repens.*
    Leaf-blades lanceolate, basal lobes half as long, spread-
      ing, acute.   5. *C. Nashii.*
Stem erect or ascending.   6. *C. spithamaeus.*

1. C. americanus (Sims) Greene. Stem twining, 1–3 m. long, glabrate. Leaf-blades broadly hastate or ovate-hastate, 5–12 cm. long, acuminate or apiculate: peduncles as long as the leaves or longer: bracts 2–3 cm. long: corolla pink or rose-purple, 5–7 cm. broad.—(HEDGE-BINDWEED.) —Thickets, various provinces, N of Coastal Plain, N. C. to Utah, Mont., and N. S.— *C. japonicus* Thunb. Similar to *C. americanus* in habit, but usually smaller: leaf-blades narrowly hastate: corolla double, pink, mostly 4–5.5 cm. wide, occurs locally in cult. grounds and waste-places.

2. C. sepium L. Similar to *C. americanus* in habit: leaf-blades relatively broader and more rounded at the apex, basal lobes directed backward, not spreading: corolla white or pink.—Thickets and waste-places, locally naturalized in N. Am., except the extreme north. Nat. of O. W.

3. C. sericatus House. Stem twining, 5–10 dm. long, tomentose: leaf-blades elliptic-ovate, acuminate, slightly hastate-cordate, white beneath with a dense silky-tomentulose indument, 6–8 cm. long: peduncles longer than the leaves: bracts 2.5–3 cm. long: corolla white, 5–6 cm. long.—Thickets, Blue Ridge, Ga.

4. C. repens L. Stem twining or trailing: leaf-blades narrowly or broadly sagittate, 5–8 cm. long, cordate at the base: peduncles as long as the leaves or longer: bracts 1.5–2.5 cm. long: corolla white or pinkish, 4–5 cm. long.—Dry soil and old fields, various provinces, Fla. to Tex., S. Dak., and Va.

5. C. Nashii House. Stem softly and finely sericeous-pubescent, twining, 1–2 m. long: leaf-blades lanceolate or the lower elliptic-lanceolate, 3–4 cm. long: basal lobes 1–2 cm. long, spreading or produced: peduncles 1-flowered, shorter than the leaves: bracts ovate, subacute, 14–18 mm. long: corolla white, or the limb bordered with pink, 4–5 cm. long.—Swampy places, Fla.

6. C. spithamaeus L. Stem finely pubescent, 1–7 dm. long: leaf-blades elliptic-ovate or fiddle-shaped, 4–10 cm. long, rounded or subcordate at the base: peduncles usually from the lower axils: bracts 1.5–3 cm. long: corolla white or pink, 4–6 cm. long.—(LOW-BINDWEED.)—Fields and roadsides, often in calcareous soil, various provinces, Fla. to Tenn., NW Terr., Ont., and N. S.

13. STROPHOCAULOS Small. Perennial procumbent or twining vines. Leaf-blades sagittate to hastate, petioled. Flowers solitary or few together on peduncles. Calyx naked, not subtended by bracts. Calyx-lobes nearly equal. Corolla short-funnelform, white or pink, sometimes pubescent without. Ovary mostly 2-celled. Capsule globose or ovoid. Seeds glabrous.— About 40 species, widely distributed. One species.—BINDWEEDS.

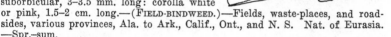

1. S. arvensis (L.) Small. Stem branched at the base, the branches prostrate or low-twining: leaf-blades elliptic, ovate-sagittate, or linear-hastate, 1–5 cm. long: peduncles shorter than the leaves: calyx-lobes oval or suborbicular, 3–3.5 mm. long: corolla white or pink, 1.5–2 cm. long.—(FIELD-BINDWEED.)—Fields, waste-places, and road-sides, various provinces, Ala. to Ark., Calif., Ont., and N. S. Nat. of Eurasia. —Spr.–sum.

14. TURBINA Raf. Perennial, high climbing or trailing vines. Leaf-blades ovate, cordate, glabrate, entire. Flowers in many-flowered, corymbose, axillary, peduncled clusters, near the ends of branches. Sepals coriaceous. Corolla funnelform from the base. Ovary 2-celled, 2-ovuled. Capsules turbinate, twice as long as broad, acute, indehiscent, 1-celled and 1-seeded by abortion. Seeds oblong, finely pubescent.—About 20 species, in tropical regions.

1. T. corymbosa (L.) Raf. Stems trailing, several m. long. Sepals narrowly ovate or elliptic, subacute, 6–8 mm. long, dark-colored with whitish scarious margins: corolla white with green bands, 3–4 cm. long; sapsule 8–10 mm. long. [*Ipomoea sidaefolia* Choisy *I. antillana* Millsp.]—Hammocks, Coastal Plain Cape Sable region, Florida and the Keys and S Tex.—Fall–wint.

15. ARGYREIA Lour. Twining vines, the pubescence commonly sericeous. Leaf-blades broad, cordate, usually entire. Flowers in axillary peduncled cymes. Calyx often colored within: lobes leathery. Corolla showy, campanulate-funnelform. Ovary 2-celled. Stigma slightly 2-lobed. Fruit baccate, indehiscent.—About 25 species, in tropical Asia and Africa.

1. A. speciosa (L.) Sweet. Stem and branches tomentose: leaf-blades broadly ovate, 12–20 cm. long, glabrate above, silvery-pubescent beneath, the veins conspicuous: bracts ovate-elliptic, unequal, glabrous within: sepals 4–5 mm. long: corolla-tube inflated-cylindric, about 5 cm. long; limb purple.—Hammocks along Everglades, Fla. Nat. of trop. Asia, and cult.—(*W. I.*)

Family 3. **CUSCUTACEAE** — Dodder Family

Herbaceous parasitic vines, with pale foliage. Leaves mere alternate scales. Flowers perfect, cymose. Calyx of 4 or 5 distinct or partly united sepals. Corolla regular, of 4 or 5 partly united petals, usually bearing fringed scales below the sinuses. Androecium of 4 or 5 stamens, the filaments partly adnate to the corolla-tube. Gynoecium of 2 partly united carpels, the styles distinct, or partly united: stigmas capitate. Capsule circumscissile or indehiscent.—Only the following genus, and about 160 species, widely distributed.

1. **CUSCUTA** [Tourn.] L. Annual, slender, yellow or reddish vines twining on herbs and shrubs and adhering to the bark by means of suckers. Flowers white, greenish, or yellowish. The plants arise from the ground, but later become wholly parasitic, the stems and branches often matted.—Sum.–fall or all year S.—Dodders. Love-vines. Strangle-weeds.

Styles distinct. (Subgenus Grammica.)
  Capsule remaining closed, a utricle.
    Flowers subtended by several bracts: sepals nearly or
      quite distinct.   I. Glomeratae.
    Flowers not subtended by bracts: sepals partly united.   II. Platycarpae.
  Capsule circumscissile, a pyxis.   III. Umbellatae.
Styles more or less united. (Subgenus Monogyna.)   IV. Exaltatae.

I. Glomeratae

Bracts subtending the calyx obtuse, with appressed tips.   1. *C. compacta.*
Bracts subtending the calyx acute, with spreading tips.   2. *C. glomerata.*

II. Platycarpae

Capsule subglobose, more or less depressed.
  Calyx and corolla smooth, neither fleshy nor papillate.
    Corolla persistent at the base of the capsule.
      Corolla-lobes obtuse; scales reaching the filaments:
        flowers pentamerous.   3. *C. glandulosa.*
      Corolla-lobes acute.
        Corolla-lobes triangular; scales with few proc-
          esses at the apex: flowers mostly tetramerous.   4. *C. Polygonorum.*
        Corolla-lobes ovate; scales with numerous proc-
          esses: flowers pentamerous.   5. *C. pentagona.*
    Corolla persistent at the apex of the capsule: flowers
      mostly tetramerous.   6. *C. Cephalanthi.*
  Calyx and corolla fleshy, papillate by the lens-like cells:
    corolla with inflexed tips.
    Flowers mostly tetramerous: corolla-scales rudimen-
      tary, represented by toothed wings.   7. *C. Coryli.*
    Flowers mostly pentamerous: corolla-scales copiously
      fringed.   8. *C. indecora.*
Capsule ovoid, conic, or flask-shaped.
  Corolla about 1 mm. long; lobes inflexed at the tip:
    flowers frequently tetramerous.   9. *C. Harperi.*
  Corolla 2–6 mm. long; lobes not inflexed: flowers pen-
    tamerous.
    Capsule flask-shaped, with a long neck: flowers 4–6
      mm. long.   10. *C. rostrata.*
    Capsule globose-conic or globose-ovoid: flowers 2–4 mm.
      long.   11. *C. Gronovii.*

III. Umbellatae

Corolla-lobes lanceolate as long as the tube: corolla-scales long
  and narrow, reaching the sinuses.   12. *C. umbellata.*
Corolla-lobes ovate, shorter than the tube: corolla-scales short
  and broad, not reaching the sinuses.   13. *C. americana.*

IV. Exaltatae

Plant with very coarse tangled stems, large flowers (corolla
  4–5 mm. long) and large capsules, 6–9 mm. long.   14. *C. exaltata.*

1. C. compacta Juss. Branches stout or stoutish, often widely matted: calyx-lobes orbicular to oval, subtended by 3–5 appressed bracts: corolla-lobes elliptic, spreading or reflexed, much shorter than the tube: corolla-scales shorter than the corolla-tube or reaching the filaments, long-fringed: anthers oval: capsule globose-conic: seeds about 2.5 mm. long.—On shrubs mostly in swamps, various provinces, Fla. to Tex., Kans., Ont., and Mass.

2. C. glomerata Choisy. Branches rather slender, wound tightly around the stems of the host, and floriferous: calyx-lobes elliptic-oval, subtended by bracts with recurved tips: corolla-lobes elliptic to lanceolate, spreading or sometimes reflexed, shorter than the tube: corolla-scales shorter than the corolla-tube, most abundantly fringed at the apex:

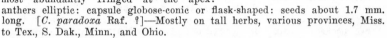

anthers elliptic: capsule globose-conic or flask-shaped: seeds about 1.7 mm. long. [*C. paradoxa* Raf. ?]—Mostly on tall herbs, various provinces, Miss. to Tex., S. Dak., Minn., and Ohio.

3. C. glandulosa (Engelm.) Small. Branches rather slender, commonly matted: flowers in globular compact clusters: calyx-lobes ovate: corolla-lobes ovate obtuse, shorter than the tube: corolla-scales as long as the corolla-tube, fimbriate: capsule depressed-globose: seeds oval. [*C. obtusiflora glandulosa* Engelm.]—On herbs, various provinces, Fla. to Tex., Calif., Tenn., and Ga.—(*W. I., Mex.*)

4. C. Polygonorum Engelm. Branches rather coarse to slender, often loosely matted: flowers in compact clusters: calyx-lobes triangular: corolla-lobes triangular, acute, longer than the tube: corolla-scales as long as the corolla-tube or nearly so, with few short processes on the upper part: capsule subglobose: seeds roundish.—On herbs in wet places, various provinces, Tenn., to Tex., Minn. and Md.

5. C. pentagona Engelm. Branches slender, loosely matted: calyx-lobes deltoid ovate to orbicular-ovate, obtuse: corolla-lobes as long as the tube or slightly longer, reflexed or spreading, the acute tips inflexed: corolla-scales longer than the corolla-tube, deeply fringed: anthers ellipsoid: capsule subglobose: seeds 1–1.2 mm. long. [*C. arvensis* Beyr.]—On herbs and low shrubs, various provinces, Fla. to Tex., Calif., Wash., and Mass.—(*W. I., Mex.*)

6. C. Cephalanthi Engelm. Branches rather coarse, seldom matted: calyx-lobes elliptic-ovate, obtuse: corolla-lobes much shorter than the tube, erect or spreading, obtuse: corolla-scales nearly or quite as long as the corolla-tube, with scattered processes: anthers oval to subglobose: capsule depressed-globose: seeds about 1.6 mm. long.—On shrubs and tall herbs, various provinces, Tenn. to Tex., Calif., Wash., Me., and Va.

7. C. Coryli Engelm. Branches slender or rather stout, sometimes loosely matted: calyx-lobes triangular, acute: corolla cylindric-campanulate in anthesis; lobes triangular-ovate: corolla-scales rudimentary, shorter than the corolla-tube, with few irregular processes on either side below the notched or truncate top: anthers oval or slightly ellipsoid: capsule depressed-globose. [*C. inflexa* Engelm.]—On shrubs or woody herbs, various provinces, N. C. to Tex., Ariz., Mont., Mich., and R. I.

8. C. indecora Choisy. Branches stout, loosely matted: calyx-lobes lanceolate to triangular-lanceolate, acute or obtusish: corolla campanulate in anthesis; lobes lanceolate or triangular-lanceolate: corolla-scales broad, as long as the corolla-tube or longer, copiously fringed: anthers broadly oval: capsule globose. [*C. decora pulcherrima* Engelm.]—On herbs and low shrubs, various provinces, Fla. to Tex., Calif., Ida., and Mich.—(*W. I., Mex.*)

9. C. Harperi Small. Branches very slender, rather loosely matted: flowers in loose clusters: calyx orbicular-ovate to reniform: corolla broadly campanulate, about 1 mm. long; lobes triangular-ovate, as long as the tube or slightly shorter, acute: corolla-scales exceeding the corolla-tube, with few short processes, especially above: anthers subglobose: capsule depressed-globose or globose-ovoid, depressed at the apex: seeds about 1 mm. long.—On low herbs, Appalachian Provinces, Ala.

10. C. rostrata Shuttlw. Branches rather coarse, sometimes loosely matted: flowers in compact clusters: calyx-lobes ovate: corolla campanulate, 4–6 mm. long; lobes ovate, much shorter than the tube, obtuse: corolla-scales shorter than the corolla-tube, with many long processes: anthers oval: capsule flask-shaped, beaked, seeds 2.5 mm. long or nearly so.—On herbs or rarely on shrubs; various provinces, Ga. to Tenn. and Md.—Very common on herbs and brambles above 5000 feet alt. in the Blue Ridge.

11. C. Gronovii Willd. Branches slender to rather coarse, more or less matted: flowers in lax or dense clusters: calyx shorter than the corolla; lobes broadly ovate, obtuse: corolla broadly campanulate; lobes ovate, shorter than the tube: corolla-scales nearly or quite as long as the tube, deeply fringed, the larger processes near the top: anthers oval: capsule globose-ovoid: seeds about 1.5 mm. long.—On herbs and low shrubs, often in wet grounds, various provinces, Fla. to Tex., Ariz., Man., and N. S.

12. C. umbellata H. B. K. Branches slender, sometimes filiform, loosely matted: flowers in unusually dense clusters: calyx fully as long as the corolla-tube; lobes triangular to ovate-triangular: corolla broadly campanulate; lobes lanceolate, as long as the tube or longer: corolla-scales as long as the corolla-tube or exceeding it, with numerous short processes: anthers oval or ellipsoid: capsule depressed-globose: seeds about 1 mm. long.—On herbs, Coastal Plain and southwestern provinces, Fla. to Ariz.—(*W. I., Mex.*)

13. C. americana L. Branches rather slender, in separate strands or sometimes matted: flowers in small (1 cm. in diameter) spaced or crowded clusters: calyx not as long as the corolla-tube; lobes somewhat reniform: corolla narrowly campanulate; lobes ovate, much shorter than the tube: corolla-scales shorter than the corolla-tube, with rather many very short processes: anthers subglobose: capsule ovoid: seeds about 1 mm. long.—Hammocks and pinelands, S Fla.—(*W. I., Mex., C. A., S. A.*)

14. C. exaltata Engelm. Branches very stout, copiously but sometimes loosely matted: flowers sessile or nearly so in spike-like panicles: calyx nearly or quite as long as the corolla-tube; lobes orbicular-ovate: corolla cylindric-campanulate: lobes ovate-orbicular, much shorter than the tube: corolla-scales 2-lobed, appearing as a wing on either side of the filament-attachment, toothed above: anthers ovoid: capsule oval-ovoid or cylindric-ovoid, 6–9 mm. long: seeds 3–5 mm. long.—On shrubs, especially scrub-oaks, coastal sand dunes, Fla.; also various provinces, Tex.

FAMILY 4. **HYDROLEACEAE** — WATER-LEAF FAMILY

Annual or perennial herbs, or shrubby plants. Leaves alternate or opposite: blades toothed, lobed, or dissected, or rarely entire. Flowers purple, blue, or white, rarely pink, in scorpioid racemes, or in cymes. Calyx of 5 partly united sepals. Corolla regular, of 5 partly united petals, the tube often appendaged within. Androecium of 5 stamens, the filaments partly adnate to the corolla. Gynoecium 2-carpellary. Fruit a capsule.—About 20 genera and 175 species, mostly natives of Western North America.

Styles wholly or partly united: ovary 1-celled: leaf-blades usually toothed or lobed.
    Corolla-lobes convolute in the bud: placentae dilated.   I. HYDROPHYLLEAE.
    Corolla-lobes imbricate in the bud: placentae narrow.   II. PHACELIAE.
Styles distinct: ovary 2-celled: leaf-blades entire.
    Corolla funnelform or salverform: capsule loculicidal,
      the valves bearing the seeds.   III. MARILAUNIDIEAE.
    Corolla rotate or campanulate: capsule septicidal, the
      axils bearing the seeds.   IV. NAMEAE.

I. HYDROPHYLLEAE

Calyx not conspicuously enlarged at maturity.
    Calyx without reflexed appendages at the sinuses.   1. HYDROPHYLLUM.
    Calyx with reflexed appendages at the sinuses.
      Styles united to near the tips: stamens exserted.   2. DECEMIUM.
      Styles united to about the middle: stamens included.   3. NEMOPHILA.
Calyx conspicuously enlarged at maturity.   4. NYCTELEA.

II. PHACELIEAE

Annual or rarely perennial herbs: flowers in scorpioid
    raceme-like cymes: corolla showy.   5. PHACELIA.

III. MARILAUNIDIEAE

Low, often prostrate herbs: flowers axillary: corolla small.   6. MARILAUNIDIUM.

IV. NAMEAE

Perennial erect herbs or partly woody plants: flowers in
    axillary or terminal cymes: corolla showy.   7. NAMA.

1. **HYDROPHYLLUM** [Tourn.] L. Perennial herbs. Leaf-blades lobed, pinnatifid, or pinnately divided. Cymes long-peduncled. Calyx but little changed in fruit. Corolla white or colored. Filaments surpassing the corolla-lobes, bearded at the middle. Seeds reticulate.—About 12 species, North American.—WATER-LEAFS.

Leaf-blades pinnate or pinnatifid: inflorescence conspicuously hirsute.
    Stems barely pubescent: calyx-lobes nearly distinct, linear.   1. *H. virginicum.*
    Stems hispid or hirsute: calyx-lobes elliptic-lanceolate.   2. *H. macrophyllum.*
Leaf-blades palmately 5–7-lobed.   3. *H. canadense.*

1. **H. virginicum** L. Plant 2–7 dm. tall: leaf-segments coarsely toothed or incised: cymes open: calyx-lobes linear, about 5 mm. long, much longer than the tube: corolla white or purplish, 8.5–10 mm. long; lobes rounded at the apex.—Rich woods, various provinces, in Coastal Plain only northward, S. C. to Kans., Man., and Que.—Spr.–sum.

2. **H. macrophyllum** Nutt. Plant 2–6 dm. tall: leaf-segments coarsely serrate or incised: cymes compact: calyx-lobes lanceolate to elliptic lanceolate, somewhat longer than the tube: corolla white, 9–11 mm. long; lobes notched at the apex.—Rich woods, various provinces, N of Coastal Plain, Ga. to Ill. and Va.—Spr.

3. **H. canadense** L. Plant 2–7 dm. tall:

leaf-lobes coarsely toothed or again lobed: cymes open: calyx-lobes linear to linear-lanceolate, much longer than the tube: corolla white, 9–10 mm. long, the lobes notched at the apex.—Rich soil, woods and river-banks, various provinces N of Coastal Plain, N. C. to Ky., Ont., and Mass.

2. **DECEMIUM** Raf. Biennial upright herbs. Leaf-blades pinnately or palmately lobed or divided. Cymes long-peduncled. Calyx somewhat accrescent. Corolla violet or purple. Filaments surpassed by the corolla-lobes, beardless. Seeds minutely pitted.—One species.

1. **D. appendiculatum** (Michx.) Small. Plant 3–6 dm. tall: leaf-lobes coarsely toothed, acute or acuminate: cymes open: calyx-lobes narrowly lanceolate or subulate-lanceolate, much longer than the tube: corolla 9–11 mm. long; lobes rounded at the apex. [*Hydrophyllum appendiculatum* Michx.]—Rich soil, usually in damp woods, various provinces N of Coastal Plain, N. C. to Kans., and Ont.

3. **NEMOPHILA** Nutt. Annual diffuse herbs. Leaf-blades pinnately lobed or pinnatifid. Flowers solitary on axillary peduncles. Calyx not much enlarged at maturity. Corolla white or colored. Filaments included, glabrous. Styles partially united.—About 10 species, North American.

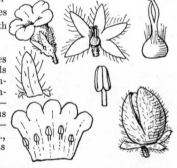

1. **N. microcalyx** (Nutt.) F. & M. Branches 0.5–4 dm. long: leaf-segments 3–5: pedicels 0.5–1.5 mm. long: calyx with minute appendages: corolla white or bluish, the appendages obsolete: capsule 4–5 mm. long.— Shaded banks and moist woods, various provinces, W Fla. to Tex., Ark., and Va.— Spr.—Another species, *N. phacelioides* Nutt., occurs west of the Mississippi River. It has a large corolla 2–2.5 cm. wide.

4. **NYCTELEA** Scop. Annual herbs. Leaf-blades pinnately divived or 1–3-pinnatifid. Flowers solitary in the axils. Calyx accrescent. Corolla white or bluish, commonly smaller than the calyx. Filaments included, often unequal, not dilated. Styles united.—About three species, North American.

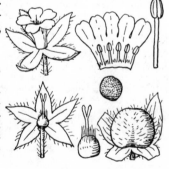

1. **N. Nyctelea** (L.) Britton. Plant 0.5–3 dm. tall, ultimately diffusely branched: leaf-blades with spreading segments: pedicels 1–2 cm. long: calyx-lobes triangular-lanceolate, becoming 7–8 mm. long: corolla 4–6 mm. long: capsule 5–6 mm. in diameter. —Rich soil, woods and stream-banks, various provinces, N of Coastal Plain, N. C. to Kans., Sask. and Ont.—Spr.–sum.

5. PHACELIA Juss. Annual, biennial, or perennial herbs. Leaf-blades toothed or dissected. Flowers in scorpioid racemes or cymes. Calyx slightly accrescent. Corolla white or variously colored: lobes entire to fimbriate. Filaments not dilated at the base. Styles partly united.—About 90 species, American—Spr.

Corolla-lobes entire or merely crenulate.
Appendages of the corolla-tube between the stamens conspicuous.   I. Bipinnatifidae.
Appendages of the corolla-tube between the stamens inconspicuous or obsolete.   II. Dubiae.
Corolla-lobes fimbriate, laciniate, or fimbriate-dentate.   III. Fimbriatae.

I. Bipinnatifidae
Stamens longer than the corolla: style over 8 mm. long.   1. *P. bipinnatifida.*
Stamens shorter than the corolla: style less than 5 mm. long.   2. *P. brevistyla.*

II. Dubiae
Plant puberulent: corolla white or lilac, 8–10 mm. wide.   3. *P. dubia.*
Plant hirsute: corolla violet-purple, 12–15 mm. wide.   4. *P. hirsuta.*

III. Fimbriatae
Pedicels as long as the calyx-lobes or a little longer at maturity: style-branches longer than the united portion.
Calyx-lobes elliptic: corolla about 8 mm. broad; lobes laciniate toothed.   5. *P. Boykinii.*
Calyx-lobes linear: corolla about 4 mm. broad; lobes irregularly toothed.   6. *P. Bicknellii.*
Pedicels fully twice as long as the calyx-lobes at maturity: style-branches shorter than the united portion.
Corolla blue with white eye: stem erect.   7. *P. Purshii.*
Corolla white or pinkish: stem spreading or decumbent.   8. *P. fimbriata.*

1. P. bipinnatifida Michx. Plant 1–6 dm. tall, glandular-pubescent above: leaves 4–11 cm. long; blades pinnately divided, the segments incised or pinnatifid: calyx-lobes narrowly linear to linear-subulate, 4–6 mm. long: corolla violet-blue, 9–11 mm. long; lobes mostly longer than the tube; appendages about ⅓ as long as the corolla: capsule 5–6 mm. long.—Damp slopes, calcareous cliffs, and thickets, various provinces N of Coastal Plain, Ga. to Ala., Ill., Ohio, and Va.—Spr.–sum.

2. P. brevistyla Buckl. Plant 1–4 dm. tall, glandular-pubescent above: leaves similar to those of *P. bipinnatifida*, but often smaller: calyx-lobes linear to linear-subulate, 4–5 mm. long: corolla bluish, 4–5.5 mm. long; lobes mostly shorter than the tube; appendages about ½ as long as the corolla: capsule 4–5 mm. long.—Shaded slopes, Blue Ridge to Appalachian Plateau, Ala. to N. C.—Spr.–sum.

3. P. dubia (L.) Small. Plant 0.5–4 dm. tall, often diffuse, strigillose, as well as glandular: stem-leaves with 3–5 oval, ovate, or obovate lobes: calyx-lobes narrowly elliptic or nearly so, 3–4 mm. long: corolla mainly pale-lilac, 5–6 mm. long; appendages obsolete: stamens longer than the corolla: ovary and style-base pubescent: capsule 2.5–3 mm. long. [*P. parviflora* Pursh]—Sterile hillsides and thickets, various provinces, N of Coastal Plain, Ga. to Tex., Kans., and W N. Y.—Spr.

4. P. hirsuta Nutt. Plant 0.5–3 dm. tall, sometimes sparingly branched, hirsute: stem-leaves with 5–7 lanceolate, elliptic, or ovate lobes: calyx-lobes elliptic to linear-spatulate, 5–6 mm. long: corolla dark-purple or purplish-blue, 8.5–11 cm. long: stamens shorter than the corolla: ovary and style-base pubescent: capsule 3.5–4 mm. long.—Dry soil, rocks, and open woods, various provinces, N of Coastal Plain, Ga. to Kans. and Va.—Spr.

5. P. Boykinii (A. Gray) Small. Plant 1–2 dm. long, the branches becoming glabrous: stem-leaves with 5–7 broadly ovate lobes: calyx-lobes elliptic, 3–3.5 mm. long: corolla bluish, 3–4 mm. long; lobes laciniate-toothed: appendages less than ½ as long as the corolla: filaments sparingly pubescent: capsule 2.5 mm. long.—Dry soil, inner edge of Coastal Plain, Ga.—Spr.

6. P. Bicknellii Small. Plant 1–3 dm. tall, the branches strigose: stem-leaves with 5–7 mostly triangular lobes: calyx-lobes linear, 4–5 mm. long: corolla pale-blue, 3–4 mm. long; lobes irregularly toothed; appendages fully ½ as long as the corolla: filaments glabrous: capsule about 2 mm. long.—Barren soil, Interior Low Plateaus, Tenn.—Spr.

7. P. Purshii Buckl. Plant 1–3 dm. tall, with rather stiff stems; stem-leaves with 5–9 lanceolate or elliptic lobes: calyx-lobes linear to elliptic-spatulate, 4–5 mm. long: corolla light-blue with white eye, 6–7 mm. long; lobes short-fimbriate; appendages manifest: filaments about as long as the corolla: capsule about 4 mm. long.—Moist thickets and rich woods, various provinces, N of Coastal Plain, N. C. to Ala., Mo., Minn., and Pa.; locally becoming a field-weed.—Spr.

8. P. fimbriata Michx. Plant 1–4 dm. tall, with weak stem: stem-leaves with 5–7 triangular, lanceolate, or ovate, or partly elliptic lobes: calyx-lobes elliptic to elliptic-spatulate, 5–6 mm. long: corolla white or pinkish, 8–9 mm. long; appendages obsolete: filaments shorter than the corolla: capsule about 5 mm. long.—Wooded slopes, Blue Ridge to Appalachian Plateau, Ala. to Va.—Spr.

6. MARILAUNIDIUM Kuntze. Annual or perennial herbs. Leaf-blades entire. Flowers solitary in axils. Calyx slightly accrescent: lobes narrow. Corolla often blue, funnelform to nearly salverform: filaments often unequal, filiform. Styles distinct.—About 18 species, natives of warm and tropical regions.

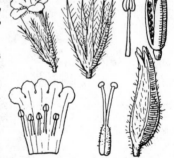

1. M. jamaicense (L.) Kuntze. Branches 1–4 dm. long, spreading or prostrate: leaf-blades spatulate, often broadly so, 1–5 cm. long: calyx-lobes narrowly linear or nearly so, 5–8 mm long, ciliate: corolla white or purple, about as long as the calyx or slightly longer: capsule 8–10 mm. long. [*Nama jamaicensis* L.]—Hammocks and waste-places, Coastal Plain, Fla. to Tex.—(*W. I.,* *Mex., C. A., S. A.*)—Spr.–fall.

7. NAMA L. Perennial herbs, or shrubby plants, sometimes spiny. Leaf-blades entire. Flowers in axillary or terminal cymes. Calyx slightly accrescent: lobes broad. Corolla blue or rarely white, rotate to campanulate. Filaments widely dilated at the base. Styles distinct. [*Hydrolea* L.]—About 45 species, natives of warm and tropical regions.

Styles several times longer than the ovary: filaments nearly or quite as long as the
corolla: top of the ovary and bases of the style glandular-pubescent.
Leaf-blades ovate to elliptic: calyx-lobes mostly less than
7 mm. long.   1. *N. ovatum.*
Leaf-blades elliptic to elliptic-lanceolate: calyx-lobes mostly
over 7 mm. long.   2. *N. corymbosum.*
Styles slightly longer than the ovary: filaments much shorter
than the corolla: ovary and styles glabrous.
Calyx-lobes linear or linear-lanceolate, sparingly ciliate:
stem villous-hirsute.   3. *N. quadrivalve.*
Calyx-lobes ovate to ovate-lanceolate, closely ciliate: stem
glabrous or puberulent.   4. *N. affine.*

1. N. ovatum (Nutt.) Britton. Plant 2–7 dm. tall, soft-pubescent, spine-
armed, paniculate above: leaf-blades somewhat acuminate: calyx-lobes simply
ciliate: corolla mainly purplish or white,
12–15 mm. long: capsule about 5 mm. long.
[*H. ovata* Nutt.]—Swamps, ponds, and
ditches, Coastal Plain, Ga. to Tex. and
Mo.—Sum.

2. N. corymbosum (Macbride) Kuntze.
Plant 2–7 dm. tall, unarmed or nearly so,
corymbose above: leaf-blades elliptic to
elliptic-lanceolate, acute: calyx-lobes glandular-ciliate: corolla mainly azure-blue, 11–
15 mm. long: capsule 4–6 mm. long. [*H.
corymbosa* Macbride]—Swamps, often calcareous, and stream-banks, Coastal Plain,
Fla. to S. C.—Sum.

3. N. quadrivalve (Walt.) Kuntze. Plant 2–10 dm. long, often decumbent,
spine-armed: leaf-blades narrowly elliptic or nearly so, 4–12 cm. long: calyx-
lobes 6–8 mm. long: corolla blue or lilac, 7–8 mm. long: capsule 5–6 mm. long,
surpassed by the calyx. [*H. quadrivalvis* Walt.]—Sandy places, swamps,
ponds, and ditches, Coastal Plain, Fla. to La. and Va.—Sum.

4. N. affine (A. Gray) Kuntze. Plant 2–7 dm. long, often creeping, spine-
armed: leaf-blades linear-elliptic or nearly so, 3–10 cm. long: calyx-lobes 4.5–5
mm. long: corolla violet, 9–10 mm. long: capsule 6–7 mm. long, surpassing
the calyx. [*H. affinis* A. Gray]—Swampy places, Coastal Plain and adj.
provinces, Miss. to Tex., Mo., and Ind.—Sum.–fall.

Family 5.   **POLEMONIACEAE** — Phlox Family[1]

Plants of moderate size. Calyx of 5 partly united sepals, their free
parts (lobes) deltoid to subulate. Corolla of 5 partly united petals, the
free parts (lobes) conspicuous, convolute in bud. Androecium of 5
stamens, often unequal. Gynoecium of 3 united carpels, the styles united.
Fruit a loculicidal capsule.—Comprises 20 genera and 200 species, most
numerous in western North America; all but about 10 of the species are
limited to the New World.

Corolla campanulate: stamens in part declined.   1. Polemonium.
Corolla funnelform to salverform: stamens erect.
Leaf-blades pinnately parted: corolla funnelform: filaments
equally adnate up to the corolla-throat (in our species).   2. Gilia.
Leaf-blades entire or nearly so: corolla salverform: filaments
unequally adnate to the corolla-tube.   3. Phlox.

[1] Contributed by Edgar Theodore Wherry.

1. POLEMONIUM L. Plants perennial with well-developed rootstocks, or in a few species annual. Leaves alternate: blades pinnately divided. Inflorescence primarily cymose, the cymes corymbose or paniculate. Calyx tubular: lobes broad. Corolla violet, yellow, or white, rotate to campanulate, with spreading lobes. Filaments equally adnate to the corolla-tube, two or more declined. Capsule ovoid to ellipsoid.—About 25 species, mostly North American, but at least 7, including the type of the genus, Eurasian.

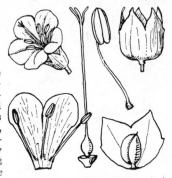

1. P. reptans L. Tufted perennial, the ascending or erect stems up to 50 (exceptionally 75) cm. tall: leaves up to 20 cm. long and 7 cm. wide; segments variable in outline, but usually elliptic: corymb lax, some of the flowers nodding: calyx-tube 3–5 mm. long; lobes 2–4 mm. long during anthesis, doubling in size as the capsule ripens: corolla pale violet, exceptionally white, campanulate, the tube 5–7 mm. long; lobes obovate, as long as the tube: stamens normally included: style exserted. — (BLUE-BELL VALERIAN. GREEK-VALERIAN. SWEAT-ROOT.)—Rich woods and thickets, often in circumneutral soil, various provinces, though rare on the Coastal Plain, Ga. to Miss., E Kans., Minn., and N. Y.— Late spr.—A delicate plant, occasionally cultivated, though blooming for but a short period. A related species, *P. Van-Bruntiae* Britton, grows in S W. Va., and may enter our range in the Blue Ridge; it is taller and has a narrow panicle of larger flowers with the stamens exserted.

2. GILIA R. & P. Perennial, biennial, or annual plants. Leaves usually alternate, with numerous narrow segments, or in some species incised or entire. Calyx tubular to campanulate; lobes narrow, acute. Corolla red, yellow, blue, or white, exceptionally purple. Filaments unequally adnate to the corolla-tube, or equally adnate but unequally exserted. Capsule ellipsoid to ovoid.—About 100 species, all American and mostly in western United States.

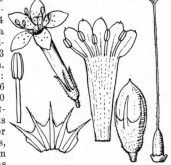

1. G. rubra (L.) Heller. Plant biennial, forming a large rosette the first year and producing a stout stem up to 100 (exceptionally 175) cm. tall the second year: leaves numerous, pinnately-parted into linear-filiform divisions: panicle long, slender: flowers short-pedicelled: calyx-tube 3–4 mm. long; teeth 4–6 mm. long: corolla usually brilliant scarlet-red without and yellow streaked with red within; tube 20–23 mm. long; lobes elliptic-ovate, 9–11 mm. long, terminally undulate or mucronulate: stamens unequally exserted, extending 2–6 mm. beyond the corolla-throat: capsule 8–10 mm. long. [*G. coronopifolia* Pers.]—(SPANISH-LARKSPUR. STANDING-CYPRESS.)—Fields and margins of woods, usually in sandy or sterile soil, Coastal Plain and adj. provinces, Fla. to Tex., Okla., and N. C.; escaped from cultivation in various provinces as far N as

Mich. and Mass.—Sum.—A very showy plant. The flowers are adapted to cross-pollination by humming-birds.

3. PHLOX L. Dwarf-shrubby, perennial, or annual plants. Leaves mostly opposite, with their bases connected by stipular lines, in some species alternate, the blades entire. Inflorescence primarily cymose, the cymes often arranged in corymbs or panicles, bracted. Calyx tubular; lobes narrow, acute or awned. Corolla typically bright-purple, but ranging to rose-red, to blue-violet, or to white, the pale eye often striate with 5 groups of deeper-colored lines: lobes cuneate to broadly obovate. Capsule subglobose to ellipsoid, 4–6 mm. long.—About 50 species, all North American except that one extends from Alaska into Siberia. Several of these, as well as hybrids between them are in cultivation and have escaped locally. Many of the species are markedly variable.

Stems woody, trailing or decumbent; axillary latent shoots prominent: leaves mostly persistent: inflorescence a few-flowered cyme; pedicels often elongate.   I. SUBULATAE.

Stems herbaceous, decumbent or erect; axillary latent shoots inconspicuous: leaves deciduous or a few persistent: inflorescence a few to many-flowered cyme, corymb, or panicle; pedicels rather short.

Calyx-lobes mostly longer than the tube, conspicuously awn-tipped: stamens and style much shorter than the corolla-tube.

Plant perennial: leaf-blades obtuse to acute with short awn-tips: inflorescence bilaterally symmetrical.   II. DIVARICATAE.

Plant annual: leaf-blades acute, with prominent awn-tips: inflorescence asymmetrical.   III. DRUMMONDIANAE.

Calyx-lobes mostly shorter than the tube, obscurely awn-tipped: one or more stamens and style nearly or quite equalling the corolla-tube.

Leaves medium-sized, their margins roughish or ciliate with soft hairs, and their lateral veins obscure.   IV. OVATAE.

Leaves relatively large, their margins ciliate-serrulate with stiff bristles and their lateral veins prominent, areolate.   V. PANICULATAE.

I. SUBULATAE

Corolla-lobes entire, erose, or shallowly notched; stamens all included; style 1–3 mm. long.

Corolla-lobes conspicuously notched (exceptionally nearly entire); stamens partly exserted; style 4–12 mm. long.   1. P. nivalis.

Nodes numerous, crowded; lower leaves 8–20 mm. long; sinuses in corolla-lobes averaging 1 mm. deep.   2. P. subulata.

Nodes few, more remote; lower leaves 20–60 mm. long; sinuses in the corolla-lobes averaging 3 mm. deep.   3. P. bifida.

II. DIVARICATAE

Sterile shoots becoming decumbent, often rooting at nodes; leaves rather broad; inflorescence lax; corolla-tube glabrous.

Sterile shoots erect or decumbent, not rooting at nodes; leaves mostly narrow; inflorescence more compact.   4. P. divaricata.

Leaves mostly linear to lanceolate, sparingly persistent; bracts spreading; inflorescence-hairs sometimes gland-tipped.

Nodes few; leaves pubescent or sometimes glabrous, the upper spreading, passing rather abruptly into the bracts.

Nodes numerous; leaves always glabrous, the upper ascending, passing gradually into glandular-pubescent bracts.   5. P. pilosa.

Leaves oblong elliptic to lanceolate, many of them persistent; bracts ascending; inflorescence-hairs coarse, eglandular.   6. P. floridana.

     7. P. amoena.

III. Drummondianae
Plant a branching annual with the upper leaves alternate.   8. *P. Drummondii.*

IV. Ovatae
Prostrate stems well-developed, rooting at nodes: lower leaves
    spatulate, many of them persistent.   9. *P. stolonifera.*
Prostrate stems poorly developed: lower leaves never typically
    spatulate, sparingly if at all persistent.
Flowering shoots mostly arising from the tip of a decum-
    bent stem: nodes few: leaves elliptic to ovate: calyx
    averaging 10 mm. long.   10. *P. ovata.*
Flowering shoots mostly arising from the rootstocks:
    nodes numerous: calyx averaging less than 10 mm.
    long.
Cymes in a corymb or broad corymbose panicle.
    Upper leaves lanceolate to ovate: calyx 6–11 mm.
        long.   11. *P. carolina.*
    Upper leaves linear to lanceolate: calyx 5–8 mm.
        long.   12. *P. glaberrima.*
Cymes in a narrow-conical or cylindrical panicle.   13. *P. maculata.*

V. Paniculatae
Hairs on the few opposite leaves, when present, coarse, and
    those on the inflorescence mostly gland-tipped: corolla-tube
    glabrous: stamens all included.   14. *P. amplifolia.*
Hairs on the numerous sub-opposite leaves, when present, fine,
    those on the inflorescence pointed or rarely gland-tipped;
    corolla-tube pubescent: 1 or 2 stamens exserted.   15. *P. paniculata.*

1. P. nivalis Lodd. Low evergreen shrub, with erect pubescent and often
glandular flowering shoots 10–20 cm. tall: leaf-blades sessile, up to 25 mm.
long and to 4 mm. wide; blades linear-subu-
late to lanceolate-elliptic: calyx-tube about
5 mm. and lobes 4 mm. long: corolla light-
purple to white, the eye often dark-striate:
tube 11–19 mm. long; lobes cuneate to
obovate, 8–15 mm. long, terminally entire or
erose, or with a sinus to 0.5 (rarely 1 or 2)
mm. deep. [*P. Hentzii* Nutt.]—(Trailing-
phlox.)—Open oak woods, pine woods, or
scrub, in sterile and often rather acid gravelly or sandy soil, Coastal Plain and Piedmont, Fla. to Ala. (or Miss. acc. to Chapman) and S Va.—Spr., and occasionally
fall.—This species probably represents the
ancestor of the next following, with which
it is often confused.

2. P. subulata L. Low matted evergreen shrub with numerous erect pubescent,
and in our range usually glandular, flowering shoots 5–10 cm. tall: leaves much
as in the preceding, but rarely exceeding 15 mm. in length and 2 mm. in width:
calyx-tube about 4 mm. long; lobes somewhat shorter: corolla of various purple
hues, rarely white, the eye often deep-purple striate: tube 9–15 mm. long;
lobes cuneate to obovate, 6–11 mm. long, terminally sub-entire or usually with
a sinus 0.5–3 mm. deep.—(Moss-phlox. Mountain pink.)—Bare gravelly or
sandy slopes, often in circumneutral soil over calcareous or magnesian rocks,
various provinces, in Coastal Plain only northward, N. C. and E Tenn. to S
Mich., S Ont., and N. Y.—Spr., and occasionally fall.—Presumably a descendant from *P. nivalis*, exhibiting its greater specialization in the more densely
matted stems, more consistently notched corolla-lobes, and more elongate
stamens and style.—*P. Brittonii* Small, differing from typical *P. subulata* in
the pale-lilac or white corolla with deeper sinuses in the lobes, was included in
Fl. SE. U.S., but is not now regarded as specifically distinct, nor as growing
within our area.

3. P. bifida Beck. Trailing subevergreen shrub, with long ascending flowering shoots; the young foliage glabrate to glandular-pubescent: leaf-blades sessile, up to 5 cm. long and to 5 mm. wide, linear to lanceolate: calyx-tube about 4 mm. long; lobes slightly shorter: corolla lavender to white, the eye faintly striate; tube 9–12 mm. long; lobes nearly as long, cuneate, with a sinus 2–6 mm. deep.—(SAND-PHLOX.)—Exposed slopes and cliffs in rocky or sandy, sterile soil, Central Lowland and occasionally adj. provinces, Tenn. to N Okla., E Kans., Iowa, and SW Mich.—Spr.—*P. Stellaria* A. Gray, with glabrate or simply puberulent young foliage, appears not to be specifically distinct.—The plant usually cultivated under the name *P. Stellaria* is a garden form of *P. subulata*.

4. P. divaricata L. Plant in an open-mat, with the lower leaves evergreen, the erect flowering shoots up to 50 cm. tall: leaf-blades sessile or nearly so, elliptic to elliptic-lanceolate or ovate, up to 5 cm. long and to 2 cm. wide: cymes corymbose-paniculate: calyx-tube about 4 mm. long; lobes somewhat longer: corolla of mauve to blue-violet hues, ranging to white, the eye faintly violet-striate; tube 10–16 mm. long, glabrous; lobes cuneate to obovate, varying greatly in length, entire, erose, apiculate, or with a sinus as much as 2 mm. deep.—(BLUE-PHLOX.)—Rich woods, often in circumneutral soil over calcareous rocks, various provinces, rarely Coastal Plain, N Fla. to E Tex., E Nebr., Minn., W Que., and N Vt.—Spr.—The flowers of this species are more consistently of a bluish color than those of any other *Phlox*.—Several showy garden forms and hybrids with other species are in cultivation.

5. P. pilosa L. Plant tufted, the stems up to 60 cm. tall, glabrous or pubescent: leaf-blades sessile, up to 10 cm. long and to 5 (rarely 10) mm. wide, opposite or alternate, linear to broadly lanceolate or ovate, somewhat ciliate, and more or less pubescent on both surfaces, deciduous or sometimes in part persistent: cymes in a terminal corymb: calyx-tube 3–4 mm. and lobes 4–7 mm. long: corolla bright-purple, pale violet, or white, the eye sometimes purple-striate; tube 10–18 mm. long, glabrous or pubescent; lobes obovate, variable in length, entire, erose, mucronulate or apiculate.—(DOWNY-PHLOX.)—Open woods, hammocks, barrens, thickets, and prairies, often in sterile soil, various provinces, Fla. to Tex., S Man., S Ont., and W Conn.—Spr.–early sum. or all year in pen. Fla.—Variable in extent and character of pubescence, on the basis of which a number of forms have been segregated.—*P. detonsa* (A. Gray) Small, with glabrous or glabrate foliage, grades too freely into *P. pilosa* to be maintained as specifically distinct. *P. glutinosa* Buckl. is regarded as a hybrid between this species and *P. divaricata*.

6. P. floridana Benth. Plant tufted, the stems up to 80 cm. tall, glabrous below the inflorescence; leaf-blades sessile, up to 10 cm. long and 7 mm. wide, linear to lanceolate, the upper gradually shortened and conspicuously appressed: cymes in a terminal corymb, glandular-pubescent; calyx-tube 4–5 mm. and lobes 4–6 mm. long: corolla bright-purple; tube 15–20 mm. long; lobes obovate, entire, often larger than in the next preceding species.—(FLORIDA PHLOX.)—Sterile woods, thickets, and swamp-margins, NW Fla. and adj. Ala. and Ga.—Blooms about a month later than *P. pilosa*, in early summer.—One of the most restricted in area of all our Phloxes. Sometimes seems to grade toward *P. pilosa*, but usually quite distinct in aspect.

7. P. amoena Sims. Plant in an open-mat, with the lower leaves evergreen, becoming purplish beneath, the flowering shoots up to 30 cm. tall: leaf-blades sessile, up to 5 cm. long and to 8 mm. wide, the lowermost spatulate but the majority linear-elliptic to elliptic-lanceolate: bracts conspicuous, lanceolate to elliptic: calyx-tube 4–5 mm. long; lobes of the same or a slightly greater length: corolla bright-purple, pale-violet, lilac, or white, the eye faintly striate; tube 12–16 mm. long, glabrous or puberulent; lobes obovate, 8–11 mm. long, terminally entire, undulate, or mucronulate.—(HAIRY PHLOX.)—Open woods and pine barrens, in acid sandy or rocky soil, various provinces, Fla. to Miss., Ky., and N. C.—Spr.—The plant usually cultivated under the name *P. amoena* is a hybrid between *P. subulata* and *P. stolonifera*, with gland-tipped hairs and long stamens and style.—*P. Lighthipei* Small, with flowering shoots up to 50 cm. tall and often longer leaves may not be specifically distinct.

8. **P. Drummondii** Hook. Stem branching, up to 40 cm. tall, pubescent with gland-tipped hairs: leaf-blades up to 9 cm. long and to 15 mm. wide, sessile, the lower opposite and oblanceolate, and the upper alternate, and lanceolate to elliptic, conspicuously awn-tipped: cymes corymbosely compound: calyx-tube 4–5 mm. and lobes 4–7 mm. long: corolla rose-red to purple, ranging to white, the eye often strongly striate; tube 14–17 mm. long, pubescent; lobes obovate, 8–15 mm. long.—(ANNUAL GARDEN-PHLOX.)—Prairies, Coastal Plain and adj. provinces, Tex.; naturalized E to Fla. and Ga.—Spr.–sum.—Cultivation has produced in this species hundreds of forms, of varying types of corolla-lobing, and numerous different colors.

9. **P. stolonifera** Sims. Plant in a dense mat, with decumbent evergreen sterile shoots rooting freely at the nodes, and erect deciduous glandular-pubescent flowering shoots up to 30 cm. tall: leaf-blades up to 8 cm. long and 2 cm. wide, obovate-spatulate to .elliptic-lanceolate: cyme simple or somewhat compound: calyx-tube about 5 mm. long; lobes as long or somewhat shorter: corolla bright-purple, violet, or rarely white, the eye purple-striate; tube 20–25 mm. long; lobes 10–12 mm. long. [*P. reptans* Michx.]—(CREEPING-PHLOX.)—Woods, in humus-rich and slightly acid soils, Blue Ridge, Appalachian Plateau and rarely adj. provinces, Ga. to Ohio and Pa.—Spr.—Rare, though occurring locally in large colonies formed by repeated rooting of the sterile shoots; having developed the ability to propagate itself in this manner, it produces seed only sparingly.

10. **P. ovata** L. Plant in an open-mat, with the lower leaves somewhat persistent, and the glabrate flowering-shoots up to 50 cm. tall; leaf-blades up to 10 cm. long and to 4 cm. wide, the lower and middle petioled, the upper subsessile, elliptic to lanceolate or ovate: cyme simple or corymbosely compound: calyx-tube 6–8 mm. and lobes 3–5 mm. long: corolla bright-purple or rarely white, the eye slightly striate; tube 18–23 mm. long; lobes 10–15 mm. long.—(MOUNTAIN-PHLOX.)—Thickets and open woods, in rather acid soil, higher Piedmont to Central Lowland and to New England Upland, Ga. to E Ind. and E Pa.—Late spr.–sum.—Specimens lacking the decumbent stems tipped with petioled leaves are difficult to distinguish from the next-following species, to which this is probably ancestral.

11. **P. carolina** L. Plant tufted, puberulent or sometimes pubescent, the stems up to 100 (rarely 125) cm. tall, often purple-streaked: leaf-blades up to 12 cm. long and 35 mm. wide, the lower linear but the upper usually conspicuously broader, elliptic-lanceolate to ovate: cymes in a corymb or broad corymbose panicle, exceptionally conical: calyx-tube usually 4–6 mm. and lobes 2.5–4.5 mm. long: corolla deep- or sometimes pale-purple, the eye somewhat striate; tube 15–26 mm. long; lobes 7–15 mm. long.—(THICK-LEAF PHLOX.)—Open woods and occasionally meadows, in subacid soil, chiefly in the Blue Ridge and Appalachian provinces, but occasionally in Piedmont or even Coastal Plain, W Fla. to Miss., S Ind. and W Md.—Late spr.–fall.—Represents an apparent intermediate between Nos. 10, 12 and 13, and grades into them in some colonies.

12. **P. glaberrima** L. Plant tufted, glabrous or essentially so, the stems all erect, up to 60 (rarely 100) cm. tall: leaf-blades up to 15 cm. long and to 15

mm. wide, often numerous and crowded below, remote above, obscurely peti-oled, linear to lanceolate: cymes in a corymb or short, irregularly interrupted panicle: calyx-tube 3–4 mm. long, the lobes somewhat shorter: corolla purple, often pale though rarely white, the eye faintly striate: tube 18–24 mm. long: lobes variable in length.—(SMOOTH-PHLOX.)—Roadsides, prairies and open woods, various provinces, Fla. to E Tex., Wisc. and SE Va.—Late spr.–sum.

13. P. maculata L. Plant tufted, the erect stems up to 125 cm. tall, often purple-streaked: leaves numerous but scarcely crowded; blades subsessile, sca-brous-ciliolate, up to 12 cm. long and to 25 (rarely 35) mm. wide, linear to ovate: cymes in a panicle 3–30 cm. long, its branches exceptionally exceeding the subtending leaves: calyx-tube 4–5 mm. and lobes 2.5–3.5 mm. long: corolla purple to white, the eye faintly striate; tube 18–24 mm. long; lobes 8–10 mm. long.—(MEADOW PHLOX.)—Damp thickets, meadows, and moist open woods, in circumneutral soil, various provinces, N. C. to E Mo., Minn., S. Que., and W Conn.—Late spr.–early fall.—The purple streaks on the stem, although often striking, are not diagnostic for this species. In some occurrences, especially those with white flowers, they are lacking while other species of the genus, and in particular *P. carolina*, of which *P. maculata* appears to be a direct descendant, may be similarly streaked. The non-recognition of this fact has led to many erroneous reports of the occurrence of this species in our region, whereas it seems to be one of the rarest.

14. P. amplifolia Britton. Plant tufted, the stems up to 125 cm. tall, often purple-streaked: leaves up to 18 cm. long and 8 cm. wide, with short broad petioles widening abruptly into the ovate blades, glabrate or usually hirsute with coarse hairs above, and hirsute-pubescent beneath: cymes in a fairly large subcorymbose panicle, the leaves subtending its elongate branches much reduced and the bractlets very small: calyx-tube 3–4 mm. and lobes about as long: corolla pale-purple or rarely white; tube about 2 cm. long; lobes 9 mm. long.—(BROAD-LEAF PHLOX.)—Open woods and thickets, various provinces N of Coastal Plain, Ga. to E Mo., S Ind., and E Ky.—Sum.–early fall.—This species has been confused with the next following, and was no doubt derived from the same ancestor, but is quite distinct in aspect.

15. P. paniculata L. Plant tufted, the stems up to 150 cm. tall: leaves numer-ous, rather crowded, often subopposite: blades somewhat petioled, undu-late-margined, glabrous or puberulent, up to 18 cm. long and 4 (rarely 5) cm. wide, elliptic: cymes in a corymbose panicle 5–35 cm. long, the branches often exceeding their subtending leaves, the bractlets rather conspicuous: calyx-tube 4–5 mm. and lobes 3–6 mm. long: corolla purple to white, the eye often distinct; tube 2–3 cm. long; lobes 9–11 mm. long.—(PERENNIAL GARDEN-PHLOX.)—Thickets along streams and damp woods, often in circumneutral soil, various provinces, N Ga. to Miss., E Nebr., and S N. Y.—Sum.–fall.—*P. paniculata* is extensively cultivated, the majority of the garden forms of perennial phlox having arisen from it or its hybrids with other species, and frequently escapes. —*P. acuminata* Pursh., with the leaves copiously soft-pubescent beneath and decurrent on the stem as angles, may not be specifically distinct.

FAMILY 6. SOLANACEAE — POTATO FAMILY

Herbs, shrubs, trees, or vines. Leaves alternate: blades entire, toothed, or lobed. Calyx of 5, (4–6), more or less united sepals. Corolla of 5, (4–6), more or less united petals. Androecium of 5, (4–6), stamens, the filaments partially adnate to the corolla-tube. Gynoecium 2-carpellary or 3–5-carpellary. Fruit a berry or a capsule.—About 75 genera and 1,750 species, most abundant in the tropics.

Fruit a berry.
  Corolla plicate; lobes usually induplicate.   I. SOLANEAE.
  Corolla little, if at all plicate; lobes imbricate, valvate, or valvate-induplicate.
    Stamens adnate to the lower part of the corolla-tube: corolla rotate or urceolate.   II. CAPSICEAE.
    Stamens adnate up to the upper part of the corolla-tube: corolla salverform to funnelform.
      Seeds flattened: stamens exserted.   III. ATROPEAE.
      Seeds turgid: stamens included.   IV. CESTREAE.
Fruit a capsule.
  Capsule prickle-armed: calyx circumscissile at the base.   V. DATUREAE.
  Capsule unarmed: calyx not circumscissile.
    Flowers in racemes or panicles: filaments nearly equal in length.   VI. NICOTIANEAE.
    Flowers solitary in the axils or opposite the leaves: filaments unequal in length.   VII. PETUNIEAE.

I. SOLANEAE

Berry enclosed in the accrescent calyx.
  Calyx inflated in fruit: anthers not connected; sacs opening lengthwise.
    Ovary 3–5-celled: sepals nearly distinct, auricled.   1. PHYSALODES.
    Ovary 2-celled: sepals united to near the tips.   2. PHYSALIS.
  Calyx not inflated, fitting close to the berry: anthers connected; sacs opening by terminal pores.   3. ANDROCERA.
Berry seated in the little changed calyx (exceptionally enclosed in species of *Solanum*): anthers connate or converging.
  Anther-sacs commonly opening by terminal pores or slits.   4. SOLANUM.
  Anther-sacs opening lengthwise and introrsely.   5. LYCOPERSICON.

II. CAPSICEAE

Anthers converging around the style: corolla urceolate.   6. PERIZOMA.
Anthers not converging: corolla rotate.   7. CAPSICUM.

III. ATROPEAE

Shrubs with herbaceous or succulent leaves.   8. LYCIUM.

IV. CESTREAE

Shrubs or trees: flowers in axillary clusters, sometimes aggregated in a terminal panicle or corymb.   9. CESTRUM.

V. DATUREAE

Herbs, shrubs, or trees, usually rank-smelling: flowers often fragrant, the corolla usually showy.   10. DATURA.

VI. NICOTIANEAE

Herbs, heavy-scented, with usually clammy-pubescent stems and leaves: flowers few or many in the panicles or racemes.   11. NICOTIANA.

VII. PETUNIEAE

Herbs with clammy-pubescent stem and leaves: corolla funnelform, showy.   12. PETUNIA.

1. **PHYSALODES** Boehm. Annual herbs. Leaf-blades sinuate or lobed. Flowers axillary, nodding. Calyx accrescent: lobes cordate or sagittate converging, inflated. Corolla open-campanulate, slightly 5-lobed. Ovary 3–5-celled. Berry surrounded by the calyx-lobes.—One species.

1. **P. Physalodes** (L.) Britton. Plant nearly glabrous, 3–9 dm. tall: leaf-blades ovate, oval, or elliptic, 5–15 cm. long, angulate-lobed or sinuate: calyx 1.5 cm. long, becoming 3.5 cm. long: lobes broadly ovate: corolla blue or violet, about 2.5 cm. wide: berry 1.5–2 cm. in diameter. [*Nicandra Physalodes* Pers.] — (APPLE-OF-PERU.)— Fence-rows, waste-grounds and roadsides, various provinces, Ala. to Miss. and S Can. Nat. of Peru.—Sum.

2. PHYSALIS L.[1]   Annual or perennial branching, often diffuse herbs. Leaf-blades entire or sinuate. Flowers axillary, nodding, mostly solitary. Calyx bladder-like at maturity: lobes short and converging. Corolla campanulate, mainly yellow or whitish, often dark in the center. Ovary 2-celled. Berry globular, enclosed in the papery calyx.—About 80 species, mostly American.—Sum. or all year S.—GROUND-CHERRIES. JERUSALEM-CHERRIES.

Annual plants, with much branched roots.
  Fruiting calyx sharply 5-angled, deeply sunken at the base: calyx-lobes at flowering time fully as long as the tube.   I. PUBESCENTES.
  Fruiting calyx obtusely or indistinctly 5- or 10-angled:
    calyx-lobes at flowering time shorter than the tube
    (except sometimes in *P. Carpenteri*).
    Leaf-blades acute: flowers solitary in the axils.   II. ANGULATAE.
    Leaf-blades acuminate: flowers often fascicled.   III. CARPENTERIANAE.
Perennial plants, with horizontal rootstocks.
  Pubescence of simple hairs.
    Pubescence sparse, seldom if at all glandular or viscid.   IV. LANCEOLATAE.
    Pubescence dense, viscid or glandular, generally a
    mixture of fine short hairs and long flat-jointed
    ones.   V. HETEROPHYLLAE.
  Pubescence mainly of stellate hairs.   VI. VISCOSAE.

I. PUBESCENTES

Plants more or less viscid pubescent.
  Fruiting calyx not long-acuminate: leaf-blades very oblique.
    Leaf-blades ovate, subentire at the base: stem slender, diffuse, sharply angled.   1. *P. pubescens.*
    Leaf-blades cordate, strongly sinuately toothed to the
    base: stem obtusely angled.
      Leaves broadly rounded, cordate, 2–5 cm. long: stem weak, diffuse.   2. *P. floridana.*
      Leaves elongated, cordate, 4–10 cm. long: stem stout.   3. *P. pruinosa.*
  Fruiting calyx long-acuminate: leaf-blades scarcely oblique at the base, cordate, abruptly acuminate.   4. *P. barbadensis.*
Plants glabrous or puberulent when young.   5. *P. turbinata.*

II. ANGULATAE

Plant pubescent and more or less viscid.   6. *P. missouriensis.*
Plant glabrous.   7. *P. angulata.*

III. CARPENTERIANAE

Plant resembling that of *Solanum nigrum* in habit, the leaf-blades thin.   8. *P. Carpenteri.*

IV. LANCEOLATAE

Leaves glabrous: upper part of the stem, calyx and veins of the leaves with few, if any, short appressed hairs.   9. *P. subglabrata.*
Leaves and stem sparingly hairy with longer, flat, spreading or reflexed, often jointed, hairs (some of the species are slightly viscid).
  Fruiting calyx ovoid, scarcely angled and scarcely sunken at the base: leaf-blades thick, subentire.   10. *P. lanceolata.*
  Fruiting calyx pyramidal, more or less 5-angled and deeply sunken at the base: leaf-blades thin.
    Fruiting calyx ovoid-pyramidal: leaf-blades mostly ovate or lanceolate, tapering at the base.
      Leaf-blades more or less sinuately dentate.
        Calyx strigose or puberulent.   11. *P. virginiana.*
        Calyx villous.   12. *P. monticola.*
      Leaf-blades subentire or wavy margined.
        Leaf-blades firm: plant not at all viscid.   13. *P. rigida.*
        Leaf-blades very thin: plant more or less viscid above when young.   14. *P. intermedia.*
    Fruiting calyx oblong-pyramidal or nearly cylindrical: leaf-blades broadly ovate, truncate or cordate at the base.
      Leaf-blades rather firm, reticulate: stem and leaves puberulent.   15. *P. arenicola.*

[1] Contributed by the late Per Axel Rydberg.

Leaf-blades very thin, the veins not prominent: stem and leaves pilose.   16. *P. ciliosa.*

V. Heterophyllae

Leaf-blades generally over 5 cm. long, more or less cordate.
  Apex, and teeth of the leaves rounded.   17. *P. sinuata.*
  Apex, and teeth (if any) of the leaves acutish to acuminate.
    Stem densely and leaves more sparingly pubescent with very long (2 mm. or more) white hairs.
      Stem erect: anthers purple: leaf-blades rounded or subcordate at the base.   18. *P. ambigua.*
      Stem spreading: anthers yellow: leaf-blades usually cuneate or acute at the base.   19. *P. nyctaginea.*
    Stem and leaves very densely pubescent with short, very viscid hairs: anthers yellow.   20. *P. heterophylla.*
Leaf-blades generally 5 cm. long or less: stem with long hairs.   16. *P. ciliosa.*

VI. Viscosae

Plants densely white-pubescent or grayish pubescent.
  Hairs all stellate.
    Leaf-blades cordate, reniform or round, angulately toothed.   21. *P. mollis.*
    Leaf-blades elliptic, sometimes cordate at the base, to oblanceolate, subentire or repand.   22. *P. viscosa.*
  Hairs partly simple, partly stellate: leaf-blades elliptic, subentire.   23. *P. fuscomaculata.*
Plants nearly glabrous, except on the margins of the calyx-lobes, rarely stellate all over when young.
  Leaf-blades oblong, oblanceolate or spatulate, the lateral veins distinct.   24. *P. Elliottii.*
  Leaf-blades linear, thick; midrib prominent, the lateral veins obsolete.   25. *P. angustifolia.*

1. P. pubescens L. Stem more or less villous and viscid: leaf-blades thin 2–6 cm. long, ovate, acute or acuminate, repand-denticulate or entire, pubescent, becoming nearly glabrous except along the nerves: calyx-lobes narrow, not subulate tipped: corolla 5–10 mm. broad, yellow with dark center: anthers purplish: fruiting calyx 2–3 cm. long, pyramidal-ovoid, acuminate, more or less retuse at the base.—Sandy soil, sand-dunes, fields, and pastures, various provinces, Fla. to Tex., Calif., and Pa. —(*W. I., Mex., C. A., S. A., O. W.*)

2. P. floridana Rydb. Stem densely villous with long white viscid hairs: leaf-blades rounded-cordate, 2–5 cm. long, coarsely sinuate-toothed, obtuse, sparingly viscid-pubescent on both sides: calyx densely viscid pubescent; lobes lanceolate, acuminate: corolla 6–8 mm. broad, yellow with purple spots: anthers purplish: fruiting calyx 2–2.5 cm. long, 5-angled, deeply retuse at the base.—Pinelands and hammocks, Fla.

3. P. pruinosa L. Stem more hairy and viscid than in the two preceding and the next following species, stout, generally erect or often ascending, finely villous or viscid: leaf-blades ovate-cordate 3–10 cm. long, finely pubescent, bluntly sinuate-toothed; calyx villous or viscid; lobes as long as the tube, narrow, but without subulate tips; corolla 3–8 mm. broad, yellow: anthers yellow or purplish: fruiting calyx of a little firmer texture and more pubescent than that of the two preceding species, reticulate, 2–3 cm. long, ovoid-cordate.— Rich soil and sandy woods, various provinces, Fla. to Ala., Ia., and Mass.

4. P. barbadensis Jacq. Stem generally pubescent and viscid, stouter than those of *P. pubescens*, tall and erect, or widely spreading: leaf-blades 3–6 cm. long, cordate, acute or generally abruptly acuminate, sharply repand-dentate, pubescent with short hairs: calyx generally densely viscid-hirsute; lobes lanceolate, acuminate, but not subulate-tipped: corolla 5–10 mm. broad, yellow: anthers purplish: fruiting calyx 2.5–3 cm. long, attenuate, almost conical, reticulate, retuse at the base.—Rich soil, often in open woods, and waste-places, various provinces, Fla., to Tex., Mo., and Pa. (*W. I., Mex., C. A., S. A.*)

5. P. turbinata Medic. Stem glabrous, or minutely puberulent when young rather stout: leaf-blades broadly ovate, obtuse or cordate and slightly oblique at the base, thin and dark-green, repand-dentate; short acuminate: calyx minutely ciliate on the margins and veins or glabrate: calyx-lobes lanceolate, acuminate: corolla 8–10 mm. broad, yellow with purplish spots: fruiting calyx 3–3.5 cm. long, long-attenuate, almost pyramidal, deeply retuse at the base.— Rich soil and thickets, various provinces, Fla. to Tex., Mo., and Pa.—(*W. I., Mex.*)

6. P. missouriensis Buch. Stem villous with short hairs, sometimes slightly viscid, spreading, often zigzag: leaf-blades 1–8 cm. long, ovate, acute, cuneate, obtuse or cordate at the base, repand or sinuately dentate, hairy at least on the nerves: calyx villous; lobes shorter than the tube, triangular: corolla 3–8 mm. broad, yellow, generally with a dark center: anthers generally yellow: fruiting calyx 1.5–2 cm. long, globose-ovoid, nearly filled with the berry, not sunken at the base. [*P. Lagascae* Rydb. not R. & S.]—Rich soil and open woods, Coastal Plain, Fla. and Ala.—(*W. I., Mex.*)

7. P. angulata L. Stem glabrous, often diffuse: leaf-blades ovate, 4–7 cm. long, with a more or less cuneate base, sharply sinuate, with acuminate teeth, thin: calyx glabrous; lobes triangular to lanceolate, generally shorter than the tube: corolla 5–10 cm. broad, yellow: anthers more or less purplish: fruiting calyx about 3 cm. long, ovoid, not prominently 5–10 angled, sometimes purple-nerved and at length nearly filled with the yellow berry.—Rich soil, fields, and pastures, various provinces, rarely Coastal Plain, Fla. to Tex., Minn., and Pa. (*W. I., Mex., C. A., S. A., O. W.*)—Forms occur in S Florida with linear to lanceolate sinuate leaf-blades.

8. P. Carpenteri Riddell. Stem rather closely and finely puberulent: leaf-blades very thin, oval or ovate, abruptly contracted into a long acumination, entire or slightly wavy, nearly glabrous or puberulent: corolla about 1 cm. broad, open-campanulate: fruiting calyx small, only 1 cm. in diameter, nearly globose, scarcely angled, faintly nerved, the lobes sometimes very unequal.— Sandy soil, Coastal Plain, N Fla. to La. and Ark.

9. P. subglabrata Mackenzie & Bush. Stem glabrous or sparingly hairy, especially above with short appressed hairs: leaf-blades ovate or ovate-lanceolate, 2.5–7.5 cm. long, undulate or entire, oblique and rounded or subcordate at the base, glabrous or with a few scattered hairs on the veins: calyx 6–8 mm. long, appressed-hairy on the veins and at the base; lobes triangular, about the length of the tube: corolla yellow, with a darker center, 10–15 mm. broad: fruiting calyx ovoid, slightly depressed at the base, slightly angled.—Loose soil roadsides, fields, and river-bottoms, various provinces N of Coastal Plain, Tenn. to Ark., Nebr., and Ont.

10. P. lanceolata Michx. Stem sparingly hirsute with flat hairs, at first erect, later spreading or diffuse: leaf-blades broadly oblanceolate or spatulate, tapering into the petiole, acute or obtuse, nearly always entire, rarely wavy, but not sinuate-toothed, thickish, sparingly pubescent with short hairs: calyx strigose or villous, rarely glabrous; lobes triangular-lanceolate: corolla dullish-yellow with a brownish center, about 1.5 cm. broad: fruiting calyx round-ovoid, not sunken at the base, indistinctly 10-angled.—Prairies, bluffs, and sandy hillsides, various provinces, rarely Coastal Plain, S. C. to N. Mex., Wyo., and Ill.

11. P. virginiana Mill. Stem pubescent with appressed hairs, sometimes somewhat glandular, or in some forms nearly glabrous: leaf-blades ovate-lanceolate, tapering to both ends, 3–6 cm. long, generally more or less sinuately dentate, often yellowish-green: calyx strigose-hirsute, or at least puberulent; lobes triangular or broadly lanceolate, nearly equalling the tube in length: corolla sulphur-yellow with purplish spots, 1.5–2.5 cm. broad: anthers yellow: fruiting calyx pyramidal-ovoid, 5-angled and sunken at the base. [*P. lanceolata* Chapm. not Michx.]—Rich soil, fields, and borders of woods, various provinces, Fla. to La., Colo., Man., and Ont.

12. P. monticola C. Mohr. Stem strigose below, villous above with simple flat jointed hairs: leaf-blades ovate, oval, or elliptic, 2–6 cm. long, repand, with the teeth obtuse or rarely acutish, slender-petioled: calyx villous; lobes broadly lanceolate: corolla dingy-yellow, with a purplish center: anthers pale-yellow: fruiting calyx ovoid, acuminate, obtusely 5-angled, deeply sunken at the base.— Exposed gravelly or rocky places, Piedmont to Appalachian Plateau, Ala.

13. P. rigida Pollard & Ball. Stems strict, more or less branching, hispid-pubescent with flat hairs, especially above: leaf-blades firm, ovate-lanceolate, wavy-margined, densely pubescent when young, tapering at both ends: calyx pubescent with flat hairs, especially on the veins and at the base: lobes triangular: corolla 1–1.5 cm. wide, yellow with purple center: fruiting calyx ovoid, nearly glabrous, obscurely 10-angled, 2.5–3 cm. long, somewhat retuse at the base.—Roadsides and waste-places, Coastal Plain, Miss. to La., Ark., and Tenn.

14. P. intermedia Rydb. Stem with long hairs and somewhat viscid, especially on the upper parts: leaf-blades ovate or ovate-lanceolate, acute, 4–6 cm. long, often oblique at the base, slightly sinuate-toothed or nearly entire, very thin, light green, puberulent or glabrate: calyx puberulent or strigose; lobes broadly lanceolate, about equalling the tube: corolla sulphur-yellow with purplish spots, 1–2 cm. broad: anthers yellow: fruiting calyx ovoid, slightly 5-angled and slightly sunken at the base.—Thickets and dry hillsides, various provinces, Fla. to Tex., Ind., and Pa.

15. P. arenicola Kearney. Stem diffuse, light-green, puberulent, but sometimes a little glandular, with a few longer hairs on the nerves of the calyx: leaf-blades relatively small, 1.5–6 cm. long, but sometimes 8 cm., ovate-cordate, truncate or cuneate at the base, irregularly angulate-dentate, puberulent, mainly along the veins, which are generally prominent and conspicuous; calyx-lobes triangular-lanceolate, equalling the tube in length: corolla 1.5–2 cm. broad, light yellow: anthers yellow: fruiting calyx 3 cm. long, narrowly ovoid or rather ellipsoid pyramidal or nearly cylindric, conspicuously reticulated.—Pinelands, scrub, sandhills, and cypress-heads, Fla.

16. P. ciliosa Rydb. Stem upright, 2–3 dm. tall, together with the pedicels and calyxes ciliate with long and white jointed hairs: leaf-blades 4–7 cm. long, ovate, truncate or slightly cordate at the base, nearly entire or with a few coarse teeth, sparsely hairy on the nerves, long-petioled, thin and not conspicuously veiny: calyx turbinate, resembling that of *P. arenicola* but more pilose: corolla funnelform-campanulate, yellow without dark markings: fruiting calyx ovoid-pyramidal, sunken at the base.—Thickets, hammocks, and borders of woods, Coastal Plain and adj. provinces, Fla. to Tenn. and Ga.

17. P. sinuata Rydb. Stem decumbent, villous with long flat hairs and very viscid: leaf-blades rounded ovate, very oblique at the base and often subcordate, pubescent with long flat hairs especially on the veins, obtuse, undulate-sinuate: calyx densely villous with flat hairs and viscid; lobes triangular-lanceolate, about equalling the tube: corolla yellow with darker spots: fruiting calyx and berry unknown.—Pinelands (?), Fla.

18. P. ambigua (A. Gray) Britton. Stem 3–8 dm. tall, light green, villous with long flat hairs: leaves with the finer pubescence sparse; blades over 5 cm. long, thin, light-green, round, scarcely at all viscid, ovate or cordate, somewhat sinuately toothed or nearly entire, acute, but rarely acuminate: calyx villous; lobes triangular, generally shorter than the tube: corolla 1.5–2 cm. broad, yellow with dark spots; anthers generally purple: fruiting calyx ovoid, somewhat sunken at the base.—Rich soil, especially in thickets, various provinces N of Coastal Plain, Tenn. to Ia., Vt., and Va.

19. P. nyctaginea Dunal. Stem puberulent and villous with long flat hairs and somewhat viscid, generally zigzag: leaf-blades dark-green, ovate, often oblique, but very rarely cordate at the base, more or less acuminate, mostly entire, or occasionally sinuately dentate and rather thick, sparingly hairy, not at all puberulent, the long hairs often confined to the veins of the lower surface: calyx villous; lobes triangular, shorter than the tube: corolla 1–1.5 cm. broad, yellow with darker spots: anthers yellow: fruiting calyx ovoid, 5-angled and sunken at the base.—Dry soil, often in pinelands, various provinces, Ga. to La., Ia., and R. I.

20. P. heterophylla Nees. Stem erect, or later generally decumbent and spreading, viscid and glandular, villous with moderately long, jointed flat hairs: leaf-blades generally over 5 cm. long, generally broadly cordate, often acute but very rarely with an acumination, thick, more or less sinuately toothed, or sometimes subentire, pubescent with short and fine and longer flat jointed hairs: calyx long-villous; lobes triangular, generally shorter than the tube: corolla 1–1.5 cm. broad, yellowish: anthers yellow: fruiting calyx 2.5–5 cm. long, ovoid to conic-ovoid, somewhat sunken at the base.—Woods, sandy fields, and alluvial banks, various provinces, Fla. to Tex., Sask., and N. B.—Plants with leaves up to 10 cm. in diameter sometimes occur on the Florida prairies.

21. P. mollis Nutt. Stem 3–6 cm. high, densely whitish- or grayish-tomentose with stellate pubescence: leaf-blades rounded cordate or the upper broadly ovate, coarsely sinuately toothed: calyx densely stellate; lobes triangular, generally a little shorter than the tube: corolla 1.5–2 cm. in diameter, bright-yellow and with a purplish center, more or less stellate-pubescent without: anthers yellow or tinged with purple: fruiting calyx 3–5 cm. long, ovoid, acuminate, slightly 5-angled and a little sunken at the base.—Thickets, stream-banks, and pinelands, various provinces, Fla. to Tex., Calif., and Ark.—(Mex.)

22. P. viscosa L. Stem slender, creeping, cinereous with a dense stellate pubescence or in age rarely glabrate: leaf-blades elliptic, oval, or ovate, obtuse, thinnish, entire or undulate: calyx stellate-pubescent; lobes triangular, generally shorter than the tube: corolla greenish-yellow, with a darker center, 1.5–2 cm. broad: fruiting calyx 2–2.3 cm. long, rounded-ovoid, scarcely sunken at the base.—Coastal sand-dunes, sandy woods near the coast, pinelands and prairies, Fla. to Tex. and Va.—(W. I., Mex., C. A., S. A.)

23. P. fuscomaculata De Rouv. Stem decumbent or ascending, terete, with decurrent ridges, a little pruinose-stellate: leaf-blades 2–4 cm. long, ovate, somewhat oblique at the base, entire or repand, the upper often opposite: calyx pruinose, a little stellate and stellate-ciliate; lobes triangular, shorter than the tube: corolla yellow, with a dark eye: fruiting calyx subglobose, 10-angled, somewhat sunken at the base.—Waste-places and ballast, Mobile, Ala. Nat. of S. Am.

24. P. Elliottii Kunze. Stem ascending branched, slightly stellate or glabrate, 3–5 dm. tall sparingly stellate-pubescent when young: leaf-blades very thin and veiny, elliptic, spatulate, broadly oblanceolate, or in luxuriant specimens broadly oval, entire or wavy-margined, decurrent into a winged petiole: calyx generally glabrous except the margin which is stellate-ciliate; lobes triangular: corolla 1.5–2 cm. broad, yellow, with dark center: fruiting calyx generally a little shorter than in the next following species.—Coastal sand dunes and pinelands, Fla. to Tex.

25. P. angustifolia Nutt. Stem often glabrous, or sparsely stellate when young, diffusely branched: leaf-blades linear or linear-oblanceolate, tapering into the petiole, entire, thickish; the veins, except the midrib, generally obsolete: calyx glabrous, except the stellate-ciliate margins of the rounded triangular lobes: corolla about 2 cm. broad, yellow, with purple center: anthers yellow: fruiting calyx small, 1.5–2 cm. long, ovoid, obscurely angled and scarcely sunken at the base.—Sea-beaches and coastal sand-dunes, Fla. to La.

3. ANDROCERA Nutt. Annual herbs, usually prickle-armed. Leaf-blades once or twice pinnatifid. Flowers in erect cymes. Calyx spreading, accrescent, densely prickly. Corolla rotate, 5-lobed, yellow, purple, or violet. Stamens 5: anthers very unequal, the lowest one much the longest, all opening by terminal pores. Berry dry, closely invested by the calyx.— Three or 4 species, in western North America.

1. A. rostrata (Dunal) Rydb. Herbaceous annual, hoary-pubescent, or yellowish-pubescent, 2–7 dm. tall: leaf-blades mostly ovate or oval, 1–2-pinnatifid, 5–22 cm. long: calyx spinescent; lobes lanceolate or linear-lanceolate: corolla yellow, about 25 mm. wide; lobes ovate to lanceolate, shorter than the tube: berry enclosed. [*Solanum rostratum* Dunal.]—(BUFFALO-BUR.)—Waste-places, roadsides, and along railroads, various provinces, Miss. to N. Mex., Wyo., N. Dak., and Tenn.; Adv. eastward to Fla. and N. H.—(*Mex.*)—Spr.–fall.

4. SOLANUM [Tourn.] L. Annual or perennial herbs, or vines or trees. Leaf-blades entire, toothed, or lobed. Flowers variously clustered. Calyx sometimes slightly accrescent. Corolla rotate, of various colors: lobes longer than the tube. Anthers narrow, converging or united, much longer than the filaments. Berry exposed.—About 1,000 species, widely distributed, most abundant in tropical America.—NIGHTSHADES.

Woody, at least partly so, vine, with climbing often twining stem and branches.
                  I. DULCAMARA.
Herbs or erect shrubs or trees, rarely somewhat twining in
    S. bahamense.
    Annual or perennial herbs.
        Annuals.
            Plants not prickly.   II. NIGRA.
            Plants prickly.
                Corolla plicate in the bud: plant annual.   III. SISYMBRIIFOLIA.

SOLANACEAE 1113

Corolla not plicate: plant perennial.
Perennials, prickle-armed.
Shrubs or trees.
Plants glabrous.
Plants pubescent.
Cymes on recurving peduncles: berries nodding: anthers tapering at the apex.
Cymes on erect peduncles or straight: berries erect: anthers blunt at the apex.
Cymes terminal: anthers short, ellipsoid.
Cymes lateral: anthers long, nearly linear.

IV. ACULEATISSIMA.
V. CAROLINENSIA.

VI. GLAUCA.

VII. BAHAMENSIA.

VIII. VERBASCIFOLIA.

IX. TORVA.

I. DULCAMARA
Leaf-blades entire and ovate to lanceolate or with 1 or 2 basal lobes or divisions: berries in drooping clusters. — 1. *S. Dulcamara.*

II. NIGRA
Foliage glabrous or nearly so: corolla 6–8 mm. broad: calyx-lobes spreading at maturity. — 2. *S. nigrum.*
Foliage puberulent or finely pubescent: corolla 8–10 mm. broad: calyx-lobes appressed to the berry.
Stem and branches sparingly appressed pubescent. — 3. *S. gracile.*
Stem and branches villous-tomentose. — 4. *S. alatum.*

III. SISYMBRIIFOLIA
Rather coarse plant: stem, branches, leaves, and calyx armed with flat yellow or yellowish prickles. — 5. *S. sisymbriifolium.*

IV. ACULEATISSIMA
Leaf-lobes acute: corolla less than 3 cm. wide, glabrous or with few long hairs without; lobes lanceolate: calyx bristly-pubescent. — 6. *S. aculeatissimum.*
Leaf-lobes obtuse: corolla over 3 cm. wide, tomentulose without; lobes deltoid: calyx tomentulose. — 7. *S. Melongena.*

V. CAROLINENSIA
Foliage green or brown: leaf-blades broad: prickles stout, much flattened.
Corolla 2–2.5 cm. wide: pedicels and calyx prickly: berry 1–1.5 cm. in diameter.
Leaf-blades undulate or angulately lobed. — 8. *S. carolinense.*
Leaf-blades pinnatifid. — 9. *S. floridanum.*
Corolla 4–5 cm. wide: pedicel and calyx not prickly: berry 2.5–4 cm. in diameter. — 10. *S. perplexum.*
Foliage silvery: leaf-blades narrow: prickles slender, not flattened. — 11. *S. elaeagnifolium.*

VI. GLAUCA
Corolla 11–14 mm. wide: berry mainly over 1 cm. thick: leaf-blades with pale margins. — 12. *S. Pseudo-capsicum.*
Corolla 25–30 mm. wide: berry mainly less than 1 cm. thick: leaf-blades without distinct margins. — 13. *S. glaucum.*

VII. BAHAMENSIA
Shrub or rarely a vine, with prickly stems and branches, and often with prickles on the more or less harshly pubescent leaves. — 14. *S. bahamense.*

VIII. VERBASCIFOLIA
Corolla-lobes ovate to oval-ovate: ovary pubescent: berry yellow. — 15. *S. verbascifolium.*
Corolla-lobes linear to linear-lanceolate or lanceolate: ovary glabrous: berry red. — 16. *S. Blodgettii.*

IX. TORVA
Corolla 15–20 mm. wide: leaf-blades manifestly petioled. — 17. *S. torvum.*
Corolla 8–14 mm. wide: leaf-blades nearly sessile by a cuneate base. — 18. *S. jamaicense.*

1. **S. Dulcamara** L. Partially woody climber: leaf-blades ovate, 3–10 cm. long, entire or with 1 or 2 basal lobes, thin: corolla white or purple, 8–10 mm. long; lobes lanceolate to elliptic-lanceolate: berry oval, 9–15 mm. long.—(BITTERSWEET.)—Roadsides, thickets, and waste-places, various provinces, rarely

1114   SOLANACEAE

Coastal Plain, Ga. to Kans., Minn., and N. B.
—Nat. of Eu.—Sum.–fall.

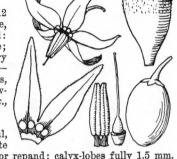

2. **S. nigrum** L. Herbaceous annual, 1–12
dm. tall: leaf-blades ovate to elliptic-ovate,
2–8 cm. long, undulate or deeply repand:
calyx-lobes fully 1 mm. long: corolla white;
lobes lanceolate to oblong-lanceolate: berry
subglobose, 4–8 mm. in diameter, black.—
(COMMON-NIGHTSHADE.) — Fields, thickets,
cult. grounds, and waste-places, various provinces, U. S. and S Canada.—(*W. I., Mex.,
C. A., S. A., O. W.*)—Spr.–fall.

3. **S. gracile** Link. Herbaceous annual,
1–14 dm. tall: leaf-blades lanceolate to ovate
or elliptic-ovate, 2.5–11 cm. long, undulate or repand: calyx-lobes fully 1.5 mm.
long: corolla white or bluish; lobes lanceolate to elliptic-lanceolate: berry subglobose, 6–10 mm. in diameter, black.—Pinelands, coastal sand-dunes, and
waste-places, near the coast, Fla. to La., and N. C.—Spr.–fall, or all year southward.

4. **S. alatum** Moench. Annual, erect, villous-hirsute. Stems mostly 2–8 dm.
tall, branched: leaf-blades ovate to suborbicular, 1–4 cm. long, obtuse or acute,
coarsely toothed, rather long-petioled: calyx copiously pubescent; lobes ovate,
about as long as the tube: corolla white, about 8 mm. wide; lobes ovate, ciliate:
berry scarlet, 7–9 mm. in diameter.—Roadsides, cult. grounds, and waste-
places, N Fla.—Nativity uncertain.

5. **S. sisymbriifolium** Lam. Herbaceous annual 3–7 dm. tall, villous: leaf-
blades elliptic to oval in outline, 1–2-pinnatifid, 8–20 cm. long: calyx spinescent;
lobes lanceolate, 5–8 mm. long: corolla white or light-blue, 3–4 cm. wide; lobes
ovate: gynoecium pubescent: berry 15–20 mm. in diameter, red.—Waste-places,
roadsides and river-banks, Coastal Plain, Fla. to La., and contiguous regions.
Nat. of S. Am.—(*W. I.*)

6. **S. aculeatissimum** Jacq. Partially woody perennial 3–8 dm. tall, often
sparingly pubescent: leaf-blades ovate to suborbicular in outline, angulately
toothed or sinuate-pinnatifid, 6–12 cm. long: calyx copiously spinescent: lobes
lanceolate to elliptic-ovate, or ovate, about 2 mm. long: corolla white, 12–18
mm. wide; lobes lanceolate: gynoecium glabrous: berry 3–6 cm. in diameter,
yellow, orange, or scarlet.—(SODA-APPLE.)—Sandy soil, fields, thickets, and
roadsides, Coastal Plain, Fla. to Tex., and N. C.—(*W. I., Mex., C. A., S. A.*)—
Spr.–fall.

7. **S. Melongena** L. Partially woody annual or perennial, 3–9 dm. tall, felty-
tomentose: leaf-blades oval to ovate, 8–30 cm. long, sinuate-lobed or shallowly
pinnate-lobed: calyx-lobes ovate, abruptly pointed, 5.5–12 mm. long, pubescent:
corolla purplish or violet, except the yellow eye, 40–50 mm. wide; lobes deltoid:
berry ellipsoid or obovoid, 5–30 cm. long, purplish or whitish, edible.—(EGG-
PLANT.)—Cult. grounds, Coastal Plain, Fla. to Tex. Nat. of Old World trop.
—Spr.–fall.

8. **S. carolinense** L. Herbaceous perennial, 2–7 dm. tall, hirsute or rough-
pubescent: leaf-blades elliptic to ovate in outline, 5–12 cm. long, sinuate or
pinnately sinuate-lobed, the lobes of a triangular type: calyx spinescent; lobes
lanceolate, often narrowly so, acuminate: corolla violet or rarely white, 25–30
mm. wide; lobes ovate: berry globular, 10–15 mm. in diameter, orange-yellow.
—(HORSE-NETTLE.)—Thickets, fields, and roadsides, various provinces, Fla. to
Tex., and Ont.—Spr.–fall.

9. **S. floridanum** Shuttlw. Similar to *S. carolinense* in habit: leaf-blades deeply pinnatifid, the lobes of an oblong type: calyx pubescent; lobes lanceolate, abruptly acuminate: corolla violet, 20–25 mm. wide; lobes oblong to oblong-lanceolate: gynoecium pubescent: berry globular, 15 mm. in diameter, orange.—Sandy soil, mostly in pinelands, Fla.—Spr.–fall.

10. **S. perplexum** Small. Herbaceous perennial, 5–8 dm. tall, villous-hirsutulous: leaf-blades ovate or oval in outline, prominently sinuate-lobed, mostly 5–20 cm. long, the lobes broadly ovate to triangular: calyx spineless; lobes ovate to triangular-lanceolate: corolla purplish or nearly white, 35–40 mm. wide; lobes ovate: berry depressed-globose, 30–40 mm. in diameter, yellow.—Pine-lands and cult. grounds, Coastal Plain, N Fla. and S Ga.—Spr.–sum.

11. **S. elaeagnifolium** Cav. Partially woody perennial, 3–11 dm. tall, silvery-canescent: leaf-blades broadly elliptic to linear-elliptic, 5–15 cm. long, undulate or repand: calyx-lobes linear-subulate from a broad base, 4–10 mm. long: corolla violet or white, 22–25 mm. wide; lobes undulate, each with a broad base and an ovate or triangular tip: berry globose, 10–15 mm. in diameter, yellow or black.—(WHITE HORSE-NETTLE.)—Roadsides, cult. grounds, and waste-places, various provinces, Tex. to Ariz., Kans., and Mo. Naturalized E to Fla.—Spr.–fall.

12. **S. Pseudo-capsicum** L. Shrub 8–19 dm. tall: leaf-blades elliptic to oblanceolate, 3–10 cm. long, undulate or repand: calyx-lobes lanceolate, about 2.5 mm. long, eciliate: corolla white, 11–14 mm. wide; lobes oval to ovate-oval, eciliate: anthers elliptic: berry globose, 10–15 mm. in diameter, scarlet, orange, or yellow.—(JERUSALEM-CHERRY.)—Roadsides, thickets, and open woods, Coastal Plain, Fla. to Tex. Nat. of Eu.

13. **S. glaucum** Dunal. Woody perennial, 9–25 dm. tall: leaf-blades narrowly elliptic to elliptic-lanceolate, 8–18 cm. long, glabrous, entire: calyx-lobes longer than wide, abruptly pointed, ciliate at the tip: corolla blue, 25–30 mm. wide; lobes broadly ovate, acute, ciliate at the tip: ovary glabrous: berry globose-ovoid, 6–8 mm. in diameter, glaucous.—Waste-places, Pensacola, Fla. Nat. of S. Am.

14. **S. bahamense** L. Shrub with much-branched stem, 5–20 dm. tall: leaf-blades elliptic to elliptic-lanceolate, 4–12 cm. long, thinly rough-pubescent, undulate: calyx-lobes ovate to elliptic-ovate, as long as the tube or shorter: corolla violet-blue, sometimes pale, 10–12 mm. wide; lobes linear or nearly so, acute or acutish: anthers linear: ovary glabrous: berry red, 6–8 mm. in diameter.—Hammocks and coastal sand-dunes, S pen. Fla. and Florida Keys.—(*W. I.*)—All year.

15. **S. verbascifolium** L. Shrub 4–30 dm. tall or small tree: leaf-blades elliptic to elliptic-ovate or ovate, 10–30 cm. long, velvety-tomentose, entire: calyx-lobes ovate, ciliate, obtuse: corolla white, 15–18 mm. wide; lobes ovate to oval-ovate, acutish, ciliate: anthers oblong: ovary pubescent: berry globular, 10–20 mm. in diameter, yellow.—(POTATO-TREE.)—Hammocks, pinelands, and roadsides, pen. Fla. and Florida Keys.—(*W. I., Mex., C. A., S. A.*)—All year.

16. **S. Blodgettii** Chapm. Shrub with simple or sparingly branched stems, 3–38 dm. tall: leaf-blades elliptic, often narrowly so, 5–15 cm. long, hoary-scurfy and tomentulose, undulate: calyx-lobes elliptic: corolla white or bluish, 14–17 mm. wide; lobes linear to linear-lanceolate or lanceolate, obtuse: anthers linear: ovary glabrous: berry red, 4–6 mm. in diameter.—Hammocks and lime-sinks in pinelands, Everglade Keys, adj. Everglades, Fla. and Florida Keys.—(*W. I.*)—All year.

17. **S. torvum** Sw. Shrub with widely branched stems, the prickles straight or nearly so: leaf-blades oval, varying to ovate or obovate, irregularly sinuate-lobed, 7–25 cm. long: cymes mostly 5–10 cm. wide: calyx-lobes ovate to lanceo-

late: corolla white, 10–20 mm. wide; lobes triangular or triangular-lanceolate:
anthers 5–6 mm. long: ovary glabrous: berry yellow, 9–14 mm. in diameter.—
(Turkey-berry.)—Roadsides, waste-places, and swamps, pen. Fla. Nat. of
W. I.—(*Mex., C. A., S. A.*)—Spr.-fall.

18. S. jamaicense Mill. Shrub with a much-branched stem and diffuse branches,
armed with flat somewhat curved prickles: leaf-blades ovate, oval, or obovate
in outline, shallowly lobed and somewhat rhombic, mostly 8–14 cm. long:
cymes 2–3.5 cm. wide: calyx-lobes lanceolate: corolla white, 8–12 mm. wide;
lobes lanceolate: anthers about 4 mm. long: ovary glabrous: berry red or
orange, 8–10 mm. in diameter.—Roadsides and woods, in pen. Fla. Nat. of
W. I.—(*Mex., C. A., S. A.*)—Spr.-fall.

5. LYCOPERSICON Mill. Annual or perennial heavy-scented herbs.
Leaf-blades 1–2-pinnately divided. Flowers in cymes. Calyx not accrescent.
Corolla rotate, yellow: lobes longer than the tube.—Four species, tropical
American.

Berry more or less depressed, several-celled.	1. *L. Lycopersicon.*
Berry globular, cherry-like, 2-celled.	2. *L. cerasiforme.*

1. L. Lycopersicon (L.) Karst. Plants clammy-pubescent, 3–12 dm. tall:
leaf-blades 1–4 dm. long, the divisions ovate to elliptic, coarsely toothed or
incised: calyx-lobes narrow, acute: corolla
mainly 1.5–2 cm. wide: berry depressed,
mainly 5–15 cm. wide, red or yellow.—
(Tomato. Love-apple.) — Cult. grounds,
fields, pinelands, and waste-places, Coastal
Plain, Fla. to Tex. Nat. of trop. Am. and
cult.—(*W. I.*)—Sum.

2. L. cerasiforme Dunal. Similar to the
preceding species, but smaller and weaker:
leaves with many small separated leaflets
between the larger ones: berry about 1–2
cm. in diameter, bright red.—(Cherry-
tomato.)—Dry soil, hammocks and roadsides, Florida Keys and S Tex. Nat. of
trop. Am.

6. PERIZOMA Miers. Herbs or shrubby plants. Leaf-blades entire.
Flowers solitary in the axils. Sepals slightly united. Corolla white or yellow,
urceolate or short-tubular: lobes much
shorter than the tube. Filaments adnate up
to near the middle of the corolla-tube:
anthers much shorter than the filaments.
Ovary depressed. Stigma dilated.—One
species.

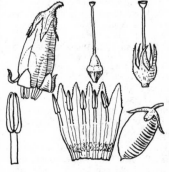

1. P. rhomboidea (Hook.) Small. Plants
much branched: leaf-blades ovate, 1–2.5 cm.
long: calyx-lobes lanceolate to subulate-
lanceolate, 2.5–3 mm. long; corolla 6–8 mm.
long; lobes lanceolate, spreading: filaments
webby near the base: berry elliptic, 2–2.5
cm. long.—Waste-places, Fla. Nat. of S.

Am.—Sum.–fall.—A related plant, *Jaborosa integrifolia* Lam. with prostrate stems, long-petioled entire elliptic leaf-blades and greenish-white salverform corollas 7–10 cm. long, has been found on ballast at Mobile, Ala. It is native of S. Am.

7. CAPSICUM [Tourn.] L. Herbs or shrubs, unarmed. Leaf-blades flat, entire or repand. Flowers axillary or cymose. Calyx truncate or minutely lobed. Corolla usually white, nearly rotate: lobes nearly as long as the tube. Filaments adnate to the lower part of the corolla-tube, glabrous: anthers longer than the filaments. Ovary not depressed: stigma minute.—About 30 species, mostly in tropical America.—CAYENNE-PEPPERS.

Corolla 7–10 mm. long: anthers over 2 mm. long: annual introduced plant.
　　　　　　　　　　　　　　　　　　　　　　　　　　　　1. *C. annuum.*
Corolla 4–5 mm. long: anthers less than 2 mm. long: perennial
　　native hammock plants.
　　Calyx markedly toothed at maturity: berry subglobose.　　2. *C. baccatum.*
　　Calyx truncate at maturity: berry ellipsoid to conic.　　3. *C. frutescens.*

1. C. annuum L. Plants mostly 1 m. tall or less, with glabrous or nearly glabrous branches: leaf-blades ovate, oval or ovate-lanceolate, mostly 7–14 cm. long, acuminate, entire: pedicels clavate: calyx 3–4 mm. long, truncate: corolla white or pinkish, 7–10 mm. long: lobes ovate, sometimes longer than the tube: berry conic or ellipsoid, 2–3 cm. long, red; or variously shaped and larger in cultivation.—(RED-PEPPER. CAYENNE-PEPPER.)—Roadsides, old-fields, and waste-places, Fla. Nat. of S. A. and cult.—All year.

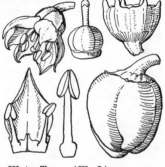

2. C. baccatum L. Stem 1–3 m. tall: leaf-blades ovate, elliptic-ovate to ovate-lanceolate, 2–5 cm. long: calyx mainly 2.5–3 mm. long: corolla about 5 mm. long: berry 5–10 mm. long, red.—(BIRD-PEPPER.)—Hammocks and thickets, pen. Fla. and the Keys. Also naturalized in cult. grounds and waste-places, W to Tex.—(*W. I.*)

3. C. frutescens L. Stem 0.5–2 m. tall: leaf-blades ovate to ovate-lanceolate, 1–3 cm. long: calyx mainly 1.5–2 mm. long: corolla about 4 mm. long: berry 8–12 mm. long or longer, red.—(BIRD-PEPPER.)—Hammocks, pen. Fla. and the Keys.—(*W. I.*)

8. LYCIUM L. Shrubs or woody vines, commonly spiny. Leaf-blades thick, sometimes terete, entire. Flowers axillary, sometimes clustered. Calyx markedly lobed. Corolla white or colored, funnelform, salverform, or nearly campanulate: lobes longer than the usually short tube, or shorter. Anthers shorter than the pubescent filaments. Stigma dilated.—About 75 species, widely distributed.—MATRIMONY-VINES.—The purple corollas of some species have the curious habit of fading to a greenish-yellow or greenish-tan after the pollen is shed from the anthers.

Leaf-blades flat: corolla-lobes shorter than the tube and throat. 1. *L. halimifolium.*
Leaf-blades clavate: corolla-lobes longer than the tube and
　　throat.　　　　　　　　　　　　　　　　　　　　　2. *L. carolinianum.*

1. L. halimifolium Mill. Shrub irregularly branched, sometimes vine-like: leaves herbaceous, 1.5–5 cm. long; blades elliptic, oval, ovate, lanceolate, or spatulate: calyx-lobes ovate to somewhat triangular, obtuse: corolla purplish or greenish; lobes 4–5 mm. long: berry oval or ovoid, orange or orange-red, 10–15 mm. long. — (MATRIMONY-VINE. BOX-THORN.) — Thickets, waste-places, and fence-rows, various provinces, Ga. to Kans., Minn., and Ont. Nat. of Eu.—Spr.–sum.

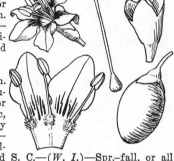

2. L. carolinianum Walt. Shrub 3–15 dm. tall, with recurving branches: leaves succulent, 0.5–2 cm. long: calyx-lobes deltoid or triangular-ovate, acute: corolla blue or lilac, or rarely white; lobes 3–6 mm. long: berry red, 8–12 mm. long.—(CHRISTMAS-BERRY.)— Coastal sand-dunes, shore-hammocks, shell-mounds, and salt-marshes, Fla. to Tex. and S. C.—(*W. I.*)—Spr.–fall, or all year S.

9. CESTRUM L. Shrubs or trees. Leaf-blades entire. Flowers in axillary clusters, sometimes aggregated in a panicle or corymb. Calyx markedly lobed. Corolla white or colored, funnelform or salverform: lobes much shorter than the tube. Filaments adnate to the middle of the corolla-tube or above it, glabrous: anthers globular. Stigma enlarged.—About 150 species, tropical American.

Corolla 15 mm. long or less: lobes as wide as long: filaments adnate to above the
    middle of the corolla-tube.   1. *C. diurnum.*
Corolla 20 mm. long or more; lobes longer than wide: filaments
    adnate to about the middle of the corolla-tube.   2. *C. Parqui.*

1. C. diurnum L. Plant minutely pubescent, 1–2.5 m. tall: leaf-blades elliptic to elliptic-lanceolate, 5–12 cm. long; petioles mostly less than 10 mm. long: calyx about 3 mm. long; tube campanulate; lobes broadly ovate: corolla white or greenish-white, 11–15 mm. long; lobes rounded.— (DAY-JESSAMINE.)—Hammocks and waste-places, Florida Keys and S. Tex.—Nat. of trop. Am.

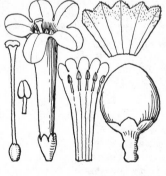

2. C. Parqui L'Her. Plant nearly glabrous, 1–2 m. tall: leaf-blades elliptic to elliptic-lanceolate, 10–20 cm. long; petioles mostly over 10 mm. long: calyx 4–4.5 mm. long; tube nearly cylindric; lobes deltoid to triangulate-ovate: corolla .greenish-white, 20–25 mm. long; lobes apiculate.—(NIGHT-BLOOMING JESSAMINE.) — Woods, thickets, waste-places, and roadsides, Coastal Plain, Fla. to Tex., and Ga. Nat. of W. I.

10. DATURA L. Herbs (ours annual), or shrubs or trees. Leaf-blades undulate or lobed. Flowers solitary in the axils. Calyx tubular, sometimes prismatic, more or less lobed. Corolla white or colored, funnelform. Filaments slightly unequal.—About 12 species, widely distributed.—Sum.–fall or all year S.

Capsule erect, dehiscent by 4 valves.   I. STRAMONIA.
Capsule inclined or nodding, opening irregularly.   II. DUTRA.

I. STRAMONIA

Herb with white or lavender corollas and capsules with nearly
     equal spines.   1. *D. Stramonium.*

II. DUTRA

Corolla, the outer one in double flowers, with a 5-toothed limb:
     fruiting pedicel curved to one side: capsule with stout-
     tubercle-like prickles which are often corrugated at the
     base.   2. *D. Metel.*
Corolla with a 10-angled limb: fruiting pedicel abruptly nod-
     ding: capsule with slender sharp prickles.
       Corolla-limb 5-toothed: foliage glaucescent.   3. *D. meteloides.*
       Corolla-limb 10-toothed: foliage softly-pubescent.   4. *D. innoxia.*

1. **D. Stramonium** L. Plant green or purple-tinged, 2–12 dm. tall: leaf-blades
ovate to elliptic, 10–20 cm. long, sinuate or laciniate-toothed: calyx 3–5 cm.
long; lobes 5–7 mm. long, the persistent
base ultimately turned downward and
frilled: corolla white, violet, or lavender,
6–10 mm. long: capsule 4–6 cm. long, the
prickles equal or the lower ones rather
shorter than the upper.—(THORN-APPLE.
JIMSON-WEED. JAMESTOWN-WEED. STRA-
MONIUM.) — Cult. grounds, roadsides, and
waste-places, various provinces, Fla. to Tex.,
Ont., and N. B.; also W U. S. Nat. of
trop. Am.—(*W. I., Mex., C. A., S. A., O.
W.*)—Sum.—The lavender-flowered variety
is sometimes separated as *D. Tatula* L.

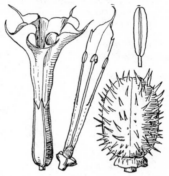

2. **D. Metel** L. Plant 1–2 m. tall, glabrous
or nearly so: leaf-blades ovate-lanceolate,
elliptic or oval, 5–15 cm. long, undulate or
repand-dentate: calyx 5–6.5 cm. long; lobes ovate to triangular-ovate: corolla
violet without, 14–18 cm. long: capsule oval or ovoid, 4–6 cm. long. [*D. fastu-
osa* L.]—Hammocks and waste-places, Coastal Plain, Fla. to Tex. Nat. of
trop. Asia and Africa.—(*W. I., Mex., C. A., S. A.*)

3. **D. meteloides** Dunal. Plant 3–11 dm. tall, glaucescent: leaf-blades ovate
to oval-ovate, 10–15 cm. long, sinuate-toothed: calyx 10–12 cm. long; lobes
lanceolate: corolla white, suffused with lavender or violet, 15–20 cm. long: capsule subglobose, 4–6 cm. in diameter.—River valleys, dry hills, and plains, Tex.
to Calif. and Colo. Naturalized on roadsides E to Fla.—(*Mex., C. A., S. A.*)

4. **D. innoxia** Mill. Plant 8–15 dm. tall, softly pubescent: leaf-blades ovate
to elliptic-ovate, 10–20 cm. long, undulate or slightly angled: calyx 7–12 cm.
long; lobes lanceolate or triangular-lanceolate: corolla white, 10–15 cm. long:
capsule oval or globose-ovoid, about 3 cm. long. [*D. Metel* (Fl. SE U. S.)]—
Roadsides and waste-places, Coastal Plain and New England coast, Fla. to
R. I. Nat. of trop. Am.—(*W. I., Mex., C. A., S. A., O. W.*)

11. **NICOTIANA** L. Herbs, shrubs, or trees, mostly clammy-pubescent.
Leaf-blades entire or repand. Flowers in racemes or panicles. Calyx markedly
lobed. Corolla white or colored, tubular, funnelform, or salverform. Filaments
equal or nearly so.—About 50 species, mostly American.—TOBACCOS.

Herbs.
     Corolla-tube stout, 2–5 times longer than the calyx.   I. RUSTICAE.
     Corolla-tube very slender, many times longer than the calyx.   II. LONGIFLORAE.
Shrubs or trees.   III. GLAUCAE.

I. RUSTICAE

Corolla 5–8 cm. long; limb becoming purplish: capsule 15–20 mm. long.   1. *N. Tabacum.*

Corolla 1–2 cm. long: limb lurid yellow or greenish: capsule 8–10 mm. long.   2. *N. rustica.*

II. LONGIFLORAE

Leaf-blades sessile: calyx-lobes narrowed upward.   3. *N. longiflora.*
Leaf-blades clasping: calyx-lobes dilated upward.   4. *N. repanda.*

III. GLAUCA

Branches and leaves very glaucous: flowers on slender stalks, the corolla nearly tubular.   5. *N. glauca.*

1. N. Tabacum L. Stem 3–30 dm. tall: leaf-blades elliptic or oval, varying to broadest above the middle or below it, acute or acuminate, those of the cauline leaves 1–3 dm. long, those of the basal leaves often much longer: calyx 1.5–2 cm. long; lobes lanceolate to triangular, shorter than the tube: corolla greenish-white or greenish-yellow; limb turning purplish, 3–4 cm. wide, the lobes somewhat reniform: capsule ovoid, 15–20 mm. long.—Fields, roadsides, and waste-places, various provinces, E U. S. Nat. of trop. Am. and widely cult.—Sum.

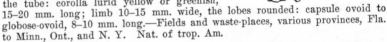

2. N. rustica L. Stem 5–12 dm. tall: leaf-blades ovate, 5–20 cm. long, entire: calyx 5–7 cm. long, or larger in age; lobes triangular to ovate-triangular, much shorter than the tube: corolla lurid yellow or greenish, 15–20 mm. long; limb 10–15 mm. wide, the lobes rounded: capsule ovoid to globose-ovoid, 8–10 mm. long.—Fields and waste-places, various provinces, Fla. to Minn., Ont., and N. Y. Nat. of trop. Am.

3. N. longiflora Cav. Stem 3–11 dm. tall: leaf-blades spatulate to elliptic, or lanceolate to linear on the upper part of the stem, 8–25 cm. long, undulate: calyx 10–12 mm. long, enlarging in age; lobes mainly shorter than the tube: corolla white or greenish-white, turning purplish, 7–10.5 cm. long; limb 2.5–3 cm. wide, the lobes ovate to ovate-lanceolate: capsule ellipsoid-ovoid, about 15 mm. long.—Waste-places, various provinces, E U. S. Nat. of S. Am. and cult. —Sum.–fall.—A shorter-flowered species *N. plumbaginifolia* Viv., with corollas only ½ or ⅓ as long as those of *N. longiflora* and with usually broader leaf-blades on the lower parts of the stem, has been found on Key West, Fla. It is native in tropical regions.

4. N. repanda Willd. Stem 3–7 dm. tall: leaf-blades suborbicular to oval-elliptic, 5–15 cm. long, repand: calyx 8–14 mm. long; lobes longer than the tube: corolla white or tinged with pink; limb 1.5–2.5 cm. wide, the lobes ovate: capsule ovoid, 8–10 mm. long.—Sandy soil, Coastal Plain, Tex., and in waste-places E to Fla.—(*W. I., Mex.*)—Spr.

5. N. glauca Graham. Shrub or small tree: leaf-blades ovate to elliptic-ovate: 5–30 cm. long or longer, undulate: calyx 11–15 mm. long; lobes lanceolate to triangular: corolla yellow or yellowish, 35–45 mm. long; limb about 10 mm. wide, the lobes very small: capsule ovoid to elliptic-ovoid, 10–12 mm. long.— Waste-places, and roadsides, Fla. to Calif. Nat. of S. Am.—(*W. I., Mex., O. W.*)

12. PETUNIA Juss. Herbs. Leaf-blades entire. Flowers solitary in the axils. Sepals united to below the middle. Corolla white or colored, funnelform or salverform. Filaments unequal, 4 of them didynamous.—About 12 species, South American.

Corolla small, the limb less than 1 cm. wide. — 1. *P. parviflora.*
Corolla large, the limb over 2 cm. wide.
  Corolla white; tube cylindric, 3 or 4 times as long as the
    calyx. — 2. *P. axillaris.*
  Corolla reddish-purple; tube campanulate, once or twice as
    long as the calyx. — 3. *P. violacea.*

1. P. parviflora Juss. Annual, pubescent: stems 1–4 dm. tall: leaf-blades spatulate to elliptic, 0.5–1.5 cm. long: calyx glandular-pubescent; lobes linear to linear-spatulate, much longer than the tube: corolla about 5 mm. long; limb purple, 6–8 mm. wide, the larger lobes wider than long, abruptly pointed: capsules ovoid, 3–4 mm. long.—Dry soil, waste-places and cult. grounds, Coastal Plain, and Basin-and-range provinces, Fla. to Tex. and Calif. —(*W. I., Mex., C. A., S. A.*)—Spr.–fall.

2. P. axillaris (Lam.) B.S.P. Stem and branches rather stout, clammy-pubescent: leaf-blades elliptic to ovate-elliptic, 3–6 cm. long, those of the lower leaves with stout petiole-like bases: calyx 1.5–2 cm. long; lobes mostly elliptic: corolla white, almost salverform; limb mostly 4–6 cm. wide.— Cult. grounds and waste-places, E U. S. Nat. of Argentina.—Sum.

3. P. violacea Lindl. Stem and branches slender: leaf-blades elliptic or oval, varying to obovate or ovate, 2–5 cm. long, those of the lower ones with slender petiole-like bases: calyx about 1 cm. long; lobes linear to linear-spatulate: corolla reddish-purple, funnelform; limb 3–4 cm. wide.—Roadsides and waste-places, E U. S. Nat. of Argentina and cult.—Sum.–fall, or all year S.

FAMILY 7. **BORAGINACEAE** — BORAGE FAMILY

Herbs or shrubby plants, the foliage usually bristly pubescent. Leaves alternate: blades mostly entire. Flowers typically perfect, the spikes or racemes often scorpioid. Calyx of 4 or 5 slightly united sepals. Corolla of 4 or 5 partly united petals. Androecium of 4 or 5 stamens, the filaments partly adnate to the corolla. Gynoecium of 4 nearly distinct carpels, the style arising from between the lobes. Fruit of 4 or fewer nutlets.— About 85 genera and 1,500 species, widely distributed.

Flowers regular: corolla with equal lobes. — I. BORAGEAE.
Flowers irregular: corolla with an oblique limb and unequal lobes. — II. ECHIEAE.

I. BORAGEAE

Nutlets armed with barbed prickles.
  Nutlets spreading, covered with prickles. — 1. CYNOGLOSSUM.
  Nutlets erect or incurved, with prickles on the back of
    angles. — 2. LAPPULA.
Nutlets unarmed.
  Receptacle conic or elongate. — 3. AMSINCKIA.
  Receptacle flat or merely convex.
    Nutlets attached obliquely to the receptacles: free por-
      tions of the filaments elongate. — 4. MERTENSIA.
    Nutlets attached to the receptacle by their bases: free
      portions of the filaments very short.

Nutlets each with a small flat scar where attached:
scales in the throat of the corolla broad.
Corolla funnelform or salverform: lobes obtuse,
spreading, broad.
Racemes without bracts: calyx-lobes about as
long as the tube.   5. Myosotis.
Racemes with bracts: calyx-lobes much longer
than the tube.
Corolla slightly longer than the calyx:
style as long as the ovary or longer.   6. Lithospermum.
Corolla much longer than the calyx: style
much elongated.   7. Batschia.
Corolla tubular: lobes acute or acuminate, erect,
narrow.   8. Onosmodium.
Nutlets each with a large hollow scar where at-
tached: scales in the throat of the corolla nar-
row.   9. Symphytum.

II. Echieae

Stamens included: corolla-throat closed by scales.   10. Lycopsis.
Stamens exserted: corolla-throat dilated and open.   11. Echium.

1. CYNOGLOSSUM [Tourn.] L.   Annual, biennial, or perennial pubescent herbs.   Calyx manifestly accrescent.   Corolla much longer than the calyx.
Style relatively long.   Fruit surpassing the calyx.—About 75 species, widely
distributed.—Sum.

Stem copiously leafy to the top: corolla slightly longer than the calyx: nutlets
flat.   1. *C. officinale.*
Stem terminated by a long peduncle: corolla much longer than
the calyx: nutlets convex.   2. *C. virginicum.*

1. C. officinale L.   Stem 2–6 dm. tall: leaf-blades elliptic to linear-elliptic or
linear-lanceolate, 5–15 cm. long: calyx-lobes becoming 6–8 mm. long or more:
corolla reddish-purple or rarely white,
mostly 8–10 mm. wide; lobes reniform:
nutlets smooth between the spines.—
(Hound's-tongue.)—Dry soil, roadsides,
fields, waste-places, and thickets, various
provinces, rarely Coastal Plain, Ga. to Ark.,
Kans., Minn., and Que. Nat. of Eu.

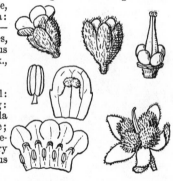

2. C. virginicum L.   Stem 2–11 dm. tall:
leaf-blades oval to elliptic, 8–32 cm. long:
calyx-lobes becoming 3–4 mm. long: corolla
blue or sometimes white, 7–8 mm. wide;
lobes ovate: nutlets coarsely wrinkled between the spines.—(Wild-comfrey.)—Dry
soil, woods, roadsides, and thickets, various
provinces, Ga. to La., Kans., and N. J.

2. LAPPULA [Rivinius] Moench.   Annual, biennial, or perennial, often
hirsute or hispid, herbs.   Calyx scarcely accrescent: lobes spreading at maturity.   Corolla pale blue, or whitish, scarcely as long as, or a little longer than
the calyx.   Style relatively short.   Fruit somewhat longer than the calyx.—
About 40 species, mostly natives of the north temperate zone.

Scales of the corolla-tube remote from the base of the lobes: fruit erect, or ascending.   1. *L. Lappula.*
Scales of the corolla-tube at the base of the lobes: fruit drooping.   2. *L. virginiana.*

1. L. Lappula (L.) Karst.   Plant 2–6 dm. tall: leaf-blades linear-spatulate to
linear, 2–5 cm. long: calyx-lobes becoming 3–10 mm. long: corolla-lobes about

2 mm. long, the appendages broadly ovate: fruit about 3 mm. wide; nutlets granulose or tuberculate on the back.—(BUR-SEED.)— Dry soil and waste-places, various provinces, N of Coastal Plain, Tenn. to Tex., B. C., Ont., N. S. and N. J. Nat. of Eu.—Spr.–fall.

2. **L. virginiana** (L.) Greene. Plant 3–9 dm. tall: leaf-blades elliptic to elliptic-lanceolate, the lower ones 10–20 cm. long: calyx-lobes becoming 2–2.5 mm. long: corolla-tube about 1.5 mm. long, the appendages reniform: fruit about 4 mm. wide; nutlets papillose and spiny. [*Echinospermum virginicum* Lehm.]—(BEGGAR'S-LICE. STICK-WEED. BUR-SEED.)—Woods, roadsides, and thickets, various provinces, Ga. to La., Kans., Minn., and N. B.—Sum.

3. **AMSINCKIA** Lehm. Annual hispid herbs. Sepals slightly united, persistent. Corolla yellow, slightly exceeding the calyx, salverform, or the tube somewhat funnelform near the throat. Stamens adnate high up on the corolla-tube. Style elongate. Nutlets crustaceous or coriaceous, attached above the base to an ellipsoid-pyramidal receptacle.—About 15 species, of western America.

1. **A. parviflora** A. Heller. Stems 5 dm. tall or less: leaves remote; blades linear-elliptic to linear, 5–6 cm. long, or shorter on the upper part of the stem; calyx-lobes linear to linear-lanceolate, about 4 mm., becoming 6–7 mm. long, both softly pubescent and hispid: corolla pale-yellow, about 5 mm. long; limb about 2.5 mm. wide: nutlets ovoid, 2–3 mm. long, sharply keeled on the back and transversely wrinkled, also sharply tuberculate.—Fields, lawns, and waste-places, Piedmont, N. C. Nat. of Calif.—Spr.–sum.

4. **MERTENSIA** Roth. Perennial glabrous (our) herbs. Calyx scarcely, if at all, accrescent. Corolla showy, conspicuously longer than the calyx. Style and free portion of the filaments elongate. Fruit barely longer than the calyx.—About 40 species, in the Northern Hemisphere.

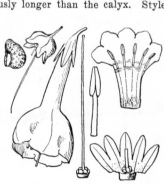

1. **M. virginica** (L.) DC. Stems often clustered 2–6 dm. tall: leaves 5–20 cm. long; blades elliptic to oval: calyx 2–3 mm. long, becoming 5–6 mm. long; lobes oblong to lanceolate or ovate: corolla blue or rarely white, 2.5–3 cm. long, the cup-like limb 10–15 mm. wide, shallowly lobed: nutlets ovoid, 2.5 mm. long.—(LUNGWORT. BLUEBELLS. VIRGINIA-COWSLIP.)—Rich woods, low grounds, and alluvial stream-banks, various provinces, rarely Coastal Plain, Ala. to Ark., Kans., Ont., and S. C.—Spr.

5. MYOSOTIS [Rupp.] L. Annual, biennial, or perennial, pubescent herbs,
Calyx slightly accrescent. Corolla manifestly longer than the calyx. Style
and free portions of the filaments short. Fruit surpassed by the calyx.—
About 35 species, of wide geographic distribution.—Spr.–sum.—FORGET-ME-
NOTS. SCORPION-GRASSES.

Calyx open at maturity, pubescent with straight hairs.
    Calyx-lobes longer than the tube: corolla-limb mostly less than 6 mm. wide:
      style short.   1. *M. laxa.*
    Calyx-lobes shorter than the tube: corolla-limb mostly over
      6 mm. wide: style elongate.   2. *M. palustris.*
Calyx closed at maturity, pubescent with hooked hairs.
    Pedicel longer than the calyx at maturity: style slender,
      about as long as the ovary.   3. *M. arvensis.*
    Pedicel shorter than the calyx: style stout, very short.
      Fruiting racemes with many approximate erect or
        ascending pedicels: calyx usually up to 5 mm. long at
        maturity: nutlets 1.5 mm. long.   4. *M. virginica.*
      Fruiting racemes with few more or less recurving pedi-
        cels: calyx over 5 mm. long at maturity: nutlets 2
        mm. long.   5. *M. macrosperma.*

1. M. laxa Lehm. Stem 1–5 dm. long: leaf-blades spatulate to elliptic-lanceolate: pedicels 5–10 mm. long: calyx-lobes triangular to triangular-lanceolate:
corolla mainly pale-blue; lobes about 1 mm.
long: nutlets about 1 mm. long.—Spring-
runs and muddy places, various provinces,
Ga. to Tenn., Ont., and N. S.

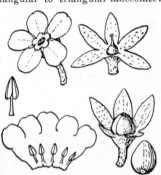

2. M. palustris (L.) Lam. Stem 2–6 dm.
long: leaf-blades spatulate to elliptic or
elliptic-lanceolate, 1–8 cm. long: pedicels
4–7 mm. long: calyx-lobes triangular:
corolla sky-blue and with a yellow eye;
lobes about 2 mm. long: nutlets about 1.5
mm. long.—Low grounds and brooks, various provinces, N of Coastal Plain, Ga. to
W. Va., and N. S. Nat. of Eu.

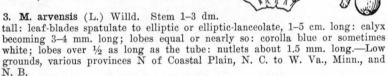

3. M. arvensis (L.) Willd. Stem 1–3 dm.
tall: leaf-blades spatulate to elliptic or elliptic-lanceolate, 1–5 cm. long: calyx
becoming 3–4 mm. long; lobes equal or nearly so: corolla blue or sometimes
white; lobes over ½ as long as the tube: nutlets about 1.5 mm. long.—Low
grounds, various provinces N of Coastal Plain, N. C. to W. Va., Minn., and
N. B.

4. M. virginica (L.) B.S.P. Stem 1–4 dm. tall, with short, stiff, often numerous branches: leaf-blades spatulate to elliptic, 1–3 cm. long: mature raceme
with numerous approximate fruiting calices: pedicels 1–3 mm. long: calyx becoming 6–7 mm. long; lobes slightly unequal: corolla white; lobes less than
⅓ as long as the tube: nutlets about 1.5 mm. long.—Dry hills and fields, various provinces, Fla. to Tex., Minn., Ont., and Me.

5. M. macrosperma Engelm. Stem 2–6 dm. tall, with few, elongate, virgate
branches: leaf-blades similar to those of *M. arvensis* but larger: mature
racemes with few widely separated fruiting calices: pedicels 3–6 mm. long:
calyx becoming 6–8 mm. long; lobes very unequal: corolla white; lobes less
than ⅓ as long as the tube: nutlets about 2 mm. long.—Hillsides, woods, and
stream-banks, Coastal Plain and adj. provinces, Fla. to Tex., Ark., Ind., and
Md.

6. LITHOSPERMUM [Tourn.] L.   Annual, biennial, or perennial herbs. Calyx slightly enlarged at maturity.   Corolla slightly longer than the calyx, white, greenish, or yellowish.   Style as long as the ovary or somewhat longer. Fruit surpassed by the calyx.—About 30 species, in the Northern Hemisphere.— Spr.–sum.—GROMWELLS.

Annual plant: corolla white or whitish, slightly surpassing the calyx.
                                                              1. *L. arvense.*
Perennial plant: corolla yellow or sometimes greenish-white.
  Pubescence of stem strictly appressed.   2. *L. latifolium.*
  Pubescence of stem more or less spreading.   3. *L. tuberosum.*

1. L. arvense L.   Stem and branches 1–8 dm. long: leaf-blades linear-oblanceolate to linear-lanceolate, 1.5–5 cm. long, acutish: calyx-lobes narrowly linear to linear-subulate, 8–10 mm. long, revolute: corolla white or pinkish; lobes ¼ to ⅕ as long as the tube: nutlets about 3 mm. long, pitted and wrinkled.—(CORN-GROMWELL.)—Roadsides, fields, and dry hills, various provinces, Ala. to Miss., Kans., Ont., and Me.

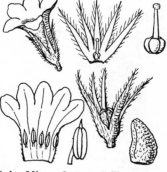

2. L. latifolium Michx.   Stem and branches 3–7 dm. tall: blades of the cauline leaves elliptic to elliptic-lanceolate, 4–12 cm. long, acuminate: calyx-lobes narrowly linear, becoming 8–10 mm. long, flat: corolla yellow-white or pale-yellow; lobes over ½ as long as the tube: nutlets ovoid, 3–3.5 mm. long, smooth.—Woods, fields, and roadsides, various provinces N of Coastal Plain, Tenn. to Ark., Minn., Ont., and Va.

3. L. tuberosum Rugel.   Stems and branches 3–7 dm. tall: blades of the cauline leaves oblanceolate to elliptic or ovate-elliptic, 2–10 cm. long, acute or abruptly pointed: calyx-lobes broadly linear to linear-spatulate, becoming 4–6 mm. long: corolla yellowish white; lobes less than ½ as long as the tube: nutlets oval-obovoid, about 2 mm. long.—River-bluffs and hammocks, Coastal Plain and adj. provinces, Fla. to Tex., and Tenn.

7. BATSCHIA G. F. Gmel.   Perennial herbs, with colored roots.   Calyx nearly unchanged at maturity.   Corolla much longer than the calyx (except in cleistogamous flowers), yellow.   Style many times longer than the ovary. Fruit surpassed by the calyx, the nutlets mainly ovoid.—About 6 species, North American.

Corolla-lobes entire, the appendages remote from them: all flowers complete: stamens
  below the throat of the corolla.
    Stem hirsute: corolla-tube beardless at the base within.   1. *B. canescens.*
    Stem hispid: corolla-tube bearded at the base within.   2. *B. carolinensis.*
Corolla-lobes erose or laciniate: the appendages close to their
  bases: later flowers cleistogamous: stamens in the throat of
  the corolla.
                                                      3. *B. linearifolia.*

1. B. canescens Michx.   Plant 1–4 dm. tall: leaf-blades linear to elliptic or ovate-elliptic, 9–21 mm. long: calyx-lobes linear or nearly so, becoming 3–5

mm. long: corolla orange-yellow: tube 9–11
mm. long: nutlets about 2.5 mm. long.
[*Lithospermum canescens* Lehm.] — (Puc-
coon.)—Rich woods and open hillsides,
various provinces N of Coastal Plain, Ga.
to Tex., Sask., and Ont.—Sum.

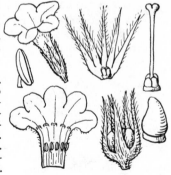

2. **B. carolinensis** (Walt.) G. F. Gmel.
Plant 1–5 dm. tall: leaf-blades linear to
elliptic or lanceolate, 1–5 cm. long: calyx-
lobes lanceolate to linear-lanceolate, becoming 7–10 mm. long: corolla orange; tube 12–
16 mm. long: nutlets 3–3.5 mm. long.
[*Lithospermum Gmelini* (Michx.) A.
Hitchc.]—Dry soil or woods, various provinces, Fla. to N. M., Minn., and N. Y.—Spr.

3. **B. linearifolia** (Goldie) Small.   Plant 1–3 dm. tall: leaf-blades linear-
lanceolate to linear, 3–9 cm. long: earlier flowers clustered: calyx-lobes linear-
tapering, becoming 7–10 mm. long: corolla light-yellow; tube slender, 25–30
mm. long: nutlets 3–4 mm. long.   [*Lithospermum linearifolium* Goldie.]—Dry
soil, hills and rock ledges, various provinces, W Fla., to Ariz., B. C. and
Ill.—Spr.

    8. ONOSMODIUM Michx.   Perennial herbs with hard roots.   Sepals
nearly distinct.   Corolla narrow, longer than the calyx, without appendages in
the throat, the lobes relatively long.—About 10 species, North American.

Corolla yellow; lobes lanceolate, acuminate: tips of the anthers not reaching up to
    the sinuses of the corolla.   1. *O. virginianum.*
Corolla whitish, often green-tinged; lobes ovate, obtuse or
        abruptly pointed: tips of the anthers reaching up to the
        sinuses of the corolla.
      Leaves, bracts, and calyx-lobes not shaggy-pubescent, the
        hairs relatively short and more or less appressed: nut-
        lets markedly pitted: anthers with long slender tips.   2. *O. molle.*
      Leaves, bracts, and calyx-lobes shaggy-pubescent, the hairs
        long and loosely spreading: nutlets little, if at all,
        pitted: anthers with short stout tips.   3. *O. hispidissimum.*

1. **O. virginianum** (L.) DC.   Stem strigose (or hirsute in *O. virginianum hirsutum*), 2–7 dm. tall or more: leaf-blades, on the upper part of the stem

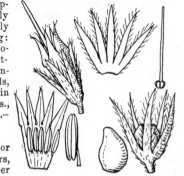

oblanceolate, narrowly elliptic, elliptic, elliptic-obovate to ovate, 2.5–12 cm. long, usually
sparingly strigose, sometimes quite copiously
so: calyx-lobes becoming 6–8 mm. long:
corolla yellow, 8–10 mm. long; lobes lanceolate, more than ½ as long as the tube: nutlets ovoid, about 2.5 mm. long, not constricted at the base.—Pinelands, dry woods,
thickets, and sandy hillsides, Coastal Plain
and adj. provinces, Fla. to La., and Mass.,
and Great Lake Lowland, W N. Y.—Spr.–
sum.

2. **O. molle** Michx.   Stem short-hirsute, or
partly strigose, with white or whitish hairs,
8 dm. tall or less: leaf-blades, on the upper

part of the stem, elliptic, lanceolate or ovate-lanceolate, not shaggy-pubescent, but with longer spreading hairs especially on the veins, and more numerous, at least beneath, short-appressed hairs: inflorescence softly pubescent: calyx-lobes narrowly linear, about 6 mm. long: corolla 9–12 mm. long; lobes ovate, about ½ as long as the tube: anthers about 2.5 mm. long: nutlets ovoid, about 3 mm. long, copiously pitted, slightly if at all constricted at the base.—Dry ridges and cedar-barrens, Interior Low Plateaus, Tenn., and Ky.—Spr.

3. **O. hispidissimum** Mackenzie. Stem copiously hirsute, with whitish hairs, 12 dm. tall or less: leaf-blades, on the upper part of the stem, narrowly elliptic, elliptics, lanceolate or ovate, pubescent as in *O. molle*, but with coarser, stiffer, and longer hairs: inflorescence copiously hirsute: calyx-lobes linear, 4–6 mm. long: corolla 10–12 mm. long or longer in the earlier flowers; lobes ovate, less than ½ as long as the tube: anthers about 2 mm. long: nutlets ovoid, 3–3.5 mm. long, smooth or slightly pitted, decidedly constricted at the base. [*O. carolinianum* (Chapm. Fl.) (Fl. SE U. S.)]—Woods, bottoms, banks and dry hillsides, various provinces N of Coastal Plain, N. C. to Tex., Minn., and Ont.—Spr.–sum.

9. **SYMPHYTUM** L. Perennial herbs with mucilaginous roots. Sepals manifestly united into a tube. Corolla much longer than the calyx, with long appendages in the throat, the lobes rela-tively short.—About 15 species, natives of the Old World.

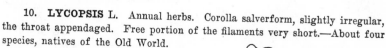

1. **S. officinale** L. Stems and branches 3–10 dm. tall, hirsute: leaf-blades oblong, lanceolate, or ovate-lanceolate, or sometimes ovate, 8–30 cm. long: calyx-lobes acuminate, each with an ovate to lanceolate body: corolla yellowish or purplish, 10–15 mm. long; lobes ovate, obtuse, the appendages lanceolate: nutlets 3–4 mm. long.—(COM-FREY. HEALING-HERB.) — Roadsides, old fields, and about gardens, various provinces N of Coastal Plain, N. C. to Tenn., Minn., and Newf. Nat. of Eu.—Sum.

10. **LYCOPSIS** L. Annual herbs. Corolla salverform, slightly irregular, the throat appendaged. Free portion of the filaments very short.—About four species, natives of the Old World.

1. **L. arvensis** L. Plants 3–7 dm. tall, bristly hispid: stems becoming widely or diffusely branched; branches often procumbent: leaf-blades oblanceolate below, to narrowly oblong or lanceolate above, 2.5–10 cm. long, undulate or sinuate, sessile or the lower ones on long petioles: racemes often 5–10 cm. long; calyx becoming 7–8 mm. long; sepals linear or linear-lanceolate, acute: corolla blue, 5–7 mm. long; tube curved: nutlets about 3 mm. long, coarsely wrinkled. — (BUGLOSS.) — Waste-places, pastures, and roadsides, various provinces N of Coastal Plain, Tenn. to Ont., N. J., and Va.—Nat. of Eurasia.—Spr.–fall.

11. ECHIUM [Tourn.] L.   Biennial or perennial herbs.   Corolla funnelform, markedly irregular, the throat unappendaged.   Free portion of the filaments elongate.—About 30 species, natives of the Old World.

1. E. vulgare L.   Plants 3–7 dm. tall, bristlypubescent: stems 3–7 dm. tall, simple or branched throughout; branches ascending: leaf-blades linear or linear-lanceolate, or linear-oblanceolate below, acute or shortacuminate, 2–15 cm. long, undulate, sessile, bristly on both sides: spikes rather dense, becoming 2–10 cm. long: bracts obliquely lanceolate, acuminate: calyx bristly; lobes linear or linear-lanceolate, 6–12 mm. long, unequal: corolla pale blue or purplish, or rarely white, obliquely campanulate, 1.6–1.8 cm. long, narrowed into a short tube which is somewhat plaited: lobes ovate or triangularovate, ciliolate: filaments and style exserted, magenta: nutlets about 3 mm. long, wrinkled.—(VIPER'S-BUGLOSS. BLUE-DEVIL. BLUEWEED.)—Old fields and roadsides, often in calcareous soil, various provinces, Ga. to Nebr., Ont., and N. B. Nat. of Eu.—Sum.

FAMILY 8. **EHRETIACEAE** — EHRETIA FAMILY

Shrubs, trees, or sometimes herbs.   Leaves mainly alternate: blades mostly entire.   Flowers perfect, cymose.   Calyx of 5 (4–6), partly united sepals.   Corolla of 5 (4–6), partially united petals.   Androecium of 5 (4–6), stamens, the filaments more or less adnate to the corolla-tube. Gynoecium 2–4-carpellary: styles 2 and distinct, or partially united, or united by pairs.   Fruit drupaceous or of 4 nutlets.—About 20 genera and 350 species, in warm or tropical regions.

Styles, and stigmas, 4, unequally united by pairs: drupe with a 4-celled stone: cotyledons plaited or corrugated.
  Corolla long-funnelform; limb deeply lobed: calyx-tube cylindric.   1. SEBESTEN.
  Corolla short-funnelform; limb slightly lobed: calyx-tube campanulate.   2. VARRONIA.
Styles, and stigmas, 2: drupe with 2 or 4 stones: cotyledons flat.   3. BOURRERIA.

1. SEBESTEN Adans.   Shrubs or trees.   Flowers in open clusters. Sepals usually united to above the middle.   Corolla bright-colored, shallowly or deeply lobed.   Filaments adnate to above or below the middle of the corolla-tube. Fruits included, adnate to the accrescent calyx.—About 12 species, of tropical and subtropical America.

1. S. Sebestena (L.) Britton.   Shrub or small tree, the twigs strigose: leaf-blades ovate or elliptic-ovate, 8–12 cm. long, undulate or repand: calyx 14–19 mm. long; tube cylindric: corolla-lobes bright-red, much shorter than the tube: fruits oval or ovoid, 2–3 cm. long.   [*Cordia Sebestena* L.]—(GEIGERTREE.)—Hammocks and sand-dunes, Everglade Keys, Fla., and Florida Keys.—(*W. I.*)

—All year.—This plant has a generic counterpart in Texas, in which the corolla
is white with a yellow center.

2. **VARRONIA** Jacq. Shrubs, trees, or vines. Flowers in open clusters or in
heads. Sepals usually united to above the middle. Corolla white or colored,
shallowly or deeply lobed. Filaments ad-
nate to above or below the middle of the
corolla-tube.—About 70 species of tropical
and subtropical America.

1. **V. globosa** Jacq. Branched shrub 1–3 m.
tall: leaf-blades ovate to elliptic-ovate, 1–5
cm. long, serrate: calyx about 8 mm. long:
corolla white, 5–7 mm. long. [*Cordia bul-
lata* (Chapm. Fl.)]—Hammocks, Cape
Sable region, Fla. and Florida Keys.—(*W.
I.*)—All year.—This plant has a generic
counterpart in Texas in which the calyx-lobes
are shorter than the tube and its corolla is
mostly 12–15 mm. long.

3. **BOURRERIA** Jacq. Shrubs or trees. Flowers in corymbose cymes.
Sepals united to above the middle. Corolla white or colored, prominently
lobed. Filaments adnate to above or below the middle of the corolla-tube.—
About 25 species, of tropical America.

Anthers about as long as the free portion of the filaments: leaf-blades short-petioled.
    Drupe 9–11 mm. wide: corolla-tube much exceeding the calyx. 1. *B. revoluta.*
    Drupe 7–8 mm. wide: corolla-tube about equalling the calyx. 2. *B. cassinifolia.*
Anthers much shorter than the free portion of the filaments:
    leaf-blades slender-petioled.   3. *B. ovata.*

1. **B. revoluta** H.B.K. Small tree or shrub, with pubescent twigs: leaf-blades
elliptic to obovate, mostly 2–7 cm. long, abruptly pointed, rounded or notched,
permanently rough-pubescent and ciliate, or
sometimes smooth: cymes several-flowered:
calyx 6–7 mm. long; lobes ovate, mostly less
than ⅓ as long as the tube: corolla white;
tube much exceeding the calyx; larger lobes
5–6 mm. wide: anthers about 2.5 mm. long:
drupe orange, slightly depressed, 9–11 mm.
wide. [*B. Radula* (Chapm. Fl.) (Fl. SE
U. S.)]—(ROUGH-STRONGBACK.)—Hammocks
and pinelands, Everglade Keys, Fla., and
Florida Keys.—(*W. I.*)—All year.

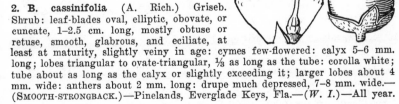

2. **B. cassinifolia** (A. Rich.) Griseb.
Shrub: leaf-blades oval, elliptic, obovate, or
cuneate, 1–2.5 cm. long, mostly obtuse or
retuse, smooth, glabrous, and eciliate, at
least at maturity, slightly veiny in age: cymes few-flowered: calyx 5–6 mm.
long; lobes triangular to ovate-triangular, ⅓ as long as the tube: corolla white;
tube about as long as the calyx or slightly exceeding it; larger lobes about 4
mm. wide: anthers about 2 mm. long: drupe much depressed, 7–8 mm. wide.—
(SMOOTH-STRONGBACK.)—Pinelands, Everglade Keys, Fla.—(*W. I.*)—All year.

3. **B. ovata** Miers. Small tree or shrub, with glabrous twigs: leaf-blades
obovate to elliptic-obovate or oval-obovate, 4–12 cm. long, smooth: calyx 6–7 cm.

long; lobes triangular, fully ⅓ as long as the tube: corolla white; tube rather short; lobes slightly shorter than the tube: stamens exserted; anthers about 2 mm. long: drupe orange, 1 cm. wide. [*B. havanensis* (Chapm. Fl.) (Fl. SE U. S.)]—(STRONGBACK.)—Hammocks, Florida Keys.—(*W. I.*)—All year.

FAMILY 9. **HELIOTROPIACEAE** — HELIOTROPE FAMILY

Herbs, shrubs, or woody vines. Leaves alternate: blades entire, or rarely toothed. Flowers perfect, mostly in scorpioid spikes or racemes. Calyx of 5 more or less united sepals. Corolla various, of 5 partially united petals. Androecium of 5 stamens, the filaments more or less adnate to the corolla-tube. Gynoecium 2–4-carpellary. Stigma annular, surmounted by an appendage. Fruit drupaceous, or dry and of 2–4 nutlets.— About 10 genera and 300 species, widely distributed.

Shrubs or woody twiners: fruit drupaceous. Tribe I. TOURNEFORTIEAE
Herbs, sometimes partly-woody: fruit dry, separating into
  nutlets. II. HELIOTROPIEAE.

I. TOURNEFORTIEAE

Corolla-lobes broad: fruit not lobed, hollowed at the base:
  anthers minutely pointed.
  Plant densely and conspicuously silky-tomentose: leaves very
    numerous and crowded: corolla-tube about as long as the
    calyx or shorter. 1. MALLOTONIA.
  Plant hirsute-inconspicuously pubescent: leaves relatively 2. TOURNEFORTIA.
    few and distant: corolla-tube much exceeding the calyx.
Corolla-lobes narrow, often subulate: fruit lobed, usually 4-lobed,
  not hollowed at the base: anthers acuminate. 3. MYRIOPUS.

II. HELIOTROPIEAE

Fruit of 4 more or less readily separating nutlets.
  Fruits 4-lobed, separating into 4 one-seeded nutlets.
    Flowers in scorpioid spikes or racemes: calyx-lobes equal
      or nearly so. 4. HELIOTROPIUM.
    Flowers axillary to narrow bracts: calyx-lobes very un-
      equal. 5. LITHOCOCCA.
  Fruits 2-lobed, separating into 2 two-seeded nutlets.
    Nutlets conic, ribbed: style obconic or turbinate. 6. TIARIDIUM.
    Nutlets subglobose, rugose: style very short or wanting. 7. SCHOBERA.
Fruit of 2 completely 2-celled nutlets, or sometimes 1-celled and
  1-seeded. 8. COCHRANEA.

1. MALLOTONIA Britton. Maritime shrubs with conspicuously pubescent foliage. Leaves numerous, crowded on the branchlets: blades narrow, succulent, sessile. Flowers in stalked scorpioid, corymbed spikes or racemes. Calyx-lobes broad, longer than the tube. Corolla white: lobes broad, spreading. Anthers ovoid, slightly cordate at the base. Stigma-appendage low-conic. Drupe not lobed, short or depressed, hollowed at the base, abruptly pointed.—Two species, in tropical and subtropical regions.

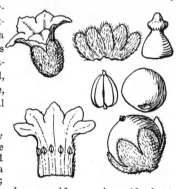

1. M. gnaphalodes (Jacq.) Britton. Fleshy shrub 2 m. tall or less, the pubescence pale or white: leaf-blades linear-spatulate, 4–11 cm. long, obtuse: calyx-lobes ovate: corolla much exceeding the calyx; tube pubescent; lobes ovate to orbicular-ovate, 2–3 mm. long: drupe ovoid or conic-ovoid, about 5 mm. long. [*Tournefortia gnaphalodes* R. Br.]—(SEA LAVENDER.)—Coastal sand-dunes, S pen. Fla. and the Keys.—(*W. I.*)—All year.

2. TOURNEFORTIA L. Hammock vines, with stout trailing or climbing stems. Leaves neither crowded nor numerous: blades broad, often coarsely or harshly pubescent, fleshy-herbaceous, petioled. Flowers in compound corymbose spikes. Calyx-lobes broad, longer than the tube. Corolla white: lobes broad, spreading, flat or crisped. Anthers lanceolate, cordate at the base. Stigma-appendage depressed. Drupe not lobed, hollow at the base.—About 100 species, of tropical and sub-tropical regions.

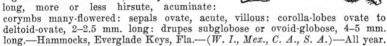

1. T. hirsutissima L. Woody or partly woody vine, the stem and branches pubescent: leaf-blades elliptic, often broadly so, varying to ovate or obovate, mostly 1–1.5 dm. long, more or less hirsute, acuminate: corymbs many-flowered: sepals ovate, acute, villous: corolla-lobes ovate to deltoid-ovate, 2–2.5 mm. long: drupes subglobose or ovoid-globose, 4–5 mm. long.—Hammocks, Everglade Keys, Fla.—(*W. I., Mex., C. A., S. A.*)—All year.

3. MYRIOPUS Small. Hammock vines with climbing, often twining stems. Leaves neither crowded nor numerous: blades broad, herbaceous, often finely pubescent, petioled. Flowers in corymbose, elongate, secund spikes or racemes. Calyx-lobes narrow or narrow-lipped. Corolla white or greenish: lobes very narrow, usually subulate. Anthers lanceolate, slightly cordate at the base. Style elongate: stigma-appendage long-conic. Drupe 2–4-lobed, with as many lobes as there are 1-seeded nutlets, usually depressed.—About 15 species, in tropical America.

Leaves glabrous or obscurely pubescent: calyx-lobes triangular or triangular-lanceolate in anthesis.   **1. *M. volubilis.***
Leaves densely white-pubescent beneath: calyx-lobes subulate or triangular-subulate in anthesis.   **2. *M. poliochros.***

1. M. volubilis (L.) Small. Woody vine, the fine pubescence usually rusty; leaf-blades ovate to elliptic-lanceolate, 2–8 cm. long, mostly acute or acuminate, green beneath: corymbs with sprawling branches: calyx-lobes much less than half as long as the corolla-tube: corolla-lobes much shorter than the tube: drupe 2–3 mm. wide, the lobes with black spots. [*Tournefortia volubilis* R. & S.]—Hammocks, S pen. Fla. and the Keys, and S Tex.—(*W. I., S. A.*)— All year.

2. M. poliochros (Spreng.) Small. Vine resembling *M. volubilis* in habit: leaf-blades ovate or elliptic, 3–6 cm. long, obtuse or abruptly pointed, pale or whitish beneath: corymbs usually copiously floriferous: calyx-lobes nearly or quite half as long as the corolla tube: corolla-lobes nearly or quite

as long as the tube: drupe 3–4 mm. wide, the lobes with magenta spots. [*Tournefortia poliochros* Spreng.]—Hammocks on kitchenmiddens, E coast, Fla.—(*W. I.*)—All year.

4. HELIOTROPIUM [Tourn.] L.   Shrubs or erect, diffuse, or prostrate herbs.   Leaves few or many: blades broad or narrow.   Calyx-lobes nearly equal.   Stamens adnate to the lower part of the corolla-tube.   Style very short.   Fruit 4-lobed, an aggregate of 4 nutlets.—About 125 species, widely distributed.—HELIOTROPES.

Inflorescence bractless.
  Calyx glabrous: nutlets finely wrinkled: leaf-blades narrow.   1. *H. curassavicum.*
  Calyx pubescent: nutlets tuberculate: leaf-blades broad.   2. *H. europaeum.*
Inflorescence bracted.
  Corolla white.
    Corolla with small puberulent swellings low down in the throat.   3. *H. phyllostachyum.*
    Corolla with prominent deflexed appendages at the top of the throat.   4. *H. polyphyllum.*
  Corolla yellow.
    Plant with erect stem and branches.   5. *H. Leavenworthii.*
    Plant with prostrate stem and branches.   6. *H. horizontale.*

1. H. curassavicum L.   Plant perennial or mainly so, 1–4 dm. tall: leaf-blades spatulate, varying to obovate or linear, mainly 2–6 cm. long: calyx-lobes lanceolate to elliptic-lanceolate, 1.5–2 mm. long: corolla white, except the yellow eye, turning blue; tube about 2 mm. long: fruit 2–2.5 mm. wide.—(SEASIDE-HELIOTROPE.)—Hammocks, shores, and waste-places, Coastal Plain and adj. provinces, Fla. to Tex. and Del.—(*W. I., Mex., C. A., S. A.*)

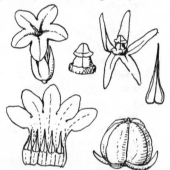

2. H. europaeum L.   Plant annual, 1–5 dm. tall: leaf-blades elliptic to oval, varying to ovate or obovate, 2–6 cm. long: calyx-lobes elliptic to elliptic-lanceolate or linear-lanceolate, 2–2.5 mm. long: corolla white or bluish; tube fully 2 mm. long: fruit about 3 mm. wide.—Waste-places and roadsides, various provinces, Fla. to Ala. and Mass. Nat. of Eu.

3. H. phyllostachyum Torr.   Plant annual, 0.5–2 dm. tall: leaf-blades elliptic, 1–2.5 cm. long: calyx-lobes lanceolate, or the larger one ovate-lanceolate, 2–3 mm. long: corolla white; tube 2–3 mm. long; lobes about 1 mm. long: fruit about 1.5 mm. wide.—Hammocks and waste-places, Key West, Fla.

4. H. polyphyllum Lehm.   Perennial, 1–2 dm. tall: leaf-blades linear-spatulate to elliptic, 0.5–2 cm. long: calyx-lobes lanceolate to ovate-lanceolate, 2–2.5 mm. long: corolla white; tube 3–4 mm. long: fruit 1.5 mm. wide.—Coastal hammocks, Everglade Keys, Fla. and Florida Keys.—(*S. A.*)—All year.

5. H. Leavenworthii Torr.   Plant with pale-pubescent erect stems, 2–11 dm. tall: leaf-blades linear to linear-elliptic, 1–2 cm. long: flowers inodorous: calyx-lobes lanceolate, 3–4 mm. long: corolla bright-yellow; lobes ovate, obtuse.—Low hammocks and wet places, mostly in Everglades, S pen. Fla. and Florida Keys.—All year.

6. H. horizontale Small.   Plant with radially prostrate branches, 1–5 cm. long, often matted: leaf-blades linear or nearly so, 0.8–1.6 cm. long: flowers fragrant: calyx-lobes lanceolate, 4–5 mm. long: corolla golden-yellow.—Pinelands, Everglade Keys, Fla.—All year.

5. LITHOCOCCA Small. Annual erect, wiry herbs. Leaves scattered: blades very narrow. Flowers scattered, axillary to narrow leaf-like bracts. Calyx-lobes very unequal in size and shape. Stamens adnate to the lower part of the corolla-tube. Style short. Fruit depressed, 4-lobed.—One species.

1. L. tenellum (Nutt.) Small. Stem 1–3 dm. tall, with several or many erect or ascending branches: leaf-blades linear to narrowly linear-lanceolate, 1.5–5 cm. long: calyx-lobes linear or nearly so, 2–6 mm. long; corolla white; tube about 4 mm. long: fruit 3–3.5 mm. wide, pubescent. [*Heliotropium tenellum* Torr.]—Dry soil, roadsides, and pastures, various provinces, Ala. to Tex., Kans., and Ky.—Sum.-fall.

6. TIARIDIUM Lehm. Annual erect herbs. Leaf-blades broad. Flowers in bractless scorpioid spikes. Sepals slightly united at the base. Corolla blue, with the anthers near the middle of the rather slender tube. Style obconic or turbinate. Fruit slightly depressed, the nutlets paired and mitriform.—One species.

1. T. indicum (L.) Lehm. Annual, 1–7 dm. tall: leaf-blades ovate, oval, or elliptic, 2–10 cm. long: calyx-lobes linear to linear-lanceolate, 1–2 mm. long: corolla blue; tube 2.5–3 mm. long: fruit 2–2.5 mm. wide. [*Heliotropium indicum* L.]—Waste-places, fields, and roadsides, various provinces, Fla. to Tex., Ill., and Va. Nat. of E. I.—(*W. I., Mex., C. A., S. A.*)—Sum.-fall, or all year S.

7. SCHOBERA Scop. Annual or perennial, erect herbs. Leaf-blades rather broad. Flowers in bractless scorpioid spikes. Sepals united at the base. Corolla white, with the anthers near the top of the very short tube. Style very short or wanting. Fruit much depressed, didymous by the nutlets uniting in pairs.—About 10 species, tropical American.

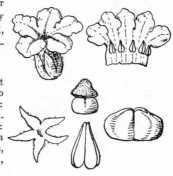

1. S. angiosperma (Murr.) Britton. Plant annual, 2–12 dm. tall: leaf-blades elliptic to elliptic-lanceolate, 2–7 cm. long, veiny: calyx-lobes lanceolate to linear, 1–1.5 mm. long: corolla white; tube 1–1.5 mm. long: fruit about 2 mm. wide. [*Heliotropium parviflorum* L.]—Hammocks and pinelands, S pen. Fla. and Florida Keys.—(*W. I., Mex., C. A., S. A.*)

8. COCHRANEA Miers. Perennial herbs, sometimes partially woody. Flowers in scorpioid cymose spikes. Sepals slightly united. Stamens adnate to the lower part of the corolla-tube. Style obsolete. Fruit 2-lobed, the typically 2-celled nutlets sometimes separating into 2 parts.—About 4 species, South American.

1. **C. anchusaefolia** (Poir.) Guerke. Plants often diffuse, 1–4 dm. tall: leaf-blades elliptic to linear-elliptic or oblanceolate, 2–8 cm. long, repand: calyx-lobes linear to linear-lanceolate, about 3 mm. long: corolla violet-blue or rose-purple; limb 4–6 mm. wide: fruits 2.5–3 mm. wide. [*Heliotropium anchusaefolium* Poir.]—Waste-places, roadsides, and cult. grounds, Coastal Plain, Fla. to Tex. and Ga. Nat. of S. Am.

FAMILY 10. **VERBENACEAE** — VERVAIN FAMILY

Herbs, shrubs, or trees. Stems commonly angled. Leaves alternate, opposite, or whorled: blades simple or rarely compound. Calyx of 4 or 5 partially or wholly united sepals. Corolla of 4 or 5 partially united petals, sometimes 2-lipped. Androecium of 2 or 4 stamens, the filaments more or less adnate to the corolla-tube. Gynoecium 2–4-carpellary, the style terminal. Fruit baccate or drupaceous or an aggregate of 2 or 4 nutlets.—About 75 genera and 1,300 species, of wide geographic distribution.

Inflorescence centripetal, spicate, racemose, or paniculate: ovules erect.
　　　　　　　　　　　　　　　　　　　　　　　　Tribe I. VERBENEAE.
Inflorescence centrifugal, cymose: ovules laterally attached. 　II. VITICEAE.

I. VERBENEAE
Flowers in heads, spikes or spike-like racemes.
　Fruit of 2 or 4 nutlets, dry.
　　Stamens 4: fruit not imbedded in the rachis.
　　　Fruit nut-like, with a broad cap-like beak. 　1. STYLODON.
　　　Fruit of 2 or 4 nutlets, not beaked.
　　　　Nutlets 4, not flattened.
　　　　　Anthers unappendaged: spikes elongate at anthesis. 　2. VERBENA.
　　　　　Anthers of the larger stamens appendaged on the back: spikes flat-topped at anthesis, elongating in fruit. 　3. GLANDULARIA.
　　　　Nutlets 2, more or less flattened.
　　　　　Calyx not inflated at maturity.
　　　　　　Herbs with procumbent or creeping stems, sometimes partly woody below. 　4. PHYLA.
　　　　　　Shrubs or shrubby plants, with upright stems. 　5. GONIOSTACHYUM.
　　　　　Calyx inflated and inclosing the fruit. 　6. PRIVA.
　　Stamens 2: fruit imbedded in excavations of the thick rachis. 　7. VALERIANOIDES.
　Fruit drupaceous. 　8. LANTANA.
Flowers in open racemes.
　Drupe seated in the calyx: nutlets 2: stigma 2-lobed. 　9. CITHAREXYLUM.
　Drupe enclosed in the calyx: nutlets 4: stigma 4-lobed. 　10. DURANTA.

II. VITICEAE
Corolla regular: leaf-blades simple. 　11. CALLICARPA.
Corolla irregular.

Drupe with 4 stones: leaf-blades simple.
Corolla short, the tube not much longer than the limb. 12. CLERODENDRON.
Corolla elongate, the tube several times longer than
the limb. 13. SIPHONANTHUS.
Drupe with a single 4-celled stone: leaf-blades compound. 14. VITEX.

1. **STYLODON** Raf. Perennial scabrous herbs. Leaf-blades serrate, sessile. Flowers in elongate, inconspicuously bracted spikes. Calyx tubular-campanulate, sharply 5–lobed. Corolla col-ored, rarely white, salverform: lobes 5, un-equal. Anthers unappendaged. Fruit nut-like, ridged, with 4 broad plain surfaces at the top which form a cap.—One species.

1. **S. carolinensis** (Walt.) Small. Stem slightly decumbent, 2–8 dm. tall, rough-pubescent: leaves 2–10 cm. long; blades of the lower ones spatulate to obovate or elliptic, those of the upper narrowly elliptic to lanceolate: spikes interrupted: calyx be-coming about 4 mm. long: corolla pink, purplish, or white; limb 5–6 mm. wide: fruit ovoid or oval, 3 mm. long. [*Phryma caroliniensis* Walt. *Verbena caroliniana* Michx.]—Sandy soil, often in woods and thickets, Coastal Plain and adj. provinces, Fla. to Miss. (La.?) and N. C.—Spr.–fall.

2. **VERBENA** [Tourn.] L. Annual, biennial, or perennial herbs. Leaf-blades entire, toothed or parted. Flowers in elongate, often very slender spikes, the bracts narrow. Calyx mainly tubular, 5-lobed. Corolla white or colored, salverform: lobes 5, unequal. Anthers unappendaged. Fruit an aggregate of 4, often narrow, readily separable nutlets filling the calyx.—About 75 species, American.—Sum.—VERBENAS. VERVAINS.

Spikes slender, sometimes very slender, continuous or interrupted, often greatly
  elongate.
  Leaf-blades toothed or incised. I. HASTATAE.
  Leaf-blades 1–2-pinnately cleft or parted.
    Bracts shorter than the calyx: plants erect. II. OFFICINALES.
    Bracts much longer than the calyx: plants prostrate or
      procumbent. III. BRACTEOSAE.
Spikes permanently short and stout.
  Bracts shorter than the mature calyx: corolla-tube less than
    twice as long as the calyx. IV. BONARIENSES.
  Bracts longer than the mature calyx: corolla-tube over
    twice as long as the calyx. V. VENOSAE.

I. HASTATAE

Spikes permanently continuous by the imbricate fruits.
  Spikes sessile or nearly so: corolla-limb 8–9 mm. wide: plants densely soft-
    pubescent. 1. *V. stricta.*
  Spikes peduncled: corolla-limb 2.5–6 mm. wide: plants
    sparingly pubescent or glabrous.
    Leaf-blades lanceolate to ovate-lanceolate: nutlets
      smooth or nearly so. 2. *V. hastata.*
    Leaf-blades linear-spatulate to linear: nutlets reticu-
      late. 3. *V. angustifolia.*
Spikes becoming interrupted, the fruits at least, not imbricate.
  Leaf-blades sessile, a spatulate type predominating. 4. *V. littoralis.*
  Leaf-blades petioled, an ovate type predominating.
    Sepals little longer than the fruit, the tips not meet-
      ing over the top. 5. *V. urticaefolia.*
    Sepals much longer than the fruit, the tips converging
      over its top and meeting. 6. *V. scabra.*

II. Officinales

Stem coarsely hirsute: flowers approximate in the spike: corolla-limb usually over 6 mm. wide: leaf-blades sessile or very short wing-petioled.   7. *V. Xutha.*

Stem glabrous or glabrate: flowers widely separated in the spike: corolla-limb usually 6 mm. wide or less: leaf-blades distinctly petioled.

Leaf-blades with blunt, rounded, or abruptly acute tips.

     Corolla-limb about 5–6 mm. wide: nutlets fully thrice as long as thick.   8. *V. Halei.*

     Corolla-limb 3–4 mm. wide: nutlets twice as long as thick.   9. *V. officinalis.*

Leaf-blades with long-tapering acute tips.   10. *V. riparia.*

III. Bracteosae

Annual plants, often forming mats: spikes leafy-bracted.   11. *V. bracteosa.*

IV. Bonarienses

Leaf-blades sessile: nutlets reticulate at the top.   12. *V. brasiliensis.*

Leaf-blades clasping: nutlets reticulate to below the middle.   13. *V. bonariensis.*

V. Venosae

Stems rigid from horizontal rootstocks: leaf-blades saliently toothed, conspicuously veined.   14. *V. rigida.*

1. V. stricta Vent. Perennial, 2–12 dm. tall, densely pale-pubescent: leaves 3–10 cm. long; blades suborbicular, oval, or elliptic, serrate or incised: spikes compact and long: calyx becoming 5 mm. long: corolla deep-blue or purple; limb 8–9 mm. wide: nutlets ellipsoid, 2.5 mm. long, or sometimes longer.—(Hoary-verbena.)—Prairies, barrens, fields, and roadsides, various provinces, Tenn. to Tex., N. Mex., Wyo., and Ont. Introduced E.—Sum.-fall.

2. V. hastata L. Perennial, 4–15 dm. tall, roughish-pubescent: leaves 4–14 cm. long: blades lanceolate, elliptic-lanceolate, or ovate-lanceolate, sharply serrate and often incised or hastate at the base: spikes relatively slender and compact: calyx becoming 2.5 mm. long: corolla blue-violet; limb 2.5–3.5 mm. wide: nutlets linear, 1.5–2 mm. long.—(Blue-verbena.)—Moist fields and meadows, various provinces, Fla. to N. M., B. C., Ont., and N. S.—Sum.

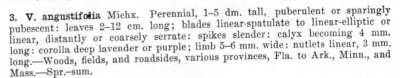

3. V. angustifolia Michx. Perennial, 1–5 dm. tall, puberulent or sparingly pubescent: leaves 2–12 cm. long; blades linear-spatulate to linear-elliptic or linear, distantly or coarsely serrate: spikes slender: calyx becoming 4 mm. long: corolla deep lavender or purple; limb 5–6 mm. wide: nutlets linear, 3 mm. long.—Woods, fields, and roadsides, various provinces, Fla. to Ark., Minn., and Mass.—Spr.–sum.

4. V. littoralis H.B.K. Perennial, 3–10 dm. tall, slightly rough-pubescent: leaves 2–8 cm. long; blades spatulate, or on shoots varying to narrowly elliptic to elliptic-lanceolate, serrate: spikes slender: calyx becoming 2 mm. long: corolla light-blue or purple; limb about 3 mm. wide: nutlets broadly linear, fully 1.5 mm. long.—Dry soil, along bayous and ditches, La. Nat. of S. A.—Spr.–sum.

5. V. urticaefolia L. Annual or perennial, 4–15 dm. tall, pubescent; leaves 8–21 cm. long; blades broadly lanceolate to ovate-lanceolate, or sometimes ovate to oval, coarsely crenate-serrate: spikes loosely-fruited: calyx becoming 2 mm.

long: corolla white: limb 3–4 mm. wide: nutlets ellipsoid, 1.5–2 mm. long.—
(WHITE-VERBENA.)—Thickets, moist fields, and meadows, various provinces,
Fla. to Tex., Minn., and N. B.—Sum.

6. V. scabra Vahl. Similar to *V. urticaefolia* in habit, the leaves relatively
smaller, and blades thicker and commonly less gradually acute or acuminate:
spikes closely fruited: calyx becoming 2 mm. long: corolla white or pinkish;
limb 2–3 mm. wide: nutlets ellipsoid, about 1.5 mm. long.—Low grounds or
sandy soil, Coastal Plain and Basin-and-Range Province, Fla. to Tex., and Calif.
—(*W. I., Mex., C. A., S. A.*)—Spr.–fall.

7. V. xutha Lehm. Perennial, 5–15 dm. tall, coarsely hirsute: leaves 4–10
cm. long; blades incised-pinnatifid, or 3-parted on the lower part of the stem,
the veins very prominent and hirsute beneath: spikes very long, not branched
or but little so, proportionately slender: calyx becoming 4 mm. long; lobes
converging over the nutlets: corolla purplish-lavender; limb 5–7 mm. wide:
nutlets linear-cylindric, 2–2.25 mm. long.—Prairies, arroyos, stream banks, roadsides, waste-places, and bayou-banks, various provinces, Miss. to Tex. and Calif.
Has been found on ballast at Mobile, Ala.—(*Mex.*)—Spr.–fall.

8. V. Halei Small. Biennial, 3–10 dm. tall, sparingly pubescent below: leaves
3–10 cm. long, pubescent, especially so beneath; blades of the lower leaves
elliptic to ovate, deeply incised-pinnatifid, often 3-parted or incised-pinnate;
those of the upper stem-leaves linear to linear-spatulate, sparingly toothed or
entire: spikes slender, usually much-branched: calyx becoming 3–3.5 mm. long,
strigillose: corolla deep-lavender; limb 4–5 mm. wide: nutlets linear-cylindric,
about 2.5 mm. long.—Prairies, stream-banks, roadsides, waste-places and bayou-
banks, various provinces, Miss. to Tex. and Okla.—Spr.–fall.

9. V. officinalis L. Annual, 2–6 dm. tall, glabrous or nearly so: leaves 2–6
cm. long; blades of the lower ones 1–2-pinnatifid and incised: spikes very
slender: calyx 2 mm. long: corolla blue or purple; tube mostly less than 3 mm.
long; lobes mainly rounded: nutlets broadly ellipsoid, about 1.5 mm. long.—
(EUROPEAN-VERBENA.)—Roadsides, fields, and waste-places, various provinces,
Fla. to Tex., Calif., and Tenn. Nat. of Eu.—(*W. I.*)—Spr.–fall.

10. V. riparia Raf. Annual, 6–15 dm. tall, sparingly pubescent: leaves 4–14
cm. long; blades of the lower ones 3-parted or 1–2-pinnatifid: spikes slender:
calyx becoming 3 mm. long: corolla light blue; tube mostly over 3 mm. long;
lobes emarginate or notched: nutlets ellipsoid, about 2 mm. long.—River banks,
Piedmont, N. C. to N. J.—Spr.–sum.

11. V. bracteosa Michx. Annual, the prostrate or procumbent branches 1–5
dm. long, hirsute: leaves 1–6.5 cm. long; blades pinnatifid, 2–3 cm. long:
spikes thick, sessile, continuous or mainly so: calyx becoming 3–4 mm. long:
corolla purple or bluish; limb 2–2.5 mm. wide: nutlets linear, 2–2.5 mm. long.
—Prairies, roadsides, fields, pastures, and waste-places, various provinces, Fla.
to Tex., Calif., B. C., Minn., and Va.—Spr.–sum.—A verbena native in the
Mediterranean region, *V. supina* L. with finely divided leaf-blades, short-bracts,
and a calyx about equalling the very thick fruit, occurs on ballast at Mobile,
Ala.

12. V. brasiliensis Vellozo. Annual, 6–25 dm. tall, finely pubescent above:
leaves 3–8 cm. long; blades elliptic to linear-elliptic or lanceolate, sharply
serrate at least above the middle: spikes not crowded: calyx becoming 3.5
mm. long or longer: corolla purple or lilac: limb about 2.5 mm. wide: nutlets
narrowly ellipsoid, 1.5 mm. long.—Waste-places and dry sandy soil, Coastal
Plain, La. Nat. of trop. Am.—Sum.

13. V. bonariensis L. Annual, 6–20 dm. tall, villous-hirsute above: leaves 4–
10 cm. long; blades elliptic to elliptic-lanceolate, broadly serrate at least above

the middle: spikes crowded: calyx becoming 3.5 mm. long: corolla purplish, or rarely white: limb about 2 mm. wide: nutlets narrowly ellipsoid, 2 mm. long.—Waste-places, roadsides, and banks, Coastal Plain, Ala. to Ark. and S. C.—Nat. of S. Am.—Spr.–sum.—This and the following species are among the most conspicuous weeds of Louisiana.

14. **V. rigida** (L.) Spreng. Perennial, the stem and branches decumbent, 2–6 dm. tall, rough-pubescent: leaves 4–12 cm. long; blades obovate, oblanceolate, or spatulate at the base of the stem, elliptic to elliptic-lanceolate or lanceolate above, with flaring coarse teeth, prominently veined, sessile and partly clasping at the base: spikes stout, continuous: calyx becoming 4–5 mm. long: corolla deep-purple, rarely paler; tube fully twice as long as the calyx; limb 6–11 mm. wide: nutlets ellipsoid, 2 mm. long. [*V. venosa* Gillies & Hook.] —Waste-places, Coastal Plain, W Fla. to Tex. and N. C. Nat. of S. Am.— Spr.–sum.—This plant forms large, spreading patches of brilliant purple along roadsides and in waste-places in Louisiana and Texas.

3. **GLANDULARIA** J. F. Gmel. Annual or (ours) perennial herbs. Leaf-blades coarsely toothed to dissected. Flowers in depressed capitate spikes which elongate somewhat in age. Calyx tubular, 5-lobed. Corolla white or colored, salverform. Anthers of the longer stamens with an appendaged connective. Fruit an aggregate of 4 nutlets in the bottom of the calyx.—About 25 species, American.—VERBENAS.

Corolla rose-purple, pink, or white.
  Leaf-blades toothed, incised, lobed, or pinnatifid, the segments broad.
    Tip of the longer calyx-lobes subulate, 1 mm. long.   1. *G. maritima.*
    Tip of the longer calyx-lobes bristle-like, 2–3 mm. long.
      Leaf-blades pinnatifid or incised-pinnatifid: nutlets
        2.5–3 mm. long, stout, pitted from near the
        base to the apex.
        Leaf-blades 1-pinnatifid: calyx 12 mm. long or
        more.
          Leaf-blades lanceolate to ovate-lanceolate,
          cuneate at the base.   2. *G. Lambertii.*
          Leaf-blades broadly ovate to deltoid, cordate
          or broadly truncate at the base.   3. *G. canadensis.*
        Leaf-blades 2-pinnatifid: calyx 10 mm. long or
        less.   4. *G. Drummondii.*
  Leaf-blades serrate or incised-serrate: nutlets about
    4 mm. long, slender, pitted from about the mid-
    dle to the apex.   5. *G. tampensis.*
  Leaf-blades pinnatisect, the segments narrowly linear to
    subulate.   6. *G. tenuisecta.*
Corolla red.   7. *G. peruviana.*

1. **G. maritima** Small. Stem and branches diffuse or widely creeping, 2–20 dm. long, often sparingly short-pubescent: leaf-blades cuneate to orbicular-obovate or ovate, 1–4 cm. long, incised, few-toothed, or lobed: calyx 10–12 mm. long, the larger lobes subulate-lanceolate: corolla rose-purple or bright-purple; tube 2 cm. long or nearly so: nutlets slender, about 4 mm. long. —Hammocks, pinelands, and Coastal sand-dunes, S pen. Fla.—All year.

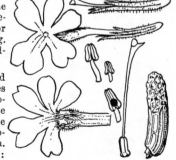

2. **G. Lambertii** (Sims) Small. Stem and branches 3–6 dm. long, hirsute: leaf-blades typically lanceolate, sometimes ovate-lanceolate, 3–9 cm. long, incised-pinnatifid, acute or acuminate at the apex, cuneate at the base: calyx becoming 11–13 mm. long: corolla showy, rose-purple; tube about 1.5 cm. long; lobes rounded or slightly notched:

nutlets mostly 3 mm. long, evenly fine-pitted.—Open woods, Coastal Plain and adj. provinces, Fla. to Tex., Ark., and S. C.—Spr.–sum.

3. G. canadensis (L.) Small. Stem and branches 3–6 dm. long, minutely pubescent: leaf-blades 3–8 cm. long, typically ovate or deltoid, incised-pinnatifid, rather rounded at the apex, truncate at the base: calyx becoming 13–16 mm. long: corolla showy, rose-purple; tube about 2 cm. long; lobes emarginate: nutlets about 3 mm. long, irregularly coarse-pitted. [*Verbena Aubletia* Jacq. *V. canadensis* Britton]—Prairies, roadsides, and thickets, various provinces, Fla. to Tex., Ill., and Va.—Spr.–sum.—Does not grow naturally in Canada.

4. G. Drummondii (Lindl.) Small. Stem and branches 2–4 dm. long, hirsute: leaf-blades 2–5 cm. long, ovate in outline, 2-pinnatifid, the segments typically narrow: calyx becoming 9–10 mm. long: corolla showy, rose-purple; tube about 1–1.5 cm. long; lobes commonly emarginate: nutlets about 3 mm. long, evenly fine-pitted. [*Verbena Drummondii* Baxt.]—Prairies, sandy bottoms, and woods, various provinces, La. to N. M., Kans., and Va.—Spr.–sum.

5. G. tampensis (Nash) Small. Stem and branches ascending or decumbent, 2–6 dm. long, usually minutely pubescent: leaf-blades lanceolate to elliptic or ovate, 2–8 cm. long, coarsely serrate or incised-serrate: calyx 12–15 mm. long, the longer lobes setaceous-subulate: corolla purple: tube fully 1.5 cm. long: nutlets 4 mm. long, coarsely pitted from the middle to the apex. [*Verbena tampensis* Nash]—Sandy hammocks, pen. Fla.—Spr.–fall.

6. G. tenuisecta (Briq.) Small. Stem and branches decumbent or procumbent, strigillose: leaf-segments narrowly linear to subulate, strigillose, diverging: calyx 9–10 mm. long; lobes short-setaceous: corolla small but showy, rose-purple, pink, or white; tube about 1 cm. long; lobes notched: nutlets 3.5 mm. long, pitted above the middle. [*Verbena tenuisecta* Briq.]—Sandy woods, clay soil and waste-places, Coastal Plain, Fla. and Ga. to La. Nat. of S. A.—Sum.–fall, or all year S.—This is the species commonly known as *Verbena erinoides* or MOSS VERBENA.

7. G. peruviana (L.) Small. Stem and branches decumbent and creeping, finely hirsute: leaf-blades ovate to elliptic-ovate, 1.5–5 cm. long, serrate, veiny: calyx about 1.5 cm. long, the larger lobes with short subulate tips: corolla red; tube about 2 cm. long; lobes notched: nutlets about 4 mm. long, striate-ribbed below the middle, cross-ribbed above it. [*Verbena chamaedrifolia* Juss.]—Hammocks and roadsides, pen. Fla. Nat. of S. Am.—(*W. I., Mex., C. A.*)—Spr.–fall.

4. PHYLA Lour. Perennial procumbent or creeping herbs. Leaf-blades toothed or lobed. Flowers in congested axillary spikes, the bracts cuneate to flabellate. Calyx short, flattened, 2-lobed. Corolla 2-lipped: tube slightly exceeding the calyx. Fruit as broad as long.—About 30 species, mostly in tropical America.—FOG-FRUITS. FROG-FRUITS.

Plant herbaceous: leaf-blades not rugose.
  Leaf-blades mostly broadest above the middle, toothed from above the middle to the apex: calyx-lobes shorter than the tube: fruit pubescent at the apex.   1. *P. nodiflora.*
  Leaf-blades mostly broadest below the middle, toothed from below the middle to the apex: calyx-lobes longer than the tube: fruit glabrous.   2. *P. lanceolata.*
Plant partly woody below: leaf-blades rugose.   3. *P. stoechadifolia.*

1. P. nodiflora (L.) Greene. Plants soft-strigillose, with creeping branches 2–13 dm. long: leaf-blades spatulate, 1–3 cm. long: spikes 10–30 mm. long:

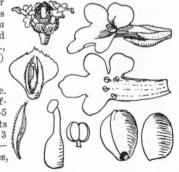

calyx about 2 mm. long: corolla purplish or nearly white, about 2 mm. long: fruits about 1 mm. long. [*Lippia nodiflora* Michx.] — (CAPE-WEED.) — Hammocks and low sandy places, Coastal Plain, Fla. to Tex., Mo., and N. C.—(*W. I., Mex., C. A., S. A.*) —All year.

2. **P. lanceolata** (Michx.) Greene. Branches creeping, 1-4 dm. long: leaf-blades elliptic-lanceolate to lanceolate, 1.5-5 cm. long: spikes 9-15 mm. long; bracts erose-ciliolate: corolla bluish-white, about 3 mm. long. [*Lippia lanceolata* Michx.]— River-banks and shores, various provinces, Fla. to Tex., Minn., and N. J.—Spr.–sum.

3. **P. stoechadifolia** (L.) Small. Plant rough-strigillose, diffuse or with vine-like branches: leaf-blades thick, narrowly elliptic to lanceolate, 2-12 cm. long, acute, serrate, rugose, the veins impressed above, prominent beneath: heads globose or depressed, becoming cylindric, sometimes elongate: calyx 2-2.5 mm. long: corolla purplish, about 3 mm. long: fruit 1.5-2 mm. long. [*Lippia stoechadifolia* H.B.K.]—Prairies, Everglade Keys, Fla.—(*W. I.*)—All year.

5. **GONIOSTACHYUM** Small. Shrubs or shrubby plants. Leaf-blades mostly toothed. Flowers in congested axillary spikes, the bracts 4-ranked, of an ovate type, keeled. Calyx flattened, 2-lobed. Corolla 2-lipped: tube glabrous within, much longer than the calyx.—Six or 8 species, in tropical America.

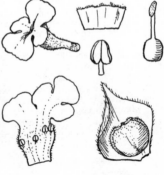

1. **G. citrosum** Small. Stems pale-gray or whitish: leaf-blades lanceolate to elliptic-lanceolate, 2.5-6 cm. long, shallowly serrate, pubescent: spikes depressed, short-peduncled, 4-6 mm. long: bracts ovate: calyx about 1 mm. long: corolla white, about 4.5 mm. long; limb about 3 mm. broad: nutlets 1.5 mm. wide.—Hammocks, Everglade Keys, Fla.—(*W. I.*)—All year.

6. **PRIVA** Adans. Perennial herbs. Leaf-blades thin, toothed. Flowers in elongate slender spikes or racemes. Calyx 5-lobed. Corolla white or lavender, slightly 2-lipped. Stamens 4. Staminodia minute or obsolete. Nutlets tuberculate or spiny.— About 10 species, of tropical regions.

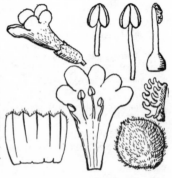

1. **P. lappulacea** (L.) Pers. Stems 2-6 dm. tall, pubescent: leaf-blades ovate, 2-10 cm. long, serrate: racemes loose-flowered: calyx with minute lobes: corolla-lobes rounded: fruit ovoid-pyramidal, included, the nutlets 3-4 mm. long, spiny-tuberculate. [*P. echinata* Juss.]—(VELVET-BUR.)—Hammocks and cult. grounds, Key West, Fla.— (*W. I., Mex., C. A., S. A.*).

Bonchea prismatica (Jacq.) Kuntze, an annual resembling *Valerianoides*, but with four perfect stamens, has been found on ballast at Mobile Bay.

7. VALERIANOIDES Boerh.   Herbs, or shrubby plants.   Leaf-blades toothed.   Flowers sessile on a stout rachis or in excavations.   Calyx often unequally 5-lobed, scarcely accrescent.   Corolla white or colored, salverform, slightly 2-lipped.   Stamens 2.   Staminodia 2.—About 40 species, of tropic regions.

1. V. jamaicensis (L.) Kuntze.   Plants with spreading or decumbent branches, 6–15 dm. long: leaf-blades elliptic, ovate, or oval, 2–8 cm. long: spikes virgate, quill-like: corolla blue-violet, 8–11 mm. long; limb 7–8.5 mm. wide.   [*Stachytarpheta jamaicensis* (L.) Vahl]—Pinelands, coastal sand-dunes, and waste-places, S pen. Fla., Florida Keys, and S Ala.—(*W. I., Mex., C. A., S. A.*)

8. LANTANA L.   Shrubs or rarely herbs, sometimes prickle-armed. Leaf-blades toothed.   Flowers in congested, flat-topped spikes.   Calyx shallowly 2–5-lobed or truncate.   Corolla white or colored: tube slightly curved: limb irregular.   Stamens 4.   Drupes more or less juicy.—About 60 species, in warm and tropical regions.—Spr.–fall or all year S.—Shrub-verbenas.

Flower-heads bracted, but not involucrate.
  Stem and branches prickle-armed: leaf-blades strigose: corolla-tube over 12 mm. long.
    Stems and branches sparingly armed with weak more or less curved prickles: corollas yellow to orange.   1. *L. Camara.*
    Stems and branches copiously armed with stout, rigid, hooked prickles: corollas yellow to purple.   2. *L. aculeata.*
  Stem and branches not prickle-armed: leaf-blades not strigose: corolla-tube 10 mm. long or less.
    Plants with prostrate stems and branches: drupes 2.5–3.5 mm. long.   3. *L. depressa.*
    Plants with erect stems and branches: drupes 4–5 mm. long.   4. *L. ovatifolia.*
Flower-heads decidedly involucrate.
  Leaf-blades acute or acutish, coarsely toothed: corolla-tube about 10 mm. long.   5. *L. Selloviana.*
  Leaf-blades rounded or retuse at the apex, crenulate: corolla-tube 2–4 mm. long.   6. *L. involucrata.*

1. L. Camara L.   Shrub with armed branches, 10–15 dm. tall: leaf-blades ovate to elliptic-ovate, 2–7 cm. long; corolla usually cream, yellow or pink, later changing to orange or scarlet; limb 6–8 mm. high.—Two forms of this species occur in Florida: one with acuminate leaf-blades, derived from plants commonly in cultivation apparently from the West Indies, the other a native plant with obtuse, relatively coarser-toothed leaf-blades.—In sandy soil, Coastal Plain, Fla. to Tex., and Ga.

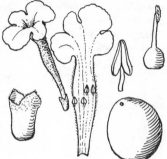

2. L. aculeata L.   Shrub with copiously and rigidly armed branches, 2.5 dm. tall or less: leaf-blades ovate, often broadly so, 3–6 cm. long: corolla yellow, changing to orange or purple; limb 7–9 mm. high.—Pinelands, and cult. grounds, pen. Fla.   Nat. of W. I.

3. L. depressa Small. Shrub with unarmed prostrate branches, 2–11 dm. long: leaf-blades ovate to elliptic, 1–3.5 cm. long: spikes less than 2.5 cm. wide: corolla yellow; tube 5–6 mm. long; stone of the drupe globose, 2.5–3.5 mm. long, scarcely beaked.—Pinelands, Everglade Keys, Fla.

4. L. ovatifolia Britton. Shrub 2 m. tall or less: leaf-blades ovate, 3–7 cm. long, crenate-serrate: spikes over 2.5 cm. wide: corolla yellow; tube 9–10 mm. long: stone of the drupe ovoid, 4–5 mm. long, beaked.—Hammocks, S. pen. Fla.—(*W. I.*)

5. L. Sellowiana Link & Otto. Shrub 3–18 dm. tall, with tomentulose foliage: leaf-blades ovate, oval, or elliptic-ovate, 1–3 cm. long, abruptly narrowed or truncate at the base: corolla magenta or lilac; tube puberulent; limb 8–18 mm. high, the lower lobe elongate.—(POLECAT-GERANIUM. WEEPING-LANTANA.)— Roadsides, waste-places, pinelands, and woods, Fla. Nat. of S. A.—(*W. I.*)

6. L. involucrata L. Shrub 4–17 dm. tall, with puberulent or tomentulose foliage: leaf-blades oval, obovate, to suborbicular, 1–3 cm. long, usually cuneate at the base: outer bracts of the involucre 4–7 mm. long, ciliolate: calyx becoming 1.5 mm. long: corolla white or pale-purple; tube 2–4 mm. long; limb 2–4 mm. high. [*L. odorata* L.]—(SAGE.)—Pinelands, hammocks, sand dunes, S pen. Fla. and Florida Keys; S Tex.—(*W. I., Mex., C. A., S. A.*)

9. CITHAREXYLUM L. Shrubs or trees, sometimes spiny. Leaf-blades mainly entire. Flowers in clusters or long spikes. Calyx obscurely 5-lobed. Corolla mainly white: tube straight or nearly so: limb slightly oblique, nearly equally 5-lobed. Staminodium present. Stigma 2-lobed. Nutlets 2.—About 20 species, tropic American.

1. C. fruticosum L. Shrub or small tree, with softly pubescent twigs: leaves 5–15 cm. long; blades elliptic or oblong-obovate, veiny: flowers in spikes or racemes: fruit black, 9–10 mm. in diameter. [*C. villosum* Jacq.] — (FIDDLEWOOD.) — Hammocks and pinelands, S pen. Fla. and Florida Keys.— (*W. I.*)—All year.

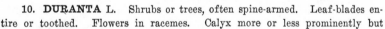

10. DURANTA L. Shrubs or trees, often spine-armed. Leaf-blades entire or toothed. Flowers in racemes. Calyx more or less prominently but minutely 5-lobed, the tube plicate. Corolla salverform or funnelform: tube mainly curved: limb slightly unequally 5-lobed, Staminodium mostly obsolete. Stigma 4-lobed or capitate. Nutlets 4. — About 8 species, tropic American.

1. D. repens L. Shrub or small tree: leaf-blades ovate-elliptic, oval or obovate, 1.5–5 cm. long: racemes 5–15 cm. long, recurving: calyx 3–4 mm. long, angled: corolla lilac or white; limb 7–9 mm. wide, the lobes ciliolate, the lower ones with magenta spots: fruit 7–11 mm. in diameter, enclosed in the

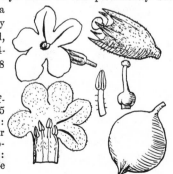

calyx. [*D. Plumieri* Jacq.]—(GOLDEN-DEWDROP.)—Hammocks, Everglade Keys, Fla. and Florida Keys.—(*W. I., Mex., C. A., S. A.*)—The accrescent calyx becomes golden-yellow.

11. CALLICARPA L. Shrubs or trees. Leaf-blades simple. Flowers in axillary cymes. Calyx shallowly 4-lobed or nearly truncate. Corolla white or colored, rotate-funnelform or funnelform, typically 4-lobed, the tube straight. Filaments adnate to the corolla-tube, glabrous. Stigmas stout. Drupe very juicy.—About 35 species, American, Asiatic, and African.—BEAUTY-BERRIES.

1. **C. americana** L. Shrub 1–2 m. tall, or a vine, stellate-pubescent: leaf-blades ovate, elliptic or oval, serrate: calyx 1–1.5 mm. long: corolla bluish or pink; limb about 5 mm. wide, the rounded lobes apiculate: fruit violet or magenta, 4–5 mm. in diameter.—(FRENCH-MULBERRY.)—Woods, thickets, hammocks and pinelands, Coastal Plain and adj. provinces, Fla. to Tex., Ark., and S Va.—Spr.–fall, or all year northward.—There are white-flowered forms.

12. CLERODENDRON [Burm.] L. Shrubs or trees, or half-shrubs. Leaves opposite: blades simple, toothed. Flowers in dense terminal cymes. Calyx prominently 5-lobed. Corolla white or highly colored, funnelform or salverform: tube slightly curved: limb 5-lobed. Filaments adnate to above the middle of the corolla-tube. Stigmas slender. Drupe lobed or ribbed.—About 100 species, in tropical regions.—GLORYBOWERS.—Spr.–fall, or all year S.

Corolla-tube slightly exceeding the calyx: calyx-lobes as long as the tube or longer.
1. *C. fragrans.*
Corolla-tube several times longer than the calyx: calyx-lobes shorter than the tube.
2. *C. foetidum.*

1. **C. fragrans** Vent. Shrub 1–3 m. tall: leaf-blades ovate to deltoid, 9–25 cm. long, mostly abruptly pointed, coarsely and irregularly toothed, finely pubescent beneath, truncate or shallowly cordate at the base, long-petioled: cymes congested: calyx 15–19 mm. long; lobes subulate or subulate-lanceolate, acuminate, ciliate: corolla 22–28 mm. long; lobes nearly as long as the tube, or shorter, white or blue-tinged.—Mostly represented by the form with double-flowers. —Thickets, roadsides, and waste-places, Fla. Nat. of eastern Asia.—(*W. I.*)

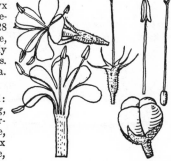

2. **C. foetidum** Bunge. Shrub 1–2 m. tall: leaf-blades deltoid-ovate, 6–15 cm. long, acute or slightly acuminate, serrate or serrate-dentate, mostly truncate at the base, long-petioled: cymes rather compact: calyx 5–6 mm. long; lobes triangular-lanceolate,

shorter than the tube: corolla 18–22 mm. long; tube very slender; lobes lilac or red-purple.—Fields and roadsides, Coastal Plain, N Fla. to La. Nat. of China.

13. **SIPHONANTHUS** L. Shrubs or half-shrubs. Leaf-blades simple, entire. Flowers in axillary cymes, sometimes aggregated in a panicle. Calyx loosely spreading. Corolla white or nearly so, slender-funnelform, 5-lobed, the tube curved. Filaments adnate to the middle of the corolla-tube. Stigmas slender. Drupe lobed.—About 6 species, natives of the Old World tropics.

1. **S. indicus** L. Plant 1–4 m. tall, the twigs glabrous: leaf-blades oblanceolate or elliptic oblanceolate to elliptic, 5–16 cm. long, entire, glabrous, short-petioled: calyx 13–16 mm. long; lobes ovate, obtuse: corolla 12–14 cm. long; lobes 12–15 mm. long: drupe 8–10 mm. long.—(TURK'S-TURBAN.) —Waste-places, roadsides, and woods, Coastal Plain, Fla. to Tex. and S. C. Nat. of E. I. and cult.—(W. I., Mex., S. A.)—The black fruits are conspicuous.

14. **VITEX** L. Shrubs or trees. Leaf-blades digitately compound or rarely 1-foliolate. Flowers in open terminal compound cymes. Calyx shallowly 3-lobed or 5-lobed. Corolla white or colored, funnelform, 2-lipped, the tube slightly curved. Filaments adnate to about the middle of the corolla-tube, pubescent at the base.—About 60 species, widely distributed in warm regions.

1. **V. Agnus-Castus** L. Shrub 1–3 m. tall, pale-pubescent: leaf-blades 7-foliolate, the leaflets with linear to linear-elliptic blades 2–10 cm. long: flowers separated: calyx 2–2.5 mm. long, campanulate: corolla blue or purplish; limb 5–6 mm. broad: fruits 3.5–4 mm. long.—(CHASTE-TREE.)—Roadsides, waste-places, and about gardens, Coastal Plain, Fla. to Tex., and N. C. Nat. of Old World, and cult.—(W. I.)—Spr.–fall.

FAMILY 11. **AVICENNIACEAE** — BLACK-MANGROVE FAMILY

Shrubs or trees of maritime regions, the branches terete, nodose. Leaves opposite, persistent: blades entire. Flowers in axillary and terminal small, long-peduncled cymes. Calyx of 5 nearly distinct sepals. Corolla of 4 partially united petals, campanulate-rotate. Androecium of 4 stamens, the filaments adnate to the lower part of the corolla-tube. Gynoecium of 2 united carpels. Fruit a compressed oblique capsule.— Only the following genus and 3 species, in tropical regions.

1. AVICENNIA L. Leaf-blades thick. Cymes peduncled. Calyx subtended by small bracts. Corolla inconspicuous, the tube and spreading lobes about equal in length. Stamens erect. Stigmas 2. Capsule thick-walled.

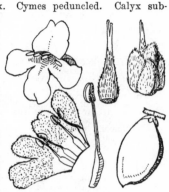

1. A. nitida Jacq. Shrub, or tree sometimes 25 m. tall: leaf-blades leathery, elliptic or nearly so, 3–8 cm. long, dark-green above, pale, minutely canescent beneath: calyx 3–4 mm. long: corolla white; lobes longer than the tube, broadly rounded or retuse: fruit ellipsoid, 3–5 cm. long, acutish. —(BLACK-MANGROVE.)—Sandy shores and coastal hammocks, Coastal Plain, Fla. to Tex.—(*W. I., Mex., C. A., S. A.*)—All year.

FAMILY 12. **PHRYMACEAE** — LOPSEED FAMILY

Perennial herbs, with angled stems. Leaves opposite: blades toothed. Flowers in slender spikes or spike-like racemes. Calyx of 5 partially united sepals, 2-lipped, the lower lip very short. Corolla white and magenta-tinged, of 5 partially united petals, 2-lipped, the lower lip 3-lobed. Androecium of 4 didynamous stamens. Gynoecium of 2 united carpels. Fruit an achene included in the deflexed accrescent calyx. Comprises only the following genus.

1. PHRYMA L. Caulescent herbs with spreading branches. Leaf-blades broad, coarsely toothed, petioled. Spikes or racemes elongate, the small flowers opposite. Achene in the bottom of the calyx. This genus is sometimes included in the Verbenaceae.

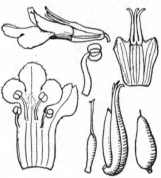

1. P. leptostachya L. Stems 3–10 dm. tall, sparingly branched above, reflexed-pubescent: leaf-blades ovate to elliptic-ovate or ovate-lanceolate, 3–15 cm. long: calyx 3–5 mm. long, accrescent; tube ribbed, little longer than the slender upper lobes during anthesis: corolla white and magenta-tinged, about 8 mm. long: achenes 4–5 mm. long. —(LOPSEED.)—Rich woods and thickets, various provinces, Fla., to Tex., Man., and N. B.—Sum.–fall. The same or a closely related species grows in eastern Asia.

FAMILY 13. **LAMIACEAE** — MINT FAMILY

Herbs or woody plants, often aromatic. Stems 4-sided. Leaves opposite or whorled: blades simple, entire, toothed, or lobed. Flowers perfect, in open or compact cymes. Calyx of 5 partially united sepals, regular or 2-lipped. Corolla of 5 partially united sepals, 2-lipped or nearly regular. Androecium of 2–4 stamens, the pairs often irregular. Gynoecium 2-carpellary. Ovary 4-celled. Fruit of 4 nutlets included in the calyx.—About 160 genera and 3,200 species, widely distributed in tropical and temperate regions. The foliage sometimes abounds in volatile oils.

Ovary of 4 united carpels, merely 4-lobed: style not basal: nutlets laterally or obliquely attached.   Tribe I. AJUGEAE.
Ovary of 4 distinct or nearly distinct carpels: style basal:
 nutlets basally attached.
  Calyx with a crest on the upper side or on the upper lip,
   the broad lips entire, closed in fruit.   II. SCUTELLARIEAE.
  Calyx without a crest on the upper side, the lips more or
   less lobed.
   Stamens included.
    Calyx with 10 narrow spreading or recurved lobes:
     corolla-tube included in the calyx: *Marrubium*
     in   III. STACHYDEAE.
    Calyx 2-lipped, the upper lip truncate or with 3
     broad lobes, the lower lip with 2 narrow lobes:
     corolla-tube exserted from the calyx. *Dicerandra*
     odoratissima in   V. SATUREIEAE.
   Stamens exserted.
    Corolla conspicuously 2-lipped: lips different, the
     upper concave.
     Anther-bearing stamens 4.   III. STACHYDEAE.
     Anther-bearing stamens 2.   IV. MONARDEAE.
    Corolla nearly regular, or if 2-lipped, the upper lip
     flat.
     Stamens 2 or 4; filaments straight and spread-
      ing, or converging under the upper lip of the
      corolla.   V. SATUREIEAE.
     Stamens 4, didynamous; lower pair longer, lying
      on the lower lip of the corolla.   VI. OCIMEAE.

I. AJUGEAE

Corolla markedly irregular, the middle lobe of the lower lip
 quite different from the other lobes: calyx 2-lipped.
 Corolla strongly bilateral, the upper lip split, very small,
  the lower lip large: stamens and style nearly straight. 1. TEUCRIUM.
 Corolla slightly bilateral, the middle lobe of the lower
  lip strongly declined: stamens and style strongly curved
  or coiled.   2. TRICHOSTEMA.
Corolla slightly irregular, the lobes of both lips nearly equal,
 spreading: calyx nearly regular.   3. ISANTHUS.

II. SCUTELLARIEAE

Perennial or rarely annual scentless herbs, with opposite
leaves and more or less 1-sided racemes or panicles.   4. SCUTELLARIA.

III. STACHYDEAE

Stamens included.   5. MARRUBIUM.
Stamens exserted.
 Upper pair of filaments longer than the lower.
  Anther-sacs parallel or nearly so.
   Upper pair of stamens declined, lower pair ascend-
    ing: erect herbs.   6. AGASTACHE.
   Upper and lower pair of stamens ascending: trail-
    ing herbs.   7. MEEHANIA.
  Anther-sacs diverging.
   Flowers in terminal raceme-like panicles: erect
    herbs.   8. NEPETA.
   Flowers in axillary clusters: creeping herbs. 9. GLECOMA.
 Upper pair of filaments shorter than the lower.
  Calyx manifestly 2-lipped.
   Upper lip of the calyx broad, with 3 lobes, the
    lower with 2 tooth-like lobes.   10. PRUNELLA.
   Upper lip of the calyx narrow, entire, the lower
    lip of 2 equal broad lobes.   11. MACBRIDEA.
  Calyx not 2-lipped, often slightly irregular, but the
   lobes essentially similar.
   Tube of the calyx faintly nerved, inflated at
    maturity.
    Calyx-lobes 5.   12. DRACOCEPHALUM.
    Calyx-lobes 4.   13. SYNANDRA.

Tube of the calyx prominently 5–10-nerved, not
  inflated at maturity.
  Anther-sacs transversely 2-valved.   14. GALEOPSIS.
  Anther-sacs not transversely 2-valved.
    Nutlets 3-sided, truncate above.
      Calyx-lobes not spine-tipped.   15. LAMIUM.
      Calyx-lobes spine-tipped.
        Calyx-lobes 5.   16. LEONURUS.
        Calyx-lobes 8–10.   17. LEONOTIS.
    Nutlets nearly terete, rounded above.   18. STACHYS.

IV. MONARDEAE

Connective of the anther elongate, bearing a perfect sac at
  one end and a rudimentary one at the other: calyx-throat
  glabrous or merely ciliate at the base of the lobes.   19. SALVIA.
Connective short: anther-sacs confluent.
  Calyx not 2-lipped; tube 15-ribbed; teeth nearly equal. 20. MONARDA.
  Calyx 2-lipped; tube 13-ribbed; teeth unequal.   21. BLEPHILIA.

V. SATUREIEAE

Flowers in axillary whorls or clusters; these sometimes
  forming terminal spike-like racemes or panicles.
  Corolla 2-lipped.
    Filaments curved, converging under the upper lip of
      the corolla.
      Anther-bearing stamens 2.
        Calyx gibbous; throat closed by hairs: corolla
          without folds in the throat.   22. HEDEOMA.
        Calyx not gibbous; throat not closed by hairs:
          corolla with 2 folds in the throat.   23. STACHYDEOMA.
      Anther-bearing stamens 4.
        Corolla-tube strongly bent.
          Anther-sacs divergent.   24. MELISSA.
          Anther-sacs parallel.   25. CONRADINA.
        Corolla-tube straight.
          Calyx with 5 nearly equal lobes, not or
            scarcely 2-lipped.
            Calyx-tube 10-ribbed.   26. PYCNOTHYMUS.
            Calyx-tube 13-ribbed.   27. MICROMERIA.
          Calyx 2-lipped.
            Anther-sacs awnless.   28. CLINOPODIUM.
            Anther-sacs awned.   29. DICERANDRA.
    Filaments straight, often spreading.
      Calyx-tube 15-nerved.   30. HYSSOPUS.
      Calyx-tube 10–13-nerved.
        Anther-bearing stamens 4.
          Anther-sacs divergent.
            Calyx equally 5-lobed: erect herbs.   31. ORIGANUM.
            Calyx 2-lipped: creeping herbs.   32. THYMUS.
          Anther-sacs parallel.   33. KOELLIA.
        Anther-bearing stamens 2.   34. MAPPIA.
  Corolla nearly regular, with 4–5 lobes.
    Anther-bearing stamens 2: foliage barely aromatic.   35. LYCOPUS.
    Anther-bearing stamens 4: foliage strongly aromatic. 36. MENTHA.
Flowers in loose terminal panicles.
  Lower lip of the corolla fringed: native plants.
    Anther-bearing stamens 4.   37. MICHELIELLA.
    Anther-bearing stamens 2.   38. COLLINSONIA.
  Lower lip of the corolla not fringed: naturalized plant. 39. PERILLA.

VI. OCIMEAE

Calyx with nearly equal lobes: corolla with a saccate drooping lower lip.   40. HYPTIS.
Calyx with a broad decurrent upper lobe: corolla-lips nearly
  equal in length.   41. OCIMUM.

1. TEUCRIUM [Tourn.] L. Perennial strict herbs. Leaf-blades toothed
Flowers in raceme-like panicles. Calyx 2-lipped. Corolla mainly pink, very
irregular: upper lip minute, split: lower lip 3-lobed, projecting beyond the
upper one: tube relatively long. Stamens lying against the upper side of the
corolla.—More than 100 species, widely distributed.—WOOD-SAGES. GERMAN-
DERS.

Leaf-blades mainly rounded at the base: stem closely canescent: broader calyx-lobes acute or acutish.   1. *T. canadense.*
Leaf-blades mainly narrowed at the base: stem downy-canescent:
    broader calyx-lobes obtuse.
      Calyx prominently ribbed at maturity: corolla glandular-
      puberulent.   2. *T. Nashii.*
      Calyx not ribbed at maturity: corolla pubescent.   3. *T. littorale.*

1. T. canadense L. Stem 2–12 dm. tall: leaf-blades relatively thin, ovate to elliptic-ovate, 6–14 cm. long, pubescent beneath: calyx becoming 6–8 mm. long; lower lobes acuminate: corolla purplish or pink, 15–20 mm. long: nutlets about 2.5 mm. long, wrinkled.—Low grounds, fields, river-banks, and roadsides, various provinces, Ga. to Tex., Minn., and Me.—Sum.

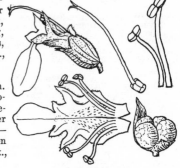

2. T. Nashii Kearney. Stem 3–14 dm. tall: leaf-blades narrowly elliptic to lanceolate, 4–14 cm. long, whitish-pubescent beneath: calyx becoming 6–7 mm. long; lower lobes blunt: corolla pink, 15–20 mm. long.— Hammocks, thickets, and wet grounds, often in calcareous soil, Coastal Plain, Fla. to Tex., and S. C.—Spr.–fall or all year S.

3. T. littorale Bicknell. Stem 3–5 dm. tall: leaf-blades narrowly elliptic to elliptic-lanceolate, 6–11 cm. long, pale or whitish-pubescent beneath: calyx becoming 5–6 mm. long; lower lobes acute: corolla pale-pink, 15–17 mm. long: nutlets 2 mm. long.—Low sandy soil, Coastal Plain and New England coast, Fla. to Me.—Sum.

2. TRICHOSTEMA L. Annual or perennial herbs or shrubby plants. Leaf-blades entire or repand. Flowers in axillary cymes. Calyx very irregular, 2-lipped. Corolla somewhat 2-lipped, the upper arching, sometimes surpassing the lower lip. Stamens lying against the lower corolla-lip.—About 10 species, North American.—The calyx becomes inverted in fruit.

Annual plant: leaf-blades of a linear or elliptic type.
    Foliage viscid-pubescent: leaf-blades elliptic or lanceolate.   1. *T. dichotomum.*
    Foliage glabrous or viscid-puberulent: leaf-blades linear.   2. *T. lineare.*
Perennial or biennial plant: leaf-blades of an obovate type.   3. *T. suffrutescens.*

1. T. dichotomum L. Plant 1–20 dm. tall: leaf-blades elliptic to broadlanceolate, 2–7 cm. long: calyx becoming 5–6 mm. long; lobes acuminate: corolla blue to white, about 5 mm. long: nutlets 1.5–2 mm. long.—(BASTARD-PENNYROYAL. BLUE-CURLS.)—Dry fields, thickets, hammocks and pinelands, various provinces, Fla. to Tex., Mo., and Me.—Sum., or all year S.

2. T. lineare Nutt. Plant 1–3 dm. tall: leaf-blades linear, 1–4 cm. long: calyx becoming 5–6 mm. long; corolla blue, sometimes pale, 6–10 mm. long: nutlets 1.5 mm. long.—Sandy soil, fields, thickets, Coastal Plain, and New England coast, Fla. to La., and Conn.—Sum.

3. T. suffrutescens Kearney. Plant 2–4 dm. tall: leaf-blades obovate to oblong-obovate,

0.5–1.5 cm. long: calyx becoming 5–6 mm. long; corolla deep-blue, 6–8 mm. long: nutlets 1.5 mm. long.—Scrub, Fla.—Spr.

3. **ISANTHUS** Michx. Annual herbs. Leaf-blades entire or sparingly toothed. Flowers in axillary cymes. Calyx nearly regular. Corolla nearly regular, the lobes spreading. Stamens slightly ascending.—One species.

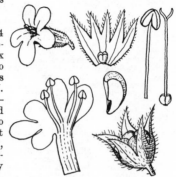

1. **I. brachiatus** (L.) B.S.P. Plant 1–4 dm. tall, viscid-pubescent: leaf-blades elliptic to linear-elliptic, 1–4 cm. long: calyx becoming 5–6 mm. long; lobes lanceolate to triangular-lanceolate: corolla blue; lobes mainly ovate: nutlets 2–2.5 mm. long. [*I. caeruleus* Michx.] — FALSE-PENNYROYAL. — Sandy soil along streams, dry fields, and calcareous rocks, various provinces, Ga. to Tex., Minn., and Que.—Sum.—This plant often acts after the manner of a fire-weed, taking almost complete possession of recently abandoned fields, especially on stony hillsides.

4. **SCUTELLARIA** L.[1] Annual or perennial herbs or shrubby plants. Leaf-blades entire or toothed. Flowers axillary or in racemes, variously colored, blue, violet, or white in our species. Calyx 2-lipped, the upper lip crested. Corolla with a long curved tube, 2-lipped, the upper lip arching.—About 100 species, widely distributed.—SKULLCAPS. HELMET-FLOWERS.

Nutlets wingless, on a low gynobase.
  Flowers in axillary, secund racemes.   I. LATERIFLORAE.
  Flowers solitary in the axils or in terminal panicles.
    Flowers solitary in the axils of the upper leaves, appearing raceme-like, but each pedicel bearing two bractlets at its base.   II. AMBIGUAE.
    Flowers in terminal or axillary panicles.
      Leaf-blades above the middle of the stem cordate.   III. CORDATAE.
      Leaf-blades above the middle of the stem abruptly or gradually narrowed at the base.
        Leaves all with toothed blades.   IV. SERRATAE.
        Leaves all, or those above the middle of stem with entire blades.   V. INTEGRIFOLIAE.
Nutlets membranous-winged, on a slender gynobase.   VI. NERVOSAE.

I. LATERIFLORAE

Slender plant with long axillary racemes of very small flowers.   1. *S. lateriflora.*

II. AMBIGUAE

Leaf-blades mainly toothed, lanceolate, cordate: corolla 1.5–2 cm. long.   2. *S. epilobifolia.*
Leaf-blades mainly entire, ovate or ovate-lanceolate: corolla less than 1.5 cm. long.
  Leaf-blades all distinctly petioled: roots fibrous.   3. *S. havanensis.*
  Leaf-blades (except basal ones) all sessile or nearly so: roots tuberous-thickened.
    Stem glabrous or puberulent: leaf-blades often revolute.   4. *S. ambigua.*
    Stem densely and softly glandular-pubescent: leaf-blades usually flat.   5. *S. parvula.*

III. CORDATAE

Foliage, especially the internodes of the stem and inflorescence, copiously pubescent.

[1] Contributed by Edward Johnston Alexander.

Larger leaves with petioles less than ½ as long as the
blades.
  Leaf-blades suborbicular to broadly ovate: inflores-
  cence pubescent with short close-set hairs.   6. *S. Ocmulgee.*
  Leaf-blades ovate to ovate-lanceolate, velvety: in-
  florescence pubescent with villous hairs.   7. *S. Cuthbertii.*
Larger leaves with petioles over ½ as long as the
blades.
  Corolla less than 15 mm. long.   8. *S. arguta.*
  Corolla over 15 mm. long.   9. *S. ovata.*
Foliage glabrous, or with scattered hairs at the nodes of
the stem and in the inflorescence.   10. *S. saxatilis.*

IV. SERRATAE

Corolla less than 2 cm. long.
  Leaf-blades glabrous above.
    Corolla pubescent: calyx not glandular-pubescent.   11. *S. incana.*
    Corolla glabrous or nearly so: calyx glandular-
    pubescent.   12. *S. alabamensis.*
  Leaf-blades pubescent above.
    Leaf-blades usually acute, serrate.   13. *S. Altamaha.*
    Leaf-blades usually obtuse, coarsely crenate.   14. *S. ovalifolia.*
Corolla over 2 cm. long.
  Foliage glabrous or nearly so: inflorescence not
  branched, appearing raceme-like.   15. *S. serrata.*
  Foliage, especially the stem, finely and closely pubes-
  cent: inflorescence branched, thus showing its
  paniculate character.
    Corolla between 2 and 2.5 cm. long.   16. *S. Mellichampii.*
    Corolla between 2.5 and 3 cm. long.
      Leaf-blades acute, relatively large: corolla nearly
      glabrous.   17. *S. montana.*
      Leaf-blades obtuse, relatively small: corolla
      pubescent.   18. *S. arenicola.*

V. INTEGRIFOLIAE

Upper lip of the corolla shorter than the throat.
  Leaf-blades and corollas glabrous or nearly so.   19. *S. glabriuscula.*
  Leaf-blades and corollas variously pubescent.
    Upper lip of the corolla exceeding the lower.   20. *S. integrifolia.*
    Upper lip of the corolla exceeded by the lower.   21. *S. multiglandulosa.*
Upper lip of the corolla longer than the throat.   22. *S. floridana.*

VI. NERVOSAE

Slender plant: blades of the lower leaves slender-petioled,
those of the upper ones sessile: bracts nearly entire.   23. *S. nervosa.*

1. S. lateriflora L. Plant erect or reclining, 2–10 dm. long, glabrous or
puberulent above: leaf-blades thinnish, ovate to ovate-lanceolate, 2–6 cm. long,
coarsely-serrate: flowers secund and crowded
in lateral racemes: calyx becoming 3–4 mm.
long: corolla 6–7 mm. long: nutlets about
1 mm. long.—(MAD-DOG SKULLCAP.)—Low
thickets, stream-banks, and swamps, various
provinces, Fla. to N. M., B. C., Ont., and
Newf.—Sum.-fall.

2. S. epilobifolia Hamilt. Plant 2–9 dm.
tall, sometimes finely pubescent: leaf-blades
lanceolate to ovate-lanceolate, 2–6 cm. long,
shallowly-serrate, very short petioled or sessile: calyx becoming 6–7 mm. long: corolla
15–20 mm. long; lower lip about 5 mm.
wide: nutlets about 1.5–2 mm. long. [*S.
galericulata* (Chapm. Fl. Fl. SE. U. S.)]—
Wet thickets and swamps, Blue Ridge and more northern provinces, N. C. to
Tenn., Nebr., N. M., Ariz., Alas., Ont., and Newf.—Sum.-fall.

3. S. havanensis Jacq. Plant 1–3 dm. tall, hoary-pubescent: leaf-blades
orbicular-ovate to ovate, 3–6 mm. long, those of the lower ones sometimes shal-

lowly toothed: calyx becoming 3 mm. long: corolla 13–14 mm. long; lower lip 7–8 mm. wide: nutlets fully 1 mm. long. [*S. cubensis* A. Rich. *S. longiflora* Small.]—Pinelands, Everglade Keys, Fla.—(*W. I.*)—All year.

4. S. ambigua Nutt. Plant 0.5–4 dm. tall, glabrous or puberulent: leaf-blades broadly ovate to lanceolate, the margins revolute, entire or sometimes the lower remotely serrate, 1–2 cm. long: calyx becoming 5–6 mm. long: corolla about 11 mm. long; lower lip 4–4.5 mm. wide: nutlets fully 1 mm. long. [*S. parvula* (Fl. SE. U. S.)]—Dry soil, various provinces, Fla. to Tex., S. D., and Que.—Spr.–sum.

5. S. parvula Michx. Plant 0.5–4 dm. tall, densely and softly glandular-pubescent: leaf-blades suborbicular to ovate, or ovate-lanceolate on the upper part of the stem, 1–2 cm. long: calyx becoming 5–6 mm. long: corolla 6–10 mm. long; lower lip 3.5–4 mm. wide: nutlets barely 1 mm. long. [*S. campestris* Britton]—Dry or damp soil, various provinces, Ga. to Tex., Kans., Ia., and Que.—Spr.

6. S. Ocmulgee Small. Plant 4–8 dm. tall, softly-pubescent: leaf-blades thickish, suborbicular to ovate, 3–8 cm. long, crenate: corolla 20–25 mm. long; lower lip 6–7 mm. wide.—River-banks, in the Piedmont of Ga.—Sum.

7. S. Cuthbertii Alexander. Plant 2–6 dm. tall, softly-pubescent, especially above: leaf-blades firm, ovate to ovate-lanceolate, acute, soft, velvety-pubescent above and beneath, petioles and larger veins usually purplish, 2–7 cm. long, crenate: inflorescence villous with glandular hairs, conspicuously bracted, the bracts entire, cordate: calyx becoming 5–7 mm. long: corolla 16–20 mm. long; lower lip about 6 mm. long, 8 mm. wide.—Rich, sandy or clay woods, Piedmont and Appalachian Valley, Ga. and Ala.—Spr.–sum.

8. S. arguta Buckl. Plant 3–5 dm. tall, pubescent: leaf-blades ovate to elliptic-ovate, 2–5 cm. long, deeply crenate-dentate; calyx becoming 5 mm. long: corolla 12–14 mm. long; lower lip 5–6 mm. wide: nutlets 1 mm. long.—Hillsides, Blue Ridge, Ga. to N. C.—Spr.–Sum.

9. S. ovata Hill. Plant 1–6 dm. tall, softly-pubescent: leaf-blades orbicular-ovate to lance-ovate, 3–10 cm. long, serrate: inflorescence inconspicuously bracted (conspicuously bracted and leaf-blades rugose beneath in *S. ovata bracteata*): calyx becoming 6–7 mm. long: corolla 19–21 mm. long; lower lip about 6 mm. long and 6 mm. wide, deeply notched at the apex: nutlets about 1.5 mm. long. [*S. cordifolia* Muhl. *S. versicolor* Nutt.]—Moist banks, various provinces, Fla. to Tex., Minn, and Pa.—Spr.–sum.

10. S. saxatilis Riddell. Plant 1–3 dm. tall, nearly glabrous, pubescent: leaf-blades suborbicular or ovate to ovate-lanceolate, 1–4 cm. long, coarsely crenate or serrate-crenate: calyx becoming 4–5 mm. long: corolla 12–18 mm. long; lower lip 5–6 mm. wide: nutlets 1 mm. long.—Sandy soil, various provinces, Ga. to Ark., Ohio, and Del.—Spr. & sum.

11. S. incana Muhl. Plant 5–12 dm. tall, finely-pubescent: leaf-blades 4–12 cm. long, serrate or crenate-serrate, usually pubescent beneath: calyx becoming 6–7 mm. long, canescent with white, eglandular hairs: corolla 15–20 mm. long; lower lip 6–8 mm. wide: nutlets about 1.5 mm. long. [*S. canescens* Nutt. *S. villosa* Ell.]—Woods, stream-banks, and thickets, various provinces N of Coastal Plain, Ga. to Ala., Mich., and Ont.—Sum.

12. S. alabamensis Alexander. Plant 4.5–7 cm. tall, finely short-pubescent below: leaf-blades ovate or ovate-lanceolate to elliptic, 4–5 cm. long, serrate-crenate, ciliate on the margin and veins beneath: inflorescence narrow and crowded, hirsute with eglandular hairs: calyx glandular pubescent: corolla glabrous or nearly so, 18–20 mm. long; upper lip as long as the throat or slightly longer; lower lip 6–8 mm. wide.—Dry woods, Appalachian Valley, Ala.—Sum.

13. S. Altamaha Small. Plant 2–4 dm. tall, hirsute-canescent: leaf-blades ovate to elliptic, short-petioled, 1.5–5 mm. long, serrate, the terminal lobe usually acute: inflorescence very narrowly crowded: calyx becoming 4 mm. long: corolla 11–14 mm. long; lower lip 5–6 mm. wide.—Pinelands, Coastal Plain, Fla. and Ga.—Spr.–sum.

14. S. ovalifolia Pers. Plant 1–6 dm. tall, finely pubescent with long, spreading hairs: leaf-blades ovate or deltoid-ovate, 1.5–4.5 cm. long, coarsely crenate, the terminal lobe usually obtuse: calyx becoming about 5 mm. long: corolla 12–15 mm. long; lower lip 5–7 mm. wide: nutlets about 1 mm. long. [*S. pilosa* Michx.]—Dry banks, woods, and meadows, various provinces, Fla. to Tex., Mich., and N. Y.—Spr.

15. S. serrata Andr. Plant 2–7 dm. tall, sometimes puberulent: leaf-blades thin, oval, elliptic, or ovate, 4–10 cm. long, serrate or crenate-serrate: calyx becoming 6–7 mm. long: corolla 20–25 mm. long; lower lip 7–8 mm. wide: nutlets about 1.5 mm. long.—Woods, various provinces N of Coastal Plain, Ala. to Ill., N. Y., and S. C.—Spr.

16. S. Mellichampii Small. Plant 4–6 dm. tall, closely-pubescent: leaf-blades ovate to elliptic-oval, 3–6 cm. long, crenate: calyx becoming 4–5 mm. long: corolla 20–25 mm. long; lower lip 8–9 mm. wide.—Sandy soil, Coastal Plain, Ga. and S. C.—Sum.

17. S. montana Chapm. Plant 3–5 dm. tall, softly pubescent: leaf-blades ovate to ovate-lanceolate or elliptic, 2–8 cm. long, coarsely crenate-serrate, cuneate at the base: calyx becoming 7 mm. long: corolla 28–35 mm. long; lower lip 10–12 mm. wide.—Woods and thickets, Blue Ridge and Appalachian Valley, Ga. and Ala.—Sum.

18. S. arenicola Small. Plant 2–4 dm. tall, finely pubescent: leaf-blades ovate to elliptic, 1.5–3 cm. long, sharply serrate or crenate-serrate: calyx becoming 5 mm. long: corolla 20–26 mm. long; lower lip 9–10 mm. wide: nutlets 1–1.5 mm. long.—Sandy pinelands and scrub, pen. Fla.—Sum.

19. S. glabriuscula Fernald. Plant 3–6 dm. tall, puberulent: blades of the lower leaves elliptic, those of the upper linear-spatulate, entire: inflorescence short-branched: calyx becoming 5–5.5 mm. long: corolla nearly glabrous, 23–26 mm. long; lower lip 8–9 mm. wide, deeply notched.—Sandy soil, N Fla.—Spr.–fall.

20. S. integrifolia L. Plant 2–6 dm. tall, softly pubescent: blades of the lower leaves ovate to elliptic-ovate, coarsely crenate, those of the upper ones elliptic to elliptic-lanceolate or linear, entire: inflorescence branched or unbranched: calyx becoming 6–7 mm. long: corolla usually blue-violet, 21–25 mm. long; lower lip shallowly notched: nutlets fully 1 mm. long.—Woods, pastures, and thickets, various provinces, Fla. to Tex., Mo., and Mass.—Spr.–sum.

21. S. multiglandulosa (Kearney) Small. Plant 1–3.5 dm. tall, glandular-pubescent: leaf-blades various, those of the lower leaves oval to elliptic 1–2 cm. long, often coarsely crenate, those of the upper leaves elliptic to linear-spatulate, entire: inflorescence not branched; calyx becoming 5–6 mm. long: corolla pale-blue or often white, 20–25 mm. long; lower lip 4-lobed, 10–11 mm. wide: nutlets 1.5 mm. long.—Dry pinelands and sandy fields, Coastal Plain, Fla. and Ga.—Spr.

22. S. floridana Chapm. Plant 2–4 dm. tall, puberulent: leaf-blades narrowly linear, 1–2.5 cm. long, entire: inflorescence not branched; calyx becoming 7 mm. long: corolla blue-violet, 20–25 mm. long; lower lip 12–13 mm. wide, deeply notched.—Pineland swamps, Fla.—Sum.

23. **S. nervosa** Pursh. Plant 1–4 cm. tall, minutely pubescent: leaf-blades suborbicular to ovate or lanceolate above, 2–4 cm. long, undulate or coarsely serrate: calyx becoming about 5 mm. long: corolla 6–10 mm. long; lower lip about 5 mm. wide: nutlets 1–2 long.—Thickets and woods, various provinces N of Coastal Plain, N. C. to Mo. and Ont.—Spr.–sum.

5. **MARRUBIUM** [Tourn.] L. Perennial low or diffuse herbs. Leaf-blades toothed, often rugose. Flowers in dense axillary clusters. Calyx nearly regular, 10-lobed; lobes slender, spreading or recurved, sometimes unequal. Corolla 2-lipped: upper lip erect: lower lip spreading, the broad middle lobe much larger than the 2 lateral ones. Filaments somewhat longer than the anthers.—About 40 species, natives of the Old World.

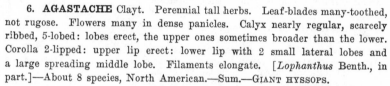

1. **M. vulgare** L. Plant 2–9 dm. tall, white-woolly: leaf-blades suborbicular, oval, or ovate, 1–4 cm. long, crenate, rugose: calyx 4–5 mm. long; lobes hooked: corolla white, 5–6 mm. long; upper lip deeply notched: nutlets about 2 mm. long.—(HOARHOUND.)— Pastures, waste-places, and on roadsides, various provinces, Fla. to Tex., Calif., B. C., and Me. Native of Eu.—(*Mex.*)—Spr.–sum.

6. **AGASTACHE** Clayt. Perennial tall herbs. Leaf-blades many-toothed, not rugose. Flowers many in dense panicles. Calyx nearly regular, scarcely ribbed, 5-lobed: lobes erect, the upper ones sometimes broader than the lower. Corolla 2-lipped: upper lip erect: lower lip with 2 small lateral lobes and a large spreading middle lobe. Filaments elongate. [*Lophanthus* Benth., in part.]—About 8 species, North American.—Sum.—GIANT HYSSOPS.

Calyx-lobes obtuse or acute: corolla greenish-yellow: bracts acute or acutish.
　　　　　　　　　　　　　　　　　　　　　　　　1. *A. nepetoides.*
Calyx-lobes acuminate: corolla purplish: bracts acuminate. 　2. *A. scrophulariaefolia.*

1. **A. nepetoides** (L.) Kuntze. Stem glabrous or nearly so, 1–2 m. tall: leaf-blades ovate to ovate-lanceolate, 5–12 cm. long: calyx 5–6 mm. long; lobes ovate or elliptic-ovate: corolla 7–9 mm. long, slightly exceeding the calyx: nutlets minutely pubescent. [*L. nepetoides* Benth.]—Hill-sides, thickets and woods, various provinces, Ga. to Ky., Minn., Que., and Mass.

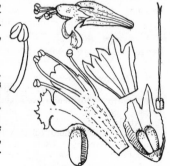

2. **A. scrophulariaefolia** (Willd.) Kuntze. Stem finely hirsute, 1–2 m. tall: leaf-blades ovate to ovate-lanceolate, or elliptic above: calyx 6–7 mm. long; lobes lanceolate: corolla 6–8 mm. long, much exceeding the calyx: nutlets hispidulous. [*L. scrophulariaefolius* Benth.]—Thickets, woods, and fence-rows, various provinces, rarely Coastal Plain, N. C., to Mo., Ont., and N. H.

7. **MEEHANIA** Britton. Perennial decumbent or creeping herbs. Leaf-blades few, crenate. Flowers few in a 1-sided raceme. Calyx nearly regular, 15-ribbed, 5-lobed; lobes erect. Corolla 2-lipped: upper lip arched: lower lip spreading, the middle lobe much broader, but scarcely longer than the 2 lateral ones. Filaments not exceeding the upper corolla-lip.—One species.

1. **M. cordata** (Nutt.) Britton. Stem and runners 1.5–11 dm. long, sparingly hirsute: leaf-blades ovate to orbicular-ovate, 2–7 cm. long, cordate: calyx 10–14 mm. long; lobes triangular to triangular-lanceolate: corolla blue or rarely white, 2.5–3 cm. long; nutlets about 2 mm. long. [*Cedronella cordata* Benth.]—Rich woods, various provinces N of Coastal Plain, N. C. to Tenn., Ky., and Pa.—Spr.–sum.

8. **NEPETA** L. Annual or perennial, erect, branching herbs. Leaf-blades toothed or incised. Flowers in axillary clusters which are sometimes borne in racemes. Calyx slightly irregular, 15-ribbed, 5-lobed: lobes relatively long, the upper lobes slightly longer than the lower. Corolla 2-lipped: upper lip erect: lower lip spreading, the larger middle lobe toothed. Filaments relatively slender, usually filiform.—Amount 150 species, Eurasian.

1. **N. Cataria** L. Plant pale-green, 3–11 dm. tall, closely-pubescent: leaf-blades ovate to tri-angular-ovate, 4–7 cm. long, crenate or serrate-crenate, mostly cordate: calyx 5–6 mm. long; lobes subulate or lanceolate-subulate: corolla pale, magenta-spotted, 6–7 mm. long: nutlets about 1 mm. long.—(CAT-MINT. CATNIP.)—Waste-places, fields, woods, and roadsides, various provinces, Ga. to La., Kans., Minn., and N. B. Nat. of Eu.—Sum.–fall.

9. **GLECOMA** L. Perennial creeping herbs. Leaf-blades toothed. Flowers in axillary clusters. Calyx slightly 2-lipped, 15-ribbed, 5-lobed: lobes unequal, relatively short. Corolla 2-lipped: upper lip erect: lower lip spreading, the large middle lobe notched. Filaments relatively slender.—About 6 species, Eurasian.

1. **G. hederacea** L. Plant dark-green, the branches 1–11 dm. long, hirsute: leaf-blades reniform to suborbicular, 2–4 cm. in diameter, coarsely crenate: calyx 5–7 mm. long; lobes subulate-tipped: corolla blue or white, 10–15 mm. long: nutlets about 1.5 mm. long. [*Nepeta Glechoma* Benth.] — GROUND-IVY. GILL-OVER-THE-GROUND.)—Banks and thickets, various provinces, Ga. to Kans., Ont., and Newf. Nat. of Eu.—Spr.

10. PRUNELLA L. Perennial erect or diffuse herbs. Leaf-blades toothed or laciniate. Flowers mostly in compact panicles. Calyx 2-lipped: upper lip with 3 broad lobes: lower lip with 2 narrow lobes. Corolla 2-lipped: upper lip arched: lower lip with the broad middle lobe generally toothed. Filaments relatively long, 2 of them forked at the apex. [*Brunella* L.]—About 5 species, widely distributed.—SELF-HEALS. HEALS-ALLS. BLUE-CURLS.

Leaf-blades entire or shallowly toothed: calyx 10–11 mm. long; lobes of the lower lip subulate tipped.   1. *P. vulgaris.*
Leaf-blades, at least the upper ones, pinnatifid: calyx 8–9 mm. long; lobes of the lower lip lanceolate.   2. *P. laciniata.*

1. P. vulgaris L. Stem 0.5–4 dm. long: leaf-blades ovate, elliptic, or lanceolate, 2–7.5 cm. long, undulate: bracts mostly reniform: calyx 10–11 mm. long; lobes of the upper lip mucronate: corolla purple or white, mainly 14–18 mm. long: nutlets about 2 mm. long.—(CARPENTER-WEED.)—Fields, thickets, and waste-places, U. S. and S Can., Nat. of Eu.—Spr.–fall.— Also called SNAKEWEED from the belief that a snake hole is hidden under the plant.

2. P. laciniata L. Plant similar to *P. vulgaris* in habit, but often hoary-pubescent: blades of the stem-leaves more or less pinnatifid: corolla white or pale.—Roadsides, fields, and lawns, various provinces, N. C. to Mass. Nat. of Eu.—Sum.—The rôle of a weed through a long period has developed many forms in the above two species.

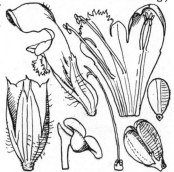

11. MACBRIDEA Ell. Perennial erect herbs. Leaf-blades entire or repand. Flowers in axillary clustered broad-leafed cymes. Calyx strongly 2-lipped, the upper lip of a narrow lobe, the lower lip of 2 broader lobes. Corolla 2-lipped: upper lip arching: lower lip 3-lobed. Stamens 4: anthers pubescent. —Two species.

Corolla white, the upper lip notched; lateral lobes of the lower lip as wide as the middle one.   1. *M. alba.*
Corolla rose-purple, streaked, the upper lip entire: lateral lobes of the lower lip much narrower than the middle one.   2. *M. pulchra.*

1. M. alba Chapm. Stem 3–5 dm. tall, simply or rarely branched: leaf-blades cuneate-spatulate to elliptic, rather fleshy, 2–8 cm. long, obtuse, undulate or repand, the lower ones with margined petioles, the upper sessile: panicles few flowered: bracts elliptic-ovate to orbicular, obtuse: pedicels very short: calyx becoming 10–12 mm. long, glabrous or nearly so; lobes about as long as the tube, the larger ones slightly notched: corolla white, 2.5–3 cm. long the upper lip hooded, nearly erect, the lower lip spreading, the lobes emarginate or nearly truncate.—Pineland swamps and low prairies, N Fla.—Sum.

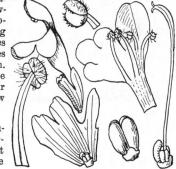

2. M. pulchra Ell. Stem 3–6 dm. tall, usually simple: leaf-blades elliptic to linear-elliptic, 4–8 cm. long, acute or acuminate at both ends, undulate or repand-serrate, the lower ones slender-petioled, the upper sessile: panicles few-flowered: bracts ovate or elliptic, mostly obtuse: pedicels very short: calyx becoming 9–10 mm. long; lobes shorter than the tube, entire or the larger ones emarginate: corolla rose-purple striped with white and purple, 3–3.5 cm. long; tube abruptly dilated near the middle, the upper lip suborbicular, 1 cm. in diameter, the lower lip with a notched middle lobe and truncate lateral lobes.—Swamps and marshes, Coastal Plain, Fla. to Ala. and N. C.—Sum.–fall.

12. **DRACOCEPHALUM** [Tourn.] L. Perennial, erect or reclining herbs. Leaf-blades typically narrow, usually toothed, at least near the apex. Flowers purplish-pink to white, in spike-like racemes. Calyx essentially regular: lobes 5, shorter than the tube. Corolla 2-lipped: upper lip arched, entire: lower lip 3-lobed. Stamens 4: filaments elongate, one pair sometimes glabrous. [*Physostegia* Benth.]—About 7 species, North American.—Sum.—FALSE DRAGON-HEADS. OBEDIENT PLANTS.

Corolla over 2 cm. long.
　Leaf-blades entire or with blunt teeth.
　　Mature calyx short-tubular, 9–11 mm. long: upper leaves conspicuously reduced. 1. *D. denticulatum.*
　　Mature calyx campanulate, 5–6.5 mm. long: upper leaves but slightly reduced. 2. *D. leptophyllum.*
　Leaf-blades copiously toothed with very acute serrations. 3. *D. virginianum.*
Corolla less than 2 cm. long: mature calyx tubular, 8–9 mm. long: stem copiously leafy up to the inflorescence. 4. *D. veroniciformis.*

1. **D. denticulatum** Ait. Stems 3–9 dm. long: leaves few; blades spatulate to oblong, 2–14 cm. long, thick, repand-crenate, mostly obtuse: calyx-lobes deltoid: corolla 20–25 mm. long: nutlets about 2 mm. long. [*P. denticulata* Britton] —Swamps and river-banks, often in calcareous soil, various provinces, Fla. to Tex., Kans. and Md.—Sum.–fall.

2. **D. leptophyllum** Small. Stems 6–10 dm. long: leaf-blades thin, oblong or nearly so, mostly 3–7 cm. long, repand: calyx-lobes lanceolate to triangular-lanceolate: corolla 20–23 mm. long: nutlets 3–3.5 mm. long. [*P. leptophylla* Small]—River-banks and swamps, pen. Fla.—Spr.–fall.

3. **D. virginianum** L. Stems 3–15 dm. long: leaves many; blades narrowly oblong to linear-oblong or oblong-lanceolate, 3–12 cm. long, thickish, saliently serrate or incised-serrate, mostly acuminate or acute: calyx-lobes lanceolate to ovate-lanceolate: corolla 25–30 mm. long: nutlets about 3 mm. long. [*P. virginiana* Benth.]—Swamps, low woods, and thickets, often in somewhat acid soil, various provinces, Fla. to Tex., Kans., and Que.—Sum.

4. **D. veroniciformis** Small. Stems 5–7 dm. long: leaf-blades lanceolate to oblong-lanceolate on the lower part of the stem, narrowly pandurate to lanceolate above, 5–10 cm. long, undulate to crenate-undulate: calyx-lobes mainly lanceolate: corolla-lobes retuse: shorter filaments pubescent. [*P. veroniciformis* Small]—Low grounds, Coastal Plain, Ga.—Sum.

13. **SYNANDRA** Nutt. Annual or biennial erect herbs. Leaf-blades broad, toothed. Flowers in interrupted racemes. Calyx nearly regular: lobes

4, shorter than the tube, herbaceous. Corolla 2-lipped: upper lip arched, entire: lower lip 3-lobed. Stamens 4: filaments pubescent.—One species.

1. S. hispidula (Michx.) Britton. Stem 2-8 dm. long, hispid or somewhat villous: leaf-blades ovate to orbicular-ovate, 2-10 cm. long, crenate or serrate, cordate: calyx becoming 10 mm. long; lobes lanceolate: corolla white, 2.5-3 cm. long: nutlets about 4 mm. long. [*S. grandiflora* Nutt.]—Wet woods and stream-banks, Interior Low Plateaus and adj. provinces, Tenn. to Ill., Ohio, and Va.—Spr.

14. GALEOPSIS L. Annual often spreading herbs. Leaf-blades broad, toothed. Flowers in crowded cymes. Calyx nearly regular: lobes 5, narrow, spine-tipped. Corolla 2-lipped: upper lip notched or erose: lower lip 3-lobed, the lateral lobes often as large as the middle one, sometimes appendaged at the base. Stamens 4: filaments glabrous.—About 6 species, Eurasian.

1. G. Tetrahit L. Plant 2-5 dm. tall, hispid: stem swollen at the nodes: leaf-blades ovate to ovate-lanceolate or oblong-lanceolate, 2.5-7 cm. long, serrate: flower-clusters bristly: calyx becoming 10-13 mm. long; lobes about as long as the tube: corolla pink-purple or white, mostly 15-20 mm. long: nutlets about 3 mm. long.—(HEMP-NETTLE.)—Waste-places, fields and roadsides, various provinces, N. C. to Alas. and Newf. Nat. of Eu.—Sum.-fall.

15. LAMIUM L. Annual, biennial or perennial, diffuse herbs. Leaf-blades broad, toothed or incised. Flowers in axillary cymes. Calyx somewhat irregular: lobes 5, the upper ones usually the larger. Corolla blue, purple, or white, 2-lipped: upper lip entire or merely notched: lower lip 3-lobed, the middle lobe with a dilated blade, the lateral lobes with slender tips. Stamens 4: filaments pubescent.—About 40 species, natives of the Old World.—DEAD-NETTLES. MONKEY-FLOWERS.

Plant annual or biennial: corolla small, less than 2 cm. long: middle lobe of the lower corolla-lip less than 5 mm. wide; lateral lobes each with a short sharp tooth and a very broad one: nutlets about 2 mm. long.
    Upper leaves with sessile or clasping blades: corolla-tube slender, longer than the throat and lower lip; middle lobe of the lower lip cuneate or reniform.   1. *L. amplexicaule.*
    Upper leaves with petioled blades: corolla-tube stout, about as long as the throat and lower lip; middle lobe of the lower lip somewhat reniform.   2. *L. purpureum.*
Plant perennial: corolla mostly over 2 cm. long: middle lobe of the lower corolla-lip 1 cm. wide or nearly so; lateral lobes each with a caudate appendage and a broad lobe: nutlets about 3 mm. long.   3. *L. maculatum.*

1. L. amplexicaule L. Stem and branches decumbent, sparingly retrorse-pubescent: leaf-blades suborbicular to orbicular-reniform, 1–3.5 cm. wide, crenate-lobed: calyx becoming 5–6 mm. long: corolla purple, 13–17 mm. long; tube slender, the lower lip with mucronate lateral lobes and a cuneate or reniform middle lobe: nutlets about 2 mm. long.—(HENBIT.) —Roadsides, fields, thickets, cult. grounds, and waste-places, various provinces, Fla. to La., Ark., Calif., B. C., and N. B. Nat. of Eu.—(W. I.)—Wint.–spr.

2. L. purpureum L. Stem and branches decumbent, often creeping at the base, minutely retrorse-pubescent: leaf-blades orbicular-ovate to orbicular-reniform: calyx less than 9 mm. long at maturity, pubescent with short hairs: corolla purple or purplish, mostly less than 1.5 cm. long, the upper lip less than 5 mm. long: nutlets about 2 mm. long.—(DEAD-NETTLE.)—Cult. grounds, roadsides, and shaded places, various provinces, N. C. to Mo., and Newf. Nat. of Eu.—Spr.–sum.

3. L. maculatum L. Stem and branches more or less creeping, rather coarsely but sparingly retrorse-pubescent: leaf-blades ovate to triangular-ovate: calyx over 10 mm. long at maturity, pubescent with long hairs: corolla purple or white, mostly over 2 cm. long, the upper lip about 1 cm. long: nutlets about 3 mm. long.—Waste-places, roadsides, and thickets, various provinces, N. C. and Tenn. to Me. Nat. of Eu.—Spr.–sum.

16. LEONURUS L. Annual, biennial, or perennial, erect herbs. Leaf-blades broad, toothed or parted. Flowers in dense axillary cymes. Calyx somewhat irregular: lobes firm, slender. Corolla 2-lipped: upper lip nearly erect: lower lip 3-lobed, the middle lobe much larger than the lateral ones. Stamens 4: filaments pubescent.—About 10 species, Eurasian.—MOTHERWORTS.

Blades of the lower leaves lobed and incised : corolla twice as long as the calyx.
    Upper corolla-lip hirsute : lower calyx-lobes spreading :
        blades of the lower leaves coarsely lobed.   1. *L. Cardiaca.*
    Upper corolla-lip puberulent : lower calyx-lobes erect :
        blades of the lower leaves finely lobed.   2. *L. sibiricus.*
Blades of the lower leaves coarsely toothed : corolla slightly
    longer than the calyx.   3. *L. Marrubiastrum.*

1. L. Cardiaca L. Perennial, 3–12 dm. tall: leaves various; blades of the lower ones suborbicular in outline, coarsely palmately lobed, those of the upper leaves ovate to cuneate, mostly 3-lobed; calyx 6–6.5 mm. long; lobes short-subulate, half as long as the tube: corolla pale-purple, 9–10 mm. long; nutlets about 1.5 mm. long. —Roadsides, waste-places, and old fields, various provinces, N. C., to Ala., Tex., Utah, and S. Can. Nat. of Eu.—Spr.–fall.

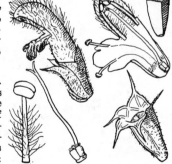

2. L. sibiricus L. Biennial, 9–12 dm. tall: leaves various; blades of the lower ones suborbicular in outline, deeply and more finely lobed than in *L. Cardiaca*, those of the upper leaves, or their lobes, finely pinnatisect; calyx 6–7 mm. long; lobes triangular-subulate, erect, about ⅓ as long as the tube: corolla purplish, 10–12 mm. long:

nutlets about 2 mm. long.—Roadsides and waste-places, various provinces, Fla. to La., Pa., and Del. Nat. of Eurasia.—(*W. I., C. A., S. A.*)—Spr.–fall.

3. **L. Marrubiastrum** L. Biennial, 8–16 dm. tall: leaf-blades ovate to elliptic-ovate, coarsely toothed: calyx about 5 mm. long; lobes subulate, about half as long as the tube: corolla whitish, about 5 mm long: nutlets about 1.5 mm. long.—Waste-places, roadsides, and stream-banks, Fla. to Pa. and Del. Nat. of Eurasia.—Sum.–fall.

17. **LEONOTIS** L. Annual or perennial erect herbs or woody plants. Leaf-blades broad, toothed. Flowers in dense, globular, remote cymes. Calyx curved, 2-lipped, the 8–10 lobes unequal, bristle-tipped. Corolla 2-lipped, curved: upper lip erect, long: lower lip much shorter than the upper, with 3 small lobes. Stamens 4: filaments minutely pubescent.—About 12 species, African.

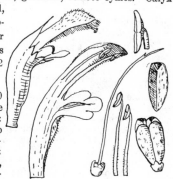

1. **L. nepetaefolia** R. Br. Annual, 3–20 dm. tall, soft-pubescent: leaf-blades ovate to ovate-deltoid, 4–12 cm. long, crenate: calyx becoming 2 cm. long; the upper lip longer than the tube: corolla orange-yellow or scarlet, 2–2.5 cm. long: nutlets about 3 mm. long.—(Lion's-ears.)—Cult. grounds, roadsides, and waste-places, various provinces, Fla. to La., Tenn., and N. C. Nat. of S. Africa.—Sum.–fall.

18. **STACHYS** [Tourn.] L. Annual or (ours) perennial, erect or spreading herbs. Leaf-blades entire or toothed. Flowers in continuous or interrupted panicles. Calyx nearly regular: lobes 5, shorter than the tube. Corolla mainly purple, 2-lipped: upper lip erect: lower lip spreading, 3-lobed, the middle lobe somewhat larger than the lateral ones. Stamens 4, all anther-bearing: anthers short.—About 160 species, mostly in the north temperate zone. Hedge-nettles.

Plants native in Tex., introduced eastward: leaf-blades not rugose: pubescence coarse and spreading.
  Plant with annual or biennial roots.   I. Agrariae.
  Plant with perennial rootstocks.
    Leaf-blades narrowed at the base.   II. Hyssopifoliae.
    Leaf-blades, all, or some of them cordate or truncate at the base.
      Petioles less than one-fourth as long as the blades.
      Petioles one-third to one-half as long as the blades.   III. Nuttallianae.
Plants introduced from Old World: leaf-blades rugose: pubescence lanate-tomentose.   IV. Cordatae.
           V. Italicae.

I. Agrariae
Slender plant: lower lip of the corolla little surpassing the calyx: mature calyx 2–4 mm. long.   1. *S. agraria.*

II. Hyssopifoliae
Leaf-blades glabrous, entire or with shallow teeth.
  glabrous at maturity.
    Calyx-lobes subulate-tipped: leaf-blades entire or nearly so.   2. *S. hyssopifolia.*
    Calyx-lobes not subulate-tipped: leaf-blades markedly but shallowly toothed.
Leaf-blades pubescent, prominently serrate.   3. *S. lythroides.*
    4. *S. ambigua.*

III. Nuttallianae

Lower leaves with petioles but little longer than those of the
    upper.
    Foliage copiously pubescent: corolla-tube slightly longer
        than the calyx.   5. *S. Nuttallii.*
    Foliage glabrous or nearly so: corolla-tube much longer
        than the calyx.   6. *S. latidens.*
Lower leaves with petioles several times longer than those of
    the upper.
    Calyx-lobes merely acute or acuminate, not awn-tipped.
        Foliage of the inflorescence glabrous or bristly pubes-
            cent.
            Inflorescence glabrous or nearly so.   7. *S. tenuifolia.*
            Inflorescence bristly-pubescent.   8. *S. aspera.*
        Foliage of the inflorescence puberulent or puberulent-
            pubescent.   9. *S. salvioides.*
    Calyx-lobes awn-tipped.   10. *S. Clingmanii.*

IV. Cordatae

Leaf-blades acuminate, 6–15 cm. long: species Alleghenian.   11. *S. cordata.*
Leaf-blades obtuse or merely acute, 1–4 cm. long: species
    Floridian.   12. *S. floridana.*

V. Italicae

Hoary-pubescent plant with obtuse, crenate leaf-blades.   13. *S. italica.*

1. S. agraria Cham. & Schlecht. Plant 1–3 dm. tall: leaf-blades elliptic to ovate, 1–4 cm. long, crenate: calyx 2–4 mm. long; lobes shorter than the tube: corolla lavender or pinkish, 5–6 mm. long: nutlets about 1 mm. long.—Shaded ground, La. to Tex.; introduced into the Coastal Plain of Ala.—Spr.–fall.

2. S. hyssopifolia Michx. Stem 2–4 dm. tall, glabrous or merely hirsute at the nodes: leaf-blades linear or nearly so, 1–5 cm. long: calyx 6–7 mm. long, generally glabrous; lobes about as long as the tube: corolla 11–13 mm. long: nutlets about 2 mm. long.—Swamps, meadows, and thickets, various provinces, Fla. to Mich., and Mass.—Sum.

3. S. lythroides Small. Stem 4–9 dm. tall, sparingly hirsute: leaf-blades broadly linear to elliptic-linear, 1.5–6 cm. long, smooth and glabrous: calyx 6–7 mm. long, mostly pubescent; lobes shorter than the tube: corolla about 10 mm. long: nutlets not seen.—Sandy soil, near Tallahassee, Fla.—Sum.

4. S. ambigua (A. Gray) Britton. Stem 3–10 dm. tall, hirsute: leaf-blades narrowly elliptic to elliptic-lanceolate, 3–6 cm. long, pubescent: calyx 6–8 mm. long; lobes lanceolate, as long as the tube or nearly so: corolla 11–13 mm. long: nutlets over 2 mm. long.—Moist sandy soil, various provinces, Ga. to Wisc., and Mass.—Sum.

5. S. Nuttallii Shuttlw. Stem 4–11 dm. tall, copiously hirsute: leaf-blades elliptic to elliptic-lanceolate, 5–10 cm. long, serrate-dentate: calyx 5–6 mm. long; lobes triangular-lanceolate, less than ½ as long as the tube: corolla 11–13 mm. long: nutlets about 2 mm. long.—Mt. slopes, Blue Ridge, Tenn. to Va.—Spr.

6. S. latidens Small. Stem 3–7 dm. tall, glabrous or nearly so: leaf-blades oval, ovate, or elliptic, and 4–10 cm. long on the lower part of stem, larger and narrower above, finely crenate-serrate: calyx 5–6 mm. long; lobes triangular, very short: corolla 11–13 mm. long: nutlets fully 2 mm. long.—Slopes and summits, Blue Ridge, N. C., and Tenn. to Va.—Sum.

7. S. tenuifolia Willd. Stem 3–9 dm. tall, glabrous or nearly so: leaf-blades mainly elliptic to elliptic-lanceolate, 3–10 cm. long, serrate: calyx 6–7 mm. long, sometimes sparingly pubescent; lobes lanceolate, as long as the tube or nearly so: corolla 10–12 mm. long: nutlets about 2 mm. long.—Roadsides, fields, and moist thickets, various provinces, Fla. to La., Kans., Ia., and N. Y.—Sum.

8. S. aspera Michx. Stem 5–12 dm. tall, hirsute: leaf-blades elliptic, elliptic lanceolate, or ovate-elliptic, 3–10 cm. long, crenate-serrate: calyx 6–8 mm. long, hirsute; lobes triangular-lanceolate, shorter than the tube: corolla mainly 12–15 mm. long: nutlets about 2 mm. long.—Woods and thickets, various provinces, Fla. to La., Ont., and Mass.—Sum.

9. S. salvioides Small. Stem 3–9 dm. tall, puberulent or puberulent-pubescent: leaf-blades elliptic to elliptic-ovate or rarely ovate, 6–12 cm. long, crenate: calyx 4–5 cm. long, hirsutulous and short pubescent; lobes triangular, acute: corolla 9–10 mm. long; lower lip shorter than the tube: nutlets nearly 2.5 mm. long.—Stony soil, Appalachian Plateau, Tenn. to W. Va., and Va.—Sum.

10. S. Clingmanii Small. Stem 5–9 dm. tall, hispid, hirsute: leaf-blades elliptic to elliptic-lanceolate, 6–12 cm. long, dentate: calyx 6–7 mm. long, villous; lobes lanceolate-subulate, at least ½ as long as the tube: corolla about 15 mm. long; lower lip about as long as the tube: nutlets 2 mm. long.—Open slopes, Clingman's Dome, in the Blue Ridge of N. C. and Tenn.—Sum.

11. S. cordata Riddell. Stem 3–10 dm. tall, hirsute: leaf-blades ovate, oval or elliptic, 6–15 cm. long, crenate: calyx 4–6 mm. long, hirsute; lobes deltoid: corolla 10–14 mm. long; lower lip shorter than the tube: nutlets about 2 mm. long.—Thickets and banks, various provinces, N. Ala. and N. C. to Ohio.—Sum.

12. S. floridana Shuttlw. Stem 1–4 dm. tall, hirsute: leaf-blades elliptic to ovate, 1–4 cm. long, serrate or dentate: calyx 5–7 mm. long, puberulent; lobes lanceolate: corolla 10–13 mm. long; lower lip as long as the tube: nutlets 1.5 mm. long or rarely smaller.—Sandy soil, Fla.—Spr.-fall.—The plant spreads by means of elongate, sometimes branching tubers.

13. S. italica Mill. Plant 1 m. tall or less, the stem simple or sparingly branched: leaf-blades elliptic, elliptic-ovate or ovate, 3–15 cm. long, obtuse, crenate, rugose, pubescent: flower-whorls dense: calyx 9–12 mm. long; lobes slender-tipped, much shorter than the tube: corolla 12–16 mm. long, pubescent: nutlets about 1 mm. long.—(Mouse-ear.)—Waste-places, cult. grounds, and roadsides, various provinces, Fla. to Tenn., and Ont. Nat. of Eu.—Sum.-fall.

19. SALVIA [Tourn.] L. Annual or perennial, herbs, or woody plants. Leaf-blades entire, toothed, or lobed. Flowers in interrupted or continuous panicles. Calyx short, 2-lipped: upper lip 3-lobed: lower lip 1-lobed. Corolla 2-lipped: lower lip 3-lobed, the middle lobe much larger than the lateral ones. Stamens 4, but only 2 anther-bearing, or only 2: each filament surmounted by a transverse connective, one end of which bears a long anther. Stigmas very unequal.—About 500 species, widely distributed.—Sages.

Lower anther-sac wanting.
 Anterior part of the connective linear or nearly so. I. Azureae.
 Anterior part of the connective abruptly dilated. II. Verbenaceae.
Lower anther-sac present. III. Lyratae.

I. Azureae

Corolla scarlet. 1. *S. coccinea.*
Corolla blue, purplish, or white.
 Leaf-blades narrow, usually over 4 times as long as wide. 2. *S. azurea.*

Leaf-blades broad, mostly less than twice as long as wide.
  Calyx over 5 mm. long at maturity.
    Leaf-blades very slightly decurrent on the petioles.
      Calyx-lobes merely acute: flower-clusters approximate or contiguous.   3. *S. serotina.*
      Calyx-lobes awn-tipped: flower-clusters widely separated.   4. *S. privoides.*
    Leaf-blades decurrent on the petioles to their bases.
      Corolla over 1 cm. long: calyx-lobes nearly erect.   5. *S. urticifolia.*
      Corolla less than 1 cm. long: calyx-lobes spreading.   6. *S. Chapmanii.*
  Calyx less than 5 mm. long at maturity.
    Petioles filiform, wingless: stigmas subulate.   7. *S. Blodgettii.*
    Petioles winged by the decurrent blades: stigmas broad.   8. *S. occidentalis.*

II. VERBENACEAE

Plant villous or villous-hirsute: leaf-blades incised to pinnatifid.   9. *S. verbenacea.*

III. LYRATAE

Plant with the leaves mainly basal; blades lyrate-pinnatifid.   10. *S. lyrata.*

1. S. coccinea L. Stems 3–7 dm. tall, softly pubescent: leaf-blades ovate to deltoid-ovate, 3–6 cm. long, crenate-serrate: calyx 10–12 mm. long; corolla scarlet; lower lip with a notched middle lobe 7–8 mm. wide: nutlets 2.5 mm. long.— Sandy soil, hammocks, waste-places, and roadsides, Coastal Plain, Fla. to Tex., and S. C.—(*Mex.*)—Spr.–fall.

2. S. azurea Lam. Stems 3–12 dm. tall, puberulent above: leaf-blades oblong to lanceolate or linear, or rarely broader, 3–10 cm. long, undulate or shallowly serrate: calyx 7–9 mm. long; lower lobes ovate: corolla azure-blue or white, 13–15 mm. long: style pubescent at the top: nutlets about 3 mm. long.—Dry soil, pinelands, sand-hills and woods, Coastal Plain, Fla. to Tex., and S. C.—Spr.–fall.

3. S. serotina L. Stems 1–7 dm. tall, finely pubescent: leaf-blades ovate to orbicular-ovate, 1–4 cm. long, crenate-serrate: inflorescence usually rather shortened, sometimes elongate, but always densely flowered: calyx glandular-pubescent, 6–8 mm. long: corolla 6–10 mm. long: nutlets fully 2 mm. long.— Pinelands, hammocks, and cult. grounds, Fla.—Spr.–fall.

4. S. privoides Benth. Stem 5–18 dm. tall, pubescent: leaf-blades ovate, 1–3 cm. long, sharply serrate: inflorescence elongated and slender, the flowers scattered along the rachis: calyx glandular-pubescent, 5–7 mm. long; lower lobes awn-tipped: corolla 5.5–6 mm. long: nutlets barely 2 mm. long.—Sandy places, pen. Fla., and the Keys.—(*W. I., Mex., C. A.*)—Spr.–fall.

5. S. urticifolia L. Stem 2–7 dm. tall, finely pubescent: leaf-blades ovate to deltoid, 3–8 cm. long, dentate or crenate: calyx 6–8 mm. long; lower lobes cuspidate: corolla deep-blue, 11–13 mm. long, lower lip about 8 mm. wide: nutlets about 2 mm. long.—Woods and thickets, various provinces, Fla. to La., Ky., and N. C.—Spr.–sum.

6. S. Chapmanii A. Gray. Stem 10–20 dm. tall, closely pubescent: leaf-blades ovate to ovate-lanceolate, 2.5–8 cm. long, crenate-serrate: calyx 4–6 mm. long; lower lobes acute: corolla 8–9 mm. long; lower lip about 4 mm. wide: nutlets about 1.5 mm. long.—Sandy soil, Coastal Plain, Fla. and Ala.—Spr.

7. S. Blodgettii Chapm. Stem 1–7 dm. tall, minutely pubescent: leaf-blades ovate to suborbicular, 1–2 cm. long, shallowly toothed: calyx about 4 mm. long; lower lobes acute: corolla about 8 mm. long.—Hammocks, Key West, Fla.—All year.

8. S. occidentalis Sw. Stem 5–20 dm. tall, pubescent: leaf-blades ovate, 2–5 cm. long, serrate: calyx 3–3.5 mm. long; lower lobes acute: corolla about 5 mm. long: nutlets 2 mm. long.—Sandy soil, pen. Fla.—(*W. I., Mex., C. A., S. A.*)—Spr.–fall.

9. S. verbenacea L. Stem 1–6 dm. tall, hirsute or villous-hirsute; leaf-blades ovate to elliptic, 3–15 cm. long, incised or pinnatifid: calyx 6–8 mm. long, shaggy-pubescent; lower lobes lanceolate: corolla bluish, 8–10 mm. long: nutlets nearly smooth.—Sandy soil, various provinces, Ga., to Ala., Ohio, and S. C. Nat. of Eu.—Sum.—*Salvia Sclarea*—CLARY—a native of Europe, with viscid foliage, large cordate, coarsely toothed leaf-blades and white and purple corollas, has been found in N. Car.

10. S. lyrata L. Stem 1–6 dm tall, scape-like, pilose or hirsute: leaves mainly basal; blades spatulate, oblanceolate, elliptic, or oval, 5–20 cm. long, lyrate-pinnatifid: calyx 9–11 mm. long, hirsute; lower lobes lanceolate: corolla blue-purple, 20–25 mm. long: nutlets granular.—(LYRE-LEAVED SAGE.)—Woods, hammocks, pinelands, various provinces, Fla. to Tex., Mo., and Conn.—Early sum.

20. MONARDA L. Shrubs, or perennial erect herbs. Leaf-blades toothed. Flowers in remote or approximate dense cymes. Calyx elongate, nearly regular: lobes 5, slender, shorter than the tube. Corolla 2-lipped, elongate: upper lip narrow, erect or arched: lower lip 3-lobed, the middle lobe much longer than the lateral ones. Stamens 2: filaments elongate: anthers with divergent sacs. About 20 species, North American.—HORSE-MINTS.

Flower-clusters terminal and solitary: stamens exserted beyond the straight upper corolla-lip.	Subgenus I. EUMONARDA.
Flower-clusters mainly axillary, borne in spike-like interrupted panicles: stamens not exceeding the curved upper corolla-lip.	Subgenus II. CHEILYCTIS.

Subgenus I. EUMONARDA

Leaf-blades relatively long-petioled or manifestly petioled.	
Corolla scarlet.	1. *M. didyma.*
Corolla white, pink, or purple.	
Leaf-blades membranous, deep-green: corolla greenish or cream-colored.	2. *M. Clinopodia.*
Leaf-blades firmer, barely membranous, dull- or bright-green: corolla pink, purple, or purple-red.	
Pubescence of spreading hairs.	
Corolla, and often the bracts, lilac or purplish.	3. *M. fistulosa.*
Corolla, and the bracts, deep-purple or purple-red.	4. *M. media.*
Pubescence of very short appressed hairs.	
Leaves on the upper part of the stem with petioles less than 5 mm. long.	5. *M. scabra.*
Leaves on the upper part of the stem with petioles over 5 mm. long.	6. *M. mollis.*
Leaf-blades sessile or nearly so: calyx pubescent at the mouth; lobes not glandular.	7. *M. Bradburiana.*

Subgenus II. CHEILYCTIS

Plants perennial: calyx-lobes acuminate: corolla yellowish, or rarely white.	8. *M. punctata.*
Plants annual or biennial: calyx-lobes setaceous: corolla pink or purplish.	9. *M. dispersa.*

1. M. didyma L. Stem 3–12 dm. tall, sometimes sparingly pubescent: leaf-blades lanceolate or elliptic-lanceolate to ovate, 8–15 cm. long, serrate: heads

showy: calyx 7–11 mm. long; lobes subulate:
corolla 35–50 mm. long; middle lobe of the
lower lip acute.—(BEE-BALM. OSWEGO-TEA).
—Moist woods, stream-banks, thickets, and
roadsides, Blue Ridge and more northern
provinces, Ga. to Ala., Ont., and N. B.—
Sum.–fall.

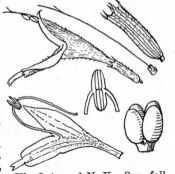

2. M. Clinopodia L.   Stem 3–8 dm. tall,
glabrous or sparingly pubescent: leaf-blades
ovate to lanceolate, 3–12 cm. long, serrate:
bracts pale: calyx 7–9 mm. long, somewhat
bearded in the throat; lobes short-subulate:
corolla 24–28 mm. long; lower lip with
rounded lateral lobes: nutlets fully 1 mm.
long.—Hillsides, woods, and moist thickets,
various provinces, rarely Coastal Plain, Ga. to Ill., Ont., and N. Y.—Spr.–fall.

3. M. fistulosa L.   Stem 5–12 dm. tall, villous or villous-hirsute: leaf-blades
ovate to lanceolate, 2–12 cm. long, remotely sharp-serrate: bracts usually
colored: calyx 8–12 mm. long, copiously bearded in the throat; lobes long-
subulate: corolla 30–34 mm. long; lower lip with acute lateral lobes: nutlets
fully 1.5 mm. long.—(HORSE-MINT. WILD-BERGAMOT).—Dry hillsides, fence-
rows, rocky woods, and thickets, often in calcareous soil, various provinces, Fla.
to La., Ont., and Me.—Sum.–fall.

4. M. media Willd.   Stem 6–12 dm. tall, hirsute or glabrate: leaf-blades
ovate, lanceolate, or elliptic, 8–12 cm. long, serrate: calyx 9–10 mm. long;
lobes subulate: corolla 15–22 mm. long; lower lip with rounded lateral lobes.—
Thickets and stream-banks, Blue Ridge, and more northern provinces, N. C. to
Tenn., Pa., and Me.—Sum.

5. M. scabra Beck.   Stem 2–10 dm. tall, velvety-pubescent: leaf-blades ovate
to lanceolate, 2–8 cm. long, sharply, often remotely, serrate: calyx 7–9 mm.
long; lobes subulate: corolla 20–25 mm. long, pale-purple; lower lip with
rounded lateral lobes.—Dry soil, various provinces, rarely Coastal Plain, Ala.
to Tex., Ariz., B. C., and Man.—Sum.

6. M. mollis L.   Similar to *M. fistulosa* in habit and to *M. scabra* in pubescence: leaf-blades ovate to lanceolate, 5–11.5 cm. long, coarsely serrate: calyx
8–10 mm. long; lobes subulate: corolla 24–27 mm. long, pink to lilac.—Dry
soil, Blue Ridge and more northern provinces, Ga. to Tenn., S. Dak., and
Me.—Sum.

7. M. Bradburiana Beck.   Stem 3–6 dm. tall, more or less villous-hirsute
above: leaf-blades ovate to lanceolate, 3–10 cm. long, serrate or nearly entire:
calyx 9–10 mm. long; lobes subulate: corolla pink or whitish, 20–27 mm. long.
—Thickets and hillsides, various provinces N of Coastal Plain, Ala. to Kans.
and Ill.—Spr.–sum.

8. M. punctata L.   Stem 3–10 dm. tall, finely pubescent: leaf-blades linear-
elliptic to lanceolate, 2–8 cm. long, serrate: calyx 8–10 mm. long; lobes short-
acuminate, spreading: corolla yellowish and purple-spotted (white in *M. punctata leucantha*), 20–25 mm. long; upper lip mainly elliptic-ovate.—Sandy fields,
pastures, woods and roadsides, in rather acid soil, various provinces, Fla. to
Tex., Minn., and N. Y.—Sum.–fall.

9. M. dispersa Small. Stem 2–8 dm. tall, puberulent: leaf-blades elliptic to elliptic-spatulate or oblanceolate on the lower part of the stem, narrowly elliptic or linear above, 2–11 cm. long, shallowly serrate: calyx-tube 8–9 mm. long; lobes spreading: corolla pink or purplish, 20–25 mm. long; lower lip with an elliptic middle lobe.—Low grounds, various provinces, Fla. to Tex., N. M., Mo., and Ga.—(*Mex.*)—Native westward.—Spr.–sum.

21. BLEPHILIA Raf. Perennial erect herbs. Leaf-blades shallowly toothed. Flowers in dense axillary cymes. Calyx 2-lipped: upper lip 3-lobed: lower lip 2-lobed. Corolla 2-lipped: upper lip erect, entire: lower lip 3-lobed, the narrow middle lobe much longer than the others. Stamens 2, long-exserted. —Only the following species.—Sum.

Cauline and floral leaves with short-petioled or nearly sessile blades : bractlets acute or short-acuminate.   **1. B. ciliata.**
Cauline and floral leaves with rather long-petioled blades : bractlets long-acuminate.   **2. B. hirsuta.**

1. B. ciliata (L.) Raf. Stem 3–6 dm. tall, softly villous-pubescent: leaf-blades lanceolate, 5–10 cm. long, shallowly toothed, short-petioled or nearly sessile: outer bractlets usually broadly ovate; all with acute or short acuminate tips; calyx 8–11 mm. long: corolla pink or purplish, 10–12 mm. long; middle lobe of the lower lip truncate or notched.—Thickets and dry woods, various provinces, Ga. to Tex., Wis., and Mass.

2. B. hirsuta (Pursh) Torr. Stem 3–10 dm. tall, hirsute or villous-hirsute: leaf-blades ovate to lanceolate, 5–12 cm. long serrate, rather long-petioled: outer bractlets usually ovate-lanceolate; all with long acuminate tips; calyx 6–8 mm. long: corolla pale or almost white, 10–11 mm. long; middle lobe of the lower lip rounded or slightly notched.—Shaded grounds, various provinces, Ga. to Tex., Wis., and Vt.

22. HEDEOMA Pers. Annual or perennial often diffuse herbs. Leaf-blades entire or sparingly toothed. Flowers in remote or contiguous axillary cymes. Calyx 2-lipped, sometimes obscurely so: lobes of the upper lip broader and shorter than those of the lower lip. Corolla 2-lipped: upper lip sometimes notched: lower lip 3-lobed, commonly broader than the lateral one. Stamens 2, accompanied by more or less reduced ones. One stigma obsolete.—About 15 species, American.

1. H. pulegioides (L.) Pers. Plant very fragrant: stem 1–4 dm. tall, finely pubescent: leaf-blades oval-elliptic to elliptic, 9–20 mm. long, sparingly serrate, mostly purple beneath: calyx becoming 4–5 mm. long; tubes strongly ribbed: corolla 4–5 mm. long, pale lilac, with a deep purple blotch on the lower lip.—(PENNYROYAL. MOCK-PENNYROYAL. AMERICAN-PENNY-

ROYAL.)—Dry fields and open woods, various provinces, Fla. to Nebr., Minn., and N. S.—Sum.

23. **STACHYDEOMA** Small. Perennial erect herbs. Leaf-blades toothed. Flowers pale-lilac, in long leafy-bracted spike-like panicles. Calyx strongly 2-lipped; lobes of the upper lip broad, those of the lower lip subulate. Corolla 2-lipped: upper lip entire: lower lip drooping, 3-lobed, the lateral lobes about equalling the terminal one. Stamens 2, exserted: anthers shorter than the filaments. Staminodia present. Style glabrous.—One species.

1. **S. graveolens** (Chapm.) Small. Stem 2–6 dm. tall, hirsute: leaf-blades suborbicular to ovate, 10–15 mm. long: calyx becoming 7–9 mm. long; upper lip ovate: nutlets 0.5 mm. long. [*Hedeoma graveolens* Chapm.] —Low pinelands, N Fla.—Sum.

24. **MELISSA** [Tourn.] L. Perennial, erect herbs. Leaf-blades broad, toothed. Flowers in axillary clusters. Calyx 2-lipped, the broad upper lip with 3 minute lobes, the 2 lobes of the lower lip slender. Corolla 2-lipped: upper lip mostly notched: lower lip 3-lobed, the middle lobe very broad. Stamens 4, exserted.— About 4 species, Eurasian.

1. **M. officinalis** L. Plant lemon-scented, 3–9 dm. tall: leaf-blades ovate to ovate-oblong, 2–8 cm. long, crenate-serrate: calyx ringent, 7–8 mm. long; upper lip curved upward: corolla white or cream-colored, about 10 mm. long: nutlets 1.5 mm. long.— (BEE-BALM. LEMON-BALM.)—Roadsides and waste-places, various provinces, Fla. to Ark., Mo., and Me. Nat. of Eu.—Sum.

25. **CONRADINA** A. Gray. Shrubs with virgate branches. Leaf-blades narrow, entire, revolute, fasciculate. Flowers 1–few together in axillary cymes which are sometimes approximate. Calyx 2-lipped; upper lip with 3 short and broad lobes; lower lip with 2 long and narrow lobes: corolla bluish or purplish, 2-lipped; upper lip erect, slightly concave; lower lip divergent, 3-lobed, usually dotted, the terminal lobe about the same size as the lateral ones or smaller. Stamens 4, exserted or lying under the upper corolla lip.— Four species, the following:

Lower corolla-lip 12–15 mm. long; lateral lobes wider than long.
        1. *C. grandiflora.*
Lower corolla-lip 8–10 mm. long; lateral lobes longer than wide.
  Calyx-tube hirsute, villous-hirsute, or hirsutulous.
    Leaf-blades pubescent on both sides: calyx-tube hirsute or villous-hirsute.
        2. *C. canescens.*
    Leaf-blades glabrous above: calyx-tube hirsutulous.
        3. *C. montana.*
  Calyx-tube minutely canescent.
        4. *C. puberula.*

1. C. grandiflora Small. Shrub 1 m. tall or less with few, virgate, often curved branches: leaf-blades narrowly spatulate, clavate on account of the revolute margins, mostly 10–25 mm. long, white-canescent beneath, otherwise glabrous or nearly so, at least at maturity, punctate: calyx becoming 6.5–7.5 mm. long, finely pubescent: upper lip of corolla 7–9 mm. long: nutlets nearly 1.5 mm. long.—Scrub, lower E coast region, Fla.—All year.

2. C. canescens (T. & G.) A. Gray. Shrub less than 0.5 m. tall, with numerous stiff branches: leaf-blades broadly spatulate, but tightly revolute and thus clavate, 5–9 mm. long, finely canescent: calyx becoming 4.5–5.5 mm. long: upper lip of corolla 4–5 mm. long: nutlets fully 1 mm. long.—Pinelands, upper Gulf coast region, Fla. and Ala.—Spr.

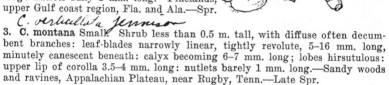

C. verticillata Jennison

3. C. montana Small. Shrub less than 0.5 m. tall, with diffuse often decumbent branches: leaf-blades narrowly linear, tightly revolute, 5–16 mm. long, minutely canescent beneath: calyx becoming 6–7 mm. long; lobes hirsutulous: upper lip of corolla 3.5–4 mm. long: nutlets barely 1 mm. long.—Sandy woods and ravines, Appalachian Plateau, near Rugby, Tenn.—Late Spr.

4. C. puberula Small. Shrub about 0.5 m. tall, with rather numerous slender branches: leaf-blades narrowly spatulate, but revolute and slenderly clavate, mostly 12–20 mm. long, puberulent: calyx becoming 5–7 mm. long; lobes hirsute: upper lip of corolla 4–5 mm. long: nutlets fully 1 mm. long.—Pinelands, N Gulf coast region, Fla.—Spr.

A plant of this genus collected near Bristol, Fla., has the small flowers of *C. canescens* and *C. puberula*, but differs in the foliage and inflorescence being glabrous or nearly so, except the ciliate calyx-lobes, and in the abortive anthers.

26. PYCNOTHYMUS Small. Shrubs. Leaf-blades narrow, entire. Flowers in dense raceme-like panicles. Calyx slightly irregular, the upper lip with 3 narrow lobes, the lower lip with 2 longer lobes. Corolla 2-lipped: lower lip 3-lobed, the middle lobe slightly larger than the lateral ones.—One species.

1. P. rigidus (Bart.) Small. Plant 1–7 dm. tall or low and diffuse, hirsute: leaf-blades lanceolate, 5–12 mm. long: calyx 2.5–3 mm. long; lobes lanceolate to elliptic-lanceolate: corolla light-purple, 7–8 mm. long; lobes rounded. — (PENNYROYAL.) — Pinelands, pen. Fla.—All year.—This plant is rather wide-spread in southern pen. Florida. It is commonly used for making a tea. The plants of the eastern coastal region grow more erect and have lighter colored flowers than those of the western coastal region.

27. **MICROMERIA** Benth. Perennial, diffuse or creeping herbs. Leaf-blades entire or sparingly toothed. Flowers in axillary cymes, the cymes in ours one-flowered. Calyx with a fringe of hairs in the throat; almost equally 5-lobed, the lobes short. Corolla 2-lipped, pink, lavender-pink, or whitish: upper lip erect: lower lip 3-lobed, the middle lobe very broad. Stamens 4, more or less exserted.—About 60 species, widely distributed.

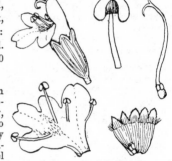

1. **M. pilosiuscula** (A. Gray) Small. Stem and branches sparingly pubescent or glabrate, the branches ascending or spreading, 1–4 dm. long: leaf-blades suborbicular to broadly ovate, 5–25 mm. long, sparingly pubescent: calyx glabrate or sparingly pilose, 4–5 mm. long, shorter than the pedicel or sometimes equalling it in length; lobes 1–1.5 mm. long, ovate-deltoid, those of the upper lip abruptly acute, acutish, or even acuminate; corolla 7–8 mm. long, pink, lavender-pink, or whitish; tube much dilated; middle lobe of the lower lip about as wide as long, notched.—Swamps, marshes, stream-banks, woods, and ditches. Coastal Plain, Fla. to Tex.—(*Mex.*)—Spr.–sum.

M. Brownei (Sw.) Benth., a West Indian species with which the above species has been confused, but which differs in the size of the calyx and the shape of the calyx-lobes, as well as in size of plant, leaf, and flower, is not known to occur in the continental U. S.

28. **CLINOPODIUM** L. Shrubs or annual or perennial herbs. Leaf-blades entire or toothed. Flowers in sessile or peduncled axillary cymes. Calyx 2-lipped, the upper lip with 3 short lobes, the lower lip with 2 long, narrow lobes. Corolla 2-lipped: upper lip sometimes notched: lower lip 3-lobed. Stamens 4: anthers awnless.—Spr.–fall, or all year southward.—About 60 species, natives of the north temperate zone.—Basils.

Flowers in dense axillary clusters, thus forming head-like whorls, accompanied by
   linear-filiform bractlets.   I. Vulgaria.
Flowers few together or solitary in the axils of the leaves, with
   minute bractlets.
    Plants herbaceous.   II. Herbacea.
    Plants woody.   III. Fruticosa.

I. Vulgaria

Stem hirsute: calyx-lobes hirsute: corolla slightly exceeding the
   calyx.   1. *C. vulgare.*

II. Herbacea

Stem and leaves pubescent: leaf-blades ovate, often broadly so. 2. *C. Nepeta.*
Stem and leaves glabrous or nearly so: leaf-blades linear to
   elliptic.   3. *C. glabellum.*

III. Fruticosa

Corolla over 2.5 cm. long, scarlet.
   Calyx less than 1.5 cm. long: corolla 3–4 cm. long.   4. *C. coccineum.*
   Calyx over 1.5 cm. long: corolla 4–5 cm. long.   5. *C. macrocalyx.*
Corolla less than 2 cm. long, white or purplish.
   Leaf-blades toothed, broad and flat.
    Clusters 5–6-flowered: leaf-blades sessile or nearly so. 6. *C. georgianum.*
    Clusters 1–3-flowered: leaf-blades petioled.   7. *C. dentatum.*
   Leaf-blades entire, narrow and strongly revolute.   8. *C. Ashei.*

1. **C. vulgare** L. Stem 1–5 dm. tall, hirsute: blades of the upper leaves ovate to ovate-lanceolate, 1–4 cm. long, undulate or crenate: calyx becoming 8–9

mm. long, villous-hirsute: corolla white or pink, 11–13 mm. long; middle lobe of the lower lip broadened upward: nutlets about 1 mm. long.—(WILD-BASIL. BASIL-WEED. DOG-MINT.) — Roadsides, old fields, and woods, various provinces, N. C. to Okla., Ariz., Man., and Newf. — (*Eurasia.*) — Sum.–fall.

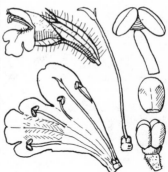

2. C. Nepeta (L.) Kuntze. Plant 2–9 dm. tall, copiously pubescent: leaf-blades ovate to orbicular-ovate, 10–20 mm. long, slightly toothed: calyx becoming 5–6 mm. long: corolla light-purple or nearly white, 8–9 mm. long.—(FIELD-BALM. BASIL-THYME.)— Fields and waste-places, various provinces, Ga. to Ark., and Md. Nat. of Eu.—Sum.–fall.

3. C. glabellum (Michx.) Kuntze. Stem 1–4 dm. tall, glabrous or nearly so: blades of the upper leaves linear-elliptic or elliptic, sparingly serrate: calyx becoming 5–6 mm. long: corolla purplish, 8–12 mm. long.—Wet or damp banks, Interior Low Plateaus, Tenn. and Ky.—Spr.–sum.

4. C. coccineum (Nutt.) Kuntze. Shrub 3–9 dm. tall: leaf-blades obovate to spatulate, linear-spatulate or linear-elliptic, 0.5–2 cm. long, entire: calyx 8–11 mm. long; lateral lobes of the upper lip triangular: corolla scarlet, 3–4 cm. long; lobes of the upper lip shorter than those of the lower.—Sandy shores, sandhills, and hammocks, Coastal Plain, Fla. to Ala. and Ga.—All year.

5. C. macrocalyx Small. Similar to *C. coccineum* in habit: leaf-blades broadly spatulate, 1–1.5 mm. long: calyx 16–18 mm. long; lateral lobes of the upper lip lanceolate-subulate: corolla scarlet, 4–5 cm. long; lobes of the upper lip longer than those of the lower.—Pinelands, E pen. Fla.—All year.

6. C. georgianum Harper. Shrub 2–6 dm. tall: leaf-blades ovate, oval or elliptic, 10–30 mm. long, shallowly serrate: calyx 5–6 mm. long: corolla white or pink-purple, and purple-spotted, 11–13 mm. long; middle lobe of the lower lip quite similar to the lateral ones and scarcely longer. [*C. carolinianum* (Michx.) Heller.]—River-banks, dry woods, and hammocks, Coastal Plain, and rarely adj. provinces, Fla. to Miss. and N. C.—Sum.–fall.

7. C. dentatum (Chapm.) Kuntze. Shrub 3–7 dm. tall: leaf-blades obovate to elliptic-cuneate, 5–12 mm. long, mainly toothed at the apex: calyx 7–8 mm. long: corolla white or purplish, 11–13 mm. long; middle lobe of the lower lip broader than the lateral ones and extending beyond them.—Sand-ridges, middle Fla.—Spr.–fall.

8. C. Ashei (Weatherby) Small. Shrub 1–5 dm. tall: leaf-blades linear to narrowly linear-elliptic, 0.5–1 cm. long, entire, strongly revolute: calyx 6–8 mm. long; lobes of the upper lip completely fused, the tip merely shallowly tridentate: corolla pinkish-purple with darker spots, 12–15 mm. long; middle lobe of the lower lip broader and longer than the lateral lobes.—Scrub, Lake Region, Fla.—Spr.

29. **DICERANDRA** Benth. Annual erect herbs. Leaf-blades narrow, entire. Flowers in axillary cymes. Calyx 2-lipped, the upper lip entire or with 3 minute lobes, the lower lip with 2 broad lobes. Corolla 2-lipped: upper lip broad: lower lip 3-lobed, the middle lobe sometimes scarcely as wide as the lateral ones. Stamens 4: anthers awned.—Three species, as follows:

Corolla pink-purple: anthers exserted: calyx purple-tinged: lobes of the lower lip deltoid or triangular: style pubescent to below the middle.

Cymes nearly sessile: anther-horns blunt or acute. 1. *D. densiflora.*
Cymes markedly peduncled: anther-horns acuminate. 2. *D. linearifolia.*
Corolla white: anthers included: calyx white above; lobes of
the lower lip subulate: style pubescent near the tip. 3. *D. odoratissima.*

1. D. densiflora Benth. Stem 1–4 dm. tall: leaf-blades narrowly elliptic to linear-elliptic, 2–4 cm. long: calyx becoming 6–8 mm. long: corolla 11–14 mm. long. [*Ceranthera densiflora* A. Gray.]—
Pinelands, Coastal Plain, E Fla. and Ga.—
Sum.–fall.

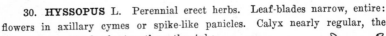

2. D. linearifolia (Ell.) Benth. Stem 2–4 dm. tall: leaf-blades linear or lanceolate, 1–3 cm. long: calyx becoming 6–7 mm. long: corolla 14–16 mm. long. [*Ceranthera linearifolia* Ell.]—Pinelands and sandhills, Coastal Plain, Fla. to Ala. and Ga.—Fall.

3. D. odoratissima Harper. Stem 2–4 dm. tall: leaf-blades linear, 2–4 cm. long: calyx becoming 8–11 mm. long: corolla 14–17 mm. long.—Sandhills, Coastal Plain, S E Ga. —Fall.

30. HYSSOPUS L. Perennial erect herbs. Leaf-blades narrow, entire: flowers in axillary cymes or spike-like panicles. Calyx nearly regular, the lobes nearly equal, shorter than the tube. Corolla 2-lipped: upper lip notched: lower lip 3-lobed, the middle lobe very broad. Stamens 4. Stigmas very short.—One species.

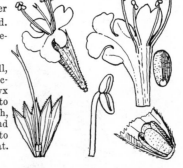

1. H. officinalis L. Stem 2–9 dm. tall, puberulent: leaf-blades elliptic to elliptic-lanceolate or linear, 1–3 cm. long: calyx becoming about 7 mm. long; lobes ovate to lanceolate, ribbed: corolla blue or purplish, 8–10 mm. long.—(HYSSOP.)—Roadsides and waste-places, various provinces, N. C. to Ont. and Me., also on Pacific slope. Nat. of Eu.—Sum.

31. ORIGANUM [Tourn.] L. Perennial herbs, or partially woody plants. Leaf-blades broad, often notched. Cymes mostly borne in corymbs. Calyx stout, nearly equally 5-lobed. Corolla 2-lipped: upper lip broad, slightly lobed: lower lip with 3 rather broad lobes. Stamens 4. Stigmas short.—About 30 species, natives of the Old World.

1. O. vulgare L. Stem mostly simple below, sparingly branched above, villous-hirsute: leaf-blades ovate, mostly 1.5–2.5 cm. long, shallowly toothed or entire: calyx 2–2.5 mm. long; lobes ovate, shorter than the tube: corolla pale-magenta or rarely white, 6–7 mm. long; lobes of the upper lip rounded, the lateral lobes of the lower lip rounded, the lateral lobes of the lower lip broadly ovate: nutlets less than 1 mm. long.—(WILD-MARJORAM.)—Thickets, roadsides, and fields, various provinces, N. C. to Ont., and Mass. Nat. of Eu.—Sum.—A related Old World plant and similar in habit, *Majorana Majorana*—the SWEET-MARJORAM of the gardens.— with a 2-lipped calyx, sometimes escapes from cultivation.

32. THYMUS [Tourn.] L. Perennial depressed or creeping herbs. Leaf-blades short, mostly entire. Flowers in axillary cymes or raceme-like panicles. Calyx 2-lipped, the upper lip with 3 short lobes, the lower lip with 2 longer lobes. Corolla 2-lipped: upper lip erect: lower lip 3-lobed, the middle lobe scarcely larger than the lateral ones. Stamens 4. Stigmas long. —About 50 species, mostly European.

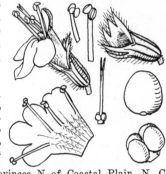

1. T. Serpyllum L. Plant fragrant, form-ing depressed mats: leaf-blades elliptic to oval or ovate, 3–10 mm. long: calyx becom-ing 3.5–4 mm. long; lobes of the lower lip about as long as the tube: corolla purplish, about as long as the calyx: nutlets less than 1 mm. long.—(CREEPING-THYME. THYME.) Meadows, roadsides, and fields, various provinces N of Coastal Plain, N. C. to W. Va. and N. S. Nat of Eu.—Sum.

33. KOELLIA Moench. Perennial erect herbs. Leaf-blades entire or shallowly toothed, those of the upper leaves, like the bracts, often more or less whitened. Flowers in dense axillary and terminal cymes, pale with purplish spots. Calyx nearly regular or somewhat 2-lipped, the lobes short or elongate. Corolla 2-lipped: upper lip erect: lower lip 3-lobed, the middle lobe larger than the lateral ones. Stamens 4.—[*Pycnanthemum* Michx.]—Sum.—MOUNTAIN-MINTS. HORSE-MINTS. BASILS.—About 20 species, North American.

Flower-clusters apparently naked, the bracts small and incon-
spicuous.   I. NUDAE.
Flower-clusters conspicuously bracted.
   Calyx not 2-lipped, lobes equal or nearly so.
      Corolla much exceeding the calyx: calyx-lobes not aris-
tate.   II. LANCEOLATAE.
      Corolla about as long as the calyx: calyx-lobes aristate. III. ARISTATAE.
   Calyx somewhat 2-lipped, the three upper lobes partly united. IV. INCANAE.

I. NUDAE
Stem strict, topped by a corymb-like cyme: flower-clusters
permanently small.   1. *K. nuda.*
II LANCEOLATAE
Bractlets ciliolate.
   Calyx-lobes triangular or ovate-triangular.   2. *K. virginiana.*
   Calyx-lobes subulate to lanceolate, triangular-lanceo-
late, or deltoid.
      Leaf-blades or most of them over 3 times as long
as broad.
        Leaves with strictly entire blades.   3. *K. flexuosa.*
        Leaves, or the larger ones, with toothed blades.
           Flower-clusters 1–2 cm. broad at maturity,
compact.
              Flower-clusters conspicuously woolly at
maturity: stems copiously pubes-
cent.
                Calyx-lobes acute: leaf-blades firm;
species campestrian.   4. *K. pilosa.*

Calyx-lobes acuminate: leaf-blades
thin: species Alleghenian. 5. *K. leptodon.*
Flower-clusters not woolly at maturity:
stems minutely pubescent. 6. *K. verticillata.*
Flower-clusters 2–3 cm. broad at maturity,
not crowded. 7. *K. clinopodioides.*
Leaf-blades or most of them less than 3 times as
long as broad. 8. *K. mutica.*
Bractlets copiously villous-ciliate. 9. *K. montana.*

III. Aristatae

Calyx-lobes, at least the lower ones, shorter than the
tube: bracts with tips mostly shorter than the
body: coastal species.
Calyx-lobes lanceolate to lanceolate-subulate, less than
⅓ as long as the tube: leaf-blades broad. 10. *K. aristata.*
Calyx-lobes subulate-filiform, over ½ as long as the
tube: leaf-blades narrow. 11. *K. hyssopifolia.*
Calyx-lobes, at least the lower ones, longer than the tube:
bracts with tips mostly longer than the body: Alleghenian species. 12. *K. Hugeri.*

IV. Incanae

Calyx-lobes minutely pubescent, without long hairs (except a rare form of 13): bractlets pubescent like
the calyx and usually without long hairs.
Calyx-lobes ovate or lanceolate.
Calyx-lobes ovate, obtuse or acutish: mature calyx
about 4 mm. long. 13. *K. albescens.*
Calyx-lobes lanceolate, acuminate: mature calyx
about 5 mm. long. 14. *K. pauciflora.*
Calyx-lobes deltoid.
Corolla much exceeding the calyx: calyx-lobes
mostly slightly longer than wide. 15. *K. multiflora.*
Corolla slightly exceeding the calyx: calyx-lobes
mostly slightly wider than long. 16. *K. curvipes.*
Calyx with long hairs in addition to the minute ones, at
least when young: bractlets finely bristly pubescent
or plumose.
Leaf-blades mostly whitened, at least, beneath.
Calyx-lobes conspicuously long-hairy; the upper
ones subulate. 17. *K. pycnanthemoides.*
Calyx-lobes inconspicuously long-hairy; the upper
ones lanceolate. 18. *K. incana.*
Leaf-blades not whitened, glabrous or nearly so, or
hirsutulous beneath.
Calyx-lobes copiously long-hairy, often plumose:
leaf-blades hirsutulous beneath, usually cuneate
at the base. 19. *K. dubia.*
Calyx-lobes sparingly long-hairy, not plumose:
leaf-blades glabrous or nearly so, rounded or
subcordate at the base. 20. *K. Beadlei.*

1. K. nuda (Nutt.) Kuntz. Stem 3–7 dm. tall, glabrous or nearly so: leaf-
blades oval or elliptic, 1–2 cm. long, entire or nearly so: calyx 3–4 mm. long;
lobes deltoid: corolla about 5 mm. long;
upper lip obtuse.—Pinelands, Coastal Plain,
Fla. to Ala. and N. C.—Sum.–fall.

2. K. virginiana (L.) Britton. Stem 4–9
dm. tall, minutely pubescent: leaf-blades
lanceolate to linear-lanceolate, 2–5 cm. long,
mostly entire: calyx 3.5–4 mm. long; lobes
triangular to ovate-triangular: corolla 6–7
mm. long; upper lip notched; middle lobe of
the lower lip slightly narrower than the
lateral ones.—Woods, fields, and thickets,
various provinces, rarely Coastal Plain, Ga.
to Ala., Kans., N. D., and Que.—Sum.–fall.

3. K. flexuosa (Walt.) MacM. Stem 3–8

dm. tall, glabrous: leaf-blades narrowly linear to linear-filiform, 1–4 cm. long, entire: calyx about 3.5 mm. long; lobes lanceolate to triangular-lanceolate: corolla 6–7 mm. long; upper lip minutely notched; middle lobe of the lower lip much narrower than the lateral ones.—Meadows, fields, and thickets, various provinces, Fla. to Tex., Minn., and Me.—Sum.–fall.

4. K. pilosa (Nutt.) Britton. Stem 4–13 dm. tall, cinereous-pubescent: leaf-blades lanceolate to linear-lanceolate, 2–6 cm. long, entire or sparingly denticulate: calyx 4–5 mm. long, minutely pubescent; lobes broad-lanceolate: corolla 7–8 mm. long.—Prairies and dry woods, various provinces, rarely Coastal Plain, Ga. to Ark., Mo., and Pa.—Sum.–fall.

5. K. leptodon (A. Gray) Small. Stem 5–11 dm. tall, soft-pubescent. at least above: leaf-blades lanceolate to elliptic-lanceolate, 2–5 cm. long, serrate or entire: calyx 4.5–5.5 mm. long, rather villous; lobes narrow-lanceolate: corolla 6–7 mm. long.—Mt. woods, Blue Ridge, N. C.—Sum.

6. K. verticillata (Michx.) Kuntze. Stem 4–12 dm. tall, minutely pubescent: leaf-blades lanceolate to almost linear, 2–6 cm. long, remotely or shallowly serrate: calyx 4–5 mm. long; lobes subulate-lanceolate: corolla 6–7 mm. long, or rarely longer.—Fields, thickets, and woods, various provinces, Ga. to Mass. and Que.—Sum.–fall.

7. K. clinopodioides (T. & G.) Kuntze. Stem 4–12 dm. tall, softly-pubescent: leaf-blades lanceolate, narrowly elliptic, 2–8 cm. long, more or less serrate: calyx 4–4.5 mm. long; lobes lanceolate-subulate, nearly ½ as long as the tube: corolla about 6 mm. long.—Open woods and dry thickets, various provinces N of Coastal Plain, Tenn. to Pa., Conn., and Va.—Sum.

8. K. mutica (Michx.) Britton. Stem 6–10 dm. tall, finely pubescent: leaf-blades thick, ovate to lanceolate, 2–6 cm. long, serrate: calyx 3.5–4 mm. long; lobes deltoid to triangular-lanceolate, very short: corolla 6–8 mm. long: filaments short.—Sandy banks, open woods, and thickets, various provinces, Fla. to Mo. and Me.—Sum.–fall.

9. K. montana (Michx.) Kuntze. Stem 3–9 dm. tall, glabrous or nearly so: leaf-blades thin, lanceolate to elliptic-lanceolate or ovate-lanceolate, 7.5–12 cm. long, sharply serrate: calyx 4–5 mm. long, often villous above; lobes lanceolate: corolla 7–8 mm. long: filaments elongate.—Mt. woods, Blue Ridge to Appalachian Plateau, Ga. to Ala., W. Va., and Va.—Sum.

10. K. aristata (Michx.) Kuntze. Stem 4–9 dm. tall, puberulent: leaf-blades elliptic-lanceolate to ovate-lanceolate, 1.5–5 cm. long, sometimes shallowly serrate: calyx 5–6 mm. long; tube faintly ribbed; lobes lanceolate to subulate-lanceolate: corolla 6–7 mm. long.—Pinelands and sandy fields, Coastal Plain, Fla. to La. and N. J.—Sum.–fall.

11. K. hyssopifolia (Benth.) Britton. Stem 4–10 dm. tall, puberulent: leaf-blades narrowly elliptic to linear 1–3.5 cm. long, usually entire: calyx 5–6 mm. long; tube prominently ribbed: corolla much surpassing the calyx.—Low pinelands, Coastal Plain, Fla. to La. and Va.—Sum.

12. K. Hugeri Small. Stem 5–9 dm. tall, cinereous-tomentulose: leaf-blades elliptic, 1.5–4 cm. long, entire or sparingly serrate: calyx 7–8 mm. long; tube prominently ribbed: corolla scarcely, if at all, longer than the calyx.—Mt. woods, Blue Ridge, N. C.—Sum.

13. K. albescens (T. & G.) Kuntze. Stem 4–10 dm. tall, more or less finely, often minutely, pubescent: leaf-blades ovate to elliptic or lanceolate, 2–7 cm.

long, serrate, usually greenish above, whitish beneath: calyx 3–4 mm. long; lobes ovate, obtuse or acutish, beardless: corolla 5–6 mm. long: nutlets ovoid, fully 1 mm. long.—Pinelands and woods, Coastal Plain, Fla. to Tex., Mo., and N. C.—Sum.–fall.

14. **K. pauciflora** Small. Stem mostly 12 dm. tall or less, minutely close-pubescent, at least above: leaf-blades lanceolate to elliptic-lanceolate, 2–5 cm. long, distantly serrate, acute or slightly acuminate, whitish or pale-green above, whitish beneath: calyx 4–5 mm. long; lobes lanceolate, acuminate, beardless: corolla about 6 mm. long: nutlets narrowly ovoid, fully 1 mm. long.—Pinelands and edges of hammocks, Albany, in the Coastal Plain of Ga.—Sum.

15. **K. multiflora** Small. Stem 15 dm. tall or less, closely and minutely soft-pubescent, at least above: leaf-blades ovate or elliptic-ovate, 2–8 cm. long, rather remotely serrate, acute or acutish, pale-green above, white or whitish beneath: flower-clusters becoming open at maturity, the branches somewhat elongate, each with many secund calyces: calyx 4–4.5 mm. long; lobes deltoid, mostly slightly longer than wide, beardless: corolla about 6 mm. long: nutlets ovoid, fully 1 mm. long.—Dry woods and open sunny slopes, various provinces, Ga. to Ala., N. C., and Pa.—Sum.

16. **K. curvipes** Greene. Stem mostly less than 10 dm. tall, closely and minutely pale-pubescent throughout: leaf-blades ovate, 1.5–3.5 cm. long, mostly obtuse, shallowly serrate, closely and densely fine-pubescent, greenish-white above, white and prominently veined beneath: flower-clusters permanently glomerate: calyx 3.5–4 mm. long; lobes deltoid, mostly wider than long: corolla about 4 mm. long: nutlets oval, about 1 mm. long.—Open woods, Stone Mt. in the Piedmont of Ga.—Sum.

17. **K. pycnanthemoides** (Leavenw.) Kuntze. Stem 6–16 dm. tall, minutely pale-pubescent, at least above, and sometimes finely hirsute: leaf-blades ovate, elliptic or elliptic-lanceolate, 2–10 cm. long, thin, shallowly and usually remotely serrate: flowerclusters rather dense and somewhat plumose when young, looser in age, the branches somewhat elongate and bearing the secund calyces: bractlets conspicuously long and narrow: calyx 5–6 mm. long; lobes slender, the upper ones subulate, the lower ones often lanceolate-subulate: corolla 7–8 mm. long: nutlets ovoid, fully 1 mm. long.—Mt. woods and thickets, Blue Ridge to Appalachian Plateau, Ga. to Ala., Ky., and Va.—Sum.

18. **K. incana** (L.) Kuntze. Stem 5–12 dm. tall, softly and closely pubescent at least above, and often finely hirsute: leaf-blades ovate, elliptic, or lanceolate, 3–10 cm. long, thickish, shallowly, but rather prominently and remotely serrate: flower-clusters permanently compact, not conspicuously plumose: calyx 3.5–4 mm. long; lobes stout, the upper ones lanceolate, the lower ones triangular-lanceolate: corolla 6–7 mm. long: nutlets broadly ovoid, about 1 mm. long.—Hillsides, dry thickets, and open woods, various provinces, Fla. to Mo., Ont., and Me.—Sum.–fall.

19. **K. dubia** (A. Gray) Small. Stem 4–11 dm. tall, finely hirsute: leaf-blades lanceolate to linear-elliptic or linear-lanceolate, 2–9.5 cm. long, remotely serrate or nearly entire, green, except some of the upper ones, hirsutulous, especially beneath: calyx 4.5–5 mm. long, pubescent; lobes each with a triangular or lanceolate body and a subulate bearded tip: corolla 6–7 mm. long: tube pubescent within: nutlets broadly ellipsoid, 1.5 mm. long.—Mt. slopes, Blue Ridge, N. C.—Sum.

20. **K. Beadlei** Small. Stem 5–9 dm. tall, minutely pubescent with short hairs: leaf-blades elliptic-lanceolate to ovate-lanceolate, or those of the branches

lanceolate to ovate, 3–8 cm. long, shallowly serrate, glabrous or nearly so, and often prominently veined beneath: calyx 4–5 mm. long, puberulent; lobes triangular-lanceolate and subulate-tipped: corolla 6–7 mm. long; tube glabrous within: nutlets narrowly ovoid, about 1.5 mm. long.—Woods in the Blue Ridge, N. C. and Tenn.—Sum.–fall.

34. MAPPIA House. Perennial erect herbs, or woody plants. Leaf-blades broad, entire or toothed. Flowers in axillary cymes. Calyx nearly regular, the lobes shorter than the tube. Corolla 2-lipped: upper lip erect: lower lip 3-lobed. Stamens 2, long-exserted.—About 15 species, American.

1. **M. origanoides** (L.) House. Stem 2–4 dm. tall, wiry: leaf-blades ovate to ovate-lanceolate, 1.5–2.5 cm. long, serrate: calyx 2–2.5 mm. long; lobes ovate to deltoid: corolla purplish, 4–5 mm. long. [*Cunila mariana* L. *C. origanoides* (L.) Britton]— (DITTANY. STONE-MINT.)—Woods, thickets, and open hillsides, often in somewhat acid soil, N Fla. to Tex., Mo., and N. Y.—Sum.–fall.—This aromatic plant found its way into the materia medica of both the American aborigines and of the early settlers from Europe. It was used in cases of "colds" and of fevers, and also for making a tea!

35. LYCOPUS [Tourn.] L. Perennial, erect or creeping, often stoloniferous herbs. Leaf-blades entire, toothed, or pinnatifid. Flowers whitish to lavender in dense axillary cymes. Calyx regular or nearly so: lobes longer than the tube or shorter. Corolla slightly 2-lipped: upper lip notched: lower lip nearly equally 3-lobed. Stamens 2.—About 15 species, natives of the north temperate zone.—Sum.—BUGLE-WEEDS. WATER-HOARHOUNDS.

Calyx-lobes ovate to elliptic or elliptic-lanceolate, 4 or 5: nutlets exceeding the calyx.   I. VIRGINICI.
Calyx-lobes subulate to lanceolate (ovate, acuminate in No. 8), mostly 5: nutlets not exceeding the calyx.
    Corolla twice as long as the calyx: bracts minute: blades of the lower leaves merely toothed.   II. RUBELLI.
    Corolla but little longer than the calyx; blades of the lower leaves pinnatifid.   III. PINNATIFIDI.

I. VIRGINICI
Corolla 1.5–2 mm. long: style included.   1. *L. virginicus.*
Corolla 2–3 mm. long: style exserted.   2. *L. uniflorus.*

II. RUBELLI
Leaf-blades manifestly petioled, or with petiole-like bases.
    Stem glabrous or merely puberulent: calyx glabrous or nearly so; lobes straight.   3. *L. rubellus.*
    Stem copiously pubescent: calyx closely pubescent; lobes, at least the upper ones, recurved.   4. *L. velutinus.*
Leaf-blades sessile or nearly so, sometimes partly clasping.
    Stem glabrous, at least below: bracts subtending the cymes gradually narrowed at the base.   5. *L. sessilifolius.*
    Stem densely puberulent or finely pubescent: bracts subtending the cymes truncate at the base.   6. *L. pubens.*

III. PINNATIFIDI
Stem and leaves usually glabrous or glabrate: calyx-lobes acute, short awn-tipped: leaf-blades with acute serrations.   7. *L. americanus.*

Stem and leaves usually pubescent, sometimes slightly so : calyx-
lobes acuminate, long awn-tipped: leaf-blades with obtuse
serrations.   8. *L. europaeus.*

1. **L. virginicus** L. Stem 1–8 dm. tall, purplish or greenish-purple, obtuse-
angled, not usually tuberous at the base, but with tuber-bearing stolons: leaf-
blades ovate to elliptic-ovate or elliptic, 2–14
cm. long, coarsely toothed, manifestly petioled: calyx about 2 mm. long; lobes narrow.
—Common, in meadows and rather moist
soil, various provinces, Ga. to Ark., Nebr.,
and N. H.—Sum.-fall.

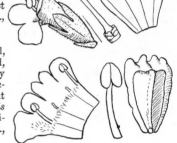

2. **L. uniflorus** Michx. Stem 1–8 dm. tall,
green or sometimes purplish, sharp-angled,
tuberous at the base, the stolons rarely
tuber-bearing: leaf-blades elliptic to elliptic-
lanceolate, 2–8 cm. long, serrate, calyx about
1.5 mm. long; lobes wide. [*L. communis*
Bicknell]—Low grounds, and thickets, various provinces, N. C. to Nebr., Ore., B. C.,
Ont., and Newf.—Sum.-fall.

3. **L. rubellus** Moench. Stem 5–10 dm. tall: leaf-blades elliptic, lanceolate,
or ovate-elliptic, 3–15 cm. long, sharply serrate or dentate-serrate: calyx becoming fully 2.5 mm. long; lobes straight, about as long as the tube: corolla
3.5–4 mm. long.—Low grounds, borders of swamps and ditches, Coastal Plain
and adj. provinces, Fla. to La., Mo., and N. Y.—Sum.-fall.

4. **L. velutinus** Rydb. Similar to *L. rubellus* in habit, but copiously pubescent, the branches often densely so: leaf-blades elliptic, sometimes broadly so,
or elliptic-lanceolate, coarsely toothed: calyx becoming 2.5 mm. long; lobes
curved, much longer than the tube: corolla 3–3.5 mm. long.—Low grounds,
various provinces, Miss. to Tex. and Colo.—Sum.-fall.

5. **L. sessilifolius** A. Gray. Stem 2–6 dm. tall: leaf-blades ovate to elliptic
or lanceolate, 1.5–6 cm. long, shallowly serrate: calyx 2–2.5 mm. long; lobes
as long as the tube: lower corolla-lip with a reniform notched middle lobe:
filaments pubescent at the base.—Wet soil and low grounds, Coastal Plain and
New England Coast, Fla. to Miss. and Mass.—Sum.-fall.

6. **L. pubens** Britton. Stem 6–12 dm. tall: leaf-blades elliptic, elliptic-lanceolate or linear-elliptic, 4.5–10 cm. long, sharply serrate: calyx mainly 2.5–3 mm.
long; lobes longer than the tube: lower corolla-lip with an ovate obtuse middle
lobe: filaments glabrous—Low pinelands, Coastal Plain, Fla. to Miss. and S. C.
—Sum.-fall.

7. **L. americanus** Muhl. Stem 1–9 dm. tall, often much-branched: leaf-blades
lanceolate to ovate-lanceolate, 2–10 cm. long, those on the lower part of the
stem pinnatifid, those near the top merely toothed: calyx 2.5–3 mm. long:
corolla about as long as the calyx: staminodia thickened at the tip. [*L. sinu-
atus* Ell.]—Moist thickets and pastures, wet banks and meadows, various provinces, Fla. to Tex., Calif., B. C., Ont., and Newf.—Sum.-fall.

8. **L. europaeus** L. Stem 1 m. tall or less: leaf-blades ovate or elliptic-
ovate, 2–8 cm. long, obtuse or acutish, coarsely toothed, and the lower ones, at
least, incised or pinnatifid near the base: calyx 2.5–3 mm. long: corolla only
slightly exceeding the calyx: nutlets scarcely exceeding the calyx-tube.—Waste-

places and roadsides, various provinces, Ala. to La. and Mass. Nat. of Eu.—Sum.–fall.

36. MENTHA [Tourn.] L. Perennial erect or diffuse herbs. Leaf-blades toothed or incised. Flowers in dense axillary cymes, these sometimes disposed in spike-like panicles. Calyx nearly regular, the lobes shorter than the tube. Corolla obscurely 2-lipped: upper lip mostly notched: lower lip of 3 nearly equal lobes. Stamens 4.—About 30 species, natives of the north temperate zone.—Sum.—MINTS.

Flower-clusters all axillary, not in terminal spikes.   I. ARVENSES.
Flower-clusters, at least most of them, aggregated in terminal spike-like panicles.   II. SPICATAE.

I. ARVENSES

Stem and branches glabrous or with short scattered hairs: calyx glabrous or nearly so, except for the ciliate lobes.   1. *M. gentilis.*
Stem and branches with retrorse or spreading hairs: calyx pubescent all over.
    Stem and branches with short retrorse or retrorse-appressed hairs: larger calyx-lobes deltoid: calyx-tube closely pubescent with short hairs.   2. *M. arvensis.*
    Stem and branches with long lax or spreading hairs: larger calyx-lobes typically lanceolate: calyx-tube loosely pubescent with long hairs.   3. *M. canadensis.*

II. SPICATAE

Flowers in short and stout raceme-like panicles, or clustered in the upper leaf-axils: longer calyx-lobes decidedly shorter than the tube: leaf-blades petioled.
    Calyx, at least the lobes, pubescent.
      Stem and leaves copiously pubescent: leaf-blades ovate or orbicular-ovate: calyx pubescent all over.   4. *M. aquatica.*
      Stem and leaves glabrous: leaf-blades elliptic, or lanceolate: calyx with pubescent lobes.   5. *M. piperita.*
                        6. *M. citrata.*
    Calyx glabrous.
Flowers in slender or relatively slender, often elongate spike-like panicles: longer calyx-lobes as long as the tube or nearly so: leaf-blades sessile.
    Stem and inflorescence not canescent: calyx-tube glabrous or nearly so: corolla-tube not exceeding the calyx.   7. *M. spicata.*
    Stem and inflorescence canescent or villous-canescent: calyx-tube copiously pubescent: corolla-tube much exceeding the calyx.   8. *M. rotundifolia.*

1. M. gentilis L. Stem 2–7 dm. tall, glabrous or nearly so: leaf-blades oval, ovate, obovate, or elliptic, 1.5–5 cm. long, serrate, the floral ones not conspicuously reduced, with petioles often longer than the flower-clusters: calyx 1.5–2 mm. long; tube glabrous or nearly so: corolla lavender or lilac; upper lip notched. —Stream-banks, waste-places, and roadsides, various provinces N of Coastal Plain, Ga. to Ia. and N. S. Nat. of Eu.—Sum.–fall.

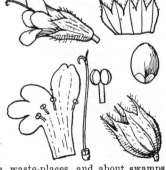

2. M. arvensis L. Stem 4 dm. tall or less, often diffuse, copiously, often closely pale-pubescent: leaf-blades ovate, elliptic, or oval, 1.5–5 cm. long, coarsely serrate above the middle, copiously pubescent with short hairs, broad at the base: calyx 1.5–2 mm. long, minutely pubescent; lobes short-tipped: corolla usually lavender, mostly 3 mm. long, the upper lip mostly notched.—Stream-banks, waste-places, and about swamps, various provinces, Fla. to Tex., Calif., Nebr., and Newf. Nat. of Eu.—(*Mex.*) —Sum.-fall.

3. M. canadensis L. Stem 2–6 dm. tall, loosely pubescent: leaf-blades lanceolate, elliptic, or elliptic-lanceolate, 2–7 cm. long, serrate, narrow-based, the floral ones with petioles as long as the flower-clusters: calyx about 2.5–3 mm. long; tube loosely pubescent: corolla lavender or white; upper lip mostly obtuse.—Thickets and low sandy places, various provinces, rarely Coastal Plain, N. C. to N. M., B. C., Man., and N. B.—Sum.-fall.

4. M. aquatica L. Stem 2–6 dm. long or more, pubescent with recurved hairs: leaf-blades broadly ovate, or orbicular-ovate, 1–4 cm. long, or rarely more, rather sharply serrate, those of the floral leaves reduced: calyx 3–3.5 mm. long: tube pubescent with short spreading hairs; lobes lanceolate, about ⅓ as long as the tube: corolla lavender, about 5 mm. long.—(WATER-MINT.)—Roadside ditches and wet places, various provinces, Ga. to N. S. Nat. of Eu.— Sum.-fall.

5. M. piperita L. Stem 2–7 dm. tall, glabrous: leaf-blades elliptic, ellipticovate, elliptic-lanceolate, or lanceolate, 1.5–5 cm. long, sharply serrate: calyx 2.5–3 mm. long; lobes subulate, much shorter than the cylindric-campanulate tube: corolla light-violet, 3.5–4 mm. long.—(PEPPERMINT.)—Waste-places, roadsides, and stream-banks, various provinces, Fla. to Ark., Calif., Ont., and N. S. Nat. of Eu.—(*W. I.*)—Sum.-fall.

6. M. citrata Ehrh. Stem 3–11 dm. long, glabrous or nearly so: leaf-blades ovate to orbicular-ovate, 1.5–4 cm. long, sharply serrate: calyx 3.5–4 mm. long; lobes subulate, shorter than the cylindric-turbinate tube: corolla lavender or whitish, about 4.5 mm. long.—Wet places, various provinces, Ga. to Mo. and Conn. Nat. of Eu.—(*W. I.*)—Sum.-fall.

7. M. spicata L. Stem 2–5 dm. tall, glabrous or nearly so: leaf-blades elliptic or elliptic-lanceolate, 3–6 cm. long, sharply serrate: calyx 1–1.5 mm. long; lobes about as long as the campanulate tube: corolla lavender, 2–2.5 mm. long. [*M. viridis* L.]—(SPEAR-MINT.)—Waste-places, fields, and roadsides, various provinces, Fla. to Kans., Ont., and N. B. Nat. of Eu.—(*W. I.*)—Sum.-fall.

8. M. rotundifolia (L.) Huds. Stem 3–9 dm. tall, canescent-tomentulose: leaf-blades elliptic, oval, or ovate, 2–9 cm. long, finely serrate, often partly clasping: calyx becoming about 1.5 mm. long; lobes slightly shorter than the campanulate tube: corolla lavender or pale-lilac, 2.5–3 mm. long.—Open grounds and thickets, various provinces, Fla. to Tex., Ark., and Me. Nat. of Eu.—(*W. I., Mex., S. A.*)—Sum.-fall.

37. MICHELIELLA Briq. Perennial erect herbs. Leaf-blades rather coarsely toothed. Flowers in panicles. Calyx 2-lipped: upper lip with 3 short lobes: lower lip with 2 narrow lobes. Corolla 2-lipped, middle lobe of the lower lip fringed. Stamens 4.—Two species.—STONE-ROOTS.

Leaves 4, or rarely 6, approximate, sometimes almost whorled at the top of the stem. 1. *M. verticillata.*
Leaves several, in pairs along the stem. 2. *M. anisata.*

1. M. verticillata (Baldw.) Briq. Stem 1–5 dm. tall, finely pubescent: leaf-blades thin, ovate to obovate or cuneate-obovate, 8–16 cm. long: calyx becoming

8 mm. long: corolla tawny, 11–13 mm. long. [*Collinsonia verticillata* Baldw.] — Rich woods, Blue Ridge and Piedmont, Ga. to Miss., Tenn., and N. C.—Spr.-sum.

2. M. anisata (Sims) Briq. Stem 3–6 dm. tall, glandular-pubescent: leaf-blades thickish, elliptic or broadly oval, 8–15 cm. long: calyx becoming 10 mm. long: corolla cream-colored, 8–12 mm. long. [*Collinsonia anisata* Sims]—Dry woods, Blue Ridge and Piedmont, Fla. to Ala. and S. C.—Sum.— The plants of this genus and of the following have long been used medicinally. The woody root and the leaves contain a number of principles, viz. starch, tannin, resin, wax, mucilage, and volatile oil. The plants are lemon-scented.

38. COLLINSONIA L. Perennial erect or reclining herbs. Leaf-blades toothed. Flowers in panicles. Calyx 2-lipped: upper lip with 3 short lobes: lower lip with 2 longer lobes. Corolla 2-lipped, elongate, middle lobe of the lower lip lacerate or fringed.—Three species as follows.—HORSE-BALMS.

Branches of the inflorescence puberulent.
    Stem rigid: leaf-blades mostly over 10 cm. long, many-toothed: pedicels becoming 6–9 mm. long.   1. *C. canadensis.*
    Stem reclining: leaf-blades mostly less than 8 cm. long,
        coarsely few-toothed: pedicels becoming 2–4 mm. long.   2. *C. tuberosa.*
Branches of the inflorescence glandular-pubescent.   3. *C. punctata.*

1. C. canadensis L. Stem erect, 3–9 dm. tall, from a thick hard root: leaf-blades thickish, elliptic or oval, 9–16 cm. long, rather coarsely dentate-serrate: calyx becoming 5–7 mm. long: corolla about 1.5 cm. long, yellowish: nutlets obscurely reticulate, nearly 2 mm. in diameter.— (HORSE-BALM. RICH-WEED. STONE-ROOT.)— Rich, moist woods and thickets, various provinces, Fla. to Ark., Kans., Ont., and Me. —Sum.-fall.

2. C. tuberosa Michx. Stem spreading or reclining, 3–10 dm. long: leaf-blades thin, ovate, 5–8 cm. long, coarsely serrate.—Rich woods, various provinces, Ga. to La. and N. C.—The corolla of this species and that of the following are yellowish, either dark or pale.

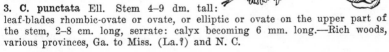

3. C. punctata Ell. Stem 4–9 dm. tall: leaf-blades rhombic-ovate or ovate, or elliptic or ovate on the upper part of the stem, 2–8 cm. long, serrate: calyx becoming 6 mm. long.—Rich woods, various provinces, Ga. to Miss. (La.?) and N. C.

39. PERILLA L. Annual erect herbs. Leaf-blades often coarsely toothed. Flowers in spike-like panicles. Calyx 2-lipped: upper lip with 3 broad lobes: lower lip with 2 longer lobes. Corolla 2-lipped: upper lip broad: lower lip 3-lobed, the middle lobe largest. Stamens 4.—Two species, Asiatic.

1. P. frutescens (L.) Britton. Stem 2–6 dm. tall, minutely pubescent: leaves usually red or red-tinged; blades ovate or oval, 4–10 cm. long, serrate or crenate-serrate: calyx 2–2.5 mm., becoming 6 mm. long; lower lobes lanceolate: corolla 3–3.5 mm. long, white, with a ring of hairs within; lobes obtuse: nutlets prominently reticulate, nearly 1.5 mm. in diameter.—(BEEFSTEAK-PLANT.)—Waste-places, and roadsides, various provinces, Fla. to Tex., Mo., and Conn. Nat. of Asia.—Sum.—The plants, especially when bruised, give off a strong odor.

40. HYPTIS Jacq. Herbs or woody plants. Leaf-blades commonly toothed. Flowers in often dense axillary cymes. Calyx nearly regular, sometimes oblique, accrescent and ribbed or veiny at maturity. Corolla 2-lipped, white to purple: lower lip 3-lobed, the middle lobe saccate. [*Mesosphaerum* P. Br.]—About 300 species, mostly tropical American.

Flowers borne in few remote peduncled involucrate heads: bracts foliaceous.
              I. RADIATAE.
Flowers borne in numerous axillary separated clusters or in
    contiguous or approximate glomerules which thus form
    terminal thyrsoid panicles: bracts minute.
Flowers in unilateral cymules which are aggregated into
    a thyrsus: mature calyx persistent.   II. SPICATAE.
Flowers in small separated axillary clusters: mature calyx
    deciduous.   III. VERTICILLATAE.

I. RADIATAE
Stem typically simple or branched at the base, leafy to the top. 1. *H. radiata.*

II. SPICATAE
Calyx-lobes short-subulate, at maturity less than ½ as long as
    the tube: terminal portion of the inflorescence composed of
    elongate slender interrupted thyrsi, open. 2. *H. mutabilis.*
Calyx-lobes setaceous-subulate, at maturity much more than ½
    as long as the tube: terminal portion of the inflorescence
    composed of short continuous thyrsi, compact. 3. *H. pectinata.*

III. VERTICILLATAE
Tall plant with virgate stems and very slender branches, the
    flower-clusters inconspicuously bracted. 4. *H. verticillata.*

1. H. radiata Willd. Stem 2 m. tall or less, finely pubescent, simple or rarely branched: leaf-blades ovate to lanceolate or linear-lanceolate, 2–8 cm. long or more, coarsely and often irregularly serrate, cuneately narrowed into petiole-like bases: calyx becoming 6–8 mm. long: tube strongly cross-ribbed at maturity; lobes subulate-lanceolate, short-hairy: corolla 8–10 mm. long: nutlets oval, nearly 1.5 mm. long.—Low pinelands, hammocks, swamps, and marshes, Coastal Plain, Fla. to Tex. and N. C.—(*W. I.*)—Spr.–fall or all year S.

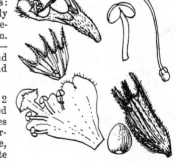

2. H. mutabilis (A. Rich.) Briq. Stem 2 m. tall or less, pubescent with short crisped hairs and more or less muricate: leaf-blades rhombic-ovate to deltoid, or orbicular-reniform, 2–7 cm. long or rarely more, crenate-serrate, broadly cuneate to truncate at the base, slender-petioled: calyx becoming 6–7 mm. long; tube prominently cross-ribbed; lobes short-subulate, about 1 mm. long: corolla 3.5–4 mm. long; tube stout: nutlets oval, about 1.5 mm. long.—Woods, waste-places, cult.-grounds, and roadsides, Fla. Nat. of trop. Am.—(*W. I., Mex., C. A., S. A.*)

3. H. pectinata (L.) Poir. Stem 1.5 m. tall or less, sparingly pubescent with short crisped hairs and more or less muricate: leaf-blades ovate, 2–8 cm. long, irregularly serrate, cuneate to rounded at the base: calyx becoming 4–5 mm. long; tube faintly cross-ribbed; lobes setaceous-subulate, 1.5–2 mm. long: corolla about 4 mm. long; tube slender: nutlets ellipsoid, about 1 mm. long.—Hammocks, cult.-grounds, and roadsides, S pen. Fla. Nat. of trop. Am.—(*W. I., Mex., C. A., S. A.*)—All year.—Two related species included in Fl. SE. U. S., *H. spicata* Poir. and *H. spicigera* Lam., are not now definitely known from our range.

4. H. verticillata Jacq. Stem 1–2 m. tall, sparingly pubescent, leaf-blades lanceolate to linear-lanceolate, mostly 5–12 cm. long, rather sharply serrate, acuminate: calyx becoming 2–2.5 mm. long; tube slightly ribbed; lobes deltoid to triangular-lanceolate, shorter than the tube: corolla white, about twice as long as the calyx: nutlets ellipsoid, about 1.5 mm. long.—Hammocks and roadsides, pen. Fla. Nat. of trop. Am.—(*W. I., Mex., C. A., S. A.*)—Sum.-fall.

41. OCIMUM [Tourn.] L. Herbs or woody plants. Leaf-blades often of an ovate type and toothed. Flowers in raceme-like panicles. Calyx strongly 2-lipped, accrescent: upper lip a broad lobe decurrent as wings on the sides of the tube: lower lip of 2 broad lobes and 2 narrow lobes. Corolla 2-lipped: lower lip of 3 broad lobes.—About 40 species, widely distributed in warm and tropical regions.

Corolla slightly exceeding the calyx; lips obscurely fine-pubescent without, the lower
  lobe entire: nutlets about 1 mm. long. 1. *O. micranthum.*
Corolla much exceeding the calyx; lips hirsutulous without, the
  lower lobe sharply toothed: nutlets about 1.5 mm. long. 2. *O. basilicum.*

1. O. micranthum Willd. Stem 2–5 dm. tall, minutely and obscurely pubescent: leaf-blades ovate, often narrowly so, evidently but shallowly toothed: panicles rather loosely flowered: calyx purple, 2–3 mm. long at anthesis: crest-like upper lobe oval-orbicular in fruit: corolla purple or paler, about 4 mm. long: posterior stamens without spurs: fruiting calyx narrowly campanulate, the lateral lobes with slender tips as long as the body.—(WILD-BASIL. MOSQUITO-PLANT.)—Hammocks, pine-lands, and waste-places, S Fla.—(*W. I., Mex., C. A., S. A.*)—Spr.-fall or all year.

2. O. basilicum L. Stem 2–5 dm. tall, finely pubescent: leaf-blades ovate, usually broadly so, obscurely toothed: panicles densely flowered: calyx green, about 5 mm. long at anthesis; crest-like upper lobe orbicular-reniform in fruit: corolla white, about 7 mm. long: posterior stamens with hairy spurs at the base of the filaments: fruiting calyx campanulate, the lateral lobes with stout tips much shorter than the body.—(BASIL.)—Hammocks, shell-mounds, and pinelands, pen. Fla. Nat. of Asia.—(*W. I.*)—Sum.-fall.

Coleus pumilus Blanco, with small, obtuse, deeply toothed leaf-blades, red along midrib and lateral veins, the stem somewhat prostrate and rooting along the lower portion, has been found as an escape in pen. Fla. Native of the Philippine Islands.

FAMILY 14. **RHINANTHACEAE**[1] — FIGWORT FAMILY

Herbs or rarely shrubs or trees. Stems commonly terete. Leaves opposite, whorled or alternate: blades entire, toothed, or divided. Flowers perfect, axillary, racemose, or paniculate, the peduncles sometimes bearing a pair of bractlets. Calyx regular or irregular, of 4 or 5 distinct or united sepals. Corolla irregular, of 5 partly or wholly united petals. Androecium usually of 4 didynamous stamens, sometimes 2 or 5 or the fifth one represented by a staminodium. Gynoecium 2-carpellary. Ovary 2-celled, rarely becoming 1-celled. Fruit capsular or rarely baccate.—About 200 genera and 3000 species, of wide geographic distribution.

Corolla with the posterior lobes external—overlapping in the bud.—(**Antirrhinoideae**)
  Tree: calyx coriaceous: corolla large, about 5 cm. long:
    capsule woody.   Tribe I. PAULOWNIEAE.
  Herbs: calyx membranous or herbaceous: corolla smaller:
    capsule membranous to coriaceous.
    Stigmas distinct, flattened (scarcely so in *Capraria*,
      Bramia, and *Scoparia*): seeds reticulate or finely
      lined, wingless (except in *Ilysanthes grandi-
      flora*): capsule-walls membranous: inflorescence
      simply racemose, with the bracts foliaceous, ex-
      cept in *Mazus*, and the flowers axillary: leaves
      opposite (except in *Capraria*).
      Sepals distinct or nearly so (except in *Hemi-
        anthus*): corolla small (3–18 mm. long): leaves
        and capsule usually glandular-punctate.   II. GRATIOLEAE.
      Sepals united over half their length: corolla large
        (25–35 mm. long): leaves and capsule not
        glandular-punctate.   III. MIMULEAE.
    Stigmas wholly united, punctiform or capitate: seeds
      not simply reticulate, either smooth, tubercu-
      late, ridged, alveolate, or winged: capsule-walls
      firm, chartaceous or coriaceous: inflorescence
      racemose or paniculate, the bracts usually much
      smaller than the leaves.
      Filaments 5: capsule septicidal.
        Corolla rotate, slightly zygomorphic, its lobes
          longer than the tube: filaments all anther-
          iferous: leaves alternate.   IV. VERBASCEAE.
        Corolla tubular-campanulate, strongly zygo-
          morphic, its lobes shorter than the tube:
          posterior filament without an anther: leaves
          opposite.   V. CHELONEAE.
      Filaments 4 (the posterior one present as a
        minute knob only in *Collinsia*): capsule
        loculicidal.
        Corolla red, tubular: capsule filled with tortu-
          ous hairs between which are scattered rough-
          ened seeds: leaves mostly scale-like.   VI. RUSSELIEAE.
        Corolla yellow, blue, violet, or white, saccate
          or spurred: capsule lacking hairs within:
          leaves with expanded blades.
          Capsule loculicidal by a simple median slit:
            seed alveolate or smooth: corolla vio-
            let or blue, not pouched or spurred
            anteriorly: leaves opposite.
          Corolla broadly saucer-shaped or dipper-
            shaped, with a fine horn-like appen-
            dage at the base of the anterior lobes:
            posterior stamen lacking: capsule
            globose: sepals distinct.   VII. ANGELONIEAE.

[1] Contributed by Francis Whittier Pennell.

Corolla seemingly papilionaceous, the tube gibbous at the base posteriorly: posterior stamen represented by a callose knob: capsule slightly flattened: sepals partly united.　VIII. COLLINSIEAE.

Capsule opening by transverse loculicidal ruptures: seed angled, ridged, or winged: corolla yellow or violet-blue, bilabiate, with a narrow pouch or spur at the base anteriorly: leaves alternate.　IX. ANTIRRHINEAE.

Corolla with the anterior lobes external—overlapping in the bud: herbs.—(**Rhinanthoideae**)

Stamens 2, the postero-laterals alone present: corolla small (2-5 mm. long), the antero-lateral lobes external: plants not parasitic.　X. VERONICEAE.

Stamens 4, the antero-lateral usually the longer: corolla larger, the mid-anterior lobes usually external: plants usually root-parasites.

Sepals 5, alike: corolla-lobes nearly equally distinct.　XI. BUCHNEREAE.

Sepals unequal, the posterior one very short or lacking: corolla strongly bilabiate, the 2 posterior lobes united nearly to the apex.　XII. RHINANTHEAE.

I. PAULOWNIEAE

Tree, with cordate leaf-blades, large panicles of horizontal flowers, and erect pointed capsules.　1. PAULOWNIA.

II. GRATIOLEAE

Leaves alternate: stamens 5: corolla nearly regular, white.　2. CAPRARIA.

Leaves opposite: stamens 4 or 2 (the posterior one obsolete).

Leaf-blades entire or toothed: seeds brown or yellow.

Corolla with the ridges to the antero-lateral sinuses low and not projecting beyond those points (anterior filaments simple): posterior lobes of the corolla, little if at all, shorter than the anterior.

Leaves uniform: capsule turgid, longer than wide, acute or obtuse: stem elongate.

Sepals 4: corolla rotate, with recurved lobes much longer than the tube.　3. SCOPARIA.

Sepals 5: corolla campanulate, tubular, or salverform, the lobes equalling or shorter than the tube.

Corolla campanulate, nearly regular; lobes equalling, or little shorter than the tube, the posterior united, little if at all higher than the others.

Pedicels not bracteolate: capsule obtuse.

Stamens 4: capsule globose or ovoid, nearly equalling the sepals: outer sepal oval.　4. MACUILLAMIA.

Stamens 2: capsule ellipsoid-ovoid, much shorter than the sepals: outer sepal of an orbicular-cordate type.　5. HERPESTIS.

Pedicels bibracteolate: capsule acute.

Corolla pubescent in the throat: ovary surrounded by a circle of bristles: outer sepal cordate: leaf-blades clasping: plant lemon-scented.　6. HYDROTRIDA.

Corolla glabrous within: ovary not surrounded by bristles: outer sepal ovate: leaf-blades cuneate at the base: plant odorless.　7. BRAMIA.

Corolla narrower, decidedly zygomorphic, the lobes shorter than the tube, the posterior united over half their length or throughout.

Corolla tubular or tubular-campanulate, relatively broad at the throat, pubescent within at the base of the posterior lobes: capsule septicidal, or secondarily (in *Gratiola*) also loculicidal: leaf-blades toothed.

Pedicels bibracteolate at the base:
outer sepals much wider than the
inner: polleniferous stamens 4. .... 8. MECARDONIA.

Pedicels bibracteolate at the apex
(or in *Gratiola* bractlets occasionally one or lacking): sepals
nearly even in width: polleniferous stamens 2.

Anther-sacs transverse across the
tip of the filament, often somewhat separated on the ex-
panded connective: corolla
mostly over twice as long as
the calyx: capsule broadly
acute to globose, only slightly
furrowed: sepals nearly or
quite equal in length. .... 9. GRATIOLA.

Anther-sacs vertical, contiguous:
corolla slightly exceeding the
calyx: capsule narrowly pyramidal, deeply furrowed: sepals
very unequal in length. .... 10. TRAGIOLA.

Corolla salverform, very narrow at the
throat and short-pubescent within on
all sides: capsule loculicidal: leaf-
blades entire. .... 11. SOPHRONANTHE.

Leaves dimorphic, several narrow submerged ones
on the short caudex-like stem and a pair of
broad ones (bracts), which serve as floats at
the tip of the elongate scape: capsule wider
than long, deeply notched. .... 12. AMPHIANTHUS.

Corolla with 2 raised ridges (each formed by the
adherence of a filament) to the antero-lateral
sinuses, and which project as knob-like processes beyond this point: posterior lobes of the
corolla less than two-thirds the length of the
anterior.

Corolla violet-blue, 6 mm. long or more: only the
postero-lateral filaments with anthers: style
with enlarged callose semi-persistent base: capsule 2 mm. long or more, ellipsoid to ovoid,
permanently 2-celled, septicidal: sepals 5. ...... 13. ILYSANTHES.

Corolla white, 2 mm. long or less: only the
antero-lateral stamens present: style not
enlarged at the base, wholly deciduous:
capsule 1 mm. long or less, globose, ·1-celled
(by lack of septum distally), rupturing
irregularly: sepals 4.

Sepals united only at the base: corolla with
posterior lobes wholly united, about half the
length of the anterior: styles united fully
three-fourths their length: leaf-blades orbicular or nearly so. .... 14. GLOBIFERA.

Sepals united at least half their length, except on the anterior side: corolla open
nearly to the base on the posterior side, the
posterior lobe lacking: styles united half to
two-thirds their length: leaf-blades ·obovate-
elliptic. .... 15. HEMIANTHUS.

Leaf-blades bipinnatifid: seeds pale greenish-yellow, or
nearly colorless: corolla lavender. .... 16. LEUCOSPORA.

III. MIMULEAE

Tall glabrous perennial herbs: corolla personate, violet. ... 17. MIMULUS.

IV. VERBASCEAE

Tall perennial or biennial herbs, with sessile or decurrent
leaf-blades and yellow or white corollas. .... 18. VERBASCUM.

V. CHELONEAE

Flower-stalk bibracteolate, the simple inflorescence nearly
spicate, the flowers crowded: bracts and bractlets broad:
corolla with orifice closed by the lower lip: anthers lanose:
seed flattened, winged. .... 19. CHELONE.

Flower-stalk not bracteolate: inflorescence compound, paniculate or thyrsoid, of axillary cymose flower-clusters:

bracts attenuate: corolla with orifice open: anthers barbate or glabrous: seeds turgid, wingless.

Corolla purple, violet-blue, or white: posterior filament slender, as long as the others: cauline leaves with clasping blades: stem terete.
20. PENSTEMON.

Corolla greenish-purple or brownish: posterior filament scale-like. 2-lobed: cauline leaves with petioled blades: stem 4-angled.
21. SCROPHULARIA.

VI. RUSSELIEAE

Tall diffuse perennial herb, with rush-like stems and scale-like leaves (except on shoots).
22. RUSSELIA.

VII. ANGELONIEAE

Erect perennial herb with leafy stems: corolla violet.
23. ANGELONIA.

VIII. COLLINSIEAE

Low annual herb with broad leaf-blades and axillary flowers, the corollas partly blue and partly white.
24. COLLINSIA.

IX. ANTIRRHINEAE

Capsule dehiscing by irregular distal ruptures: corolla with the posterior lobes arched and distally spreading: filaments and anthers glabrous: flowers in terminal racemes: leaf-blades narrow, sessile: plants erect.
25. LINARIA.

Capsule dehiscing by a lid: corolla with the posterior lobes projecting: filaments and anthers pubescent: flowers axillary: leaf-blades broad, petioled: plant prostrate.
26. KICKXIA.

X. VERONICEAE

Corolla with lobes much shorter than the tube: capsule ovoid, turgid, acute: sepals 5: leaves whorled.
27. VERONICASTRUM.

Corolla with lobes longer than the tube: capsule as wide as long or wider, flat: acutish to deeply notched: sepals 4: leaves opposite or alternate.
28. VERONICA.

XI. BUCHNEREAE

Stamens with both anther-sacs equally developed: corolla not salverform, the throat open: capsule partly exserted from the calyx: pedicel not bracteolate.

Corolla tubular, orange, fleshy, semi-persistent: anthers much exserted.
29. MACRANTHERA.

Corolla campanulate or rotate, yellow or rose-purple, membranous, early falling: anthers little or not at all exserted.

Anther-sacs glabrous (or in *Afzelia cassioides* with few bristle-like hairs at apex): corolla rotate: stigma punctiform or capitate.

Corolla densely pubescent within on all sides: filaments didynamous: anther-sacs somewhat cuspidate at the base, opening lengthwise: style persistent on the capsule.
30. DASISTOMA.

Corolla finely pubescent in a ring about the base of the filaments: filaments nearly or quite equal: anther-sacs obtuse at the base, opening by apical slits: style deciduous.
31. AFZELIA.

Anther-sacs lanose: corolla semi-campanulate: stigma somewhat elongate.

Corolla yellow: anther-sacs with rigid awns at the base: stigma ovoid-capitate.
32. AUREOLARIA.

Corolla purple or pink, nearly always with red-purple spots within: anther-sacs rounded or mucronate-setaceous at the base: stigma linguliform.

Leaf-blades of a filiform, linear, or spatulate type, entire: calyx-lobes shorter than the tube or about equalling it: anther-sacs of both pairs of stamens equal.
33. AGALINIS.

Leaf-blades of a lanceolate type, some, at least, auriculate-lobed at the base: calyx-lobes longer than the tube: anther-sacs of the posterior stamens smaller.
34. TOMANTHERA.

Stamens with only one anther-sac developed, the other wholly abortive: corolla salverform, the throat nearly closed: capsule nearly or quite included in the calyx-tube: pedicel bibracteolate.
35. BUCHNERA.

XII. RHINANTHEAE

Pedicel bibracteolate: calyx-lobes 5: capsule turgid, septicidal, and tardily also slightly loculicidal: seeds narrow,
winged.   36. SCHWALBEA.
Pedicel not bracted: calyx-lobes 4: capsule loculicidal:
seeds broad, wingless.
   Corolla yellowish-green, its posterior lobes long-project-
   ing, not hooded at the apex, its anterior lobes very
   short: capsule cylindric-ovoid, equally 2-celled: calyx
   and foliaceous bracts distally scarlet.   37. CASTILLEJA.
   Corolla yellow, purplish, or white, its posterior lobes
   arched and hooded, its anterior lobes developed on
   a flat or ridged plane: capsule flattened, ensiform,
   unequally 2-celled: calyx and bracts green.
      Anterior lip not raised into a palate: anthers
      glabrous: seeds flat: sepals of each side united to
      the apex: plant perennial.   38. PEDICULARIS.
      Anterior lip raised into a yellow densely pubescent
      palate: anthers pubescent: seeds turgid: sepals of
      each side united at the base: plant annual.   39. MELAMPYRUM.

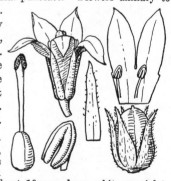

1. **PAULOWNIA** Sieb. & Zucc.   Trees resembling *Catalpa*.   Leaves opposite; blades ample, long-petioled.   Flowers in a large panicle.   Sepals 5,
united half their length.   Corolla violet-blue,
zygomorphic, the throat broad and two-
ridged within, the lips slightly spreading.
Stamens 4, didynamous.   Stigmas distinct,
plate-like.   Capsule ovoid, acute, loculicidal.
Seeds flat, broadly winged.—Eight species,
Asiatic.

1. **P. tomentosa** (Thunb.) Baill.   Large
tree with flaky bark: leaf-blades 15–40 cm.
long, ovate, to suborbicular, cordate, entire
or somewhat three-lobed, densely pubescent
beneath with stellate hairs: calyx 10–15 mm.
long; lobes triangular-ovate: corolla 45–55
mm. long; capsule 30–40 mm. long.—(PRINCESS-TREE.   KARRI-TREE.)—Roadsides and open woods, occasional throughout E U. S.   Nat. of China.—Late Spr.

2. **CAPRARIA** L.   Erect branched herb, the root perennial.   Leaves
alternate: blades sessile, serrate, not glandular-punctate.   Flowers axillary to
leaf-like bracts.   Sepals 5, distinct, equal.
Corolla white: tube campanulate, slightly
pubescent anteriorly: lobes 5, nearly equal,
spreading, longer than the tube.   Stamens 5.
Stigmas scarcely distinct, short.   Capsule
ovoid, acute, glandular-dotted, septicidal, the
valves only slightly splitting loculicidally at
apex.   Seeds numerous, reticulate, wingless.
—Two or three species, tropical American.

1. **C. biflora** L.   Stem 3–15 dm. tall, glabrous or pubescent: leaf-blades 2–7 cm. long,
oblanceolate, cuneate, or elliptic: pedicels
5–20 mm. long, slender, usually two to an
axil: sepals 5–7 mm. long, linear: corolla about 10 mm. long, white or violet-
tinged: capsule 4–6 mm. long: seeds ellipsoid, brown.—Sandy soil, on or near
beaches, S Fla.—(*W. I., Mex., C. A., S. A.*)—All year.

3. **SCOPARIA** L. Erect, much-branched herb, the root perennial. Leaves opposite: blades petioled, serrate, glandular-punctate. Flowers axillary to leaf-like bracts. Sepals 4, equal. Corolla white, rotate, lanose-pubescent on all sides: lobes much longer than the tube, the posterior united throughout (so that lobes appear to be only four). Stamens 4. Stigmas minute, mainly united. Capsule ovoid, acute, septicidal, and only slightly loculicidal at apex. Seeds numerous, cylindric-ellipsoid, reticulate, wingless.—About 20 species, tropical and South American.

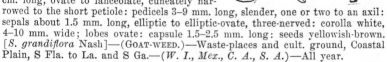

1. **S. dulcis** L. Stem 3–8 dm. tall, glabrous or slightly pubescent: leaf-blades 1–3 cm. long, ovate to lanceolate, cuneately narrowed to the short petiole: pedicels 3–9 mm. long, slender, one or two to an axil: sepals about 1.5 mm. long, elliptic to elliptic-ovate, three-nerved: corolla white, 4–10 mm. wide; lobes ovate: capsule 1.5–2.5 mm. long: seeds yellowish-brown. [*S. grandiflora* Nash]—(GOAT-WEED.)—Waste-places and cult. ground, Coastal Plain, S Fla. to La. and S Ga.—(*W. I., Mex., C. A., S. A.*)—All year.

4. **MACUILLAMIA** Raf. Creeping and floating succulent, odorless herbs. Leaves opposite: blades entire, palmately 7–9-veined, obscurely glandular-punctate, narrowed to a clasping base. Flowers axillary to leaf-like bracts. Sepals 5, unequal, the posterior one orbicular-oval to oval; the two lateral ovate; the two innermost lanceolate, as long as the others. Corolla white, nearly regular, campanulate: lobes slightly shorter than the tube, equally distinct or the posterior slightly united. Stamens 4. Stigmas peltately flattened. Capsule globose or ovoid, obtuse, nearly equalling the persistent calyx, septicidal or also loculicidal. Seeds numerous, cylindric, finely reticulate, wingless.—About 10 species, natives of tropical and temperate America.

Pedicels 10–15 mm. long, pubescent: corolla 6–8 mm. long: capsule 4–5 mm. long, both septicidal and loculicidal.   1. *M. rotundifolia.*
Pedicels 5–7 mm. long, nearly glabrous: corolla 3–4 mm. long:
    capsule 3 mm. long, apparently only loculicidal.   2. *M. repens.*

1. **M. rotundifolia** (Michx.) Raf. Stem and branches 2–6 dm. long, pubescent, especially above, forming dense mats in water: leaf-blades 1.5–3.5 cm. long, obovate to obovate-orbicular: pedicels 10–15 mm. long, shorter than the bracts: sepals becoming 4–6 mm. long: corolla 6–8 mm. long, with yellow throat: seeds 0.5 mm. long, yellowish-brown. [*Herpestis rotundifolia* (Michx.) Pursh *Monniera rotundifolia* Michx.]—Ponds, Interior Low Plateaus, Tenn., and more western provinces, Tex. to Colo., N. D., and Ind.—Sum.

2. **M. repens** (Sw.) Pennell. Stem and branches 2–4 dm. long, pubescent, especially above, forming mats in water: leaf-blades 1–2 cm. long, obovate: pedicels 5–7 mm. long, nearly glabrous, much shorter than the bracts: sepals becoming 3–4 mm. long:

corolla 3–4 mm. long. [*Gratiola repens* Sw.]—Pools, near the coast, George-town, S. C.—(*W. I.*)—Sum.

5. HERPESTIS Gaertn. f.   Creeping succulent, odorless herbs.   Leaves opposite: blades entire, palmately 3–5-veined, obscurely glandular-punctate, cor-date-clasping.   Flowers axillary to leaf-like bracts.   Sepals 5, very dissimilar, the posterior one orbicular-cordate, the two lateral half-cordate; the two inner-most linear-lanceolate, attenuate, slightly shorter than the others.   Corolla white, nearly regular, campanulate: lobes shorter than the tube, the posterior united about half their length.   Stamens 2.   Stigmas dis-tinct, peltately flattened and semi-capitate. Capsule ellipsoid-ovoid, obtuse, enclosed with-in and much shorter than the persistent calyx, both septicidal and loculicidal.   Seeds numerous, ellipsoid-cylindric, finely ridged, wingless.—One species.

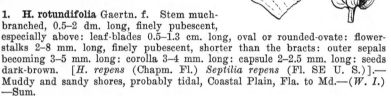

1. H. rotundifolia Gaertn. f.   Stem much-branched, 0.5–2 dm. long, finely pubescent, especially above: leaf-blades 0.5–1.3 cm. long, oval or rounded-ovate: flower-stalks 2–8 mm. long, finely pubescent, shorter than the bracts: outer sepals becoming 3–5 mm. long: corolla 3–4 mm. long: capsule 2–2.5 mm. long: seeds dark-brown.   [*H. repens* (Chapm. Fl.) *Septilia repens* (Fl. SE U. S.)].—Muddy and sandy shores, probably tidal, Coastal Plain, Fla. to Md.—(*W. I.*)—Sum.

6. HYDROTRIDA Small.   Aromatic, succulent, creeping or floating herbs, the roots perennial.   Stems distally erect.   Leaves opposite: blades entire or obscurely crenate, with 5–7 longitudinal veins, punctate with resinous dots, rounded, clasping at base.   Flowers axillary to leaf-like bracts.   Bractlets two, borne just beneath the calyx.   Sepals 5, very dissimilar, the posterior one cor-date, the two lateral half-cordate; the two innermost lanceolate-attenuate, much shorter than the others.   Corolla blue, nearly regular, campanulate: lobes slightly shorter than the tube and all pubescent within at base, the posterior lobes somewhat united. Stamens 4.   Ovary surrounded by a circle of bristles.   Stigmas distinct, lip-like.   Cap-sule narrowly ovoid, acute, glabrous, in-cluded in the persistent calyx, septicidal and loculicidal.   Seeds numerous, ellipsoid or oval, reticulate, wingless.—About 5 species, American.

1. H. caroliniana (Walt.) Small.   Stem and branches 2–6 dm. long, distally lanose: leaf-blades 1–2.5 cm. long, ovate to suborbicular or nearly elliptic: pedicels 3–15 mm. long, shorter than the bracts: sepals all exceeding the minute, subulate bractlets, the outer becoming 6–11 mm. long: corolla 9–11 mm. long: capsule

4-5 mm. long: seeds grayish-brown. [*Herpestis amplexicaulis* Pursh *Septilia caroliniana* (Walt.) Small]—Ponds and ditches in pineland, Coastal Plain, S Fla. to E Tex. and Va.—Spr.–fall, or all year S.

7. **BRAMIA** Lam. Creeping, glabrous, succulent, odorless herbs, the root perennial. Stems distally ascending. Leaves opposite, blades entire or obscurely toothed, obscurely glandular-punctate, narrowed to a sessile base. Flowers axillary to leaf-like bracts. Bractlets two, just beneath the calyx. Sepals 5, dissimilar; the posterior one ovate; the two lateral narrower; the two innermost lanceolate, attenuate, slightly shorter than the others. Corolla nearly regular, campanulate, glabrous: lobes equalling the tube, all equally distinct. Stigmas flat, mainly united and semi-capitate. Capsule ovoid, acute, glabrous, more deeply loculicidal than septicidal. Seeds numerous, cylindric or ovoid, finely-ridged, wingless.— About 5 species, tropical.

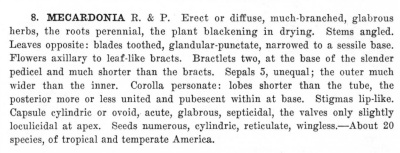

1. **B. Monnieri** (L.) Pennell. Stem and branches 1-6 dm. long, often forming mats: leaf-blades 0.5-1.7 cm. long, cuneate to elliptic-cuneate: pedicels 5-25 mm. long, usually as long as or longer than the bracts: sepals becoming 5-7 mm. long, much exceeding the linear-attenuate, spreading bractlets: corolla 8-10 mm. long, white or pinkish-white: capsule 4-5 mm. long: seeds grayish-brown. [*Herpestis Monnieria* (L.) H.B.K. *Monniera Monniera* (L.) Britton]—Sandy shores of rivers and ponds, most frequently within reach of tides, near the coast, Fla. to Tex., and Va.—(*W. I., Mex., C. A., S. A., O. W.*)—Spr.–fall, or all year S.

8. **MECARDONIA** R. & P. Erect or diffuse, much-branched, glabrous herbs, the roots perennial, the plant blackening in drying. Stems angled. Leaves opposite: blades toothed, glandular-punctate, narrowed to a sessile base. Flowers axillary to leaf-like bracts. Bractlets two, at the base of the slender pedicel and much shorter than the bracts. Sepals 5, unequal; the outer much wider than the inner. Corolla personate: lobes shorter than the tube, the posterior more or less united and pubescent within at base. Stigmas lip-like. Capsule cylindric or ovoid, acute, glabrous, septicidal, the valves only slightly loculicidal at apex. Seeds numerous, cylindric, reticulate, wingless.—About 20 species, of tropical and temperate America.

Corolla white, the posterior lobes united half to two-thirds their length: sepals unequal, the outer lanceolate, rarely more than twice the width of the inner: plant erect or diffuse. 1. *M. acuminata.*
Corolla yellow, the posterior lobes united nearly to apex: sepals nearly equal in length, the outer ovate, more than thrice the width of the inner: plant procumbent or ascending.
Outer sepals narrowly ovate to ovate, narrowed or slightly rounded at base: pedicels 2-4 times the length of the bracts. 2. *M. tenuis.*
Outer sepals ovate to widely ovate, broadly rounded or cordate at the base: pedicels 1-2 times the length of the bracts. 3. *M. procumbens.*

1. **M. acuminata** (Walt.) Small. Plant erect or nearly so, 1-6 dm. tall: (lower, diffuse, with leaf-blades 1.3-2 cm. long, outer sepals 5-6 mm. long, and

corolla usually 7–8 mm. long, in *M. acumi-*
nata peninsularis of S Fla.; laxly ascending,
with ovate leaf-blades only 1–1.7 cm. long
and pedicels only 8–12 mm. long, in *M. acu-*
minata microphylla of longleaf pinelands
from N Fla. to Tex. and S Ga.) leaf-blades
3–5 cm. long, spatulate-elliptic or nearly
elliptic, serrate-dentate: pedicels 12–30 mm.
long, usually exceeding the bracts: sepals
6.8 mm. long: corolla about 10 mm. long,
white, with longitudinal purple veins on the
posterior side: capsule 5–6 mm. long: seeds
dark-gray. [*Herpestis nigrescens* Benth.]—
Moist sand or loam, especially near streams,
in partial shade, various provinces, Fla. to
Tex., Mo., Ky., and Md.—Spr.–fall.

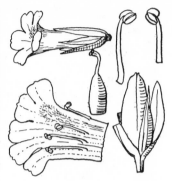

2. **M. tenuis** Small. Plant 0.5–4 dm. long, diffusely ascending or prostrate:
leaf-blades 1–2 cm. long, oval, serrate: pedicels 15–35 mm. long, sepals 5–6 mm.
long: corolla 7–8 mm. long, deep lemon-yellow, with longitudinal dark veins on
the posterior side: capsule 5–6 mm. long.—Light loam or humus over limestone,
hammocks and thickets, Everglade Keys, Fla., and lower Florida Keys.—
(*W. I.*).—All year, but mostly in spr.

3. **M. procumbens** (Mill.) Small. Plant 0.5–4 dm. long, procumbent and somewhat ascending: leaf-blades 1–2 cm. long, oval or ovate, serrate: pedicels 7–25
mm. long, sepals 6–9 mm. long: corolla 6 mm. long, lemon-yellow, with longitudinal dark veins on the posterior side: capsule 4–6 mm. long.—Moist loam or
sand, meadows and edges of hammocks, S Florida.—(*W. I., Mex., C. A., S. A.*)
—All year.

9. **GRATIOLA** L. Erect or ascending, branching herbs, the roots perennial or annual. Leaves opposite: blades toothed to rarely entire, more or less
glandular-punctate, sessile, or on young shoots petioled. Flowers axillary to
leaf-like bracts. Bractlets usually present, borne just beneath the calyx.
Sepals 5, nearly equal. Corolla yellow or white, personate: lobes shorter than
the tube, the posterior united nearly or quite to apex and pubescent within at
base. Two postero-lateral stamens perfect, the antero-lateral represented by
rudimentary filaments or wholly lacking, the connective expanded to a pale
membrane spreading beyond the anther-sacs, which are turned transversely to
axis of flower. Stigmas lip-like. Capsule ovoid-pyramidal to globose, acute or
rounded, glabrous, both septicidal and loculicidal nearly or quite to base. Seeds
numerous, irregularly tetrahedral, reticulate, wingless.—About 30 species, widely
distributed.—HEDGE-HYSSOPS.

Capsule 3–6 mm. long, equalling or slightly exceeding the sepals: stem-leaves narrowed to a sessile or scarcely clasping base: plant annual.
   Pedicel slender, 10–45 mm. long: corolla within throat on posterior side pubes-
      cent with clavate hairs: capsule ovoid, equalled or exceeded by the sepals.
      Corolla 8–10 mm. long; tube greenish-yellow, unlined:
         leaf-blades elliptic-lanceolate, acute to acuminate.   1. *G. neglecta.*
      Corolla (at least of earlier flowers) 15–18 mm. long, the
         tube white and lined with purple: leaf-blades obovate
         to oval, obtuse or rounded.   2. *G. floridana.*
   Pedicel stout, 1–12 mm. long: corolla within throat on pos-
      terior side pubescent with filiform hairs: capsule globose,
      usually slightly exceeding the sepals.   3. *G. virginiana.*
Capsule 1–3 mm. long, much exceeded by the sepals: stem-leaves
   clasping by a wide base: plant perennial.

Corolla golden-yellow: capsule 3 mm. long: leaf-blades entire or slightly toothed.   4. *G. aurea.*
Corolla at least with white lobes; tube delicately lined with purple-brown: capsule 1-2 mm. long: leaf-blades with sharp salient teeth.
Leaf-blades linear-lanceolate to lanceolate, coarsely toothed towards the tip: sepals linear to linear-subulate: corolla-tube dull-yellow.
Capsule usually wider than long: sepals 5-7 mm. long, usually subtended by one or two sepal-like bractlets.   5. *G. brevifolia.*
Capsule as long as wide or longer: sepals 3-5 mm. long, subtended by one small bractlet or none.   6. *G. ramosa.*
Leaf-blades elliptic-ovate to ovate, finely serrate throughout: sepals lanceolate to elliptic-lanceolate: corolla-tube white.   7. *G. viscidula.*

1. G. neglecta Torr. Stem 1-3 dm. tall, usually much-branched, glandular-pubescent especially above: leaf-blades 1-6 cm. long, elliptic-lanceolate, serrate-dentate, acute or acuminate: pedicels 10-30 mm. long, slender, glandular-pubescent: bractlets equaling or usually longer than the calyx: sepals 3-6 mm. long, linear to linear-lanceolate: corolla 8-10 mm. long; lobes white or pinkish-tinged; throat greenish-yellow: capsule 3-5 mm. long, pyramidal-ovoid, acute: seeds yellow, with longitudinal much more pronounced than transverse reticulations. [*G. virginiana* (Chapm. Fl. Fl. SE U. S.)].—Wet loam, usually in deciduous woodland, Piedmont and more northern provinces, Ga. to Tex., Calif., B. C., Ont., and Me.; north of our area more common. —Spr.-sum., then until fall fruiting cleistogamously.

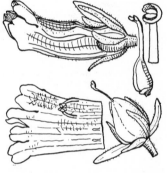

2. G. floridana Nutt. Stem 1-4 dm. tall, simple or somewhat branched, finely glandular-pubescent above or glabrate throughout: leaf-blades 2-4 cm. long, obovate or oval, dentate to nearly entire, obtuse or rounded, obscurely glandular-punctate: pedicels mostly 20-45 mm. long, slender, finely glandular-pubescent to glabrate: bractlets equalling or usually longer than the calyx: sepals 3-6 mm. long, linear: corolla 15-18 mm. long, white; throat lined with purple, yellow posteriorly: capsule 3-5 mm. long, ovoid, acute: seeds cylindric, yellow, with longitudinal much more pronounced than transverse reticulations. [*G. macrantha* Chapm.]—Muddy banks and wet woods, Coastal Plain and adj. provinces, N Fla. to Ala. and Ga.—Spr.

3. G. virginiana L. Stem 1-4 dm. tall, stout, often much branched, glabrous or nearly so throughout: leaf-blades 2-5 cm. long, elliptic-lanceolate to oval, repand to dentate-serrate, acute or obtuse, obscurely glandular-punctate: pedicels 1-12 mm. long, stout, puberulent or glabrate: bractlets shorter or slightly longer than the calyx: sepals 4-6 mm. long, linear: corolla 9-14 mm. long, white; throat lined with purple on the upper side: capsule 4-7 mm. long, globose: seeds linear-cylindric, yellow, with longitudinal and transverse reticulations equally pronounced. [*G. sphaerocarpa* Ell.]—Wet shaded places, along streams and ponds, Coastal Plain from C pen. Fla. to E Tex., and N. J.; inland through the Blue Ridge and Appalachian Valley, and in the Mississippi Valley to Ia. and Ohio.—Spr., then until fall fruiting cleistogamously.

4. G. aurea Pursh. Stem 1-4 dm. long, erect or weakly ascending, usually branched, glandular-puberulent above: leaf-blades 1-2.5 cm. long, linear-lanceolate to lanceolate-ovate, conspicuously glandular-punctate, clasping at base: pedicels becoming 10-25 mm. long, slender, glandular-puberulent: bractlets shorter than the calyx: sepals 4–7 mm. long, linear-lanceolate to lanceolate: corolla 10–15 mm. long, golden-yellow, unlined; capsule 3 mm. long: seeds strongly reticulate, brown. [*G. georgiana* Pennell]—Wet pine-barrens, occasional or rare, Coastal Plain, N Fla. to Ala. and N. C.; more abundant northward, to Que. and Newf.—Spr.–fall.

5. G. brevifolia Raf. Stem 2–4 dm. long, laxly ascending, simple or little branched, glandular-puberulent above: leaf-blades 1–2.5 mm. long, linear-lanceolate, clasping at base: pedicels becoming 12–20 mm. long, slender, glandular-puberulent: bractlets equalling the calyx: sepals 5–7 mm. long, linear: corolla 10–12 mm. long; lobes white, the throat yellow, lined with brown; capsule 1–2 mm. long, wider than long: seeds strongly reticulate, brown. [*G. Drummondii* Benth.]—Moist or wet sandy soil in pinelands, Coastal Plain from N Florida to E Texas and S Ga.; inland on sandstone ridges to northwestern Georgia and the Cumberland Plateau of E Tenn.—Spr.–fall.

6. G. ramosa Walt. Rootstock much branched: stem 1–3 dm. tall, simple or little branched, densely glandular-puberulent above: leaf-blades 0.7–1.5 cm. long, linear to lanceolate, clasping at base: pedicels becoming 6–17 mm. long, glandular-puberulent: bractlets vestigial or wholly lacking: sepals 3–5 mm. long, linear-subulate: corolla 10–14 mm. long; lobes white; throat yellow, lined with brown: capsule 1–2 mm. long, as long as or longer than wide: seeds finely reticulate, brown.—Moist or wet sandy soil in pinelands, Coastal Plain, S Fla. to La. and Md.—Spr.

7. G. viscidula Pennell. Rootstock short and nearly simple: stem 2–6 dm. tall, simple or little branched, viscid-puberulent or pubescent: leaf-blades 1–2 cm. long, oblong-ovate to ovate, widely clasping at base: pedicels 10–15 mm. long, glandular-pubescent: bractlets nearly equalling the calyx: sepals 5–7 mm. long, lanceolate to elliptic-lanceolate: corolla 8–11 mm. long, white; throat lined with purple: capsule 2 mm. long, globose-ovoid: seeds strongly reticulate, brown. [*G. viscosa* Schwein. not Hornem.]—Swales and along streams, Blue Ridge and Piedmont, C Ga. to E Tenn. and N Del.—Sum.

10. TRAGIOLA Small & Pennell. Erect herbs, from a short rootstock. Leaves opposite: blades serrate, glandular-punctate, the cauline rounded to a clasping base, the basal short-petioled, forming a winter-rosette. Flowers axillary to bracts. Bractlets two, just beneath the calyx. Sepals 5, unequal. Corolla white, personate, nearly tubular: lobes short, the posterior united nearly to apex and pubescent within at base. Two postero-lateral stamens polleniferous, the antero-laterals represented by rudimentary filaments. Connective not dilated. Stigmas lip-like. Capsule narrowly pyramidal, acuminate, deeply-sulcate, glabrous, septicidal, the valves only slightly loculicidal at apex. Seeds numerous, irregularly tetrahedral, obscurely lined, wingless.—One species.

1. T. pilosa (Michx.) Small & Pennell. Stem 2–6 dm. tall, hirsute (or nearly or quite glabrous and with shorter leaves and bracts in *T. pilosa epilis*, which occurs in S Fla.); leaf-blades 1–2 cm. long, ovate or oval, slightly serrate to nearly entire: pedicels less than 1 mm. long: sepals 5–7 mm. long, linear to linear-subulate, somewhat exceeded by the bractlets: corolla 5–9 mm. long, the throat with faint bluish-purple lines: capsule 4–5 mm. long: seeds yellowish. [*Gratiola pilosa* Michx. *Sophronanthe pilosa* (Michx.) Small]—Pinelands, Coastal Plain, C pen. Fla. to E Tex. and N. J.; inland through northern Ala. and northern Ga., reaching the mountain-valleys of E Tenn. and W N. C.—Sum.–fall.

11. **SOPHRONANTHE** Benth. Erect much branched herbs, with perennial roots, the plant covered nearly throughout with stiff white bristle-like hairs. Leaves opposite; blades entire, strongly revolute, obscurely glandular-punctate, sessile. Flowers sessile, axillary to leaf-like bracts. Bractlets two. Sepals 5, very unequal, the outer three longer than the inner two. Corolla white, salverform, slightly personate: tube very narrow, short-pubescent within on all sides; lobes shorter than the tube, the posterior united to apex. Two postero-lateral stamens polleniferous, the antero-laterals represented by rudimentary filaments or lacking. Connective not dilated. Stigmas lip-like. Capsule narrowly pyramidal, acuminate, deeply-sulcate, glabrous, loculicidal. Seeds numerous, nearly rectagonal, finely lined, wingless. —One species.

1. **S. hispida** Benth. Stem 0.5–2 dm. tall, hispid: leaf-blades 0.8–1.5 cm. long, firm, linear, glabrous and whitened as by an incrustation above, with hispid midrib beneath: sepals 3–6 mm. long, linear to linear-lanceolate, all exceeded by the bractlets: corolla 10–13 mm. long: capsule 4–5 mm. long: seeds nearly black. [*Gratiola subulata* Baldw.]—Dry pinelands, Coastal Plain, S Fla. to Miss. and S Ga.—Spr.–fall.

12. **AMPHIANTHUS** Torr. Delicate glabrous annual herb, from a caudex sending up several lax stems each buoyed to the surface of the water by the pair of leaves that act as floats. Leaves opposite; blades obscurely glandular-punctate, dimorphic; the basal immersed ones lanceolate, acute, widely sessile; the distal floating ones oval, rounded at apex, narrowed to a semipetiolar base. Flowers axillary to both types of leaves, although from the two floating leaves there is usually only one, seemingly terminal, the basal flowers probably cleistogamic. Bractlets none. Sepals 5, slightly united, somewhat unequal. Corolla of emersed flowers white or whitish, campanulate, slightly personate; lobes shorter than the tube: while not seen, the corollas of the basal flowers probably do not open. Stamens 2. Stigmas plate-like. Capsule wider than long, flattened contrary to septum, of two rounded cavities, loculicidal to base, even splitting the septum. Seeds numerous, cylindric, reticulate, wingless.—One species.

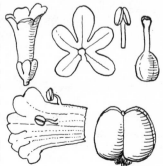

1. **A. pusillus** Torr. Stem filiform, 0.1–0.5 dm. long branched only at base: leaf-blades about 0.5 cm. long: pedicels 0.5–2 mm. long,

shorter than the bracts: sepals 1 mm. long: corolla (of emersed flowers) 6–8 mm. long: capsule 2 mm. long, 3 mm. wide: seeds 1–1.2 mm. long, those of the basal capsules smaller.—Aquatic in shallow depressions in granite rocks, Piedmont, Ga. —Spr.—The seeds of this plant apparently lie dormant during dry seasons, and germinate in years of heavy winter precipitation. It is accordingly to be found only at long or irregular intervals.

13. ILYSANTHES Raf. Erect, diffuse or creeping herbs, usually much-branched, with biennial or annual roots. Leaves opposite: blades toothed to entire, glandular-punctate, sessile or somewhat petioled. Flowers axillary to leaf-like bracts. Bractlets none. Sepals 5, distinct or united, linear, slightly unequal in length. Corolla blue-violet or paler, zygomorphic: lobes shorter than the tube, the two posterior arched and united over half their length, the three anterior projecting and with two conspicuous yellow pubescent ridges formed by the adnate proximal portions of the anterior filaments. Filaments four, didynamous, the two posterior shorter, anther-bearing; the two anterior projecting distally as two short yellow pubescent processes, at or near the apex of which a reflexed glabrous upcurving prolongation may be evident. Stigmas plate-like. Capsule narrowly ellipsoid to ovoid, somewhat oblique by the greater development of the anterior carpel and with the callose white style-base attached posteriorly; glabrous, septicidal throughout. Seeds numerous, yellowish, nearly ellipsoid, prismatic-angled or winged, with fine transverse lines. —About 70 species, widely distributed, especially in warm regions.—FALSE-PIMPERNELS.

Stem prostrate and extensively creeping: leaf-blades orbicular to ovate-orbicular, rounded at base, all closely sessile: seeds winged.   I. BAZINA.
Stem erect or ascending: leaf-blades more or less elongate, at least the lowermost narrowed at the base: seeds not winged.   II. EUILYSANTHES.

I. BAZINA
Matted plant, conspicuous when in flower by the numerous mottled corollas.   1. *I. grandiflora.*

II. EUILYSANTHES
Seeds much longer than wide, truncate: basal leaves small or lacking, not tending to form a rosette: stem and pedicels slightly ridge-angled.
  Seeds pale-yellow, mostly twice or thrice as long as wide: leaf-blades 1–3 cm. long, the lower obviously narrowed at base: pedicels shorter or longer than the bracts: later flowers cleistogamous.   2. *I. dubia.*
  Seeds brownish-yellow, mostly less than twice as long as wide: leaf-blades 0.5–1.5 cm. long, nearly all widest near base and rounded-clasping: pedicels much exceeding the bracts: corollas throughout the season all open.   3. *I. inaequalis.*
Seeds as wide as long, apiculate: basal leaves usually larger, present most of the season and forming a winter-rosette: stem and pedicels prominently ridge-angled.
  Stem 0.3–1 dm. tall, uniformly leafy, the cauline leaves being little smaller than the basal: pedicels 7–15 mm. long: capsule 1–2 mm. long.   4. *I. saxicola.*
  Stem 1–3 dm. tall, nearly bare above, the upper leaves being reduced to subulate bracts: pedicels 15–50 mm. long: capsule 3–5 mm. long.   5. *I. monticola.*

1. I. grandiflora (Nutt.) Benth. Stems 0.2–4 dm. long, much-branched, extensively creeping: leaf-blades 0.5–1 cm. long, orbicular or ovate-orbicular, crenate-serrate to entire, finely glandular-punctate: pedicels 15–40 mm. long, erect, obscurely puberulent: sepals 2–4 mm. long, glabrate: corolla 8–10 mm. long, violet-blue, within paler, the posterior lobes pale and with violet-blue median streaks, the anterior lobes white, but with two violet-blue blotches near the bases of the lobes: capsule 4–6 mm. long: seeds brownish-yellow, cylindric, scarcely longer than wide, slightly curved, with 5 to 7 thin wings. [*Bazina nudiflora* Raf.]—Moist sandy soil, Coastal Plain, S Fla. to S Ga.—Spr.–fall or all year S.

2. I. dubia (L.) Barnhart. Stems 0.5–2.5 dm. tall, often much branched and diffusely spreading: leaf-blades dentate, serrate, or nearly entire: those of the lower leaves obovate or elliptic narrowed at base, 1–3 cm. long; the upper smaller and frequently ovate, with rounded clasping base: pedicels 3–20 mm. long: sepals 3–5 mm. long, usually finely pubescent: corolla 7–10 mm. long, pale-lavender, deeper in color near margin of lobes: capsule 3–5 mm. long: seeds nearly cylindric, pale-yellow. [*I. gratioloides* (L.) Benth. *I. attenuata* (Muhl.) Small.]—Swamps and stream-margins, usually loam, open or shaded, various provinces, N Fla. to Tex., Nebr., Wis., and N. B.—Sum.; in fall fruiting cleistogamously.

3. I. inequalis (Walt.) Pennell. Stems 0.3–2 dm. tall, much-branched and diffusely spreading: leaf-blades 0.5–1.5 cm. long, remotely toothed or usually entire, mostly ovate and rounded-clasping, only the lowermost sometimes narrowed at base: pedicels 10–20 mm. long: sepals 2–3 mm. long, glabrate or glabrous: corolla 6–8 mm. long, white or faintly tinged with lavender: capsule 2–4 mm. long: seeds cylindric-angled, brownish-yellow. [*I. gratioloides* (Fl. SE. U. S.)]—Wet sandy places, usually open, Coastal Plain and more northern provinces, Fla. to Tex., N. Dak., and N. H.—Sum.–fall.

4. I. saxicola (Curtis) Chapm. Stems 0.3–1 dm. tall, somewhat tufted, simple or sparingly branched: blades of the cauline leaves 0.3–0.7 mm. long, narrowly elliptic or somewhat spatulate, entire, obviously glandular-dotted, narrowed at base: pedicels 7–15 mm. long, obscurely glandular-puberulent: sepals 1–2 mm. long, glabrous: corolla 9–12 mm. long (not seen fresh): capsule 1–2 mm. long: seeds ovoid, brownish-yellow.—On rocks in rapid streams, Blue Ridge, Ga. to N. C.—Sum.–fall.

5. I. monticola (Nutt.) Raf. Stems 1–3 dm. tall, rising from out a rosette of leaves that persists most of the year, simple or laxly branched: basal leaf-blades elliptic-oval to oval, undulate-dentate to entire, obviously glandular-punctate, 15–23 mm. long, narrowed to short petiolar bases; blades of the cauline leaves smaller, rapidly diminishing above, the upper being slender subulate-linear scales only 2–3 mm. long: pedicels obscurely glandular-puberulent to glabrous: sepals 1.5–3 mm. long, glabrous: corolla 9–11 mm. long, violet-purple, within paler, streaked and blotched: capsule 3–5 mm. long: seeds globose-ovoid, brownish-yellow. [*I. refracta* (Ell.) Raf.]—Moist sandy open soil, various provinces, N Fla. to Ala., and N. C.—Spr.–fall.

14. GLOBIFERA J. F. Gmel. Creeping glabrous annual herbs, extensively branching and forming soft mats. Leaves opposite: blades entire, obscurely or not glandular-punctate, sessile or nearly so. Flowers axillary to leaf-like bracts. Bractlets none. Sepals 4, slightly united, elliptic, uniform.

Corolla white, glabrous, rotate, lobes longer than the tube, the 2 posterior
united to apex, so appearing as one lobe which is smaller than the other 3.
Filaments two (only the antero-lateral pres-
ent), exserted, arising from swollen, but
scarcely projecting bases. Stigmas lip-like,
borne on the distinct style-tips. Capsule
globose, glabrous, at maturity one-celled,
rupturing irregularly by the break-down of
the thin wall. Seeds numerous, yellowish,
cylindric, prismatic-angled, with fine transverse lines.—Two or 3 species, American.

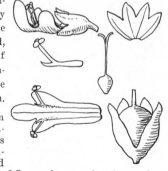

1. **G. umbrosa** (Walt.) J. F. Gmel. Stem
0.5–3 dm. long, slender: leaf-blades 0.3–1.1
cm. long, somewhat cuneately narrowed at
base: pedicels 0.5–1 mm. long: sepals 1.5
mm. long: corolla 1.5 mm long: capsule 1 mm. long.   [*Micranthemum orbiculatum* Michx.]—Wet shaded loam, often in shallow pools, Coastal Plain, C pen.
Fla. to Tex., and N. C.—(*W. I., S. A.*)—Spr.–fall.—The suborbicular leaf-blades
are usually much less than 1 cm. long.

15. **HEMIANTHUS** Nutt. Creeping glabrous annual herbs, extensively
branching and forming small mats. Leaves opposite or in threes: blades entire, not glandular-punctate, sessile. Flowers axillary to leaf-like bracts.
Bractlets none. Sepals 4, united at least half their length, but on the anterior
side distinct nearly to base. Corolla 1-lipped, open nearly to base on the
posterior side (the posterior lobes wholly lacking), the lip deflexed-spreading, 3-lobed, pubescent with short yellow hairs on the two ridges to the
sinuses. Filaments two (only the antero-lateral present), projecting distally
as two yellow-pubescent processes just below the bases of which upcurve the
glabrous anther-bearing portion of the fila-
ment. Stigmas narrowly flattened, widely
divaricate on the free style-tips. Capsule
globose, glabrous, at maturity 1-celled,
rupturing irregularly by the break-down of
the thin wall. Seeds numerous, yellow, cylindric, prismatic-angled, with fine transverse
lines.—About 7 species, mostly West Indian.

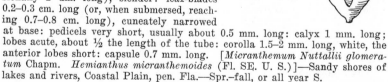

1. **H. glomeratus** (Chapm.) Pennell. Stem
0.2–0.5 dm. long (or, when submersed, occasionally 2 dm. long), slender: leaf-blades
0.2–0.3 cm. long (or, when submersed, reaching 0.7–0.8 cm. long), cuneately narrowed
at base: pedicels very short, usually about 0.5 mm. long: calyx 1 mm. long;
lobes acute, about ½ the length of the tube: corolla 1.5–2 mm. long, white, the
anterior lobes short: capsule 0.7 mm. long.   [*Micranthemum Nuttallii glomeratum* Chapm. *Hemianthus micranthemoides* (Fl. SE. U. S.)]—Sandy shores of
lakes and rivers, Coastal Plain, pen. Fla.—Spr.–fall, or all year S.

16. **LEUCOSPORA** Nutt. Erect, hairy, annual, much branched herbs.
Leaves opposite: blades deeply-pinnatifid, not punctate, petioled. Bractlets
none. Sepals 5, distinct, linear-attenuate, uniform. Corolla personate: lobes
shorter than the tube, the two posterior united nearly to apex, the anterior

spreading-projecting and slightly pubescent at base. Filaments four, didynamous. Stigmas plate-like. Capsule ovoid, glabrous, septicidal nearly to base, the valves only slightly loculicidal near apex. Seeds numerous, pale greenish-yellow or nearly colorless, ellipsoid-cylindric, ridged and with fine transverse lines.—One species.

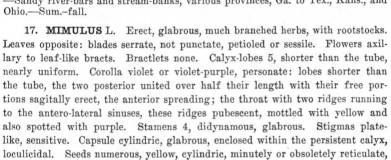

1. **L. multifida** (Michx.) Nutt. Stem 1-3 dm. tall, glandular-pubescent: leaf-blades with two pairs of divaricately spreading segments that, like the terminal segment, are slightly dentate to sharply lobed, the larger leaf-blades 1-2 cm. long on ill-defined petioles 0.5-1 cm. long: pedicels 3-7 mm. long, pubescent: sepals 3-5 mm. long, finely pubescent: corolla 3-4 mm. long; lobes with violet-purple lines; tube within yellow and purplish: capsule 3-4 mm. long. [*Conobea multifida* (Michx.) Benth.] —Sandy river-bars and stream-banks, various provinces, Ga. to Tex., Kans., and Ohio.—Sum.-fall.

17. **MIMULUS** L. Erect, glabrous, much branched herbs, with rootstocks. Leaves opposite: blades serrate, not punctate, petioled or sessile. Flowers axillary to leaf-like bracts. Bractlets none. Calyx-lobes 5, shorter than the tube, nearly uniform. Corolla violet or violet-purple, personate: lobes shorter than the tube, the two posterior united over half their length with their free portions sagitally erect, the anterior spreading; the throat with two ridges running to the antero-lateral sinuses, these ridges pubescent, mottled with yellow and also spotted with purple. Stamens 4, didynamous, glabrous. Stigmas plate-like, sensitive. Capsule cylindric, glabrous, enclosed within the persistent calyx, loculicidal. Seeds numerous, yellow, cylindric, minutely or obsoletely reticulate, wingless.—About 70 species, mostly American.—MONKEY-FLOWERS.

Leaf-blades petioled: angles of stem usually slightly winged: calyx-lobes setaceous-tipped, 0.5-2 mm. long. 1. *M. alatus.*
Leaf-blades clasping (or rarely only sessile): angles of stem not winged: calyx-lobes lanceolate, 3-5 mm. long. 2. *M. ringens.*

1. **M. alatus** Ait. Stem 4-12 dm. tall, simple or somewhat branched: leaf-blades 5-15 cm. long, elliptic-oval, oval, or ovate: pedicels 0.5-1.5 (-3) cm. long: calyx-lobes setaceous-tipped: corolla 25-35 mm. long, as in *M. ringens,* but frequently more purplish, with smaller spots and fainter brownish patches: capsule 10-12 mm. long.—Shaded swamps, Piedmont and more northern provinces, and along river-bottoms in the Coastal Plain, N Fla. to E Tex., Nebr., Mich., and Conn.—Sum.

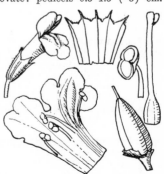

2. **M. ringens** L. Stem 5-12 dm. tall, usually much branched: leaf-blades 5-12 cm. long, narrowly lanceolate to ovate-lanceolate: pedicels 3-6 cm. long: calyx-lobes lanceolate-attenuate: corolla 25-30 mm. long, pale hortense-violet, throat anteriorly with purpled-red spots and proximally two yellow areas

mottled with faint brownish patches: capsule 10–12 mm. long. [*M. menthoides* Greene]—Swamps and swales, Piedmont and more northern provinces, C Ala. to Colo., Minn., and N. S.; descending along rivers into Coastal Plain as reported from Quincy, Fla.—Sum.

18. VERBASCUM L. Erect, simple or virgately branched herbs, with a perennial or biennial tap-root. Leaves alternate: blades toothed or entire, those of the cauline sessile, clasping, or sometimes decurrent. Flowers in spikes, racemes, or panicles, the bracts much smaller than the leaves. Bractlets none. Sepals 5, uniform. Corolla rotate, slightly zygomorphic: lobes longer than the tube, all equally distinct, the anterior larger than the posterior. Stamens 5, exserted, the filaments more or less lanose-pubescent. Stigma capitate. Capsule ellipsoid to subglobose, septicidal. Seeds numerous, gray, minutely tuberculate-lined, wingless.—About 250 species, natives of the Old World.—MULLENS.

Stem glabrous or with simple gland-tipped hairs above: leaves glabrous: filaments all densely lanose with knobbed purple hairs: capsule subglobose, glandular-puberulent. 1. *V. Blattaria.*
Stem pubescent with stellate, glandless hairs: leaves pubescent, at least beneath: filaments lanose with filiform yellow hairs, the two anterior sparingly so or glabrous: capsule ovoid to ellipsoid, stellate-pubescent.
  Leaf-blades crenate, glabrate above, the cauline sessile: pedicels usually several in an axil: sepals about half length of capsule: inflorescence not densely crowded.
    Inflorescence a simple raceme, the pedicels one to five to an axil: capsule globose, 7–8 mm. long: leaves green and slightly pubescent beneath. 2. *V. virgatum.*
    Inflorescence a panicle of racemes, the pedicels three to twelve to an axil: capsule oblong or oblong-ovoid, 4–5 mm. long: leaves white and densely stellate-tomentose beneath. 3. *V. Lychnitis.*
  Leaf-blades entire or only obscurely crenate, densely pubescent above, the cauline decurrent: pedicels one to an axil: sepals as long as the capsule: inflorescence densely crowded. 4. *V. Thapsus.*

1. V. Blattaria L. Stem 4–12 dm. tall, simple or slightly branched, glandular-pubescent above: cauline leaf-blades 2–12 cm. long, elliptic to ovate, doubly serrate-crenate, bright-green above and scarcely paler beneath: pedicels 10–15 mm. long, glandular-pubescent: sepals 5–8 mm. long, linear-lanceolate: corolla 25–30 mm. wide, yellow or white: capsule 6–8 mm. long, glandular-puberulent. — (MOTH-MULLEN.)—Old fields and roadsides, various provinces, C Fla. to Calif., B. C., and Que. Nat. of Eurasia.—Sum.-fall.

2. V. virgatum With. Stem 6–12 dm. tall, simple or slightly branched, stellate-pubescent: cauline leaf-blades 7–15 cm. long, lanceolate, crenate, deep-green above and scarcely paler beneath: pedicels 2–5 mm. long, pubescent: sepals 5–6 mm. long, lanceolate: corolla about 25 mm. wide, yellow: capsule 7–8 mm. long, stellate-pubescent.—Waste-places, Coastal Plain, S. C.; Calif.—Nat. of Eu.—Sum.

3. V. Lychnitis L. Stem 8–10 dm. tall, usually much branched especially above, floccose-tomentose with short stellate hairs: cauline leaf-blades 10–20 cm. long, elliptic-lanceolate to ovate-lanceolate, crenate, dark-green above, whitened beneath: pedicels 2–10 mm. long, stellate-tomentose: sepals 2–3 mm. long, lanceolate: corolla 10–15 mm. wide, yellow: capsule 3–4 mm. long, ovoid.—(WHITE-MULLEN.)—Old fields and roadsides, various provinces, N. C. to Ont., and N. J.—Nat. of Eurasia.—Sum.

4. **V. Thapsus** L. Stem 3–12 dm. tall, usually simple, densely tomentose with floccose stellate hairs: leaf-blades 5–30 cm. long, elliptic to elliptic-ovate, finely crenate to entire, densely stellate-tomentose: pedicels less than 2 mm. long, woolly: sepals 7–9 mm. long, lanceolate or ovate with caudate tip: corolla 15–20 mm. long, yellow: capsule 8 mm. long.—(GREAT-MULLEN. WOOLLY-MULLEN. VELVET-PLANT.)—Old fields, roadsides and thickets, various provinces, Fla. to Calif., S. Dak., and N. S.—Nat. of Eurasia.—Sum.-fall.

19. **CHELONE** L. Odorless glabrous herbs, the erect stems arising from a rootstock. Leaves all cauline, opposite: blades toothed, acuminate, not punctate. Flowers in spike-like racemes, the bracts, excepting the lower ones, sepal-like, broad, entire. Bractlets 2, similar to the bracts but smaller. Sepals 5 uniform, rounded. Corolla purple, greenish, or white, 2-lipped, externally glabrous, internally lanose on the margins of the palate: tube abruptly expanded into an inflated throat: lips shorter than the throat, the posterior lip arched, slightly lobed, the anterior lip projecting, slightly lobed. Polleniferous stamens 4, didynamous, included: anther-sacs divaricate, lanose. Sterile posterior filament (staminodium) shorter than the stamens, usually glabrous. Stigma capitate, capsule pyramidal-globose or pyramidal-cylindric, glabrous, distally septicidal. Seeds numerous, winged.—About 8 species, eastern North American.—SNAKE-HEADS. TURTLE-HEADS.

Leaf-blades widest at or near the middle, above the cuneately narrowed base: corolla purple to white, not or only faintly lined within throat on the anterior side, the beard of the anterior lip pale-yellow to white: sterile filament less than half the length of the polleniferous ones: blooming chiefly in September.   I. EUCHELONE.

Leaf-blades widest near the rounded, truncate, or rarely slightly narrowed base: corolla purple to violet, with well-defined lines of deeper color within the throat on the anterior side, the beard of the anterior lip yellow: sterile filament over half the length of the polleniferous ones: blooming chiefly in August.

Petioles very short or lacking: flowers conspicuously 4-ranked, in nearly leafless, usually elongate spikes: bracts, bractlets, and sepals finely ciliolate: corolla tending toward violet, the color-lines wide, the beard light-yellow: sterile filament purple.   II. SESSILES.

Petioles mostly 1.5–3 cm. long: flowers obscurely ranked, in short spikes subtended by scarcely reduced leaves: bracts, bractlets, and sepals strongly ciliolate: corolla tending toward purple, the color lines narrow, the beard deep-yellow: sterile filament white or pinkish-tipped.   III. PETIOLATAE.

I. EUCHELONE

Corolla white throughout, or distally purple or green: sterile filament green or greenish: sepals obscurely ciliolate: leaf-blades rather thick and usually duller green.

Distal portion of corolla white or green, externally only faintly if at all purplish.

Leaf-blades 2–4 cm. wide, with ascending teeth, decidedly paler beneath, on petioles 0.2–0.6 cm. long: corolla rounded or slightly keeled posteriorly, distally often purplish, and with purple tinge internally.   1. *C. glabra.*

Leaf-blades 3–6 cm. wide, with spreading teeth, only slightly paler beneath, on petioles 0.6–1.2 cm. long: corolla strongly keeled posteriorly, distally yellowish-green, without purple tinge even internally.   2. *C. chlorantha.*

Distal portion of corolla purple: petioles 0.5–1.5 cm. long, and leaf-blades lanceolate to elliptic-oval, the larger 2–6 cm. wide.   3. *C. montana.*

Corolla purple throughout: sterile filament white or rarely
   greenish-tipped: sepals manifestly ciliolate: leaf-blades rather
   thin and deep-green.   4. *C. obliqua.*

II. SESSILES
Tall plant with leaf-blades rounded to the stem.   5. *C. Cuthbertii.*

III. PETIOLATAE
Low plant with wide-spreading ample leaf-blades.   6. *C. Lyoni.*

1. C. glabra L. Stem 8–16 dm. tall: leaf-blades 7–15 cm. long, lanceolate
to elliptic-lanceolate (or linear-lanceolate and the spikes usually much elongate
in *C. glabra elongata* of W Tenn. and S
Ind.), slightly to moderately serrate, glaucous and glabrous or pubescent beneath,
acuminate, at base cuneately narrowed:
spike slightly or considerably elongate, the
flowers obscurely ranked: bractlets 4–7 mm.
long, oval or elliptic-oval, rounded: sepals
7–10 mm. long, elliptic or widely elliptic,
rounded: bracts, bractlets, and sepals
minutely ciliolate and scarious, the sepals
somewhat erose: corolla 25–33 mm. long,
rounded or slightly keeled posteriorly, white,
sometimes distally faintly purplish and normally dull-purple within the lips (or with
greenish-yellow corolla-tips that are only
slightly or not at all purple within and a
tendency to more elongate and laxer spikes, in *C. glabra ochroleuca*, of the
Coastal Plain from N. C. to Md.), the anterior lip with white or faintly yellowish beard and with the lateral margins somewhat deflexed: sterile filament ⅓
to ½ the length of the polleniferous ones: capsule 10–12 mm. long.—Swamps
and along streams, Piedmont and more northern provinces, Ga. to Minn. and
Newf.—Fall.

2. C. chlorantha Pennell & Wherry. Stem 9–15 dm. tall: leaf-blades 9–18
cm. long, elliptic-lanceolate to elliptic-ovate, sharply dentate-serrate, glabrous
and slightly glaucous beneath, long-acuminate, at base cuneately narrowed to
the petiole: spike becoming elongate, the flowers obscurely ranked: bractlets
4–6 mm. long, oval or elliptic, obtuse or rounded: sepals 6–9 mm. long, elliptic,
obtuse or rounded: bracts, bractlets, and sepals minutely ciliolate, the sepals
with narrow scarious margin: corolla 23–28 mm. long, proximally white, the
anterior lip with pale-yellow beard and with the lateral margins much deflexed: sterile filament ⅓ to ½ the length of the polleniferous ones: capsule
not seen.—Swamps and along streams, Blue Ridge and adj. Piedmont, N. C.—
Fall.

3. C. montana (Raf.) Pennell & Wherry. Stem 6–12 dm. tall: leaf-blades
9–18 cm. long, lanceolate (or elliptic or elliptic-oval and dentate-serrate borne
on a larger plant; corolla usually 30–36 mm. long, and capsule 10–12 mm.
long, in *C. montana elatior,* a plant of lower elevations and occurring as far
south as N Ga.), sharply serrate, glabrous and slightly glaucous beneath, long-
acuminate, at base cuneately narrowed: spike only slightly elongate, the flowers
obscurely ranked: bracts acute to acuminate: bractlets 3–5 mm. long, broadly
oval, rounded: sepals 8–10 mm. long, elliptic, rounded: bracts, bractlets, and
sepals minutely ciliolate and somewhat erose, the margin somewhat scarious
and purplish: corolla usually 25–30 mm. long, slightly keeled posteriorly, proximally white, the anterior lip with slightly yellowish beard and usually with
spreading lateral margins: sterile filament ⅓ the length of the polleniferous

ones: capsule not seen.—Sphagnous bogs and stream-margins, at high elevations, Blue Ridge to Appalachian Plateau, N. C. to Ky. and Pa.—Sum.–fall.

4. C. obliqua L. Stem 8–15 dm. tall: leaf-blades 8–18 cm. long, elliptic to ovate-elliptic, irregularly serrate, slightly pubescent or glabrous, slightly paler beneath, acute to usually acuminate, at base cuneately narrowed to the petiole which is 0.5–1.5 cm. long: spike usually somewhat elongate, the flowers obscurely ranked: bracts 6–10 mm. long, broadly ovate, acute to acuminate: bractlets 5–7 mm. long, obtuse: sepals 6–10 mm. long, widely elliptic, rounded: bracts, bractlets, and sepals ciliolate, and the sepals with pale or purplish scarious margins: corolla 25–32 mm. long, rounded and faintly keeled posteriorly, purple (paler and duller, with the sterile filament usually green-tipped, and leaf-blades decidedly paler beneath, in *C. obliqua Erwiniae* of the Blue Ridge, N. C.), the anterior lip with faintly yellowish or dull-yellow beard and with the lateral margins somewhat deflexed: sterile filament ⅓ to ½ the length of the polleniferous ones: capsule not seen.—Alluvial swamps, Coastal Plain and Mississippi Valley, Fla. to Ark., Iowa, and Md.—Fall.

5. C. Cuthbertii Small. Stem 4–15 dm. tall: leaf-blades 5–10 cm. long, lanceolate to ovate, finely to rather coarsely serrate, glabrous, pale and slightly lustrous beneath, attenuate-acuminate, rounded at base, nearly sessile to somewhat clasping: spike usually elongate, the flowers conspicuously 4-ranked: bractlets 3–5 mm. long, broadly oval, rounded: sepals 7–9 mm. long, elliptic or widely elliptic, rounded: bracts, bractlets, and sepals finely ciliolate, with purple scarious margins: corolla 20–25 mm. long, slightly keeled posteriorly, violet-purple, broadly striped on the anterior side, the anterior lip with light yellow beard and with the lateral margins strongly deflexed: sterile filament purple, ½ to ¾ the length of the polleniferous ones: capsule 10–12 mm. long: seeds 3 mm. long. [*C. Grimesii* Weatherby]—Boggy meadows and thickets, Piedmont and Blue Ridge, N. C.; and in the Coastal Plain of Va.—Sum.

6. C. Lyoni Pursh. Stem 6–10 dm. tall: leaf-blades 10–20 cm. long, ovate, evenly serrate, finely pubescent to glabrous, somewhat glaucous beneath, conspicuously acuminate, at base broadly rounded or somewhat narrowed to the slender petiole: spike short, the flowers obscurely ranked: bractlets 3–4 mm. long, broadly oval, rounded: sepals 7–9 mm. long, elliptic or widely elliptic, rounded: bracts, bractlets, and sepals strongly ciliolate, sometimes with pale or purplish scarious margins: corolla 25–30 mm. long, sharply keeled posteriorly, purple, narrowly striped on the anterior side, the anterior lip with dark-yellow beard and with the lateral margins strongly deflexed: sterile filament white or pinkish-tipped, nearly as long as the polleniferous ones: capsule 10–12 mm. long, not seen mature. [*C. latifolia* Muhl.]—Moist mountain slopes in forest, Blue Ridge, N. C. and Tenn.—Sum.

20. PENSTEMON [Mitch.] Schmidel. Strong-scented herbs with erect solitary or several nearly terete stems arising from a short rootstock or caudex, the inflorescence usually glandular. Leaves dimorphic: those of the winter rosettes narrowed into petiole-like bases: cauline-leaves opposite, the blades entire or toothed, or rarely pinnatifid, the upper ones sessile and usually clasping. Flowers paniculate, often thyrsoid. Bractlets none. Sepals 5, uniform. Corolla often somewhat nodding, colored and mostly blue or purple or white, 2-lipped: tube rather abruptly expanded into a more or less inflated throat, whose orifice may remain open or be partly or wholly closed by the uparching of the anterior lip: lobes shorter than the tube. Polleniferous stamens 4, didynamous, included: anther-sacs usually divaricate. Sterile posterior filament (staminodium) equalling the fertile stamens or longer, with yellow hairs. Stigma capitate. Capsule conic-ovoid, glabrous, septicidal and secondarily slightly loculicidal. Seeds numerous, angled, wingless.—About 300 species, North American.—BEARD-TONGUES.

Leaf-blades of 2 types, the cauline bipinnatifid, those of the basal rosettes entire or few-toothed: staminodium conspicuously exserted. I. DISSECTI.
Leaf-blades all entire or toothed; those of the basal rosettes petioled: staminodium included or slightly exserted.
  Anther-sacs dehiscent their entire length, not pouch-like: inflorescence-branches less elongate.
    Corolla pubescent with glandless hairs within over the bases of the anterior lobes, the throat well inflated: leaf-blades more or less serrate. II. GRACILES.
    Corolla glandular-puberulent within on all sides, the throat slightly inflated: leaf-blades entire or nearly so. III. TUBIFLORI.
  Anther-sacs dehiscent by short proximal slits, the distal part of each sac pouch-like: inflorescence-branches elongate. IV. MULTIFLORI.

I. DISSECTI
Plant puberulent: corolla purple and lined. 1. P. dissectus.

II. GRACILES
Corolla with throat much inflated, only slightly 2-ridged within: anterior lobes little exceeding the posterior: staminodium slightly or moderately bearded.
  Anthers normally somewhat bearded: corolla-throat amply inflated, white or slightly tinged or lined with purple: sepals ovate and acuminate-tipped.
    Corolla 23–30 mm. long: sepals evidently scarious-margined: inflorescence of 3–5 fascicles, markedly glandular-pubescent. 2. P. Digitalis.
    Corolla 17–23 mm. long: sepals scarcely scarious-margined: inflorescence of 5–7 fascicles, glabrous or sparsely glandular. 3. P. alluviorum.
  Anthers glabrous: corolla-throat less strongly inflated, more or less violet-purple: sepals ovate-lanceolate to linear-attenuate.
    Sepals ovate-lanceolate, 3–6 mm. long: corolla 15–20 mm. long: blades of the cauline leaves lanceolate, sometimes narrowly so. 4. P. Pentstemon.
    Sepals linear-lanceolate, long-attenuate, 5–12 mm. long: corolla 20–35 mm. long: blades of the cauline leaves broadly lanceolate to ovate. 5. P. calycosus.
Corolla with throat narrower, strongly 2-ridged within: anterior corolla-lobes projecting considerably beyond the posterior: staminodium densely bearded.
  Corolla lined with deeper color: orifice to the throat open: anther-sacs longer than wide.
    Lower bracts of inflorescence foliose, scarcely smaller than the leaves: cauline leaf-blades usually tapering from a wide base, evenly and sharply serrate: radical leaf-blades truncate to cordate at base: corolla 28–35 mm. long: capsule 8–10 mm. long. 6. P. Smallii.
    Lower bracts of inflorescence much smaller than the leaves: cauline leaf-blades lanceolate or elliptic-lanceolate, more irregularly or less sharply serrate: radical leaf-blades narrowed to petiole: corolla usually smaller.
      Throat of corolla moderately inflated, nearly cylindric: corolla 20–32 mm. long.
        Leaf-blades essentially glabrous, deep green above, the cauline rather sharply serrate: stem 2–5 dm. tall: corolla strongly purple. 7. P. Brittonorum.
        Leaf-blades somewhat pubescent, dull green above, usually less sharply serrate: stem 3–8 dm. tall: corolla pale-purple or nearly white. 8. P. canescens.
      Throat of corolla slightly inflated, nearly tubular: corolla 15–25 mm. long.
        Corolla white, merely lined with purple: leaves densely and softly pubescent, velvety to the touch. 9. P. pallidus.
        Corolla purple or purplish: leaves finely pubescent or puberulent.

Sepals less than half the length of the capsule: corolla pale violet-purple, anteriorly with nearly or quite distinct fine
lines: primary peduncles ascending-
spreading.

    Capsule 5–7 mm. long: sepals 2–3 mm.
long, obtusish to acute: blades of the
cauline leaves elliptic-lanceolate to nar-
rowly ovate, obtuse to acute.   10. *P. brevisepalus.*

    Capsule 8–9 mm. long: sepals 3–6 mm.
long, acute to acuminate: blades of the
cauline leaves lanceolate, acute to acu-
minate.   11. *P. pauciflorus.*

Sepals half the length of the capsule or
more: corolla reddish-purple, on all sides
with lines that anastomose distally: primary peduncles strongly ascending or
erect.   12. *P. australis.*

Corolla unlined; orifice to the throat closed by the uparching lower lip: anther-sacs as wide as long.

    Corolla-throat purplish to violet, the lobes white:
sepals usually over half the length of the capsule:
leaf-blades soon glabrous, except for coarse hairs
beneath on midrib.   13. *P. hirsutus.*

    Corolla-throat and lobes white: sepals less than half
the length of the capsule: leaf-blades pubescent on
both surfaces, only in age becoming glabrate.   14. *P. tenuiflorus.*

III. TUBIFLORI

Plant glabrous: corolla white, unlined; lobes wide spreading. 15. *P. tubiflorus.*

IV. MULTIFLORI

Plant glabrous: corolla white, unlined; throat campanulate;
lobes slightly spreading.   16. *P. multiflorus.*

1. P. dissectus Ell.   Stem 3–4 dm. tall, puberulent: blades of the cauline
leaves bipinnatifid, the segments linear: panicle lax, of 1–3 fascicles: sepals

3–4 mm. long, broadly ovate, acute or
abruptly acuminate, the scarious margins
erose: corolla 20–25 mm. long, externally
violet-purple and paler within, and lined
with violet-purple, the throat much inflated;
lobes of both lips widely spreading: capsule
not seen.—Gravelly soil and rock-ledges,
Altamaha Grit, Coastal Plain, Ga.—Sum.

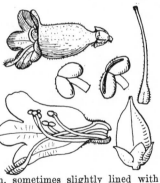

2. P. Digitalis Nutt. Stem 7–15 dm. tall,
glabrous, frequently purple, slightly shining: blades of the cauline leaves lanceolate,
sharply serrate, acuminate: panicle lax, of
3–5 fascicles: sepals 5–8 mm. long, oval or
ovate, caudate-acuminate, glandular-pubescent, the margins scarious and erose: corolla

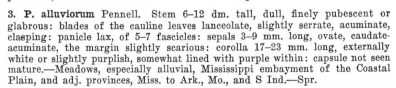

23–30 mm. long, white or externally purplish, sometimes slightly lined with
amparo-purple within: capsule 8–9 mm. long.—Fields and roadsides, various
provinces, N Ala. to Kans. and Me. Adv. E.—Spr.

3. P. alluviorum Pennell. Stem 6–12 dm. tall, dull, finely pubescent or
glabrous: blades of the cauline leaves lanceolate, slightly serrate, acuminate,
clasping: panicle lax, of 5–7 fascicles: sepals 3–9 mm. long, ovate, caudate-
acuminate, the margin slightly scarious: corolla 17–23 mm. long, externally
white or slightly purplish, somewhat lined with purple within: capsule not seen
mature.—Meadows, especially alluvial, Mississippi embayment of the Coastal
Plain, and adj. provinces, Miss. to Ark., Mo., and S Ind.—Spr.

4. P. Pentstemon (L.) MacM. Stem 4–10 dm. tall, dull, puberulent to nearly
glabrous, sometimes slightly purple: blades of the cauline leaves lanceolate,
finely or obscurely serrate, acuminate: panicle lax, of 3–5 fascicles: sepals 3–6

mm. long, ovate-lanceolate, acute or short-attenuate, proximally with erose somewhat scarious margin: corolla 15–20 mm. long, externally violet-purple, within usually white, and faintly lined with purple: capsule 6–7 mm. long. [*P. laevigatus* (L.) Ait.]—Meadows and river-banks, various provinces, N Fla. to S Ala., E Tenn., and Pa.—Spr.

5. P. calycosus Small. Stem 6–12 dm. tall, finely pubescent to nearly glabrous, dull or slightly purple: blades of the cauline leaves broadly lanceolate to ovate, finely serrate, acute to acuminate: panicle lax, of 3–5 fascicles: sepals 5–12 mm. long, linear-lanceolate, long-attenuate, the margin sometimes slightly scarious: corolla 20–35 mm. long, externally more or less violet-purple, within paler and with more or less evident purple lines: capsule 7–8 mm. long. —Woods and meadows, limestone ledges and river-banks, Interior Low Plateaus and adj. provinces, N Ala. to Ill. and Ohio.—Spr.

6. P. Smallii Heller. Stem 4–8 dm. tall, finely puberulent: blades of the cauline leaves broadly lanceolate to triangular-ovate, sharply serrate: panicle lax, of 3–5 fascicles: sepals 5–7 mm. long, ovate-acuminate, the margins sometimes slightly scarious: corolla 28–35 mm. long, externally amparo-purple, within paler and with many sharply defined purple lines: capsule 8–10 mm. long.—Woods, Blue Ridge and Appalachian Valley, N. C. and Tenn.—Spr.

7. P. Brittonorum Pennell. Stem 2–5 dm. tall, finely pubescent or hirsute below, green or purplish: blades of the cauline leaves elliptic-lanceolate, sharply serrate, acute to acuminate: panicle lax, of 3–5 fascicles: sepals 4–5 mm. long, lanceolate or ovate-lanceolate, acuminate, the margin scarious proximally: corolla 25–30 mm. long, purple, paler than *P. Smallii*, and with the color-lines narrower: capsule 7–8 mm. long.—Woods, Blue Ridge, S. C. to Va.—Spr.

8. P. canescens Britton. Stem 3–8 dm. tall, pubescent: blades of the cauline leaves elliptic-lanceolate, irregularly serrate: panicle lax, of 3–6 fascicles: sepals 4–7 mm. long, ovate-lanceolate, acuminate to attenuate, the margin obscurely scarious: corolla 22–32 mm. long, externally pale amparo-purple, within white and with many sharply defined purple lines: capsule 6–8 mm. long.— Rocky or sandy woods, Blue Ridge and Appalachian provinces, Ala. to Ky., Pa., and N. C.; rarely in the Piedmont in S Va.—Spr.

9. P. pallidus Small. Stem 4–8 dm. tall, pubescent, hirsute below: blades of the cauline leaves lanceolate, serrate or serrate-dentate, acuminate: panicle of 4–7 fascicles: sepals 3–7 mm. long, ovate, acuminate, the margin slightly scarious: corolla 17–22 mm. long, white, within with violet-purple lines: capsule 6–7 mm. long.—Rocky or sandy woods and old fields, N. C. to Ark., Ia., and Vt. Adv. E.

10. P. brevisepalus Pennell. Stem 6–8 dm. tall, finely pubescent: blades of the cauline leaves elliptic-lanceolate to ovate-lanceolate, crenate-serrate or serrate, obtuse to somewhat acuminate: panicle lax, of 4–7 fascicles: sepals 2–3 mm. long, ovate, obtusish to acute, the margin slightly scarious: corolla 15–23 (–25) mm. long, externally pale lavender-violet or amparo-purple, within paler and with violet-purple lines: capsule 5–7 mm. long.—Sandy or rocky woods, Appalachian Plateau, Tenn. and Ky.—Spr.

11. P. pauciflorus Buckl. Stem 4–8 dm. tall, puberulent: blades of the cauline leaves narrowly lanceolate, sharply serrate, acute to attenuate-acuminate: panicle lax, of 3–6 fascicles: sepals 3–5 mm. long, ovate, acute to acuminate, the margin slightly scarious: corolla 20–25 mm. long, pale-purple, within with fine violet-purple lines: capsule 7–9 mm. long.—Sandy soil, open woodland and prairies, Coastal Plain and adj. provinces, N Fla. to Tex., Okla., and Ark.—Spr.

12. P. australis Small. Stem 3–8 dm. tall, finely pubescent, or at the base coarsely pubescent: blades of the cauline leaves lanceolate, usually narrowly so, slightly serrate, attenuate-acuminate: panicle strict, of 3–7 fascicles: sepals 4–8 mm. long, ovate, acute to acuminate, the margin slightly scarious: corolla 20–25 mm. long, externally reddish-purple, within paler and with conspicuous red-purple lines which are most pronounced on the anterior side: capsule 8–9 mm. long.—Pinelands, granite hills and sandy fields, Coastal Plain and Piedmont, C Fla. to Miss. and S Va.—Spr.

13. **P. hirsutus** (L.) Willd. Stem 4–8 dm. tall, hirsute: blades of the cauline leaves lanceolate, serrate-dentate or sinuately serrate, acuminate, clasping: panicle lax, of 3–6 fascicles: sepals 3–8 mm. long, ovate, acuminate, the margin sometimes slightly scarious: corolla 23–28 mm. long, the tube externally amparo-purple to light-violet, the lobes white: capsule 8–9 mm. long. [*P. pubescens* Ait.]—Rocky bluffs and woods, various provinces, N of Coastal Plain, Tenn. to Wis., Que., and Me.—Spr.

14. **P. tenuiflorus** Pennell. Stem 4–8 dm. tall, hirsute: blades of the cauline leaves lanceolate to ovate, slightly serrate or undulate, acuminate: panicle lax, of 4–7 fascicles: sepals 2–5 mm. long, ovate, acute or short-acuminate, the margin sometimes scarious: corolla 25–30 mm. long, externally glandular-pubescent and white: capsule 8–9 mm. long.—Stony or rocky soil, especially in cedar-glades, Interior Low Plateaus, Ala. to Ky.—Spr.

15. **P. tubiflorus** Nutt. Stem 5–10 dm. tall, glabrous: blades of the cauline leaves elliptic-lanceolate to lanceolate, entire or the upper occasionally finely serrate, acuminate: panicle (thyrsus) strict, of 4–7 fascicles: sepals 3–4 mm. long, triangular-ovate, acuminate, the margin scarious: corolla 20–25 mm. long, white, within glandular-pubescent; lobes of both lips spreading: capsule 7–8 mm. long.—Gravelly banks, mostly along the Mississippi River and tributaries and Ozark Plateau, Tenn. to Tex., Kans., and Ind.—Sum.

16. **P. multiflorus** Chapm. Stem 8–15 dm. tall, glabrous: blades of the cauline leaves oblanceolate, entire or slightly undulate-crenate, acute: panicle diffuse, of 5–8 fascicles: sepals 3–5 mm. long, ovate, obtuse or acutish, the margin slightly scarious: corolla 20–22 mm. long, white or faintly purplish, the throat much inflated; lobes of both lips projecting-spreading: capsule 7–9 mm. long.—Sandy soil, pinelands and scrub, S Fla. to S Ga.—Spr.–sum, or all year S.

21. **SCROPHULARIA** L. Erect strong-scented herbs. Stem arising from a stout rootstock, 4-angled. Leaves opposite: blades relatively broad, toothed, petioled. Flowers in panicles. Bractlets none. Calyx-lobes 5, much longer than the tube. Corolla greenish-purple or purplish-brown, two-lipped: tube cylindric; posterior lip as long as the tube, projecting and flattened, the lobes well united; anterior lip with the lateral lobes vertical, the middle lobe reflexed. Stamens 4, slightly didynamous, barely exserted: anther-sacs divergent. Sterile posterior filament (staminodium) scale-like. Stigma semi-capitate. Capsule conic-ovoid, septicidal. Seeds numerous, plump, furrowed.—Over 100 species, native of the Northern Hemisphere.

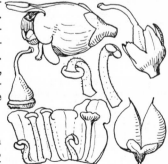

1. **S. marilandica** L. Stem 8–15 dm. tall: leaf-blades 10–17 cm. long, ovate, often broadly so, serrate or rather finely dentate, rounded or cordate at the base, on nearly

wingless petioles: panicle usually ample and lax, of 4–10 fascicles, often with several pairs of the lower bracts foliaceous: calyx-lobes triangular-rounded, 2–3 mm. long: corolla 5–8 mm. long: staminodium purple: capsule 4–7 mm. long, globose-ovoid, acute.—(Figwort. Heal-all.)—Rich woods, Blue Ridge and more northern provinces, Fla. and Ala. to Nebr., Ont., and Mass.—Sum.

22. RUSSELIA Jacq.　Erect-arching herbs or shrubby plants, with several or many striate-angled stems in a clump on the perennial root, and whorled branches. Leaves all cauline, whorled, with small or scale-like blades. Flowers in lateral cymes, the bracts minute. Bractlets none. Sepals 5, only slightly if at all united. Corolla red, 2-lipped: tube nearly cylindric: lips short, the posterior with partly united arched lobes, the anterior spreading. Stamens 4, slightly didynamous: anther-sacs explanate. Stigma punctiform-capitate. Capsule globose, mucronate, loculicidal, filled with slender or tortuous hairs among which are embedded the seeds. Seeds numerous, cylindric, reticulate-roughened, long-funicled.— About 30 species, tropical American.

1. R. juncea Zucc.　Stem 8–25 dm. long, with many striations and 4–6 ridges, virgately branched: leaves scale-like or if developed the blades oval or elliptic, less than 1 cm. long, short-petioled: cymes lax or diffuse, 1–2-flowered: sepals ovate, 2 mm. long, acuminate: corolla 20–25 mm. long: capsule 5–6 mm. long, prominently caudate-mucronate. — (Fountain-plant. Coral-plant.) — Waste-places and roadsides, pen. Fla. and cult. Nat. of Mex.—Spr.–sum. or all year S.

23. ANGELONIA H. & B.　Herbs with erect stems arising from a rootstock. Leaves opposite: blades often toothed. Flowers in racemes, the bracts much smaller than the leaves. Bractlets none. Sepals 5, uniform. Corolla violet-blue, zygomorphic: anterior lip like a shallow cup or saucer: lobes spreading, the anterior the longer, with a yellow palate at the base and a projecting horn on the mid-anterior lobe. Stamens 4, scarcely didynamous: filaments pubescent: anthers glabrous; the sacs explanate. Stigma punctiform-capitate. Capsule globose, loculicidal. Seeds numerous, with raised wing-like reticulations.—About 30 species, tropical American.

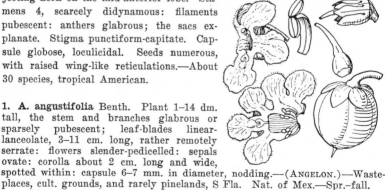

1. A. angustifolia Benth.　Plant 1–14 dm. tall, the stem and branches glabrous or sparsely pubescent; leaf-blades linear-lanceolate, 3–11 cm. long, rather remotely serrate: flowers slender-pedicelled: sepals ovate: corolla about 2 cm. long and wide, spotted within: capsule 6–7 mm. in diameter, nodding.—(Angelon.)—Waste-places, cult. grounds, and rarely pinelands, S Fla. Nat. of Mex.—Spr.–fall.

24. **COLLINSIA** Nutt. Delicate annual herbs, the stem erect, much-branched. Leaves opposite: blades toothed, the upper ones sessile or clasping. Flowers in loose racemes, long-pedicelled, axillary to foliaceous bracts, sometimes in whorls of 3–6. Bractlets none. Calyx-lobes 5, uniform, half as long as the tube or more, acute. Corolla two-lipped: tube gibbous on the posterior side: posterior lip pale or white, shorter than the anterior, proximally with a concave-arched portion which abruptly terminates in a transverse-rounded, puberulent, palate-like ridge, beyond which the lip becomes upcurved-erect with free fan-like lobes; anterior lobes projecting, blue, the median one with margins upcurved, so that the petal is boat-like, slightly exceeded by the flat lateral lobes. Stamens 4, slightly didynamous: filaments slender: anthers scarcely exserted; sacs divaricate, glabrous. Posterior stamen represented by a callose knob. Stigma capitate. Capsule subglobose, somewhat flattened laterally, loculicidal and also slightly septicidal. Seeds few, smooth, wingless.— About 30 species, North American.

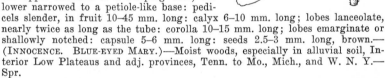

1. **C. verna** Nutt. Stem 1–5 dm. tall, pubescent chiefly in 2 lines: leaf-blades elliptic-ovate to ovate, crenately serrate-dentate, the upper rounded to a clasping base, the lower narrowed to a petiole-like base: pedicels slender, in fruit 10–45 mm. long: calyx 6–10 mm. long; lobes lanceolate, nearly twice as long as the tube: corolla 10–15 mm. long; lobes emarginate or shallowly notched: capsule 5–6 mm. long: seeds 2.5–3 mm. long, brown.— (INNOCENCE. BLUE-EYED MARY.)—Moist woods, especially in alluvial soil, Interior Low Plateaus and adj. provinces, Tenn. to Mo., Mich., and W. N. Y.— Spr.

25. **LINARIA** Mill. Erect annual or perennial herbs, the stem branched, sometimes with basal shoots. Leaves alternate, or opposite on the basal shoots: blades narrow, entire, sessile. Flowers in racemes, the bracts foliaceous, or much reduced. Bractlets none. Sepals 5, uniform. Corolla 2-lipped, yellow or violet: tube spurred at the base anteriorly: posterior lobes more or less united and arched: anterior lobes united and spreading, at times with a definite palate. Stamens 4, didynamous, included: filaments glabrous: anther-sacs divaricate. Stigma capitate. Capsule globose to cylindric, loculicidal by irregular ruptures. Seeds numerous, prismatic-angled and wingless, or flattened and broadly winged.—About 120 species, widely distributed, but most abundant in the old World.—SPURRED-SNAPDRAGON. TOADFLAXES.

Corolla violet or violet-purple; anterior lip with 2 rounded ridges, but no palate: capsule globose or nearly so: seeds less than 0.5 mm. long, wingless: plant annual, or perhaps biennial, with prostrate basal shoots. — — — — — — — — — — — — — I. LEPTOPLECTRON.

Corolla yellow; anterior lip with a prominent orange-colored palate: capsule ovoid: seeds about 1.5 mm. long, winged: plant perennial, all stems erect. — — — — — — — — — — II. EULINARIA.

I. LEPTOPLECTRON

Pedicels nearly glabrous, shorter than the corolla: corolla 7–12 mm. long, the spur slender, decurved: capsule 2–3.5 mm. long. — — — — — — — — — — — — — — — — 1. *L. canadensis*.

Pedicels glandular-pubescent, longer than the corolla: corolla
5–6 mm. long, the spur very short: capsule 1.5–2 mm. long.   2. *L. floridana.*

II. EULINARIA

Flowers in stiffly erect dense racemes: corolla strongly 2-lipped;
the stout spur tapering.   3. *L. Linaria.*

1. **L. canadensis** (L.) Dum.   Stems slender, 2–6 dm. tall: leaves scattered
but usually numerous on the flowering stems, linear, 1.5–2.5 cm. long, those on
the basal shoots opposite or in 3's and
shorter and wider: raceme elongate, nearly
glabrous: pedicels 1–5 mm. long: sepals 2–3
mm. long, lanceolate: corolla 7–10 mm. long,
the spur decurved 2–6 mm. long, (corolla
10–12 mm. long with a slender spur 5–9 mm.
long, and densely tuberculate seeds, in *L.
canadensis texana* which predominates westward): posterior lip with erect lobes about
as long as the body; anterior lip with a
ridged body and 3 spreading lobes: capsule
2–3 mm. long.—(BLUE-TOADFLAX.)—Open
sandy soil, often a weed in fields and on
roadsides, various provinces, chiefly Coastal
Plain, Fla. to Tex. and Mass.—(*Mex., C. A.,
S. A.*)—Spr.; in sum. ripening its fruit
cleistogamously.—The species name is a misnomer, as it is not found in Canada.

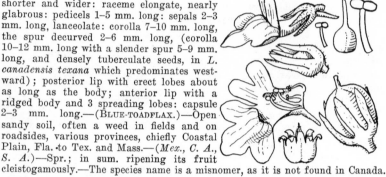

2. **L. floridana** Chapm.   Stems slender, 1–3 dm. tall: leaf-blades filiform, 1–2.5
cm. long, those on the basal shoots whorled in 3's: raceme zigzag, glandular-
pubescent: pedicels 5–10 mm. long: sepals 1–2 mm. long, lanceolate: corolla
5–6 mm. long, the subulate spur about 0.5 mm. long; posterior lip with erect
lobes about twice as long as the body; anterior lip with spreading lobes: capsule 1.5–2 mm. long.—Dry sandy soil, often in scrub or on sandhills, Coastal
Plain, Fla. to Miss. and Ga.—Spr.

3. **L. Linaria** (L.) Karst.   Stems 4–8 dm. tall, usually several together;
leaf-blades 3–6 cm. long, linear to linear-lanceolate: raceme stout: pedicels 3–8
mm. long: sepals 3–4 mm. long, lanceolate-ovate: corolla 15–20 mm. long, the
spur 10–15 mm. long; posterior lip with recurved lobes shorter than the body;
lobes of the anterior lip deflexed-spreading: capsule 9–12 mm. long.   [*L. vulgaris* Mill.]—(BUTTER-AND-EGGS.   WILD-SNAPDRAGON.   YELLOW-TOADFLAX.)—
Fields, roadsides, and waste-places, various provinces, Ala. to Ark., N. Dak., Ont.,
and N. S.   Nat. of Eurasia.—Sum.

26. **KICKXIA** Dumort.   Pubescent perennial herbs, the stems prostrate, often matted.   Leaves alternate: blades broad, entire, sometimes hastate
at the base.   Flowers axillary to leaf-like bracts, slender-pedicelled.   Bractlets
none.   Sepals 5, uniform.   Corolla 2-lipped, proximally yellow: tube with a
deflexed spur: posterior lip with lobes shorter than the body, distally purple;
anterior lip raised anteriorly into a prominent russet palate, the lobes mostly
yellow.   Stamens 4, didynamous, included: filaments pubescent: anthers horse-
shoe-shaped, the sacs opening proximally, densely white-hairy.   Stigmas somewhat united.   Capsule globose, glandular-pubescent, loculicidal by the falling
away as a lid of most of the wall of each carpel.   Seeds few, with reticulations or convolutions.—About 25 species, natives of the Old World.—FLUELLINS.

Leaf-blades hastate-lobed at the base: sepals lanceolate: corolla 5 mm. long, with
straight spur: anthers wholly cohering.   1. *K. Elatine.*

Leaf-blades rounded or cordate at base: sepals ovate: corolla 6–8 mm. long, with curved spur: anthers usually more or less cohering.   2. *K. spuria.*

1. K. Elatine (L.) Dumort. Stem 2–8 dm. long: leaf-blades 1–2 cm. long, ovate, hastate at the truncate or slightly cordate base, the petioles 2–4 mm. long: sepals 3–5 mm. long, triangular-lanceolate: corolla-spur 3–5 mm. long: capsule 3 mm. long, equalling or exceeding the calyx: seeds with strongly raised and wing-like convolutions. — (CANKER-ROOT.) — Waste-places, sandy fields, and roadsides, various provinces, Ga. to La., Mo., Mass., and Del. Nat. of Eurasia.—Sum.

2. K. spuria (L.) Dumort. Stem 2–8 dm. long or more: leaf-blades 1–4 cm. long, broadly oval, the petioles 1–4 mm. long: sepals 4–6 mm. long, ovate: corolla-spur 5 mm. long: capsule 3.5–4 mm. long, nearly concealed in the calyx: seeds with slightly raised reticulations and convolutions.—

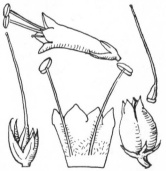

(FEMALE FLUELLIN.)—Waste-places and ballast, various provinces, Ala. to Mo., N. Y., and N. C. Nat. of Eu.—Sum.

27. VERONICASTRUM Fabr. Tall virgate herbs, the solitary stem erect from an elongate rootstock. Leaves whorled: blades narrow or relatively so, toothed, short-petioled. Flowers in a terminal spike-like raceme which is usually accompanied by several smaller racemes axillary to the upper leaf-whorl. Bracts very small. Bractlets none. Sepals 5, uniform. Corolla tubular, white or pinkish-white: lobes broad, less than half the length of the tube, the posterior ones wholly united. Stamens 2 (only the 2 postero-laterals present): filaments slender: anthers exserted, glabrous, the sacs parallel. Stigma capitate. Capsule ovoid, glabrous, septicidal and slightly loculicidal. Seeds numerous, obscurely reticulate.—Two species, the following and one Asiatic.

1. V. virginicum (L.) Farwell. Stem 10–20 dm. tall: leaves whorled in 3's–6's, usually in 5's: blades lanceolate to elliptic-ovate, 3–15 cm. long, finely serrate: racemes 20–30 cm. long, dense, the bracts setaceous-

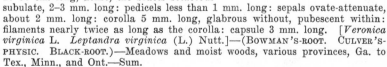

subulate, 2–3 mm. long: pedicels less than 1 mm. long: sepals ovate-attenuate, about 2 mm. long: corolla 5 mm. long, glabrous without, pubescent within: filaments nearly twice as long as the corolla: capsule 3 mm. long. [*Veronica virginica* L. *Leptandra virginica* (L.) Nutt.]—(BOWMAN'S-ROOT. CULVER'S-PHYSIC. BLACK-ROOT.)—Meadows and moist woods, various provinces, Ga. to Tex., Minn., and Ont.—Sum.

28. VERONICA L. Low creeping or spreading perennial or annual herbs. Leaves opposite or alternate above: blades linear to cordate, toothed or nearly entire. Flowers in terminal or axillary racemes or spikes. Bractlets none. Sepals 4 (the posterior one lacking), uniform or the anterior longer. Corolla rotate, blue, violet, or white: lobes spreading, longer than the tube, the posterior ones wholly united to form one rounded lobe. Stamens 2 (only the 2 postero-laterals present): anthers slightly exserted, glabrous, the sacs parallel. Stigma capitate. Capsule flattened contrary to the septum, as wide as long or wider, deeply loculicidal. Seeds numerous or few, smooth.—About 250 species, widely distributed.—SPEEDWELLS.

Main stem terminating in an inflorescence, whose flowers are densely crowded or remote and axillary: bract-leaves alternate.　　　　　　　　I. VERONICELLA.
Main stem not terminating in an inflorescence, leaves opposite throughout and flowers all in axillary racemes.　　　　　　II. EUVERONICA.

I. VERONICELLA

Plant perennial: flowers in terminal racemes: corolla pale, with deep-blue lines only on the posterior side.　　　　　　1. *V. serpyllifolia.*
Plant annual: flowers axillary to most of the leaf-axils: corolla more uniformly colored.
　　Pedicels shorter than the linear to lanceolate sepals: capsule strongly flattened: seeds many, less than 1 mm. long, flat, smooth: stem erect.
　　　　Leaf-blades, except the lowermost, sessile; those of the lower stem-leaves oblanceolate, nearly entire to dentate: corolla whitish throughout: capsule greenish, notched, the minute style hidden between the capsule-lobes: plant glabrous or with gland-tipped hairs.　　2. *V. peregrina.*
　　　　Leaf-blades petioled or the upper ones sessile, those of the lower stem-leaves ovate, crenate-serrate: corolla deep violet-blue: capsule yellowish-brown, notched one-third its length or nearly so, the style reaching to about the capsule-lobes: plant pubescent with white glandless or obscurely gland-tipped hairs.　　3. *V. arvensis.*
　　Pedicels longer than the ovate sepals: capsule relatively turgid: seeds few, 1.5–3 mm. long, turgid, rough: stem creeping.
　　　　Leaf-blades ovate: sepals short-ciliate, not accrescent: capsule slightly flattened, deeply notched, pubescent: seeds 1.5–2 mm. long, brown.
　　　　　　Corolla-lobes not exceeding the ovate sepals: capsule-lobes rounded, the distal point of each about midway between the style and the lateral margin: style shorter than the capsule.　　4. *V. polita.*
　　　　　　Corolla-lobes much exceeding the sepals: capsule-lobes acutish in profile, the most distal point of each near the lateral margin: style as long as the capsule.　　5. *V. persica.*
　　　　Leaf-blades broadly and shallowly cordate, 3–5-lobed: sepals conspicuously ciliate, accrescent: capsule turgid, scarcely notched, glabrous: seeds 2.5–3 mm. long, blackish.　　6. *V. hederaefolia.*

II. EUVERONICA

Capsule pubescent, wider than long, the most distal point of each lobe near the lateral margin: pedicel shorter than the calyx: stem, leaves, pedicels, and calyx with glandless hairs: leaf-blades oval, with petiole-like bases: herbage pubescent: plant of dry soil.　　7. *V. officinalis.*
Capsule glabrous or sparingly glandular-pubescent, as wide as long or narrower, the most distal point of each lobe about midway between the style and the lateral margin: pedicel longer than the calyx: leaf-blades rounded at the base, lanceolate or narrowly ovate: herbage glabrous or glandular: plant aquatic.
　　Leaf-blades all petioled: racemes usually 10–25-flowered: corolla 2.5–3 mm. long, violet-blue: style 2–3 mm. long: plant glabrous.　　8. *V. americana.*
　　Leaf-blades of the flowering stem sessile and clasping; those of the autumnal shoots petioled: racemes usually 30–60-flowered: corolla 2 mm. long, pale-violet: style 1–1.5 mm. long: inflorescence with gland-tipped hairs.　　9. *V. glandifera.*

1. V. serpyllifolia L. Stem 0.3–2 dm. long, finely pubescent with incurved hairs, creeping, distally erect and floriferous: leaf-blades elliptic-ovate or oval,

0.9–1.6 cm. long, obscurely crenate, obtuse:
pedicels 2–3 mm. long, ascending: sepals 3
mm. long, elliptic-oval, glabrous: corolla
about 2 mm. long: style 2 mm. long: capsule 3 mm. long, shallowly notched, slightly
glandular-pubescent.—Fields, roadsides, and
cult. grounds, Blue Ridge and more northern provinces, N. C. to Mo., Minn., Ont.,
and Newf.; also introduced on the Pacific
slope.—Nat. of Eu.—Spr.-sum.

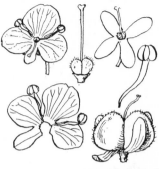

2. V. peregrina L. Stem 1–3 dm. tall,
glabrous (glandular-pubescent throughout,
even to the capsules, in *V. peregrina xalapensis*), much-branched, floriferous nearly
throughout: leaf-blades oblanceolate to

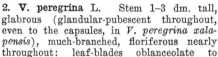

elliptic, 1.5–3.5 cm. long, obtuse, entire or the larger crenate-dentate: pedicels
0.5–1 mm. long: sepals 3–5 mm. long, linear-elliptic: corolla about 2 mm. long:
style 0.1–0.2 mm. long: capsule about 3 mm. long, shallowly notched, glabrous.
—(NECKWEED.)—Cult. grounds and moist fields, various provinces, Fla. to
Tex., Ia., Mich., and N. B.—Spr.

3. V. arvensis L. Stem 1–3 dm. tall, pubescent with glandless or obscurely
gland-tipped hairs, usually much-branched, floriferous nearly throughout: leaf-
blades ovate, 0.5–1.5 cm. long, obtuse, crenate-serrate: pedicels 0.5–1 mm. long:
sepals 3–4 mm. long, broadly linear: corolla about 2 mm. long, deep-blue, the
lobes with deeper-blue lines: style 0.5 mm. long: capsule 2.5–3 mm. long, deeply
notched, pubescent. — (WALL-SPEEDWELL.) — Fields, dry woods, and cult.
grounds, various provinces, C Ga. to Okla., Kans., Ont., and Newf.; also introduced on the Pacific slope. Nat. of Eurasia.—Spr.

4. V. polita Fries. Stem 1–2 dm. long, finely pubescent, much branched:
leaf-blades ovate, 0.5–1.2 cm. long, acutish, with rounded teeth: pedicels 5–10
mm. long, recurving: sepals ovate, 3–4 mm. long, reticulate, obscurely ciliate:
corolla 3 mm. long, violet-blue: style 1 mm. long: capsule 3–3.5 mm. long,
deeply notched, minutely pubescent.—Fields and cult. grounds, various provinces, Fla. to Tex. and N. Y. Nat. of Eu.—Spr.

5. V. persica Poir. Stem 1–3 dm. long, pubescent, distally ascending: leaf-
blades ovate, 1–2 cm. long, dentate: sepals ovate, 4–6 mm. long, finely ciliate:
corolla 5 mm. long, blue, anteriorly paler, the lobes with deep-blue lines: style
3 mm. long: capsule 3–4 mm. long, broadly notched, pubescent.—Fields, roadsides, and waste-places, various provinces, Fla. to Calif., Alas., and Newf.
Nat. of Eu.—(*W. I.*)—Spr.

6. V. hederaefolia L. Stem 0.5–3 dm. long, white-hirsute, much branched,
distally ascending: leaf-blades broadly ovate, 0.5–1.5 cm. long, 3–5-lobed, the
lobes rounded, entire: pedicels 7–18 mm. long: sepals broadly ovate, at anthesis 2–3 mm. long, becoming 5–7 mm. long, densely ciliate: corolla 2 mm. long,
purplish: style 0.5 mm. long: capsule 3 mm. long, scarcely notched, glabrous.
—(IVY-SPEEDWELL.)—Roadsides, orchards, and waste-places, various provinces,
S. C. to N. Y. Nat. of Eu.—Spr.

7. V. officinalis L. Stem 1–4 dm. long, pubescent, much-branched: leaf-blades
oval, 2–5 cm. long, crenate-serrate: racemes mostly 5–10 cm. long: pedicels 1–2
mm. long: sepals elliptic-lanceolate, 2 mm. long: corolla 3–4 mm. long, pale-
lavender, on the posterior side with lavender-blue lines: style 2.5–3.5 mm. long:
capsule 3–4 mm. long.—(GIPSY-WEED.)—Fields and open woods, various provinces, in Coastal Plain only N, N. C. to Tenn., S. Dak., Ont., and N. S. Nat.
of Eu.—Sum.

8. V. americana Schwein. Stem 2–8 dm. long, creeping at the base, glabrous: leaf-blades lanceolate to narrowly ovate, 2–8 cm. long, serrate with low teeth, acute or acutish: racemes mostly 5–10 cm. long: pedicels 5–8 mm. long: sepals elliptic-lanceolate, 2–3 mm. long, acuminate: corolla 2.5–3 mm. long, violet-blue, with deeper-blue lines: capsule 2.5–3 mm. long, slightly notched.— (BROOKLIME.)—Woodland streams and spring-heads, Blue Ridge and more N provinces, N. C. to Calif., Alas., Ont., and Newf.—(*Mex.*)—Sum.

9. V. glandifera Pennell. Stem 3–6 dm. long, creeping at the base, distally finely and sparsely glandular-pubescent: leaf-blades lanceolate, sometimes broadly so, 4–9 cm. long, sharply crenate-serrate, acuminate: racemes mostly 10–15 cm. long: pedicels 3–5 mm. long: sepals lanceolate to narrowly ovate, 2–3 mm. long, acuminate: corolla 2 mm. long, pale violet-blue, with few deeper-blue lines: style 1–1.5 mm. long: capsule 2.5–3 mm. long, rounded.—Shallow streams and stream-margins, various provinces, N. C. to Ind. and Pa.—Sum.

29. MACRANTHERA Torr. Tall annual or biennial herb, the stem retrorse-pubescent. Leaves opposite: blades pinnatifid. Flowers in terminal racemes, the pedicels reflexed in fruit, the bracts entire. Bractlets none. Calyx-lobes 5, uniform. Corolla tubular, orange, fleshy, semi-persistent: lobes shorter than the tube, the 2 posterior erect, the 3 anterior spreading. Stamens 4, equal: anthers conspicuously exserted on the elon-

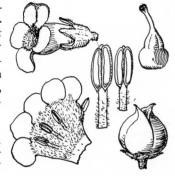

gate filaments, the sacs parallel. Stigma linear-clavate. Capsule ovoid, pubescent, loculicidal. Seeds angular-lunate, reticulate, winged.—One species.

1. M. flammea (Bartr.) Pennell. Stem 15–30 dm. tall, obtusely 4-angled: leaf-blades lanceolate to ovate in outline, the larger 8–10 cm. long, with 5–7 pairs of lateral lobes: pedicels 10–20 mm. long, upcurved at the apex: calyx-lobes, at anthesis, linear, becoming 10–15 mm. long and toothed: corolla 20–25 mm. long, rusty-tomentulose without, glabrous within above; lobes obtuse: filaments lanose: capsule broadly ovoid, 15–18 mm. long: seeds 3–4 mm. long, thick-winged. [*M. fuchsioides* (Nutt.) Benth. *M. LeContei* Torr.]—Borders of wet sandy thickets, Coastal Plain, N Fla. to E La. and Ga.—Sum.–fall.

30. DASISTOMA Raf. Tall annual herbs, the stem retrorse-pubescent. Leaves opposite: blades bipinnatifid-lobed. Flowers axillary to foliaceous narrow entire bracts, spicate. Bractlets none. Calyx-lobes 5, about as long as the tube. Corolla yellow, evanescent: tube pubescent all over within: lobes spreading, equally distinct, slightly shorter than the tube. Stamens 4, didynamous, included; anther-sacs slightly divaricate, glabrous. Stigmas 2, semi-capitate. Capsule globose-ovoid, loculicidal. Seeds winged.—One species.

1. D. macrophylla (Nutt.) Raf. Stem 15–20 dm. tall, obtusely 4-angled, much-branched: leaf-blades ovate to ovate-lanceolate, the larger 10–30 cm. long, with 7–12 pairs of lateral lobes: calyx-lobes triangular-ovate, ultimately longer' than the tube: corolla 15–16 mm. long, externally glabrous; lobes ovate-reniform, about 7 mm. long: capsule 9–10 mm. long, glabrous, black: seeds 2 mm. long, short-winged. [*Seymeria macrophylla* Nutt. *Brachygyne macrophylla* (Nutt.) Small.]—(MULLEN-FOXGLOVE.)—Moist woodlands, Appalachian Valley and more N & W provinces, Ga. to NE Tex., Nebr., and Ohio.—Sum.—A root-parasite.

31. AFZELIA J. F. Gmel. Relatively low annual herbs, the stem more or less glandular-pubescent. Leaves opposite: blades pinnatifid or bipinnatifid. Flowers axillary to foliaceous pinnatifid or bipinnatifid bracts, loosely racemose. Bractlets none. Calyx-lobes 5, longer than the tube. Corolla rotate, yellow, evanescent, glabrous or nearly so within above the bases of the filaments; lobes longer than the tube, the 2 posterior partly united. Stamens 4, nearly equal, slightly exserted: anther-sacs parallel, glabrous or nearly so, dehiscing by short apical slits. Stigma punctiform or capitate. Capsule ovoid or urceolate. Seeds numerous, winged or wingless.—About 22 species, North American, mostly Mexican.

Capsule ovoid, brown-tomentose: seeds winged: corolla deep-yellow, externally pubescent: leaf-segments lanceolate or wider: stem viscid-pubescent. 1. *A. pectinata.*
Capsule urceolate-acuminate, glabrous: seeds wingless: corolla pale-yellow, externally glabrous: leaf-segments filiform: stem sparsely pubescent, obscurely glandular. 2. *A. cassioides.*

1. A. pectinata (Pursh) Kuntze. Stem 2–6 dm. tall, widely and stiffly branched, retrorsely pubescent (with ascending hairs and glandular-pubescent capsules, in *A. pectinata peninsularis* of S Fla.): leaf-blades mostly pinnatifid, the longer ones 1.5–3 cm. long, with 3 or 4 pairs of lateral segments: calyx glandular-pubescent; lobes 3–4.5 mm. long, lanceolate: corolla 10 mm. long; lobes ovate: filaments lanose at the apex: capsule 5–7 mm. long, rounded or acute: seeds with 3 or 4 wings.— Dry pinelands, Coastal Plain, Fla. to Miss. and S. C.—Sum.–fall.

2. A. cassioides (Walt.) J. F. Gmel. Stem 5–10 dm. tall, virgately branched, sparsely pubescent with ascending incurved hairs: leaf-blades pinnatifid, the larger ones 1–1.5 cm. long, with 4–7 pairs of lateral segments: calyx glabrous or nearly so: lobes 2–2.5 mm. long, linear: corolla 9 mm. long; lobes lanceolate: filaments glabrous: capsule 4–4.5 mm. long, acuminate: seeds furrowed. [*Seymeria tenuifolia* Pursh.]—Pinelands, Coastal Plain and adj. provinces, C pen. Fla. to La., Tenn., and N. C.—(*W. I.*)—Fall.

32. AUREOLARIA Raf. Perennial or annual herbs parasitic on the roots of oaks, the stem simple or branched. Leaves opposite: blades narrow or broad, entire, toothed, or pinnatifid. Flowers axillary to more or less foliaceous bracts, in spikes or racemes. Bractlets none. Calyx-lobes 5, uniform or nearly so, longer than the tube. Corolla yellow, the throat nearly campanulate, somewhat inflated anteriorly; lobes spreading. Stamens 4, didynamous: filaments flattened, lanose: anthers lanose on the valvular surfaces, the sacs parallel. Stigma slightly elongate or semi-capitate. Capsule cylindric-ellipsoid to globose-ovoid, acute to acuminate, loculicidal. Seeds irregularly tetrahedral, reticulate, wingless or winged. [*Dasystoma* Benth. not Raf.]—About 11 species, in eastern North America.—YELLOW-FOXGLOVES. FALSE-FOX-GLOVES.

Seeds wingless: capsule glandular-pubescent: corolla externally glandular-pubescent: calyx-lobes toothed or pectinate: leaf-blades bipinnatifid, more or less pectinately cut: plant annual.   I. PANCTENIS.

Seeds winged: capsule glandless: corolla externally glabrous: calyx-lobes entire: leaf-blades entire to coarsely bipinnatifid: plant perennial.   II. EUAUREOLARIA.

I. PANCTENIS

Calyx-tube turbinate, glandular-puberulent: capsule ellipsoid, half enclosed in the calyx-tube: pedicels 1–3 cm. long: leaf-blades with mostly rounded teeth.   1. *A. pedicularia.*

Calyx-tube hemispheric, glandular-hirsute or -lanose: capsule ovoid, only the base enclosed in the calyx-tube: pedicels 0.4–2 cm. long: leaf-blades with acute or acutish teeth.   2. *A. pectinata.*

II. EUAUREOLARIA

Capsule pubescent: pedicels 1.5–3 mm. long: stem pubescent or puberulent, at least above.

Stem pubescent or puberulent throughout: leaf-blades permanently pubescent: capsule 12–15 mm. long.   3. *A. virginica.*

Stem glabrous below: leaf-blades becoming glabrous: capsule 9–12 mm. long.   4. *A. microcarpa.*

Capsule glabrous: pedicels 3–25 mm. long: stem glabrous or minutely puberulent.

Leaf-blades lanceolate to ovate-lanceolate, widest below the middle, long-acuminate: corolla 30–35 mm. long: capsule 10–12 mm. long.   5. *A. laevigata.*

Leaf-blades elliptic-ovate in outline, widest about the middle, less acuminate: corolla 35–60 mm. long: capsule 12–24 mm. long.

Stem glabrous, glaucous: pedicels and calyx externally glabrous.   6. *A. flava.*

Stem puberulent, not glaucous: pedicels and calyx externally puberulent.

Pedicels 4–10 mm. long: calyx-lobes 5–7 mm. long, triangular-lanceolate: corolla 40–50 mm. long.   7. *A. dispersa.*

Pedicels 10–25 mm. long: calyx-lobes 10–12 mm. long, linear: corolla 35–45 mm. long.   8. *A. patula.*

1. A. pedicularia (L.) Raf. Stem 4–12 dm. tall, glandular-hirsute below, but nearly or quite glandless above (glandular-pubescent throughout, calyx-lobes 10–16 mm. long, and capsule broadly ellipsoid, in *A. pedicularia austromontana,* Blue Ridge, Ga. to Va.): leaf-blades lanceolate to ovate-lanceolate, deeply bipinnatifid (⅔ to the midrib), (less deeply cut and rather copiously glandular, but stem and pedicels less glandular or nearly glabrous, in *A. pedicularia carolinensis,* Piedmont and Coastal Plain, N. C.), the larger 3–6 cm. long, with 6–8 pairs of lateral lobes (or only 1.5–2.5 cm. long, stem less hirsute, and pedicels longer than bracts, in *A. pedicularia caesariensis,* Coastal Plain and Piedmont, N. C. to Mass.): calyx-lobes 8–10 mm. long, pinnately cut: corolla 30–40 mm. long; lobes depressed-orbicular: capsule 10–11 mm. long. [*D. pedicularia* (L.) Benth.]—Sandy and rocky woods, various provinces, Va. to Ont. and Me.; to be expected in N. C.—Sum.—Represented in our range by the subspecies as indicated above.

2. A. pectinata (Nutt.) Pennell. Stem 4–11 dm. tall, glandular-hirsute, diffusely branched (virgately branched, with the small upper leaves appressed to the branches, short pedicels and large corollas 38–45 mm. long, in *A. pectinata floridana*, Coastal Plain, C Fla. and S Ga.) : leaf-blades lanceolate to lanceolate-ovate, deeply bipinnatifid, glandular-pubescent, the larger 2–4 cm. long (larger, 3–6 cm. long, with the capsule 13–16 mm. long on pedicels 8–16 mm. long, in *A. pectinata eurycarpa*, various provinces, Ga. to Ala., Tenn., and N. C.) : pedicels 4–11 mm. long: calyx glandular-lanose (merely glandular-hirsute and with pedicels 10–20 mm. long in *A. pectinata transcedens*, sandhills, Coastal Plain, Ga. to N. C.) ; lobes 8–15 mm. long, pinnately cut: corolla 30–40 mm. long; lobes orbicular: capsule 11–13 mm. long. [*D. pectinata* (Nutt.) Benth.] Sandy oak woods, Coastal Plain, NW Fla. to La., Tenn., and N. C.; also adj. provinces, Ala. to C. Tenn.—Sum.—The stem is pubescent or puberulent.

3. A. virginica (L.) Pennell. Stem 8–12 dm. tall: leaf-blades lanceolate-ovate, rather coarsely sinuate with 2–4 rounded lobes, downy on both sides, the longer 9–15 cm. long: pedicels 1–3 mm. long: calyx-lobes 4–12 mm. long, lanceolate to ovate: corolla 30–45 mm. long; lobes 6–12 mm. long, ovate-orbicular: capsule 12–15 mm. long, ovoid to globose-ovoid. [*D. pubescens* Benth. *Gerardia flava* (Chapm. Fl.)]—Open, usually sandy oak woods, various provinces, N Fla. to La., Mich., and N. H.—Spr.-sum.—The stem is puberulent above.

4. A. microcarpa Pennell. Stem 6–10 dm. tall: leaf-blades lanceolate-ovate, rather coarsely · sinuate-lobed, puberulent on both sides, the larger 6–11 cm. long: pedicels 1–3 mm. long: calyx-lobes 3.5–7 mm. long, lanceolate to spatulate-ovate: corolla 30–40 mm. long; lobes 5–10 mm. long, ovate-orbicular: capsule 9–12 mm. long, ovoid to globose-ovoid.—Dry oak woods, Appalachian provinces and rarely Coastal Plain, N Fla. to E Tenn.—Sum.

5. A. laevigata Raf. Stem 5–12 dm. tall, glabrous, green: leaf-blades lanceolate to ovate-lanceolate, entire or the lower ones somewhat pinnately lobed, glabrous or nearly so, the larger 5–12 cm. long: pedicels 1–4 mm. long, or in fruit 3–8 mm. long: calyx glabrous; tube 3–5 mm. long; lobes 4–6 mm. long, lanceolate: corolla 30–35 mm. long; lobes 9–11 mm. long, depressed-orbicular: capsule 10–12 mm. long, ovoid. [*D. laevigata* (Raf.) Chapm.]—Rocky woods, Blue Ridge and Appalachian provinces, Ga. to Ky., Ohio, and Pa.; rarely Piedmont, N. C. and Va.—Sum.

6. A. flava (L.) Farwell. Stem 15–25 dm. tall, glabrous, glaucous: leaf-blades ovate-lanceolate to ovate, rather deeply and coarsely lobed or incised (shallowly lobed in *A. flava reticulata*, Coastal Plain, C Fla. to Md.), glabrate or glabrous, the larger 10–14 cm. long, with 5–7 pairs of lateral lobes: pedicels 4–10 mm. long: calyx glabrous; tube 4–7 mm. long; lobes 2–5 mm. long (5–14 mm. long, corolla 35–60 mm. long, and capsule 15–20 mm. long, in *A. flava macrantha*, various provinces, Ala. to Ark., Ill., and Ont.), lanceolate: corolla 35–40 mm. long; lobes 11–13 mm. long, depressed-orbicular: capsule 12–16 mm. long, ovoid. [*D. quercifolia* (Pursh) Benth. *Gerardia virginica* Auth. not L.] —Rocky and sandy oak woods, Piedmont, and more northern provinces, Ala. to Mich. and Me.—Sum.-fall.

7. A. dispersa (Small) Pennell. Stem 10–12 dm. tall, sparsely puberulent: leaf-blades lanceolate-ovate to ovate, nearly entire or rather deeply and coarsely lobed, finely puberulent, the larger 7–12 cm. long, with 1–4 pairs of lateral lobes: pedicels 4–10 mm. long: calyx-lobes 5–7 mm. long, triangular-lanceolate: corolla 40–50 mm. long; lobes 10–13 mm. long, depressed orbicular: capsule 14–18 mm. long, ovoid. [*D. dispersa* Small]—Sandy oak-woods, Coastal Plain, Ala. to La.—Sum.

8. A. patula (Chapm.) Pennell. Stems 10–12 dm. tall, sparsely puberulent: leaf-blades ovate-lanceolate to narrowly ovate, deeply and coarsely lobed or incised, puberulent or glabrate, the larger 13–16 cm. long, with 4–8 pairs of lateral lobes: pedicels 10–16 mm. long, or in fruit 15–25 mm. long: calyx-lobes 10–12 mm. long, linear: corolla 35–45 mm. long; lobes 7–10 mm. long, depressed-orbicular: capsule 13–17 mm. long, ovoid. [*D. patula* Chapm.]—Wooded river bluffs, Appalachian Valley and Interior Low Plateaus, Ga. to Tenn.—Sum.-fall.

33. AGALINIS Raf. Annual or perennial root-parasitic herbs, the stem usually branched. Leaves usually opposite, often with leaf-clusters in their axils: blades linear or filiform, or rarely subulate or broadened upward, entire, sessile. Flowers in racemes, axillary to foliaceous bracts. Calyx-lobes 5, uniform, shorter than the tube. Corolla rose-purple or pink-purple, more or less purple-spotted and usually with 2 yellow lines on the anterior side: throat campanulate or horizontally flattened, somewhat inflated anteriorly: lobes much shorter than the tube, about equal in length, spreading or the posterior arched or flattened. Stamens 4, didynamous, included: filaments more or less lanose: anthers lanose. Stigma elongate. Capsule globose to globose-ellipsoid, mucronate, loculicidal. Seeds numerous, reticulate, wingless. [*Gerardia* L. in part.] —About 50 species, American.—FALSE-FOXGLOVES. GERARDIAS. FALSE PURPLE-FOXGLOVES.

Plant annual: pedicels ascending or spreading: corolla membranous, rose-purple or
  lavender-purple, or rarely pink, nearly always with spots and yellow lines
  within: parasitic on many plants.
  Corolla with the posterior lobes spreading, pubescent within at their base.
    Calyx-tube not strongly reticulate-veined: seeds dark-brown: plant tending
      to blacken in drying.   I. PURPUREAE.
    Calyx-tube evidently reticulate-veined: seeds yellowish-
      brown: plant not tending to blacken in drying.   II. ERECTAE.
  Corolla with the posterior lobes arched or flattened over
    stamens and style, glabrous within at their base.   III. TENUIFOLIAE.
Plant with an elongate rootstock: pedicels erect: corolla pink,
  slightly fleshy, spotted, but without yellow lines in the
  throat: parasitic on pine roots.   IV. LINIFOLIAE.

I. PURPUREAE
Leaf-blades all linear or filiform, not obviously dimorphic.
  Racemes elongate, the pedicels less than 12 mm. long.
    Leaf-blades and calyx-lobes acute to acuminate: anther-
      sacs mucronate to caudate at the base: plant not
      fleshy.
      Corolla purple, the two yellow lines and dark spots
        within evident: plant dull-green or purplish.
        Stem smooth or minutely scabrellous: leaves with-
          out axillary fascicles or these small and
          shorter than the leaves.
          Fruiting pedicels 3–6 mm. long: the areas
            between the reticulations of the seed
            relatively pale.
            Plant relatively stiffly branched: stem
              sparingly scabrellous: calyx-lobes tri-
              angular-lanceolate to triangular-subulate:
              corolla 20–38 mm. long.   1. *A. purpurea.*
            Plant virgately branched: stem smooth:
              calyx-lobes subulate or nearly so: corolla
              20–25 mm. long.   2. *A. virgata.*
          Fruiting pedicels 1.5–3 mm. long: the areas
            between the reticulations of the seed
            nearly black.
            Corolla 20–25 mm. long: stigmas 2–3 mm.
              long: stem usually much branched.   3. *A. pinetorum.*
            Corolla 15–18 mm. long: stigmas 1–1.5 mm.
              long: stem simple or slightly branched.   4. *A. Harperi.*
        Stem more or less scabrous: leaves with usually
          conspicuously developed axillary fascicles.   5. *A. fasciculata.*

Corolla lavender-pink, destitute of spots and yellow
lines: plant bright-green.   6. *A. georgiana.*
Leaf-blades and calyx-lobes obtuse or acutish: anther-sacs
obtuse or acutish at the base: plant fleshy.   7. *A. maritima.*
Racemes short, much broken or lax, or if somewhat elongate
the pedicels over 10 mm. long.
Stem scabrous: corolla pubescent within in a narrow
line below the posterior sinus: anthers densely lanose
with pink hairs on the sides.   8. *A. pulchella.*
Stem smooth or nearly so: corolla pubescent within over
the entire width of the basal portions of the posterior lobes: anthers glabrous over much of the
dorsal surface.
Cauline leaves alternate: blades broadened distally
slightly fleshy: axillary leaf-fascicles abundantly
developed.   9. *A. filifolia.*
Cauline leaves opposite: blades neither broadened dis-
tally nor fleshy: axillary leaf-fascicles scarcely
or not at all developed.
Branches very widely and laxly ascending: fruiting pedicels 25–50 mm. long, 4–5 times as long
as the bracts: corolla 15–18 mm. long.   10. *A. laxa.*
Branches more closely and stiffly ascending: fruit-
ing pedicels less than twice as long as the
bracts.
Leaf-blades 2–3.5 cm. long, equalling or exceeding the internodes, slightly scabrous
to smooth on the upper surface.
Pedicels 15–40 mm. long, longer than the
bracts: corolla 17–25 mm. long: capsule 3–4 mm. long.
Racemes somewhat developed so that
only a few flowers appear as if terminal: pedicels 15–40 mm. long: corolla
18–25 mm. long: leaf-blades narrowly
linear to filiform.   11. *A. setacea.*
Racemes scarcely evident, most flowers
appearing as if terminal to the
branches: pedicels 15–20 mm. long:
corolla 17–20 mm. long: leaf-blades
filiform-setaceous.   12. *A. stenophylla.*
Pedicels 5–10 (–15) mm. long, shorter than
the bracts or equalling them: corolla
25–30 mm. long: capsule 4–5 mm. long:
most flowers appearing as if terminal to
the branches.   13. *A. Plukenetii.*
Leaf-blades 0.5–1.2 cm. long, shorter than the
internodes, scabrous on the upper surface: corolla 15–22 mm. long.
Pedicels 4–6 mm. long, about equalling the
bracts: calyx-lobes not becoming callose:
leaf-blades filiform: stem smooth or
slightly scabrellous.   14. *A. keyensis.*
Pedicels thrice to ten times the length of
the bracts: calyx-lobes becoming callose:
leaf-blades linear-subulate: stem ridged,
minutely hispidulous-roughened.   15. *A. oligophylla.*
Leaf-blades mostly minute, scale-like, appressed, those near the
base of the stem oval or ovate and spreading, but frequently
early deciduous: pedicels 1–3 mm. long.   16. *A. aphylla.*

II. Erectae

Racemes well-developed, and flowers not appearing as if terminal: stigma 1–2 mm. long: leaf-blades linear to nearly
filiform: stem evidently striate-angled.
Leaf-blades linear to nearly filiform, not widening distally,
acutish to acuminate: corolla with yellow lines and
dark spots within strongly defined: capsule globose to
globose-ovoid, somewhat flattened at the base.
Corolla 10–15 mm. long: pedicels mostly twice to thrice
the length of the bracts.   17. *A. decemloba.*
Corolla 15–20 mm. long: pedicels mostly thrice to eight
times the length of the bracts.   18. *A. tenella.*
Leaf-blades widening distally, acutish to obtuse: corolla
with yellow lines and dark spots faint or obsolete: cap-
sule globose-ovoid to ellipsoid, rounded at the base.   19. *A. erecta.*

Racemes scarcely developed, many flowers appearing as if terminal to the branches: stigma 2–3 mm. long: leaf-blades nar-
rowly linear: stem nearly terete.   20. *A. Gattingeri.*

III. Tenuifoliae

Corolla pubescent externally, its posterior lobes about two-thirds
the length of the anterior, concave-arched: pedicels, if ex-
ceeding the bracts, less than twice their length.   21. *A. tenuifolia.*
Corolla glabrous externally, its posterior lobes less than half
the length of the anterior, flattened: pedicels at least
thrice the length of the bracts.
 Leaf-blades filiform, 1.5–2 cm. long: stem evenly and stiffly
 much-branched: racemes well developed, no flowers appearing as if terminal: pedicels 15–32 mm. long: corolla
 15–18 mm. long.   22. *A. divaricata.*
 Leaf-blades minute, triangular-subulate, 0.1–0.2 cm. long:
 stem sparingly very laxly branched: racemes scarcely
 developed, the flowers scattered and mostly appearing as
 if terminal to the branches: pedicels 5–10 mm. long:
 corolla 10–13 mm. long.   23. *A. filicaulis.*

IV. Linifoliae

Plant with a virgate, little branched stem, corollas 30–40 mm.
long.   24. *A. linifolia.*

1. A. purpurea (L.) Pennell. Stem 4–12 dm. tall, striate-angled, sparingly
scabrellous, much branched: leaf-blades 2.5–4 cm. long, linear, scabrous above:
racemes elongate, 6–14-flowered: pedicels 2–5
mm. long: calyx-lobes triangular-lanceolate
to subulate, 0.5–2 mm. long, much shorter
than the tube: corolla 20–38 mm. long, purple; lobes spreading, the posterior ones
pubescent at the base: capsule 4.5–7 mm.
long, globose or nearly so. [*G. purpurea*
L.]—Moist sandy soil, meadows and stream-
banks, various provinces, Fla. to Tex., Minn.,
and Mass.—Sum.–fall.

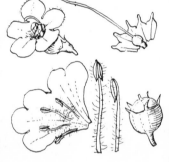

2. A. virgata Raf. Stem 3–10 dm. tall,
striate-angled, glabrous, virgately branched:
leaf-blades 1.5–4 cm. long, narrowly linear
to almost filiform, scabrous above: racemes
elongate, 8–26-flowered: pedicels 2–6 mm.
long: calyx-lobes triangular-subulate to subulate, 0.8–2 mm. long: corolla 20–25
mm. long, purple; lobes spreading, the posterior pubescent at the base: capsule
4.5–5 mm. long, globose.—Moist pinebarrens, Coastal Plain, S. C. to SE
N. Y.—Fall.

3. A. pinetorum Pennell. Stem 6–8 dm. tall, slightly angled, nearly glabrous,
much branched: leaf-blades 2–2.5 cm. long, narrowly linear (a more slender
plant, *A. pinetorum delicatula*, with filiform curled leaf-blades, calyx-lobes 1.5–2
mm. long, and an unspotted corolla, occurs on the pinehills of W Fla.) somewhat scabrous above: racemes slightly elongate, 8–14-flowered: pedicels 1–3 mm.
long: calyx-lobes triangular-subulate, 1–1.5 mm. long, shorter than the tube:
corolla 20–25 mm. long, purple; lobes spreading, the posterior ones pubescent
at the base: capsule 4.5–5 mm. long, globose.—Moist pinelands, Coastal Plain,
N Fla. to La. and Ga.—Fall.

4. A. Harperi Pennell. Stem 4–8 dm. tall, striate-angled, nearly glabrous,
simple or slightly branched: leaf-blades 2–3.5 cm. long, narrowly linear, scabrous above: racemes elongate, 8–20-flowered: pedicels 1–2 mm. long: calyx-
lobes triangular-lanceolate to triangular-subulate, 0.7–1.5 mm. long, shorter
than the tube: corolla 15–18 mm. long, pink; lobes spreading, the posterior
lobes pubescent at the base: capsule 4–5 mm. long, globose.—Moist pinelands
and marsh-borders, Coastal Plain, S Fla. to Ga.—(*W. I.*)—Fall or all year S.

5. A. fasciculata (Ell.) Raf. Stem 6–12 dm. tall, striate-angled, usually very scabrous, much branched: leaf-blades 1.5–4 cm. long, linear, scabrous above (or with the fascicles only slightly or moderately developed on a slender plant with merely scabrellous stems in *A. fasciculata peninsularis*, of the Everglades, Fla.): racemes elongate, 12–30-flowered: pedicels 2–6 mm. long: calyx-lobes triangular-lanceolate to subulate, 0.5–2 mm. long, much shorter than the tube: corolla mostly 25–35 mm. long; lobes spreading, the posterior lobes pubescent at the base: capsule 5–6 mm. long, ovoid-globose.—Sandy soil, near beaches and in cult. fields and prairies, Coastal Plain, Fla. to Tex. and S. C.; also in adj. provinces, Okla. to Mo.—(*W. I.*)—Sum.–fall, or all year S.

6. A. georgiana (Boynton) Pennell. Stem 3–8 dm. tall, striate-angled, nearly or quite glabrous, simple or branched: leaf-blades 1–1.5 cm. long, linear, somewhat scabrous above: racemes elongate, 12–20-flowered: pedicels 1–4 mm. long: calyx-lobes triangular-lanceolate, 0.5–1 mm. long: corolla 15–18 mm. long; lobes spreading, the posterior pubescent at the base: capsule 3.5–5 mm. long, ovoid-globose.—Dry pinelands, Coastal Plain, N Fla. to Ala. and Ga.—Fall.

7. A. maritima Raf. Stem 0.5–4 dm. tall, nearly terete, glabrous, often bushy-branched: leaf-blades 1.5–3 cm. long, broadly linear, somewhat scabrous above: racemes elongate, 4–10-flowered: pedicels 2–10 mm. long: calyx-lobes triangular, 0.5–1.5 mm. long, obtuse, shorter than the tube: corolla 12–17 mm. long, pink-purple; lobes spreading, somewhat pubescent below and adjacent to the posterior sinus: capsule 5–6 mm. long, globose to globose-ovoid. [*G. maritima* Raf.]—Saltmarshes, Va. to Me.—The species is represented in our range by *A. maritima grandiflora* (Benth.) Pennell (*G. spiciflora* Engelm.), larger plant up to 6 dm. tall, with leaves 2–4 cm. long and corolla 15–20 mm. long, ranging in salt marshes from S Fla. to Tex. and N. C.—(*W. I., Mex.*)

8. A. pulchella Pennell. Stem 6–10 dm. tall, striate-angled, scabrous, much branched: leaf-blades 2–3 cm. long, narrowly linear, very scabrous above: racemes slightly elongate, 4–6-flowered: pedicels 15–30 mm. long, much longer in fruit: calyx-lobes subulate, 0.1–0.5 mm. long: corolla 25–30 mm. long; lobes spreading: capsule 5–6 mm. long, globose.—Pinelands, Coastal Plain, N Fla. to La. and Ga.—Fall.

9. A. filifolia (Nutt.) Raf. Stem 3–8 dm. tall, terete, glabrous, much branched: leaf-blades 1–2 cm. long, narrowly linear to filiform, slightly scabrous above: racemes slightly elongate, 3–12-flowered: pedicels 10–30 mm. long or in fruit nearly twice this length: calyx-lobes linear-subulate, 0.5–1 mm. long: corolla 22–28 mm. long, purple; lobes spreading: capsule 4–5 mm. long, ovoid-globose. [*G. filifolia* Nutt.]—Pinelands, Coastal Plain, S Fla. to Ga.—Fall.

10. A. laxa Pennell. Stem 6–10 dm. tall, nearly terete, glabrous, widely and laxly branched: leaf-blades 2–3 cm. long, narrowly linear to nearly filiform, nearly or quite glabrous above: racemes slightly elongate, 3–8-flowered: pedicels 15–30 mm. long, or in fruit nearly twice as long: calyx-lobes subulate, 0.2–0.5 mm. long: corolla 15–18 mm. long; lobes spreading: capsule 4–5 mm. long, ovoid-globose.—River handhills and old dunes, Coastal Plain, C Fla. to S. C.—Fall.

11. A. setacea (Walt.) Raf. Stem 3–7 dm. tall, somewhat striate-angled, glabrous, much branched: leaf-blades 2.5–3.5 mm. long, narrowly linear to filiform, scabrellous to nearly glabrous above: racemes slightly elongate, 6–10-flowered: pedicels 15–40 mm. long: calyx-lobes triangular-subulate, 0.2–0.5 mm. long: corolla mostly 18–25 mm. long; lobes spreading: capsule 3–4 mm. long, globose-ovoid. [*G. Holmiana* Greene]—Dry pinelands, Coastal Plain and rarely adj. provinces, Ga. to SE N. Y.—Sum.–fall.

12. A. stenophylla Pennell. Stem 6–7 dm. tall, slightly striate-angled, glabrous, much-branched: leaf-blades 2–3 cm. long, filiform-setaceous, nearly or quite glabrous: racemes scarcely elongate, 1–6-flowered: pedicels 8–12 mm. long or in fruit nearly twice this length: calyx-lobes triangular-subulate, 0.1–0.3 mm. long: corolla 17–20 mm. long, not seen fresh; lobes spreading; capsule 3–4 mm. long, globose-ovoid.—Pinelands, C Fla.—Fall.

13. A. Plukenetii (Ell.) Raf. Stem 5–8 dm. tall, striate-angled, glabrous or nearly so, much-branched: leaf-blades 2–3.5 cm. long, setaceous-filiform, scabrellous above: racemes scarcely developed, 1–6-flowered: pedicels mostly 5–10 mm. long: calyx-lobes triangular-subulate to subulate, 0.3–0.5 mm. long; corolla mostly 25–30 mm. long, purple; lobes spreading: capsule 4–5 mm. long, globose. [*G. Plukenetii* Ell.]—Dry pinelands, Coastal Plain, N Fla. to E Miss. and Ga.; also adj. provinces, Ga. to Ala. and SE Tenn.—Fall.

14. A. keyensis Pennell. Stem at least 7 dm. tall, slightly striate-angled, glabrous or nearly so, much branched: leaf-blades (lowest not seen) 0.8–1.2 cm. long, filiform, scabrous above: racemes scarcely developed, only 1–4-flowered: pedicels in flower 3–4 mm. long, in fruit 4–6 mm. long: calyx-lobes triangular-subulate, 0.4–0.6 mm. long: corolla 18–20 mm. long, not seen fresh; lobes spreading: capsule 3–3.5 mm. long, globose.—Pinelands, Big Pine Key, Fla.

15. A. oligophylla Pennell. Stem 3–8 dm. tall, striate-angled, hispidulous, simple or branched: leaf-blades 0.5–1 cm. long, linear-filiform to subulate, scabrous above: racemes scarcely developed: pedicels in flower 5–15 mm. long (2–8 mm. long and calyx-lobes very callose, 0.2 mm. long, in *A. oligophylla pseudaphylla* of long-leaf pineland of S Miss.), in fruit not seen: calyx-lobes triangular-subulate, 0.4–0.6 mm. long; corolla 15–22 mm. long; lobes spreading: capsule not seen. [*G. microphylla* (A. Gray) Small, not *A. microphylla* Raf.]—Long-leaf pineland, Coastal Plain, S La. to E Tex.—Doubtfully E of the Mississippi River, except in above subspecies.

16. A. aphylla (Nutt.) Raf. Stem 5–12 dm. tall, striate-ridged and minutely hispidulous, or sometimes terete and hirsute at the base, simple or branched: leaf-blades appressed, 0.1–0.3 (–0.6) mm. long, triangular-subulate, glabrous above; those near the base with oval more or less pubescent blades: racemes somewhat elongate, 8–20-flowered: pedicels 1–3 mm. long: calyx-lobes subulate tips 0.05–0.2 mm. long; corolla 15–20 mm. long, pink; lobes spreading, the posterior ones pubescent at the base: capsule 3–4 mm. long, globose.—Moist pinelands, Coastal Plain, N Fla. to La. and N. C.—Fall.

17. A. decemloba (Greene) Pennell. Stem 2–5 dm. tall, striate-angled, glabrous, simple or somewhat branched: leaf-blades mostly 2–2.5 cm. long, filiform-linear, scabrous above: racemes somewhat elongate, 3–10-flowered: pedicels in flower 5–15 mm. long, in fruit 12–25 mm. long: calyx-lobes minute, 0.05–0.2 (–0.3) mm. long: corolla 10–15 mm. long, pink; lobes spreading, the posterior pubescent at the base: capsule 3.5–4 mm. long, globose-ovoid. [*G. decemloba* Greene]—Open sterile soil, Piedmont, Blue Ridge, and Appalachian Valley, Ala. to Pa.—Fall.

18. A. tenella Pennell. Stem 5–8 dm. tall, striate-angled, glabrous, branched: leaf-blades mostly 1–1.5 cm. long, linear-filiform to filiform, scabrellous above: racemes somewhat elongate, 8–12-flowered: pedicels 8–25 mm. long, calyx-lobes minute, 0.05–0.2 mm. long: corolla 15–20 mm. long, pink; lobes spreading, the posterior ones pubescent at the base: capsule 3–4 mm. long, globose-ovoid.—Dry pinelands, Coastal Plain, N Fla. to E Ala. and S. C.—Fall.

19. A. erecta (Walt.) Pennell. Stem 3–8 dm. tall, striate-angled, nearly glabrous, simple or branched: leaf-blades mostly 1–1.5 cm. long, linear-cuneate, scabrous above: racemes slightly elongate, 6–14-flowered: pedicels 3–25 mm. long: calyx-lobes minute, subulate, 0.05–0.15 mm. long: corolla 12–16 mm. long; lobes spreading, the posterior ones pubescent at the base: capsule 3–4 mm. long, globose-ovoid to globose-ellipsoid. [*G. parvifolia* (Benth.) Chapm.]— Pinelands, Coastal Plain, Fla. to La. and Del.—Fall.

20. **A. Gattingeri** Small. Stem 2–5 dm. tall, nearly terete, nearly glabrous, much-branched: leaf-blades 2–3 cm. long, narrowly linear, scabrellous above: racemes scarcely developed, 1–5-flowered: pedicels in flower 2–25 mm. long, in fruit 8–30 mm. long; calyx-lobes triangular-lanceolate, 0.5–1.8 mm. long, much shorter than the tube: corolla 12–18 mm. long, pink; lobes spreading, the posterior ones pubescent at the base: capsule 4–5 mm. long, globose to globose-ovoid. [*G. Gattingeri* Small]—Open woods, in sterile soil, barrens, and bluffs, Appalachian Valley and more N and W provinces, Ala. to Tex., Minn., and Ont.—Sum.–fall.

21. **A. tenuifolia** (Vahl) Raf. Stem 1–8 dm. tall, striate-angled, nearly glabrous, much branched: leaf-blades 2–5 cm. long, narrowly linear (linear-filiform to filiform and corollas 9–12 mm. long, in *A. tenuifolia polyphylla* of the granite regions of Ga.; widely linear and 3–7 cm. long, calyx-lobes 1–2 mm. long, and capsules 5–7 mm. long, in *A. tenuifolia macrophylla* of the Miss. Valley), scabrous above: racemes much elongate, 6–34-flowered: pedicels in flower 7–20 mm. long, in fruit 12–27 mm. long: calyx-lobes triangular-subulate to subulate, 0.2–1 mm. long: corolla 10–15 mm. long (15–23 mm. long and capsule 5–7 mm. long, in *A. tenuifolia leucanthera* of the Coastal Plain, N Fla. to Tex. and Ga.), purple, the posterior lobes concave-arched, glabrous: capsule 3–4 (–7) mm. long, globose. [*G. tenuifolia* Vahl.]—Woodlands, various provinces, Ga. to La., Mo., Mich., and Me.—Sum.–fall.

22. **A. divaricata** (Chapm.) Pennell. Stem 3–8 dm. tall, striate-angled, glabrous, much-branched: leaf-blades 1.5–2 cm. long, filiform, scabrellous above: racemes elongate, 6–12-flowered: pedicels 15–32 mm. long: calyx-lobes subulate, 0.1–0.3 mm. long, much shorter than the tube: corolla 15–18 mm. long, the posterior lobes flattened-projecting and glabrous at the base: capsule 3–4 mm. long, globose to ovoid-globose, not seen mature. [*G. divaricata* Chapm.]—Dry pineland, NW Fla. and SE Ala.—Fall.

23. **A. filicaulis** (Benth.) Pennell. Stem 1–5 dm. tall, obscurely striate, glabrous, with a few lax branches: leaf-blades 0.1–0.2 cm. long, triangular-subulate, appressed, scabrellous above: racemes not developed, the flowers nearly always solitary: pedicels in flower 5–8 mm. long, in fruit 6–10 mm. long: calyx-lobes triangular-subulate, 0.1–0.3 mm. long: corolla 10–13 mm. long, the posterior lobes flattened-projecting and glabrous at the base: capsule about 3 mm. long, globose. [*G. filicaulis* Benth.]—Moist grassy pinelands, Coastal Plain, N Fla. to E La. and Ga.—Fall.

24. **A. linifolia** (Nutt.) Britton. Stem 8–15 dm. tall, terete, glabrous, simple or virgately branched: leaf-blades 3–5 cm. long, linear, glabrous: racemes elongate, 8–20-flowered: pedicels 5–25 mm. long: calyx-lobes minute, subulate: corolla 30–40 mm. long; lobes spreading, lanose on the basal portions of the posterior: capsule 6–7 mm. long, globose to globose-ovoid. [*G. linifolia* Nutt.] —Wet pinelands, Coastal Plain, S Fla. to La. and Del.—Sum.–fall.

34. **TOMANTHERA** Raf. Annual root-parasitic herbs, the stems simple or branched, pubescent. Leaves opposite, cauline: blades entire, lobed at the base, or pinnately parted, sessile. Flowers in spikes with foliaceous bracts. Calyx-lobes 5, unequal, longer than the tube. Corolla purple: throat campanulate, somewhat inflated anteriorly: lobes much shorter than the tube, the 2

posterior arched, the 3 anterior spreading. Stamens 4, didynamous, included: anthers lanose. Stigma elongate. Capsule short, glabrous, loculicidal. Seeds numerous, reticulate, wingless. [*Otophylla* Benth.]— Two species, eastern North American.

1. **T. auriculata** (Michx.) Raf. Stem 1.5–8 dm. tall, 4-angled, hispid: leaf-blades 2.5–5.5 cm. long, lanceolate to lanceolate-ovate, rough-pubescent above: calyx-tube 5–8 mm. long, retrorse-pubescent; lobes 9–12 mm. long, ovate-lanceolate; corolla 20–23 mm. long, externally pubescent; the throat spotted with deep-purple anteriorly: capsule broadly ovoid, 10–13 mm. long, mucronate. [*O. Michauxii* Benth. *O. auriculata* (Michx.) Small]—Prairies and old fields, various provinces; introduced, Ala. to Tenn. and Pa.; native from Ill. to Tex., Kans., and Minn.—Sum.

35. **BUCHNERA** L. Perennial mostly pubescent herbs with short rootstocks, the stem simple. Leaves opposite, the lower sessile or nearly so, the upper clasping, toothed, all rough-pubescent. Flowers in a slender terminal spike, each axillary to a bract and with 2 narrower bractlets. Calyx-lobes 5, short. Corolla violet or white, salverform: tube very slender, pubescent: lobes nearly uniform. Stamens 4, included, slightly didynamous: anthers 1-celled. Stigma linear-cylindric. Capsule ovoid, included, loculicidal. Seeds numerous, reticulate, wingless.—About 100 species, in warm regions.—BLUEHEARTS.

Leaf-blades obscurely, if at all, 3-veined, repand-dentate or entire: capsule usually about 5 mm. long: stem finely rough-pubescent or nearly glabrous.
  Corolla-tube about twice as long as the calyx: calyx-lobes triangular-acute, the anterior sinus only slightly deeper than the others: bracts 1.5–3 mm. long.
    Blades of the lower leaves lanceolate to linear-lanceolate, acute or acuminate: corolla-lobes usually 6–9 mm. long.   1. *B. elongata.*
    Blades of the lower leaves elliptic-lanceolate, obtuse: corolla-lobes 3–5 mm. long.   2. *B. floridana.*
  Corolla-tube little longer than the calyx: calyx-lobes lanceolate-acuminate, the anterior sinus much deeper than the others: bracts 3–4 mm. long.   3. *B. breviflora.*
Leaf-blades clearly 3-veined, sinuate-toothed or lacerate: capsule usually 6–7 mm. long: stem hirsute.   4. *B. americana.*

1. **B. elongata** Sw. Stem 3–7 dm. tall, sparsely pilose or glabrate: leaf-blades rough-pubescent, the larger lanceolate to linear-lanceolate, 3–8 cm. long: bracts 1.5–3 mm. long, spreading or ascending-appressed: calyx-lobes triangular-acute to triangular-acuminate, 0.5–1 mm. long, the anterior sinus scarcely deeper than the others: corolla violet or white; tube 7–10 mm. long; lobes 6–9 mm. long, oblanceolate to narrowly obovate: capsule 5 mm. long.— Prairies and pinelands, S Fla.—[*W. I.*]— All year.

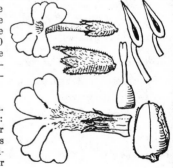

2. **B. floridana** Gandoger. Stem 3–6 dm. tall, slightly pilose, or glabrate above: leaf-blades rough-pubescent, the larger elliptic-lanceolate, 2.5–5.5 cm. long: bracts 2–3 mm. long, spreading: calyx-lobes triangular-acute, 0.5–1 mm. long, the anterior

sinus the deeper: corolla violet or white; tube 7–8 mm. long; lobes 3–5 mm. long, triangular-obovate: capsule about 5 mm. long.—Pinelands, Coastal Plain, pen. Fla. to Tex. and N. C.—Spr.–fall.

3. B. breviflora Pennell. Stem 3–6 dm. tall, pilose below: leaf-blades rough-pubescent, the larger lanceolate to elliptic, 4–8 cm. long: bracts 3–4 mm. long, ascending-appressed: calyx-lobes lanceolate-acuminate, 1–2 mm. long: corolla violet; tube 6–7 mm. long, very densely pilose at the mouth; lobes 2–4 mm. long, triangular-obovate, rounded or slightly emarginate: capsule not seen mature.—Prairies and pinelands, Coastal Plain, C pen. Fla. to Tex. and S. C.—Spr.

4. B. americana L. Stem 3–8 dm. tall, most copiously hirsute below: leaf-blades hispid, the larger ovate-lanceolate or elliptic-lanceolate, 3–7 cm. long: bracts 2–4 mm. long, ascending or spreading: calyx-lobes acuminate-cuspidate, mostly 1–1.5 mm. long: corolla violet; tube 9–11 mm. long, strongly pilose at the mouth; lobes 5–8 mm. long, oblanceolate, rounded or emarginate: capsule usually 6–7 mm. long: seeds about 0.5 mm. long.—Sandy or sterile open soil, often in meadows, various provinces N of Coastal Plain, Ga. to Tex., Ill., Ont., and Pa.—Spr.–early sum.

36. SCHWALBEA L.   Perennial pubescent herbs, the stem simple. Leaves alternate, all cauline: blades entire, rather broad, 3-veined, sessile. Flowers in a raceme, each pedicel subtended by 2 bractlets, the short stalks axillary to bracts which are shorter than the calyx.   Calyx-lobes 5, unequal, the posterior one short, narrow, the anterior pair well united, broad.   Corolla 2-lipped: posterior lip nearly entire: anterior lip 3-lobed, the throat with 2 slightly pubescent ridges. Stamens 4, in-cluded, didynamous: anthers nearly gla-brous.   Stigma capitate.   Capsule stout, included in the calyx, septicidal and secon-darily slightly loculicidal.   Seeds narrow, flat, winged.—Two species, eastern North American.

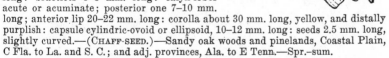

1. S. australis Pennell. Stem 4–8 dm. tall, finely pubescent with ascending hairs: leaf-blades 3–4 cm. long, elliptic-oval, obscurely reticulate, strigillose; pedicels 3–5 mm. long: bractlets 5–8 mm. long: calyx-lobes acute or acuminate; posterior one 7–10 mm. long; anterior lip 20–22 mm. long: corolla about 30 mm. long, yellow, and distally purplish: capsule cylindric-ovoid or ellipsoid, 10–12 mm. long: seeds 2.5 mm. long, slightly curved.—(CHAFF-SEED.)—Sandy oak woods and pinelands, Coastal Plain, C Fla. to La. and S. C.; and adj. provinces, Ala. to E Tenn.—Spr.–sum.

37. CASTILLEJA Mutis.   Annual pubescent herbs, the stem simple or branched.   Leaves alternate, the basal ones forming a semi-persistent rosette: blades entire or pinnately cleft, sessile or nearly so.   Flowers spicate.   Bracts foliaceous, shorter and broader than the leaves, red or yellowish towards the ends.   Bractlets none.   Calyx-lobes 4 (the posterior sepal lacking), united sagitally about half their length, those of each side completely fused; distally

red or yellowish. Corolla 2-lipped, yellowish-green: posterior lip long and narrowly
arched: anterior lip very short, of 3 thickened lobes. Stamens 4, included, didynamous: anthers coherent, glabrous. Stigma
capitate. Capsule stout, the carpels equal,
loculicidal. Seeds turgid, reticulate, wingless.—About 200 species, mostly American;
2 or 3 Asiatic.

1. **C. coccinea** (L.) Spreng. Stem 2–6 dm.
tall, arising from a rosette of elliptic to
ovate, nearly or quite entire leaf-blades:
cauline leaves few; blades linear-lanceolate,
with 1 or 2 pairs of divaricate lobes: bracts overlapping, ovate, 3-lobed, distally scarlet, or exceptionally yellow: calyx 18–23 mm. long: corolla 18–25 mm.
long: capsule narrowly-ovoid, 11–13 mm. long.—(PAINTED-CUP. INDIAN PAINT-
BRUSH.)—Grassy meadows and moist woods, various provinces, in Coastal Plain
only northward, Ga. to Ark., Kans., Man., and Me.—Spr.

38. **PEDICULARIS** L. Perennial herbs, the stems often gregarious, glabrous or pubescent. Leaves opposite or alternate, all cauline or tufted on
basal shoots: blades pinnately lobed, often thickish. Flowers closely spicate,
usually leafy-bracted. Bractlets none. Calyx-lobes 4 (the posterior sepal lacking), shorter than the tube, those of each side completely fused. Corolla
2-lipped, yellow or purple: posterior lip arched and decurved: anterior lip 3-
lobed, obliquely spreading. Stamens 4, included, slightly didynamous. Stigma
capitate. Capsule ensiform-lanceolate, the carpels unequal, the posterior loculicidal. Seeds few, flat, wingless.—About 350 species, of the Northern Hemisphere,
mainly in the Old World.—LOUSEWORTS. FERNLEAFS.

Stem hirsute: leaves alternate; blades deeply pinnatifid: calyx-lobes broadly acute,
    entire: capsule twice as long as the calyx.   1. **P. canadensis.**
Stem glabrous: leaves opposite; blades shallowly pinnatifid:
    calyx-lobes with a slightly enlarged crenate tip: capsule scarcely
    exceeding the calyx.   2. **P. lanceolata.**

1. **P. canadensis** L. Stem 1–3 dm. tall: leaf-blades petioled, elliptic-oval, with
long crenate lobes separated by deep broad sinuses: flower-rachis lanate: calyx

7–9 mm. long, hirsute, on each side entire:
corolla 18–23 mm. long, yellow, or with the
posterior lip purple, or purplish throughout,
the anterior lip not close to the posterior
one: capsule 13–16 mm. long, nearly beakless: seeds 1.5 mm. long, finely lined.—
(WOOD-BETONY.)—Sandy or sterile soil,
woods and knolls in meadows, various provinces, N Fla. to Tex., Man., and N. S.—Spr.

2. **P. lanceolata** Michx. Stem 4–8 dm.
tall: leaf-blades sessile or nearly so, elliptic-
lanceolate, with short crenulate lobes separated by shallow narrow sinuses: flower-
rachis glabrous: calyx 9–11 mm. long, glabrous or nearly so, on each side terminating
in a crenate leaf-like tip: corolla 18–23 mm.

long, yellow, the anterior lip appressed to or partly investing the posterior one: capsule 10–12 mm. long, obliquely pointed: seeds 2.5 mm. long.—(SWAMP-LOUSEWORT.)—Wet meadows and swales, Blue Ridge and more N provinces, N. C. to Nebr., Man., and Mass.—Sum.–fall.

39. **MELAMPYRUM** L. Annual herbs, the stem minutely pubescent. Leaves opposite, all cauline: blades usually entire, thin. Flowers loosely racemose, axillary to foliaceous, entire or basally fimbriate bracts. Bractlets none. Calyx-lobes 4 (the posterior sepal lacking), as long as the tube or longer, nearly equal, the posterior and anterior pairs divaricate. Corolla 2-lipped, mainly white: posterior lip arched and hooded: anterior lip slightly 3-lobed with a densely puberulent palate. Stamens 4, included, didynamous: filaments glabrous: anthers cohering, pubescent, mucronate at base. Stigma capitate. Capsule somewhat decurved, the carpels unequal, the posterior cavity loculicidal. Seeds 2 in each cavity, plump, smooth, wingless.—About 50 species, of the Northern Hemisphere.

1. **M. lineare** Desr. Stem 1–4 dm. tall: leaf-blades linear to lanceolate-linear: 2–6 cm. long: bracts conspicuously fimbriate: calyx-lobes ovate-caudate, 2–4 mm. long: corolla 7–10 mm. long: posterior lip yellowish-tipped, ciliolate; anterior lip flat, the palate egg-yellow: capsule ensiform-ovate, 5–7 mm. long: seeds ovoid, 2–3 mm. long, mostly brown. [*M. americanum* (Chapm. Fl.)]—(COW-WHEAT.)—Open woods, old fields, and pastures, Coastal Plain and adj. provinces, N. C. to N. Y.—*M. latifolium* Muhl. perhaps not specifically distinct, with larger leaf-blades varying from ovate to linear-lanceolate, shortly fimbriate or entire bracts, a broader capsule, and seeds 3–4 mm. long, ranges, in the Blue Ridge and adj. provinces, from Ga. to Wis., Que., and N. S.

FAMILY 15. **ACANTHACEAE** — ACANTHUS FAMILY

Herbs or shrubs. Leaves alternate, opposite, or whorled: blades simple. Flowers perfect, irregular. Calyx of usually 5 partly united sepals. Corolla of 5 partly united petals, 2-lipped or sometimes essentially regular. Androecium of 4 didynamous, or of 2 equal stamens, one pair being abortive or obsolete. Gynoecium of 2 united carpels. Ovary 2-celled. Ovules commonly 2 in each cavity. Fruit a capsule, often with a stipe-like base, the valves opening elastically.—About 175 genera and 2,000 species, widely distributed in temperate and tropical regions.

Vines: seeds globular.   1. THUNBERGIA.
Erect or diffuse herbs: seeds flat.
  Leaves normal only at the base of the stem, those on the
    stem reduced to firm sheathing imbricate scales and pass-
    ing into the inflorescence.   2. TUBIFLORA.
  Leaves normal on the stem.
    Corolla convolute in the bud.
      Corolla conspicuously 2-lipped: capsule terete, not
        constricted at the base.   3. HYGROPHILA.
      Corolla barely if at all 2-lipped: capsule constricted
        into a stipe-like base.

Anther-sacs mucronate or aristulate at the base:
corolla with a short tube and a campanulate
throat.   4. DYSCHORISTE.
Anther-sacs rounded at the base: corolla with a
long tube and a funnelform or campanulate
throat.   5. RUELLIA.
Corolla imbricated in the bud.
Stamens 4: anthers 1-celled.   6. GERARDIA.
Stamens 2: anthers 2-celled.
Anther-sacs parallel, closely contiguous.
Corolla strongly 2-lipped.   7. DIAPEDIUM.
Corolla slightly 2-lipped.   8. YEATESIA.
Anther-sacs separated on a dilated connective.
Anther-sacs nearly similar in size and shape,
the lower sac short-stalked.   9. DIANTHERA.
Anther-sacs dissimilar, more or less unequal,
and the lateral one, at least, pointed at the
base, sessile.   10. JUSTICIA.

1. **THUNBERGIA** L. f. Climbing vines (ours). Leaf-blades more or
less hastate or sagittate and toothed. Flowers on axillary peduncles, subtended by a pair of foliaceous bracts. Calyx persistent: lobes 10–16, narrow.
Corolla salverform, with a short tube, a long throat, and a limb with 5
broad lobes. Stamens 4, didynamous. Capsule subtended by the persistent
bracts, with a roundish body and a flat beak.—About 40 species, in the Old
World tropics.—Sum. or all year S.

Petioles wing-margined: corolla yellow or ochroleucous, with a purple eye: capsule-
beak somewhat longer than the body.   1. *T. alata.*
Petioles not wing-margined: corolla white: capsule-beak much
longer than the body.   2. *T. fragrans.*

1. **T. alata** Bojer. Leaf-blades triangular-ovate to hastate, 3–11 cm. long,
undulate or sinuate-toothed, cordate at the base: calyx-lobes subulate, mostly
10–12, longer than the tube: corolla-limb
2.5–3.5 cm. wide, the lobes rounded or undulate: capsule-beak somewhat longer than
the diameter of the body.—(BLACK-EYED
SUSAN.)—Prairies, roadsides, and waste-
places, Fla. Nat. of Africa.

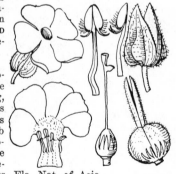

2. **T. fragrans** Roxb. Leaf-blades lanceolate to ovate, coarsely toothed near the base
and more or less hastate, 4–11 cm. long,
truncate to cordate at the base: calyx-lobes
lanceolate, 12–16, unequal, about half as
long as the tube or longer: corolla-limb
3.5–4.5 cm. wide, the lobes truncate: capsule-beak nearly twice as long as the
body. — (WHITE-THUNBERGIA.) — Fence-
rows, roadsides, waste-places, and hammocks, Fla. Nat. of Asia.

2. **TUBIFLORA** J. F. Gmel. Rigid herbs with several basal leaves and
flower stems with many rigid sheathing scales. Flowers in terminal spikes,
subtended by bractlets somewhat shorter than the calyx. Calyx-lobes glumace-
ous, 4 or 5, the lateral ones the narrower. Corolla white or blue, slightly 2-
lipped. [*Elytraria* Vahl.]—About 10 species, American.

Basal leaves more or less spreading: blades narrow and elongate. 1. *T. angustifolia.*
Basal leaves erect; blades broad and relatively short.   2. *T. carolinensis.*

1. T. angustifolia (Fernald) Small. Stem 2–6 dm. tall: basal leaves' 4–30 cm. long; blades linear, elongate linear-spatulate or narrowly oblanceolate: bracts ciliate: bractlets very narrow: calyx-lobes 6–7.5 mm. long, short-ciliate at the tip: corolla-lobes much shorter than the tube: capsule about equalling the calyx, the body 4–5 mm. long. Everglades, S Fla.— Spr.–fall.

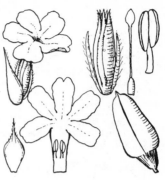

2. T. carolinensis (Walt.) J. F. Gmel. Stem 2–5 dm. tall: basal leaves 5–20 cm. long; blades elliptic to spatulate: bracts ciliate: bractlets rather broad: calyx-lobes 8–9.5 mm. long, long-ciliate at the tip: corolla-lobes nearly as long as the tube: capsule often exserted at the tip, the body 5–7 mm. long. [*E. virgata* Michx.]—Low grounds, especially calcareous, Coastal Plain, Fla. to S. C.—Sum.

3. HYGROPHILA R. Br. Annual or perennial weak herbs. Flowers solitary or clustered in the axils. Calyx 5-lobed, the lobes nearly equal. Corolla mainly white, strongly 2-lipped. Stamens 4, didynamous. Capsule cylindric.—About 30 species, tropical.

1. H. lacustris (Schlecht.) Nees. Stem 3–9 dm. long: leaf-blades nearly linear or narrowly linear-lanceolate, 5–12 cm. long: calyx-lobes narrowly linear-subulate, 5–7 mm. long: corolla 7 mm. long: lobes of the lower lip ovate: capsule 7–8 mm. long.— Swamps and muddy banks, Coastal Plain, Fla. to Tex.— (*Mex.*) — Sum.–fall.—The score and a half species of this genus are all swamp or marsh inhabitants. The sole species in the continental United States inhabits the river-bottoms from western Florida to Texas. It reaches its greatest development in the lower Mississippi Delta.

4. DYSCHORISTE Nees. Herbs or woody plants: leaf-blades entire. Flowers solitary or clustered in the axils. Calyx-lobes 5, very slender. Corolla blue, purple, or rarely white, somewhat 2-lipped. Capsule 2–4-seeded. [*Calophanes* D. Don.]—About 30 species widely distributed in warm and tropical regions.

Calyx-lobes nearly as long as the corolla; corollas and the bractlets about equal in
  length.   1. *D. humistrata.*
Calyx-lobes less than ½ as long as the corolla; which is fully
  twice as long as the bractlets.
    Corolla 1 cm. long or shorter: leaf-blades of a linear type. 2. *D. angusta.*
    Corolla fully 2 cm. long: leaf-blades mainly of an elliptic
      type.   3. *D. oblongifolia.*

1. D. humistrata (Michx.) Kuntze. Stem 1–4 dm. long: leaves few; blades 2–3 cm. long, elliptic to elliptic-ovate: calyx puberulent; lobes subulate-seta-

ceous from a lanceolate base, 6–8 mm. long:
corolla about 1 cm. long; limb about 10 mm.
wide: capsule 8–10 mm. long.—River-
swamps, Coastal Plain, Fla. and Ga.—Spr.

2. D. angusta (A. Gray) Small. Stem
1–2 dm. tall: leaves numerous; blades 1–2.5
cm. long, spatulate below to linear-elliptic
or linear above: calyx-lobes linear-subulate,
9–11 mm. long: corolla limb about 10 mm.
wide: capsule 7–8 mm. long.—Pinelands and
open sandy hammocks, S Fla.—All year.

3. D. oblongifolia (Michx.) Kuntze. Stem
1–3 dm. tall: leaves few; blades 1–3 cm.
long, obovate to cuneate below, elliptic
above: calyx-lobes 12–15 mm. long: corolla-limb 15 mm. wide: capsule 10–13
mm. long.—Sandhills and pinelands, Coastal Plain, Fla. to Va.—Spr.–fall.

5. RUELLIA [Plum.] L.   Caulescent herbs.   Leaf-blades entire or
toothed.   Flowers axillary or sometimes in terminal clusters.   Calyx 5-lobed,
the lobes narrow.   Corolla nearly regular.   Capsule 6–20 seeded.—About 200
species, mostly tropical American.

Flowers or flower-clusters sessile or essentially so.   I. PARVIFLORAE.
Flowers or flower-clusters peduncled.   II. PEDUNCULATAE.

I. PARVIFLORAE
Calyx-lobes linear-filiform or with filiform tips, longer than the capsule.
  Corolla 4–6 cm. long.
    Stem less than 1 dm. tall.   1. *R. humilis.*
    Stem over 2 dm. tall.
      Leaf-blades sessile or essentially so.   2. *R. ciliosa.*
      Leaf-blades manifestly petioled.
        Plant green or purple-tinged: leaf-blades not
          conspicuously veined beneath.
            Leaf-blades thick: stem succulent, fistulose. 3. *R. succulenta.*
            Leaf-blades thin: stem woody, not fistulose. 4. *R. parviflora.*
        Plant grayish-pubescent: leaf-blades prominently
          veined beneath.   5. *R. hybrida.*
  Corolla 7–10 cm. long.   6. *R. noctiflora.*
Calyx-lobes linear-lanceolate or broadly linear, scarcely longer
  than the capsule.   7. *R. strepens.*
II. PEDUNCULATAE
Erect gregarious plant with narrow leaf-blades.   8. *R. malacosperma.*

1. R. humilis Nutt. Stem 1–3 cm. tall, hirsute or villous-hirsute, or almost
wanting: leaf-blades spatulate to elliptic or oval, 3–10 cm. long: calyx hirsute;
lobes linear-subulate, 15–20 mm. long: co-
rolla blue or nearly white, 4–5 cm. long;
tube 1–2 mm. thick: capsule 15–17 mm.
long.—Sandy soil, Coastal Plain, Fla. to
Miss. and Ga.—Spr.–fall.

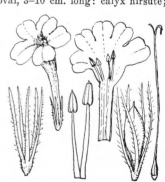

2. R. ciliosa Pursh. Stem 2–6 dm. tall,
hirsute: leaf-blades oval, ovate, or elliptic,
2–5 cm. long: calyx hirsute; lobes filiform-
subulate, 15–20 mm. long: corolla blue, 5–7
cm. long: tube 1–2 mm. thick: capsule 10–
15 mm. long.—Dry soil, various provinces,
Fla. to Tex., Kans., Mich., and N. J.—Spr.–
fall.

3. R. succulenta Small. Stem 1.5–5 dm.
tall, inconspicuously puberulent: leaf-blades

narrowly elliptic to spatulate, 2.5–4.5 cm. long; calyx sparingly ciliate or glabrous; lobes linear-filiform, 13–16 mm. long: corolla deep purplish-blue, about 4 cm. long.—Everglades, Fla.—All year.

4. R. parviflora (Nees) Britton. Stem 2–6 dm. tall, sparingly pubescent but green: leaf-blades elliptic to elliptic-lanceolate, 3–10 cm. long: calyx hirsute; lobes linear-filiform, 15–20 mm. long: corolla blue, 4–5 cm. long; tube 1.5–2 mm. thick: capsule barely 15 mm. long.—Sandy soil, Coastal Plain and adj. provinces, Fla. to Tex., Ind., and N. J.—Spr.–fall.

5. R. hybrida Pursh. Stem 2–6 dm. long, often diffusely spreading, grayish pubescent: leaf-blades elliptic to elliptic-lanceolate, 3–10 cm. long: calyx hirsute; lobes linear-filiform, 15–20 mm. long: corolla light-blue, 4–5 cm. long: capsule 10–16 mm. long.—Pinelands, Fla.—Spr.–sum.

6. R. noctiflora (Nees) A. Gray. Stem 1–3 dm. tall, minutely pubescent: leaf-blades elliptic, sometimes narrowly so or elliptic-lanceolate, 4–7 cm. long: calyx softly pubescent; lobes linear-filiform, 25–35 mm. long: corolla blue or nearly white, about 9 cm. long; tube about 2 mm. thick: capsule about 25 mm. long.—Pinelands, Coastal Plain, Fla. to Miss. and Ga.—Spr.–sum.

7. R. strepens L. Stem 2–12 dm. tall, glabrous or finely pubescent; leaf-blades ovate to elliptic, 5–15 cm. long: corolla blue or nearly white, 5–6 cm. long: capsule 10–15 mm. long.—Dry soil, often calcareous, various provinces, Fla. to Tex., Wisc., and Pa.—Spr.–sum.

8. R. malacosperma Greenm. Stem up to 1 m. tall, glabrous in age: leaf-blades linear-elliptic or linear-spatulate on the lower part of the stem, elongate-linear and attenuate above, mostly 1–2 dm. long: flowers in open cymes: calyx sparingly pubescent; lobes linear-subulate, about 1 cm. long: corolla bluish-purple, 3.5–4 cm. long; tube about 1 cm. long, shorter than the throat: capsule about 2.5 cm. long.—Roadsides, cult. grounds, and ditch-banks, Coastal Plain, Fla. to La. Nat. of C. A. and cult.—Spr.–fall.

Blechnum Blechnum (L.) Millsp., with conspicuously bracted epike-like panicles, has been found in Fla.; it is a native of S. A.

6. GERARDIA L. Mostly scapose herbs. Leaves mainly basal. Flowers in terminal spikes. Calyx-lobes 5, nearly equal. Corolla with slightly unequal broad spreading lobes. [*Stenandrium* Nees.]— About 25 species, of tropical America.

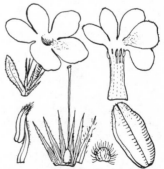

1. G. floridana (A. Gray) Small. Plant 2–6 cm. tall: leaf-blades ovate to elliptic or oval, 2–3 cm. long: calyx-lobes linear-subulate, becoming 9–11 mm. long: corolla rose-purple, 16–20 mm. long: capsule 9–12 mm. long. [*S. floridanum* (A. Gray) Small.]— Pinelands, S pen. Fla.—All year.—The genus-name *Gerardia* has long been mistakenly applied to certain groups of the Figwort Family.

7. DIAPEDIUM Konig. Annual or usually perennial herbs. Leaf-blades entire. Flowers in conspicuously bracted spikes. Calyx 5-lobed, the lobes narrow, nearly equal. Corolla 2-lipped, the upper lip erect. Filaments elongate. Capsule with an ovoid or suborbicular body. [*Dicliptera* Juss.]— About 60 species of tropical and warm regions.

Corolla red or crimson, curved: tube longer than the lips.   1. *D. assurgens.*
Corolla purple or pink, nearly straight: tube and lips about
    equal in length.   2. *D. brachiatum.*

1. **D. assurgens** (L.) Kuntze. Plant 3–11 dm. tall, often diffuse: leaf-blades
ovate to elliptic or elliptic-lanceolate, 2–10 cm. long: calyx 3–4 mm. long; lobes
lanceolate: corolla crimson or red, 2–2.5 cm.
long: capsule 7–8 mm. long.—Hammocks,
S pen. Fla. and the Keys.—(*W. I., Mex., C.
A.*)—All year.

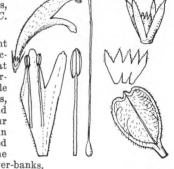

2. **D. brachiatum** (Pursh) Kuntze. Plant
3–8 dm. tall: leaf-blades ovate to elliptic-
ovate, 2–10 cm. long, acute or somewhat
acuminate: calyx 4–5 mm. long; lobes linear-
subulate: corolla 15–20 mm. long: capsule
about 5 mm. long.—River-banks and swamps,
Coastal Plain, Fla. to Tex., Kans, Mo., and
N. C.—Sum.-fall.—The two species in our
range are as distinct in their habitats as in
the color of their corollas. The first cited
species thrives in saline habitats, while the
second one inhabits fresh swamps and river-banks.

8. **YEATESIA** Small. Perennial herbs. Leaf-blades entire. Flowers
in conspicuously bracted spikes. Calyx 5-lobed, the lobes slender. Corolla
slightly 2-lipped: upper lip entire or nearly
so: lower lip 3-lobed. Capsule with an
ovoid body.—One species.

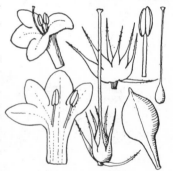

1. **Y. viridiflora** (Nees) Small. Plant 2–6
dm. tall: leaf-blades elliptic or elliptic-lanceolate, 5–15 cm. long: calyx 4–5 mm. long;
lobes slender: corolla white, pale-purple, or
pink, 12–15 mm. long: capsule about 1 cm.
long, the body longer than the stipe-like
base.   [*Dicliptera Halei* Ridd.]—Shaded
stream-banks, woods, and thickets, Coastal
Plain and adj. provinces, Fla. to Tex.,
Tenn., and Ga.—Sum.

9. **DIANTHERA** [Gronov.] L. Perennial herbs. Leaf-blades entire or
rarely toothed. Flowers in dense spikes on axillary peduncles. Calyx 4–5
lobed, the lobes narrow or slender. Corolla
2-lipped: upper lip slightly notched: lower
lip 3-lobed. Anther-sacs borne obliquely,
each at the tip of a fork of the connective.
Capsule mostly 4-seeded.—One species.

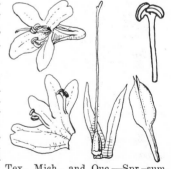

1. **D. americana** L. Stem 3–10 dm. tall:
leaf-blades linear to linear-lanceolate or narrowly elliptic, 5–15 cm. long: peduncles ascending, about as long as the leaves or
longer: spikes 1–3 cm. long, continuous:
calyx-lobes linear, 4–5 mm. long: corolla
white, pink, or purplish: capsule 1.5–2 cm.
long.—(WATER-WILLOW.)—Beds, shores, and
banks of streams, various provinces, Ga. to Tex., Mich., and Que.—Spr.–sum.

10. **JUSTICIA** L. Perennial herbs. Leaf-blades entire. Flowers in more or less interrupted spikes on axillary peduncles. Calyx 5-lobed, the lobes narrow. Corolla 2-lipped: upper lip notched: lower lip 3-lobed. Anther-sacs unequal, one borne oblique or horizontal at the top of the connective, the other perpendicular or nearly so below it. Capsule 4-seeded.—About 100 species, mostly tropical American.

Corolla 2–2.5 cm. long.   1. *J. crassifolia.*
Corolla 1 cm. long or shorter.
  Flowers scattered along one side of the upper part of the
    peduncle.
    Leaves remote, reflexed: corolla-tube 5–6 mm. long.   2. *J. angusta.*
    Leaves approximate, spreading or ascending: corolla-tube
      8–10 mm. long.   3. *J. lanceolata.*
  Flowers in head-like spikes terminating the peduncles, or
    approximate at the end.   4. *J. ovata.*

1. **J. crassifolia** Chapm. Stem 2–4 dm. tall: leaf-blades linear, usually narrowly so, or spatulate near the base of the stem, 3–15 cm. long, fleshy: calyx-lobes linear, 11–15 mm. long, acuminate: corolla bright-purple, 2–2.5 cm. long: capsule 2–2.5 cm. long.—Swamps, wet woods, and low pinelands, Fla.—Spr. or all year S.

2. **J. angusta** (Chapm.) Small. Stem 2–5 dm. tall: leaf-blades linear or narrowly linear-lanceolate, 2–7 cm. long, or elliptic-spatulate at the base of the stem, more or less reflexed: peduncles bearing 2–few flowers near the end: calyx-lobes linear, 5–7 mm. long: corolla pale-purple about 10 mm. long: capsule about 1.2 cm. long.—Pineland ponds, Fla.—Spr.

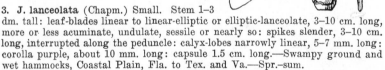

3. **J. lanceolata** (Chapm.) Small. Stem 1–3 dm. tall: leaf-blades linear to linear-elliptic or elliptic-lanceolate, 3–10 cm. long, more or less acuminate, undulate, sessile or nearly so: spikes slender, 3–10 cm. long, interrupted along the peduncle: calyx-lobes narrowly linear, 5–7 mm. long: corolla purple, about 10 mm. long: capsule 1.5 cm. long.—Swampy ground and wet hammocks, Coastal Plain, Fla. to Tex. and Va.—Spr.–sum.

4. **J. ovata** Walt. Stem 1–3 dm. tall: leaf-blades elliptic, 3–11 cm. long; spike long-peduncled, 1–2 cm. long, continuous: calyx-lobes narrowly linear-acuminate, 6–12 mm. long: corolla pale-purple to violet, about 10 mm. long: capsule about 1 cm. long.—About pineland ponds, Coastal Plain, Fla. to Tex. and Va.—Spr.–sum.

Family 16. **PINGUICULACEAE**[1] — Bladderwort Family

Herbs, growing in water or in wet places. Leaves submersed and dissected, sometimes resembling rootlets and often bladder-bearing, or aerial and entire, or rarely wanting. Scapes naked or minutely scaly, 1–many-flowered. Flowers irregular, perfect. Calyx 2–5-lobed, the lobes often nearly distinct. Corolla 2-lipped: tube spurred or saccate. Androecium of 2 stamens, adnate to the base of the corolla-tube on its upper side. Filaments flattened, twisted. Anthers 1-celled. Gynoecium a single 1-celled pistil, with a free-central, usually globose placenta. Style thick, very short. Ovules usually numerous but sometimes only two. Fruit a

[1] Contributed by John Hendley Barnhart.

capsule, 2-valved or irregularly dehiscent. Seeds numerous (in *Biovularia* only one).

Calyx-lobes 5 : scape without bracts, always 1-flowered.   1. PINGUICULA.
Calyx-lobes 2 : scape with 1 or more bracts, 1-many-flowered.
   Calyx with a pair of bractlets resembling exterior lobes :
      scales, bracts, bractlets, and calyx-lobes fimbriate.   2. ARANELLA.
   Calyx without bractlets ; lobes not fimbriate.
      Pedicels each with a bract and 2 bractlets at base.
         Racemes spike-like, the pedicels rarely exceeding the
            bracts : bractlets free.   3. STOMOISIA.
         Racemes not spike-like, the pedicels longer, commonly
            many times longer than the bracts : bractlets more
            or less adnate to the bracts.   4. CALPIDISCA.
      Pedicels each with a bract at base, but no bractlets.
         Branches, if any, alternate : lateral lobes (if any) of
            lower corolla-lip not saccate.
            Bracts peltate.   5. SETISCAPELLA.
            Bracts not peltate, attached by the base.
               Bracts tubular, solitary : corollas purple.   6. LECTICULA.
               Bracts not tubular, 1 or more : corollas yellow.
                  Scape below lowest bract well developed,
                    with several scales ; ovules and seeds
                    numerous.   7. UTRICULARIA.
                  Scape below lowest bract obsolete ; ovules
                    2 ; seed 1.   8. BIOVULARIA.
         Branches and branchlets whorled : lateral lobes of
            lower corolla-lip saccate.   9. VESICULINA.

1. **PINGUICULA** [Tourn.] L. Terrestrial scapose herbs. Leaves in a basal rosette: blades flat. Scapes usually several, 1-flowered, without scales or bracts. Calyx-lobes 5, more or less united. Corolla spurred at the base, the palate (in ours) subulate or clavate, included in the tube.—About 35 species, widely distributed.—BUTTERWORTS.

Corolla, including spur, less than 2 cm. long.   1. *P. pumila.*
Corolla, including spur, 2 cm. long, or longer.
   Spur slender : plant glandular-pubescent.
      Corolla golden-yellow : scape not villous.   2. *P. lutea.*
      Corolla violet : scape villous toward the base.   3. *P. caerulea.*
   Spur short and sac-like : plant almost wholly glabrous.   4. *P. planifolia.*

1. **P. pumila** Michx. Leaves 1–2.5 cm. long, clammy-pubescent: scapes very slender, 5–20 cm. tall: corolla white, pale violet, or pale rose, very rarely yellow, 1–2 cm. broad; spur subulate, about 3 mm. long, longer than the sac-like base of the corolla.—Low pinelands. Coastal Plain, Fla. to Tex. and S. C.—(*W. I.*)—Spr. or all year S.

2. **P. lutea** Walt. Leaves 1.5–6 cm. long, clammy-pubescent; scapes 1–3 dm. tall, pubescent: corolla golden-yellow, 2–3.5 cm. broad; lobes longer than the tube, usually obtusely 2–4-lobed; spur subulate or subcylindric, 5–10 mm. long.—Low pinelands, Coastal Plain, Fla. to La. and N. C.—Spr.

3. **P. caerulea** Walt. Leaves 1.5–6 cm. long, clammy-pubescent; scapes 1–3 dm. tall, pubescent, villous at the base; corolla violet, 2–2.5 cm. broad, the lobes obtusely 2-cleft; spur slender, subcylindric, 4–8 mm. long, obtuse. [*P. elatior* Michx.] —Low pinelands, Coastal Plain, Fla. to N. C.—Spr.

4. **P. planifolia** Chapm. Leaves 1.5–8 cm. long, glabrous or nearly so: scapes 1–3.5 dm. tall, nearly glabrous, not villous at the base: corolla violet, 1–2 cm.

broad, the lobes usually acutely 2-cleft; spur rather sac-like, only 1–3 mm. long, obtuse.—Shallow water, near the Gulf coast, Fla. to Miss.—Spr.

2. **ARANELLA** Barnh. Terrestrial herbs. Leaves in a basal rosette, often fugacious. Scapes 1–several-flowered: scales below the lowest pedicel numerous, peltate, fimbriate: bracts fimbriate: bractlets above the base of the very short pedicels, mimicking exterior calyx-lobes, fimbriate. Calyx-lobes 2, nearly distinct, fimbriate. Corolla 2-lipped. [*Cosmiza* Small, not Raf.]—Three or 4 species, tropical American.

1. **A. fimbriata** (H.B.K.) Barnh. Leaves linear, 5–6 mm. long: scapes 5–15 cm. tall: racemes 1–7-flowered, spike-like or subcapitate: corolla yellow, 6–8 mm. broad; spur subconic, about as long as the lower lip. [*Cosmiza longeciliata* Small.]—Low pinelands, especially along the Everglades, pen. Fla.—(*W. I., S. A.*)—All year.

3. **STOMOISIA** Raf. Terrestrial herbs. Stems delicate, root-like. Leaves delicate, rarely seen: blades linear. Bladders minute, beaked but without bristles. Scapes 1–many-flowered: scales below the lowest pedicel several, attached by the base: bracts each accompanied by a pair of bractlets. Calyx-lobes 2, nearly distinct. Corolla 2-lipped, the lips nearly distinct, the upper one clawed, the lower consisting chiefly of the helmet-shaped, laterally compressed palate.—About 50 species, widely distributed.

Corolla much exceeding the calyx.
    Lower lip of corolla 1.2 cm. long or more; spur about 12 mm. long.
                                                1. *S. cornuta.*
    Lower lip of corolla 1 cm. long or less; spur about 6 mm. long.   2. *S. juncea.*
Corolla about as long as the calyx, or shorter.   3. *S. virgatula.*

1. **S. cornuta** (Michx.) Raf. Scape rooting in mud, erect, 1–3 dm. tall: racemes spike-like, 2–5-flowered, the flowers approximate: corolla yellow, 1.2–1.6 cm. broad: lower lip much larger than the upper, abruptly pointed; spur horn-shaped, acute, slightly curved, pendent, 7–12 mm. long. [*Utricularia cornuta* Michx.]—Margins of ponds, various provinces, Fla. to Tex., Minn., and Newf.—(*W. I.*)—Sum.-fall.

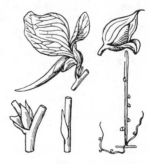

2. **S. juncea** (Vahl.) Barnh. Scape rooting in mud, erect, 1–4 dm. tall: racemes spike-like, 3–12-flowered: corolla yellow, 0.8–1 cm. broad; lower lip larger than the upper, rather pointed; spur horn-shaped, acute, slightly curved, pendent, 5–7 mm. long. [*Utricularia juncea* Vahl.]—Margins of ponds, Coastal Plain and rarely adj. provinces, Fla. to Miss. and N. Y.—(*W. I., S. A.*)—Sum.-fall.

3. S. virgatula Barnh. Scape rooting in mud, erect, 0.3–2 dm. tall: racemes spike-like, 1–6-flowered: corolla yellow, 4 mm. broad, little if at all surpassing the calyx; spur conic, pendent, 2–3 mm. long. [*Utricularia simplex* Wright.] —Margins of ponds, Coastal Plain, Fla. to Miss. and N. Y.—(*W. I.*)—Fall.

4. CALPIDISCA Barnh. Terrestrial herbs. Leaves in a basal rosette, often fugacious. Scapes 1–several-flowered: scales below the lowest pedicel several, acute: bracts each accompanied by a pair of bractlets more or less adnate to it, making an apparently 3-lobed bract. Calyx-lobes 2, nearly distinct. Corolla 2-lipped, the lower lip abruptly reflexed from the aperture of the spur.—About 60 species, mostly tropical.

1. C. Standleyae Barnh. Leaves 1–6, subspatulate, 3–5 mm. long: scapes filiform, 1.5–15 cm. tall: racemes 1–6-flowered: pedicels filiform, ascending, 1.5–11 mm. long: corolla probably pale-purple; upper lip entire, 3 mm. long; spur compressed-conic, 4–5 mm. long, longer than the lower lip.—Low pinelands, pen. Fla.—Fall.

5. SETISCAPELLA Barnh. Terrestrial herbs, with short root-like branches from the base of the scape. Leaves delicate, evanescent and rarely seen: blades linear. Bladders minute, 2-horned. Scapes 1–many-flowered: scales below the lowest pedicel scarious, peltate: bracts scarious, peltate: bractlets none. Calyx-lobes 2, nearly distinct, scarious, ribbed. Corolla 2-lipped, the lower lip commonly stiff, divergently 3-lobed, with a 2-lobed palate.—About 12 species, mostly American.—Spr.–sum. or all year S.

Corolla yellow, 6–12 mm. long: capsule 2 mm. in diameter. 1. *S. subulata*.
Corolla white or purplish, subglobose, about 1 mm. in diameter:
   capsule 1 mm. in diameter. 2. *S. cleistogama*.

1. S. subulata (L.) Barnh. Scape rooting in mud, filiform, 3–20 cm. tall: racemes 1–12-flowered: rachis becoming zigzag when well-developed: pedicels ascending, 2–10 mm. long, surpassing the bracts: calyx becoming 2 mm. long: corolla yellow, 6–12 mm. long, 4–8 mm. broad, the lower lip much larger than the upper one, equally 3-lobed; spur flattened-conic, obtuse, appressed, nearly as long as the lower lip: capsule 2 mm. in diameter. [*Utricularia subulata* L.]—Wet sandy soil, Coastal Plain and New England coast, Fla. to Tex. and Mass.—Sum.

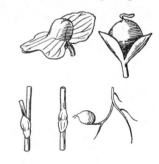

2. S. cleistogama (A. Gray) Barnh. Scape rooting in mud, filiform, stiff, 1–6 cm. tall: racemes 1–3-flowered: pedicels ascending 2–6 mm. long, surpassing the bracts: corolla dirty-white or purplish, not more than 1 mm. in diameter, consisting chiefly of the large saccate spur, the tips minute: capsule 1 mm. in diameter.—Wet sandy soil, Coastal Plain and New England coast, Fla. to Miss. and Mass.—(*Cuba.*)

6. LECTICULA Barnh. Herbs. Stems radiating from the base of the scape, usually submerged. Leaves alternate, usually 3-parted, the segments linear. Scapes 1-flowered, the pedicel continuous with the scape: bract tubular, the free margin truncate, notched: bractlets none. Calyx-lobes 2, nearly distinct. Corolla transverse at the summit of the scape, 2-lipped, the palate a mere convexity.—Two species, the following and one in South America.

1. L. resupinata (B. D. Greene) Barnh. Stem short, root-like: leaves scattered; blades simple or forked near the base, the segments slender, capillary, often bladder-bearing: scape erect, 2-10 cm. tall: calyx 1.5-2 mm. long: corolla violet-purple, 8-12 mm. long; spur conic. obtuse, distant from the lower lip. [*Utricularia resupinata* B. D. Greene.]—Shallow water, various provinces, Fla. to Ont. and N. B.—Fall.

7. UTRICULARIA L. Aquatic herbs. Stems submersed, the branches alternate or from the base of the scapes. Leaves alternate, dissected. Bladders borne on the leaf-segments, the mouth with a pair of bristles. Scapes 1–many-flowered: scales below the lowest pedicel several: bractlets none. Calyxlobes 2, nearly distinct. Corolla 2-lipped: lower lip flat, spreading, with a prominent 2-lobed palate.—About 75 species, very widely distributed.—BLADDERWORTS.

Scape without floats.
  Stem creeping on the bottom in shallow water: some or all of the leaves root-like.
    Spur slender, equalling or exceeding the lower lip.
      Spur conic at base, linear above: leaves not all bladder-bearing: scapes 10–40 cm. tall.   1. *U. fibrosa.*
      Spur tapering from base to apex: leaves all alike, bladder-bearing: scapes 5–12 cm. tall.   2. *U. pumila.*
    Spur stout, conic, shorter than the lower lip.   3. *U. gibba.*
  Stem free-floating, except for the single point of attachment.
    Corolla 12–15 mm. broad: leaves forked, each fork twice or thrice dissected.
      Scapes erect: pedicels recurving at maturity: capsule 3–4 mm. in diameter.   4. *U. macrorhiza.*
      Scapes flexuous: pedicels straight at maturity: capsule 5 mm. in diameter.   5. *U. floridana.*
    Corolla 15–20 mm. broad: leaves forked, each fork 4–5 times dissected: pedicels recurving at maturity: capsule 5 mm. in diameter.   6. *U. foliosa.*
Scape with a whorl of conspicuous, inflated, more or less united floats.
  Scape from floats to lowest pedicel 5 cm. long or less.   7. *U. radiata.*
  Scape from floats to lowest pedicel 7.5 cm. long or more.   8. *U. inflata.*

1. U. fibrosa Walt. Stems radiating from the base of the scape or scapes, often 1–2 dm. long and free-swimming at the tip: leaves numerous; blades 2–3-

dichotomously dissected, or the bladder-bearing ones much reduced: scapes 1–4 dm. tall:
raceme 2–6-flowered, usually 3-flowered:
pedicels ascending, 5–20 mm. long: corolla
yellow, about 15 mm. broad; spur conic at
base, linear above, appressed, about as long
as the lower lip, obtuse or emarginate at the
apex.—Ponds, chiefly in pinelands, Coastal
Plain, Fla. to Miss., (La.?) and N. Y.—
Spr.–fall.

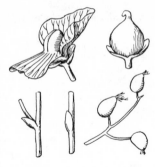

2. **U. pumila** Walt. Stems radiating from
the base of the scape or scapes, short, root-
like: leaves few; blades mostly bladder-
bearing and much reduced: scapes 5–12 cm.
tall: raceme 1–4-flowered, usually 2-flow-
ered: pedicels ascending, 5–16 cm. long: corolla yellow, about 12 mm. broad;
spur slenderly conic, appressed, usually longer than the lower lip, obtuse or
emarginate at the apex. [*U. biflora* Lam. *U. macrorhyncha* Barnh.]—Shallow water, mostly Coastal Plain, and New England coast, Fla. to La. and Mass.
—Spr.–fall.

3. **U. gibba** L. Stems radiating from the base of the scape or scapes, several
cm. long, delicate, root-like: leaves scattered, sparingly divided; segments
capillary, with few minute bladders: scapes 2–10 cm. tall: raceme 1–3-flowered,
usually 2-flowered: pedicels very slender, erect or ascending, 2–10 mm. long:
corolla yellow, 5–8 mm. broad; spur conic, very obtuse, shorter than the lower
lip.—Shallow water, various provinces, Fla. to Tex., Mich., and Me.—Spr.–
fall or all year S.

4. **U. macrorhiza** Le Conte. Stems submersed, leafy, 3–10 dm. long: leaves
numerous, alternate, 1.5–5 cm. long: blades forked, each fork 2–3-pinnately
dissected into filiform segments, usually bearing numerous bladders; bladders
when fully developed 3–5 mm. long: scapes erect, 1–3 dm. tall: raceme 5–20-
flowered: pedicels 0.5–2 cm. long, recurving at maturity: corolla yellow, 12–15
mm. broad, the lower lip slightly 3-lobed; spur not appressed, subulate, slightly
curved, shorter than the lower lip: capsule 3–4 mm. in diameter, many-seeded.
[*U. vulgaris americana* A. Gray.]—In water, various provinces, (N. C.?), Va.
to Tex., Mo., Yukon, and Newf.—Sum.

5. **U. floridana** Nash. Stems submersed, leafy, 6–15 dm. long: leaves numerous, alternate, 3–5 cm. long; blades forked, each fork 2–3-pinnately dissected
into very delicate capillary segments, the segments fewer, shorter, and stiffer
when bladder-bearing; bladders 2 mm. long or less: scapes more or less flexuous,
1.5 dm. tall when the first flower expands, becoming 3–6 dm. tall: raceme very
laxly 8–25-flowered: pedicels 0.5–1.5 cm. long, ascending or spreading at
maturity: corolla yellow, 12–15 mm. broad, both lips nearly entire: spur not
appressed, subulate, slightly curved, shorter than the lower lip: capsule about
5 mm. in diameter.—Ponds, Coastal Plain, Fla. and Ga.—Spr.–sum.

6. **U. foliosa** L. Stems submersed, leafy, 9–30 dm. long: leaves numerous,
alternate, 3–10 cm. long; blades forked, each fork 4–5-pinnately dissected into
very fine or capillary segments, the segments fewer when the bladders are more
numerous: bladders 2 mm. long or less: scapes erect, 1–3 dm. tall: raceme
rather closely 10–20-flowered: pedicels 1–2 cm. long, recurving at maturity:
calyx becoming 4–5 mm. long: corolla yellow, 15–20 mm. broad, the upper
lip erect, nearly entire, the lower lip spreading, slightly 3-lobed; spur not appressed, slenderly conic, slightly curved, shorter than the lower lip: capsule
about 5 mm. in diameter, few-seeded. [*U. oligosperma* St. Hil.]—Ponds and
brackish water, Coastal Plain, Fla. to La.—(W. I.)—Spr.–fall or all year S.

7. U. radiata Small. Stems elongate: leaves 6–10-dichotomously dissected, copiously bladder-bearing: scapes erect, 6–12 cm. tall, bearing near the middle a single whorl of 4–7 conspicuous inflated floats, which are more or less confluent at the base, less than 4 cm. long, and pinnately dissected near the tip: raceme 1–3-flowered: pedicels 8–20 mm. long, spreading or recurved in fruit: corolla yellow, about 1.5 cm. broad, the lower lip 3-lobed, about twice as long as the appressed conic emarginate spur.—Ponds, Coastal Plain and New England coast, Fla. to Tex. and Me.—Spr.–fall.

8. U. inflata Walt. Stems submersed, often stout, elongate: leaves 10–12-dichotomously dissected, copiously bladder-bearing: scapes erect, 2–6 dm. tall, bearing a whorl of 4–9 conspicuous inflated bracts, which are more or less confluent at the base, 5–7 cm. long, and pinnately dissected from near the middle: raceme 4–12-flowered: pedicels 16–32 mm. long, spreading or recurved in fruit: corolla yellow, about 2 cm. broad, the lower lip 3-lobed, about twice as long as the appressed conic emarginate spur.—Ponds and ditches, Coastal Plain, Fla. to Del.—Spr.–fall.

8. BIOVULARIA Kam. Minute aquatic herbs. Stems submerged. Leaves alternate, dissected. Bladders borne on the leaf-segments, the mouth 2-beaked. Scapes 1–3-flowered, the part below lowest bract obsolete, the lowest bract hence sessile on the main stem; bractlets none. Calyx-lobes 2, nearly distinct. Corolla 2-lipped, the lips entire, the palate not prominent. Ovules only 2. Fruit indehiscent, with a single seed.—One species, in tropical and subtropical America.

1. B. olivacea (Wright) Kam. Stems delicate, capillary, forming mats on or a little beneath the surface of the water: leaves mostly of a single ségment, bearing one bladder; scape scarcely any, the bracts and pedicels, if more than one, approximate at its base; longest pedicel less than 1 cm. long; calyx about 0.5 mm. long; corolla yellowish, less than 2 mm. long: spur saccate. [*Utricularia olivacea* Wright.]—Shallow water, near Sanford, Seminole Co., Fla.—(*W. I., S. A.*) One of the smallest (perhaps the smallest by weight) of all flowering plants.

9. VESICULINA Raf. Aquatic herbs. Stems submersed, the branches whorled, decompound. Leaves none. Bladders terminal, the mouth (in ours) naked. Scapes 1–4-flowered: scales below the lowest pedicel none: bractlets none. Calyx-lobes 2, nearly distinct. Corolla 2-lipped: lower lip 3-lobed, the lateral lobes saccate, forming together a prominent divergently 2-lobed palate, the middle lobe short.—About 6 species, American.

1. V. purpurea (Walt.) Raf. Stems elongate, the branches numerous, whorled, verticillately decompound: bladders solitary, terminating many of the ultimate branchlets, the orifices without projecting processes: scapes erect, slender, spongy-

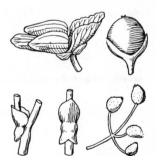

thickened below, 0.5–1.5 dm. tall: pedicels erect or ascending: calyx becoming 2.5–3 mm. long: corolla violet-purple, 12 mm. broad; spur conic, somewhat flattened, about ½ as long as the lower lip. [*Utricularia purpurea* Walt.]— Ponds, various provinces, Fla. to La., Minn., Ont., and Me.—(*W. I.*)—Sum.–fall.

Family 17. **OROBANCHACEAE** — Broom-rape Family

Parasitic, commonly perennial herbs, without green coloring matter. Leaves alternate, scale-like. Flowers perfect, or rarely dioecious, sometimes cleistogamous and complete on the same plant. Calyx of 4 or 5 partly united sepals, sometimes spathe-like. Corolla of 4 or 5 partially united petals, the limb irregular or 2-lipped. Androecium of 4 didynamous stamens partially adnate to the corolla. Gynoecium of 2, or rarely of 3, united carpels. Ovary 1-celled. Ovules mostly numerous. Fruit a capsule. Seeds wingless.—About 11 genera and more than 200 species, most abundant in the Northern Hemisphere.

Flowers perfect and complete throughout.
    Calyx irregular, spathe-like, the lower side split, the upper with 3 or 4 tooth-
      like lobes : stamens exserted.   1. Conopholis.
    Calyx regular or nearly so, with 2–5 equal or unequal lobes :
      stamens included.
      Calyx with a deep sinus above and below.   2. Orobanche.
      Calyx nearly equally 5-lobed.   3. Thalesia.
Flowers various, cleistogamous on lower part of spike, complete
    but mostly sterile above.   4. Leptamnium.

1. CONOPHOLIS Wallr. Yellow or brownish herbs, with very stout stems and inflorescence. Leaves numerous. Flowers sessile, yellowish, crowded in the spike.— Three species, North American.

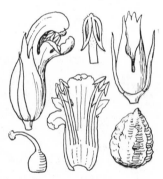

1. C. americana (L. f.) Wallr. Plant clustered, 1–2 dm. tall: leaves (scales) ovate to lanceolate, 10–12 mm. long: calyx 7–9 mm. long, erose-toothed: corolla yellowish or pale-yellow, 10–12 mm. long: capsule ovoid, 10–15 mm. long. — (Squaw-root. Cancer-roots.)—Rich woods, various provinces, Fla. to Mich. and Me.—Spr.—The squaw-root frequently grows in oak-woods. The young plant resembles a fir or spruce cone. It is pale, often creamy when young, but soon becomes brown.

2. OROBANCHE L. Whitish, yellowish, reddish, or violet herbs, with relatively slender stems. Leaves few. Flowers sessile, in a spike.—About 85 species, natives of the Old World.

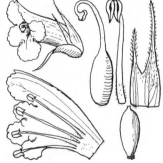

1. O. minor J. E. Smith. Plant 1–5 dm. tall: leaves (scales) ovate to lanceolate, 6–20 mm. long: calyx about 10 mm. long; lobes lanceolate-subulate: corolla 11–15 mm. long; lips bluish, the lobes erose: filaments pubescent: capsule about 8 mm. long.—(Broom-rape.)—Fields, various provinces N. C. to N. J. Nat. of Eu.—Spr.–sum.—Usually parasitic on clover roots. *Orobanche* is the most wide-spread genus of this family. The plants of some species are restricted to a single host, while others are not particularly selective. Different hosts seem to influence variations in the parasite, a fact that may have led to too much multiplication of species.

3. **THALESIA** Raf. Pale, often pink herbs, with short, mostly subterranean stems. Leaves few. Flowers solitary on long pedicels, often more deeply colored than the foliage.—About 5 species, North American.

1. **T. uniflora** (L.) Britton. Plant 5–16 cm. tall: leaves (scales) ovate to obovate, 5–10 mm. long: calyx 4–11 mm. long; lobes lanceolate, about as long as the tube: corolla cream-colored and purple-tinged, 14–18 mm. long; lobes elliptic to obovate: capsule conicovoid, about 10 mm. long. [*Aphyllon uniflorum* T. & G.]—(BROOM-RAPE. CANCERROOT.)—Rich woods, various provinces, rarely Coastal Plain, Ga. to Tex., Calif., B. C., Ont., and Newf.—Spr.

4. **LEPTAMNIUM** Raf. Dark-purplish or yellowish-brown herbs, with branching stems. Leaves very few. Flowers racemose or paniculate, paler than the stem, separated.—One species.

1. **L. virginianum** (L.) Raf. Plant 1–4 dm. tall: leaves (scales) few at the base of the plant: complete flowers larger than the cleistogamous ones: calyx 2.5–3 mm. long; lobes triangular to ovate-triangular, shorter than the tube: corolla 10–13 mm. long; upper lip notched; lobes of the lower lip acute: capsule 3–5 mm. long. [*Epiphegus virginiana* Bart.]—(BEECH-DROPS. CANCERROOT.)—Under beech trees, various provinces, Fla. to La., Mich., and N. B.—Spr.

FAMILY 18. **BIGNONIACEAE** — TRUMPET-CREEPER FAMILY

Shrubs, trees, woody vines, or rarely herbs. Leaves opposite, or rarely alternate or whorled, often tendril-bearing: blades simple or pinnately compound. Flowers perfect, usually showy. Calyx of usually 2–5 more or less united sepals. Corolla 5-lobed, irregular, or 2-lipped. Androecium of 5 stamens with 1 or 3 of them reduced to staminodia, or of 4 didynamous stamens. Anthers with mostly divaricate sacs. Gynoecium of 2 united carpels. Ovary 1-celled or 2-celled by the meeting of the placentae. Ovules numerous. Fruit a capsule. Seeds winged or appendaged.—About 60 genera and more than 500 species, mostly tropical.

Leaf-blades compound: vines or rarely herbaceous plants: calyx 5-lobed.
  Calyx with an undulate margin: capsule flattened parallel with its partition.
                                                        1. ANISOSTICHUS.
  Calyx with 5 lobes: capsule flattened at right angles with its partition.

Erect plant: pod linear, not stipitate.   2. TECOMA.
Climbing plant: pod clavate or fusiform, stipitate.   3. BIGNONIA.
Leaf-blades simple: shrubs or trees: calyx 2-lobed.
   Anther-bearing stamens 2: leaves opposite: fruit slender,
     dehiscent.   4. CATALPA.
   Anther-bearing stamens 4: leaves alternate or scattered:
     fruit thick, roundish, indehiscent.
     Leaves clustered on spurs; blades of a spatulate or ob-
      lanceolate type: fruit rounded at the apex, with fleshy
      placentae.   5. CRESCENTIA.
     Leaves alternate; blades of a broad type: fruit umbonate
      at the apex, with dry placentae.   6. ENALLAGMA.

1. **ANISOSTICHUS** Bureau. Vines. Leaf-blades 2-foliolate or rarely 1-foliolate, often tendril-bearing: leaflets usually with entire blades. Calyx campanulate or cupulate. Corolla with a short tube abruptly expanded into a campanulate throat. Capsule narrow. Seeds winged.—One species.

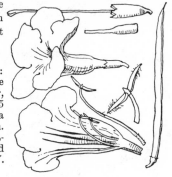

1. **A. crucigera** (L.) Bureau. Glabrous vine: leaves prolonged into tendrils; leaflets mostly 2; blades elliptic to elliptic-lanceolate, 5-15 cm. long, cordate or auricled at the base: calyx 5-8 mm. long, shallowly lobed: corolla red-orange without, yellow within, 4-5 cm. long: filaments villous at the base: capsule linear, 10-17 cm. long. [*Bignonia capreolata* L.]—(CROSS-VINE. TRUMPET-FLOWER.)—Swamps, stream-banks, thickets, and woods, Coastal Plain and adj. provinces, Fla. to La., Ill., and Va. (or Md.?)—Spr.—Also called smoke vine, as sections of the stems which show a strikingly cross-shaped pith, are smoked as cigars.

2. **TECOMA** Juss. Shrubs or partly herbaceous plants. Leaf-blades unequally pinnate. Flowers clustered. Calyx tubular-campanulate, nearly equally 5-lobed. Corolla with the tube gradually enlarged into the funnelform throat. Seeds membranous-winged.—About 10 species, mostly tropical American.

1. **T. stans** (L.) Juss. Plant 1-8 m. tall: leaves 1-2.5 dm. long; leaflets 7-13, the blades lanceolate to elliptic, or narrower, 4-10 cm. long, coarsely serrate: calyx 3-5 mm. long; lobes often triangular: corolla yellow, 3.5-4.5 cm. long: capsule 10-20 cm. long.—(YELLOW TRUMPET-FLOWER. YELLOW-ELDER.) — Hammocks, woods, and thickets, Coastal Plain, Fla. to Tex.—(*W. I., Mex., C. A., S. A.*).—All year.

3. **BIGNONIA** [Tourn.] L. Vines. Leaf-blades unequally pinnate: leaflets with toothed blades. Flowers clustered. Calyx tubular-campanulate,

nearly equally 5-lobed. Corolla tubular-funnelform. Capsule stout, fusiform. Seeds membranous-winged.—Two species, the following and 1 in Japan.

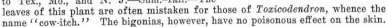

1. **B. radicans** L. Stout vine: leaves many, 2–2.5 dm. long; leaflets 7–11, the blades oval, ovate, or elliptic, 2–6 cm. long, coarsely serrate: calyx 14–18 mm. long; lobes triangular to triangular-ovate: corolla red or orange, 5–9 cm. long: capsule fusiform, 10–18 cm. long. [*Tecoma radicans* Juss.]—(TRUMPET-CREEPER. COW-ITCH. TRUMPET.) —Woods, river-swamps, thickets, and fence-rows, Coastal Plain and adj. provinces, Fla. to Tex., Mo., and N. J.—Sum.-fall.—The leaves of this plant are often mistaken for those of *Toxicodendron*, whence the name "cow-itch." The bigonias, however, have no poisonous effect on the skin.

4. **CATALPA** L. Shrubs or trees, with scaly bark. Leaves deciduous: blades broad, membranous. Flowers paniculate. Calyx 2-lobed. Corolla mainly white or yellow, the tube abruptly expanded into the throat. Capsule slender and elongate. Seeds fimbriate-winged. About 5 species, North American and Japanese.—INDIAN-BEANS. INDIAN-CIGARS. CIGAR-TREES. SMOKING-BEANS. CATALPAS. CATAWBAS.

Panicles many-flowered, crowded: corolla with a limb 4–5 × 5–6 cm. 1. *C. Catalpa.*
Panicles few-flowered, lax: corolla with a limb 6–7 × 7–8 cm. 2. *C. speciosa.*

1. **C. Catalpa** (L.) Karst. Tree becoming 20 m. tall: leaf-blades ovate, 1–3 dm. long: calyx 8–12 mm. long; lobes abruptly pointed: corolla 3–4 cm. long, or sometimes larger; throat campanulate, channeled and keeled on the lower side, with yellow blotches along the ridges within and purple or magenta spots except on the top within; limb oblique, the lower lobe erect: capsule 1.5–4 dm. long.—Woods and stream-banks, various provinces, Fla. to Tex., and naturalized as far N as N. Y.—The dried capsules are frequently smoked by children wherever the tree is found.—Spr.-sum.

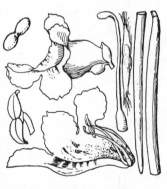

2. **C. speciosa** Warder. Tree becoming 40 m. tall: leaf-blades ovate to oblong-ovate, 1–3 dm. long: calyx 10–11 mm. long; lobes abruptly acuminate: corolla 3.5–5.5 cm. long, rather less copiously spotted within than *C. Catalpa;* throat conic-campanulate: capsule 3.5–5 dm. long.—(BOIS-PLANT.)—Damp soil or swamps, various provinces N of Coastal Plain, Tenn. to Tex., Mo., and Ind.—Spr.

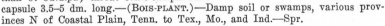

5. **CRESCENTIA** L. Trees with scaly bark. Leaves clustered on spurs: blades of a spatulate or oblanceolate type. Flowers in clusters or solitary, on

the spurs, pediceled. Calyx 2-lobed, leathery. Corolla mainly yellowish-green and magenta-streaked, with a fold between the tube and the campanulate throat: lobes 5, unequal. Anthers mostly included. Fruit relatively large, rounded at the apex, with a thick, hard pericarp. Seeds flat, obcordate. —About 5 species, tropical American.

1. **C. Cujete** L. Tree becoming 12 m. tall: leaf-blades 8–15 cm. long, abruptly acuminate or obtuse, narrow-based: calyx 2–3 cm. long: corolla yellowish-green and magenta-streaked; lobes undulate: capsule subglobose, oval, or ellipsoid, 15–30 cm. long.— (CALABASH-TREE.)—Hammocks, Florida Keys. Nat. of tropical America.— Spr.–sum.

6. **ENALLAGMA** Baill. Trees with scaly bark. Leaves alternate: blades of an oblong, oval, or obovate type. Flowers solitary or clustered at the ends of the branchlets, long-pedicelled. Calyx 2-lobed, leathery. Corolla mainly whitish, purplish or greenish-yellow, with a fold between the tube and the campanulate throat: lobes 5, unequal. Anthers mostly exserted. Fruit relatively small, umbonate at the apex, with a thin brittle pericarp. Seeds convex, notched at both ends.—Four species, tropical American.

1. **E. latifolia** (Mill.) Small. Tree becoming 8 m. tall: leaf-blades 7–15 cm. long, abruptly pointed, broad-based: calyx 2.5–4 cm. long: corolla 5–6 cm. long, pale-purple to yellowish-white; lobes toothed: capsule ellipsoid or oval, 5–11.5 cm. long. [*Crescentia ovata* Fl. SE. U. S.]—(BLACK-CALABASH.)—Hammocks, often along the coast, S pen. Fla. and Florida Keys.— (*W. I.*)—Spr.–sum.

FAMILY 19. **PEDALIACEAE** — BENNE FAMILY

Herbs or rarely shrubs. Leaves opposite or sometimes alternate: blades entire, toothed or lobed, usually petioled. Flowers perfect, in axillary or terminal clusters. Calyx of 5 partly united unequal sepals. Corolla irregular: tube long or short, rarely spurred at the base: limb 2-lipped, the 5 lobes usually broad. Androecium of 4 didynamous stamens and one staminodium. Gynoecium of usually 2 united carpels. Style elongate. Stigmas 2, often somewhat foliaceous. Fruit a capsule, unarmed or with simple or hooked spines.—About 14 genera and 45 species, in the Old World.

Ovary slightly 2-lobed at the apex: capsule abruptly pointed or short-beaked at the apex.   1. SESAMUM.
Ovary truncate at the apex: capsule truncate and with 2 lateral horns at the apex.   2. CERATOTHECA.

1. SESAMUM L. Herbs. Leaves opposite or partly alternate: blades broad or narrow. Flowers axillary. Calyx-lobes slightly unequal. Corolla horizontal: tube very short: throat campanulate: limb 2-lipped, the lower lip much larger than the upper one. Stamens included. Capsule angled or somewhat flattened. Seeds wingless.—About 12 species, in tropical Asia and Africa.

1. S. indicum L. Plant 1.5 m. tall or less, finely pubescent: leaf-blades ovate, toothed or lobed and long-petioled on the lower part of the stem, lanceolate to linear-lanceolate, undulate or entire and short-petioled above: calyx-lobes lanceolate or linear-lanceolate, 5–7 mm. long: corolla pink, yellowish, or white, 2–2.5 cm. long; lobes rounded: capsule ellipsoid, 2.5–3 cm. long, abruptly pointed.—(BENNE.)—Roadsides, cult. grounds, and waste-places, Coastal Plain, Fla. to Tex. Nat. of East Indies.— (*W. I., Mex., C. A., S. A.*)—All year.

2. CERATOTHECA Endl. Differs from Sesamum chiefly in the 2-horned capsule and in the case of our species in the broader leaf-blades. Leaves alternate on the upper part of the stem: blades toothed or lobed, petioled, subpalmately veined. Flowers axillary, opposite or alternate, subtended by bracts narrower than the leaves. Calyx-lobes unequal. Corolla nodding: tube mostly shorter than the calyx: throat subcampanulate: limb very oblique, the lower lip much longer than the upper one. Stamens included. Capsule somewhat flattened, truncate at the top. Seeds margined. —Five species, African.

1. C. triloba E. Meyer. Plant 1–2 m. tall, the stem 4-angled and with grooved sides: leaves clammy-pubescent: blades sub-orbicular or ovate-orbicular, mostly 1–5 cm. long, crenate, those of the lower leaves more or less 3-lobed, all petioled: calyx-lobes lanceolate to linear-lanceolate, 6–7 mm. long: corolla lavender or pale-violet, 4.5–6.5 cm. long; blades obtuse: capsule slightly broadened upward, 1.5–2 cm. long, the horns divergent, pubescent, the sides grooved. —High pinelands and roadsides, pen. Fla. Nat. of Africa.—Sum.–fall.

FAMILY 20. **MARTYNIACEAE** — UNICORN-PLANT FAMILY

Annual or perennial, stocky herbs, with stout weak stems. Leaves opposite or rarely alternate: blades undulate or lobed. Flowers perfect, irregular, in racemes. Calyx of mostly 5 well-united sepals, oblique, the lobes short. Corolla of 5 partly united petals: tube often decurved: limb 5-lobed, oblique. Androecium of 4 didynamous stamens (or the posterior pair mere staminodia). Gynoecium 2-carpellary. Ovary 1-celled, the placentae parietal.—Three genera and 12 species, mostly tropical.

1. MARTYNIA L. Annual or perennial, very stout, herbs with clammy, strong-scented pubescence. Leaf-blades broad. Corolla declined, the limb oblique. Capsule 2-valved, the body crested, terminating in a curved or hooked beak.— About 8 species, American.

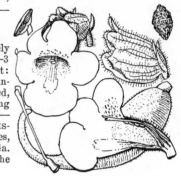

1. M. louisiana Mill. Annual, densely viscid-pubescent: leaf-blades sinuate, 0.5–3 dm. wide, petioled: flowers not fragrant: calyx-lobes ovate, obtuse: corolla-lobes undulate: capsule stout, 8–15 cm. long, curved, separating into 2 elastically spreading valves, the beak longer than the body.— (UNICORN-PLANT. RAM'S-HORN. PROBOSCIS-FLOWER.)—River-banks, fields, waste-places, and about gardens, various provinces, Ga. to N. M., Utah. Ia., and Pa. Nat. of the Miss. valley.—(*Mex.*)—Sum.-fall.

ORDER **PLANTAGINALES** — PLANTAGINAL ORDER

Annual or perennial herbs, or partially woody plants. Leaves wholly or mainly basal, or crowded on a simple or branched caudex: blades typically 1–several-ribbed. Flowers perfect, monoecious or dioecious, spicate. Calyx of 4 (3–5), partly united sepals. Corolla of 4 (3–5), partly united scarious and veinless petals. Androecium of 4 or 2 stamens, (or of 1 stamen). Gynoecium typically 2-carpellary. Ovary superior. Fruit capsular, usually a pyxis.

FAMILY 1. **PLANTAGINACEAE** — PLANTAIN FAMILY

Herbs. Leaf-blades typically 1–several-ribbed. Calyx-lobes, and corolla-lobes, 4. Style and stigma elongate.—Three genera and 225 species, widely distributed.

1. PLANTAGO [Tour.] L.[1] Acaulescent (ours) or caulescent herbs. Leaf-blades broad or narrow. Spikes usually elongate, green, or brown or grayish. Filaments partially adnate to the corolla-tube. More than 200 species, of wide geographical distribution.—PLANTAINS.

Flowers mainly dioecious : corolla lobes erect or closing over the capsule : plants
    annual or biennial.
    Stamens 2 : leaf-blades narrow, linear or filiform.   I. PUSILLAE.
    Stamens 4 : leaf-blades relatively broad.   II. VIRGINICAE.
Flowers perfect : corolla-lobes spreading or reflexed on the top
    of the capsule.
    Plants annual : flowers heterogonous, mostly cleistogamous.   III. ARISTATAE.
    Plants perennial : flowers proterogynous.
        Calyx-lobes various, the lower united, the upper distinct. IV. LANCEOLATAE.
        Calyx-lobes all essentially distinct.   V. MAJORES.

I. PUSILLAE

Capsule about twice as long as the calyx : seeds 10–30.   1. *P. heterophylla.*
Capsule slightly surpassing the calyx : seeds 2–4.   2. *P. pusilla.*

[1] Prepared from matter contributed by Edward Lyman Morris.

II. Virginicae

Plant with spatulate, obovate or elliptic, usually repand denticulate leaf-blades, and obtuse calyx-lobes. ... 3. *P. virginica.*

III. Aristatae

Rigid plant with narrow entire leaf-blades and a stiff spike with long spreading bracts. ... 4. *P. aristata.*

IV. Lanceolatae

Plant with narrow leaf-blades and short cylindric spikes which terminate wiry peduncles. ... 5. *P. lanceolata.*

V. Majores

Lateral nerves of the leaf-blades free and remote from the midrib.

 Spikes interrupted throughout: bracts much shorter than the calyx: seeds 2. ... 6. *P. sparsiflora.*

 Spikes continuous at least above the base: bracts one half the length of the calyx or more: seeds 4–18.

  Capsules conic or ellipsoid-conic, circumscissile below the middle. ... 7. *P. Rugelii.*

  Capsules ovoid, circumscissile at about the middle. ... 8. *P. major.*

Lateral nerves of the leaf-blades partially confluent with the midrib. ... 9. *P. cordata.*

1. **P. heterophylla** Nutt. Leaves basal, 2–18 cm. long; blades linear or nearly filiform, acute, entire or with several remote teeth or spreading narrow lobes, narrowed to the dilated base: scapes usually numerous, 2–25 cm. long, equalling or surpassing the leaves: spike slender, 2–15 cm. long, loosely-flowered: bracts ovate, 1.5–2 mm. long, blunt: flowers dioecious or polygamous: calyx-lobes oval to rhombic-obovate, about 1.5 mm. long, obtuse, mostly shorter than the bracts: corolla glabrous; lobes erect, ovate, 0.5 mm. long, acute: capsule ellipsoid, 3–3.5 mm. long, circumscissile below the middle: seeds mainly 0.5–0.7 mm. long, dark-red.—Moist soil, fields and pastures, Coastal Plain and adj. provinces, Fla. to Tex., Ark., and N. J.—Spr.–sum.

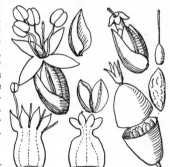

2. **P. pusilla** Nutt. Leaves basal, several 2–12 cm. long; blades linear or nearly filiform, blunt-tipped, entire, obscurely 1-nerved, sometimes early deciduous: scapes usually several together, nearly filiform, 5–25 cm. long, surpassing the leaves, often glabrate above: spike rather loosely-flowered, slender: bracts ovate, 1–1.3 mm. long, acutish: flowers dioecious or polygamous: calyx-lobes oval to obovate, 1.3–1.5 mm. long, obtuse, about equalling the bracts: corolla glabrous; lobes erect, lanceolate to ovate-lanceolate: capsule ellipsoid or ovoid-ellipsoid, about 2 mm. long, circumscissile below the middle: seeds 1–1.5 mm. long, dark-red. —Dry sandy soil, various provinces, Ga. to Tex., Kans., and Mass.—Spr.–sum.

3. **P. virginica** L. Leaves basal, spreading or ascending, 1–15 cm. long; blades spatulate to obovate or elliptic, obtuse or acutish, entire or repand-denticulate, 3–5-nerved, narrowed into margined petioles or nearly sessile: scapes erect or ascending, 0.5–20 dm. tall, much surpassing the leaves: spike dense, sometimes interrupted below: flowers dioecious: bracts linear-lanceolate to lanceolate: calyx-lobes elliptic or ovate, 2–2.5 mm. long, obtuse, surpassing the bracts: corolla various, those of staminate flowers with spreading lobes, those of pistillate flowers with lobes usually unequally erect after fertilization: capsule ovoid or oval-ovoid, 1.5–2 mm. long, circumscissile at about the middle: seeds 2–4, 1.3 mm. long, golden-yellow.—Dry soil, Fla. to Tex., Ariz., Mich., and R. I.—Spr.–sum.

4. P. aristata Michx. Leaves nearly basal, 5–25 cm. long: blades linear, acuminate, entire and callous-tipped, narrowed into margined petioles, 3–5-nerved: scapes erect, 10–50 cm. tall, rigid, surpassing the leaves: spike dense, 2–15 cm. long, pubescent but not woolly: bracts linear, puberulent, 1–3 cm. long, surpassing the flowers by several times their length: flowers perfect: calyx-lobes spatulate-elliptic or cuneate, 2–2.5 mm. long, obtuse, the outer herbaceous, the inner widely scarious-margined: corolla glabrous; lobes ovate or orbicular- ovate, 2 mm. long, obtuse, cordate: capsule slightly narrowed upward, 2.5–3 mm. long, slightly surpassing the calyx, circumscissile at the middle: seeds 2, 2–3 mm. long.—Dry plains and prairies, various provinces, La. to N. M., B. C., Alas., and Ill.; naturalized eastward to Fla. and Me.—Spr.–fall.

5. P. lanceolata L. Leaves basal, often numerous, 4–30 cm. long; blades linear-elliptic to broadly elliptic, acute and callous-tipped at the apex or acuminate at both ends, 3–7-nerved, entire or denticulate, narrowed into margined petioles; which are dilated and hairy at the base: scapes erect or nearly so, 1–7 dm. tall, ridged: spike cylindric, dense, 1–8 cm. long, 6–8 mm. thick: bracts rhombic, 4–5 mm. long, the tip bent: flowers perfect: calyx-lobes 2–3 mm. long, broadly elliptic to oval, obtuse, the 2 lower ones usually united, their midribs closely subparallel: corolla glabrous; lobes broadly lanceolate, 2–2.5 mm. long: capsule ellipsoid, 3 mm. long, slightly longer than the calyx, circumscissile at about the middle: seeds 2, fully 2 mm. long.—(RIB-GRASS. ENGLISH-PLANTAIN. RIPPLE-GRASS.)—Fields, roadsides, and waste-places, various provinces, Fla. to Tex., N. M., Alas., Sask., and N. B. Nat. of Eurasia.—(W. I.) —Spr.–fall.

6. P. sparsiflora Michx. Leaves basal, 8–30 cm. long; petioles shorter than the blades, margined; blades lanceolate to very narrowly elliptic-lanceolate, acute or acuminate, 5(–7)-nerved, entire or indistinctly denticulate: scapes erect, 2–7 dm. tall, slender, simple: spike slender, sometimes 3.8 dm. long, glabrous or nearly so, loosely-flowered: bracts ovate, very much shorter than the calyx: flowers perfect: calyx-lobes orbicular to obovate, about 2 mm. long, rounded, each with a green midrib and scarious margins: corolla with tube slightly surpassing the calyx, glabrous; lobes reflexed: capsule ellipsoid-cylindric, 3–4 mm. long, nearly twice as long as the calyx, circumscissile at the lower third: seeds 2, fully 2 mm. long.—Low marshy pinelands, Coastal Plain, Fla. to N. C.—Spr.–fall.

7. P. Rugelii Decne. Leaves basal, 5–40 cm. long; petioles usually purple at the base; blades broadly ovate to elliptic, longer than the petioles or sometimes shorter, 5–7-nerved, entire or shallowly toothed, cuneately or abruptly narrowed at the base: scapes often surpassing the leaves, 10–50 cm. tall: spike 2–30 cm. long, sometimes broadly bracted near the base: bracts fully one half as long as the calyx, acute: flowers perfect: sepals elliptic, acute 2–2.5 mm. long, keeled, often scarious-margined: corolla glabrous; tubes slightly surpassing the calyx; lobes spreading: capsule conic or ellipsoid-conic, 4–4.5 mm. long, circumscissile below the middle: seeds 4–9, 1.5–2 mm. long.—Roadsides, fields, waste-places and woods, various provinces, Fla. to Tex., N. D., and N. B.; naturalized further westward.—Spr.–fall.—The leaves are shining green.

8. P. major L. Leaves basal, 5–35 cm. long; petioles usually green at the base; blades ovate or oval, or rarely elliptic, obtuse or acutish, 5–7-nerved, entire or coarsely toothed, rounded or cordate at the base, longer than the petioles or shorter: scapes surpassing the leaves, 8–40 cm. tall: spikes 4–20 cm. long, dense: bracts ovate, barely equalling the calyx: flowers perfect:

calyx-lobes ovate to obovate, obtuse, not keeled, scarious-margined: corolla inconspicuous; tubes about as long as the calyx; lobes spreading or reflexed: capsule ovoid, about 3 mm. long, slightly surpassing the calyx-lobes, circumscissile at the middle: seeds 6–18, 0.7 mm. long.—Waste-places, roadsides, cult. grounds, and damp banks, various provinces, U. S. and S Can. In part naturalized from Eu.—(*W. I., Mex.*)—Spr.–fall.—The leaves are dull-green.

9. **P. cordata** Lam. Leaves basal, 1–4.5 dm. long; blades ovate to suborbicular, 5–30 cm. long, acute or obtuse, 7–9-nerved, these confluent with the midrib below the middle of blade, entire or shallowly toothed, rounded or cordate at the base: scapes erect, surpassing the leaves, 15–50 cm. tall: spike loosely-flowered, sometimes interrupted: bracts orbicular-ovate or reniform, 1.5–3 mm. long: calyx-lobes ovate to suborbicular, 2.5–3 mm. long, obtuse or acutish: corolla surpassing the calyx; lobes ovate or orbicular-ovate, spreading or reflexed in age: capsule globose-ovoid, 4–5 mm. long, circumscissile at the middle or slightly below it: seeds 1–4, 3.5–4 mm. long. —Stream-banks, shaded swamps, various provinces, Ala. to La., Ont., and Va.—Spr.–sum.

Order SANTALALES — Santalal Order

Herbs, shrubs, or trees, mostly root- or tree-parasites. Leaves with expanded blades or scale-like. Flowers inconspicuous, perfect or imperfect. Calyx present, but often a mere border. Corolla present or wanting. Androecium of as many stamens as there are sepals, or petals, or twice as many. Gynoecium of several united carpels. Ovary more or less inferior. Fruit a drupe, a nut, or a berry.

Stamens as many as the petals or sepals: ovules not freely pendulous from an erect placenta.
Leaves opposite: fruit a berry: tree-parasites.   Fam. 1. LORANTHACEAE.
Leaves mainly alternate: fruit a drupe or a nut: rootparasites.   Fam. 2. SANTALACEAE.
Stamens twice as many as the petals, except in *Schoepfia*:
ovules freely pendulous from the erect placenta.   Fam. 3. OLACACEAE.

Family 1. LORANTHACEAE[1] — Mistletoe Family

Green or olive-brown shrubs or half-shrubs, with chlorophyll-bearing tissues, growing on woody plants from which they take sap through specialized roots (*haustoria*). Leaves opposite, sometimes scale-like. Flowers regular, minute, dioecious and seemingly apetalous in our species. Calyx of mostly 3 valvate sepals, each with a minute opposed stamen. Gynoecium compound, often 2-carpellary, but ovary inferior, 1-celled with a single little-differentiated ovule. Style single or wanting: stigma blunt or capitate. Fruit a berry or a drupe, the mesocarp very viscid.— About 21 genera and 500 species, most abundant in the tropics.

1. **PHORADENDRON** Nutt. Stem rather fleshy about a woody axis, brittle at the nodes. Leaves opposite, scale-like or fleshy-coriaceous. Inflorescence 1- to several-jointed. Spikes solitary or clustered in the axils. Flowers very small, apetalous, dioecious: staminate with a 3-lobed (rarely 2- to 5-lobed) calyx: anthers nearly sessile, 2-celled, dehiscing upwards: pistillate similar, the stigma nearly sessile. Berry subglobose, sessile, crowned with the per-

[1] Contributed by William Trelease.

sistent sepals. Seed solitary.—About 100 species, American.—AMERICAN-MISTLETOES. MISTLETOES.

Spikes permanently short (2–3 cm.), rather closely covered with berries.
  Leaf-blades relatively broad, oblanceolate to obovate, or
    orbicular.   1. *P. flavescens.*
  Leaf-blades relatively narrow, spatulate or elliptic-spatu-
    late.   2. *P. Eatoni.*
Spikes elongating (6–7 cm.) with the berries in separated
  whorls.   3. *P. macrotomum.*

1. **P. flavescens** (Pursh) Nutt. Stem minutely puberulous, becoming glabrate: leaf-blades oblanceolate to obovate (or orbicular in the southwestern *P. flavescens orbiculatum*), obtuse, cuneately subpetioled, 20–50 mm. long: spikes short, mostly 10–15 mm. long, short-peduncled, with about 4 short joints, some joints 6-flowered when pistillate, others 12-flowered when staminate: berries white or slightly yellowish, 4 mm. in diameter, covering the spike, with inflexed sepals.—On many kinds of deciduous trees, various provinces, Fla. to E Tex., Okla., W. Va., and N. J.—Plants forming large rather compact tufts.

2. **P. Eatoni** Trelease. Stem slender, glabrescent: leaves elliptic-spatulate or spatulate, obtuse, gradually attenuate at base, 25–50 mm. long: spikes moderately short, 20–30 mm. long, short-peduncled, with 2 or 3 to 6 ellipsoid joints 6–12-flowered or even 30-flowered when staminate, and about 3 short joints some 6-flowered when pistillate: berries nearly white, broadly ellipsoid, 4×5 mm. in diameter, with inflexed sepals.—On ash trees or sometimes on oaks and other trees, S pen. Fla.—Plants in dense much-branched tufts.

3. **P. macrotomum** Trelease. Stem minutely puberulous or glabrescent: leaf-blades oblanceolate, obtuse, cuneately subpetioled, 50–70 mm. long: spikes rather long, 20–30 mm., reaching 60–70 mm. in fruit, short-peduncled, with about 5 rather short joints, some joints 6-flowered when pistillate, others 20-flowered when staminate: berries greenish-white, ellipsoid, 4 mm. in diameter, in separated whorls, with inflexed sepals.—On various deciduous trees, Fla.—Plants forming large rather open tufts.

FAMILY 2. **SANTALACEAE** — SANDAL-WOOD FAMILY

Herbs, shrubs, or trees, parasitic on the roots of other plants. Leaves opposite or alternate: blades entire. Flowers perfect, polygamous, or dioecious, the staminate clustered, the pistillate often solitary. Calyx of 3–6 sepals. Corolla wanting. Androecium of 3–6 stamens opposite the sepals on the edge of the hypanthium. Gynoecium compound. Fruit mostly drupaceous.—About 26 genera and 250 species, mostly tropical.

Herbaceous perennials: flowers perfect: stigma capitate.   1. COMANDRA.
Shrubs: flowers dioecious or polygamous: stigma 2–4-lobed.
  Staminate flowers in umbels or umbel-like clusters: leaves
    leaves opposite or nearly so.
    Hypanthium of the staminate flowers turbinate: anthers
      connected with the sepals by a tuft of hairs.   2. NESTRONIA.
    Hypanthium of the staminate flowers flat: anthers not con- 3. BUCKLEYA.
      nected with the sepals.   4. PYRULARIA.
  Staminate flowers in racemes: leaves alternate.

1. **COMANDRA** Nutt. Herbs with long rootstocks. Leaves alternate: blades narrow. Flowers perfect, cymose. Style columnar: stigma capitate. Drupe crowned with the persistent calyx.— Five species, one of them European.

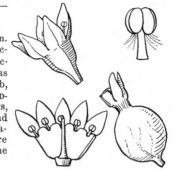

1. **C. umbellata** (L.) Nutt. Plant 2–4 dm. tall: leaf-blades elliptic, oval, or elliptic-lanceolate, 1–3.5 cm. long: sepals elliptic-ovate, 2–2.5 mm. long, white; stamens ½ as long as the sepals: drupe greenish-drab, about 5 mm. in diameter.—(BASTARD-TOAD-FLAX.)—Dry ground, thickets, and banks, various provinces, Ga. to Ark., Alb., and N. B.—Spr.–sum.—This is the only santalaceous genus in North America with more than one species, three additional to the above occurring in western North America.

2. **NESTRONIA** Raf. Shrubs with spreading branches. Leaves opposite: blades broad. Flowers polygamo-dioecious, the staminate umbellate: sepals not veiny. Style conic; stigma 3–4-lobed. Drupe of an oval type.—One species.

1. **N. umbellula** Raf. Shrub 3–10 dm. tall, the branches glabrous: leaf-blades oval, varying to ovate or obovate, 2–7 cm. long: sepals broad at the base, greenish, those of the staminate flowers elliptic-ovate, 2–2.5 mm. long: stamens ⅔ as long as the sepals: drupes 10–13 mm. long.—Woods and stream-banks, Piedmont to Appalachian Plateau, Ga. to Ala. and Va.—Spr.—This shrub, un-like *Buckleya*, is, as far as we know, para-sitic on the roots of the deciduous-leaved shrubs and trees with which it grows. Coniferous trees are often wanting there.

3. **BUCKLEYA** Torr. Shrubs with 2-ranked branches. Leaves opposite or nearly so, distichous: blades rather broad. Flowers dioecious, the staminate umbellate: sepals veiny. Style conic: stigma 4-lobed. Drupe of an ellipsoid type.—One species.

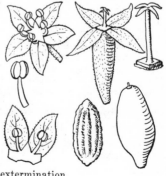

1. **B. distichophylla** (Nutt.) Torr. Shrub 2–4 m. tall, the branches pubescent: leaf-blades lanceolate to ovate-lanceolate, 2–7 cm. long: sepals rounded at the base, green-ish, those of the staminate flowers ovate, 2.5–3 mm. long: drupe 2–2.5 cm. long.— River-banks, Blue Ridge, N. C. and Tenn. —Spr.–sum.—Parasitic on the roots of hemlock trees. The geographic range is very restricted, only three localities being defi-nitely known at present, although others have been reported. The species is in danger of extermination.

4. PYRULARIA Michx. Shrubs or trees, with diffuse branches. Leaves alternate: blades broad. Flowers dioecious or polygamous, racemose. Style very short: stigma depressed. Drupe pyriform.—Three species, the following and 2 Asiatic.

1. P. pubera Michx. Shrub 1–3 m. tall, with pubescent branches: leaf-blades elliptic or commonly broadest above the middle, 4–15 cm. long: sepals ovate, green, 2–2.5 mm. long: drupe 2–2.5 cm. long.—(BUFFALO-NUT. OIL-NUT. MOUNTAIN-COCONUT.)—River-banks and woods, Blue Ridge to Appalachian Plateau, Ga. to Ala. and Pa.—Spr.–sum.—A curious shrub, inconspicuous in flower, but obvious in fruit by the dangling drupes, which are, at first light-green and later yellowish. An oil, resembling olive oil, but ill-scented and poisonous, has been pressed from the drupes.

FAMILY 3. **OLACACEAE** — XIMENIA FAMILY

Shrubs, trees, or vines. Leaves usually alternate: blades entire or rarely toothed. Flowers perfect or polygamous, regular, in dichotomous or raceme-like cymes. Calyx of 4–6 small sepals, surmounting the hypanthium. Corolla of 4–6 distinct or united petals. Androecium of 4–12 stamens. Gynoecium 3–4-carpellary. Fruit a drupe.—About 25 genera and 140 species, mostly tropical.

Petals united to above the middle: stamens as many as the corolla-lobes and opposite them: drupe nearly enclosed in the disk.   1. SCHOEPFIA.
Petals nearly distinct: stamens twice as many as the petals: drupe naked.   2. XIMENIA.

1. SCHOEPFIA Schreb. Unarmed shrubs or trees. Leaf-blades entire. Hypanthium filled with an elevated disk. Sepals broad. Petals united to above the middle. Filaments adnate to about the middle of the corolla-tube. Anthers oval or ovoid. Ovary about ½ inferior.—About 15 species, tropical American and Asiatic.

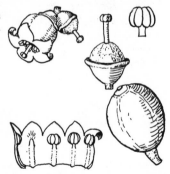

1. S. chrysophylloides (A. Rich.) Planch. Shrub or small tree, with pale branches: leaf-blades ovate to oblong-ovate, 2–6 cm. long: corolla red or reddish, about 4 mm. long: lobes ovate, glabrous: drupes ovoid or oval-ovoid, 10–12 mm. long. [*S. Schreberi* (Fl. SE. U. S.)]—(WHITEWOOD.)—Coastal and inland hammocks, pen. Fla. and the Keys.—(*W. I.*)—All year.

2. XIMENIA [Plum.] L. Thorny shrubs or trees. Leaf-blades entire. Hypanthium without an elevated disk. Sepals minute. Petals nearly dis-

tinct. Anthers linear. Ovary nearly superior.—About 5 species, tropical.

1. X. americana L. Shrub or small tree,
with dark branches: leaf-blades oblong to
elliptic or nearly so, 3–7 cm. long: corolla
yellow or yellowish-white, about 10 mm.
long; lobes linear, densely pubescent within:
drupes subglobose or broadly oval, 14–17
mm. long. — (TALLOW-WOOD.) — Hammocks,
pen. Fla. and hammocks and pine-lands,
Everglade Keys, Fla. and Fla. Keys.—(W.
I.)—Spr.–fall, or all year southward.—The
tallow tree has become accommodated to a
variety of soils and habitats. These factors
are reflected in its habits. In the sterile soil of the "scrub" it is a sprawling
shrub often only knee high; in hammocks it is an erect shrub or small tree.

Order **RUBIALES** — Rubial Order

Herbs, shrubs, or trees. Leaves opposite, sometimes whorled. Flowers perfect or polygamous, axillary or cymose. Hypanthium present.
Calyx of 2 or more often small sepals. Corolla of 3 or more partially
united petals. Androecium of as many stamens as there are petals or
twice as many. Gynoecium 2–several-carpellary. Ovary wholly or partially inferior. Fruit a capsule, a berry, or a drupe.

Leaves with stipules adnate to the stem between the leaf-bases.
                                                         Fam. 1. RUBIACEAE.
Leaves without stipules, or if present these adnate to the
   petiole.
                                                Fam. 2. CAPRIFOLIACEAE.

Family 1. **RUBIACEAE** — Madder Family

Herbs, shrubs, trees, or vines. Leaves opposite or whorled, with
interpetiolar or foliaceous stipules. Flowers perfect or polygamous, regular or nearly so. Calyx of 2–6, or more, sepals surmounting the hypanthium, or obsolete. Corolla of 3–6, or more, more or less united petals.
Androecium of as many stamens as there are petals and alternate with
them. Gynoecium 2–several-carpellary. Fruit a capsule, a drupe, or a
berry.—About 340 genera and 6,000 species, widely distributed; most
abundant in the tropics.

Cavities of the ovary with several to many ovules each: seeds several to many.
                                                     Subfamily I. CINCHONOIDEAE.
Cavities of the ovary with a single ovule each:
   seed solitary.
     Stipules not foliaceous, usually minute.   Subfamily II. COFFEOIDEAE.
     Stipules foliaceous, nearly or quite as large as
       the leaf-blades, thus making the leaves ap-
       pear as in whorls.   Subfamily III. GALIOIDEAE.

Subfamily I. CINCHONOIDEAE
Fruit dry.
   Seed wingless.
     Ovules very numerous: shrubs or trees.   1. PINCKNEYA.
     Ovules several: herbs, sometimes woody at the base.
       Sepals and corolla-lobes 4.
         Top of the capsule not extending beyond the hy-
           panthium.   2. OLDENLANDIA.
         Top of the capsule extending beyond the hy-
           panthium.   3. HOUSTONIA.

Sepals and corolla-lobes 5.   4. PENTODON.
 Seed winged.   5. EXOSTEMA.
Fruit pulpy.
 Fruit 2-celled.
  Flowers in cymes.   6. CASASIA.
  Flowers solitary.
   Corolla-lobes 5, convolute.   7. RANDIA.
   Corolla-lobes 4, valvate.   8. CATESBAEA.
 Fruit 5-celled.   9. HAMELIA.

      Subfamily II. COFFEOIDEAE

Flowers in dense heads.   10. CEPHALANTHUS.
Flowers solitary or in open inflorescences.
 Ovule pendulous.
  Filaments wholly or partly adnate to the corolla-tube. 11. GUETTARDIA.
  Filaments not adnate to the corolla-tube.
   Inflorescence terminal.   12. ERITHALIS.
   Inflorescence axillary.   13. CHIOCOCCA.
 Ovule not pendulous.
  Corolla-lobes imbricate.   14. STRUMPFIA.
  Corolla-lobes valvate.
   Ovule or seed with a basal attachment.
    Flowers not paired, the ovaries distinct.
     Corolla funnelform : seed wingless : erect. 15. PSYCHOTRIA.
     Corolla campanulate : seed winged : vines. 16. PAEDERIA.
    Flowers paired, the ovaries united. 17. MITCHELLA.
   Ovule or seed with a lateral attachment.
    Shrubs or trees.   18. MORINDA.
    Herbs.
     Ovary 3- or 4-celled.   19. RICHARDIA.
     Ovary 2-celled.
      Fruit drupaceous, the carpels neither de-
       hiscent nor separating.   20. ERNODEA.
      Fruit not drupaceous, the carpels dehis-
       cent or separating.
       Mature carpels merely separating.
        Styles partly united : stigmas slen-
         der : corolla salverform. 21. DIODIA.
        Styles united to the top : stigma
         capitate or 2-lobed : corolla fun-
         nelform.   22. DIODELLA.
       Mature carpels dehiscent.
        Fruit septicidal, and both carpels
         ventrally dehiscent.   23. BORRERIA.
        Fruit separating into carpels, one
         of which opens through the ven-
         tral face, the other remaining
         closed.   24. SPERMACOCE.

      Subfamily III. GALIOIDEAE

Stipules foliaceous, usually resembling the leaves. 25. GALIUM.

   1. **PINCKNEYA** Michx. Shrubs or trees. Leaves with broad entire
blades. Flowers in corymbose cymes. Sepals 5, 1 or 2 of them, at least in the
outer flowers, transformed into leaf-like
members. Corolla with a stout tube and 5
rather broad lobes. Stamens 5 : filaments
adnate to the lower part of the corolla-tube,
glabrous : anthers ellipsoid, exserted. Capsule as wide as long. Seeds flat, wingless.—
One species.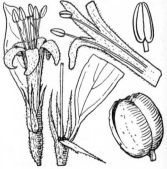

   1. **P. pubens** Michx. Shrub or small tree,
with pubescent foliage : leaf-blades elliptic,
oval, or ovate, 5–20 cm. long, short-petioled :
foliaceous sepals like the leaves in shape, but
smaller and pink : unchanged sepals linear
to linear-lanceolate, 1–1.5 cm. long : corolla

greenish, mottled with brown or purple: tube 1.5–2 cm. long; lobes as long as the tube or shorter: capsule subglobose or obovoid, nearly 2 cm. in diameter.— (FEVER-TREE.)—Sandy swamps, Coastal Plain, W Fla. to S. C.—Spr.–sum.— The numerous bright-pink foliaceous sepals make the plants conspicuous on the edges of swamps.

2. **OLDENLANDIA** L. Annual or perennial, often diffuse herbs, or woody plants. Leaf-blades mostly narrow. Flowers in axillary or terminal congested cymes. Sepals 4, broad. Corolla rotate, minute: tube very short: lobes broad. Stamens 4: filaments adnate to the base of the corolla-tube. Style very short or wanting. Capsule scarcely longer than the hypanthium, terete or angled.—About 175 species, most abundant in tropical Asia.

Flowers sessile or nearly so, solitary or glomerate.
  Annual plants: sepals ciliate, acute.
    Stem hirsute: leaf-blades short-petioled.   1. *O. uniflora.*
    Stem glabrous: leaf-blades sessile.   2. *O. fasciculata.*
  Perennial plants: sepals eciliate, acuminate.   3. *O. Boscii.*
Flowers on filiform pedicels and peduncles.   4. *O. corymbosa.*

1. **O. uniflora** L. Stem 1–4 dm. long, often much branched: leaf-blades ovate to elliptic, 0.5–2.5 cm. long: sepals about 1.5 mm. long: petals about ½ as long as the sepals, white or nearly so, ciliate at the tip: capsule 1–1.5 mm. long.—Moist sandy soil, Coastal Plain, Fla. to Tex. and N. Y.—Spr.–fall, or all year southward.

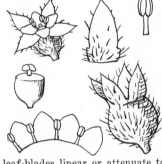

2. **O. fasciculata** (Bertol.) Small. Stem 1–5 dm. long, sometimes diffusely branched: leaf-blades elliptic to lanceolate or ovate-lanceolate, 0.5–2 cm. long: sepals about 1.5 mm. long: petals about ½ as long as the sepals, pearl-blue, eciliate: capsule 1.5–2 mm. long.—Sandy beaches, swamps, muddy banks about tide-water, Coastal Plain, Fla. to Miss.—Sum.–fall.

3. **O. Boscii** (DC.) Chapm. Stem weak, commonly diffusely branched, 1–3 dm. long: leaf-blades linear or attenuate to the bases, 1–2 cm. long: sepals barely 1.5 mm. long: petals triangular or ovate-triangular, about 0.5 mm. long, white or purplish: filaments finely pubescent: capsule about 2 mm. long.—Wet soil, borders of ponds, and ditches, Coastal Plain and adj. provinces, Fla. to Tex., Ark., Tenn., and S. C.—Spr.–fall.

4. **O. corymbosa** L. Stem erect or decumbent and diffuse, 2–5 dm. long: leaf-blades linear to linear-lanceolate, 1–4 cm. long: sepals about 1 mm. long: corolla white, about 2 mm. long; lobes ovate, pubescent within: filaments glabrous: capsule about 2 mm. long.—Roadsides and waste-places, S pen. Fla.—(*W. I., C. A., S. A., O. W.*)—Spr.–sum.

3. **HOUSTONIA** L. Annual or perennial, erect or creeping herbs. Leaf-blades narrow or broad. Flowers in open or compact cymes. Sepals 4, commonly narrow. Corolla funnelform or salverform: tube long: lobes mostly shorter than the tube. Stamens 4: filaments adnate to above the middle of the corolla-tube. Style slender. Capsule seated on or in the hypanthium, flattened. —About 35 species, North American.

Flowers solitary on terminal pedicels or also on pedicels axillary to leaf-like bracts,
not aggregated into a terminal cyme.
  Pedicels erect in fruit.   I. CAERULEAE.
  Pedicels recurved in fruit.   II. ROTUNDIFOLIAE.
Flowers borne in terminal, more or less effuse cymes.   III. ANGUSTIFOLIAE.

I. CAERULEAE

Plant perennial by slender horizontal rootstocks or creeping
stems.
  Plant erect: sepals lanceolate: corolla-tube glabrous
  within.   1. *H. caerulea.*
  Plant diffusely creeping: sepals elliptic: corolla-tube pubescent within.   2. *H. serpyllifolia.*
Plant annual, with slender roots.
  Sepals much surpassed by the corolla-tube: capsule about
  equalling the sepals.   3. *H. pusilla.*
  Sepals about equalling the corolla-tube: capsule much exceeded by the sepals.   4. *H. minima.*

II. ROTUNDIFOLIAE

Plant prostrate, usually in light-green mats: corolla bright-
white, starry.   5. *H. procumbens.*

III. ANGUSTIFOLIAE

Sepals fully as long as the hypanthium.
  Sepals conspicuously surpassing the capsule.
    Corolla less than twice as long as the sepals: sepals
    4–8 mm. long.   6. *H. lanceolata.*
    Corolla over twice as long as the sepals: sepals 2–3
    mm. long.
      Sepals subulate to linear-lanceolate during anthesis:
      corolla-tube 6–7 mm. long.   7. *H. purpurea.*
      Sepals ovate to ovate-lanceolate during anthesis:
      corolla-tube 9–11 mm. long. 8. *H. montana.*
  Sepals slightly surpassing the capsule.
    Leaf-blades, especially those of basal leaves, conspicu-
    ously ciliate.   9. *H. canadensis.*
    Leaf-blades perfectly glabrous, at least never ciliate.
      Corolla 8–9 mm. long: mature hypanthium and calyx
      3.5–4 mm. long.   10. *H. longifolia.*
      Corolla 4–5.5 mm. long: mature hypanthium and
      calyx 2.5–3 mm. long. 11. *H. tenuifolia.*
Sepals shorter than the hypanthium.
  Stem erect or ascending, sometimes diffusely branched at
  the base, the branches neither spreading nor prostrate.
    Capsule much longer than broad, 2.5–3 mm. long. 12. *H. angustifolia.*
    Capsule fully as broad as long, 1–1.5 mm. long. 13. *H. filifolia.*
  Stem branched at the base, the branches prostrate or
  spreading.   14. *H. pulvinata.*

1. H. caerulea L. Plant often matted, the stem slender, 2–15 cm. tall: leaf-
blades oval, ovate, or spatulate, 2–5 mm. long: corolla lilac, blue, or white,
except the yellow eye, lobes 5–7 mm. long:
capsule 3–4 mm. wide.—(BLUETS. INNO-
CENCE.)—Damp grassy places and meadows,
various provinces, Ga. to La., Ont., N. S.,
and Miquelon.—Spr.–sum.

2. H. serpyllifolia Michx. Plant matted,
the stems creeping: leaf-blades ovate, oval,
or suborbicular, 1–6 mm. long: corolla
usually deep-blue, except the yellowish or
white eye; lobes 5–7 mm. long: capsule 2–3
mm. wide.—Mt. tops and damp slopes, Blue
Ridge to Appalachian Plateau, Ga. to W.
Va. and Pa.—Spr.–sum.—Introduced locally
into the Coastal Plain.

3. H. pusilla Schoepf. Plant 1–10 cm. tall, sometimes sparingly branched:
leaf-blades oval, elliptic, or ovate, or sometimes narrowly spatulate to nearly

linear, 2–10 mm. long: sepals becoming 2–2.5 mm. long: corolla deep-blue; limb 6.5–8 mm. wide: capsule 4–5 mm. wide. [*H. minor* (Michx.) Britton.]— Sandy soil, Coastal Plain, and adj. provinces, Fla. to Tex., Ark., Ill., and Va.—Spr.

4. **H. minima** Beck. Plant more or less diffusely branched, the branches 1–10 cm. long: leaf-blades spatulate to obovate or ovate, 2–8 cm. long: sepals becoming 3–3.5 mm. long: corolla lilac or bluish; limb 7.5–9 mm. wide: capsule 3–4 mm. wide.—Dry hillsides, various provinces N of Coastal Plain, Tenn. to Tex. and Mo.—Spr.

5. **H. procumbens** (Walt.) Standley. Plant with prostrate, often creeping stems and branches 0.5–4 dm. long, sparingly pubescent or nearly glabrous: leaf-blades oval to suborbicular, 5–18 mm. long: sepals broadly elliptic to ovate, 1–1.5 mm. long: corolla white, glabrous within: capsule 4–4.5 mm. wide, sparingly pubescent. [*H. rotundifolia* Michx.]—Sandy soil, often in damp pinelands. Coastal Plain, Fla. to La. and S. C.—Spr.–fall.

6. **H. lanceolata** (Poir.) Britton. Plant 1–3 dm. tall: blades of the stem-leaves elliptic-lanceolate to lanceolate, acute; sepals linear, 4–8 mm. long, recurved at the tip, fully twice as long as the hypanthium: corolla lilac or bluish; tube 5–6 mm. long: capsule 3 mm. thick.—Woods, Coastal Plain and adj. provinces, Ala. to Okla., Ill., and N. C.—Spr.

7. **H. purpurea** L. Plant 0.5–4 dm. tall: blades of the stem-leaves suborbicular to ovate or elliptic-ovate (elliptic to lanceolate and relatively small in *H. purpurea pubescens*), 2.5–4.5 cm. long: sepals subulate or linear-lanceolate, 2–3.5 mm. long, about as long as the hypanthium: corolla lilac, light-purple or white; tube 6–7 mm. long: capsule 2.5–3 mm. thick.—Moist soil, various provinces, rarely Coastal Plain, Ga. to Ark., Ia., and Md.—Spr.–fall.

8. **H. montana** (Chickering) Small. Similar to *H. purpurea* in habit, but typically smaller: blades of the stem-leaves ovate, 0.5–1.5 cm. long: sepals lanceolate to elliptic-lanceolate at maturity, about 2 mm. long, about as long as the hypanthium: corolla purple; tube 9–11 mm. long: capsule 3–3.5 mm. thick.—Cliffs, Roan Mt. and vicinity, in the Blue Ridge of N. C. and Tenn. —Sum.

9. **H. canadensis** Willd. Plant 0.5–2 dm. tall, with the leaves mainly approximate on a caudex: blades of the stem-leaves elliptic or spatulate, mainly 1–3 cm. long: sepals elliptic to elliptic-lanceolate, 2–3 mm. long, longer than the hypanthium: corolla blue; tube 7–9 mm. long: capsule 2–2.5 mm. thick. [*H. ciliolata* Torr.]—Woods or rocky soil, various provinces, Tenn. to Ark., Ont., and Me.— Spr.–sum.

10. **H. longifolia** Gaertn. Plant 1–4 dm. tall, often tufted; blades of the stem-leaves linear to linear-lanceolate or linear-elliptic, 1–3 cm. long: sepals linear-subulate to lanceolate-subulate, 1.5–2 mm. long, slightly longer than the hypanthium: corolla pinkish or bluish; tube about 4 mm. long: capsule 2–2.5 mm. thick.—Sandy soil and rocky banks, various provinces, Ga. to Miss., Mo., Man., and Me.—Sum.

11. **H. tenuifolia** Nutt. Plant 1–4 dm. tall, slender: blades of the stem-leaves linear to linear-filiform, 1–4 cm. long: sepals lanceolate to subulate-lanceolate, 1–1.5 mm. long, slightly longer than the hypanthium: corolla pale-blue or whitish; tube 4–5.5 mm. long: capsule 1.5–2 mm. thick.—Dry soil and rocky banks Blue Ridge to Appalachian Plateau, Ga. to Ala., Ohio, and Va.— Spr.–sum.

12. H. angustifolia Michx. Plant 0.5–3 dm. tall, tufted or diffuse: blades o the stem-leaves narrowly linear to linear-filiform, 4 cm. long: sepals lanceolat 1–1.5 mm. long, much shorter than the hypanthium at maturity: corolla whit or purple-tinged; tube about 3 mm. long: capsule 2.5–3 mm. long, nearly ellir soid, nearly equalling the sepals.—Dry soil, limestone rocks, barrens, an prairies, various provinces, Fla. to Tex., Kans., and Ill.—Spr.–sum.

13. H. filifolia (A. Gray) Small. Plant loosely or diffusely branched, 0.5– dm. tall: blades of the stem-leaves narrowly linear to subulate, 0.5–3 cm. long sepals lanceolate, becoming deltoid, scarcely 1 mm. long: corolla white o purplish; tube about 3 mm. long, sparingly pubescent within: capsule globose obovoid, about 1.5 mm. long.—Pinelands and sandy places, Everglade Keys Fla. and Fla. Keys.—All year.

14. H. pulvinata Small. Plant compactly much branched, 0.8–1.2 dm. tall, th branches angled: blades of the stem-leaves linear or nearly so, mainly 1–1. cm. long, often curved: sepals ovate to elliptic-ovate, fully 1 mm. long: coroll bluish; tube about 3 mm. long, copiously pubescent within: capsule obovoid about 2.5 mm. long.—Sand-dunes, pen. Fla.—Spr.–fall.

4. PENTODON Hochst. Annual tender herbs. Leaf-blades broad Flowers in axillary or terminal cymes. Sepals 5, rather long. Corolla funnel form: tube short: lobes somewhat shorter than the tube. Stamens 5: filaments adnate to above the middle of the corolla-tube. Style columnar. Capsule included in the hypanthium, 2-lobed.—Two species, the following and 1 African.

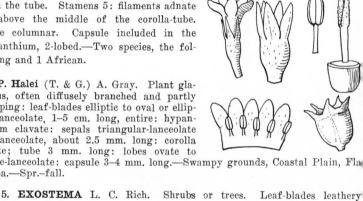

1. P. Halei (T. & G.) A. Gray. Plant gla brous, often diffusely branched and partly creeping: leaf-blades elliptic to oval or ellip tic-lanceolate, 1–5 cm. long, entire: hypan thium clavate: sepals triangular-lanceolate or lanceolate, about 2.5 mm. long: corolla white; tube 3 mm. long: lobes ovate to ovate-lanceolate: capsule 3–4 mm. long.—Swampy grounds, Coastal Plain, Fla to La.—Spr.–fall.

5. EXOSTEMA L. C. Rich. Shrubs or trees. Leaf-blades leathery Flowers axillary or in paniculate cymes. Sepals 5, short. Corolla with slende tube and 5 narrow lobes. Stamens 5: fila ments adnate to the base of the corolla-tube, pubescent below: anthers narrowly linear, exserted. Capsule elongate. Seeds winged. —About 30 species, tropical American.

1. E. caribaeum (Jacq.) R. & S. Shrub or small tree, the foliage glabrous: leaf blades elliptic, 2–6 cm. long: sepals 1–2 mm. long: corolla white or rose-tinged, the tube 3.5–4 cm. long; lobes narrowly linear: cap sule ellipsoid, 10–12 mm. long.—(PRINCE WOOD.)—Hammocks, Everglade Keys, Fla. and Florida Keys.—(W. I.)—Spr.–sum.

6. CASASIA A. Rich. Unarmed shrubs or trees. Leaf-blades leathery. Flowers in axillary cymes. Sepals 5, broad or narrow. Corolla with a stout tube and 5 relatively broad lobes. Stamens 5: filaments adnate to the lower part of the corolla-tube: anthers elongate, linear-sagittate, included. Berry thick. Seeds angled. —About 8 species, West Indian.

1. **C. clusiifolia** (Jacq.) Urban. Shrub or small tree, the bark pale: leaves clustered at the branch-tips; blades cuneate to obovate, 5-15 cm. long: hypanthium turbinate: sepals subulate: corolla white; tube 16-20 mm. long; lobes acuminate, shorter than the tube: berry mainly obovoid, 5-7 cm. long. [*Genipa clusiifolia* Jacq.] — SEVEN-YEAR APPLE.)—Coastal sand-dunes and hammocks, near the coast, S pen. Fla. and Florida Keys.—(*W. I.*)—All year.

7. RANDIA [Houst.] L. Armed shrubs or trees. Leaves relatively few: blades leathery. Flowers axillary. Sepals 4-5, short. Corolla with a short tube and 5 often very broad lobes. Stamens 4 or 5: filaments adnate to near the top of the corolla-tube: anthers ellipsoid or linear, partly exserted or included. Berry globular or elongate.—About 100 species, tropical.

1. **R. aculeata** L. Shrub 0.3-3 m. tall: leaves 1.5-5 cm. long; blades spatulate to oval, elliptic, or suborbicular: sepals triangular to ovate, about 1 mm. long: corolla white; tube 5-7 mm. long; lobes elliptic to ovate: berry oval to subglobose, 8-10 mm. long, greenish-white.—Hammocks and pinelands, S pen. Fla., and Florida Keys.—(*W. I.*)—All year.

8. CATESBAEA L. Armed shrubs. Leaves very numerous: blades leathery. Flowers axillary. Sepals 4, short. Corolla with a long tube and 4 short lobes. Stamens 4: filaments adnate to the base of the corolla-tube: anthers narrow or linear. Berry thick.—About 8 species, West Indian.

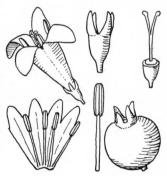

1. **C. parviflora** Sw. Shrub 1-3 m. tall: leaves 5-15 mm. long; blades spatulate, obovate or suborbicular, lustrous: sepals triangular to triangular-lanceolate, 1-1.5 mm. long: corolla white; tube campanulate, 3.5-4 mm. long; lobes deltoid, acutish: berry subglobose, 6-18 mm. long, blue or black.— Hammocks and dunes, Florida Keys.— (*W. I.*)—All year.—Fires and storms have greatly depleted the naturally rather limited growth of this shrub. The most extensive

growth now extant is on the sand-dunes behind the barrier dune on Bahia Honda Key.

9. HAMELIA Jacq. Unarmed shrubs or trees. Leaf-blades membranous. Flowers in dichotomous cymes. Sepals 5, minute. Corolla with a narrow fluted tube and 5 very short lobes. Stamens 5: filaments adnate to the base of the corolla-tube: anthers linear, included. Berry thick. —About 25 species tropical American.

1. H. patens Jacq. Shrub or small tree: leaf-blades elliptic, or elliptic-ovate, 8–15 cm. long: hypanthium turbinate: sepals about 1 mm. long: corolla crimson, 1.5–2.3 cm. long; lobes 2–3 mm. long: berry oval or ovoid, 5–7 mm. long, black. [*H. erecta* Jacq.?]—(HAMELIA.)—Hammocks, S pen. Fla. and Fla. Keys.—(*W. I.*)—All year.— Sometimes popularly known as fire-bush on account of the red inflorescence. This shrub or small tree is most conspicuous on the edges of hammocks. Not only are the calyx and corolla red, but also the inflorescence branches and the hypanthium.

10. CEPHALANTHUS L. Shrubs or trees. Leaf-blades thinnish. Flowers in capitate cymes. Sepals usually 4, rounded. Corolla with a long tube and usually 4 short lobes. Stamens usually 4: filaments adnate to the throat of the corolla: anthers ellipsoid or nearly so. Nut-like fruit obpyramidal.—About 6 species, American and Asiatic.

1. C. occidentalis L. Shrub or small tree: leaf-blades elliptic-lanceolate, or ovate-lanceolate, 5–20 cm. long, short-petioled: flower-heads globose, 2.5–3.5 cm. thick: sepals about 0.5 mm. long: corolla white, about 10 mm. long; lobes ovate to elliptic ovate: nutlets 7–8 mm. long.—(BUTTONBUSH.)— Swamps, ponds, low hammocks, and stream-banks, various provinces, Fla. to Tex., Calif., Ont., and N. B.—(*W. I., Mex.*)— Sum.–fall, or all year southward.

11. GUETTARDA L. Shrubs or trees. Leaf-blades thin or thickish. Flowers in axillary peduncled cymes. Sepals 2–4 or more, short, or obsolete. Corolla with a long tube and 4, or more, shorter lobes. Stamens 4–9: filaments adnate to near the top of the corolla-tube: anthers narrow, but short. Drupe globular, pubescent.—About 65 species, mostly tropical American.—All year.

Corolla 6–8 mm. long: leaf-blades strigillose or glabrate, not rugose. 1. *G. elliptica.*
Corolla 20–25 mm. long: leaf-blades scabro-pubescent, rugose. 2. *G. scabra.*

1. G. elliptica Sw. Shrub or small tree: leaf-blades thin, mainly elliptic, oval, or obovate, 2–4 cm. long: corolla pink or reddish; lobes mostly 4: style

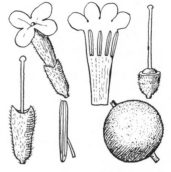

glabrous: drupe 8–11 mm. in diameter.—
(Velvet-seed.)—Hammocks and pinelands,
Everglade Keys, Fla. and Florida Keys.—
(*W. I.*)

2. **G. scabra** Vent. Shrub or small tree:
leaf-blades thick, mainly elliptic, oval, or
elliptic-ovate, 4.5–8 cm. long, or rarely
smaller: corolla white or reddish; lobes
mostly 6 or 7: style pubescent: drupe about
6 mm. in diameter.—(Rough velvet-seed.)
—Hammocks and pinelands, Everglade Keys,
Fla. and Fla. Keys, and coastal hammocks,
pen. Fla.—(*W. I.*)—The pinelands are not
the normal habitat for these plants. Where
hammocks have been destroyed some of the
trees become adapted to the conditions of the pinelands and persist in much
reduced stature, the soil being scant and poor in plant foods.

12. **ERITHALIS** P. Br. Shrubs. Leaf-blades leathery. Flowers in terminal cymes. Sepals 5–10, short or obsolete. Corolla with a short tube and
5–10 narrow lobes. Stamens 5–10: filaments
adnate to the base of the corolla-tube:
anthers ellipsoid to linear. Drupe berry-
like.—About 6 species, tropical American.

1. **E. fruticosa** L. Shrub with glabrous
foliage: leaf-blades oval to elliptic-obovate,
2.5–5 cm. long, lustrous: sepals minute:
corolla white; lobes elliptic, 3–5 mm. long:
drupe subglobose, 3–4 mm. thick, dark-
purple.—Sand-dunes and coastal hammocks,
S pen. Fla. and the Keys.—(*W. I.*)—This,
like many of the coastal dune plants thrive
in the sands apparently devoid of nourish-
ment. It often grows in large colonies. These vary much in height—in some
the shrubs are knee high in others head high.

13. **CHIOCOCCA** P. Br. Shrubs or vines. Leaf-blades leathery. Flowers on axillary raceme-like cymes. Sepals 5, short. Corolla with a relatively
short tube and 5 shorter lobes. Stamens 5: filaments long, essentially free
from the corolla-tube and united around the base of the style: anthers linear.
Drupe somewhat flattened, globular.—About 10 species, tropical American.—
All year.—Snowberries.

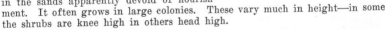

Corolla-lobes about 3 mm. long: anthers about 3 mm. long: seed 4–5 mm. long.
1. *C. alba.*

Corolla-lobes about 2 mm. long: anthers about 2 mm. long: seed
2–2.5 mm. long.
2. *C. pinetorum.*

1. **C. alba** (L.) A. Hitchc. Large, erect, diffuse, or reclining plants: leaf-
blades elliptic, oval, or ovate, 3–7 cm. long: corolla white, often becoming

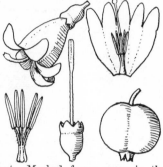

yellow; tube 7–8 mm. long: drupe white,
5.5–6.5 mm. in diameter. [*C. racemosa* L.]
—Hammocks, pen. Fla. and the Keys.—
(*W. I.*)

2. C. pinetorum Britton. Small, trailing
plant: leaf-blades elliptic or sometimes oval,
broadest below the middle, 1–3 cm. long:
corolla permanently white; tube 3.5–4 mm.
long: drupe white, 4–4.5 mm. in diameter.—
Pinelands, Everglade Keys, Fla. and Florida
Keys.—(*W. I.*)—On the lower Keys a form
grows in the hammocks which is more robust
than the typical form, but is here referred to
this species. The Florida representatives of
this genus need extensive study. Variations
in the leaves, flowers, and fruits are frequent. Marked forms occur in the
hammocks of the lower eastern coast, in the Big Cypress Swamp, and on the
Florida Keys. *Chiococca alba* is rarely found in the form of a small tree on
the upper Keys.

14. STRUMPFIA Jacq. Shrubs. Leaf-blades rigid-leathery. Flowers
in axillary raceme-like panicles. Sepals 5, short. Corolla rotate, with a very
short tube and 5 longer lobes. Stamens 5:
filaments very short, scarcely adnate to the
base of the corolla-tube, united: anthers
adnate by their broad connectives. Drupe
thick.—One species.

1. S. maritima Jacq. Much-branched pubescent shrub, the branches short-jointed:
leaf-blades linear to linear-elliptic, 1–2.5 cm.
long, revolute: sepals triangular to ovate-
triangular, becoming about 1 mm. long,
acute: corolla white, pubescent; lobes lanceolate to elliptic, 3–4 mm. long: drupe 4–6 mm.
long, white or red.—Coastal sand-dunes, and
hammocks, Florida Keys.—(*W. I.*)—All year.—Dried fruits have the fragrance
of red-cedar wood.

15. PSYCHOTRIA L. Shrubs or trees. Leaf-blades thinnish. Flowers
in terminal or axillary cymes. Sepals 4–6, short and broad. Corolla with a
relatively short tube and 4–6 usually somewhat shorter lobes. Stamens 4–6:
filaments adnate to near the top of the corolla-tube: anthers ellipsoid to oval.
Drupe thick, often berry-like.—More than 300 species, tropical American.—Spr.–
sum., or sporadically all year.

Inflorescence, twigs, and leaves pubescent: corolla-lobes as long
    as the tube: stone with high ridges.   1. *P. Sulzneri.*
Inflorescence, twigs, and leaves glabrous: corolla-lobes shorter
    than the tube: stone with flat ridges.
    Cymes sessile: sepals very shallow.   2. *P. nervosa.*
    Cymes peduncled: sepals deltoid.   3. *P. bahamensis.*

1. P. Sulzneri Small. Shrub, the branches pubescent: leaf-blades narrowly
oblong, elliptic, or elliptic-lanceolate, 8–15 cm. long: corolla green; tube 2–2.5

mm. long: anthers ellipsoid: drupe 5–6 mm. long, scarlet, orange, or yellow. [*P. tenuifolia* Griseb. Not Sw.]—(WILD-COFFEE.)—Hammocks, S pen. Fla. and adj. islands.—(*W. I.*)

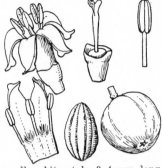

2. P. nervosa Sw. Shrub or small tree, the twigs glabrous: leaf-blades oval, elliptic, or elliptic-lanceolate, 6–15 cm. long: corolla white; tube 2.5–3 mm. long: anthers oval: drupe ellipsoid, 7–9 mm. long, red or rarely yellow.—(WILD-COFFEE.)—Hammocks, pen. Fla. and the Keys.—(*W. I.*)

3. P. bahamensis Millsp. Shrub or small tree, the twigs glabrous: leaf-blades lanceolate, elliptic, or oblanceolate, 3–12 cm. long: anthers oblong: drupe oval or ellipsoid, corolla white; tube 3–4 mm. long: 6–8 mm. long, bright-orange.— (BAHAMAN WILD-COFFEE.)—Hammocks, Fla. Keys.—(*W. I.*)

16. **PAEDERIA** L. Woody vines. Leaves opposite: blades broad, at least relatively so, entire. Flowers borne in dichotomous cymes. Sepals 4 or 5, narrow. Corolla campanulate: lobes 4 or 5, relatively short. Filaments almost wholly adnate to the corolla-tube: anthers narrow. Styles slender, united at the base. Berry rather dry, the outer coat brittle and early falling away. Seeds flat, margined.—About 18 species, mostly Asiatic.

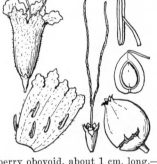

1. P. foetida L. Stem twining, often slightly pubescent in lines: leaf-blades elliptic to elliptic-lanceolate, 3–11 cm. long, acuminate at the apex, rounded, truncate or subcordate at the base, slender-petioled: sepals acute: corolla pale-lilac, 7–9 mm. long; lobes about ¼ as long as the tube, apiculate: berry obovoid, about 1 cm. long.—Thickets and fence-rows, pen. Fla. Nat. of East Indies.—Spr.–fall.

17. **MITCHELLA** L. Undershrubs with creeping stems. Leaf-blades leathery. Flowers in pairs, the hypanthia coalescent. Sepals usually 4, short. Corolla with a relatively long tube and usually 4 short lobes. Stamens 4: filaments adnate to the corolla-tube. Drupes paired.— Two species, the following and 1 Asiatic.

1. M. repens L. Stem and branches matted, 1–4 dm. long: leaf-blades ovate to orbicular, or elliptic, 8–30 mm. long: sepals deltoid, less than 1 mm. long: corolla white or pinkish; tube 9–12 mm. long; lobes ovate to elliptic: fruit globular, 7–10 mm. thick, red or white, aromatic.—(TWIN-BERRY. PARTRIDGE-BERRY.)—Damp woods, sandy hammocks, and shaded banks, often in acid soil, various provinces, Fla. to Tex., Minn., and N. S.—Spr.–fall.

18. **MORINDA** [Vaill.] L. Shrubs or trees. Leaf-blades rather thin. Flowers in capitate cymes, the hypanthia coalescent. Sepals usually 5, minute or obsolete. Corolla with a relatively short tube and usually 5 somewhat shorter lobes. Stamens usually 5: filaments adnate to near the top of the corolla-tube: anthers linear. Drupe united into a fleshy syncarp.—About 40 species, tropical.

1. **M. Roioc** L. Shrub or vine: leaf-blades elliptic to cuneate, 5–10 cm. long: flowers several in a head: corolla white or reddish; lobes elliptic or elliptic-lanceolate, 2.5–3.5 mm. long: syncarp 2–3.5 cm. long, yellow.— Hammocks and pinelands, pen. Fla. and the Keys.—All year.

19. **RICHARDIA** L. Annual or perennial diffuse herbs. Leaf-blades herbaceous. Flowers in contracted involucrate cymes. Sepals 4–8, rather broad. Corolla with a relatively short tube and 4–8 shorter lobes. Stamens 4–8: filaments adnate to the top of the corolla-tube: anthers ellipsoid to oval. Mature carpels separating from each other. [*Richardsonia* Kunth.]—About 8 species, in the warm part of America.—Spr.–fall or all year.

Corolla 5–6.5 mm. long; tube about twice as long as the calyx: mature carpels 3–3.5 mm. long.   1. *R. scabra.*
Corolla 3.5–4 mm. long; tube about thrice as long as the calyx: mature carpels 2–2.5 mm. long.   2. *R. brasiliensis.*

1. **R. scabra** St. Hil. Annual, the stems more or less branched: leaf-blades elliptic, lanceolate, or ovate, 2–8 cm. long: sepals lanceolate to ovate-lanceolate, becoming 2–2.5 mm. long: corolla white; lobes less than ⅓ as long as the tube: anthers ellipsoid: mature carpels ellipsoid.—Sandy soil, especially in cult fields, Coastal Plain, Fla. to Tex. and N. C.; also in Ind.—(*Mex.*) —Nat. of Trop. Am.

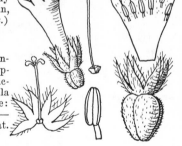

2. **R. brasiliensis** (Moq.) Gomez. Perennial, the branches diffuse: leaf-blades elliptic, 1.5–4 cm. long: sepals ovate to elliptic-ovate, becoming about 1 mm. long: corolla white; lobes fully ⅓ as long as the tube: anthers oval: mature carpels obovoid.— Waste-places and pinelands, pen. Fla. Nat. of S. Am.

20. **ERNODEA** Sw. Diffuse or vine-like shrubs. Leaf-blades leathery. Flowers axillary. Sepals 4–6, narrow. Corolla with a long tube and 4–6 relatively long lobes. Stamens 4–6: filaments adnate to the top of the corolla-tube: anthers narrow. Drupe thin-fleshy.—About 6 species, tropical American. —The plants of the following species flower throughout most of the year.

Sepals about one-third as long as the corolla-tube: anthers linear.   1. *E. littoralis.*
Sepals about one-half as long as the corolla-tube: anthers narrowly ellipsoid.   2. *E. angusta.*

1. E. littoralis Sw. Stem and branches prostrate: leaves fleshy; blades mainly elliptic, sometimes narrowly so, 2–3.5 cm. long: corolla white; tube mostly over 10 mm. long: anthers over 2 mm. long: drupe mostly globular.—Coastal sand-dunes and rocky shores, southern pen. Fla. and the Keys.—(*W. I.*)

2. E. angusta Small. Stem and branches more slender than those of *E. littoralis*: leaves firm; blades linear, 2–4 cm. long: corolla usually reddish; tube mostly less than 10 mm. long: anthers over 1.5 mm. long: drupe mostly oval.—Pinelands, Everglade Keys, Fla. and Florida Keys.— (*W. I.*)—Our two species occupy quite different habitats, but they are both sprawling or creeping vine-like shrubs. The first species grows in the poorest soil, the coastal dunes, where it completely covers large areas of sand with its wiry stems and myriad leaves.

21. DIODIA [Gronov.] L. Perennial creeping herbs. Leaf-blades soft-herbaceous. Flowers axillary. Sepals 2. Corolla white or pink, salverform, with a long slender tube and 4 narrow lobes. Stamens 4: filaments adnate to the top of the corolla-tube, the free portion elongate: anthers linear. Stigmas filiform. Drupe thin-fleshy, ribbed. About 20 species, mostly American.— Spr.–fall, or all year S.—BUTTONWEEDS.

Corolla-tube over 6 mm. long: capsule oval or ellipsoid: sepals ciliate.
  Stem sparingly pubescent on the angles or nearly glabrous.
    Capsules ellipsoid: leaf-blades narrowed at the base.   1. *D. virginiana.*
    Capsules oval: leaf-blades truncate or subcordate at the
      base.   2. *D. tetragona.*
  Stem hirsute.   3. *D. hirsuta.*
Corolla-tube less than 5 mm. long: capsule globular: sepals
  eciliate.   4. *D. Harperi.*

1. D. virginiana L. Stem branching, 1–15 dm. long, sparingly pubescent on the angles: leaf-blades thinnish, spatulate, to linear-elliptic, 3–8 cm. long, acute or acuminate: sepals linear to linear-lanceolate, 4–6 mm. long: corolla-tube 6–8 mm. long: fruit 7–9 mm. long.—Low grounds, swamps, and stream banks, Coastal Plain, Fla. to Tex., Mo., and N. J.

2. D. tetragona Walt. Stem branching, 2–10 dm. long, the angles often pubescent: leaf-blades spatulate to obovate, usually somewhat rhombic: sepals ovate to ovate-lanceolate, 4–5 mm. long: corolla-tube 6.5–7 mm. long: fruit 4.5–5.5 mm. long.—Damp sandy soil, Coastal Plain, Fla. to La. and N. C.

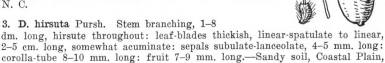

3. D. hirsuta Pursh. Stem branching, 1–8 dm. long, hirsute throughout: leaf-blades thickish, linear-spatulate to linear, 2–5 cm. long, somewhat acuminate: sepals subulate-lanceolate, 4–5 mm. long: corolla-tube 8–10 mm. long: fruit 7–9 mm. long.—Sandy soil, Coastal Plain, Fla. to N. C.

4. D. Harperi Small. Plant smaller than that of the three preceding species, glabrous throughout: leaf-blades spatulate to linear, 1–3 cm. long, acute, eciliate: sepals lanceolate, 3–4 mm. long: corolla-tube 3.5–4.5 mm. long: fruit about 5 mm. long.—Pond margins, Coastal Plain, S Ga.

22. DIODELLA Small. Annual diffuse herbs. Leaf-blades firm-herbaceous. Flowers axillary. Sepals 4. Corolla with a relatively short thick tube and 4 broad lobes. Stamens 5: filaments adnate up to the top of the corolla-tube, the free portions very short: anthers oval or ovoid. Stigma capitate or 2-lobed. Capsular fruit crustaceous, lobed. About 15 species, American.—BUTTON-WEEDS.

Corolla 4–5 mm. long: fruit hispidulous.   1. *D. teres.*
Corolla 6–10 mm. long: fruit strigillose.   2. *D. rigida.*

1. D. teres (Walt.) Small. Stem or branches 1–4 dm. long, spreading or creeping, pubescent: leaf-blades linear or narrowly linear-lanceolate, 1–4 cm. long: sepals 4, acute, 1.5–2 mm. long: corolla white or pinkish, 4–5 mm. long; lobes broadly ovate to deltoid: fruit obovoid, 4–4.5 mm. long. [*Diodia teres* Walt.]—Stony soil, fields, roadsides, open woods, dry sandy banks, various provinces, Fla. to Tex., Kans., Mich., and Conn.—Sum.–fall.

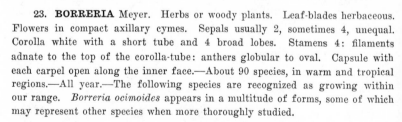

2. D. rigida (Cham. & Schlecht.) Small. Stem and branches procumbent or prostrate, finely pubescent: leaf-blades thick, linear to linear-lanceolate, mostly 1–3.5 cm. long, acute, minutely rough-pubescent; stipules long-setose: sepals ovate to ovate-lanceolate, 1.5–2 mm. long: corolla white or pinkish, 6–10 mm. long or rarely larger; lobes ovate to ovate-lanceolate: fruit obovoid, 3–3.5 mm. long.—Pinelands, Everglade Keys, Fla.—(*W. I.*)—All year.

23. BORRERIA Meyer. Herbs or woody plants. Leaf-blades herbaceous. Flowers in compact axillary cymes. Sepals usually 2, sometimes 4, unequal. Corolla white with a short tube and 4 broad lobes. Stamens 4: filaments adnate to the top of the corolla-tube: anthers globular to oval. Capsule with each carpel open along the inner face.—About 90 species, in warm and tropical regions.—All year.—The following species are recognized as growing within our range. *Borreria ocimoides* appears in a multitude of forms, some of which may represent other species when more thoroughly studied.

Plant perennial: flowers in a dense terminal glomerule, and sometimes in supplementary glomerule in the upper leaf-axils: leaves fleshy; blades of the upper ones, at least, narrowly linear.   1. *B. terminalis.*
Plant annual: flowers in clusters in all or many of the leaf-axils:
  leaves herbaceous; blades not linear.
    Sepals subulate, nearly or quite as long as the capsule.   2. *B. ocimoides.*
    Sepals ovate, much shorter than the capsule.   3. *B. laevis.*

1. B. terminalis Small. Perennial, 0.5–3 dm. tall, the stems often in colonies: leaf-blades linear-spatulate to linear, often narrowly so, 1–3 cm. long, veinless:

corolla about 3 mm. long; lobes ovate, about as long as the tube. [*B. podocephala* (Fl. SE. U. S.)]—Pinelands, Everglade Keys, Fla. and lower Florida Keys.—A related species, *B. tenella* (H.B.K.) C. & S., has been collected at Pensacola, Fla. It has subulate calyx-lobes and a corolla about 5 mm. long, with the lobes much shorter than the tube.

2. B. ocimoides (Burm.) DC. Annual, 1–9 dm. tall: leaf-blades elliptic or linear-elliptic, 1–2.5 cm. long, veiny: corolla about equalling the calyx; lobes about 1 mm. long. [*B. parviflora* G. F. W. Meyer. *B. micrantha* F. & G.]—Pinelands, S pen. Fla. and the Keys.—(*W. I., Mex., C. A., S. A., O. W.*)

3. B. laevis (Lam.) Griseb. Annual, 2–6 dm. tall: leaf-blades elliptic or oval, 1.5–6 cm. long, veiny: corolla much exceeding the calyx; lobes about 2 mm. long. [*Spermacoce Chapmanii* T. & G.]—Woods and stream-banks, Coastal Plain, Fla. to La.—(*W. I., Mex., C. A., S. A.*)

24. SPERMACOCE [Dill.] L. Herbs or woody plants. Leaf-blades herbaceous. Flowers in dense, axillary cymes. Sepals usually 4. Corolla with a short tube and 4 broad lobes. Stamens 4: filaments adnate at least to the lower part of the corolla-tube: anthers oval or globular. Capsule with 1 dehiscent and 1 indehiscent carpel.—Four or five species, American.

Stem and leaves glabrous or nearly so.
  Plant perennial: corolla very villous in the throat.   1. *S. glabra*.
  Plant annual: corolla glabrous or slightly hairy in the throat.
    Corolla-lobes shorter than the tube; hypanthium bristly-
      pubescent.   2. *S. tenuior*.
    Corolla-lobes longer than the tube: hypanthium not
      bristly.   3. *S. keyensis*.
Stem and leaves hirsute with whitish hairs.   4. *S. tetraquetra*.

1. S. glabra Michx. Stem 1–6 dm. tall, glabrous or nearly so: leaf-blades elliptic, varying to broadest below or above the middle, 2–7 cm. long: sepals becoming 1.5 mm. long, eciliate or nearly so: corolla white; lobes elliptic-ovate: fruit about 3 mm. long.—River-banks and low grounds, various provinces, Fla. to Tex., Kans., and Ohio.—Sum. or all year S.

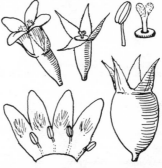

2. S. tenuior (L.) Lam. Stem 1–5 dm. tall, or prostrate: leaf-blades elliptic, or elliptic-lanceolate, 2–5 cm. long: sepals finely bristly-pubescent: corolla white; lobes ovate, shorter than the tube: fruit over 2 mm. long, coarsely hispidulous.—Hammocks, Coastal Plain, Fla. to La. and Ga.—Spr.–sum.

3. S. keyensis Small. Stem and branches prostrate, 1–4 dm. long, glabrous: leaf-blades elliptic, varying to broadest below or above the middle, or elliptic-lanceolate, mostly 1–2 cm. long: sepals minutely pubescent: corolla white; lobes ovate, longer than the tube: fruit 1.5–2 mm. long, minutely hispidulous. [*S. porto-*

ricensis (Fl. SE. U. S.)]—Open hammocks and sandy places, Florida Keys.—All year.

4. S. tetraquetra A. Rich. Stem 2–14 dm. tall, usually branched, hirsute, four-sided: leaf-blades elliptic, often narrowly so, varying to broadest above or below the middle, acute; flower-clusters dense: hypanthium hispid: sepals lanceolate to subulate-lanceolate, 1–1.5 mm. long; corolla white, 2–2.5 mm. long; lobes ovate, much shorter than the tube, pubescent at the base within: fruit ellipsoid, fully 2–2.5 mm. long, hispid.—Pinelands, Everglade Keys, Fla.—(*W. I.*)—All year.

25. GALIUM L. Perennial, or sometimes annual, weak spreading herbs. Leaves with blades and stipules about equal in size. Flowers in simple or branched cymes. Sepals usually obsolete. Corolla rotate, with 3–5 lobes. Stamens 3–5. Fruit globular or didymous. About 250 species, widely distributed.—BEDSTRAWS. CLEAVERS.

Fruit dry.
  Plants annual.
    Flowers in axillary cymules.
      Fruit densely uncinate-hispid.   I. APARINA.
      Fruit slightly granular or smooth.   II. PARISIENSA.
    Flowers solitary in the axils.   III. VIRGATA.
  Plants perennial.
    Fruit uncinate-hispid.
      Leaves and stipules in 4's; blades not bristle-tipped.   IV. PILOSA.
      Leaves and stipules in 6's; blades bristle-tipped.   V. TRIFLORA.
    Fruit smooth and glabrous or merely warty.
      Corolla brownish or brownish-purple.   VI. LATIFOLIA.
      Corolla white or greenish.   VII. TINCTORIA.
Fruit fleshy.   VIII. BERMUDENSA.

I. APARINA

Plant with the long weak reclining stems retrorse-scabrous or prickly on the angles.   1. *G. Aparine.*

II. PARISIENSA

Plant diffusely branched, the branches minutely scabrous on the angles.   2. *G. parisiense.*

III. VIRGATA

Plant with slender stems and remote whorls of very short leaves and stipules.   3. *G. virgatum.*

IV. PILOSA

Flowers manifestly pedicelled.   4. *G. pilosum.*
Flowers sessile or nearly so.
  Leaf-blades elliptic-ovate to oval: corolla pubescent.   5. *G. circaezans.*
  Leaf-blades lanceolate or ovate-lanceolate: corolla glabrous or nearly so.   6. *G. lanceolatum.*

V. TRIFLORA

Plant fragrant in drying: leaf-blades bristle-tipped.   7. *G. triflorum.*

VI. LATIFOLIA

Leaf-blades broadly lanceolate, 3-veined: fruit smooth.   8. *G. latifolium.*
Leaf-blades narrowly or linear-lanceolate, mostly 1-veined: fruit minutely warty.   9. *G. arkansanum.*

VII. TINCTORIA

Leaf-blades obtuse or merely acute.
  Corolla-lobes 3, obtuse: stem scabrous.   10. *G. Claytonii.*
  Corolla-lobes 4, acute: stem smooth.
    Stipules as large as the leaves or nearly so: fruits when didymous 3–3.5 mm. wide.   11. *G. tinctorium.*
    Stipules much smaller and narrower than the leaves: fruits when didymous 4–5 mm. wide.   12. *G. filifolium.*
Leaf-blades cuspidate.   13. *G. asprellum.*

VIII. BERMUDENSA

Leaf-blades linear or nearly so.   14. *G. uniflorum.*
Leaf-blades elliptic to oval.   15. *G. bermudense.*

1. G. Aparine L. Plant reclining, 1–15 dm. long, the stem retrorse-scabrous or prickly: leaves, and stipules, with linear-spatulate blades 1–8 cm. long, the upper side with short stout hairs (small-leaved, abundantly fruited, and with longer-hispidulous fruits in *G. Aparine Vaillantii*): corolla white; lobes ovate, 1–1.5 mm. long, acute: fruit 3–5 mm. thick, densely uncinate-hispid.—(Goose-grass. Spring-cleavers.) —Thickets, rich shaded soil, and waste-places, various provinces, Fla. to Tex., Alas., Ont., and N. B.—(*Eurasia.*)—Spr.–sum.

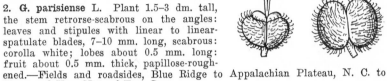

2. G. parisiense L. Plant 1.5–3 dm. tall, the stem retrorse-scabrous on the angles: leaves and stipules with linear to linear-spatulate blades, 7–10 mm. long, scabrous: corolla white; lobes about 0.5 mm. long: fruit about 0.5 mm. thick, papillose-roughened.—Fields and roadsides, Blue Ridge to Appalachian Plateau, N. C. to Tenn. and Va. Nat. of Eu.—Sum.

3. G. virgatum Nutt. Plant 1–3 dm. tall, the stem hispid, with short internodes: leaves and stipules with linear-elliptic blades, 3–10 mm. long, very hispid on the margin and midrib: corolla white; lobes ovate, less than 1 mm. long, glabrous: fruit about 3 mm. thick, uncinate-hispid, (glabrous and smooth like the foliage, *G. virgatum leiocarpum*).—Dry soil, Coastal Plain and adj. provinces, Tenn. to La., Tex., and Mo.—Spr.

4. G. pilosum Ait. Plant 3–8 dm. tall, the stem hirsute, 4-angled above the swollen nodes (or internodes merely pubescent with uncinate hairs on the angles in *G. pilosum puncticulosum*; glabrous in *G. pilosum laevicaule*): leaves and stipules, with oval-ovate or elliptic blades 8–10 mm. long, sparingly pubescent, pellucid-punctate beneath: corolla yellowish or purplish; lobes ovate to lanceolate, about 1.5 mm. long: fruit about 4 mm. thick, uncinate-hispid.—Open woods, shaded banks, fence-rows, and thickets, various provinces, Fla. to Tex., Kans., Ont., and Mass.—(*W. I.*)—Sum.

5. G. circaezans Michx. Plant 2–4 dm. tall, the stem glabrous or sparingly pubescent: leaves and stipules with elliptic-ovate or oval blades 15–30 mm. long, or more, sparingly pubescent: corolla greenish; lobes ovate, acute, less than 2 mm. long: fruit about 5 mm. thick, uncinate-hispid.—(Wild-liquorice.) —Dry woods, thickets, and open banks, various provinces, Fla. to Tex., Minn., and Que.—Sum.

6. G. lanceolatum Torr. Plant sparingly pubescent in parts, the stem branched at the base, mostly 2.5–6 dm. tall: leaves and stipules shorter than the internodes, 30–75 mm. long; blades of the upper leaves lanceolate or ovate-lanceolate, acute or slightly acuminate, sparingly pubescent, especially on the veins beneath, 3-ribbed: flowers few, sessile on the spreading cyme-branches: corolla glabrous or nearly so, 3–5 mm. broad, greenish, or yellowish, becoming purple; lobes 4, slender-tipped: fruit as in *G. circaezans.*—(Wild-liquorice.)—Dry thickets and rocky woods, various provinces, N of Coastal Plain, N. C. to Ky., Ont., and Que.—Sum.

7. G. triflorum Michx. Plant reclining, sweet-scented in drying, the stem 3–10 dm. long, sparsely hispid or rarely glabrous: leaves and stipules in 6's, with broadly linear to elliptic blades 1–8 cm. long, the margins and midrib hispid: flowers relatively few, 3 together on the ultimate peduncles: corolla greenish or yellowish-white; lobes fully 1.5 mm. long: fruit about 3 mm. thick, uncinate-hispid.—(SWEET-SCENTED BEDSTRAW.)—Thickets and woods, various provinces, Fla. to Tex., Calif., Alas., Ont., and Newf.—(*Eurasia.*)—Spr.–sum.

8. **G. latifolium** Michx. Plant 3–6 dm. tall, the stem glabrous (hispid, like the leaves, in *G. latifolium hispidifolium*): leaves and stipules with broadly lanceolate blades 3–6 cm. long: corolla brownish; lobes ovate-lanceolate, acuminate, about 2.5 mm. long: fruit about 2.5 mm. thick, glabrous, slightly fleshy.—Woods, Blue Ridge to Appalachian Plateau, Ga. to Ala. and Pa.—Sum.–fall.

9. **G. arkansanum** A. Gray. Plant about 3 dm. tall, the stem glabrous below, retrorse-scabrous above: leaves and stipules with narrowly or linear-lanceolate blades 25–40 mm. long, scabrous on the margin and midrib, densely pellucid-punctate beneath: corolla brownish purple: lobes ovate-lanceolate, acuminate, about 2.5 mm. long: fruit 2–2.5 mm. thick, glabrous.—Dry soil, often in rocky woods, various provinces N of Coastal Plain, Tenn. to Okla. and Mo.—Sum.

10. **G. Claytonii** Michx. Plant more or less diffuse, 1.5–6 dm. tall, the stem retrorse-scabrous on the angles: leaves and stipules mostly in 5's or 6's, with linear-spatulate or spatulate-elliptic blades 8–15 mm. long, obtuse, with scabrous margins and midrib: corolla white; lobes about 1 mm. long: fruit about 1.5 mm. thick, glabrous.—Marshes and ditches, various provinces, N. C. to Tex., Nebr., and Que.—Spr.–sum.

11. **G. tinctorium** L. Plant 1.5–2.5 dm. tall, the stem glabrous or nearly so: leaves and stipules mostly in 4's, with linear-lanceolate blades 15–25 mm. long; (plants decumbent with linear-spatulate leaves, in *G. tinctorium floridanum*): flowers 2 or 3 in terminal clusters: corolla white; lobes about 1 mm. long: fruit, when didymous, 3–3.5 mm. wide, smooth.—Damp shaded places, swamps, and wet thickets, various provinces, Fla. to Tex., Ariz., Nebr., and Que.—Spr.–sum., or all year southward.

12. **G. filifolium** (Wiegand) Small. Plant 1.3 dm. tall, the stem and branches diffuse, more or less sprawling in age, glabrous: leaves and stipules mostly in 4's, with very narrowly linear blades mostly 1–1.5 cm. long: flowers in open cymes, filiform-pedicelled: corolla white, about 1 mm. long: fruit, when didymous, 4–5 mm. wide, glabrous.—Low pinelands, swamps, and stream-banks, Coastal Plain, Ga. to N. C.—Spr.–sum.

13. **G. asprellum** L. Plant reclining, the stem 3–16 dm. long, retrorsely scabrous or prickly: leaves and stipules in 6's, with elliptic-spatulate to elliptic blades 1–2 cm. long, the margins and midrib scabrous: flowers very numerous: corolla white; lobes fully 1.5 mm. long: fruit about 2.5 mm. thick, smooth and glabrous.—(ROUGH-BEDSTRAW.)—Open swamps and moist thickets, various provinces, N. C. to Nebr., Ont., and Newf.—Spr.–sum.

14. **G. uniflorum** Michx. Plant evergreen, about 3 dm. tall, the stem smooth and glabrous: leaves and stipules with linear blades 25–28 mm. long, acute, glabrous beneath: flowers solitary in pairs: corolla white; lobes broadly ovate, about 2 mm. long: fruit about 1.5–2 mm. thick, baccate, glabrous.—Dry woods, Coastal Plain and adj. provinces, Fla. to Tex. and S. C.—Sum.

15. **G. bermudense** L. Plant evergreen, diffuse, the stem 1–6 dm. long, hispidulous or glabrous: leaves and stipules oval or elliptic, 5–25 mm. long, cuspidate, pellucid-punctate and pubescent beneath: flowers 3–5 together: corolla greenish-white; lobes narrowly ovate, about 2 mm. long: fruit about 5 mm. thick, baccate, usually smooth and glabrous. [*G. hispidulum* Michx.]—Dry sandy soil, Coastal Plain, Fla. to La. and N. J.—(*W. I.*)—Spr.–sum.

Sherardia arvensis L. with the habit of *Galium*, but with funnelform corollas, has been found in grass plots in northern Fla. and in Tenn.

FAMILY 2. **CAPRIFOLIACEAE** — HONEYSUCKLE FAMILY

Shrubs, trees, vines, or perennial herbs. Leaves opposite: blades entire, toothed, or pinnate. Flowers mostly perfect, in terminal or axillary cymes, or axillary. Calyx of mostly 4 or 5 minute or foliaceous sepals. Corolla of 4 or 5 partly united petals, often irregular. Androecium of 4 or 5 stamens: filaments partly adnate to the corolla-tube. Gynoecium 2–5-carpellary. Ovary inferior. Fruit baccate, drupaceous, or capsular.—About 12 genera and 300 species, mostly in the Northern Hemisphere.

Corolla rotate to urceolate, regular or nearly so: stigma 3–5-lobed: style wanting
or very short.   Tribe I. SAMBUCEAE.
Corolla tubular to tubular-campanulate or trumpet-shaped,
often irregular: stigma capitate: style elongate.   II. LONICEREAE.

I. SAMBUCEAE
Leaf-blades pinnate: drupe berry-like with 3–5 nutlets.   1. SAMBUCUS.
Leaf-blades simple: drupe with one nutlet.   2. VIBURNUM.

II. LONICEREAE
Flowers axillary: herbs.   3. TRIOSTEUM.
Flowers in axillary or terminal clusters or open cymes:
    shrubs or vines.
  Fruit baccate.
    Corolla regular or nearly so; tube short or elongate:
        limb with ascending or spreading lobes.
      Corolla short, more or less campanulate; tube
        short: stamens adnate up to the top of the
        corolla-tube.   4. SYMPHORICARPOS.
      Corolla elongate, nearly tubular; tube gradually
        enlarged upward: stamens not adnate up to the
        top of the corolla-tube.   5. PHENIANTHUS.
    Corolla irregular; limb 2-lipped.
      Flowers in pairs each of which terminates an axil-
        lary peduncle, accompanied by a pair of
        bracts and bractlets.
        Bracts minute, very different from the leaves:
          corolla-tube gibbous at the base: upright
          shrubs.   6. XYLOSTEON.
        Bracts foliaceous, resembling the leaves:
          corolla-tube not gibbous at the base: vines.   7. NINTOOA.
      Flowers in whorls at or near the ends of the
        branches, the bracts and usually some of the
        upper pairs of leaves connate-perfoliate.   8. LONICERA.
  Fruit capsular.   9. DIERVILLA.

1. **SAMBUCUS** [Tourn.] L. Shrubs or trees, with pithy stems. Leaf-blades pinnate. Flowers white, in thyrsoid or flat-topped cymes. Sepals small. Anthers ellipsoid or oval. Ovary 3–5-celled. Drupe with 3–5 nutlets—About 25 species, widely distributed.—Spr. or all year S.—ELDERS.

Cyme flat-topped or slightly convex: fruit dark-purple to black.
  Lateral leaflets merely toothed, or the lower pair rarely with a
    lateral pinna.   1. *S. canadensis.*
  Lateral leaflets, at least the lower pair, pinnately 2- or 3-
    foliolate.   2. *S. Simpsonii.*
Cyme compact, rounded: fruit red.   3. *S. pubens.*

1. **S. canadensis** L. Shrub with soft wood and white pith: leaflets mostly 5–11, the blades of the lateral ones elliptic, lanceolate, ovate or oval, 3–14 cm.

long, serrate with incurved teeth: cyme merely convex: corolla 5–6 mm. wide: drupe 4–5 mm. in diameter.—(COMMON-ELDER.)— Open places, woods, river-banks, and swamps, various provinces, Ga. to Tex., Man., and N. B.

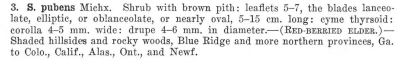

2. S. Simpsonii Rehder. Tall shrub or small tree with white pith: leaflets 5–9, the blades of the lateral ones elliptic or nearly so, 3–8 cm. long, serrate: cyme flat: corolla 5–7 mm. wide: drupe 5–6 mm. in diameter. [*S. intermedia* (Fl. SE. U. S.)]—(GULF-ELDER. SOUTHERN-ELDER.)—Hammocks and marshes, Coastal Plain, Fla. to La.—Forms vast thickets in the Lake Okeechobee region and the coastwise lagoons of southern Florida, where it blooms throughout the year.

3. S. pubens Michx. Shrub with brown pith: leaflets 5–7, the blades lanceolate, elliptic, or oblanceolate, or nearly oval, 5–15 cm. long: cyme thyrsoid: corolla 4–5 mm. wide: drupe 4–6 mm. in diameter.—(RED-BERRIED ELDER.)— Shaded hillsides and rocky woods, Blue Ridge and more northern provinces, Ga. to Colo., Calif., Alas., Ont., and Newf.

2. VIBURNUM [Tourn.] L. Shrubs or trees, the stems not pithy. Leaf-blades simple. Flowers in round-topped cymes. Sepals small. Corolla white. Anthers oblong. Ovary 1-celled. Drupe with a single stone.—About 100 species, widely distributed.—Spr.–sum.—ARROW-WOODS.

Cyme with some of the marginal flowers radiant and sterile: drupe red to scarlet.   I. ALNIFOLIA.
Cyme without radiant marginal flowers: drupe blue or dark-purple to black.
  Leaf-blades palmately veined or palmately lobed.   II. ACERIFOLIA.
  Leaf-blades pinnately veined, entire or toothed.
    Filaments as long as the corolla or longer: leaves with manifest distinction between blades and petiole.
      Leaf-blades with straight pinnate veins which terminate in the teeth: stone of the drupe usually grooved.   III. DENTATA.
      Leaf-blades with curved veins which anastomose near the entire or toothed margin: stone flat and even.   IV. PRUNIFOLIA.
    Filaments much shorter than the corolla: leaves without distinction between blade and petiole.   V. OBOVATA.

I. ALNIFOLIA
Shrub with diffuse or procumbent, sometimes creeping (rooting) branches.   1. *V. lantanoides.*

II. ACERIFOLIA
Leaf-blades with salient lobes, the teeth manifestly acute or flaring.   2. *V. acerifolium.*
Leaf-blades merely toothed or obscurely lobed, the teeth rounded or relatively blunt.   3. *V. densiflorum.*

III. DENTATA
Leaf-blades sessile or very short-petioled.   4. *V. Rafinesquianum.*
Leaf-blades decidedly petioled, sometimes relatively long-petioled.
  Lower surfaces of the leaf-blades glabrous or merely with tufts of hairs in the axils of the veins.
    Corolla 5–6 mm. wide: drupe globose-ovoid.   5. *V. dentatum.*
    Corolla about 8 mm. wide: drupe oval or ovoid.   6. *V. bracteatum.*
  Lower surfaces of the leaf-blades stellate-pubescent.   7. *V. semitomentosum.*

IV. PRUNIFOLIA

Cyme peduncled.
Peduncles shorter than the cymes. 8. *V. cassinoides.*
Peduncles as long as the cymes or longer. 9. *V. nudum.*
Cyme sessile or nearly so.
Leaf-blades prominently acuminate, serrate. 10. *V. lentago.*
Leaf-blades obtuse or merely acute, serrulate.
Petioles and leaf-surfaces glabrous or nearly so:
stone of the drupe elliptic. 11. *V. prunifolium.*
Petioles and leaf-surfaces more or less densely red-
tomentose: stone orbicular or nearly so. 12. *V. rufotomentosum.*

V. OBOVATA

Drupe 6–7 mm. long; stone turgid, suborbicular. 13. *V. obovatum.*
Drupe 10–11 mm. long; stone flat, elliptic-obovate. 14. *V. Nashii.*

1. **V. lantanoides** Michx. Straggling shrub: leaf-blades ovate to suborbicular, 9–20 cm. long, serrate: sepals ovate, about 1.5 mm. long, pubescent:
corolla 5–6 mm. wide (those of the marginal
ones larger), the lobes ovate: drupe 10–15
mm. long. [*V. alnifolium* (Fl. SE. U. S.)]
—(HOBBLE-BUSH. MOOSEWOOD. WITCH-
HOBBLE.)—Damp woods, Blue Ridge, and
more northern provinces, N. C. to Mich. and
N. B.

2. **V. acerifolium** L. Erect shrub: leaf-
blades prominently 3-lobed, 4–10 cm. long:
sepals reniform, about 0.5 mm. long: hypanthium glabrous or nearly so: corolla-
lobes mostly reniform: drupe oval, 9–10
mm. long, black or purple-black.—Rocky
hillsides, woods, and thickets, various provinces, Ga. to Ont., and N. B.

3. **V. densiflorum** Chapm. Erect shrub: leaf-blades undulate, shallowly
toothed or sometimes slightly 3-lobed: sepals deltoid, about 0.7 mm. long:
hypanthium pubescent: corolla-lobes mostly ovate: drupe ellipsoid, 8–9 mm.
long.—Wooded hillsides, Coastal Plain, W Fla. (and Ala.?)

4. **V. Rafinesquianum** Schult. Shrub: leaf-blades ovate to elliptic or suborbicular, sharply serrate-dentate, 2–7 cm. long: corolla-lobes broadly ovate:
filaments about equalling the corolla-lobes: drupe ellipsoid, 7–9 mm. long, black
or nearly so. [*V. pubescens* (Ait.) Pursh]—Rocky woods, Blue Ridge and
more northern provinces, Ga. to Minn. and Que.

5. **V. dentatum** L. Shrub: leaf-blades suborbicular, oval, or ovate, sharply
dentate, 3–8 cm. long; petioles over 1.5 cm. long: corolla-lobes reniform: filaments much exceeding the corolla-lobes: drupe globose-ovoid, 5–6 mm. long,
deep-blue or nearly black.—(ARROW-WOOD.)—Wet thickets, swamps, and
meadows, various provinces, Fla. to Ont. and N. B.

6. **V. bracteatum** Rehder. Shrub: leaf-blades ovate, often broadly so, crenate-
dentate, 5–12 cm. long; petioles mostly less than 1.5 cm. long: corolla-lobes
obovate: filaments mostly longer than the corolla-lobes: drupe oval or ovoid,
about 1 cm. long, bluish-black.—Banks of the Coosa River, Appalachian Valley, Ga.

7. **V. semitomentosum** (Michx.) Rehder. Shrub: leaf-blades suborbicular,
broadly ovate or elliptic, crenate-dentate, 3–9 cm. long: corolla 5–8 mm. wide:
filaments slightly exceeding the corolla-lobes: drupe globose-ovoid, 8–9 mm. long

deep-blue.—Low ground and swamps, Coastal Plain, Fla. to Tex. and Pa.— A counter-part of this species in the Blue Ridge province of Ga. and adj. Tenn. and N. C., with large coarsely-toothed leaf-blades in *V. carolinianum* Ashe. A plant with sparingly pubescent foliage and small leaves (2.5–6 cm.) in S Miss., has been described as *V. Ashei* Bush.—*V. molle* Michx., with ellipsoid fruits about 1 cm. long, ranges from Ky. to Mo. and La.

8. **V. cassinoides** L.   Shrub: leaf-blades thickish, ovate-elliptic, ovate-lanceolate, or oblanceolate, undulate or crenate, 3–8 cm. long: corolla 4–5 mm. wide: filaments much exceeding the corolla-lobes: drupe ovoid or globose-ovoid, 6–9 mm. long, deep-blue or rarely pink.—(WITHE-ROD. WILD-RAISIN. SWAMP-HAW.)—Swamps and wet woods, various provinces, Fla. to Miss., Man., and Newf.

9. **V. nudum** L.   Shrub: leaf-blades thick, oval-ovate, elliptic, broadly lanceolate, or oblanceolate (linear-elliptic or narrowly elliptic-lanceolate in *V. nudum angustifolium* = *V. nitidum*), undulate or obscurely toothed, 5–15 cm. long (up to 30 cm. long in *V. nudum grandifolium*): corolla often larger than that of *V. cassinoides* (smaller in *V. nudum serotinum*): drupe oval to subglobose, 6–10 mm. long, deep-blue.—(POSSUM-HAW. SWAMP-HAW.)—Swamps and low grounds, often in acid soil, Coastal Plain and adj. provinces, Fla. to Tex., Ky., and Conn.

10. **V. Lentago** L.   Shrub or tree: leaf-blades ovate to obovate or rarely suborbicular, finely and sharply serrate, 4–10 cm. long: sepals mostly acute or acutish: corolla-lobes ovate: filaments twice as long as the corolla or nearly so: drupe oval, 10–12 mm. long, bluish-black.—(NANNYBERRY. SHEEPBERRY. WILD-RAISIN. SWEET-VIBURNUM.)—Woods and banks of streams, various provinces, Ga. to Mo., Man., and Que.

11. **V. prunifolium** L.   Shrub or tree: leaf-blades thinnish, oval varying to ovate or obovate, or rarely suborbicular, finely, sometimes obscurely, serrulate, 2.5–5 cm. long: sepals obtuse: corolla-lobes suborbicular: filaments much less than twice as long as the corolla: drupe elliptic, sometimes broadly so, 7–9 mm. long bluish-black under the bloom.—(BLACK-HAW. STAG-BRUSH. SLOE.)— Thickets, woods and open banks, various provinces, Ga. to Ark., Kans., Mich., and Conn.

12. **V. rufidulum** Raf.   Shrub or small tree: leaf-blades thick, elliptic, or nearly so, serrate, 4–10 cm. long: corolla 7–10 mm. wide: drupe broadly oblong, 10–14 mm. long, deep-blue under the bloom.   [*V. rufotomentosum* Small.]— (SOUTHERN BLACK-HAW.)—Woods, thickets, hammocks, and bluffs, various provinces, Fla. to Tex., Kans., and Va.

13. **V. obovatum** Walt.   Shrub or small tree: leaf-blades oblanceolate, cuneate, or obovate, 1.5–6 cm. long, entire or slightly toothed near the apex: corolla 5–6 mm. wide: filaments scarcely equalling the corolla-tube: drupe oval, 6–8 mm. long, black.—(SMALL-VIBURNUM.)—River-swamps and low hammocks, Coastal Plain, Fla. to Va.

14. **V. Nashii** Small.   Shrub or small tree: leaf-blades suborbicular or broadly obovate to spatulate, 4–5 cm. long, more or less crenate: drupe ellipsoid, 10–12 mm. long, black.—(NASH'S-VIBURNUM.)—River-swamps, Fla.

3. **TRIOSTEUM** L.   Herbs with simple stems. Leaf-blades entire, sometimes connate-perfoliate. Flowers axillary. Sepals foliaceous. Corolla yellow, greenish-yellow, or maroon. Filaments adnate to the lower part of the corolla-

tube. Anthers linear. Ovary 3–5-celled. Drupe leathery or fleshy. About 6 species, the following and 3 Asiatic.—Sum.—HORSE-GENTIANS. FEVERWORTS.

Leaf-blades narrowed to the sessile or slightly connate-perfoliate bases.
   Leaves less than thrice as long as broad : corolla dull-red.   1. *T. aurantiacum.*
   Leaves over thrice as long as broad : corolla yellowish.   2. *T. angustifolium.*
Leaf-blades with broadly dilated connate-perfoliate bases.   3. *T. perfoliatum.*

1. T. aurantiacum Bicknell. Similar to *T. angustifolium* in habit: blades of the upper leaves ovate-elliptic to elliptic-lanceolate, 15–25 cm. long: sepals 12–20 mm. long: corolla 14–20 mm. long: drupe 12–14 mm. long.—Rocky woods, sandy thickets, and rich hillsides, various provinces, rarely Coastal Plain, N. C. to Minn. and Que.

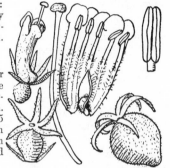

2. T. angustifolium L. Stem hirsute or softly hispid, 3–9 dm. tall: blades of the upper leaves usually narrowly elliptic, varying to lanceolate or oblanceolate, 3–15 cm. long: sepals 8–10 mm. long: corolla 12–15 mm. long: drupe about 10 mm. long.—Rich soil and edges of thickets, Coastal Plain and adj. provinces, Ala. to La., Mo., and Conn.

3. T. perfoliatum L. Stem softly pubescent: blades of the upper leaves ovate to broadly oval, 10–25 cm. long: sepals 11–15 mm. long: corolla 12–15 mm. long: drupe 8–12 mm. long.—(WILD-COFFEE. TINKER'S-WEED.)—Rich woods and thickets, various provinces, rarely Coastal Plain, Ala. to Nebr. and Mass.

4. SYMPHORICARPOS [Dill.] Ludwig. Shrubs with much branched stems. Leaf-blades entire, or lobed on shoots. Flowers in spikes or racemes. Sepals minute. Corolla white or red. Filaments adnate to the top of the corolla-tube. Anthers ellipsoid. Ovary 4-celled. Berry drupe-like, fleshy, with 2 nutlets. About 10 species, North American.—Sum.

Style glabrous : drupe white: corolla pale.   1. *S. albus.*
Style pubescent: drupe red or purple : corolla dark.   2. *S. Symphoricarpos.*

1. S. albus (L.) Blake. Shrub 1–2 m. tall, the twigs and leaves glabrous: leaf-blades elliptic or suborbicular, 3–6 cm. long: flowers short-pedicelled: corolla white or pinkish, 6–7 mm. long: drupe 6–10 mm. long. [*S. racemosus* Michx.]—(SNOWBERRY.)—Rocky woods and river-banks, various provinces, N. C. to Calif., B. C., and N. S.

2. S. Symphoricarpos (L.) MacM. Shrub 1–2 m. tall, the twigs and leaves pubescent: leaf-blades ovate, oval, or elliptic, 1–4 cm. long, or rarely larger: flowers sessile or nearly so: corolla greenish-red, 2.5–3.5 mm. long: drupe 3–4 mm. long. [*S. vulgaris* Michx.]—(CORAL-BERRY. INDIAN-CURRANT.) —Thickets, edges of woods, and roadsides, various provinces, Ga. to Tex., N. D. and N. Y.; naturalized eastward.

5. PHENIANTHUS Raf. Woody vines or diffuse shrubs. Leaf-blades entire, the upper pairs of bracts often connate-perfoliate. Flowers in sessile axillary clusters. Sepals very small. Corolla-elongate, bright-colored: tube slightly ventricose near the base. Berries subglobose, usually clustered.— About 6 species, mostly North American.

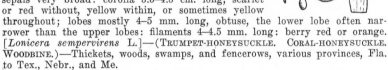

1. P. sempervirens (L.) Raf. Twining vine, the twigs glabrous: leaf-blades narrow or broad, mostly 2–9 cm. long, glaucous and often glabrous beneath: sepals very broad: corolla 3.5–4.5 cm. long, scarlet or red without, yellow within, or sometimes yellow throughout; lobes mostly 4–5 mm. long, obtuse, the lower lobe often narrower than the upper lobes: filaments 4–4.5 mm. long: berry red or orange. [*Lonicera sempervirens* L.]—(TRUMPET-HONEYSUCKLE. CORAL-HONEYSUCKLE. WOODBINE.)—Thickets, woods, swamps, and fencerows, various provinces, Fla. to Tex., Nebr., and Me.

6. XYLOSTEON B. Juss. Erect shrubs. Leaf-blades entire. Flowers in pairs at the end of an axillary peduncle, accompanied by 2 minute bracts and 2 bractlets, the hypanthia more or less united. Sepals minute or obsolete. Corolla relatively short: tube gibbous at the base. Berry distinct or didymous. —About a dozen species, in the north temperate zone.—HONEYSUCKLE.

Corolla funnelform, the lobes shorter than the tube.　　　　1. *X. ciliatum.*
Corolla 2-lipped, the lobes as long as the tube.　　　　　　2. *X. fragrantissimum.*

1. X. ciliatum (Muhl.) Pursh. Shrub 0.5–2 m. tall: leaf-blades thin, ovate or oval-ovate, 3–8 cm. long, ciliate: corolla yellowish, about 1.5 cm. long; tube prominently gibbous at the base: stamens and style included or style exserted: berry ovoid or oval-ovoid, 6–10 mm. long, red.—(FLY-HONEYSUCKLE.)—Rocky woods, Blue Ridge and more northern provinces, N. C. to Minn. and N. S.—Spr.

2. X. fragrantissimum (Lindl. & Paxton) Small. Shrub 3 m. tall or less with glabrous or nearly glabrous twigs: leaf-blades ovate, oval, elliptic, or obovate, 1.5–4 cm. long, pale beneath: corolla white or nearly so, about 1 cm. long; tube slightly gibbous at the base: berry 6–8 mm. long.—Roadsides and about gardens, Augusta, in the Piedmont of Ga. Nat. of China.— Wint.–spr.

7. NINTOOA Sweet. Woody vines. Leaf-blades entire, or pinnatifid on young shoots. Flowers in pairs terminating axillary peduncles, accompanied by 2 foliaceous bracts and 2 small bractlets, the hypanthia distinct. Sepals slender or subulate. Corolla relatively long: ‘tube not gibbous: limb 2-lipped. Berries distinct.—Four or 5 species, Asiatic.

1. N. japonica (Thunb.) Sweet. Diffusely creeping or climbing vine: leaf-blades elliptic-ovate or orbicular-ovate, 2–5 cm. long: evergreen or nearly so: corolla white or pink, becoming yellow; tube about 2 cm. long: stamens and style exserted: berries subglobose or oval, 4–6 mm. long, black.—(JAPANESE-

HONEYSUCKLE.)—Woods, banks, sand-dunes, throughout the E U. S. Nat. of Asia. This species has a red-leaved, red-stemmed, and red-flowered form.

8. LONICERA L. Woody vines. Leaf-blades entire, or lobed on shoots. Flowers in sessile axillary clusters. Hypanthium short. Sepals minute. Corolla mostly 2-lipped: tube more or less gibbous at the base. Berries clustered. —About 80 species, mostly in the north temperate zone.—Spr.–sum.—HONEY-SUCKLES. WOODBINES.

Corolla-tube glabrous within.	1. *L. Caprifolium.*
Corolla-tube pubescent within.	
Corolla-tube abruptly gibbous at the base.	
Corolla glabrous without.	2. *L. dioica.*
Corolla pubescent without.	3. *L. glaucescens.*
Corolla-tube scarcely gibbous at the base.	
Style pubescent : corolla pale-yellow : filaments pubescent at the base.	4. *L. Sullivantii.*
Style glabrous : corolla deep-yellow or orange: filaments glabrous.	
Corolla-tube about 15 mm. long, copiously pubescent within : filaments as long as the corolla-lips.	5. *L. flavida.*
Corolla-tube about 20 mm. long, glabrous or sparingly pubescent within : filaments shorter than the corolla-lips.	6. *L. flava.*

1. L. caprifolium L. A twining vine, the twigs often pubescent: leaf-blades elliptic, oval, or obovate, 2–7 cm. long: corolla purple without; tube 2.5–3 cm. long; limb white within, fading yellow: berry red.—Thickets and woods, various provinces, Ga. to La., Mich., and N. Y. Nat. of Eu.

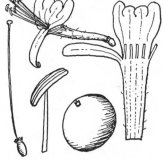

2. L. dioica L. A diffuse or twining vine, the twigs glabrous: leaf-blades elliptic, ovate, oval, or obovate, 5–12 cm. long: corolla yellowish-green tinged with purple; tube 10–12 mm. long. [*L. glauca* Hill]—(MOUNTAIN-HONEYSUCKLE.)—Rocky banks and dry hillsides, Blue Ridge and more northern provinces, Ga. to Mo., Man., and Que.—In the typical plant the swelling of the corolla-tube is close to the base. A form occurs in the mountains of N. Carolina with the swelling higher up, thus leaving a stipe-like base to the corolla-tube.

3. L. glaucescens Rydb. A twining vine, the twigs sometimes sparingly pubescent: leaf-blades elliptic, 5–12 cm. long: hypanthium glaucous (or glandular and more or less pubescent in *L. glaucescens dasygyna*): corolla yellow, becoming reddish; tube 8–10 mm. long.—Thickets and ravines, Blue Ridge and more northern provinces, N. C. to Okla., Sask., and Ont.

4. L. Sullivantii A. Gray. A twining vine, the twigs glabrous: leaf-blades elliptic, oval, or obovate, 2.5–8 cm. long: corolla pale-yellow; tube stout, as long as the lips or slightly longer.—Rocky woods, various provinces N of Coastal Plain, Tenn. to Wisc. and Ont.

5. L. flavida Cockerell. A trailing or twining vine, the twigs green: leaf-blades oblanceolate to elliptic or rhombic-ovate, 8–12 cm. long: corolla light-yellow; tube stout, longer than the lips. [*L. flavescens* Small not Dippel]—Bluffs and shaded banks, Interior Low Plateaus, Tenn. and Ky.

6. **L. flava** Sims. A twining vine, the twigs green, glabrous: leaf-blades oval or ovate, or rarely obovate or elliptic, 3–9 cm. long: corolla orange-yellow; tube slender, much longer than the lips.—Rocky woods, various provinces N of Coastal Plain, Ga. to Ala., Tenn., and N. C.

9. **DIERVILLA** [Tourn.] Mill. Shrubs. Leaves with mostly toothed blades. Flowers in dichotomous cymes. Hypanthium elongate. Sepals 5, narrow. Corolla unequally 5-lobed. Capsule elongate. Three species, as follows:—Spr.–sum.

Leaf-blades petioled, ciliate.	1. *D. Diervilla.*
Leaf-blades sessile or nearly so, not ciliate.	
Leaf-blades glabrous beneath or essentially so: capsule 9–12 mm. long.	2. *D. sessilifolia.*
Leaf-blades pubescent beneath: capsule 5–6 mm. long.	3. *D. rivularis.*

1. **D. Diervilla** (L.) MacM. Shrub 5–15 dm. tall, the twigs terete: leaf-blades oval to elliptic-ovate, 3–15 cm. long: sepals 4–5 mm. long: corolla yellow, turning red or reddish: capsule gradually long-beaked. [*D. trifida* Moench.]—(BUSH-HONEYSUCKLE.)—Rocky woods, various provinces, in Coastal Plain only northward, Ga. to Mich., Man., and Newf.

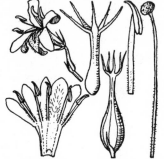

2. **D. sessilifolia** Buckl. Shrub 5–18 dm. tall, the twigs pubescent in lines: leaf-blades lanceolate to ovate-lanceolate or sometimes ovate, 5–15 cm. long: sepals 2–3 mm. long: corolla greenish-yellow: capsule abruptly short-beaked, the body ellipsoid.—Mt. woods, Blue Ridge to Appalachian Plateau, Ga., to Ala., Tenn., and N. C.

3. **D. rivularis** Gattinger. Shrub 5–20 dm. tall, the twigs densely pubescent: leaf-blades ovate to elliptic-lanceolate, 3–8 cm. long: sepals 1.5–2 mm. long: corolla yellow: capsule gradually long-beaked, the body ellipsoid-ovoid.—Damp mt. woods and rocky banks, Blue Ridge to Appalachian Plateau, Ga. to Ala., Tenn., and N. C.

ORDER **VALERIANALES** — VALERIANAL ORDER

Caulescent or rarely acaulescent, succulent, coarse or woody plants. Leaves opposite: blades entire, toothed, or divided. Flowers mainly perfect. Calyx of partly united sepals, pappus-like, or obsolete. Corolla of 2–5 partly united petals. Androecium of usually fewer stamens than there are petals. Gynoecium 1–3-carpellary. Ovary inferior, 2 of the carpels commonly abortive. Fruit an achene, or nut-like.

Gynoecium 3-carpellary, but with two of the cavities empty: flowers not in involucrate heads.	Fam. 1. VALERIANACEAE.
Gynoecium 1-carpellary: flowers in dense involucrate heads.	Fam. 2. MORINACEAE.

FAMILY 1. **VALERIANACEAE** — VALERIAN FAMILY

Annual or perennial, caulescent, succulent herbs. Leaves opposite: blades entire or pinnately divided. Flowers in variously disposed cymes. Calyx of 3–5 sepals, or sometimes pappus-like, or obsolete. Corolla of 3–5 partially united petals: tube often swollen or spurred. Androecium of 1–4 stamens: filaments adnate to the corolla-tube. Gynoecium 3-carpellary but only 1 carpel fructiferous. Ovary inferior. Fruit a kind of leathery or crustaceous nutlet.—About 9 genera and 300 species, widely distributed.

Sepals becoming bristle-like or awn-like: fruit 1-celled: tall herbs often with divided leaf-blades. 1. VALERIANA.
Sepals minute or wanting: fruit .3-celled: low herbs with undivided leaf-blades. 2. VALERIANELLA.

1. VALERIANA [Tourn.] L. Perennial heavy-scented herbs or vines. Leaf-blades entire, toothed, or pinnatifid. Flowers perfect, in compact cymes. Calyx with an inrolled limb which ultimately expands and develops 5–15 plumose bristles. Corolla funnelform or salverform. Stamens 3 or fewer. Fruit 1-celled, the 2 abortive carpels appearing as 4 ridges.—About 175 species, most abundant in the cooler parts of the north temperate zone and the mts. of South America.

Corolla 1.5–2 mm. long: fruit pubescent: upper stem-leaves ternate. 1. V. scandens.
Corolla 16–20 mm. long: fruit glabrous: upper stem-leaves pinnate. 2. V. pauciflora.

1. V. scandens L. Vine: blades of the basal leaves ovate, entire: bracts 1–2 mm. long: inflorescence open: corolla pinkish; lobes nearly ½ as long as the tube: fruit ovoid, 2.5–3 mm. long.—Thickets and hammocks, pen. Fla.—(W. I., Mex., C. A., S. A.)—All year.

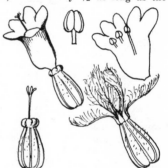

2. V. pauciflora Michx. Plants 1 m. tall or less: blades of the basal leaves ovate or triangular-ovate, mostly toothed: bracts 4–8 mm. long: inflorescence congested: corolla pale-pink; lobes less than ⅛ as long as the tube: fruit oblong, 5–6 mm. long.—Streambanks and rich woods, various provinces N of Coastal Plain, Tenn. to Mo., Pa., and Va.—Late spr.—These two species of Valeriana are of very diverse habits, the one a rampant vine with inconspicuous flowers, the other an erect herb with flowers showy.

2. VALERIANELLA [Tourn.] Mill. Annual, vernal, succulent herbs, the stems dichotomous. Leaf-blades entire, toothed, lobed, or pinnatifid. Flowers perfect, in clustered or corymbose cymes. Calyx shallowly lobed or obsolete. Corolla funnelform, white, pink, or blue. Stamens 3. Fruit with the abortive carpels more or less elongate. About 50 species, natives of Northern Hemisphere.—Spr.–sum.—CORN-SALADS. LAMB'S-LETTUCES.

Corolla blue or purplish: fruit about twice as broad as thick. 1. V. Locusta.
Corolla white: fruit about as broad as thick: species native.
  Fruit with the fertile portion fully as wide as the sterile portion: fruit ovoid-tetragonal, with a broad and shallow groove between the sterile portions. 2. V. radiata.
  Fruit with the fertile portion much smaller and narrower than the sterile portion.
    Empty cavities broad, bladder-like by the infolding of the edges and forming a cross-shaped umbilication. 3. V. umbilicata.
    Empty cavities never infolded so as to make a bladder-like body.
      Empty cavities dilated and divergent, forming a saucer-shaped body notched at both ends. 4. V. patellaria.
      Empty cavities contiguous, with an elliptic depression between them. 5. V. Woodsiana.

1. **V. Locusta** (L.) Bettke. Stem 1–4 dm. tall: blades of the stem-leaves elliptic-lanceolate: corolla 2 mm. long: fruit about twice as long as thick. [*V. olitoria* Poll.]—Stream-banks, thickets, meadows, and waste-grounds, various provinces, Ala. to La., Idaho, Ont., Me., and N. C. Nat. of Eu.

2. **V. radiata** (L.) Dufr. Stem 2–7 dm. tall: blades of the upper stem-leaves oblanceolate to elliptic or ovate: fruits obovoid-tetragonal.—Stream-banks, moist hillsides, and meadows, various provinces, Fla. to Tex., Minn., and N. Y.

3. **V. umbilicata** (Sulliv.) Krok. Stem 1–3 dm. tall: blades of the upper stem-leaves lanceolate; empty portion of the fruit with a cross-shaped umbilication.—Low grounds, various provinces N of Coastal Plain, Tenn. to Ohio, N. Y., and Pa.

4. **V. patellaria** (Sulliv.) Krok. Stem 1–4 dm. tall: blades of the upper stem-leaves similar to those of *V. radiata:* empty carpels of the fruits with a saucer-shaped body notched at each end.—Fields, meadows, and low grounds, various provinces N of Coastal Plain, Tenn. to Ohio and Pa.

5. **V. Woodsiana** (T. & G.) Walp. In habit and leaves resembling *V. radiata*: fruits about 2 mm. long, with the fertile portions much smaller and narrower than the sterile, the cavities of this latter contiguous, with an elliptic depression between them.—Moist banks and low grounds, various provinces, Tenn. to N. Y. and Pa.

FAMILY 2. **MORINACEAE** — TEASEL FAMILY

Annual or perennial, often prickly herbs, or woody plants. Leaves opposite: blades entire, toothed, or dissected. Flowers perfect, each subtended by an involucel, commonly crowded on a receptacle and involucrate. Calyx a cup-like border or of several bristles. Corolla of 2–5 partially united petals, sometimes 2-lipped. Androecium of 2–4 stamens: filaments adnate to the corolla-tube. Gynoecium 1-carpellary. Ovary inferior. Fruit an achene crowned with a calyx.—About 7 genera and 150 species, natives of the Old World.

1. **DIPSACUS** [Tourn.] L. Coarse prickly herbs. Leaf-blades often connate-perfoliate. Flower-heads globular or elongate. Involucral bracts rigid. Calyx cup-like, sometimes 4-lobed. Corolla tubular-funnelform. Ovary enclosed in the involucel. Achenes 8-ribbed.—About 15 species, natives of the Old World.

1. **D. sylvestris** Huds. Biennial, 1–2.5 m. tall: blades of the stem-leaves lanceolate, entire: heads ovoid, 5–6 cm. long, the involucral bracts rough: calyx fully 1 mm. long: corolla 11–13 mm. long; lobes 4, lilac, broadly ovate: stamens exserted: achenes 5 mm. long.—(TEASEL.)—Fields and waste-places, various provinces, Fla. to Tex., Ont., and Me. Nat. of Eu.—Sum.

ORDER ARISTOLOCHIALES — ARISTOLOCHIAL ORDER

Herbs, shrubs, or vines. Leaves alternate: blades mostly cordate or hastate. Flowers perfect, often conspicuous. Hypanthium mostly adnate to the ovary. Calyx regular or very irregular. Corolla wanting or rudimentary. Androecium of as many stamens as there are calyx lobes or more. Gynoecium of usually 6 united carpels. Fruit a capsule.

FAMILY 1. ASARACEAE — BIRTHWORT FAMILY

Perennial herbs, shrubs, or vines. Leaves alternate: blades sometimes lobed, generally cordate. Flowers perfect, regular or very irregular. Calyx usually colored, the tube often bent or inflated. Androecium of 6–many stamens. Gynoecium of 4–6 united carpels. Ovary mostly inferior. Fruit capsular.—About 6 genera and 200 species, widely distributed.

Acaulescent herbs: calyx regular, persistent: capsule fleshy.
  Ovary superior: filaments shorter than the anthers: styles distinct: leaves persistent.
        1. HEXASTYLIS.
  Ovary inferior: filaments longer than the anthers: styles united: leaves deciduous.
        2. ASARUM.
Caulescent herbs or vines: calyx irregular, deciduous: capsule dry.
        3. ARISTOLOCHIA.

1. HEXASTYLIS Raf. Acaulescent gingerous herbs. Leaves 1 every year: blades lustrous above. Flower-stalk subtended by a bract. Hypanthium terete, glabrous without. Sepals green or purplish without, dark-purple, and sometimes blotched within, persistent. Capsule enveloped in the calyx and hypanthium. Seeds flattened.—Eight species, as follows.—Spr. or spr.–sum.—The leaves are evergreen with coriaceous blades.—HEART-LEAFS.

Leaf-blades of a broadly ovate type, varying to suborbicular or·reniform, not hastate.
  Hypanthium and calyx of an urceolate type in anthesis.
    Hypanthium and calyx 3–4 cm. long, the lobes over 1 cm. wide.
          1. H. Shuttleworthii.
    Hypanthium and calyx 1–2 cm. long, the lobes less than 1 cm. wide.
      Calyx-limb over 1.5 cm. wide in anthesis; lobes nearly or quite half as long as the tube.
            2. H. virginica.
      Calyx-limb less than 1.5 cm. wide in anthesis; lobes very short.
            3. H. Memmingeri.
  Hypanthium and calyx of a turbinate or turbinate-campanulate type in anthesis.
        4. H. heterophylla.
Leaf-blades of a hastate type.
  Calyx without any decided limb, the lobes erect or somewhat spreading.
    Hypanthium and calyx ovoid-urceolate, the small lobes erect, the tube not constricted.
          5. H. Ruthii.
    Hypanthium and calyx campanulate-urceolate, the large lobes spreading, the tube constricted.
      Leaf-blades predominantly of an ovate type.
            6. H. callifolia.
      Leaf-blades predominantly of a triangular-hastate type.
            7. H. arifolia.
  Calyx with a salver-campanulate limb surmounting the tube.
        8. H. speciosa.

1. H. Shuttleworthii (J. Britten) Small. Leaf-blades orbicular, varying to ovate or somewhat rhombic, 5–8 cm. long, the sinus narrow: hypanthium and

calyx long-urceolate, 3–5 cm. long; lobes
broad, ascending or spreading, and more or
less incurved at the tip: anther-sacs 3 mm.
long, exceeded by the broad blunt connective-
tip: styles 5–5.5 mm. long: seed 3 mm. long.
—Rich or somewhat acid woods, inner Piedmont to Appalachian Valley, Ala. to Tenn.,
and S Va.

2. **H. virginica** (L.) Small. Leaf-blades
broadly ovate, varying to orbicular-ovate or
deltoid-ovate, 4–9 cm. long, the sinus often
narrow: hypanthium and calyx short-urceolate, 1–2 cm. long; lobes broad, somewhat
spreading: anther-sacs 2–2.5 mm. long,
scarcely exceeded by the minute connective-

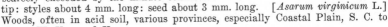

tip: styles about 4 mm. long: seed about 3 mm. long.   [*Asarum virginicum* L.]
Woods, often in acid soil, various provinces, especially Coastal Plain, S. C. to
Tenn., W. Va., and Va.

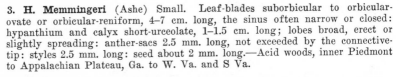

3. **H. Memmingeri** (Ashe) Small. Leaf-blades suborbicular to orbicular-
ovate or orbicular-reniform, 4–7 cm. long, the sinus often narrow or closed:
hypanthium and calyx short-urceolate, 1–1.5 cm. long; lobes broad, erect or
slightly spreading: anther-sacs 2.5 mm. long, not exceeded by the connective-
tip: styles 2.5 mm. long: seed about 2 mm. long.—Acid woods, inner Piedmont
to Appalachian Plateau, Ga. to W. Va. and S Va.

4. **H. heterophylla** (Ashe) Small. Leaf-blades orbicular-reniform to orbicular-
ovate or triangular-ovate, 4–10 cm. long: hypanthium and calyx turbinate or
turbinate-campanulate, 2–2.5 cm. long; lobes very broad, somewhat spreading:
anther-sacs about 2.5 mm. long, slightly exceeded by the minute connective-tip:
styles 2–2.5 mm. long: seed about 2.5 mm. long.—Woods, Piedmont, to Appalachian Plateau, Ga. to Ala., W. Va., and S Va.

5. **H. Ruthii** (Ashe) Small. Leaf-blades hastate, varying from individually
ovate to broadly triangular in outline, 8–15 cm. long: hypanthium and calyx
narrowly urceolate, with 3 short ovate, erect or converging lobes surmounting
the narrow neck: anther-sacs 2–2.5 mm. long, much exceeded by the narrow
connective-tips: seed fully 3 mm. long.—Rich woods, Blue Ridge to Appalachian
Plateau, Ala. to Tenn. and S Va.

6. **H. callifolia** Small. Leaf-blades ovate, 5–9 cm. long: hypanthium and
calyx broadly urceolate, with reniform, more or less spreading lobes surmounting a broad neck: anther-sacs about 4 mm. long, much exceeded by the broad
connective-tip—Woods, N Fla.

7. **H. arifolia** (Michx.) Small. Leaf-blades hastate, varying from individually
ovate to deltoid or reniform in outline, 5–1.2 cm. long: hypanthium and calyx
urceolate, with 3 broad spreading lobes surmounting the constricted neck:
anther-sacs 2.5 mm. long, slightly exceeded by the minute connective-tips: seeds
about 3 mm. long. [*Asarum arifolium* Michx.]—Rich or sterile woods, various
provinces, Fla. to Ala., Tenn., and S Va.

8. **H. speciosa** Harper. Leaf-blades ovate-hastate, 6–12 cm. long: hypanthium
and calyx campanulate-salverform, calyx conspicuous, the hemispheric base surmounted by a cap-like limb with 3 broad spreading parallel-lined lobes: anther
sacs 3 mm. long, the connective broadly rounded at the apex which slightly ex-
ceeds the sacs: styles 2–2.5 mm. long.—Rich woods, Autauga Co., in the Coastal
Plain of Ala.

2. **ASARUM** [Tourn.] L. Acaulescent gingerous herbs. Leaves in pairs: blades not lustrous. Flower-stalks arising between the petioles. Hypanthium angled, pubescent. Sepals brown within, deciduous. Capsule inferior. Seeds turgid.—About 20 species, natives of the north temperate zone.—Spr.—The leaves are not evergreen, with thick-membranous blades.—WILD-GINGERS.

Sepals triangular, merely acute, about as long as the hypanthium or shorter.
  1. *A. reflexum.*
Sepals lanceolate-acuminate, longer than the hypanthium.
  Sepals slightly longer than the hypanthium, the tubular portion 4–8 mm. long: species mainly Alleghenian.
  2. *A. canadense.*
  Sepals much longer than the hypanthium, the tubular portion 10–20 mm. long: species campestrian.
  3. *A. acuminatum.*

1. **A. reflexum** Bicknell. Leaf-blades reniform, 6–14 cm. wide, the sinus open: flowers smaller than those of the preceding species: sepals 8–10 mm. long, early reflexed, obtuse at the tip—Rocky hillsides and rich woods, various provinces N of Coastal Plain, N. C. to Kans., Ia., and Conn.

2. **A. canadense** L. Leaf-blades reniform, 6–15 cm. wide, the sinus closed: hypanthium thinly pubescent: sepals abruptly acuminate, the tubular portions curving upward.—Rich woods and rocky hillsides, various provinces, N. C. to Ark., (La.?), Ont., and N. B.

3. **A. acuminatum** (Ashe) Bicknell. Similar to *A. canadense,* but more pubescent: hypanthium densely pubescent: sepals gradually acuminate, the tubular tips recurved-spreading.—Woods, Blue Ridge and more northern provinces, Tenn to Minn.

A. rubrocinctum Peattie is said to differ from *A. canadense* and *A. acuminatum* by its larger flowers and less pubescent leaf-blades, and also from the former by its longer sepals. It occurs in the mountains of N. C.

3. **ARISTOLOCHIA** [Tourn.] L. Caulescent herbs, shrubs, or vines. Leaves with narrow or broad blades. Flowers irregular, often S-shaped or resembling a "dutch pipe," the calyx usually corolloid. Hypanthium often ribbed. Ovary inferior. Styles united into an angled column. Capsule pendulous.—About 200 species, in tropical and temperate regions.—BIRTHWORTS.

Erect herbs: flowers borne at the base of the stem: calyx-tube swollen at each end.
  I. HASTATAE.
Twining vines: flowers borne along the branches.
  Herbaceous vines: calyx-tube swollen at the base: calyx-limb expanded on one side: stamens 5.
  II. PENTANDRAE.
  Woody vines: calyx-tube swollen in the middle: calyx-limb expanded on all sides: stamens 6.
  III. MACROPHYLLAE.

I. HASTATAE

Plant sparingly and indistinctly pubescent with soft hairs: capsule sparingly pubescent.
  Leaf-blades hastate, delicate: capsule 5–6 mm. long or rarely longer.
  1. *A. hastata.*
  Leaf-blades not hastate, membranous: capsule about 1 cm. long.
  2. *A. Serpentaria.*
Plant manifestly pubescent with stiff spreading hairs: capsule copiously pubescent.
  3. *A. convolvulacea.*

II. PENTANDRAE

Diffusely twining vine with fleshy leaf-blades and globular
drooping capsules.   4. *A. pentandra.*

III. MACROPHYLLAE

Young foliage densely tomentose: leaf-blades coriaceous:
hypanthium tomentose.   5. *A. tomentosa.*
Young foliage minutely pubescent or glabrous: leaf-blades
membranous: hypanthium glabrous.   6. *A. macrophylla.*

1. **A. hastata** Nutt. Plant light-green, 1–3 dm. tall: leaf-blades very thin,
linear to lanceolate, hastate, 2–12 cm. long: flowers about 1.5 cm. long:
hypanthium densely hirsutulous: calyx pur-
ple or greenish-purple: capsule 5–11 mm. in
diameter: seed 3.5–4 mm. long, with minute
scattered papillae on the face. [*A. Nashii*
Kearney] — (SNAKEROOT.) — Damp woods,
various provinces, Fla. to La. and S Va.—
Sum.

2. **A. Serpentaria** L. Plant dark-green, 1–4
dm. tall: leaf-blades elliptic-lanceolate to
oval-lanceolate, or rarely lanceolate, 4–15 cm.
long: flowers 1–1.5 cm. long: hypanthium
villous-hirsutulous: calyx purple; limb obtusely 3-lobed: capsule about 10 mm. in
diameter: seed about 4 mm. long, with many
approximate papillae on its face.—(VIR-
GINIA-SNAKEROOT.)—Rich woods, various provinces, Fla. to Tex., Mo., Mich.,
and Conn.—Spr.–fall.

3. **A. convolvulacea** Small. Plant bristly-pubescent, 1–3 dm. tall: leaf-blades
broadly ovate to oval, 2–8 cm. long: flowers about 1.5 cm. long: hypanthium
densely hirsute: calyx purplish; limb 3-lobed: capsule 6–8 mm. in diameter.
—Woods, Piedmont to Appalachian Plateau, Ga.—Spr.–sum.

4. **A. pentandra** Jacq. Stem reclining and twining: leaf-blades ovate, 4–10
cm. long: hypanthium minutely pubescent: calyx nearly straight, greenish or
purplish, the limb narrow, nearly erect: capsule globular, 15–20 mm. long, wing-
angled: seed black, 5–6 mm. long.—Coastal hammocks, S Pen. Fla. and the
Keys.—(*W. I.*)—All year.

5. **A. tomentosa** Sims. Stem woody, high-climbing, the branches downy;
leaf-blades ovate to suborbicular, 10–18 cm. long, rounded at the apex: peduncle
wanting: calyx abruptly bent above the ovary, the limb 2–2.5 cm. wide, yellowish or greenish-yellow, except the purple orifice, rugose: capsule 4–6 cm. long.
(PIPEVINE.)—Woods, various provinces, Fla. to Okla., Mo., Ill., and N. C.—Spr.

6. **A. macrophylla** Lam. Stem greatly elongate, climbing, the branches glabrous or nearly so: leaf-blades suborbicular to broadly ovate, 5–25 cm. long,
abruptly acute or obtuse: peduncles 1–2 cm. long: calyx abruptly bent above
the ovary, the limb 2–3 cm. wide, brown or yellowish, veiny: capsule 5–6 cm.
long. [*A. Sipho* L'Her.]—(DUTCHMAN'S PIPE.)—Woods, various provinces
N of Coastal Plain, Ga. to Kans., Minn., and Pa.—Spr.–sum.

Aristolochia maxima L. of tropical America and cultivated, with large
variegated flowers and capsules 1–1.5 dm. long, has escaped from cultivation
into hammocks in S Fla.

Order **CAMPANULALES** — Campanulal Order

Herbs, or rarely shrubs or trees. Leaves mainly alternate: blades simple, entire, or divided. Flowers perfect, monoecious or dioecious, sometimes irregular. Hypanthium well-developed. Calyx of several distinct or partly united sepals. Corolla of several distinct or partly united petals. Androecium of 1–5 stamens. Anthers distinct or connate. Gynoecium of 1–several united carpels, the ovary wholly or partially inferior. Fruit capsular, baccate, or drupaceous.

Flowers variously disposed, but not in heads.
  Flowers monoecious or dioecious: plant usually tendril-
    bearing vines: endosperm wanting.   Fam. 1. Campanutaceae.
  Flowers perfect or mainly so: herbs or shrubs: endo-
    sperm present.
    Corolla regular.   Fam. 2. Campanulaceae.
    Corolla irregular, split on one side:
      Anthers united around the style: stigma naked:
        herbs.   Fam. 3. Lobeliaceae.
      Anthers separate: stigma surrounded by a cup-
        like indusium: succulent shrubs.   Fam. 4. Brunnoniaceae.
Flowers capitate, on a flat or elongate receptacle.   Fam. 5. Calyceraceae.

Family 1. **CUCURBITACEAE** — Gourd Family

Vines, usually tendril-bearing. Leaves alternate: blades palmately or pedately veined, and commonly lobed. Flowers monoecious or dioecious. Calyx of 4 or 5, or rarely 6, distinct or partly united sepals. Corolla of 4 or 5, or rarely 6, distinct or partly united petals, sometimes adherent to the calyx. Androecium of 3 stamens (2 anthers 2-celled and 1 anther 1-celled), or rarely of 1, 2, 4, or 5 stamens. Filaments sometimes united. Anthers straight or bent. Gynoecium 1–several-carpellary. Styles united. Fruit a fleshy or partly dry berry (pepo).—About 90 genera and 700 species, mostly tropical.

Stamens distinct or with the filaments partly united.
  Anther-sacs straight or merely curved.   Tribe   I. Melothrieae.
  Anther-sacs S-shaped or V-shaped.   Tribe II. Cucurbiteae.
Stamens united into a column.   Tribe III. Sicyoideae.

I. Melothrieae

Slender trailing or climbing, mostly monoecious vines.   1. Melothria.

II. Cucurbiteae

Ovules horizontal, numerous.
  Corolla rotate.
    Anthers distinct.
      Calyx with 2 or 3 scales at the bottom within.   2. Momordica.
      Calyx without basal scales within.
        Staminate flowers racemose: fruit dry.   3. Luffa.
        Staminate flowers solitary or in clusters: fruit
        fleshy.
          Anther-sacs not surpassed by the connective:
            tendrils branched.   4. Citrullus.
          Anther-sacs surpassed by the connective: ten-
            drils simple.   5. Cucumis.
    Anthers capitate.   6. Cucurbita.
  Corolla campanulate.   7. Pepo.
Ovules erect or ascending: 1–4 in each cavity.   8. Cayaponia.

III. Sicyoideae

Corolla campanulate: fruit smooth.   9. Coccinea.
Corolla rotate: fruit bristly or echinate.
  Pistillate flowers mostly solitary: ovary 2- or 3-celled, with
  few ovules: fruit bladdery, few-seeded, opening at the
  apex.   10. Micrampelis.
  Pistillate flowers clustered: ovary 1-celled, with one ovule:
  fruit succulent, indehiscent.   11. Sicyos.

1. MELOTHRIA L.   Slender perennial vines.   Leaves with toothed or lobed blades.   Flowers mainly monoecious.   Hypanthium of the pistillate flowers relatively short.   Corolla yellow, that of the pistillate flowers relatively short, about 8 mm. broad (in our species), that of the staminate flower smaller. Berry juicy, the rind tender.   Seed flat.—About 70 species, natives of warm and tropical regions.—CREEPING-CUCUMBERS.   MELONETTES.

Berry ellipsoid or oval.
    Stem climbing: leaf-blades longer than wide, the lobes angular: berry dark-
        purple or blackish.   1. *M. pendula.*
    Stem trailing or creeping: leaf-blades wider than long, the
        lobes low and rounded: berry green and somewhat varie-
        gated.   2. *M. crassifolia.*
Berry globose or subglobose.
    Berry over 10 mm. in diameter: leaf-blades deeply lobed.   3. *M. Nashii.*
    Berry less than 10 mm. in diameter: leaf-blades shallowly
        lobed.   4. *M. microcarpa.*

1. M. pendula L.   Leaves glabrous or nearly so (or with hispidulous petioles and deeply lobed blades in *M. pendula aspera*); blades suborbicular to ovate in outline, 3–8 cm. wide, with 3–5 angular shallow-toothed lobes; petioles hispid: hypanthium glabrous or pubescent: berry ellipsoid or oval, 10–25 mm. long.—Swamps and thickets, various provinces, Fla. to Tex., Mo., and S Pa.—(*Mex.*)—Spr.–fall.

2. M. crassifolia Small.   Leaf-blades suborbicular, reniform, or ovate in outline, 3–8 cm. wide, with 3–5 angular shallow-toothed lobes: hypanthium glabrous or pubescent: berry ellipsoid or oval, 10–25 mm. long.—Hammocks, pen. Fla. and the Keys.—All year.

3. M. Nashii Small.   Leaf-blades fleshy, suborbicular to triangular-ovate in outline, 2–3.5 cm. long, 5-lobed, the lobes entire or with 1 or 2 teeth or small lobes; petioles hispid: berry globose, 12–15 mm. in diameter.—Pinelands, pen. Fla.—Spr.–fall.

4. M. microcarpa Shuttlw.   Leaf-blades thinnish, commonly as long as wide, 1–3 cm. long, 3–5-lobed, the lobes irregularly toothed: petioles hispidulous: berry globose, 7–9 mm. in diameter.—Thickets, Appalachian Plateau, Ala.—Spr.–sum.

2. MOMORDICA L.   Annual or perennial vines.   Leaves with entire, lobed, or pedately dissected blades.   Flowers monoecious or dioecious.   Staminodia of the pistillate flowers gland-like, or wanting.   Stalk of the staminate flowers bracted.   Style slender.   Stigmas 3.   Berry warty.—About 25 species, native of the Old World Tropics.—The plants flower most of the year.

Leaf-blades with obtuse or acutish teeth: bract entire, at the middle or base of the
    staminate peduncle.   1. *M. Charantia.*
Leaf-blades with acuminate teeth: bract toothed, at the apex of
    the staminate peduncle.   2. *M. Balsamina.*

1. M. Charantia L.   Stem creeping or climbing, often greatly elongate: leaf-blades 4–12 cm. wide, 5–7-lobed, the lobes with acutish or obtuse teeth, villous

or glabrate: sepals oval or oval-ovate, 3–4.5
mm. long: corolla yellow about 2 cm. wide:
berry 4–12 cm. long, golden-yellow: seed
elliptic, 9–12 mm. long or rarely larger.—
(WILD BALSAM-APPLE.)—Hammocks, thickets, and waste-places, outer Coastal Plain,
Fla. to Tex.—(*W. I., Mex., C. A., S. A.*)

2. **M. Balsamina** L. Stem mostly climbing,
much-branched: leaf-blades 3–8 cm. wide,
3–5-lobed, the lobes with acuminate teeth;
petioles usually puberulent: sepals elliptic,
about 6 mm. long: corolla golden-yellow and
dark or black at the center, about 2.5 cm.
wide: berry 3–6 cm. long, orange: seed
ovoid or oval, 10–12 mm. long—(BALSAM-
APPLE.)—Sandy soil, Coastal Plain, La. and
Tex.—(*W. I., Mex., C. A., S. A.*)

3. **LUFFA** L. Annual vines. Leaves with 5–7-lobed blades. Flowers
monoecious. Corolla yellow, pink, or whitish. Staminodia of the pistillate
flowers 3. Style columnar. Stigmas 3, each
2-lobed. Berry elongate, ribbed.—About 7
species, all but 1 in the Old World tropics.

1. **L. cylindrica** (L.) Roem. Stem and
branches ribbed: leaf-blades suborbicular in
outline, mostly 1–3 dm. broad and 5–7-
lobed, the lobes coarsely toothed: sepals
lanceolate to triangular-lanceolate, those of
the pistillate flowers about twice as long as
those of the staminate: corolla yellow, that
of the pistillate flower 10–12 cm. wide, that
of the staminate flower smaller: berry
cylindric or clavate, 2.5–6.5 dm. long.—
(VEGETABLE-SPONGE. DISHCLOTH-GOURD.)—
Roadsides, waste-places, and thickets, pen.
Fla. Nat. of Old World tropics.—(*W. I., Mex., C. A., S. A.*)—All year.

4. **CITRULLUS** Schrad. Annual or perennial vines. Leaves with lobed
blades. Flowers monoecious. Staminodia of the pistillate flowers prominent.
Style short. Stigmas reniform. Berry
smooth. — About 4 species, Asiatic and
African.

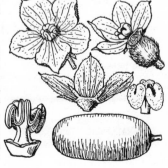

1. **C. Citrullus** (L.) Small. Stem trailing,
with spreading hairs: leaf-blades ovate in
outline, 3–7-lobed: sepals linear or nearly
so: corolla pale-yellow; lobes ovate or elliptic: berry globose to ellipsoid-cylindric, 1–
6 dm. long, smooth, edible: seed flat.—
(WATERMELON.) — Waste-places, woods,
pinelands, and roadsides, various provinces,
Fla. to Tex. and N. C. Nat. of tropical
Africa.—Spr.-fall.—The watermelon plant
is too sensitive to cold to become a per-
manent member of our flora.

5. **CUCUMIS** L. Annual or perennial vines. Leaves with toothed or prominently lobed blades. Flowers monoecious. Corolla rotate. Staminodia of the pistillate flowers obsolete or wanting. Style short. Stigmas obtuse. Berry rugose or echinate.—About 25 species, mostly Asiatic and African.

Corolla 3–5 cm. broad: fruit not prickly.   1. *C. Melo.*
Corolla 1–1.5 cm. broad: fruit prickly.   2. *C. Anguria.*

1. **C. Melo** L. Stem stout: leaf-blades reniform to suborbicular, 1.5 dm. long or less, merely toothed or shallowly lobed: corolla 3–5 cm. wide, yellow: fruit elongate or depressed, rugose. — (MELON. CANTA-LOUPE. MUSKMELON.)—Pinelands, cult. grounds, and waste-places, Coastal Plain, Fla. to Tex. Nat. of Asia and cult.—(*W. I., Mex., C. A., S. A.*)

2. **C. Anguria** L. Stem slender: leaf-blades mostly 5–8 cm. long, deeply 3–5-lobed: corolla 1–1.5 cm. wide, yellow: fruit oval to ellipsoid.—(BUR-GHERKIN. WEST-INDIAN GHERKIN. GOOSE-BERRY GOURD.)—Thickets and waste-places, Coastal Plain, Fla. to Tex., and Ga.—(*W. I., Mex., C. A., S. A.*)—These two species of *Cucumis*, although not permanently naturalized in our range, continue to appear.

6. **CUCURBITA** [Tourn.] L. Annual vines. Leaves with lobed blades. Flowers monoecious or rarely dioecious. Corolla rotate. Staminodia wanting. Stigmas erect, 2-lobed. Berry variable in shape, the rind smooth, woody.—One species.

1. **C. Lagenaria** L. Plant musk-scented, clammy-pubescent: leaf-blades ovate to triangular or orbicular-ovate, 1–3 dm. long, sinuate or denticulate: corolla white with greenish veins, 5–7 cm. wide; lobes broadened upward, erose-crenate: berry usually somewhat clavate. [*Lagenaria Lagenaria* Cockerell.]—(BOTTLE-GOURD. GOURD. CALABASH.)—Thickets and waste-places, Coastal Plain, Fla. to Tex. Nat. of Old World tropics and cult.—(*W. I., Mex., C. A., S. A.*)

7. **PEPO** [Tourn.] Mill. Annual or perennial vines. Leaves with toothed or lobed blades. Flowers monoecious. Corolla campanulate, typically large. Pistillate flowers with staminodia. Ovary 1-celled. Stigmas 2-lobed. Berry fleshy, with a tough rind.— About 10 species, American, African, and Asiatic.— PUMPKINS. GOURDS.

1. **Pepo okeechobeensis** Small. Annual with clammy pubescent foliage and unequally forked tendrils: leaf-blades suborbicular or orbicular-reniform in outline, 1–2 dm. wide, deeply cordate, shallowly 5–7-lobed, the lobes irregularly dentate: flowers pedi-celled: hypanthium pubescent: sepals subulate or subulate-lanceolate: corolla cream-colored, campanu-late, finely pubescent, the lobes erose-crenulate: berry (pepo) globular, 7–9 cm. in diameter, bright-green and usually flecked and somewhat streaked with whitish or dark-green spots: seeds obovate, 8–12 mm. long, thick-margined.—

(OKEECHOBEE-GOURD).—Hammocks, about Lake Okeechobee, Fla.—Spr.–sum.—
Cultivated relatives, sometimes met with in the field are: the field-pumpkin (*Pepo
Pepo* (L.) Britton.), with harshly pubescent foliage, bright-yellow or orange
corollas and usually larger orange-colored fruits, nativity undetermined; the so-
called crookneck squash, (*Pepo moschata* (Duchesne) Britton), with fruits of
many shapes, known in Florida as the Seminole-pumpkin, may be found growing
wild about Indian settlements and abandoned camp sites.

8. **CAYAPONIA** Manso. Vines. Leaves with toothed or lobed blades.
Flowers monoecious or dioecious. Corolla rotate or broadly campanulate, rela-
tively small. Pistillate flowers with staminodia. Ovary 3-celled, smooth.
Stigmas dilated. Berry juicy, with a tender rind.—About 60 species, American.

Leaf-blade not decurrent on the petiole: anther free.
    Berry oval, less than 1.5 cm. long: leaf-blades usually less than 1 cm. wide.
                                                              1. *C. Boykinii.*
    Berry ellipsoid, over 1.5 cm. long: leaf-blades usually over
      10 cm. wide.   2. *C. grandifolia.*
Leaf-blade decurrent on the petiole: anthers coherent.   3. *C. racemosa.*

1. **C. Boykinii** (T. & G.) Cogn. Stem finely pubescent: leaf-blades thickish,
5–10 cm. long, 3-angled or 3-lobed, sparingly pubescent beneath; petioles bristly
villous: corolla greenish-white, the staminate
5–6 mm. wide: berry 12–14 mm. long: seed
6–7 mm. long. [*Trianosperma Boykinii*
Roem.]—Along streams, Coastal Plain, Ga.
to La.—Sum.

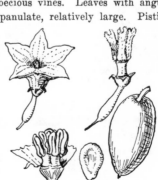

2. **C. grandifolia** (T. & G.) Small. Stem
sparingly pubescent: leaf-blades thin, 12–18
cm. long, 3-lobed; petioles softly villous:
corolla greenish-white, the staminate 7–9
mm. wide: berry 16–20 mm. long.—Bottom-
lands, Coastal Plain, Miss to La. and Ark.
—Sum.

3. **C. racemosa** (Sw.) Cogn. Stem glabrous
or nearly so: leaf-blades thick, 6–13 cm.
long, 3-lobed, closely hispidulous beneath; petioles glabrous or nearly so: staminate corolla 8–10 mm. wide, greenish: berry ellipsoid to oval, 15–20 mm. long:
seed 9–10 mm. long.—Hammocks, Everglade Keys, Fla.—(*W. I.*)—Spr.–sum.

9. **COCCINEA** W. & A. Perennial dioecious vines. Leaves with angulate or shallowly lobed blades. Corolla campanulate, relatively large. Pistillate flowers solitary, with 3 staminodia.
Ovary smooth and glabrous. Berry smooth.
Seeds numerous.—About a dozen species,
natives of the Old World tropics.

1. **C. cordifolia** (L.) Cogn. Stem glabrous,
climbing: leaf-blades ovate to orbicular in
outline, 4–10 cm. long, 3–5-lobed, cordate,
slender-petioled: sepals subulate or linear-
subulate, 3–4 mm. long, reflexed: corolla
white, 3–4 cm. wide: berry ellipsoid or obovoid, 4–5 cm. long, scarlet.—Hammocks, pen.
Fla. Nat. of Asia.—(*W. I., Mex., C. A.,
S. A.*)—All year.

10. MICRAMPELIS Raf. Annual or perennial vines. Leaves with angulate or lobed blades. Flowers monoecious. Corolla rotate, relatively small. Pistillate flowers usually solitary, with staminodia. Ovary echinate. Stigmas lobed. Berry echinate, fibrous within, the rind tough. Seeds not filling the cavities.—About 25 species, American.

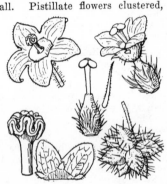

1. M. lobata (Michx.) Greene. Stem and branches tender: leaf-blades 4–15 cm. long, palmately 3–5-lobed, the lobes triangular-ovate to lanceolate: sepals 2–4 mm. long: corolla rotate, 7–9 mm. wide, white or cream-color; lobes lanceolate: berry inflated, ellipsoid to globose-ellipsoid, 3–4.5 mm. long, bursting at the apex. [*Echinocystis lobata* T. & G.]—(WILD BALSAM-APPLE. MOCK-APPLE.)—Stream-banks and thickets, various provinces, Ga. to Tex., Colo., Sask., and N. B.—Sum.

11. SICYOS L. Annual monoecious vines. Leaves with angulate or lobed blades. Corolla rotate, relatively small. Pistillate flowers clustered, without staminodia. Ovary and berry bristly. Seeds filling the cavity.—About 35 species, American and Australian.

1. S. angulata L. Stem and branches viscid-pubescent: leaf-blades 6–15 cm. wide, 5-angled or 5-lobed, the lobes distinctly toothed: hypanthium flattish: sepals of the staminate flowers triangular, 3–5 mm. long: corolla rotate, white, striped with green, 10–12 mm. wide: berries clustered, ovoid, 1.5–2 cm. long.—(NIMBLE-KATE. STAR-CUCUMBER.)—Thickets, stream-banks, and cult. grounds, various provinces, Fla. to Tex., Minn., and Que.—Sum.-fall.

FAMILY 2. **CAMPANULACEAE** — BELL-FLOWER FAMILY

Herbs or woody plants. Leaves alternate: blades entire, toothed, or lobed. Flowers perfect, regular, sometimes dimorphous. Calyx of 5 sepals, or fewer in cleistogamous flowers. Corolla of 5 partly united petals. Androecium of 5 distinct stamens. Gynoecium 2–5-carpellary, the ovary more or less inferior. Fruit capsular.—About 40 genera and more than 1,000 species, widely distributed.

Style with pollen-collecting hairs: filaments free or nearly so: corolla usually valvate or induplicate in the bud.
  Corolla campanulate or funnelform: inflorescence racemose or paniculate.   1. CAMPANULA.
  Corolla rotate.
    Flowers axillary.   2. ROTANTHA.
    Flowers in spikes.
      Style declined: flowers complete throughout.   3. CAMPANULASTRUM.
      Style straight: flowers various, the earlier ones cleistogamous.   4. SPECULARIA.
Style without collecting hairs: filaments adnate to the corolla: corolla imbricate in the bud.   5. SPHENOCLEA.

1. CAMPANULA [Tourn.] L. Perennial or sometimes annual herbs.
Leaf-blades entire, toothed, or lobed. Flowers perfect, all alike and complete. Hypanthium relatively short in age. Corolla campanulate to funnelform. Stamens included. Capsule opening by lateral or basal perforations or valves. —About 250 species, natives of the Northern Hemisphere.—BELLFLOWERS.

Style shorter than the corolla or sometimes about equalling it: leaf-blades entire or
   slightly toothed.   1. *C. aparinoides.*
Style exceeding the corolla: leaf-blades laciniately toothed.   2. *C. flexuosa.*

1. C. aparinoides Pursh. Stem 2–6 dm. long, prickly throughout: leaf-blades 1–3.5 cm. long, those of the upper leaves linear to lanceolate: sepals ovate to triangular-ovate, 1.5–2 mm. long: corolla white, pale blue, or pink, 5–8 mm. long: capsule globose-obovoid: seed about 0.5 mm. long, smooth. — (MARSH - BELLFLOWER.) — Acid swamps, meadows and spring-runs, various provinces, Ga. to Ky., Colo., and Me.—Sum.

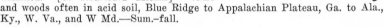

2. C. flexuosa Michx. Stem 2–10 dm. tall, smooth: leaf-blades 2–12 cm. long, lanceolate to ovate-lanceolate or elliptic: sepals subulate, 4–6 mm. long: corolla violet-blue or white, 6–8 mm. long: capsule turbinate-campanulate: seed fully 1 mm. long, wrinkled. [*C. divaricata* Michx.] — Cliffs and woods often in acid soil, Blue Ridge to Appalachian Plateau, Ga. to Ala., Ky., W. Va., and W Md.—Sum.–fall.

Campanula persicifolia L., a native of Europe, up to 1 m. tall, with spatulate to linear leaf-blades and large blue or white corollas 2–2.5 cm. wide, has escaped from gardens, W N. C.

2. ROTANTHA Small. Annual or perennial, smooth, diffuse herbs.
Leaf-blades entire, or obscurely or shallowly toothed. Flowers perfect, all alike and complete. Hypanthium short. Corolla rotate. Stamens exserted. Capsule opening by perforations.—Two species, natives of Florida.

Corolla 14–18 mm. wide: sepals nearly or quite as long as the
   corolla-lobes: capsule obovoid.   1. *R. floridana.*
Corolla 7–8 mm. wide: sepals less than half as long as the
   corolla-lobes: capsule subglobose.   2. *R. Robinsiae.*

1. R. floridana (S. Wats.) Small. Perennial: stems and branches diffusely spreading and often intertwined, 2–4 dm. long: leaf-blades narrowly elliptic-oblanceolate, linear, or linear-lanceolate, 1–4 cm. long, obscurely toothed: hypanthium obovate-turbinate: sepals linear-lanceolate to linear-subulate, 6–9 mm. long: corolla violet; lobes narrowly lanceolate: anthers 3–4 mm. long: capsule obovoid, 3–4 mm. long. [*Campanula floridana* S. Wats.]— Grassy swamps and marshes, E Fla. and the pen.—All year.

2. R. Robinsiae Small. Annual: stem with several or many slender erect branches, 0.5–1 dm. tall: leaf-blades spatulate to elliptic, lanceolate, or ovate, or rarely narrower, 0.3–1.2 cm. long, entire or sharply few-toothed: hypanthium subglobose: sepals lanceolate to subulate-lanceolate, 1–1.5 mm. long: corolla violet or blue; lobes elliptic; anthers 1–1.5 mm. long: capsule subglobose, 2–2.5 mm. in diameter. [*Campanula Robinsiae* Small]—Grassy slopes of Chinsegut Hill, near Brooksville, Fla.—Spr.–fall.

3. **CAMPANULASTRUM** Small. Annual or biennial herbs. Leaf-blades toothed. Flowers perfect and complete. Hypanthium elongate in age. Corolla rotate. Stamens exserted. Capsule opening by subapical valves. Seed flattish, broad, margined.—One species.

1. **C. americanum** (L.) Small. Plant 2–20 dm. tall, often widely branched: blades of the upper leaves usually lanceolate, 5–12 cm. long, acuminate: sepals linear-subulate, 6–10 mm. long: corolla blue or white; lobes 10–13 cm. long: capsule turbinate-clavate, 8–10 mm. long: seed oval, about 1.5 mm. long.—Rich woods and rocky river-banks, various provinces, Fla. to Ark., S. Dak., and N. B.—Sum.

4. **SPECULARIA** [Heist.] Fabr. Annual or biennial herbs. Leaf-blades toothed. Flowers dimorphous, the earlier ones with 3 or 4 sepals and undeveloped corollas, the later ones with 5 sepals and rotate corolla. Capsule prismatic, opening by lateral valves.—About 10 species, in the Northern Hemisphere.—VENUS'S LOOKING-GLASSES.

Leaf-blades clasping, usually fully as wide as long: capsule with the valves near the middle. 1. *S. perfoliata*.
Leaf-blades sessile, longer than wide: capsule with the valves at the top. 2. *S. biflora*.

1. **S. perfoliata** (L.) A. DC. Stem 1–5 dm. tall: leaf-blades suborbicular to triangular-ovate: corolla purple, 10–15 mm. wide: capsule ellipsoid-prismatic or obconic, 5–6 mm. long: seed oval, about 0.5 mm. long.—Woods, fields, and waste-places, various provinces, Fla. to Tex., Calif., B. C., and Ont.—(*W. I., Mex., C. A., S. A.*)—Sum.

2. **S. biflora** (R. & P.) F. & M. Stem 1–5 dm. tall: leaf-blades ovate to elliptic or lanceolate above: corolla purple, 15–20 mm. wide: capsule cylindric to fusiform, 6–9 mm. long: seed nearly 1 mm. long.—Fields and open places, various provinces, Fla. to Tex., Calif., Kans., and Que.—(*W. I., Mex.*)—Spr.–fall.

5. **SPHENOCLEA** Gaertn. Annual herbs. Leaf-blades entire. Flowers all alike, borne in a continuous dense spike. Sepals broad. Corolla short-

campanulate: lobes short. Stamens with very short filaments. Ovary depressed. Stigma nearly sessile. Capsule circumscissile, the lid and calyx adnate.—One species.

1. **S. zeylanica** Gaertn. Plant 2–13 dm. tall: leaf-blades mainly elliptic to almost linear, 3–12 cm. long, paler beneath than above: spikes 3–11 cm. long: sepals broadly ovate, 1.5 mm. long: corolla white or greenish, about 2 mm. long, the ovate lobes about as long as the tube: capsule 3–4 mm. wide. —Low grounds, Coastal Plain, La. to Ark. Nat. of the Old World tropics.—(*W. I., Mex., C. A., S. A.*)—Spr.–fall.

FAMILY 3. **LOBELIACEAE** — LOBELIA FAMILY

Herbs, or rarely trees, the sap often milky. Leaves alternate: blades entire, toothed, or parted. Flowers perfect, or rarely dioecious, irregular. Calyx of 5 sepals. Corolla more or less 2-lipped, the tube open on one side. Androecium of 5 stamens, the filaments sometimes cohering. Gynoecium mostly 2-carpellary, the ovary more or less inferior. Fruit capsular or baccate.—About 20 genera and 600 species, widely distributed.

1. **LOBELIA** [Plum.] L. Annual or perennial herbs. Leaf-blades entire or toothed. Flowers in spikes, racemes, or panicles. Hypanthium mostly ribbed. Sepals entire or often glandular-toothed, sometimes with basal appendages. Corolla variously colored or white: upper lip 2-lobed: lower lip 3-lobed. Anthers in a ring around the style, 2 often smaller than the others. Ovary 2-celled. Capsule 2-valved.—About 225 species, widely distributed.—In the following descriptions cauline leaves are considered.

Corolla red (pink or white forms are rare).	I. CARDINALES.
Corolla blue or white, or blue variegated with white.	
Flowers large (corolla-tube over 1 cm. long).	
Stem not scape-like, leafy to the inflorescence.	II. SIPHILITICAE.
Stem scape-like, leafy at the base, the upper leaves reduced and remote.	III. PALUDOSAE.
Flowers small (corolla-tube less than 1 cm. long).	
Raceme secund.	IV. APPENDICULATAE.
Raceme not secund.	
Blades of the cauline leaves sessile.	
Upper cauline leaves with broad blades, at least not linear: raceme spike-like, continuous.	V. SPICATAE.
Upper cauline leaves with narrow, usually linear, or filiform blades: raceme relatively few-flowered, open.	VI. NUTTALLIANAE.
Blades of the cauline leaves manifestly petioled.	VII. XALAPENSES.

I. CARDINALES

Perennial herb with offsets: raceme elongate, mostly 1-sided, very showy.	1. *L. cardinalis.*

II. SIPHILITICAE

Sepals pinnatifid, the auricles hiding the hypanthium: leaves not at all or only slightly reduced above: blades pinnatifid-toothed.	2. *L. brevifolia.*

Sepals entire or glandular-toothed, the auricles, if present, not hiding the hypanthium: leaves on the upper part of the stem much smaller than those below.
Sepals with deflexed or broadly rounded auricles at the base, the edges ciliate, not glandular-toothed.
Hypanthium hemispheric in anthesis: sepals strongly auricled at the base, erose and more or less irregularly toothed. 3. *L. siphilitica.*
Hypanthium turbinate in anthesis: sepals slightly auricled at the base, merely ciliate. 4. *L. puberula.*
Sepals without basal auricles.
Sepals entire, glandless.
Leaf-blades broad, usually bluntly toothed: sepals shorter than the corolla-tube. 5. *L. amoena.*
Leaf-blades narrow, undulate or glandular-toothed: sepals as long as the corolla-tube or longer. 6. *L. elongata.*
Sepals glandular-toothed.
Lower lip of the corolla glabrous: hypanthium glabrous: leaf-blades broad. 7. *L. glandulifera.*
Lower lip of the corolla pubescent within: hypanthium bristly-pubescent: leaf-blades narrow. 8. *L. glandulosa.*

III. PALUDOSAE

Sepals not auricled at the base: anther-head about 2 mm. long: corolla-tube less than 1 cm. long. 9. *L. paludosa.*
Sepals auricled at the base: anther-head about 4 mm. long: corolla-tube over 1 cm. long. 10. *L. floridana.*

IV. APPENDICULATAE

Sepals lanceolate, glandular-toothed, much shorter than the corolla-tube: corolla finely pubescent without: hypanthium turbinate in anthesis. 11. *L. flaccidifolia.*
Sepals subulate, entire or merely erose: nearly or quite as long as the corolla-tube: corolla glabrous or puberulent without: hypanthium campanulate in anthesis. 12. *L. Gattingeri.*

V. SPICATAE

Capsule partly inferior: mature hypanthium hemispheric: sepals more or less auricled at the base.
Sepals lanceolate, with minute spreading auricles at the base, shorter than the corolla-tube. 13. *L. spicata.*
Sepals slender-subulate, with long deflexed auricles at the base, quite as long as the corolla-tube.
Bracts elongate, nearly or quite surpassing the flowers: corolla copiously pubescent without. 14. *L. bracteata.*
Bracts short, not surpassing the flowers: corollas glabrous or slightly puberulent without. 15. *L. leptostachya.*
Capsule wholly inferior: mature hypanthium obovoid, oval, or ovoid: sepals not at all auricled. 16. *L. inflata.*

VI. NUTTALLIANAE

Pedicels mostly shorter than the bracts, shorter than the corollas in anthesis.
Sepals lanceolate: corolla less than 1 cm. long: mature hypanthium hemispheric or depressed-hemispheric. 17. *L. Nuttallii.*
Sepals linear-subulate: corolla mostly over 1 cm. long: mature hypanthium ellipsoid or turbinate-ellipsoid. 18. *L. Canbyi.*
Pedicels much exceeding the bracts, longer than the corollas. 19. *L. Boykinii.*

VII. XALAPENSES

Pedicels long, over 1 cm. long in anthesis: capsule ½ inferior or less.
Corolla 4–6 mm. long: sepals lanceolate. 20. *L. Cliffortiana.*
Corolla 8–10 mm. long: sepals subulate. 21. *L. homophylla.*
Pedicels short, less than 1 cm. long in anthesis: capsules 2/3 inferior. 22. *L. Feayana.*

1. **L. cardinalis** L. Stem 3–12 dm. tall, simple, glabrous or finely hirsute: blades of the lower leaves elliptic to elliptic-spatulate, serrate or dentate:

raceme continuous, rather conspicuously bracted: sepals linear-attenuate to linear-subulate, entire: corolla-lobes on either side of the cleft linear-oblanceolate or nearly linear: anther-head 5–6 mm. long: capsule hemispheric, short-beaked: seed about 1 mm. long. — (CARDINAL-FLOWER.) — Wet ravines, swamps and stream-banks, various provinces, Fla. to Tex., Ont., and N. B.—Sum.–fall.

2. **L. brevifolia** Nutt. Stem 3–8 dm. tall, rather copiously and evenly leafy, sometimes branched: leaf-blades fleshy, spatulate or obovate to elliptic or linear-elliptic, 0.5–2.5 cm. long, pinnatifid-toothed, the teeth gland-tipped: raceme interrupted, not conspicuously bracted: sepals lanceolate to hastate-ovate, pinnatifid, each with 2 obtuse basal auricles which invest the hypanthium: corolla blue, pubescent without; lobes of the upper lip lanceolate: capsule 5–7 mm. long: seed about 0.5 mm. long.—Moist pinelands, Coastal Plain, Fla. to La.—Sum-fall.

3. **L. siphilitica** L. Stem 2–10 dm. tall, sparingly pubescent, often branched: leaf-blades thin or thinnish, oblanceolate to elliptic or lanceolate, 2.5–20 cm. long, coarsely serrate or sinuate-dentate: sepals lanceolate, bristly ciliate, acuminate from a broad base, each with large acute basal auricles: corolla light-blue, or rarely white, straightened out, over 2 cm. long: anther-head fully 5 mm. long: capsule over 7 mm. wide, with the sepal-auricles reaching nearly or quite to the base: seed ellipsoid.—(GREAT-LOBELIA.)—Low grounds, meadows, and along streams, various provinces, Ga. to La., Colo., S. Dak., Ont., and Me. —Sum.–fall.

4. **L. puberula** Michx. Stem 3–10 dm. tall, softly fine-pubescent: leaf-blades thick, oblanceolate to obovate, elliptic, lanceolate, or ovate, 2–10 cm. long, finely toothed: sepals lanceolate, finely pubescent, each with small rounded basal auricles: corolla bright-blue, straghtened out 2 cm. long or less; anther-head less than 5 mm. long: capsule less than 7 mm. wide, finely pubescent with the sepal auricles reaching to above the middle: seed linear-cylindric.—Wet woods, low grounds, and thickets, often in acid soil, various provinces, Fla. to Tex., Ga., and N. J.—Fall.

5. **L. amoena** Michx. Stem 3–12 dm. tall, glabrous or softly hirsute: leaf-blades thinnish, elliptic, varying to obovate or ovate, undulate to sinuate, or unevenly crenate: sepals narrowly linear-subulate, 7–8 mm. long, entire, slender-tipped: corolla bright-blue, straightened out 2–2.5 cm. long or sometimes less; anther-head 2–2.5 mm. long: capsule 5–6 mm. wide: seed linear-cylindric, fully 1 mm. long.—Acid swamps or moist hillsides, Coastal Plain, Fla. to Miss. and Va.—Sum.–fall.

6. **L. elongata** Small. Stem 3–12 dm. tall, glabrous: leaf-blades linear or nearly so, or narrowly linear-lanceolate on the upper part of the stem, 2–10 cm. long, undulate, serrate, or dentate-serrate: sepals elongate, linear-subulate or linear-setaceous, entire: corolla deep-blue, straightened out about 2 cm. long: anther-head about 4 mm. long: capsule about 5 mm. wide: seed narrowly ellipsoid, barely 1 mm. long.—Low grounds, Coastal Plain, Fla. to La. and Va. —Sum.–fall.

7. **L. glandulifera** (A. Gray) Small. Stem 3–7 dm. tall, glabrous or sparingly pubescent: leaf-blades narrowly elliptic to elliptic-ovate, 3–12 cm. long, irregu-

larly dentate or undulate: hypanthium glabrous: sepals narrowly lanceolate to linear-lanceolate, 7–9 mm. long, pectinately glandular-toothed: corolla deep-blue, straightened out 2–2.5 cm. long: anther-head 3–4 mm. long: capsule about 5 mm. wide: seed ellipsoid, about 1 mm. long.—Low grounds, meadows, and swamps, Coastal Plain, Fla. to Miss. and Va.—Sum.–fall.

8. L. glandulosa Walt. Stem 3–12 dm. tall, glabrous: leaf-blades linear-oblanceolate to linear, 2–15 cm. long, repand or shallowly toothed, the teeth gland-tipped: hypanthium pubescent: sepals lanceolate or linear-lanceolate, 6–9 mm. long, prominently glandular-toothed: corolla deep-blue, straightened out 2–2.5 cm. long; lobes of the lower lip broadly ovate: capsule 6–7 mm. wide: seed ellipsoid, less than 1 mm. long.—Wet pinelands and swamps, Coastal Plain, Fla. to Va.; reported also from Miss.—Spr.–fall or all year southward.

9. L. floridana Chapm. Stem 8–15 dm. tall: leaf-blades linear or slightly linear-spatulate below, 10–40 cm. long, undulate or crenate-undulate: sepals hastate-lanceolate, 4–5 mm. long, coarsely toothed: corolla blue, sometimes pale, straightened out over 1.5 cm. long: capsule 4–4.5 mm. wide.—Swamps, and low pinelands, Coastal Plain, Fla. to Miss.—Spr.–fall.

10. L. paludosa Nutt. Stem 2–9 dm. tall: leaf-blades linear-spatulate, or rarely elliptic-obovate to linear, 3–25 cm. long, entire or sinuate-crenate: sepals lanceolate to linear-lanceolate, 3–5 mm. long, shallowly toothed or often entire: corolla light-blue or white, straightened out less than 1.5 cm. long: capsule 3–3.5 mm. wide.—Swamps, and low pinelands and ponds, Coastal Plain, Fla. to La. and Del.—Spr.–fall, or all year southward.

11. L. flaccidifolia Small. Stem 2–6 dm. tall: leaf-blades thin, obovate to elliptic-spatulate at the base of the stem, linear-elliptic or rarely linear-lanceolate above, 3–11 cm. long, undulate or crenate-undulate: hypanthium in anthesis turbinate: sepals lanceolate, 3–5 mm. long, glandular-toothed, auricled at the base: corolla 14–16 mm. long: capsule 5–8 mm. long.—River swamps, Coastal Plain, Fla. and Ga.—Sum.

12. L. Gattingeri A. Gray. Stem 2–4 dm. tall, glabrous: leaf-blades thick, obovate at the base of the stem, elliptic, oval, or ovate above, 1–4 cm. long, irregularly toothed or nearly entire: hypanthium in anthesis campanulate: sepals subulate, 4–6 mm. long, eciliate, not auricled at the base: corolla 8–9 mm. long: capsule 5–6 mm. long.—Cedar glades and limestone prairies, Interior Low Plateaus, Ala. and Tenn.—Spr. Plants, perhaps referable to *L. appendiculata* in which the ciliate sepals are auricled at the base, have been found in Ala.

13. L. spicata Lam. Stem 1–12 dm. tall, pubescent, at least near the base: leaf-blades spatulate, obovate, or suborbicular at the base of the stem, oblanceolate to lanceolate above, 1–10 cm. long, crenate-dentate or nearly entire: hypanthium in anthesis hemispheric: sepals lanceolate, 3–3.5 mm. long, with minute spreading auricles at the base: corolla blue, 6–9 mm. long: capsule 2.5–3 mm. long.—Woods, moist fields, and meadows, various provinces, Ga. to Tex., Sask., and P. E. I.—Sum.

14. L. bracteata Small. Stem 8–10 dm. tall: leaf-blades spatulate at the base of the stem, elliptic, lanceolate or elliptic-lanceolate above, 3–10 cm. long, glandular-toothed: hypanthium in anthesis somewhat depressed: sepals slender-subulate, 4–4.5 mm. long, with deflexed auricles at the base: corolla 8–9 mm. long: capsule 5–7 mm. long.—Woods, Piedmont, Ga. to N. C.—Sum.

15. **L. leptostachys** A. DC. Stem 3–12 dm. tall: leaf-blades obovate to oblanceolate at the base of the stem, elliptic to lanceolate above, 3–10 cm. long, entire or indistinctly toothed: hypanthium in anthesis depressed: sepals slender-subulate, 5–6 mm. long, with deflexed auricles at the base: corolla 6–8 mm. long: capsule 3–4 mm. long.—Dry soil, various provinces, rarely Coastal Plain, Ga. to Miss., Kans., Ohio, and Va.—Sum.

16. **L. inflata** L. Stem 1–10 dm. tall, finely hirsute: leaf-blades obovate to oval or ovate, 2–9 cm. long, crenate: hypanthium in anthesis campanulate: sepals linear, 2.5–3.5 mm. long, entire: corolla lilac, 6–8 mm. long: capsule 5–8 mm. long, inflated.—(INDIAN-TOBACCO. WILD-TOBACCO. EYEBRIGHT.)— Fields, woods, and thickets, various provinces, Ga. to Ark., Sask., and Lab. —Sum.–fall.

17. **L. Nuttallii** Roem. & Schult. Stem 2–7 dm. tall: leaf-blades obovate to ovate at the base of the stem, oblanceolate to linear above, 2–4 cm. long, entire or toothed: hypanthium in anthesis much depressed: sepals lanceolate, about 2 mm. long, entire: corolla light-blue, 6–7.5 mm. long: capsule 2.5–3 mm. long. —Low grounds or pinelands, Coastal Plain and rarely Appalachian provinces, Fla. to Miss., Pa., and S N. Y.—Spr.–fall.

18. **L. Canbyi** A. Gray. Stem 3–8 dm. tall: leaf-blades elliptic-linear to linear, 2–6 cm. long, glandular-denticulate: hypanthium in anthesis campanulate: sepals linear-subulate, 3–4 mm. long, obscurely glandular-denticulate: corolla bright-blue, 10–11 mm. long: capsule about 4 mm. long, wholly inferior.—Pineland swamps, local, Coastal Plain, S. C. to N. J.—Sum.–fall.

19. **L. Boykinii** T. &. G. Stem 3–8 dm. tall, hollow, virgate, sometimes with few virgàte branches: leaf-blades inconspicuous, linear-filiform to filiform, 1–3 cm. long or shorter, indistinctly glandular-toothed: hypanthium in anthesis turbinate: sepals slender-subulate, 3.5–4.5 mm. long, entire: corolla bright-blue, 8–10 mm. long: capsule 3–4 mm. long, half-inferior.—Pineland swamps and cypress-ponds, Coastal Plain, Fla. to S. C.—Spr.–sum.

20. **L. Cliffortiana** L. Stem 3–6 dm. tall, often finely pubescent: leaf-blades ovate to ovate-lanceolate, 2–10 cm. long, coarsely toothed or sinuate: sepals lanceolate, about 2 mm. long, entire: corolla 4–6 mm. long: capsule 5–6 mm. long.—Wet places, waste-places, and cult. grounds, Coastal Plain, Fla. to Tex. Nat. of Trop. Am.—(*W. I., Mex., C. A., S. A.*)—Spr.–fall.

21. **L. homophylla** F. E. Wimmer. Stem 2–6 dm. tall, glabrous or finely pubescent: leaf-blades ovate to suborbicular, 1–4 cm. long, rather closely and irregularly crenate or incised-dentate, cordate to truncate at the base: sepals subulate, 2.5–3.5 mm. long, entire: corolla 8–10 mm. long: capsule 6–7 mm. long. [*L. Cliffortiana xalapensis* (Chapm. Fl.). *L. xalapensis* (Fl. SE U. S.).] —Pinelands, fence-rows, and roadsides, pen. Fla.—Spr.–fall.

22. **L. Feayana** A. Gray. Stem 1–3 dm. tall, glabrous: leaf-blades reniform, suborbicular, or orbicular-ovate at the base of the stem, obovate to ovate above, 0.5–1.5 cm. long, entire or crenate: sepals lanceolate, 1.5–2 mm. long, entire: corolla 7–9 mm. long: capsule about 4 mm. long.—(BAY-LOBELIA.)—Pinelands, Fla.—Spr.–fall.

FAMILY 4. **BRUNONIACEAE** — GOODENIA FAMILY

Herbaceous or woody plants. Leaves alternate or sometimes opposite: blades entire, toothed, or pinnatifid. Flowers perfect. Calyx of 5 partially united sepals, or rarely obsolete. Corolla of 5 equally or unequally united petals. Androecium of 5 distinct stamens. Gynoecium mostly of 2 united carpels, the ovary inferior. Stigma surrounded with an indusium. Fruit drupaceous, baccate, or capsular.—Twelve genera and more than 200 species, mostly Australian.

1. **SCAEVOLA** L. Succulent herbs or shrubs. Leaf-blades mostly entire. Flowers irregular, in cymes. Calyx 5-lobed, or obsolete. Corolla-tube open to the base on one side, the lobes winged. Stigma with a ciliate indusium. Berry with a fleshy exocarp.—About 60 species, mostly Australian.

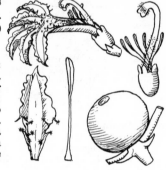

1. **S. Plumieri** Vahl. Plant 3–18 dm. tall: leaf-blades obovate to spatulate, 4–6 cm. long: calyx-lobes rounded: corolla white or pinkish, 22–28 mm. long, woolly within; lobes linear to lanceolate: berries oval to globular, 10–14 mm. long, black, very juicy.—Coastal sand-dunes, pen. Fla. and Florida Keys.—(*W. I.*)—All year.—Stems often spreading under the sand and forming large patches.

FAMILY 5. **CALYCERACEAE** — CALYCERA FAMILY

Herbs or partly woody plants. Leaves alternate: blades usually narrow, entire, toothed, or pinnatifid. Flowers small, in heads which are solitary at the end of each peduncle, or sessile, the receptacle short or elongate. Involucre of one or two series of distinct or united bracts. Calyx of 4–6 more or less accrescent sepals. Corolla elongate: tube slender, the throat shorter than the tube, the limb 4–6-lobed. Androecium of 4–6 stamens. Filaments adnate up to the throat of the corolla. Anthers erect, adnate around the style. Gynoecium of a single carpel. Ovary inferior. Style elongate. Stigma minute. Fruit an achene, often crowned with the calyx.—Three genera and 25 species, South American.

1. **ACICARPHA** Juss. Annual diffuse or procumbent herbs. Leaves various: blades of the basal ones usually petioled, those of the cauline leaves sessile or clasping, all entire or toothed. Heads sessile or short-peduncled, spiny at the base, the marginal flowers fruit-producing, the central flowers not fruit-producing. Receptacle elongate. Sepals erect, persistent. Corolla colored, with a long tube and a short throat: lobes narrow. Achenes more or less united to each other.—Three species, South American.

1. **A. tribuloides** Juss. Plant mostly 1–4 dm. tall, glabrous: basal leaves 3–11 cm. long; blades spatulate: blades of the cauline

leaves elliptic to lanceolate, clasping, all coarsely toothed: sepals about 1 mm. long, acuminate: corollas yellow, about 3 mm. long; lobes lanceolate: achene crowned with the accrescent subulate sepals, 4–5 mm. long.—Fields and road-sides, N Fla. Nat. of S. Am.—Spr.–fall.

Order CARDUALES—Cardual Order

Herbs, shrubs, or rarely trees. Leaves mainly alternate: blades entire, toothed, or divided. Flowers perfect, monoecious, or dioecious, few or many aggregated on a receptacle and surrounded with an involucre, or the involucre rarely obsolete. Calyx one or two rows of bristles, scales, a mere border or crown, or obsolete, or wanting. Corolla of several more or less united petals, or wanting. Androecium of usually 5 stamens, the anthers converging, or united. Gynoecium mostly of 2 united carpels. Ovary inferior. Styles or stigmas mostly 2. Fruit an achene.

Flowers with tubular corollas, or those of the outer ones prolonged into ligules.
  Stamens distinct, or the filaments sometimes united,
    the anthers merely converging about the stigma.   Fam. 1. AMBROSIACEAE.
  Stamens united by their anthers, thus forming a tube
    around the stigma, except in *Kuhnia*.   Fam. 2. CARDUACEAE.
Flowers with each corolla prolonged into a ligule.   Fam. 3. CICHORIACEAE.

Family 1. AMBROSIACEAE — Ragweed Family

Annual or perennial herbs, or shrubs, the plants often coarse. Leaf-blades entire, toothed, lobed, or divided. Flowers in inconspicuous heads, the bracts of the pistillate heads distinct or sometimes united and accrescent into a bur. Fruit-producing flowers apetalous or with much reduced corollas. Achenes subtended by or enclosed in an involucre. Pappus wanting or obsolete.—Eight genera and about 75 species, mostly American.

Staminate and pistillate flowers in the same head, the pistillate marginal, fewer
  than the staminate, or rarely wanting: heads neither bur-
  like nor nut-like.   Tribe I. IVEAE.
Staminate and pistillate flowers in different heads, the pistillate flowers 1–7, enclosed in a bur-like or nut-like involucre,
  which also later encloses the achenes.   II. AMBROSIEAE.

I. Iveae
Plants with androgynous nodding heads and broad or
  narrow leaf-blades.   1. IVA.

II. Ambrosieae
Bracts of the staminate involucre more or less united: re-
  ceptacle flat or merely convex: filaments free.
  Tubercles or spines of the pistillate involucres in a
    single series: fruit with a truncate or equally 3–5-
    toothed beak.   2. AMBROSIA.
  Tubercles or spines in several series: fruit with a
    2-toothed beak, the teeth incurved, the outer one the
    longer.   3. FRANSERIA.
Bracts of the staminate involucre distinct: receptacle
  elongate filaments united.
  Leaves pinnately veined or lobed, the stipules simple or
    pronged stipular spines: bur with straight beaks.   4. ACANTHOXANTHIUM.
  Leaves digitately veined or lobed, the stipules not
    spiny: bur with curved or hooked beaks.   5. XANTHIUM.

1. IVA L. Annual or perennial, glabrous, strigose, or hispidulous herbs, or shrubs. Leaves, at least the lower, opposite: blades entire or toothed. Heads axillary to leaf-like bracts. Involucre turbinate to hemispheric: bracts 3–6, or 5–9 in *I. imbricata*. Receptacle with large bractlets. Corolla of the pistillate flowers a truncate tube. Achenes slightly flattened, usually obovoid.—About 20 species, American.—MARSH-ELDERS.

Plants perennial : heads mostly peduncled : bracts of the involucre 5–9, or rarely 4.
  Bracts of the involucre 6–9, imbricate in two series : leaf-blades entire. 1. *I. imbricata.*
  Bracts of the involucre 5 or rarely 4, in one series and only slightly overlapping : leaf-blades toothed. 2. *I. frutescens.*
Plants annual : heads sessile : bracts of the involucre 3, or rarely 4 or 5.
  Leaf-blades broad, coarsely toothed, petioled : those of the inflorescence different, sessile.
    Leaves of the inflorescence with ovate to lanceolate short-acuminate blades. 3. *I. ciliata.*
    Leaves of the inflorescence with linear or linear-lanceolate caudate-acuminate blades. 4. *I. caudata.*
  Leaf-blades narrow, entire or shallowly toothed, sessile or short-petioled ; those of the inflorescence nearly similar.
    Bracts of the involucre distinct : staminate and pistillate flowers three each : leaf-blades linear. 5. *I. microcephala.*
    Bracts of the involucre partly united : pistillate flowers usually solitary : leaf-blades oblong. 6. *I. asperifolia.*

1. **I. imbricata** Walt. Perennial with a woody base: stem 1 m. tall or less, smooth and glabrous: leaf-blades linear to linear-elliptic, linear-oblanceolate, or linear-subulate above, 2–5 cm. long, glabrous, entire or shallowly toothed: involucres subtended by foliaceous bracts, 3–4 mm. high or larger in age; inner bracts suborbicular: achenes 3–3.5 mm. long.—Coastal sand-dunes and rocky shores, Fla. to La. and Va.—(*W. I.*)—Sum.–fall.

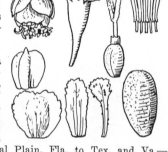

2. **I. frutescens** L. Perennial with a woody base: stem 3.5 m. tall or less, pubescent, at least above: leaf-blades elliptic, linear-elliptic, elliptic-lanceolate or nearly linear above, 4–10 cm. long, pubescent, coarsely serrate: involucres 3.5–4 mm. high; inner bracts oval or obovate: achenes 2–2.5 mm. long.—(MARSH-ELDER. HIGH-WATER SHRUB.)—Salt marshes and margins, Coastal Plain, Fla. to Tex. and Va.—Sum.–fall.

3. **I. ciliata** Willd. Annual, 1.8 m. tall or less: stem copiously rough-pubescent: leaf-blades ovate, oval, or elliptic, 4–10 cm. long, acute or short-acuminate, serrate: heads contiguous, subtended by bristly-ciliate bracts: involucres 3–4 mm. high, rough-pubescent: achenes colored, about 3 mm. long, with faint tubercular-roughened ridges.—Moist soil, various provinces, La. to N. M., Nebr., and Ill.; extending as a weed E to Ala.—Sum.–fall.

4. **I. caudata** Small. Annual, 1 m. tall or less: stem rather sparingly hispidulous: leaf-blades ovate to elliptic, 4–15 cm. long, acuminate, coarsely and unevenly serrate: heads contiguous or approximate, subtended by coarsely ciliate bracts: involucres sparingly pubescent: achenes broadly cuneate-obovoid, 3.5 mm. long, with prominent even ridges.—Swamps and low grounds, Coastal Plain and adj. provinces, Miss. to La., Mo., and Ill.—Sum.-fall.

5. **I. microcephala** Nutt. Annual, 1 m. tall or less: stem glabrous or minutely pubescent especially above, often with numerous erect branches: leaf-blades narrowly linear, 2–5 cm. long, entire or shallowly toothed, glandular-punctate: heads contiguous or nearly so, subtended by subulate or linear-filiform bracts: involucre campanulate, about 2 mm. high; bracts obovate to suborbicular:

achenes narrowly obovoid, fully 1 mm. long, muriculate.—Low pinelands and prairies, Coastal Plain, Fla. to S. C.—Sum.-winter.—Sometimes a weed.

6. I. asperifolia Less. Annual, or perhaps sometimes perennial, 0.5 m. tall or less: stem sometimes decumbent, sparingly rough-pubescent at least above: leaves narrowly elliptic to linear-oblanceolate, 1–2 cm. long, entire, glandular-punctate: heads contiguous or approximate: involucre turbinate, about 3 mm. high; bracts cuneate to suborbicular: achenes obovoid, about 2 mm. long, granular-muriculate.—Waste-places, Pensacola, Fla. Nat. of Mex.—Sum.-fall.

2. AMBROSIA L. Annual or rarely perennial coarse caulescent branching herbs. Leaves alternate or opposite: blades toothed, lobed, or dissected, long-petioled. Heads in spikes or racemes, the staminate above the pistillate, with a usually saucer-shaped 5–12-lobed involucre. Pistillate involucre erect, nut-like, usually with a single series of tubercles or spines near the apex, the beak truncate or 3- to 4-toothed.—About 20 species, mostly American.—RAG-WEEDS.

Staminate heads spicate: involucre very oblique, produced on the side away from
  the stem into a lanceolate acuminate lobe: annuals.   I. CERCOMERIS.
Staminate heads racemose: involucre slightly, if at all, oblique,
  not produced into an elongate lobe on either side: annuals or
  perennials.   II. EUAMBROSIA.

I. CERCOMERIS

A rough hirsute herb: leaf-blades of a lanceolate type, usually
  with a lobe on each side near the base.   1. *A. bidentata.*

II. EUAMBROSIA

Leaf-blades pinnatifid to tripinnatifid.
  Leaf-blades green at least above: plants annual.
    Fruit-body 2–2.5 mm. long, the beak 1 mm. long or less.
      Fruits rugose.   2. *A. monophylla.*
      Fruits smooth.   3. *A. glandulosa.*
    Fruit-body 3 mm. long or more, the beak more than 1
      mm. long.
      Blades of the lower leaves mostly bipinnatifid, the
        segments narrow: staminate heads about 3 mm.
        wide.   4. *A. elatior.*
      Blades of the lower leaves mostly pinnatifid, the seg-
        ments broad: staminate heads 4–5 mm. wide.   5. *A. Rugelii.*
  Leaf-blades canescent: plants perennial.   6. *A. hispida.*
Leaf-blades entire, toothed, or 3–5-lobed.
  Leaves with winged petioles: fruits slightly if at all pitted
    between the ridges which end in short conic spines.   7. *A. trifida.*
  Leaves with wingless petioles: fruits pitted between the
    ridges which end in tubercle-like spines.   8. *A. aptera.*

1. A. bidentata Michx. Stem 1 m. tall or less, rough hirsute: leaf-blades lanceolate, linear-lanceolate, or elliptic-lanceolate, 2–8 cm. long, each with a sharp lobe-like tooth on one or both sides near the base: staminate involucre turbi-nate: pistillate heads solitary or two together in the axils: fruit 6–7 mm. long, the body much longer than the beak, the spines subulate, directed forward, ½ as long as the beak.—Prairies, Interior Low Plateaus and adj. provinces, Miss. to Tex., Nebr., and Ky.—Sum.-fall.

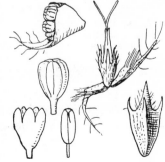

2. A. monophylla (Walt.) Rydb. Stem 1.5 m. tall or less, pubescent with lax more or less scattered hairs: leaf-blades deeply bipinnatifid, or those of the upper leaves pinnatifid or merely toothed, scabrous above, strigillose beneath, the segments lanceolate, acute: staminate involucre broadly obconic, 1.5–2 mm. high: fruit 2.5–3 mm. high, the body obovoid, short-beaked, with 5–7 short conic spines.—Prairies, coastal dunes, pinelands, and waste-places, Coastal Plain, Fla. to Tex. and N. C.—(*W. I.*)—All year.

3. **A. glandulosa** Scheele. Stem 1 m. tall or less, sparingly pubescent: leaf-blades bipinnatifid or pinnatifid, strigose on both sides, the segments linear to linear-lanceolate, acute or acuminate: staminate involucre saucer-shaped, 1–1.5 mm. high: fruit about 2.5 mm. long, the body broadly obovoid, short-beaked with usually 5 or 6 tubercle-like spines.—Low grounds, river-bottoms, and banks, Coastal Plain, W Fla. to Tex.—Sum.–fall.

4. **A. elatior** L. Stem 1.5 m. tall or less; more or less hirsute: leaf-blades bipinnatifid or those of the upper ones merely pinnatifid, strigillose above, often hirsute beneath, the segments lanceolate to subelliptic, usually acute: staminate involucre saucer-shaped, 1–1.5 mm. high: fruit 4–4.5 mm. long, the body obovoid, often broadly so, rather long-beaked, with 5–7 short-subulate spines. [*A. artemisiifolia* Fl. SE U. S.]—(Roman-Wormwood. Hot-weed. Bitter-weed.)—Dry soil, beaches, prairies, pinelands, and cult. grounds, various provinces, N. C. to Tex., Calif., Wash., and N. S.—(*W. I.*)—Spr.–fall.

5. **A. Rugelii** Rydb. Stem 1 m. tall or less, densely hirsute: leaf-blades pin-natifid or partly bipinnatifid, hispidulous and strongly veined, the segments ovate to lanceolate: staminate involucre shallowly cupulate, 1.5–2 mm. high: fruit 4–4.5 mm. long, the body obovoid, short-beaked, with 5 or 6 short-subulate or tubercle-like spines.—Sand-dunes and pinelands, Coastal Plain, Fla. and Ga.—Sum.–fall.—The short-petioled or sessile leaves turn dark in drying.

6. **A. hispida** Pursh. Stem and branches prostrate, creeping, several m. long or less, white hirsute or hispidulous: leaf-blades tripinnatifid, broadly ovate in outline, the segments divergent, ovate to obovate, obtuse or merely acutish: staminate involucre cupulate, about 2 mm. high: fruit 3.5–4 mm. long, the body obovoid, veinly, glandular, short-beaked, with 1–5 unequal short-conic spines. —Beaches and coastal dunes, Fla.—(*W. I., Mex., C. A., S. A.*)—All year.— Often efficacious as a sand-binder.

7. **A. trifida** L. Stem 5 m. tall or less, hispidulous or hirsute: leaf-blades except sometimes those of the upper ones, 3- or 5-lobed, mostly 1–3 dm. long; lobes ovate to lanceolate, serrate: staminate involucre saucer-shaped, about 1 mm. high: fruit 7–8 mm. long, the body broadly obovoid, with 6 or 7 ridges which end in short-conic spines, stout-beaked.—(Great-ragweed. Horse-cane.) —River-banks, cult. grounds, and waste-places, various provinces, Fla. to Tex., Colo., B. C., and Que.—Sum.–fall.—Plants whose juvenile main stem is cut off, produce unlobed leaf-blades.

8. **A. aptera** DC. Stem 5 m. tall or less, scabrous: leaf-blades, except some of the upper ones, 3- or 5-lobed, the lobes lanceolate to ovate, coarsely serrate or unevenly toothed: staminate involucre saucer-shaped about 1 mm. high: fruit 5–6 mm. long, the body obovoid, with 4–8 ridges which end in tubercle-like spines, short-beaked.—Low grounds and wet places, various provinces, Miss. to Ariz.—Sum.–fall.—In this and the next preceding species, the staminate in-volucre and corollas are black-streaked.

3. **FRANSERIA** Cav. Anual or perennial caulescent herbs, or low shrubs: leaves alternate or opposite: blades toothed or dissected. Heads in spikes or

racemes, the staminate with saucer-shaped or turbinate lobed involucres. Pistillate involucre of several fused bracts, nut-like, becoming a several- or many-spined bur, 2-lipped or 2-beaked at the tip.—About 25 species, American.—RAGWEEDS.

1. F. confertiflora (DC.) Rydb. Perennial, 2 m. tall or less, more or less strigose: leaf-blades bipinnately or tripinnately dissected, the segments lanceolate to linear, acute, the terminal one elongate: staminate involucre 2 mm. high or nearly so, hirsutulous: fruit ovoid or globose in outline, 2–3 mm. long, with a single beak and usually 6–18 spines.—Plains and moist grounds, various provinces, Tenn. to Tex., N. M., and Colo.—(*Mex.*)—Sum.-fall.

4. ACANTHOXANTHIUM Fourr.[1] Coarse monoecious annual herbs. Leaves alternate, with 3-pronged or simple stipular spines: blades pinnately lobed or entire. Staminate heads mostly in terminal capitate clusters: involucre of distinct bracts: corolla tubular-funnelform, 5-lobed: filaments monadelphous. Pistillate involucres axillary, closed, 1- or 2-beaked or sometimes beakless, the body cylindric-ellipsoid, 1- or 2-flowered, armed with numerous spines which are first bent backward and then hooked forward, the beaks straight, if two, unequal in length: corolla wanting: stigmas 2. Achenes 1 or 2 in each bur.—Four species, South American.

1. A. spinosum (L.) Fourr. Stem 3–10 dm. tall, in age stramineous, branched: leaf-blades lanceolate, entire or 3–5-lobed, strigose above, white-tomentose beneath, 5–10 cm. long; spines 3-pronged, up to 2.5 cm. long: bur with an ellipsoid body, 10–13 mm. long, pubescent, the prickles about 2 mm. long; the beaks up to 3 mm. long. [*Xanthium spinosum* L.]—(CLOTBUR.)—Waste-places, fields, and roadsides, various provinces, Fla. to Tex., Calif., B. C., and Me. Nat. of S. Am.—(*W. I., Mex., C. A., O. W.*) —Sum.

5. XANTHIUM L.[1] Coarse monoecious annual herbs. Leaves alternate: blades usually ovate to reniform in outline, more or less digitately 3–5-lobed, often cordate at the base. Staminate heads in terminal spikes or racemes: involucre of distinct bracts in 1–3 series: corolla tubular-funnelform, 5-lobed: filaments monadelphous. Pistillate involucre closed, 2- or 3-beaked, the body cylindric-fusiform, ellipsoid, or ovoid, 2- or 3-flowered, armed with spines which are hooked at the apex, the beaks nearly equal, more or less curved, 2-lobed, the outer lobe the longer and incurved: corolla wanting: stigmas 2. Achene

[1] Contributed by the late Per Axel Rydberg.

solitary in each cavity of the bur.—About 40 species, widely distributed.—
Sum.—CLOTBURS. BURWEEDS. COCKLEBURS.

Body of the bur 1.5–3 cm. long.
　Bur minutely glandular-puberulent, hispidulous, or glabrate.
　　Body of the bur broadly fusiform, nearly half as wide
　　　as long.　　　　　　　　　　　　　　　　　　　　　　　　　1. *X. americanum.*
　　Body of the bur almost cylindric, about a third as
　　　wide as long.　　　　　　　　　　　　　　　　　　　　　　　2. *X. cylindraceum.*
　Bur more or less coarsely hispid, especially on the lower
　　part of the spines.
　　Body of the bur cylindro-fusiform, about a third as
　　　wide as long, less than 2 cm. long; spines 5–7 mm.
　　　long.　　　　　　　　　　　　　　　　　　　　　　　　　　　3. *X. pennsylvanicum.*
　　Body of the bur ellipsoid, half as wide as long or
　　　nearly so.
　　　Body of the bur about 1.5–1.8 cm. long; spines 3–5
　　　　mm. long.　　　　　　　　　　　　　　　　　　　　　　　4. *X. echinatum.*
　　　Body of the bur about 2.5–3 cm. long; spines 8–11
　　　　mm. long.　　　　　　　　　　　　　　　　　　　　　　　5. *X. speciosum.*
Body of the bur about 1 cm. long.　　　　　　　　　　　　　　6. *X. echinellum.*

1. X. americanum Walt. Plant glabrate or finely pubescent, 2–13 dm. tall:
leaf-blades ovate to deltoid, 5–30 cm. long: body of the bur broadly fusiform,
15–18 mm. long, thickly beset with 100–200
slender, more or less hooked spines, which
are 3–4 mm. long, and nearly equalling the
beaks which are straight nearly to the
apex. [*X. chinense* Millsp. & Sherff scarcely Mill. *X. glabratum* (DC.) Britton]—
Waste-places, cult. grounds, and woodsides,
various provinces, Fla. to Tex., Nebr., and
Mass.

2. X. cylindraceum Millsp. & Sherff. Plant
rough-puberulent, 5–15 dm. tall: leaf-
blades deltoid-ovate, 8–10 cm. long: body
of the bur almost cylindric, beset with 125–
175 slender hooked spines about 3 mm.
long; beaks 4–5 mm. long, strongly in-
curved.—Waste-places, old fields, and cult. grounds, Piedmont, N. C.

3. X. pennsylvanicum Wallr. Plant rough-pubescent, at least above, 2–6 dm.
tall: leaf-blades ovate to reniform: body of the bur cylindro-fusiform, 15–20
mm. long, the spines 100–150, nearly as long as the diameter of the body;
beaks 4–6 mm. long, often incurved.—Rich soil, various provinces, Fla. to
Tex., Minn., Mass., and Va.

4. X. echinatum Murr. Plant rough-pubescent, 3–16 dm. tall: leaf-blades
ovate to deltoid, or reniform: body of the bur ellipsoid, 15–18 mm. long, hispid, the spines 100–200, stout, more or less hooked; beaks 3–5 mm. long, stout,
incurved.—River-banks, beaches, and waste-places, various provinces, N. C.
to Nebr., N. D., and Me.

5. X. speciosum Kearney. Plant somewhat pubescent, 10–15 dm. tall: leaf-
blades deltoid-ovate to somewhat reniform: body of the bur 25–30 mm. long,
pubescent and closely beset with 200 or more incurved spines; beaks 8–10 mm.
long, incurved.—Sandy bottoms, Interior Low Plateaus and adj. provinces,
Tenn. to Tex., Mont., and Minn.

6. X. echinellum Greene. Plant sparingly hispidulous and the stem striate
and reddish: leaf-blades broadly cordate, 5–18 cm. long and fully as wide, 3-

ribbed, 3–5-lobed: burs 3–8 together; body about 1 cm. long, about 5 mm. wide, sparingly glandular-puberulent, the spines 150–200, slender, about 3 mm. long; beaks stout, ascending, nearly straight, 4 mm. long.—Clay County, Miss.

FAMILY 2. **CARDUACEAE** NECK.— THISTLE FAMILY

Herbs or rarely shrubs, or sometimes trees in tropical regions. Leaves opposite or alternate, sometimes all basal, without stipules; blades various. Flowers perfect, pistillate, or neutral, or sometimes monoecious or dioecious, aggregated on a receptacle, surrounded by an involucre. Receptacle smooth, pitted, or honey-combed, naked or with scales, chaff, fimbrillae, or bristles subtending the flowers. Calyx of bristles, awns, or scales, or a crown or cup-like, forming pappus at maturity, or wanting. Corolla of 5 united petals, usually equally 5-lobed, or in the case of the marginal flowers of the head the corolla is often produced on one side into a ligule; when ray-flowers are present the head is said to be radiate, when wanting it is said to be discoid. Androecium of 5 stamens: filaments mostly adnate to the corolla-tube: anthers often appendaged at the apex and sometimes also at the base, united into a ring (syngenecious) except in *Kuhnia*. Gynoecium 2-carpellary. Ovary inferior, 1-celled. Stigmas of the fructiferous flowers 2. Ovule solitary. Fruit an achene. Seed erect.—About 800 genera and 10,000 species, of wide geographic distribution. In the following figures the filaments and the anthers are not always shown in proper proportions.

Anthers not caudate at the base.
  Heads discoid, but rarely with the corollas split on one side and thus ligulate:
    corollas varying from white to red or blue, never yellow or brown: stigmas
    half-cylindric.
    Stigmas much elongate, acute, with stigmatic part on the inside, hispidulous
      without.
      Achene not 4-angled, or if 4-angled not clavate: pappus-squamellae, if
        any, not with strong midribs.   Tribe I. VERNONIEAE.
      Achenes 4-angled, clavate: pappus of elongate
        squamellae with strong midribs (*Palafoxia* and
        Polypteris in)   VII. HELENIEAE.
    Stigmas somewhat elongate, obtuse or rounded at the
      apex, with the stigmatic part on the inside only
      near the base, the upper portion, as well as the out-
      side, hispidulous.   II. EUPATORIEAE.
  Heads radiate, or, if discoid, the disk-corollas usually
    yellow or brown: stigmas either without appen-
    dages, truncate or rounded at the apex, or with
    acute appendages.
    Leaves or bracts, or both, with conspicuous resinous
      glands.   VIII. TAGETEAE.
    Leaves and bracts without resinous glands (rarely
      punctate with oil glands).
      Pappus of squamellae or stiff bristles, or coroni-
        form, or wanting.
        Involucral bracts not scarious-margined, usu-
          ally green and more or less foliaceous.
          Receptacle chaffy (paleaceous).   VI. HELIANTHEAE.
          Receptacle naked or fimbrillate in *Gaillardia*.
            Involucral bracts imbricate in several
              series.   III. ASTEREAE.
            Involucral bracts in 1 or 2 subequal
              series.   VII. HELENIEAE.
        Involucral bracts with dry scarious or hyaline
          margins or tips.
          Pappus of squamellae: stigmas with acute
            or acutish appendages.   VII. HELENIEAE.
          Pappus coroniform or wanting: stigmas
            truncate at the apex.   IX. ANTHEMIDEAE.

Pappus, at least in part, of many capillary
bristles.
Stigmas flattened, with appendages, hairy on
the outside : involucres imbricate.   III. ASTEREAE.
Stigmas terete, truncate, or appendaged : in-
volucral bracts in one series.   X. SENECINEAE.
Anthers caudate at the base.
Stigmas without a ring of long hairs below.
Disk-corollas not 2-lipped.
Pistillate flowers with filiform corollas, without
ligules.   IV. GNAPHALIEAE.
Pistillate flowers with ligulate corollas.   V. INULEAE.
Disk-corollas 2-lipped, the upper lip 2-lobed, lower
3-lobed.   XII. MUTISIEAE.
Stigmas with a ring of long hairs at the base of the
stigmatic portion : heads discoid or the ray-corollas
actino-morphic and neutral.   XI. CYNAREAE.

I. VERNONIEAE

Corollas all alike, equal : bracts of the involucre unappendaged.
Pappus of 2 series : corollas regular : heads many-
flowered, not glomerate.
Achenes ribbed or grooved : both series of the
pappus persistent : perennials.   1. VERNONIA.
Achenes terete, ribless : inner series of the pappus
deciduous : annuals.   2. SENECIODES.
Pappus simple : corollas irregular, split on the inner
side : heads 2–5-flowered, in involucrate heads of a
second order.   3. ELEPHANTOPUS.
Corollas of the marginal flowers enlarged, oblique : an
inner series of bracts with pectinate-spinulose appendages.   4. STOKESIA.

II. EUPATORIEAE

Anthers truncate or broadly rounded at the apex, the connective without appendages : heads few-flowered.   5. HARTWRIGHTIA.
Anthers with the connective produced into an appendage
at the apex.
Achenes 3–5-angled.
Pappus of squamellae, sometimes cup-like or
crown-like.
Leaves whorled : bracts of the involucre nerve-
less : corolla-tube abruptly dilated into the
broad throat.   6. SCLEROLEPIS.
Leaves opposite, or alternate above : bracts of
the involucre striate : corolla narrow
throughout.   7. AGERATUM.
Pappus of elongate bristles or hairs.
Involucral bracts more than 4 : flowers
4–many.
Receptacle of the flowers flat.
Involucral bracts leathery or coriaceous,
in several series, striate.   8. OSMIA.
Involucral bracts thin, membranous, in
1–few series, few-ribbed or ribless.   9. EUPATORIUM.
Receptacle conic or hemispheric.   10. CONOCLINIUM.
Involucral bracts and flowers 4.   11. MIKANIA.
Achenes 8–10-ribbed or 8–10-striate.
Involucral bracts in several series, well imbricate.
Bracts not herbaceous, thin, striate.
Pappus-bristles scabrous or barbellate :
anthers united : involucral bracts usually
many.   12. COLEOSANTHUS.
Pappus-bristles plumose : anthers distinct :
involucral bracts few.   13. KUHNIA.
Bracts herbaceous or partly colored, not stri-
ate : pappus of capillary or plumose
bristles.
Receptacle chaffy : heads corymbose.   14. CARPHEPHORUS.
Receptacle naked.
Herbs : heads spicate or racemose :
bracts of the involucre spirally
imbricate.
Heads corymbose : basal leaves in
depressed rosettes ; blades rather
broad.   15. LITRISA.

Heads spicate or racemose or rarely
cymose: basal leaves not in
rosettes, erect or nearly so:
blades elongate.
  Pappus in one series of equal
bristles: leaves herbaceous:
plant usually with a globose-
woody root.   16. LACINIARIA.
  Pappus in two series, the outer
bristles shorter than the inner:
leaves succulent: plant with
an elongate fleshy root.   17. AMMOPURSUS.
Shrub: heads corymbose: bracts of the
involucre imbricate in definite vertical ranks.   18. GARBERIA.
Involucral bracts subequal, little imbricate, not
striate.   19. TRILISA.

III. ASTEREAE

Plants not dioecious.
Ray-corollas yellow or none or white in *Solidago
bicolor*.
  Pappus of squamellae or awns, or wanting, not of
capillary bristles.
    Heads small, few-flowered: involucre cam-
panulate or cylindric, not more than 5
mm. high: ligules of the ray 10 or less,
less than 5 mm. long.
      Disk-flowers sterile: leaves with narrow
entire blades.   20. AMPHIACHYRIS.
      Disk-flowers fertile: leaves with cordate
toothed blades.   33. BRACHYCHAETA
    Heads larger, many-flowered: involucre hemi-
spheric or depressed: ligules of the ray 12
or more, 1 cm. long or more (wanting in a
few species): pappus of 2–8 deciduous stout
awns.   21. GRINDELIA.
  Pappus, at least in part, of capillary bristles.
    Pappus double, at least in the disk-flowers, the
inner of capillary bristles, the outer of
short squamellae or short bristles.
      Ray-achenes flattened, with well developed
pappus.
        Leaf-blades not grass-like, glabrous or
pubescent, but not silky: achene
somewhat turgid, turbinate, obovoid,
or ellipsoid-obovoid, with no neck.   22. CHRYSOPSIS.
        Leaf-blades grass-like, silky-tomentose:
achene spindle-shaped, with more or
less of a neck.   23. PITYOPSIS.
      Ray-achenes turgid, with obsolete or
coroniform pappus.   24. HETEROTHECA.
    Pappus simple.
      Heads discoid.
        Involucre narrowly turbinate; bracts
more or less arranged in definite
(usually 5) vertical ranks.   25. CHONDROPHORA.
        Involucre broadly turbinate to hemi-
spheric; bracts squarrose, imbricate,
but not in definite vertical ranks.   26. BRINTONIA.
      Heads radiate.
        Leaf-blades pinnatifid or toothed; lobes
or teeth spinulose-tipped.   27. SIDERANTHUS.
        Leaf-blades entire or toothed, the teeth
not bristle-tipped.
          Pappus-bristles elongate, equaling or
longer than the achenes.
            Bracts of the involucre narrow,
neither longitudinally ribbed
nor striate.
              Annual or biennial herbs.   28. ISOPAPPUS.
              Perennial herbs or under-
shrubs.
                Ray-flowers not more nu-
merous than the
disk-flowers: recep-

tacle alveolate or
pitted.
Leaves with distinct
depressions; blades
veinless, entire: un-
der-shrubs.   29. CHRYSOMA.
Leaves without depres-
sions; blades veiny,
usually t o o t h e d :
herbs.   30. SOLIDAGO.
Ray-flowers more numer-
ous than the disk-
flowers: receptacle fim-
briolate; heads corym-
bose.   31. EUTHAMIA.
Bracts of the involucre longitu-
dinally ribbed or striate.   32. OLIGONEURON.
Pappus-bristles much shorter than
the achenes.   33. BRACHYCHAETA.
Ray-corollas blue, purple, pink, or white.
Pappus a mere crown or of a few squamellae, or
subulate bristles, or wanting.
Pappus of a mere crown or wanting.
Pappus wanting or obsolete: bracts of the
involucre imbricate in 2 or 3 series.   34. ASTRANTHIUM.
Pappus a small crown: bracts of the in-
volucre imbricate in few series.   35. APHANOSTEPHUS.
Pappus of a series of short squamellae and
usually also 2–4 slender bristles.   36. BOLTONIA.
Pappus, at least of the disk-flowers, of numerous
capillary bristles.
Ray-corollas conspicuous, longer than the pappus: ligules of the ray usually equaling
or exceeding the disk, spreading.
Stigma-tips lanceolate to filiform.
Pappus-bristles not in two distinct
series.
Disk-corollas as well as ray-corollas
white or stramineous.
Bracts of the involucre leathery,
with green thick tips.   37. SERICOCARPUS.
Bracts not leathery, their green
tips not thick (see *Solidago
bicolor*).   30. SOLIDAGO.
Disk-corollas typically yellow, changing to red, brown, or purple: ray-
corollas various: bracts of the involucre in several series, more or
less foliaceous, at least at the tip:
perennials with rootstocks.   38. ASTER.
Pappus distinctly double, the outer
series of short subulate bristles.
Inner pappus-bristles clavate at the
apex: bracts of the involucre thin-
coriaceous, without herbaceous
tips, shorter than the disk.   39. DOELLINGERIA.
Inner pappus-bristles filiform
throughout: bracts of the involucre equaling the disk.   40. IONACTIS.
Stigma-tips triangular or ovate, obtuse,
rarely acutish: bracts of the involucre in
1–2, rarely 3 series.   41. ERIGERON.
Ray-corollas inconspicuous, not longer than the
pappus: ligules of the ray short and erect:
stigma-tips obtuse.   42. LEPTILON.
Plants dioecious: heads unisexual, discoid: pappus-
bristles of the staminate flowers with clavate tips.   43. BACCHARIS.

IV. GNAPHALIEAE

Receptacle not chaffy.
Involucral bracts not scarious: stigmas of the perfect
(usually sterile) flowers elongate and acute.
Stem not winged by the decurrent leaves: involucral bracts persistent.
Caulescent herbs or shrubs: stem and branches
not wiry.   44. PLUCHEA.

Acaulescent herbs : scape and branches wiry.   45. SACHSIA.
Stem winged by the decurrent leaves : involucral
bracts mostly deciduous.   46. PTEROCAULON.
Involucral bracts scarious or with scarious colored
tips : stigmas of the perfect flowers short, truncate, distinct or sometimes united.
Plants dioecious or the pistillate heads with a
few hermaphrodite flowers in the center :
perfect flowers usually sterile.
Pappus-bristles of the pistillate flowers falling
off in a ring : central perfect flowers none.   47. ANTENNARIA.
Pappus-bristles of the pistillate flowers falling
off separate : central perfect flowers present
in the pistillate heads.   48. ANAPHALIS.
Plants not dioecious : flowers pistillate or perfect,
all fertile.
Pappus-bristles capillary, not plumose.   49. GNAPHALIUM.
Pappus-bristles plumose.   50. FACELIS.
Receptacle chaffy.
Receptacle subulate : perfect flowers fertile, their
achenes with capillary pappus.   51. GIFOLA.
Receptacle hemispheric : perfect flowers usually
sterile, their achenes without pappus.   52. FILAGINOPSIS.

V. INULEAE

Achene not contracted at the apex into a short neck :
pappus-bristles not united at the base into a cup.
Achene 4-angled : outer involucral bracts foliaceous.   53. INULA.
Achene not angled : involucral bracts not foliaceous.   54. VICOA.
Achene contracted at the apex into a neck : pappus-
bristles united at the base into a cup.   55. CUPULARIA.

VI. HELIANTHEAE

Disk-flowers perfect, but sterile.
Achene thick, not conspicuously flattened : pappus
wanting.
Inner involucral bracts smooth, merely embracing
the achenes.
Achenes strongly many-striate : leaves palmately lobed.   56. SMALLANTHUS.
Achenes 3–5-ribbed or 3–5-angled : leaves pinnately lobed.   57. POLYMNIA.
Inner involucral bracts prickly, closely and permanently enclosing the achenes and falling off with
them.   58. ACANTHOSPERMUM.
Achene conspicuously flattened.   59. SILPHIUM.
Achenes falling free, wing-margined.
Achenes adnate to 2 or 3 bractlets (subtending as
many sterile flowers), and falling away with
them, wingless.
Ligules of the ray well developed, plane and
exserted : receptacle flat.
Leaves opposite : pappus semicupulate, i.e.,
with the crown developed on the outside
only.   60. CHRYSOGONUM.
Leaves alternate : pappus wanting or of 2
short awns or teeth.   61. BERLANDIERA.
Ligules of the ray poorly developed, reduced to
small lobe or 2 or 3 teeth, the marginal corollas reduced to a truncate or obliquely cleft
tube.   62. PARTHENIUM.
Disk-flowers perfect and fertile.
Ray-corollas ligulate, persistent on the achenes and
becoming papery in texture : ray-flowers fertile.
Achenes of the disk-flowers flattened or compressed, 4-angled ; those of the ray-flowers often
3-angled : bractlets conduplicate around the
achenes.   63. ZINNIA.
Achenes not flattened : involucre broad : receptacle
convex or conic.   64. HELIOPSIS.
Ray-corollas ligulate, deciduous from the achenes, or
heads discoid.
Involucre conspicuously 4- (rarely 5-) angled in
the bud ; bracts (outer) 4 or 5, foliaceous, valvate, connate at the base.   65. TETRAGONOTHECA.

Involucre not 4-angled; bracts several or numerous, distinct.
  Pappus consisting of a small crown or wanting, or of a few squamellae or awns on the angles of the achenes, and rarely some minute ones interposed.
    Achenes, at least those of the disk, not obcompressed, *i.e.*, if compressed, arranged radially.
      Paleae of the receptacle mere chaffy awns or bristles: disk-corollas 4- or 5-lobed: achenes of the disk compressed; those of the ray 3-sided.   66. VERBESINA.
      Paleae of the receptacle concave or conduplicate.
        Bracts of the involucre dry or papery: heads usually discoid: pappus of few, slender awns.   67. MELANTHERA.
        Bracts of the involucre herbaceous or foliaceous: heads usually radiate.
          Receptacle high, hemispheric, conic, subulate, columnar, or globose.
            Ray-flowers fertile: stigmas of the disk-flowers truncate: pappus an awn on one or more achene-angles, or none.   68. SPILANTHES.
            Ray-flowers sterile: stigmas of the disk-flowers with acute, hispid appendages.
              Achenes 4-angled or terete, wingless.
                Disk-corollas without a tube: ligules of the ray purplish, rarely white or yellow.   69. ECHINACEA.
                Disk-corollas with a manifest but short tube: ligules of the ray yellow or none.
                  Achene 4-angled.
                    Achenes quadrilaterally compressed, apex commonly covered with the corolla-tube.   70. VIGUIERA.
                    Achenes equally 4-angled, apex not covered by the corolla-tube.   71. RUDBECKIA.
                      72. DRACOPIS.
                  Achene terete.
              Achenes compressed, winged, or wing-margined.
                Receptacle columnar: bracts of the involucre numerous.   73. RATIBIDA.
                Receptacle globose: bracts of the involucre few.   84. RIDAN.
          Receptacle flat or merely convex, or rarely somewhat conic.
            Achene not strongly compressed, not wing-margined.
              Ray-flowers fertile.
                Achenes turgid or those of the disk obscurely angled: herbs.

Pappus of several
paleae partly
united into a
cup or ring.
Achene c o r k y,
tubercled, tur-
gid, bluntly
3-angled : lig-
ules of the
r a y mostly
3-toothed.   74. WEDELIA.
Achene neither
c o r k y n o r
tubercled, com-
pressed, un-
equally 3-an-
gled ; ligules
of the ray
mostly 2-cleft.   75. STEMMODONTIA.
Pappus of several
distinct paleae,
and occasionally
with 2 additional
short awns.   76. PASCALIA.
Achenes sharply 4-an-
gled or those of
the rays 3-angled :
shrubs.   77. BORRICHIA.
Ray-flowers sterile o r
wanting : a c h e n e
more or less com-
pressed, 4-angled.
Pappus of s e v e r a l
scales and awns ; the
scales persistent : in-
volucral bracts in
two distinct series.   78. TITHONIA.
Pappus of few early
deciduous awns : in-
volucral bracts in 3
or 4 series.   79. HELIANTHUS.
Achene strongly compressed.
Receptacle flat or convex :
bracts of the involu-
cre numerous.
Intermediate squamel-
lae of the pappus
present or the awns
connected by their
bases.   80. PHOEBANTHUS.
Intermediate squamel-
lae wanting, the
awns distinct.
Involucre f l a t ;
bracts elongate,
spreading : a n -
nual herbs with
petioled l e a f -
blades.   81. XIMENESIA.
Involucre campanu-
late to hemi-
spheric ; bracts
s h o r t, a p -
pressed : peren-
nial herbs with
decurrent o r
sessile leaves.
Ray-flowers fer-
tile : heads nu-
merous, corym-
bose : achenes
long-awned.   82. PHAETHUSA.
Ray-flowers ster-
ile : heads soli-
tary or few to-
gether : achenes

with short or
obsolete awns.   83. PTEROPHYTON.
Receptacle globose: bracts
of the involucre few:
leaves decurrent.   84. RIDAN.
Achenes decidedly obcom-
pressed, *i.e.*, flattened
parallel to the involu-
cral bracts.
Involucre simple, of 1 or 2
herbaceous and sev-
eral chaffy bracts.
Achenes of the ray with
ascending marginal
bristles.   85. SYNEDRELLA.
Achenes of the ray
w i t h o u t marginal
bristles.   85a. CALYPTOCARPUS.
Involucre manifestly double,
the outer one in-
volucellate.
Pappus a pair of fim-
briolate squamellae,
short awns, a minute
crown, or wanting.   86. COREOPSIS.
Pappus of 2–4 usually
barbellate awns.
Achene beakless:
ligules of the ray
yellow or white.   87. BIDENS.
Achene distinctly
beaked: ligules of
the ray purple or
rose, or orange-
yellow.   88. COSMOS.
Pappus of many similar squamellae.
Paleae of the receptacle concreted, forming
alveoli, the receptacle resembling a
honeycomb: ray-flowers neutral.
Pits of the receptacle with broad erose-
toothed edges: head solitary: ray-
flowers 20–30.   89. ENDORIMA.
Pits of the receptacle with cuspidate
and erose toothed edges: heads corymbose: ray-flowers 8–18.   90. ACTINOSPERMUM.
Paleae of the receptacle distinct, thin.
Ray-flowers wanting: squamellae of the
pappus nerveless.   91. MARSHALLIA.
Ray-flowers present, pistillate and fertile.
Squamellae of the pappus of the disk
flowers with thick midribs and
fimbriate margins.   92. GALINSOGA.
Squamellae of the pappus aristate-
acuminate, plumose-ciliate.   93. TRIDAX.

VII. HELENIEAE

Achenes distinctly 3–5-angled, or if less distinctly so,
then obconic.
Stigmas either short or with a distinct appendage, not
hispidulous to or below the fork; either disk- or
ray-corollas or both yellow, if purple the involucre not narrow.
Bracts of the involucre wholly herbaceous, or somewhat chartaceous at the base, without scarious margins.
Involucre companulate or hemispheric; bracts
erect or ascending, not reflexed; outer
bracts more or less united below.   94. HYMENOXYS.
Involucre rotate; bracts spreading, wholly or
the tips reflexed.
Receptacle not bristly: pappus-scales thin
and scarious, the midrib, when present,
not becoming spine-like.   95. HELENIUM.
Receptacle bristly, fimbrillate, triangular-
fimbrillate, or naked: pappus-scales scari-

ous, but becoming rigid, the midrib ex-
current as a rigid spine.   96. GAILLARDIA.
Bracts of the involucre with thin, more or less
scarious and colored margins.   97. HYMENOPAPPUS.
Stigmas long and filiform, stigmatose to near the
apex, hispidulous down to the fork or below;
both disk- and ray-corollas rose-purple: involucre from elongate-turbinate to almost cylindric.
Throat of the disk-corollas short-campanulate or
scarcely any, much shorter than the long linear
lobes and the tube.   98. POLYPTERIS.
Throat of the disk-corollas cylindric, much longer
than the lanceolate lobes and the tube.   99. PALAFOXIA.
Achenes 8–10-ribbed or -striate, linear or elliptic, terete
or oval in cross-section: heads few-flowered and few-
bracted.   100. FLAVERIA.

VIII. TAGETEAE

Stigmas of the perfect flowers elongate, appendiculate or
truncate: leaves, if simple, not bristly-ciliate.
Squamellae of the receptacle few, 3–10, some of them,
usually 1 or 2, longer, linear or subulate, acute, the
rest broader and shorter, usually obtuse; bracts of
the involucre united to near the apex.   101. TAGETES.
Squamellae of the receptacle 10 or more, rarely less,
each with 9 or more stiff bristles.   102. BOEBERA.
Stigmas of the perfect flowers short, elliptic: leaves simple, bristly-ciliate, at least towards the base.   103. PECTIS.

IX. ANTHEMIDEAE

Receptacle with chaff, this consisting of usually membranous, concave, elongate paleae.
Achene more or less obcompressed, subrhombic or
obliquely triquetrous in cross-section: tube of the
disk-corollas more or less flattened: heads small:
ligules of the ray few, short.   104. ACHILLEA.
Achene terete, cylindric, obovoid, or ellipsoid: heads
large and broad: ligules of the ray conspicuous
or wanting.
Ray-flowers fertile: paleae of the receptacle membranous, or cartilaginous in *Ormenis,* subtending all the flowers.
Tube of the disk-corollas produced into a spur-
like appendage at the base: ligules of the
ray, in ours white with a yellow base.   105. ORMENIS.
Tube of the disk-corollas not appendaged at
the base: ligules of the ray white or want-
ing.   106. ANTHEMIS.
Ray-flowers neutral: paleae of the receptacle subulate, stiff, subtending only the innermost flowers. 107. MARUTA.
Receptacle without chaff, naked or hairy.
Heads radiate, with usually flat ligules: anther-tips
deltoid, mostly obtuse.
Pappus of a more or less developed crown or
margin.
Receptacle high, hemispheric, conic or subglobose: achene with 3–5 ribs on the inner half,
and nerveless on the back.   108. CHAMOMILLA.
Receptacle convex or nearly flat: achene
equally 5–10-ribbed or 5–10-angled.   109. MATRICARIA.
Pappus, at least of the disk-flowers, wanting.
Achenes all 10-ribbed or 10-angled: ligules of
the ray white or pink.   110. LEUCANTHEMUM.
Achenes of the ray-flowers 2- or 3-winged:
ligules of the ray yellow.   111. CHRYSANTHEMUM.
Heads discoid or apparently so: pistillate ray-flowers,
if present, without well-developed ligules.
Marginal pistillate flowers, if present, with corollas or sometimes wanting in *Artemisia:*
achene not flattened.
Anthers with ovate obtuse tips: corollas of
the marginal flowers oblique: pappus coroni-
form.   112. TANACETUM.
Anthers with subulate tips: corollas of the
marginal flowers regular: pappus wanting.   113. ARTEMISIA.
Marginal pistillate flowers without corollas:
achene flattened, obcompressed.

Achenes not hairy at the apex, with thin flat
wings: disk-corollas cylindric, without dif-
ferentiation between tube and throat: anthers broad, rounded at the base. 114. SOLIVA.
Achenes villous at the apex, with thick corky
wings: disk-corollas with a slender tube and
elongate-funnelform throat: anthers narrow,
somewhat sagittate at the base. 115. GYMNOSTYLES.

X. SENECINEAE

Leaves opposite, but in our species all near the base. 116. ARNICA.
Leaves alternate.
  Stigmas filiform, elongate, acute: throat of the
    corolla cylindric.
    Heads with no outer involucre: achene 5-angled. 117. EMILIA.
    Heads with outer involucre present: achene 8–10
    ribbed, terete. 118. GYNURA.
  Stigmas short, truncate at the apex: throat of the
    corolla campanulate.
    Heads discoid; corollas whitish or pinkish.
      Marginal pistillate flowers wanting, the flowers
        all perfect.
        Corolla-lobes longer than the throat: in-
          volucral bracts 5–8: center of the recep-
          tacle usually with a fleshy point. 119. MESADENIA.
        Corolla-lobes not longer than the throat:
          involucral bracts 12–15: receptacle flat. 120. SYNOSMA.
      Marginal pistillate flowers present, their corol-
        las actinomorphic, 4–5-lobed, similar to but
        more slender than those of the disk-flowers. 121. ERECHTITES.
    Heads usually radiate, if discoid the corollas
      yellow. 122. SENECIO.

XI. CYNAREAE

Achenes inserted by their very bases or nearly so, not
  obliquely.
  Bracts of the involucre hooked: leaves not with
    spinose lobes and tips. 123. ARCTIUM.
  Bracts of the involucre not hooked: leaves with
    spinose lobes and tips.
    Filaments papillose or pilose, free.
      Receptacle bristly: pappus-bristles plumose. 124. CIRSIUM.
      Receptacle deeply honeycombed, the pits with
        a toothed margin: pappus-bristles scabrous
        or barbellate. 125. ONOPORDON.
    Filaments glabrous, united into a tube: receptacles
      bristly: pappus barbellate. 126. MARIANA.
Achenes inserted obliquely on the receptacle.
  Achene truncate at the apex: pappus of several series
    of short scales or bristles of different lengths, or
    none: head not subtended by several spiny leaves. 127. CENTAUREA.
  Achene 10-toothed at the apex: pappus of 10 longer
    naked outer bristles and 10 inner fimbriolate ones:
    head subtended by several spiny leaves. 128. CNICUS.

XII. MUTISIEAE

Heads heterogamous: marginal corollas ligulate. 129. CHAPTALIA.

1. VERNONIA L. Perennial, caulescent or scapose herbs. Leaves
alternate: blades narrow or broad, mostly toothed. Heads not involucrate.
Flowers purple or white. Corolla-lobes lanceolate to linear. Anther-appendages
lanceolate to elliptic. Achene 10-ribbed or -grooved. Pappus double, the outer
series of scales or stout bristles, the inner of numerous capillary bristles, both
series persistent.—About 500 species, most abundant in South America.—IRON-
WEEDS.—Sum.-fall or all year S.

Plant caulescent: leaves mainly cauline.
  Bracts of the involucre, at least some of them, with filiform or subulate tips.
    Leaf-blades smooth above. I. NOVEBORACENSES.
    Leaf-blades scabrous above. II. SCABERRIMAE.
  Bracts of the involucre obtuse, acute, or acuminate.
    Leaf-blades, at least above the base of the stem,
      narrow, mostly of a linear type. III. ANGUSTIFOLIAE.

Leaf-blades broad, of an ovate, or lanceolate type.
  Leaf-blades glabrous or thinly pubescent and
    scabrous beneath.   IV. ALTISSIMAE.
  Leaf-blades tomentose beneath.   V. INTERIORES.
Plant scapose: leaves basal or mainly so.   VI. ACAULES.

I. NOVEBORACENSES

Pappus purple or tawny-purple.
  Head with 42 flowers or less: bracts of the involucre
    mainly ovate, each abruptly narrowed into the tip.   1. *V. noveboracensis.*
  Head with 55 flowers or more: bracts mainly lanceo-
    late, each gradually narrowed into the tip.   2. *V. Harperi.*
Pappus stramineous.   3. *V. glauca.*

II. SCABERRIMAE

Leaf-blades broad, mostly 3 or 4 times as long as wide,
  prominently serrate, sometimes coarsely so.   4. *V. pulchella.*
Leaf-blades narrow, mostly 5–16 times as long as wide,
  entire or merely serrulate.
  Bracts of the involucre closely appressed at the base,
    the tips recurved or spreading.   5. *V. recurva.*
  Bracts of the involucre loosely appressed at the base,
    the tips not recurved.   6. *V. scaberrima.*

III. ANGUSTIFOLIAE

Leaf-blades scabrous above.
  Leaf-blades linear; usually narrowly so, revolute.   7. *V. angustifolia.*
  Leaf-blades linear-lanceolate to elliptic, not revolute.   8. *V. dissimilis.*
Leaf-blades smooth and glabrous or nearly so.
  Heads about 13-flowered.   9. *V. concinna.*
  Heads about 21-flowered.   10. *V. Blodgettii.*

IV. ALTISSIMAE

Head with 13 flowers or less.   11. *V. gigantea.*
Head with 18 flowers or more.
  Pappus purple or purplish.
    Bracts of the involucre rounded at the apex,
      abruptly tipped.   12. *V. altissima.*
    Bracts of the involucre acute or cuspidate.   13. *V. ovalifolia.*
  Pappus tawny or yellowish, or stramineous.
    Involucre 5–6 mm. high; bracts acute or cuspidate,
      often stramineous.   13. *V. ovalifolia.*
    Involucre 3–4 mm. high; bracts obtuse or subacute.   14. *V. flaccidifolia.*

V. INTERIORES

Bracts of the involucre with closely appressed tips: head
  with mostly 29 flowers or more.   15. *V. missurica.*
Bracts of the involucre with spreading or reflexed tips:
  head 18–34-flowered.   16. *V. Baldwinii.*

VI. ACAULES

Blades of the basal leaves elliptic, oblanceolate, spatulate,
  or obovate, 3–7 cm. wide.   17. *V. acaulis.*
Blades of the basal leaves lanceolate, 1–2 cm. wide.   18. *V. georgiana.*

1. V. noveboracensis (L.) Willd. Stem 1–3 m. tall, glabrous or thinly
pubescent, branching above: leaves rather numerous; blades linear-lanceolate
or elliptic-lanceolate, 1–2 dm. long, acumi-
nate, finely serrate or nearly entire: corymb
1–3 dm. broad, commonly irregular: involucre hemispheric, 6–7 mm. high; bracts
purple, ovate or ovate-lanceolate, prolonged
into filiform tips, glabrous or sparingly
ciliate: corolla about 10 mm. long: achene
4–4.5 mm. long, upwardly barbed along the
sharp angles; pappus purple or tawny-
purple.—Woods, thickets, meadows, and
open places, various provinces, Ga. to Miss.,
Ont., and Mass.

2. V. Harperi Gleason. Stem 1 m. tall or
more, puberulent, divaricately branched
above: leaves numerous; blades lanceolate,

12–18 cm. long or smaller near the top of the stem, thin, acuminate, dentate-serrate: corymb 3 dm. wide or more, lax: involucre broadly campanulate, 7–9 mm. high; bracts green, with ovate or triangular-ovate bases and erect elongate tips, arachnoid-ciliate: achene 3.5 mm. long, pubescent on the ribs: pappus dull-purple.—Damp grounds and wet woods, in the Coastal Plain of Ga.

3. V. glauca (L.) Britton. Stem 1–2 m. tall, glabrous or nearly so, often widely branched above: leaves numerous; blades linear-lanceolate to elliptic or elliptic-oblanceolate, acute or short-acuminate, sharply and saliently serrate: corymb 1–3 dm. broad: involucre hemispheric, about 5–7 mm. high; bracts lanceolate to nearly elliptic, purple, the outer ones merely acuminate, glabrous or nearly so: achene 2–3 mm. long, with the sharp ribs barbed: pappus stramineous. [*V. noveboracensis latifolia* A. Gray.]—Wooded slopes and river-banks, various provinces N of Coastal Plain, Ga. to Ala., Pa., and N. J.

4. V. pulchella Small. Stem 3–10 dm. tall, pubescent, branched above: leaves firm; blades elliptic-lanceolate or elliptic or sometimes narrower above, 2–10 cm. long, acute, serrate, often sharply so, somewhat crisped, revolute, sessile, but not at all cordate: corymb 1–1.5 dm. broad: involucre campanulate, 6–7 mm. high; bracts lanceolate to linear-elliptic, prolonged into soft linear-subulate spreading or recurved tips, often purplish: achene about 3 mm. long: pappus stramineous.—Sand-hills, Coastal Plain, Ga. and S. C.

5. V. recurva Gleason. Stem about 7 dm. tall, pubescent below, glabrate above: leaves firm, mostly near the base of the stem; blades elliptic-linear to linear, 5–7 cm. long, or shorter above, acute, revolute, entire or sparingly callous-toothed, scabrous, rounded at the base: corymb about 15 cm. wide: involucre cylindric-campanulate, about 8 mm. high; bracts lanceolate to elliptic-lanceolate, long-acuminate, appressed at the base, the long tips recurved or spreading: achene 3.5 mm. long, pubescent on the angles: pappus tawny.—Dry pine-lands, Coastal Plain, SE Ga.

6. V. scaberrima Nutt. Stem 3–8 dm. tall, glabrous or puberulent below, usually dense: leaves firm; blades linear to linear-elliptic, 1.5–8 cm. long, acute, entire or remotely serrate, sessile or nearly so, cordate or truncate at the base: corymb with comparatively few heads: involucre campanulate, 5–6 mm. high: bracts subulate-linear to elliptic, prolonged into rigid subulate tips: achene about 2 mm. long, with scabrous ribs: pappus purplish.—Sandy soil, Coastal Plain, Fla. to N. C.

7. V. angustifolia Michx. Stem 0.5–1 m. tall, glabrous or pubescent, often widely branched above: leaves numerous; blades linear, usually narrowly so, 5–15 cm. long, acute, revolute: involucre turbinate or turbinate-campanulate, 5–6 mm. high, acute or somewhat rounded at the base; bracts lanceolate to elliptic, acute or apiculate, with more or less spreading tips: achene 2 mm. long, or more, with scabrous ribs: pappus purplish.—Sandy woods, pinelands, and dry hillsides, Coastal Plain, Fla. to Miss. and N. C.—*V. texana* (A. Gray) Small, with tawny pappus and lower leaf surface pitted, has been reported from Meadville in S W Miss.

8. V. dissimilis Gleason. Stem stout, 8–11 dm. tall: leaves numerous; blades linear-lanceolate to elliptic, 10–15 cm. long, firm, acuminate, sharply serrate, except the smaller upper ones, not revolute, scabrous above: corymb rather dense: involucre campanulate, about 4 mm. high; bracts ovate or ovate-lanceolate, obtuse or obtusish, or the outer ones acute, arachnoid-ciliate, appressed: achene 2.5 mm. long, with hirsute ribs: pappus bright-purple.—Dry banks and woods, Piedmont, E Ala.

9. **V. concinna** Gleason. Stem 1 m. tall or less, green, glabrous: leaves numerous; blades narrowly oblanceolate to elliptic-linear, 10–12 cm. long or less, thin, acute, entire or with minute callous teeth, glabrous above, minutely pubescent beneath, flat: corymb rather lax: involucre turbinate-campanulate, 6–7 mm. high; bracts elliptic-lanceolate, broader than the slightly spreading outer ones, acute or mucronate, glabrous or slightly ciliate: achene about 3 mm. long, minutely pubescent: pappus purplish-tawny.—Hammocks, M pen. Fla.

10. **V. Blodgettii** Small. Stem often branched near the base, 2–5 dm. tall, glabrous or nearly so, corymbose above: leaves mostly near the base of the stem; blades linear or nearly so, 2–4.5 cm. long, obtuse or acutish, entire, erect or ascending, slightly revolute: involucre campanulate, about 5 mm. high; bracts elliptic to linear-elliptic, acute or apiculate, slightly pubescent: achene 2.5 mm. long, with pubescent ribs: pappus stramineous, slightly roughened.— Low pinelands and adj. Everglades, S pen. Fla. and the Florida Keys.—The general trend of migration of native Florida plants, through the agencies of man has been southward. The range of this ironweed, however, has been extended northward. Occasional specimens have recently been found nearly half way up the eastern coast.

11. **V. gigantea** (Walt.) Trelease. Stem 1–2.5 m. tall, glabrous, often widely branched above: leaves numerous; blades mostly elliptic, 0.8–3 dm. long, acute or acuminate, sharply serrate: corymb 1–4 dm. broad: involucre cylindric, 4–5 mm. high, narrowed at the base; bracts elliptic-lanceolate to narrowly elliptic, rounded on the back, the outer acutish, the inner obtuse, lax or loosely spreading at maturity; achene 3 mm. long, with scabrous angles: pappus purplish. [*V. oligantha* Greene.]—Low grounds, river-bottoms, and swamps, Coastal Plain and rarely adj. provinces, Fla. to Ala. and S. C.

12. **V. altissima** Nutt. Stem 1–3 m. tall, glabrous, branching above: leaves rather numerous; blades narrowly elliptic to lanceolate or narrowly lanceolate, 1–3 dm. long, acuminate, sharply serrate: corymb 1–4 dm. broad; involucre hemispheric-campanulate, 4 mm. to almost 5 mm. high, rounded at the base; bracts ovate to elliptic, nearly flat, acute or mucronate, appressed, ciliate; achene 3 mm. long, with barbed ribs: pappus light-purple or deep-purple. [*V. maxima* Small.]—Low grounds, alluvial banks, bottoms and fields, various provinces N of Coastal Plain, Ga. to Ala., Mo., and Pa.

13. **V. ovalifolia** T. & G. Stem 1–2 m. tall, glabrous or puberulent, branching above: leaves rather numerous; blades elliptic, or the upper elliptic-lanceolate, all acute, or short-acuminate, rather coarsely toothed, abruptly or sometimes gradually contracted at the base: corymb 1–3 dm. broad: involucre campanulate, 5–6 mm. high; bracts lanceolate to elliptic, acute or cuspidate, mainly appressed: achene 2.5–3 mm. long, slightly barbed along the ribs: pappus stramineous or pale-purplish.—Rich woods and sandy stream-banks, Coastal Plain, N Fla. to Ala. and Ga.

14. **V. flaccidifolia** Small. Stem 1–1.5 m. tall, glabrous, glaucous, with slender branches above: leaves rather numerous; blades thin, elliptic to narrowly lanceolate, 0.8–2 dm. long, acuminate, sharply serrate, sometimes doubly so, short-petioled: corymb 1–2 dm. broad; branches slender: involucre hemispheric, 3–4 mm. high; bracts ovate to elliptic, light-green or deeper at the tip, obtuse or subacute, ciliate, not spreading: achene 3 mm. long, with sharp barbed ribs: pappus pale stramineous.—Rich woods, stream-banks, and wooded hillsides, Blue Ridge to Appalachian Plateau, Ga. to Ala., Tenn., and S. C.

15. **V. missurica** Raf. Stem 1–2 m. tall, tomentose, branching above: leaves numerous: blades elliptic to elliptic-lanceolate or lanceolate, 1–3 dm. long,

acute or short-acuminate, sharply and coarsely serrate: corymb usually 1–4 dm. broad: involucre campanulate to cylindric-campanulate, 7–8 mm. high; bracts ovate to elliptic, acute or apiculate: achene 4–5 mm. long, with smooth and glabrous ribs: pappus tawny or tinged with purple. [*V. Drummondii* Werner not Shuttl.]—Low woods, ravines, and rich sandy soil, various provinces N of Coastal Plain, Ala. to Tex., Kans., and Ont.—*V. fasciculata* Michx., with subacuate or rounded involucral scales, has been reported from Starkville in NE Miss.

16. V. Baldwinii Torr. Stem 1–1.5 m. tall, tomentose, branching above: leaf-blades elliptic to ovate, 1–2 dm. long, short-acuminate, sharply serrate: corymb 1–3 dm. wide, irregular: involucre campanulate to hemispheric, 5–7 mm. high; bracts closely imbricate at the base, spreading or reflexed at the glandular acuminate tips: achene 3 mm. long, pubescent and resinous: pappus tawny or purplish.—Dry woods and hills, Interior Plateaus, Tenn. to Okla. and Mo.

17. V. acaulis (Walt.) Gleason. Scape minutely pubescent, 2–7 dm. tall: leaves basal; blades elliptic, oblanceolate, spatulate, or obovate, mainly 1–3 dm. long, obtuse or acutish, serrate or dentate, sometimes doubly so: involucre campanulate, 7–8 mm. high; bracts linear to linear-lanceolate, narrowed into subulate tips: achene 3 mm. long, barbed upward in the ribs: pappus pale-stramineous. [*V. oligophylla* Michx.]—Dry woods or pinelands, Coastal Plain, Fla. to N. C.

18. V. georgiana Bartlett. Scape puberulent, 2–10 dm. tall: leaves basal; blades lanceolate, 5–15 cm. long, acute or obtuse, denticulate, narrowed at the base, scabrous above: involucre campanulate, 6–7 mm. high; bracts narrow, subulate at the tip, glabrous or obscurely ciliate, the outer with spreading tips: achene 3 mm. long, pubescent: pappus pale-stramineous.—Dry pinelands, Coastal Plain, Ga. and S. C.

2. SENECIODES Post & Kuntze. Annual, caulescent herbs. Leaves alternate: blades broad, toothed. Heads corymbose. Flowers pale-purple or white; nearly as in *Vernonia*. Achene terete, ribless. Pappus double, the inner series deciduous.—About 12 species, natives of the Old World.

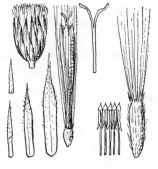

1. S. cinerea (L.) Kuntze. Stem corymbose above, 1 m. tall or less, cinereous-pubescent: leaf-blades ovate to elliptic-ovate, mostly 2–8 cm. long, shallowly toothed, paler beneath than above: peduncles slender: involucre 4–5 mm. high; bracts subulate to linear, acuminate: corolla about 4 mm. long: achene about 1 mm. long, terete or nearly so: pappus white. [*Vernonia cinerea* L.]—Hammocks, Florida Keys. Nat. of Asia.—(*W. I., Mex., C. A., S. A.*)—All year.

3. ELEPHANTOPUS [Vaill.] L. Perennial, scapose or caulescent herbs. Leaves alternate: blades shallowly toothed. Heads involucrate. Flowers lilac-purple. Corolla-lobes linear-lanceolate. Anther-appendages deltoid to ovate. Pappus single, of several rigid bristles terminating scale-like bases.—About 15 species, native of tropical and warm regions.—Sum.–fall.—ELEPHANT-FOOTS.

Stem leafy: leaves mainly cauline, all of the same type.   I. CAROLINIANI.
Stem naked or with few bract-like leaves: leaves mainly basal.   II. TOMENTOSI.

I. CAROLINIANI

A rather coarse, softly hirsute herb, with thinnish leaf-blades.　1. *E. carolinianus.*

II. TOMENTOSI

Longer bracts of the involucre 8 mm. long or less: pappus
　　bristles 3.5–5 mm. long: midrib of the leaf pubescent be-
　　neath with appressed hairs.
　Stem with spreading rather than reflexed hairs: leaf-blades
　　closely and softly pubescent: scale-like base of the pappus
　　gradually narrowed into the tip.　　　　　　　　　　2. *E. elatus.*
　Stem with appressed rather than spreading hairs: leaf-
　　blades glabrous or sparingly pubescent: scale-like base of
　　the pappus abruptly narrowed into the tip.　　　　　3. *E. nudatus.*
Longer bracts of the involucre 9–12 mm. long: pappus-bristles
　6–8 mm. long: midrib of the leaf pubescent beneath with
　spreading and reflexed hairs.　　　　　　　　　　　　4. *E. tomentosus.*

1. **E. carolinianus** Willd. Stem 3–9 dm. tall, rather hirsute: leaf-blades
elliptic or oval, 5–15 cm. long, crenate-serrate or repand: inner bracts of the
involucre 8–10 mm. long, acute: achene 3.5–4
mm. long.—Woods and thickets, various
provinces, Fla. to Tex., Kans., and N. J.

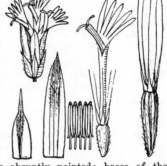

2. **E. elatus** Bertol. Stem 7–12 dm. tall,
mainly hirsute: blades of the basal leaves
spatulate to ovate-elliptic, 10–25 cm. long,
crenate-serrate: inner bracts of the involucre
obtuse: achene 2.5–3 mm. long: bases of
the pappus-bristles minute.—Dry soil,
Coastal Plain and adj. provinces, Fla. to
Ark. and S. C.

3. **E. nudatus** A Gray. Stem 2–8 dm. tall,
mainly strigose; blades of the basal leaves
oblanceolate to spatulate, crenate-serrate:
inner bracts of the involucre acuminate or abruptly pointed: bases of the
pappus-bristles shorter than the breadth of the achene.—Sandy soil, Coastal
Plain, Fla. to La., Ark., and Del.

4. **E. tomentosus** L. Stem 2–7 dm. tall, mostly hirsute above: blades of the
basal leaves elliptic, oval, or elliptic oblanceolate, crenate-serrate: inner bracts
of the involucre acuminate: bases of the pappus-bristles as long as the breadth
of the achene.—Pinelands and dry woods, various provinces, Fla. to Tex., Ky.,
and Va.

4. **STOKESIA** L'Her. Perennial, stout, pubescent herbs. Leaves alternate: blades spinulose-ciliate near the base, elongate. Heads large, showy,
bristly, solitary or few in a corymb, many-
flowered. Involucre broad and depressed:
bracts foliaceous, the outer entire, lax, the
inner with a large pectinate-spinulose appendage on a small base, the innermost, narrow, entire. Receptacle flat, naked. Corollas various, the inner ones tubular, with 5
narrow lobes; the outer ligulate, the marginal ones radiate, the blade prominently
lobed. Anther-appendages ovate. Achene
stout, 3- or 4-angled. Pappus of 4 of 5
slender caducous awns.—One species, remarkable in its group on account of the ligulate
marginal corollas.

1. S. laevis (Hill) Greene. Stem 2–5 dm. tall, woolly, permanently so above: leaves few; blades various, those of the basal and lower cauline elliptic to narrowly elliptic-lanceolate, narrowed into petiole-like bases and dilated at the base, those of the upper cauline lanceolate to elliptic-lanceolate or ovate-lanceolate, clasping: heads solitary at the ends of stem or its few branches: involucre bristly: corolla purplish-blue or rarely white, the lobes all linear-lanceolate: achene narrowly obovoid, about 5 mm. long, the angles callous-thickened. [*S. cyanea* L'Her.] —Moist pinelands, Coastal Plain, Fla. to La. and S. C.—Spr.–sum.—Rare east of Ala. Much more showy than its relatives, the ironweed and the elephant-foot. Widely cultivated.

5. HARTWRIGHTIA A. Gray. Perennial, glabrous, slender herbs. Leaves alternate: blades elongate, entire. Heads rather small, smooth, inconspicuous, loosely corymbose, few-flowered. Involucre turbinate: bracts herbaceous, entire. Receptacle elevated, with few bractlets near the edge. Corolla with a very short tube and a funnelform throat, the lobes broad. Anthers unappendaged. Achene enlarged upward. Pappus of several slender bristles or wanting.—One species representing a group of genera otherwise mainly tropical American.

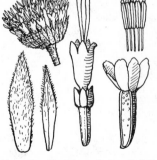

1. H. floridana A. Gray. Stem 4–15 dm. tall, branched above: basal leaves elongate: blades spatulate, elliptic, or elliptic-lanceolate, long-petioled: blades of the cauline leaves narrowly lanceolate to linear: branches of the inflorescence with small clavate scales: bracts of the involucre linear to linear-lanceolate, 4–5 mm. long, obtuse: corollas white or purple, 3–3.5 mm. long; lobes ovate: achene obpyramidal, 4.5–5.5 mm. long.—Swamps and marshes, N Fla. and N part of the pen.—Sum.–fall.—One of the rarer Florida plants. The basal leaves resemble those of *Limonium*.

6. SCLEROLEPIS Cass. Perennial, stoloniferous herbs. Leaves whorled: blades narrow, entire. Heads solitary, not showy. Involucre broad, many-flowered: bracts narrow, appressed. Receptacle conic, naked. Corollas with a very short tube and a funnelform throat, the lobes broad. Anther-appendages ovate. Achene narrow, sharply angled. Pappus of 5 broad scales.—One species.

1. S. uniflora (Walt.) B. S. P. Stem 2–7 dm. long, often decumbent: leaves 4–6 in a whorl; blades linear to narrowly linear-lanceolate or linear-filiform, 1–2.5 cm. long: heads slender-peduncled: bracts of the involucre ciliate, lanceolate or with a lanceolate or narrowly ovate tip above a thicker base, acute or acuminate: corolla rose-purple or pink, nearly 2 mm. long, the tube shorter than the throat: achene slightly broadened upward, 1 mm. long, excluding the stipe-like base: pappus-scales broad, shorter than the achene, blunt. [*S. verticillata* Cass.]—Bogs and pineland ponds, Coastal Plain and New England coast, Fla. to Ala. and N. H.—Spr.-fall.—Usually growing in water or at least in soft mud. Sometimes very densely matted and then striking on account of the very numerous whorled leaves and the numerous stems each with an erect small head.

7. **AGERATUM** L. Annual or rarely perennial, stiff herbs or partly woody plants. Leaves usually opposite: blades toothed. Heads corymbose. Involucre campanulate. Receptacle elevated. Flowers blue, purple, pink, or white. Corolla-lobes erect, deltoid. Anther-appendages ovate. Achene 5-angled short. Pappus of several short blunt or long slender-tipped scales, or cup-like or crown-like.—About 30 species, tropical American, several widely cultivated.—AGERATUMS.

Pappus cup-like or crown-like, the scales very short: achene glabrous: foliage glabrous: leaves succulent.   1. *A. littorale.*
Pappus of distinct scales as long as the pubescent achenes or longer: foliage pubescent: leaves herbaceous.
  Involucre over 4 mm. high; bracts long-tipped; pappus decidedly longer than the achene.   2. *A. Houstonianum.*
  Involucre less than 4 mm. high; bracts short-tipped: pappus about as long as the achene.   3. *A. conyzoides.*

1. **A. littorale** A. Gray. Stem 2–7 dm. tall, glabrous, often branched at the base: leaf-blades ovate, 1–5 cm. long, crenate-serrate, usually cuneate at the base: corymbs terminating long peduncle-like branches: involucre 4 mm. high in anthesis; bracts merely ciliolate: corolla about 2.5 mm. long: achene 2 mm. long: pappus very short.—Sand-dunes and shore hammocks, Florida Keys and Cape Sable.—All year.—An exceedingly showy plant both on account of the bright-green succulent leaves and the numerous blue flower-heads. Only cultivated locally.

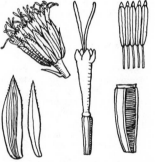

2. **A. Houstonianum** Mill. Stem 3–11 dm. tall, rather copiously pubescent with crisped hairs, sometimes branched: leaf-blades ovate to deltoid mostly 4–7 cm. long, crenate, thick: involucre about 5 mm. high in anthesis; bracts subulate to linear-lanceolate, copiously pubescent: corolla nearly 3 mm. long: achene about 2 mm. long, stout: pappus-scales nearly 2.5 mm. long, the slender tip less than twice as long as the body.—Pinelands and cult. grounds, Fla. Nat. of Mex.—(*W. I., C. A.*)—Sum.-fall.—Commonly cultivated for ornament. The flowers are very fragrant.

3. **A. conyzoides** L. Stem 1–9 dm. tall, sparingly pubescent or nearly glabrous, often branched: leaf-blades ovate to deltoid-ovate, 1.5–4 cm. long, crenate, thinnish: involucre about 3 mm. high in anthesis; bracts subulate to linear-subulate, sparingly pubescent: corolla nearly 2 mm. long: achene 1.5 mm. long, slender: pappus-scales about 1.5 mm. long, the slender tip fully twice exceeding the small body.—Waste-places and cult. grounds, Coastal Plain, Fla. to Miss. and N. C. Nat. of trop. Am.—Sum.-fall.—Has smaller heads than the preceding species and is less commonly cultivated.

8. **OSMIA** Sch. Bip. Shrubs or perennial herbs, with much-branched stems. Leaves opposite: blades broadest below the middle, often coarsely toothed. Heads borne in corymbs, relatively few-flowered. Flowers lilac, pale-purple, bluish-purple, or white. Involucre narrowly ovoid or stout-cylindric:

bracts in several series, chartaceous, the outer very short, the inner long and narrow. Corolla-lobes ovate or rounded. Anther-appendages triangular. Achene elongate, angled. Pappus of capillary bristles.—More than 50 species, tropical.

Tips of the involucral bracts spreading, bluish, much thinner than the body: inner
bracts broadened upward: achene wing-angled.   1. *O. ivaefolia.*
Tips of the involucral bracts appressed, light-green or dark-green:
 inner bracts pale, linear, each with a minute colored tip:
 achene not wing-angled.
  Bracts of the involucre 5–7-ribbed, the inner acute: involucre
   less than 8 mm. high.   2. *O. frustrata.*
  Bracts of the involucre 3-ribbed, the inner obtuse: involucre
   over 8 mm. high.   3. *O. odorata.*

1. O. ivaefolia (L.) Small. Stem 3–15 dm. tall, finely pubescent or sometimes slightly hirsute: leaf-blades lanceolate, elliptic-lanceolate, or nearly linear, 1–7 cm. long, acute, with short petiole-like bases: involucre about 6 mm. high; bracts striate and azure-tipped: corollas purplish-red or bluish-purple: receptacle small, flat-topped: achene 2–2.5 mm. long. [*Eupatorium ivaefolium* L.]—Prairies, pinewoods, and fields, Coastal Plain, Miss. to Tex.—(*W. I., Mex., C. A., S. A.*)—Sum.–fall.—One of several tropical plants that occur in our range only in or near the lower end of the Mississippi drainage basin.

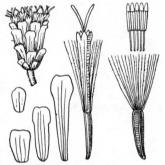

2. O. frustrata (B. L. Robinson) Small. Stem 5–20 dm. tall, minutely pubescent, with mostly ascending branches: leaf-blades ovate, deltoid-ovate, or ovate-lanceolate, 2–5 cm. long, acute or obtuse, with rather slender petiole-like bases: involucre about 7 mm. high; bracts sometimes slightly green-tipped: corolla pale-purplish or bluish, about 4 mm. long: achene stoutish, less than 4 mm. long. [*Eupatorium heteroclinum* Chapm. not Griseb.]—Hammocks, S pen. Fla. and the Keys.—All year.—An endemic species. It is particularly abundant in the Cape Sable region and in hammocks of the Ten Thousand Islands.

3. O. odorata (L.) Sch. Bip. Stem 6–28 dm. tall, pubescent, with divergent branches: leaf-blades ovate to lanceolate, 4–12 cm. long, acuminate, with long slender petiole-like bases: involucre 9–10 mm. high; bracts decidedly green-tipped: corolla white or pale-lilac, about 5 mm. long: achene very slender, over 4 mm. long. [*Eupatorium conyzoides* Vahl.]—Hammocks, S pen. Fla. and the Keys.—(*W. I., Mex., C. A., S. A.*)—All year.—The largest of our three species, often forming dense thickets on the Florida Keys.

9. EUPATORIUM [Tourn.] L. Shrubs or caulescent herbs. Leaves alternate or opposite: blades entire, toothed, or dissected. Heads borne in corymbs. Involucre campanulate, turbinate or cylindric: bracts appressed. Corollas white, pink, lilac, red, or purple. Corolla-lobes ovate or triangular. Anther-appendages ovate. Achene angled. Pappus of capillary bristles.—More than 500 species, mostly in warm and tropical region.—The leaves are sometimes whorled.

Herbs: mostly temperate plants of various habitats.
 Leaf-blades dissected or pinnatifid, the segments narrow.
                                                                                    I. Capillifolia.

CARDUACEAE 1321

Leaf-blades entire, toothed, or merely incised.
Leaves alternate or merely opposite, sometimes
  whorled on individual plants.
Involucre of closely imbricate unequal bracts in
  several series.
Leaf-blades petioled or merely sessile.
  Leaf-blades petioled, often long-petioled.
    Head 10–15-flowered: involucre cam-
      panulate: leaf-blades of a lanceolate
      type, borne horizontally.   II. SEROTINA.
    Head about 5-flowered: involucre cylin-
      dric: leaf-blades of an ovate type,
      borne vertically.   III. CRASSIFOLIA.
  Leaf-blades sessile or essentially so.
    Leaf-blades narrowed at the base.
      Bracts of the involucre acute, acu-
        minate, or mucronate.   IV. ALBA.
      Bracts of the involucre obtuse or
        individually mucronulate.   V. HYSSOPIFOLIA.
    Leaf-blades broad at the base.   VI. ROTUNDIFOLIA.
  Leaf-blades connate-perfoliate or connate-
    clasping.   VII. PERFOLIATA.
Involucre of nearly equal bracts in one row, or
  a few outer ones shorter.   VIII. URTICAEFOLIA.
Leaves in whorls of 3–6.   IX. PURPUREA.
Shrub: tropical plant of hammocks.   X. VILLOSA.

I. CAPILLIFOLIA

Leaf-segments filiform.
  Inflorescence-branches secund-recurved: inner involu-
    cral bracts prominently scarious-margined, gradually
    long-aristate.   1. *E. leptophyllum.*
  Inflorescence-branches fastigiate: inner involucral
    bracts obscurely scarious, abruptly short-aristate. 2. *E. capillifolium.*
Leaf-segments linear, linear-filiform, or lanceolate.
  Leaf-blades 1- or 2-parted.
    Inflorescence paniculate or thyrsoid.
      Heads 3–6-flowered, not glomerate on the inflo-
        rescence-branches: bracts of the involucre
        punctate and viscid.   3. *E. compositifolium.*
      Heads 6–9-flowered, glomerate or clustered at the
        ends of the inflorescence-branches: bracts of
        the involucre neither punctate nor viscid. 4. *E. Eugenei.*
    Inflorescence corymbose.   5. *E. pinnatifidum.*
  Leaf-blades mainly pectinately pinnatifid.   6. *E. pectinatum.*

II. SEROTINA

Tall, rather coarse, herb with coarsely toothed long-
  petioled leaf-blades not placed vertically.   7. *E. serotinum.*

III. CRASSIFOLIA

Low, somewhat fleshy, herbs, with repand or crenate-
  dentate petioled leaf-blades placed vertically.   8. *E. mikanioides.*

IV. ALBA

Blades of the upper cauline leaves linear or of a linear
  type.   9. *E. leucolepis.*
Blades of the upper cauline leaves ovate, lanceolate, or
  elliptic.
  Bracts of the mature involucre copiously fine-pubescent,
    not scarious-margined, the inner ones 5.5 mm. long or
    less.   10. *E. anomalum.*
  Bracts of the mature involucre glabrous or with scat-
    tered hairs, more or less scarious-margined, the
    inner ones 7 mm. long or more.
    Inner bracts of the involucre not petaloid, long-
      acuminate, linear-subulate.   11. *E. album.*
    Inner bracts of the involucre petaloid, short-
      mucronate, linear-spatulate.   12. *E. petaloideum.*

V. HYSSOPIFOLIA

Leaf-blades linear, often narrowly so or linear-filiform.
  Inner bracts of the involucre over 4 mm. long, outer
    bracts lanceolate: achene 2.5–3 mm. long.   13. *E. hyssopifolium.*

Inner bracts of the involucre less than 4 mm. long,
　　outer bracts ovate: achene about 2 mm. long.　　　　14. *E. lecheaefolium.*
Leaf-blades broader.
Inner bracts of the involucre linear: leaf-blades entire
　　or coarsely toothed, but the teeth not salient.
　　Inner bracts of the involucre 4 mm. long or more.
　　　　Leaf-blades typically or predominantly narrowed
　　　　　　upward.
　　　　　　Leaves spreading: inner bracts of the in-
　　　　　　　　volucre broadly linear: achene about 3
　　　　　　　　mm. long.　　　　　　　　　　　　　　15. *E. Torreyanum.*
　　　　　　Leaves reflexed: inner bracts of the in-
　　　　　　　　volucre narrowly linear: achene about 2
　　　　　　　　mm. long.　　　　　　　　　　　　　　16. *E. recurvans.*
　　　　Leaf-blades typically or predominantly broadened
　　　　　　upward.
　　　　　　Blades of the cauline-leaves entire or nearly
　　　　　　　　so: achene about 3 mm. long.　　　　　17. *E. tortifolium.*
　　　　　　Blades of the cauline leaves coarsely toothed:
　　　　　　　　achene about 2.5 mm. long.　　　　　　18. *E. cuneifolium.*
　　Inner bracts of the involucre 3.5 mm. long or less.　19. *E. semiserratum.*
Inner bracts of the involucre elliptic: leaf-blades stiff,
　　prominently ribbed, usually saliently toothed.　　　20. *E. altissimum.*

VI. ROTUNDIFOLIA

Leaf-blades crenate, serrate-crenate, or dentate-serrate or
　　somewhat incised: bracts of the involucre acute or
　　acuminate.
Branches of the inflorescence alternate: blades of the
　　upper leaves coarsely few-toothed.　　　　　　　　21. *E. verbenaefolium.*
Branches of the inflorescence opposite: blades of the
　　upper leaves more finely and evenly toothed.
　　Leaf-blades about as wide as long, the upper ones
　　　　of a deltoid or suborbicular type, truncate or
　　　　subcordate at the base.　　　　　　　　　　　22. *E. rotundifolium.*
　　Leaf-blades longer than wide, the upper ones of an
　　　　ovoid type, rounded or broadly cuneate at the
　　　　base.
　　　　Involucre over 6 mm. long: achene nearly 3 mm.
　　　　　　long.　　　　　　　　　　　　　　　　　23. *E. pubescens.*
　　　　Involucre less than 6 mm. long: achene about 2
　　　　　　mm. long.　　　　　　　　　　　　　　　24. *E. scabridum.*
Leaf-blades sharply serrate: bracts of the involucre ob-
　　tuse.　　　　　　　　　　　　　　　　　　　　　25. *E. sessilifolium.*

VII. PERFOLIATA

Leaf-blades connate-clasping: bracts of the involucre
　　mostly less than 12: head more than 15-flowered.
Involucre cylindric-turbinate, over 4 mm. high, acute at
　　the base; inner bracts linear, acuminate.　　　　　26. *E. Chapmanii.*
Involucre campanulate, less than 4 mm. high, rounded
　　at the base; inner bracts elliptic, abruptly short-
　　pointed or obtuse.　　　　　　　　　　　　　　　27. *E. cuneatum.*
Leaf-blades connate-perfoliate, except in *E. perfoliatum
truncatum:* bracts of the involucre mostly more than 12:
head less than 15-flowered.　　　　　　　　　　　　　28. *E. perfoliatum.*

VIII. URTICAEFOLIA

Corolla pink to pale-purple, wholly glabrous.　　　　　29. *E. incarnatum.*
Corolla white, the lobes pubescent, sometimes very slightly
　　so.
　　Leaf-blades sharply or saliently toothed, the upper
　　　　cauline-leaves slender-petioled, with petioles
　　　　nearly or quite one-half as long as the blades.
　　　　Large-leaved plants; blades of the leaves of the
　　　　　　stem typically nearly or quite 1 dm. long, of
　　　　　　an ovate type.
　　　　　　Involucre mostly less than 20-flowered, 3 mm.
　　　　　　　　wide or less at maturity; bracts mostly 13 or
　　　　　　　　fewer.　　　　　　　　　　　　　　　　30. *E. urticaefolium.*
　　　　　　Involucre mostly more than 25-flowered, 4 mm.
　　　　　　　　wide or more at maturity; bracts mostly 16
　　　　　　　　or more.　　　　　　　　　　　　　　　31. *E. roanensis.*
　　　　Small-leaved plants; blades of the leaves of the
　　　　　　stem typically less than 6 cm. long, of a hastate
　　　　　　or deltoid type.　　　　　　　　　　　　　　32. *E. jucundum.*

Leaf-blades crenate, the teeth blunt or rounded, the upper cauline leaves short-petioled or sessile.

Involucre sparingly pubescent; inner bracts nearly linear or spatulate, glabrous or sparingly ciliate, scarious-margined. — 33. *E. aromaticum.*

Involucre copiously pubescent; inner bracts spatulate or narrowly cuneate, copiously ciliate, not scarious-margined. — 34. *E. latidens.*

IX. PURPUREA

Stem hollow, very glaucous: leaf-blades elliptic-lanceolate, crenate-serrate. — 35. *E. maculatum.*

Stem normally solid, green or slightly glaucous: leaf-blades of an ovate type, sharply serrate.

Stem very purple at the nodes: leaf-blades very thin: flowers not ill-scented: corollas light-purple. — 36. *E. trifoliatum.*

Stem not purple at the nodes: leaf-blades thickish, rugose: flowers ill-scented: corollas crimson. — 37. *E. purpureum.*

X. VILLOSA

Shrub with ovate or deltoid-ovate leaf-blades. — 38. *E. villosum.*

1. E. leptophyllum DC. Stem 4–13 dm. tall, glabrous, with recurved-secund branches above: leaf-blades with filiform segments: bracts of the involucre long-tipped, the inner between 3 and 4 mm. long: corolla white, about 3 mm. long: achene fully 1.5 mm. long.—(FENNEL.)—Low grounds, margins of ponds, and swamps, Coastal Plain, Fla. to Miss. and S. C.—Sum.–fall, or all year S.

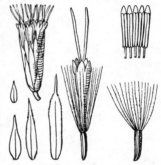

2. E. capillifolium (Lam.) Small. Stem 9–30 dm. tall, pubescent, fastigiate above: leaf-blades with filiform segments: bracts of the involucre short-tipped, the inner between 2 and 3 mm. long: corolla white, about 2 mm. long: achene fully 1 mm. long.—(DOG-FENNEL.)—Hammocks, old fields, roadsides, and banks, Coastal Plain and adj. provinces, Fla. to Tex., Tenn., and Del.—Sum.–fall.

3. E. compositifolium Walt. Stem 6–12 dm. tall, puberulent to finely pubescent, paniculate above: leaf-blades with linear or nearly linear segments: inflorescence plumose: bracts of the involucre mucronate, the inner 3.5–4 mm. long: corolla white, 3 mm. long: achene 1.5–2 mm. long.—(DOG-FENNEL.)—Dry soil, especially in pinelands, Coastal Plain and adj. provinces, Fla. to Tex., and N. C. Sum.–fall.

4. E. Eugenei Small. Stem 6–14 dm. tall, pubescent: leaf-blades with linear, entire, or toothed segments, or those of the upper leaves merely toothed or incised: inflorescence not plumose: bracts of the involucre mucronate, the inner 3–3.5 mm. long: corolla white, 2.5–3 mm. long: achene less than 2 mm. long.—Pinelands and woods, Coastal Plain and adj. Piedmont, Fla. and Ala.—Fall.

5. E. pinnatifidum Ell. Stem 6–12 dm. tall, finely pubescent: leaf-blades with linear or nearly linear segments: involucre about 3 mm. long; bracts cuspidate, the inner about 3 mm. long: corolla white, about 2 mm. long: achene fully 1 mm. long.—Dry soil and damp borders of thickets, Coastal Plain and adj. provinces, Fla. to Ala. and N. C.—Sum.–fall.

6. E. pectinatum Small. Stem 9–20 dm. tall, finely pubescent, corymbose above: leaf-blades elliptic in outline, or broadest above or below the middle: involucre 4–5 mm. long; bracts obtuse or retuse-aristulate, the inner 3.5–4 mm. long: corolla white, 3 mm. long: achene fully 1 mm. long.—Sandy soil, Coastal Plain, Fla. and Ga.—Sum.–fall.

7. E. serotinum Michx. Stem 8–20 dm. tall, finely pubescent, corymbose above: leaf-blades herbaceous, lanceolate to ovate-lanceolate, 5–25 cm. long, acute or acuminate, coarsely serrate: involucre less than 5 mm. long; bracts linear to linear-elliptic, broadened upward, rounded at the apex, white-margined, the inner 3–3.5 mm. long: corolla white, 3 mm. long: achene less than 2 mm. long.—Rich woods, banks, and wet grounds, various provinces, Fla. to Tex., Ia., and Md.—Sum.-fall.

8. E. mikanioides Chapm. Stem 5–11 dm. tall, tomentulose, at least when young: leaf-blades vertical, fleshy, deltoid-ovate to hastate-ovate, or sometimes elliptic, 3–6 cm. long, obtuse or acutish, repand or crenate-dentate: involucre over 5 mm. long; bracts linear, abruptly pointed, green-margined, the inner 4–5 mm. long: corolla white or pinkish, nearly 4 mm. long: achene fully 1 mm. long.—Low sandy soil, damp, sandy or marly pinelands, and salt marshes, Fla.—Sum.-fall.

9. E. leucolepis T. & G. Stem 3–8 dm. tall, rough-pubescent, or tomentulose above; leaf-blades linear to lanceolate, 3–8 cm. long, remotely serrate or nearly entire: involucre tomentulose; bracts slenderly acuminate, the inner ones broadly linear, 6–6.5 mm. long: corolla white, about 3.5 mm. long: achene 2.5 mm. long. [*E. Mohri* Greene.]—Pinelands, and acid, sandy bogs, Coastal Plain, Fla. to La. and N. Y.—Sum.-fall.

10. E. anomalum Nash. Stem 8–15 dm. tall, tomentulose: leaf-blades ovate-lanceolate to ovate, 3–7 cm. long, coarsely and sharply serrate: involucre finely pubescent; bracts acute or short-acuminate, the inner narrowly linear, 5–5.5 mm. long: corolla white, about 3.5 mm. long: achene 2–2.5 mm. long.—Sandy soil, Fla.—Sum.-fall.

11. E. album L. Stem 3–9 dm. tall, harshly pubescent: leaf-blades elliptic to lanceolate, or those at the base of the stem ovate to obovate, 3–10 cm. long, serrate: involucre cylindric-turbinate, the inner bracts linear-subulate, 8–9 mm. long, abruptly pointed: corolla white, about 5 mm. long: achene about 3 mm. long.—Dry, acid, sandy soil, in pinelands and deciduous woods, Coastal Plain and adj. provinces, Fla. to La., Tenn., and N. Y.—Sum.-fall.

12. E. petaloideum Britton. Stem 3–7 dm. tall, rough-pubescent: leaf-blades elliptic to ovate or ovate-lanceolate, or the lower ones oval or obovate, 2–8 cm. long, bluntly serrate or crenate-serrate: involucre trumpet-shaped, the inner bracts spatulate, 10–11 mm. long, or sometimes shorter, mucronate: corolla white, 4 mm. long: achene about 3 mm. long.—Pinelands, Coastal Plain, Fla. and Ala.—Sum.-fall.

13. E. hyssopifolium L. Stem 3–8 dm. tall, puberulent: leaf-blades linear, 2–6 cm. long, sometimes undulate: involucre 5–6 mm. high; inner bracts narrowly linear or linear-lanceolate, ciliolate, obtuse, the inner 5–5.5 mm. long: corolla white, 3.5–4 mm. long: achene 2.5–3 mm. long.—Woods, banks, and thickets, various provinces, Fla. to Tex., Ky., and Mass.—Sum.-fall.

14. E. lecheaefolium Greene. Stem 3–7 dm. tall, puberulent or finely pubescent: leaf-blades narrowly linear, 1–8 cm. long, entire: involucre 3–4 mm. high; inner bracts elliptic, ciliolate at the mucronate apex: corolla white, 2.5–3 mm. long: achene about 2 mm. long.—Sandy soil, Coastal Plain, Fla. to Ga. and Ala.—Sum.-fall.

15. E. Torreyanum Short. Stem 4–12 dm. tall, finely pubescent: leaf-blades broadly linear to narrowly lanceolate, coarsely and sharply serrate to laciniate: involucre turbinate: bracts broadly linear, ciliate, the inner 5–5.5 mm. long:

corolla white, 3 mm. long: achene 3 mm. long.—Low woods and wooded hillsides, often in acid soil, various provinces, Fla. to Tenn., Ky., and Pa.—Sum.–fall.

16. **E. recurvans** Small. Stem 4–9 dm. tall, finely pubescent: leaves more or less reflexed; blades narrowly elliptic to lanceolate, 1.5–4 cm. long, coarsely and bluntly toothed: involucre cylindric: bracts narrowly linear, slightly ciliate, the inner about 4 mm. long: corolla white, 3 mm. long: achene about 2 mm. long.—Pinelands, Coastal Plain, Fla. to Ala. and Ga.—Sum.–fall.

17. **E. tortifolium** Chapm. Stem 3–7 dm. tall, tomentulose above: leaf-blades spatulate, oblanceolate, or nearly linear, 1–3 cm. long, entire or shallowly and remotely toothed: outer bracts of the involucre ovate; inner bracts linear: corolla white, about 3 mm. long: achene about 3 mm. long.—Sandy ridges and dry pinelands, Coastal Plain, Fla. to Ala. and S. C.—Sum.–fall.

18. **E. cuneifolium** Willd. Stem 4–8 dm. tall, tomentulose above: leaf-blades cuneate, elliptic-cuneate, or linear-elliptic, 1–3 cm. long, serrate, or the upper ones individually entire: outer bracts of the involucre oval; inner bracts narrowly elliptic: corolla white, about 3.5 mm. long: achene about 2.5 mm. long.—Rich woods, Coastal Plain and adj. provinces, Fla. to Ala. and S. C.—Sum.–fall.

19. **E. semiserratum** DC. Stem 5–12 dm. tall, tomentulose: leaf-blades elliptic-spatulate to elliptic, 3–10 cm. long, sharply serrate: involucre nearly cylindric; bracts obtuse, ciliate, not pale-margined, the inner linear, 3–3.5 mm. long: corolla white, 2–2.5 mm. long: achene about 2 mm. long.—Sandy soil, wet places, and pond-margins, Coastal Plain and adj. provinces, Fla. to Tex., Mo., and Va.—Sum.–fall.

20. **E. altissimum** L. Stem 8–20 dm. tall, hoary-tomentulose: leaf-blades linear-lanceolate to linear-elliptic, mostly 4–12 cm. long, sharply serrate: involucre campanulate; bracts ciliate, obtuse, pale-margined, the inner elliptic, 4.5–5 mm. long: corolla white, about 4 mm. long: achene 3–3.5 mm. long.—Dry soil, various provinces, Miss. to Tex., Ia., Pa., and N. C.—Sum.–fall.

21. **E. verbenaefolium** Michx. Stem 6–12 dm. tall, finely pubescent: leaf-blades ovate to lanceolate, 2–12 cm. long, coarsely serrate: bracts of the involucre abruptly short-pointed, the inner mostly linear-elliptic or narrowly elliptic, 4–4.5 mm. long: corolla white, 3 mm. long: achene about 3 mm. long.—Sandy soil, moist grounds, and acid swamps, Coastal Plain and adj. provinces, Fla. to La., Tenn., and Mass.—Sum.–fall.

22. **E. rotundifolium** L. Stem 3–12 dm. tall, tomentulose: leaf-blades suborbicular to orbicular-ovate, 2–4 cm. long, crenate or crenate-dentate: intermediate bracts of the involucre acuminate, the inner ones 5.5–6 mm. long, narrowly linear: corolla white, about 3 mm. long: achene fully 2 mm. long.—(FALSE-HOARHOUND.)—Dry woods, pinelands, and swamps, Coastal Plain and adj. provinces, Fla. to Tex., Ark., and R. I.—Sum.–fall.

23. **E. pubescens** Muhl. Stem 3–15 dm. tall, canescent-tomentulose: leaf-blades ovate, 2–10 cm. long, serrate or incised-serrate: intermediate bracts of the involucre acute or abruptly pointed, the inner ones 5.5–6 mm. long, linear-elliptic: corolla white, about 3 mm. long: achene 2.5–3 mm. long.—Rocky woods, acid, sandy banks, and•thickets, Coastal Plain and adj. provinces, Fla. to Miss., Tenn., and Me.—Sum.–fall.

24. **E. scabridum** Ell. Stem 4–12 dm. tall, canescent-tomentose: leaf-blades elliptic to ovate-elliptic, 2–8 cm. long, serrate or incised-serrate: bracts of the

involucre abruptly pointed, the inner 4–5 mm. long, linear-elliptic: corolla white, 2.5–3 mm. long: achene fully 2 mm. long.—Low pinelands, Coastal Plain, Fla. to S. C.—Sum.–fall.

25. **E. sessilifolium** L. Stem 4–15 dm. tall, tomentulose above: leaf-blades lanceolate, 8–25 cm. long, acuminate, sharply serrate, sessile, sometimes slightly clasping: bracts of the involucre obtuse, the inner linear-elliptic, 4.5–5 mm. long: corolla white, 3 mm. long: achene 3–3.5 mm. long.—Thickets, open woods and rocky banks, various provinces, rarely Coastal Plain, Ga. to Ala., Mo., Vt., and Mass.—Sum.–fall.

26. **E. Chapmanii** Small. Stem 4–12 dm. tall, tomentulose above: leaf-blades elliptic to elliptic-ovate, or narrowly ovate, 2–10 cm. long, crenate; inner bracts of the involucre acuminate, linear, 4–4.5 mm. long: corolla white, 3 mm. long: achene about 1.5 mm. long.—Sandy woods, Fla.—Sum.

27. **E. cuneatum** Engelm. Stem 5–16 dm. tall, tomentose above: leaf-blades lanceolate to elliptic-lanceolate, 9–20 cm. long, finely crenate-serrate: inner bracts of the involucre abruptly short-pointed or obtuse, elliptic, 3–3.5 mm. long: corolla white, 3 mm. long: achene 1.5 mm. long.—Low grounds, Coastal Plain and adj. provinces, Ala. to La., Mo., and N. C.—Sum.–fall.

28. **E. perfoliatum** L. Stem 3–12 dm. tall, tomentulose above: leaf-blades lanceolate, 8–25 cm. long, crenate-serrate, connate-perfoliate (or truncate in *E. perfoliatum truncatum*): inner bracts of the involucres cuneate-spatulate, acuminate, 6–6.5 mm. long or shorter: corolla white, 3–4 mm. long: achene 2 mm. long, or mostly shorter.—(BONESET. THOROUGHWORT.)—Moist meadows, and swamps, various provinces, Fla. to Tex., N. D., and N. B.—Sum.–fall.

29. **E. incarnatum** Walt. Stem 5–12 dm. tall, minutely pubescent: leaf-blades thin, ovate to deltoid, and usually somewhat hastate, 2–6 cm. long, acute or acuminate, coarsely serrate, on long and slender petioles: involucre narrow; bracts linear or nearly so, or the outer subulate, often ciliolate at the apex, the outer ones often pubescent, especially near the base, the inner 4–4.5 mm. long: corolla lilac, about 3 mm. long: achene 2–2.5 mm. long.—Rich sandy woods, Coastal Plain and adj. provinces, Fla. to Tex., Ind. and Va.—(*Mex.*)—Sum.–fall.

30. **E. urticaefolium** Reichard. Stem 4–12 dm. tall, puberulent or glabrate: leaf-blades thin, ovate or rarely ovate-lanceolate, 4–12 cm. long, acuminate, coarsely serrate, long-petioled: involucre turbinate: bracts narrowly linear, ciliolate at the apex, the inner 3–5 mm. long, acuminate: corolla white, 3–4 mm. long: achene slender-fusiform, 2–2.5 mm. long.—(WHITE-SNAKEROOT. WHITE-SANICLE.)—Rich woods and thickets, various provinces, Ga. to La., Okla., Ont., and N.B.—Sum.–fall.

31. **E. roanensis** Small. Stem 1 m. tall or less, finely pubescent at least above: leaf-blades ovate, often broadly so, 7–14 cm. long, acuminate, serrate, rather coarsely so, long-petioled: involucre campanulate; bracts broadly linear or somewhat spatulate, minutely pubescent, the inner 5–6 mm. long, acute: corolla white, 3–4 mm. long: achene stout-fusiform, about 2.5 mm. long.—Woods, Roan Mt., in the Blue Ridge, N. C. and Tenn.—Sum.–fall.

32. **E. jucundum** Greene. Stem 4–12 dm. tall, glabrous or minutely pubescent above: leaf-blades thin, ovate, often broadly so or deltoid, or somewhat hastate, 1.5–6 cm. long, obtuse or acutish, coarsely crenate-serrate or incised-serrate, slender-petioled: involucre cylindric or nearly so; bracts acute or acuminate, the inner narrowly linear, 3–3.5 mm. long: corolla white, about 4 mm. long: achene about 2.5 mm. long.—Hammocks and pinelands, N and upper pen. Fla.—Fall–wint.

33. **E aromaticum** L. Stem 3–15 dm. tall, puberulent or minutely pubescent: leaf-blades thickish, ovate or orbicular-ovate to ovate-lanceolate, 2–10

cm. long, obtuse or acute, crenate, sessile or short-petioled: involucre cylindric or turbinate-cylindric: bracts narrow, linear, or the inner ones spatulate, ciliate, 4–4.5 mm. long: corolla white, 4.5–5 mm. long: achene 2.5–3 mm. long.—(WILD-HOARHOUND.)—Dry, acid, woods, thickets, and pinelands, Coastal Plain and adj. provinces, Fla. to Miss., Tenn., Pa., and Mass.—Sum.–fall.

34. E. latidens Small. Stem 7–12 dm. tall, finely pubescent often closely so above: leaf-blades deltoid-ovate or orbicular-ovate, or suborbicular or reniform-orbicular on the lower part of the stem, 4–11 cm. long, obtuse or acutish, coarsely toothed, usually crenate, sessile or short-petioled: involucre campanulate; bracts broad, elliptic, or the inner spatulate or narrowly cuneate, all copiously ciliate, obtuse or acute: corolla white, 3–3.5 mm. long: achene about 2 mm. long.—Woods, Appalachian Valley, Tenn.—Sum.–fall.

35. E. maculatum Justineus. Stem glabrous, 2–5 m. tall, usually mottled: leaves in whorls of 4–7, usually of 5 or 6; blades elliptic-lanceolate, 1–3 dm. long, acuminate, firm: corymb more or less elongate, round-topped: involucre usually 6- or 7-flowered: corolla 3.5–5 mm. long.—(JOE-PYE-WEED. SMOKEWEED.)—Moist soil, often in thickets, various provinces, Fla. to Tex., Ohio, and Me.—Sum.–fall.

36. E. trifoliatum L. Stem glabrous or sparingly pubescent, 1–2 m. tall: leaves in whorls of 3–5, mostly in fours; blades lanceolate to elliptic-lanceolate, 1.5–2 dm. long, acuminate: corymb convex: involucre usually 5–7-flowered: corolla 5.5–7.5 mm. long.—(JOE-PYE-WEED.)—Open woodlands, various provinces, Ga. to Okla., Nebr., Wis., and N. H.—Sum.–fall.

37. E. purpureum L. Stem more or less pubescent, scabrous, 0.5–2 m. tall, purplish-tinged: leaves in whorls of 2–5, usually in threes or fours; blades firm, ovate, 0.5–2 dm. long, sharply-serrate, 3-ribbed: corymb somewhat convex: involucre usually 6–9-flowered: corolla 4.5–5.5 mm. long.—(JOE-PYE-WEED.)—Moist soil, often in swamps, Coastal Plain and adj. provinces, S. C. to N. H.—Sum.–fall.

38. E. villosum Sw. Stem 5–20 dm. tall, woody, tomentulose: leaf-blades ovate to deltoid-ovate, 1.5–7 cm. long, obtuse, entire or repand: heads in small clusters: involucre campanulate: bracts obtuse, or the inner acute, 3–4 mm. long: corolla white or pinkish, barely 3 mm. long: achene 1.5–2 mm. long.—Hammocks and pinelands, Everglade Keys, Fla. and Florida Keys.—(W. I.)—All year.

10. CONOCLINIUM DC. Perennial caulescent herbs. Leaves opposite: blades toothed or lobed. Heads in open or compact peduncled clusters. Involucre campanulate or hemispheric, many flowered: bracts narrow, imbricate in several series. Corolla regular, blue or violet, very narrowly funnelform: lobes ovate or deltoid. Androecium included. Anther-appendages ovate. Achene narrowly obpyramidal or somewhat ellipsoid, angled. Pappus of few capillary bristles.—Eight or ten species, mostly trop-ical. Plants, and flower-heads, often resemble ageratum.

1. C. coelestinum (L.) DC. Stem 2–11 dm. tall, appressed-pubescent, branched: leaf-blades ovate, deltoid, triangular or triangular-lanceolate, 3–12 cm. long, crenate or serrate-crenate, sometimes coarsely so, those of the lower leaves, at least, long-petioled: involucre about

4 mm. high; bracts subulate or linear-subulate, ribbed, pubescent: corolla about 2.5 mm. long: achene barely 1.5 mm. long. [*Eupatorium coelestinum* L. *C. dichotomum* Chapm.]—(MIST-FLOWER.)—Stream-banks, marshes, and thickets, various provinces, Fla. to Tex., Kans., Mich., and N. J.—(*Cuba.*)—Sum.-fall or all year S.—Sometimes cultivated and used in place of species of *Ageratum*.

11. MIKANIA Willd. Herbaceous vines. Leaves opposite, herbaceous: blades of a hastate or deltoid type, mostly toothed. Heads borne in corymbs. Involucre cylindric. Corolla pink or white, with a campanulate throat: lobes lanceolate to triangular-ovate. Androecium exserted: anther-appendages ovate. Achene angled. Pappus of many capillary bristles. [*Willugbaeya* Neck.]—About 150 species, American.—CLIMBING HEMPWEEDS.

Bracts of the involucre acute or acuminate.
    Bracts of the involucre scarcely 4 mm. long.   1. *M. batatifolia.*
    Bracts of the involucre over 4 mm. long.   2. *M. scandens.*
Bracts of the involucre obtuse.   3. *M. cordifolia.*

1. M. batatifolia DC. Plant glabrous: leaf-blades deltoid to hastate-ovate, 1–3 cm. long, entire or repand: heads in small irregular clusters: bracts of the involucre 3–4 mm. long: corolla about 3 mm. long. [*W. heterophylla* Small.]—Hammocks, low pinelands, and Everglades, S pen. Fla. and the Keys.—(*W. I.*)—All year.

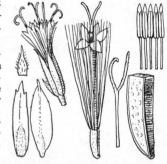

2. M. scandens (L.) Willd. Plant finely pubescent or nearly glabrous: leaf-blades deltoid-ovate to hastate, 5–8 cm. long, undulate or angulately lobed: bracts of the involucre 5–5.5 mm. long, acuminate or abruptly pointed: corolla about 4 mm. long: achene 2–2.5 mm. long.—(CLIMBING HEMP-VINE.)—Woods, thickets, and swamps, various provinces, Fla. to Tex., Ont., and Me.—Sum.

3. M. cordifolia (L.) Willd. Plant densely pubescent: leaf-blades ovate to hastate, 6–15 cm. long, coarsely toothed, or lobed, cordate at the base: corymbs rounded or rather flat-topped: heads numerous: involucre narrow, but rather stout; bracts elliptic to linear-elliptic, 7–8 mm. long, obtuse: corolla about 6 mm. long.—Hammocks, S pen. Fla. and the Keys.—(*W. I., Mex., C. A., S. A.*)—All year.—The most vigorous of the three climbing-hempweeds. Well-developed vines produce prodigious inflorescences. The flowers are very fragrant.

12. COLEOSANTHUS Cass. Perennial, branching herbs or woody plants. Leaves opposite or alternate: blades usually broad and toothed. Heads borne in corymbose cymes. Involucre cylindric to campanulate: bracts ribbed. Corolla-throat narrow, scarcely wider than the tube; lobes ovate to deltoid. Anther-appendages ovate, obtuse. Achene ribbed or striate. Pappus of many capillary bristles. [*Brickellia* Ell.]—About 70 species, mostly American.

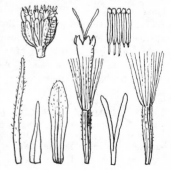

1. C. cordifolius (Ell.) Kuntze. Stem 6–12 dm. tall, puberulent or tomentulose: leaf-blades ovate to deltoid-ovate, or nearly lanceolate above, 5–10 cm. long, crenate-serrate: heads many-flowered: involucre campanulate, lax: outer bracts linear-subulate; inner bracts linear, obtuse, 9–10 mm. long: corolla pale-purple: achene slender, about 6 mm. long, sparingly pubescent: pappus purplish.—Rich soil, woods, and pinelands, Coastal Plain, Fla. to Ala. and Ga.—Sum.-fall.

13. **KUHNIA** L. Perennial, pubescent herbs. Leaves alternate: blades narrow, or rarely of an ovate type, resinous-dotted. Heads in open or compact corymbose or paniculate clusters. Involucres cylindric, often narrow. Corolla cream-colored or nearly white, narrowly funnelform, the tube and throat scarcely distinguishable: lobes triangular to lanceolate. Anther-appendages ovate, obtuse. Achene columnar, striate. Pappus of many capillary bristles.—About 10 species, North American.—FALSE-BONESETS.—Sum.-fall.

Peduncle and involucre finely close-pubescent: bracts of the involucre slenderly and not very prominently ribbed, the inner ones narrowly linear.
  Leaves, at least those of the stem, with linear or nearly linear blades: blades thick, entire or obscurely toothed. 1. *K. Mosieri.*
  Leaves, at least those of the stem, with blades predominantly of a lanceolate type: blades thin, the larger coarsely toothed. 2. *K. eupatorioides.*
Peduncle and involucre villous-tomentose: bracts of the involucre broadly and prominently ribbed, the inner ones broadly linear. 3. *K. glutinosa.*

1. **K. Mosieri** Small. Plant 3–11 dm. tall, slender, deep-green: leaves 1–3 cm. long, usually spreading or reflexed; blades linear or nearly so, entire or obscurely toothed: mature involucre 8–9 mm. high; inner bracts narrowly and sharply ribbbed: corolla mostly over 6 mm. long: pappus pale-brown or whitish. [*K. paniculata* (Fl. SE. U. S.)]—Pinelands, Everglade Keys, Fla.—Specimens from as far west as S Ala. may be referable to this species.

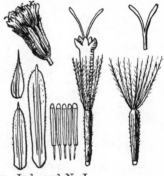

2. **K. eupatorioides** L. Plant 15 dm. tall or less, stoutish, often pale-green: leaves 3–10 cm. long, ascending; blades lanceolate, sometimes narrowly so, coarsely toothed, or entire above: mature involucre 9–10.5 mm. high; inner bracts with prominent rounded ribs: corolla mostly less than 6 mm. long: pappus tawny.—Woods and stream-banks, Coastal Plain and adj. provinces, Fla. to Miss., Ind., and N. J.

3. **K. glutinosa** Ell. Plant 12 dm. tall or less, stoutish, gray or grayish: leaves 1.5–7 cm. long, erect or ascending; blades lanceolate to ovate, coarsely toothed: heads often conspicuously glomerate: mature involucre 8–9 mm. high; inner bracts coarsely ribbed: pappus tawny.—Dry prairies or plains, various provinces, Ala., to Tex., Mont., and Ill.

14. **CARPHEPHORUS** Cass. Perennial, simple-stemmed herbs. Leaves alternate; blades narrow, flat, or acerose, entire. Heads in a terminal corymbose cyme, this sometimes cluster-like. Involucre hemispheric to campanulate: bracts in several series. Corolla rose-purple: throat narrowly funnelform, longer than the narrower tube; lobes lanceolate to deltoid. Androecium included: anther-appendages mostly notched. Achene fusiform, sharply ribbed. Pappus of many pale capillary bristles.—Four species, as follows:

Basal leaves with elongate acerose blades: outer bracts of the involucre lanceolate.

1. C. Pseudo-Liatris.

Basal leaves with broader or linear-spatulate blades: outer bracts of the involucre, especially the median ones, broad.

    Bracts of the involucre with lax or spreading thick acute or acutish tips.

2. C. tomentosus.

    Bracts of the involucre with thin or scarious erect rounded or retuse tips.

        Heads in a cluster-like cyme: stem copiously pubescent.

3. C. corymbosus.

        Heads in an open slenderly branched cyme: stem glabrous or nearly so.

4. C. bellidifolius.

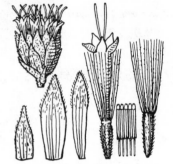

1. C. Pseudo-Liatris Cass. Stem 3–9 dm. tall, finely crisped-pubescent: leaf-blades acerose, involute, reduced to narrow scales above: outer bracts of the involucre lanceolate; inner 7–8 mm. long; broadly linear: bractlets (chaff) linear: achene about 3 mm. long.—Moist pinelands, Coastal Plain, Fla. to La. and Ga.—Fall.

2. C. tomentosus (Michx.) T. & G. Stem 3–7 dm. tall, copiously crisped-pubescent or often hirsutulous below: leaf-blades linear-spatulate below, to obovate to elliptic-oval above: outer bracts of the involucre ovate; inner narrowly linear, 9–12 mm. long, entire: bractlets narrowly linear or linear-spatulate: achene about 4 mm. long.—Pinelands, Coastal Plain, Fla. to N. C.—Sum.-fall.—Rather rare.

3. C. corymbosus (Nutt.) T. & G. Stem 3–9 dm. tall, pubescent: leaf-blades spatulate or elliptic-spatulate below to cuneate, elliptic, or ovate above: bracts of the involucre scarious-margined, erose-ciliate; outer ovate; inner 6–8 mm. long, cuneate: achene stout, about 3 mm. long.—Pinelands, Coastal Plain, Fla. to N. C.—Sum.-fall.

4. C. bellidifolius (Michx.) T. & G. Stem 3–5 dm. tall, glabrous or obscurely pubescent: leaf-blades linear-spatulate to linear: bracts of the involucre not scarious-margined, ciliolate, 8–9 mm. long, obtuse: achene slender, about 4 mm. long.—Pinelands, Coastal Plain, and adj. provinces, Fla. to N. C.—Sum.-fall.

    15. LITRISA Small. Perennial somewhat succulent caulescent herbs, the stems single or clustered from short, branched, knotty rootstocks. Leaves alternate, the basal ones larger than the cauline: blades fleshy-leathery, entire, parallel-veined. Heads corymbose. Involucre campanulate, few-flowered; bracts few, relatively broad, pubescent. Corolla bright-purple, with a short tube and a cylindric throat. Androecium included. Anther-appendages ovate, nearly entire, obtuse. Achene cuneate, ribbed. Pappus of many barbellate bristles.—One species.

    1. L. carnosa Small. Stem 3–8 dm. tall, finely pubescent; basal leaves in a rosette; blades mostly 2–8 cm. long, linear, varying to lanceolate or spatulate, acute; cauline leaves remote; blades sessile; involucre erect; bracts mostly acute or mucronate, purple-tinged, the outer ovate, the inner elliptic or broadly linear, about 4 mm. long; achene 2–2.5 mm. long, pubescent.—Prairies and low pinelands, pen. Fla.—Sum.–fall.

16. **LACINIARIA** Hill.[1] Perennial, typically simple herbs with thick roots. Leaves alternate, often numerous; blades narrow, entire. Heads in spikes, racemes, panicles, or rarely in cymes. Involucre ovoid to cylindric or turbinate: bracts few or many, imbricate, rarely petaloid. Corolla rose-purple: throat narrow-funnelform, much longer than the slightly narrower tube: lobes lanceolate. Anther-appendages entire or notched. Achene short, ribbed. Pappus of many barbellate or plumose bristles.—About 40 species, North American.—BUTTON-SNAKEROOTS. BLAZING-STARS. RATTLESNAKE-MASTERS.

Pappus bristles plumose.
  Bracts of the involucre with dilated or petal-like, rose, (or white), apical appendages. I. ELEGANTES.
  Bracts of the involucre not petal-like at the apex.
    Heads many (16–60) -flowered: corolla-lobes pubescent within. II. SQUARROSAE.
    Heads few (3–6) -flowered: corolla-lobes glabrous. III. PUNCTATAE.
Pappus bristles barbellate.
  Bracts of the involucre acute, acuminate, or mucronate at the apex.
    Bracts with recurved-spreading tips. IV. PYCNOSTACHYAE.
    Bracts with erect or appressed tips.
      Heads secund-spreading on the rachis. V. PAUCIFLORAE.
      Heads not secund, erect or appressed. VI. TENUIFOLIAE.
  Bracts of the involucre obtuse or rounded at the apex (except in No. 17).
    Involucre campanulate, nearly cylindric, or turbinate; few-flowered. VII. SPICATAE.
    Involucre hemispheric; many-flowered. VIII. SCARIOSAE.

I. ELEGANTES

Petal-like tips of the involucral bracts much longer than wide, serrulate, acuminate. 1. *L. elegans.*
Petal-like tips of the involucral bracts about as broad as long, rounded and erose-denticulate. 2. *L. flabellata.*

II. SQUARROSAE

Stout plant with approximate cauline leaves and large heads: involucral bracts with rigid, acuminate, spreading tips. 3. *L. squarrosa.*

III. PUNCTATAE

Slender plant with very narrow leaves: involucral bracts with slightly petaloid tips. 4. *L. Boykinii.*

IV. PYCNOSTACHYAE

Involucral bracts with strongly recurved, small petaloid tips. 5. *L. pycnostachya.*
Involucral bracts with slightly recurved, green tips. 6. *L. chlorolepis.*

V. PAUCIFLORAE

Stem and rachis glabrous: involucral bracts not glandular punctate. 7. *L. pauciflora.*
Stem and rachis pubescent: involucral bracts glandular punctate. 8. *L. secunda.*

VI. TENUIFOLIAE

Leaves gradually decreasing in length from the base of the stem to the inflorescence.
  Bracts of the involucre linear or nearly so, usually long-acuminate. 9. *L. Chapmanii.*
  Bracts of the involucre, ovate-lanceolate, usually mucronate.

[1] Contributed by Edward Johnston Alexander.

Bracts numerous, about 20, glabrous or sparingly
    ciliate: stem and rachis glabrous.   10. *L. regimontis.*
Bracts few, about 10, pubescent with crisped hairs:
    stem and rachis pubescent.   11. *L. Garberi.*
Leaves abruptly smaller near the base of the stem, the
    lower ones very much elongate.   12. *L. tenuifolia.*

VII. Spicatae

Involucre campanulate; heads sessile.
  Involucral bracts with broad petaloid margins.
  Involucral bracts with merely scarious margins.   13. *L. spicata.*
Involucre turbinate: heads sessile or peduncled.
  Stem and rachis copiously pubescent.   14. *L. laxa.*
  Stem and rachis glabrous or nearly so.
    Involucre 8–12-flowered.
      Pappus-bristles nearly or quite as long as the
        corolla-tube.
        Involucre nearly cylindric.   15. *L. microcephala.*
        Involucre turbinate, sometimes broadly so.
          Involucre over 9 mm. long.
            Involucral bracts rounded at the tip. 16. *L. graminifolia.*
            Involucral bracts pointed at the tip. 17. *L. Smallii.*
          Involucre less than 8 mm. long.   18. *L. gracilis.*
      Pappus-bristles about half as long as the corolla-
        tube.   19. *L. Helleri.*
    Involucre about 20-flowered.   20. *L. pilosa.*

VIII. Scariosae

Involucral bracts with broad, petaloid margins and tips. 21. *L. aspera.*
Involucral bracts with merely scarious margins or not
  margined at all.
  Involucres usually 1 cm. or more high.
    Involucral bracts only ciliate margined or glabrous,
      often with a few scattered hairs: leaves glabrous
      or scabrate-margined.   22. *L. scariosa.*
    Involucral bracts densely puberulent: leaves sca-
      brous.   23. *L. Shortii.*
  Involucre usually less than 1 cm. high.
    Leaves narrowly linear, scabrous all over.   24. *L. Tracyi.*
    Leaves elliptic to linear-elliptic, smooth, or scabrate
      merely on the margin.   25. *L. Ruthii.*

1. **L. elegans** (Walt.) Kuntze. Stem 3–12 dm. tall, finely pubescent: blades of the lower leaves linear to linear-spatulate; upper leaves reflexed: involucral bracts densely pubescent, the petaloid tips glabrous; tips of the inner ones irregularly serrulate.—Pinelands and dry, sandy woods, Coastal Plain, Fla. to Tex. and S Va.—Sum.–fall.

2. **L. flabellata** Small. Stem 3–6 dm. tall, lanuginous: blades of the lower leaves linear or nearly so: upper leaves reflexed: involucral bracts sparingly pubescent, except the outer bracts which are densely pubescent; tips of the inner bracts erose-denticulate.—Pinelands and open woods, St. Helena Id., S. C.—Fall.

3. **L. squarrosa** (L.) Hill. Stem 3–8 dm. tall, pubescent: blades of the lower leaves linear to linear-elliptic: bracts of the involucre spatulate with abruptly acuminate, spreading tips, heavily ciliate-margined, with some cilia on the bract-body (rarely glabrous, only the outermost slightly ciliate); inner bracts linear, acute, 15–22 mm. long: corollas about 15 mm. long: achene about 6 mm. long, short-pubescent.—Dry sandy soil, various provinces, Fla. to Tex., Mo., Ind., and Va.—Sum.–fall.—The constituents of this species are rather difficult to interpret at present. The following divisions may help understanding the group. *L. squarrosa intermedia* (Lindl.) DC., with

heads more narrow and bracts erect or little spreading, less prolonged, has the same range as the type. *L. squarrosa alabamensis* Alexander, with heads more narrow, bracts glabrous except the outermost, abruptly short-acuminate and very squarrose, is in Ala. and Miss.

4. **L. Boykinii** (T. & G.) Kuntze. Stem 3–6 dm. tall, glabrous or nearly so: blades of the lower leaves narrowly linear: heads loosely spicate-racemose, slender-peduncled: inner bracts of the involucre linear, 9–12 mm. long, acuminate, glabrous or nearly so: corolla 6–7 mm. long: achene 4–4.5 mm. long, or sometimes shorter.—Dry or sandy soil, Coastal Plain, Ga.—Sum.—Perhaps a hybrid between *L. elegans* and *L. tenuifolia.*

5. **L. pycnostachya** (Michx.) Kuntze. Stem 6–15 dm. tall, more or less pubescent, especially above: blades of the lower leaves linear: involucral bracts ciliate-margined, often heavily so; inner bracts 9–11 mm. long, acuminate: corollas 10–11 mm. long: filaments less than half as long as the anthers: achene 4.5–5 mm. long. [*L. macilenta* Small]—Dry soil, various provinces, Tex. to Nebr., Minn., Wis., Ky., and Miss.—Sum.–fall.—*L. Langloisii* Green, distinguished by its woolly stem and involucres, may be distinct.

6. **L. chlorolepis** Small. Stem 3–6 dm. tall, hirsute-tomentulose: blades of the lower leaves narrowly linear: involucral bracts pubescent, with short recurved green tips; inner bracts 6–7 mm. long, obtuse, long-ciliate: filaments fully half as long as the anthers: achene 3–3.5 mm. long. [*L. Garberi* Small, not Kuntze.]—Sandy pinelands, near Tampa, Fla.—Fall.

7. **L. pauciflora** (Pursh) Kuntze. Stem 2–9 dm. tall, glabrous: blades of the lower leaves narrowly linear: involucral bracts glabrous; inner bracts 12–13 mm. long, abruptly pointed or somewhat acuminate: achene 4–4.5 mm. long.—Dry sand, Coastal Plain, Fla. to S. C.—Sum.–fall.

8. **L. secunda** (Ell.) Small. Stem 3–8 dm. tall, densely short-pubescent: blades of the lower leaves linear, often narrowly so: inner bracts of the involucre linear, broadened upward, 7–10 mm. long, acuminate, scattered, short-pubescent: achene 3–5 mm. long. [*L. carinata* Small.]—Sandhills and pinelands, Coastal Plain and Piedmont, Fla. and Ala. to N. C.—Fall.

9. **L. Chapmanii** (T. & G.) Kuntze. Stem 2–6 dm. tall, tomentose: blades of the lower leaves narrowly linear, mostly less than 10 cm. long (or those of the basal and lower stem-leaves longer in *L. Chapmanii longifolia*); involucral bracts glabrous or nearly so; inner bracts 11–13 mm. long, linear-acuminate: achene 5.5–6 mm. long. [*L. Deamii* Lunell.]—Pinelands, Coastal Plain, Fla. and Ga.

10. **L. regimontis** Small. Stem 3–9 dm. tall, glabrous: blades of the lower leaves narrowly linear: involucral bracts glabrous or sparingly ciliate; inner bracts cuneate, 8–9 mm. long, acute: filaments less than half as long as the anthers: achene about 4 mm. long.—Wooded slopes, outliers of the Blue Ridge in the Piedmont, also in adj. provinces, Ga. to N. C.—Sum.–fall.

11. **L. Garberi** (A. Gray) Kuntze. Stem 2–5 dm. tall, hirsute: blades of the lower leaves narrowly linear: involucral bracts broadly elliptic, ciliate and viscid, and abruptly acuminate; inner bracts 8–9 mm. long, ciliate, viscid and glandular-punctate: achene 2.5–3 mm. long. [*L. Nashii* Small.]—Pinelands, pen. Fla.—Sum.–fall.—Unusual on account of its clustered fleshy tuberous roots.

12. **L. tenuifolia** (Nutt.) Kuntze. Stem 6–12 dm. tall, glabrous: blades of the lower leaves linear-filiform: involucral bracts minutely ciliate; inner bracts 5–6 mm. long: corollas 6–7 mm. long: filaments pubescent, less than half as long as the anthers: achene 3.5–4.5 mm. long. [*Liatris laevigata* Nutt. *L.*

laevigata Small.]—Pinelands, Coastal Plain and adj. provinces, Fla. to Ala. and N. C.—Sum.–fall.

13. L. spicata (L.) Kuntze. Stem 6–15 dm. tall, sometimes sparingly hirsute: blades of the lower leaves linear: involucral bracts glabrous; intermediate bracts oblong-ovate; inner bracts 8–9 mm. long, broadly linear: corollas 6.5–7.5 mm. long; lobes glabrous: achene 4–5 mm. long.—Moist woods, prairies, low-pinelands, and low grounds, various provinces, Fla. to La., Minn., and Mass.—Sum.–fall.—*L. spicata montana* Gray, with broader leaves and larger heads occurs in the Blue Ridge from Ga. and S. C. to Va.

14. L. laxa Small. Stem 4–6 dm. tall, thinly tomentulose: blades of the lower leaves linear: involucral bracts finely and densely ciliate; inner bracts narrowed at the tip, 4–5 mm. long: achene mostly over 3 mm. long. [*L. gracilis* Fl. SE U. S.)]—Coastal sand-dunes, Fla. to Ala. and S. C.—Spr.

15. L. microcephala Small. Stem 3–7 dm. tall, glabrous: blades of the lower leaves narrowly linear, often elongate: involucral bracts glabrous, nearly cylindric; inner bracts 7–8 mm. long: corollas 1.5–2.5 mm. long: filaments fully half as long as the anthers: achene clavate, 4 mm. long. [*L. polyphylla* Small.]—Sandy soil, Blue Ridge to Interior Low Plateaus, Ga. to Tenn.—Sum.

16. L. graminifolia (Walt.) Kuntze. Stem 2–12 dm. tall, glabrous: leaves ciliate near the base; blades of the lower ones linear: involucral bracts narrowly linear elliptic, minutely ciliate; the inner ones 7–8 mm. long, linear: achene 4–5 mm. long. [*L. vittata* Greene.]—Arid fields open woods, and damp savannas, Coastal Plain and adj. provinces, Fla. to Tenn. and N. J.—Sum.

17. L. Smallii Britton. Stem 1–8 dm. tall, glabrous: leaves ciliate near the base; blades of the lower ones broadly or narrowly linear: involucral bracts ciliate margined, broadly linear and bluntly often dark-tipped; inner bracts broadly linear, ciliolate all around, 8–9 mm. long: corolla-tube scarcely longer than the pappus: achene 4–5 mm. long.—Mt. slopes, Blue Ridge, Ga. to Va.—Sum.–fall.

18. L. gracilis (Pursh) Kuntze. Stem 4–10 dm. tall, glabrous: lower leaves with long, linear or narrowly elliptic blades: bracts of the involucre narrowly linear-elliptic, glabrous (sometimes puberulent), finely ciliate, the inner 4–5 mm. long: achene very coarsely ribbed, 2–3 mm. long.—Dry, open woods, fields and slopes, Coastal Plain and adj. provinces, Fla. to Miss. and Ga.—Late sum.–fall.—Probably *L. elegantula* and *L. elongata* of Greene belong here.

19. L. Helleri Porter. Stem 1–4 dm. tall, glabrous or nearly so: blades of the lower leaves linear: involucral bracts minutely ciliate: inner bracts narrowly linear, 7–8 mm. long: corolla-tube twice as long as the pappus: achene about 4 mm. long.—Rocky soil and cliffs, Blue Ridge, N. C. and Va.—Sum.–fall.

20. L. pilosa (Ait.) Heller. Stem 2–7 dm. tall, glabrous: blades of the lower leaves broadly linear or linear-oblong: involucral bracts narrowly linear-elliptic, glabrous; inner ones linear, 8–10 mm. long: achene fully 5 mm. long.—Dry rocky or sandy slopes, various provinces N of Coastal Plain, Ga. to Ala., W. Va., and S Va.—Sum.

21. L. aspera (Michx.) Greene. Stem 3–15 dm. tall, densely pubescent: blades of the lower leaves narrowly elliptic: involucral bracts with only the central portion herbaceous, the entire tip and sides being so broadly scarious as to appear winged, the tip usually concave, and spreading, purplish-tinged or stramineous: achene 4–5 mm. long.—Prairies and plains, various provinces, Ark. and Okla. to Nebr., Minn. and Ind.—Sum.–fall.—*L. aspera sphaeroidea* (Michx.) Alexander, a variety with glabrous leaves occurs on mountain slopes and rocky soil, in the mountains of Ga., N. C. and Tenn., and in various provinces, to Minn. and Mich.—Sum.–fall.

22. L. scariosa (L.) Hill. Stem 3–10 dm. tall, usually very closely pubescent: blades of the lower leaves linear to elliptic, often very broadly so: inner bracts of the involucre 10–15 mm. long in typical plants, shorter in some small mountain forms; glabrous or nearly so, linear with slightly spatulate tips, becoming definitely spatulate in the intermediate bracts and nearly ovate in the outer ones, apices varying from rounded in the inner bracts to nearly acute in the outer, the margins erose or ciliate, sometimes foliaceous with only a slight scarious margin, at other times markedly scarious-margined but still foliaceous and thick: achene 4–6 mm. long. [*L. squarrulosa* Michx.]—Plains, hillsides, and open woods, various provinces, Fla. to Ill., Mich., and Mass.—Sum.–fall.

23. L. Shortii Alexander. Stem 6–9 dm. tall, densely pubescent: blades of the lower leaves elliptic, very short-pubescent: bracts of the involucre with a very narrow scarious margin, otherwise quite herbaceous, densely short-pubescent, very spatulate, the inner nearly linear, 10–12 mm. long: achene about 5 mm. long.—Dry or rocky soil, various provinces, Miss. and La., to Ark. and Ohio. —Sum.–fall.

24. L. Tracyi Alexander. Stem about 4 dm. or more tall, densely pubescent: blades of the lower leaves linear, very scabrous: bracts of the involucre rounded at the tip, somewhat spatulate, pubescent; inner ones 7–8 mm. long: achene about 5 mm. long.—Baldwin Co., in the Coastal Plain of Ala.—Fall.

25. L. Ruthii Alexander. Stem 3–16 dm. tall, pubescent: blades of the lower leaves linear to elliptic glabrous or nearly so: involucral bracts rather narrowly spatulate, usually green, lightly pubescent, narrowly if at all scarious-margined, the inner bracts 8–11 mm. long: achene 4–5 mm. long.—Woods and thickets, various provinces chiefly the Blue Ridge and Appalachian, Ga. to Tenn. and N. C.—Sum.–fall.

17. AMMOPURSUS Small. Perennial, succulent, caulescent herb, the stem from a long, perpendicular, fleshy tap-root. Leaves alternate, fleshy: blades narrow, entire, punctate, sessile. Heads solitary or in panicles, showy, not radiate, erect. Involucre cylindric-campanulate, many-flowered: bracts broad, in six or more series, appressed, fimbriolate-ciliate. Receptacle naked, honeycombed. Flowers perfect. Corolla rose-purple: tube slender-cylindric: throat thicker than the tube, more or less urceolate: limb slightly zygomorphic: lobes 5, spreading, about as long as the throat. Stamens included: filaments filiform-subulate: anthers linear, rounded or emarginate at the apex, cordate at the base, the lobes rounded. Style filiform. Stigmas filiform, usually longer than the style. Achene fusiform, 10–12-ribbed, pubescent. Pappus of numerous capillary barbellate bristles in two series, the outer shorter than the inner, the inner as long as or longer than the achene. —One species.

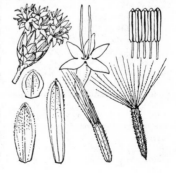

1. A. Ohlingeri (Blake) Small. Stem 2–11 dm. tall, solitary or several from the top of the root, usually paniculately branched above, minutely pubescent with pale crisped hairs: leaves fleshy, narrowly linear or linear-clavate, acute, glabrous: involucre about 2 cm. long;

bracts numerous, the outer orbicular-reniform, thence gradually longer and narrower to the linear-spatulate inner ones, all obtuse, the body deep green, punctate, the scarious margins pale: corollas bright rose-purple, about 2 cm. long: tube slender; throat cylindric-urceolate; lobes lanceolate, 5–6 mm. long, acute: achene fusiform, 8–9 mm. long, about 10-ribbed, densely pubescent with spreading hairs: pappus whitish, much shorter than the corolla, barbellate. [*Laciniaria Ohlingeri* Blake.]—Scrub, S end of lake region, Fla.—Sum.

18. GARBERIA A. Gray.   Much-branched shrubs.   Leaves alternate, evergreen: blades broad, entire.   Heads in rather dense corymbose cymes.   Involucre narrowly turbinate.   Corolla rose-purple: throat campanulate, rather shorter than the much narrower tube: lobes ovate to lanceolate.   Androecium conspicuously exserted: anther-appendages notched.   Achene long, sharply ribbed.   Pappus of scabro-barbellate capillary bristles in 2 or more rows.—One species.

1. G. fruticosa (Nutt.) A. Gray.   Plant 1–2 m. tall, the twigs scurfy: leaf-blades spatulate to obovate, 2–3 cm. long: involucre 10–12 mm. long; bracts narrow, the outer lanceolate, the inner linear-cuneate, all acute or acuminate, scurfy-puberulent: achene slender-fusiform, 7–8 mm. long or sometimes longer, pubescent.—Scrub and coastal dunes, pen. Fla.—Spr.–fall.—Conspicuous in the scrub in winter from its persistent brown pappus.

19. TRILISA Cass.   Perennial caulescent herbs; the stem from short rootstocks.   Leaves alternate, the basal ones much larger than the cauline: blades leathery, entire or shallowly toothed, sparingly pinnate-veined.   Heads thyrsoid-paniculate or corymbose.   Involucre turbinate, few-flowered: bracts few, relatively narrow, glandular.   Corolla rose-purple, with a short tube and a cylindric throat.   Androecium included.   Anther-appendages ovate.   Achene fusiform, sharply ribbed.   Pappus of many capillary barbellate bristles.—Two species:

Stem viscid-pubescent: heads thyrsoid-paniculate: involucral bracts with stalked
glands.   1. *T. paniculata.*
Stem glabrous or nearly so: heads corymbose: involucral
bracts with sessile glands.   2. *T. odoratissima.*

1. T. paniculata (Walt.) Cass.   Stem 2–17 dm. tall, sparingly hirsute: basal leaves mostly 5–20 cm. long; blades elliptic to almost linear: blades of the cauline leaves narrow, sessile: inner bracts of the involucre less than 5 mm. long: corolla-lobes rather ovate: achene fully 3 mm. long.—Low pinelands, Coastal Plain, Fla. to La., and N. C. (or S Va.?).—Fall-wint.

2. T. odoratissima (Walt.) Cass.   Stem 5–15 dm. tall, somewhat glaucous: basal leaves mostly 10–30 cm. long; blades elliptic, cuneate or spatulate: blades of the cauline leaves broad, slightly clasping: inner bracts of the involucre over 4 mm. long; corolla-lobes rather lanceolate: achene 2–3 mm. long.—(VANILLA-PLANT.   DEER'S-TONGUE.   HOUND'S-TONGUE.)—Low pinelands, Fla. to La., and N. C. (or S Va.?).—Sum.–fall.—The leaves contain coumarin and have been used as a flavoring agent.—Extreme forms often indicate the possibility of two species being involved. One with a strong coumarin odor, broad, clasping, coarsely toothed upper leaf-blades and slightly viscid involucres, the other with only a faint odor, narrow entire upper leaf-blades and very viscid involucres.

20. **AMPHIACHYRIS** DC. Annual or perennial, glabrous herbs. Leaves alternate: blades narrow, entire. Heads small. Involucre campanulate to cylindric, the bracts obtuse. Ray-flowers with small ligules. Disk-corollas with a cylindric-campanulate throat. Anthers narrow. Stigmas pubescent. Achenes of the ray with a crown-like pappus, those of the disk abortive, with bristle-like pappus-scales.—Two species, North American.

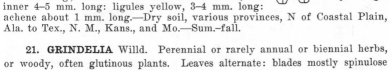

1. **A. dracunculoides** (DC.) Nutt. Stem 3–7 dm. tall: leaf-blades narrowly linear or linear-filiform, 1–5 cm. long; bracts of the involucre lustrous, the inner 4–5 mm. long: ligules yellow, 3–4 mm. long: achene about 1 mm. long.—Dry soil, various provinces, N of Coastal Plain, Ala. to Tex., N. M., Kans., and Mo.—Sum.–fall.

21. **GRINDELIA** Willd. Perennial or rarely annual or biennial herbs, or woody, often glutinous plants. Leaves alternate: blades mostly spinulose toothed. Heads large. Involucre hemispheric or depressed, the bracts slender-tipped, eciliate. Ray-flowers with conspicuous yellow ligules, or rarely wanting. Disk-corollas with a narrowly funnelform throat longer than the tube. Anthers linear; appendages lanceolate. Stigmas linear. Achene ribbed. Pappus of the disk of 2–8 smooth awns or stiff bristles, caducous.—About 30 species, western American.—GUM-PLANTS. STICKY-HEADS.

Leaf-blades coarsely spiny-toothed: achene 2-lobed at the apex.   1. *G. lanceolata.*
Leaf-blades finely spiny-toothed: achene truncate at the apex.   2. *G. squarrosa.*

1. **G. lanceolata** Nutt. Stem 5–8 dm. tall, glabrous, usually sparingly branched above: blades of the cauline leaves lanceolate to linear-lanceolate or almost linear, 2–8 cm. long, more or less acuminate: bracts of the involucre with spreading tips: achene 3–3.5 mm. long, 2-lobed at the apex, rather bluntly ribbed.—Dry soil, barrens, prairies and waste-places, various provinces, Ala. to Tex., Kans., and Tenn.—Sum.

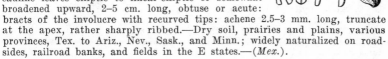

2. **G. squarrosa** (Pursh) Dunal. Stem 3–10 dm. tall, glabrous, more or less branched above and sometimes also branched at the base: blades of the cauline leaves elliptic to linear-elliptic or somewhat broadened upward, 2–5 cm. long, obtuse or acute: bracts of the involucre with recurved tips: achene 2.5–3 mm. long, truncate at the apex, rather sharply ribbed.—Dry soil, prairies and plains, various provinces, Tex. to Ariz., Nev., Sask., and Minn.; widely naturalized on roadsides, railroad banks, and fields in the E states.—(*Mex.*).

22. **CHRYSOPSIS** Nutt. Biennial herbs, with villous, hirsute, floccose, cottony, or arachnoid pubescence. Leaves alternate: blades narrow or broad, but neither nervose nor gramineous, mostly entire. Heads in a terminal corymb.

Involucre ovoid to hemispheric, the bracts narrow. Ray-flowers with conspicuous yellow ligules. Disk-corollas with a narrow funnelform throat. Anther-appendages lanceolate. Stigmas subulate. Achene somewhat turgid, ellipsoid or obovoid, 3–5-nerved. Pappus double, of numerous bristles, the outer series very short and scale-like.—About 20 species, North American.—Mostly sum.–fall.—GOLDEN-ASTERS.

Plant perennial : achene 3–5-nerved.
  Bracts of the involucre glabrous.   I. TRICHOPHYLLAE.
  Bracts of the involucre glandular or cobwebby.
    Bracts of the involucre copiously glandular, without
      cobwebby hairs.   II. MARIANAE.
    Bracts of the involucre with cobwebby hairs.   III. PILOSAE.
Plant annual, with a tap-root : achene 10-nerved.   IV. NUTTALLIANAE.

I. TRICHOPHYLLAE

Bracts of the involucre prolonged into subulate tips.   1. *C. subulata.*
Bracts of the involucre acute, mucronate, or short-acuminate.
  Cauline leaves, at least the lower ones, with spatulate,
    elliptic, or elliptic-lanceolate blades.
    Bracts of the involucre acute or short-acuminate.   2. *C. trichophylla.*
    Bracts of the involucre abruptly pointed or mucro-
      nate.   3. *C. gigantea.*
  Cauline leaves with narrowly linear blades.   4. *C. hyssopifolia.*

II. MARIANAE

Pubescence deciduous : foliage rough-glandular.   5. *C. scabrella.*
Pubescence persistent : foliage smooth or soft-glandular.
  Bracts of the involucre 1 mm. wide or less.
    Stem and leaves cobwebby-pubescent.   6. *C. mariana.*
    Stem and leaves white cottony-lanate.
      Peduncles cottony-lanate and with some glands
        under the involucre.   7. *C. arenicola.*
      Peduncles only glandular.
        Bracts of the involucre acuminate recurved :
          inflorescence conspicuously glandular.   8. *C. lanuginosa.*
        Bracts of the involucre acute, erect : inflores-
          cence inconspicuously glandular.   9. *C. floridana.*
  Bracts of the involucre 2 mm. wide or more.   10. *C. latisquama.*

III. PILOSAE

Peduncles glandular : bracts of the involucre sparingly cobwebby.   11. *C. decumbens.*
Peduncles densely villous-cobwebby : bracts of the involucre
  densely villous-cobwebby.   12. *C. pilosa.*

IV. VILLOSAE

Plant pubescent, the stem simple below the inflorescence or
  sometimes branched throughout.   13. *C. Nuttallii.*

1. C. subulata Small. Stem 3–11 dm. tall, short cobwebby : blades of the basal leaves narrowly spatulate, those of the cauline leaves spatulate to linear, usually entire : involucre 6–8 mm. long ; bracts with curved or bent caudate tips : achene 1.5–2 mm. long.—Pinelands and scrub, pen. Fla. and rarely N Fla.—Spr.–fall or all year.

2. C. trichophylla Nutt. Stem 3–11 dm. tall, more or less long cobwebby, at least when young : blades of the basal leaves broadly spatulate, those of the cauline leaves spatulate to elliptic-obovate, linear, or lanceolate, entire or sometimes sparingly toothed : involucre 7–9 mm. long : bracts acute or short-acuminate, often with slightly spreading tips : achene about 2 mm. long.—Pinelands, Coastal Plain, Fla. to S. C. and Miss., (La.?).

3. **C. gigantea** Small. Stem 8–15 dm. tall, sparingly cobwebby-pubescent, at least when old: leaves numerous, the basal and lower cauline with spatulate, to oblanceolate or oblong-oblanceolate blades; upper cauline leaves with oblong to oblong-lanceolate blades, often obscurely serrulate, sometimes apiculate: involucre 7–9 mm. high; bracts linear-lanceolate to linear, acute to slightly acuminate, glabrous: achene 2–2.5 mm. long.—Pinelands, Fla.

4. **C. hyssopifolia** Nutt. Stem 3–9 dm. tall, glabrous or sparingly cobwebby when young: leaves numerous, the basal in a dense rosette, white cottony, with spatulate or linear-spatulate blades, cauline leaves often crowded; blades narrowly linear to linear-filiform, 1–6 cm. long: involucre 6–8 mm. long; bracts rigid, acute, often abruptly so with erect tips: achenes 2–2.5 mm. long.—Dry pinelands, Coastal Plain, Fla. and Ala.

5. **C. scabrella** T. & G. Stems 3–12 dm. tall, more or less rough-glandular: leaves rather numerous, the basal in a very dense rosette, white-cottony, with spatulate, often coarsely toothed blades: blades of the cauline leaves linear-spatulate to linear, acute, entire, more or less glandular-scabrous acute, sessile: involucre 6–9 mm. high; bracts linear-subulate to linear, rigid, acute, often abruptly so: achene 2.5–3 mm. long.—Pinelands, prairies, and scrub, Coastal Plain, Fla. to Miss.

6. **C. mariana** (L.) Nutt. Stem 1–6 dm. tall, more or less cobwebby; and glandular in the inflorescence: blades of the cauline leaves spatulate to elliptic or oblong, 2–12 cm. long, often acute, entire or remotely toothed, the lower ones narrowed into petiole-like bases: heads showy: involucre 8–10 mm. long, bracts linear, acute, glandular, ciliolate: achene about 2 mm. long.—Dry woods and hillsides, various provinces, Fla. to La., Tenn., and S N. Y.

7. **C. arenicola** Alexander. Stem about 3 dm. tall, white cottony: blades of the cauline leaves various, the lower ones slightly broadened upward, 1–3 cm. long, the upper ones oblong-lanceolate to linear-lanceolate, auricled at the base, sessile, all white cottony-lanate: bracts of the involucre rather rough-glandular, the inner bracts narrowly linear, acuminate: achenes about 2 mm. long.—Sandhills, near Hartsville, S. C.

8. **C. lanuginosa** Small. Stem below the inflorescence, white-woolly, finely glandular above and in the inflorescence, 2 dm. tall or more, sometimes branched near the base: leaves white-cottony, basal and lower cauline leaves with spatulate blades mostly 1 dm. long or less; blades of the upper cauline cuneate-spatulate or cuneate, entire: involucre about 1 cm. high; bracts linear or nearly so, except the recurved or spreading slender green tips, finely, softly, and copiously glandular-pubescent.—Grassy places, near Lynn Haven, N. Fla.

9. **C. floridana** Small. Stem usually branched at the base, the branches curved, 2.5–4 dm. long, white-cottony below, glandular above: leaves white-cottony; basal and lower cauline leaves with spatulate blades mostly less than 1 dm. long; blades of the upper cauline entire: cuneate to oblong-cuneate, 1.5–2.5 cm. long, obtuse, partly clasping: peduncles inconspicuously glandular: involucre 6–8 mm. high; bracts firm, glandular, often sparingly so, acute or slightly acuminate.—Scrub, sand-dunes and pinelands, pen. Fla.

10. **C. latisquama** Pollard. Stem 3–7 dm. tall, copiously cobwebby below, glandular above, the branches often elongate: basal and lower stem-leaves with spatulate or oblanceolate blades; upper cauline leaves smaller; blades oblong to linear-oblong or broadly linear, serrulate or undulate: involucre 7–8 mm. high;

bracts mostly broadest above the middle, not woolly, glandular, deep-green, the outer rather foliaceous, usually acute.—Pinelands and hammock-borders, pen. Fla.

11. C. decumbens Chapm. Stem decumbent, 6–12 dm. long, white-cottony or cobwebby-cottony; blades of the cauline leaves spatulate to oblong or oblong-lanceolate, obtuse or abruptly acute, entire, sessile: involucre 8–10 mm. high; bracts sparingly cobwebby, acuminate.—Pinelands, Coastal Plain, Fla. to N. C.

12. C. pilosa (Walt.) Britton. Stem 3–7 dm. tall, lanate: blades of the cauline leaves spatulate, oblong, or oblong-spatulate, obtuse or apiculate, entire or sparingly toothed, often partly clasping: involucre about 1 cm. high; bracts densely villous-cobwebby, acute or acuminate. [*C. gossypina* Nutt.]—Sandhills, woods, and pinelands, Fla. to Ala. and N. C., (Va.?)

13. C. Nuttallii Britton. Stem villous or softly hirsute, 3–8 dm. tall, simple below the inflorescence or sometimes branched throughout: leaves few or numerous, 1.5–4.5 cm. long: blades oblong to linear-oblong, entire or distantly or coarsely toothed, acute, sessile, or the lower ones oblong-oblanceolate and commonly incised: heads showy: involucres 8–10 mm. high; bracts linear or linear-subulate, acuminate: ray-flowers with ligules 10–15 mm. long: achenes 10-nerved.—Rocky open woods, sandy hills, prairies, and oak-woods, Miss. to Tex., Kans., and Mo.

　　23. PITYOPSIS Nutt. Perennial herbs with silvery or lead-colored, silky pubescence, or rarely glabrate. Leaves alternate: blades elongate, nervose or gramineous, entire. Heads terminating irregular peduncles or corymbose. Involucre campanulate to turbinate: bracts narrow. Ray-flowers with yellow ligules. Disk-corollas with a narrow funnelform throat. Anther-appendages ovate to lanceolate. Stigmas lanceolate. Achene compressed-fusiform. Pappus double, the outer series very short and scale-like. About 10 species of eastern North America.

Cauline leaves numerous, filiform; glabrous or nearly so.　　I. PINIFOLIAE.
Cauline leaves few, linear, silky-lanate, sometimes narrowly
　　so, or linear-lanceolate.
　　Peduncles, branches, and stem woolly-tomentose.　　II. GRAMINIFOLIAE.
　　Peduncles, branches, and sometimes the stem, glandular.　III. ASPERAE.

I. PINIFOLIAE

Slender plant with linear-filiform leaves and not very numerous heads of flowers.　　1. *P. pinifolia*.

II. GRAMINIFOLIAE

Stem conspicuously zigzag.　　2. *P. flexuosa*.
Stem strict or essentially so.
　　Involucres 10–12 mm. high.
　　　　Inflorescence-branches few or several: ligules of the
　　　　ray-flowers mostly over 1 cm. long.　　3. *P. Tracyi*.
　　　　Inflorescence-branches many: ligules of the ray-
　　　　flowers less than 1 cm. long.　　4. *P. graminifolia*.
　　Involucres 4–7 mm. high.　　5. *P. microcephala*.

III. ASPERAE

Lower cauline leaves not markedly longer than the upper.　　6. *P. Ruthii*.
Lower cauline leaves conspicuously longer than the upper.
　　Stem-leaves numerous, approximate; blades narrow:
　　　　ligules of the ray-flowers less than 1 cm. long.　　7. *P. aspera*.
　　Stem leaves mostly 2–4, distant: blades relatively broad:
　　　　ligules of the ray-flowers over 1 cm. long.　　8. *P. oligantha*.

1. **P. pinifolia** (Ell.) Nutt. Stem 2–4 dm. tall: blades of the cauline leaves linear-filiform: inner bracts of the involucre 4–5.5 mm. long, glabrous: ligules 6–7 mm. long. [*Chrysopsis pinifolia* Ell.]— Sandhills, Taylor County in the Coastal Plain of Ga.—Fall.

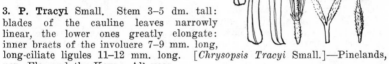

2. **P. flexuosa** (Nash) Small. Stem 2–4 dm. tall, zigzag: blades of the cauline leaves narrowly linear-lanceolate to linear: inner bracts of the involucre 10–12 mm. long: ligules 8–10 mm. long: disk-corollas 7–8 mm. long. [*Chrysopsis flexuosa* Nash]. — Dry sandy pinelands, M Fla.—Sum.–fall.

3. **P. Tracyi** Small. Stem 3–5 dm. tall: blades of the cauline leaves narrowly linear, the lower ones greatly elongate: inner bracts of the involucre 7–9 mm. long, long-ciliate ligules 11–12 mm. long. [*Chrysopsis Tracyi* Small.]—Pinelands, pen. Fla. and the Keys.—All year.

4. **P. graminifolia** (Michx.) Nutt. Stem 3–9 dm. tall: blades of the cauline leaves linear-lanceolate, linear or linear-subulate: inner bracts of the involucre 7–11 mm. long: ligules 7–9 mm. long: disk-corollas 7–8 mm. long [*Chrysopsis graminifolia* (Michx.) Nutt. *C. argentea* Pers.]—Sandy, often acid, soil, Coastal Plain and adj. provinces, Fla. to Tex., Tenn., and Md.—(*W. I.*)—Sum.—early wint. or all year S.—*P. graminifolia latifolia* Fernald, distinguished by the upper cauline leaves nearly the same length as the lower, grades into the typical form.

5. **P. microcephala** Small. Stem 4–7 dm. tall: blades of the cauline leaves linear-lanceolate: outer bracts of the involucre broadly lanceolate, not glandular; inner bracts 5–6 mm. long: ligules 3–4 mm. long: filaments shorter than the anthers. [*Chrysopsis microcephala* Small].—Sandy soil, Coastal Plain and adj. provinces, Fla. to Tex. and S. C.—Sum.–fall.

6. **P. Ruthii** Small. Stem 1–3 dm. tall: blades of the cauline leaves linear to narrowly linear-lanceolate: outer bracts of the involucre subulate, glandular; inner bracts 6.5–7.5 mm. long: filaments longer than the anthers. [*Chrysopsis Ruthii* Small.]—Rocks, Appalachian Valley, Hiawassee Valley, Tenn.—Fall.

7. **P. aspera** (Shuttlw.) Small. Stem 3–7 dm. tall: blades of the cauline leaves linear to narrowly linear-lanceolate: outer bracts of the involucre lanceolate, glandular; inner bracts 6–8 mm. long: disk corollas 4–5 mm. long: filaments much shorter than the anthers. [*Chrysopsis aspera* Shuttlw.]—Dry soil, mostly in pinelands, Coastal Plain, Fla. to La. and Va.—Sum.–fall.

8. **P. oligantha** (Chapm.) Small. Stem 3–6 dm. tall: blades of the cauline leaves linear to elliptic: outer bracts of the involucre lanceolate, glandular; inner bracts 7–9 mm. long, strongly ciliate: disk-corollas 7–8 mm. long: filaments as long as the anthers or longer. [*Chrysopsis oligantha* Chapm.].—Pinelands, Coastal Plain, N Florida and SE Ala.—Spr.

24. **HETEROTHECA** Cass. Annual or biennial, pubescent herbs. Leaves alternate: blades entire or toothed. Heads rather large. Involucre

hemispheric or campanulate, the inner bracts ciliate. Ray-flowers with conspicuous yellow ligules. Disk-corollas with a funnelform throat about as long as the tube. Anther-appendages lanceolate. Stigmas lanceolate or triangular. Achenes of the ray thickish, those of the disk flat. Pappus of the disk **of** many bristles, those of the outer series shorter and stouter than those of the inner.—About 6 species, North American.

1. H. subaxillaris (Lam.) Britt. & Rusby. Stem 3–12 dm. tall, hirsute or hispid; blades of the stem-leaves elliptic to elliptic-lanceolate, 1–7 cm. long, serrate: involucre 7–8 mm. high; outer bracts glandular-pubescent: achene about 2 mm. long. [*H. Lamarckii* Cass.].—(CAMPHOR-PLANT.)—Pinelands, sand-dunes, and waste-places, various provinces, Fla. to Tex., Ariz., Kans., and Del.—(*W. I., Mex., C. A., S. A.*)—Sum.-fall, or all year S.—A weedy plant, very variable in habit and with a great variety of leaf-forms.

25. CHONDROPHORA Raf. Perennial, glabrous, slender, virgate-stemmed herbs. Leaves alternate: blades very narrow, entire. Heads in terminal corymbs, or rarely thyrsoid. Involucre narrow, few-flowered: bracts narrow, abruptly or gradually narrowed at the apex. Ray-flowers wanting. Disk-corollas yellow, with a broadly funnelform throat about as long as the tube or longer: lobes lanceolate. Achenes 1–2-ribbed on each side. Pappus of 1 series of bristles.—Two species.—Sum.—RAYLESS-GOLDENRODS.

Stem-leaves with linear or linear-spatulate blades.   1. *C. nudata.*
Stem-leaves with filiform blades.   2. *C. virgata.*

1. C. nudata (Michx.) Britton. Stem 2–6 dm. tall: blades of the basal leaves spatulate to linear-spatulate, 3–12 cm. long: inner bracts of the involucre linear-oblong or linear-elliptic, 4.5–5 mm. long, acute or acutish.—Pinelands, Coastal Plain, Fla. to Tex. and Va. (or N. J.?).

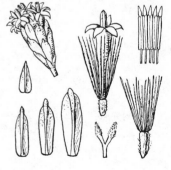

2. C. virgata (Nutt.) Greene. Similar to *C. nudata* in habit: blades of the basal leaves filiform: inner bracts of the involucre lanceolate, 4–4.5 mm. long, acuminate.—On rocks, rocky creek-banks, open woods and prairies, Coastal Plain and adj. provinces, W Fla. to Tex. and Ga.—The greenish-yellow very numerous flower-heads of these species, when the plants grow *en masse*, especially on prairies, shows a color not usually seen in this family.

26. BRINTONIA Greene. Perennial pubescent, leafy-stemmed herbs. Leaves alternate: blades broad, coarsely toothed, with wide petiole-like bases.

Heads many, racemose. Involucre campanulate, several-flowered: bracts rather narrow, the inner ones broader than the outer. Ray-flowers wanting. Disk-corollas with a funnelform throat and a somewhat shorter tube: lobes ovate. Anthers longer than the filaments: appendages lanceolate. Stigmas lanceolate or ovate. Achene ribbed. Pappus-bristles numerous, the inner clavate at the tip.—One species.

1. B. discoidea (Ell.) Greene. Stem 8–15 dm. tall, finely hirsute: leaf-blades oval, ovate, or elliptic-ovate, 4–9 cm. long: involucres 6–8 mm. high: corollas about 4 mm. long, white or whitish, and often purple-tinged.—Dry soil, borders of woods, and thickets, Coastal Plain, Fla. to La. and Ga.—Sum.–fall.

27. SIDERANTHUS Fraser. Annual or perennial, more or less widely branching herbs, or shrubs. Leaves alternate: blades spinulose-toothed,

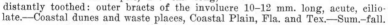

lobed, or pinnatifid. Heads terminating the branches. Involucre hemispheric or campanulate, many-flowered: bracts narrow, usually acuminate. Ray-flowers yellow, several. Disk-corollas with a narrowly funnelform throat and a shorter tube: lobes deltoid to triangular. Stigmas lanceolate. Achene pubescent, mostly 8–10-nerved. Pappus of 1–3 series of bristles.—About 20 species, American.

1. S. megacephalus (Nash) Small. Stem 8–12 dm. tall, finely pubescent: leaf-blades lanceolate to linear-elliptic, 2–7 cm. long, distantly toothed: outer bracts of the involucre 10–12 mm. long, acute, ciliolate.—Coastal dunes and waste places, Coastal Plain, Fla. and Tex.—Sum.–fall.

28. ISOPAPPUS T. & G. Annual or biennial, virgate-stemmed herbs. Leaves alternate: blades narrow, some of them coarsely toothed. Heads in open panicles. Involucre narrow: bracts subulate to linear or lanceolate. Ray-flowers few or several: corolla with a long tube and a yellow ligule. Disk-corollas with a narrowly funnelform throat and a very short tube: lobes deltoid. Anthers as long as the filaments or shorter: appendages ovate. Stigmas subulate. Achene terete, short. Pappus a series of rough capillary bristles.—Three species, North American.

1. I. divaricatus (Nutt.) T. & G. Stem 3–12 dm. tall, hispid and glandular: leaf-blades linear-oblanceolate to narrowly linear,

2–10 cm. long: involucral bracts ciliolate near the tip, the inner as well as the outer glandular: filaments longer than the anthers.—Dry soil, sandy fields, and roadsides, various provinces, Fla. to Tex., Kans., and S. C.—Sum.–fall.

29. CHRYSOMA Nutt. Shrubs or partly woody plants. Leaves evergreen, alternate: blades narrow, fleshy-leathery, conspicuously fine-pitted. Heads numerous, thyrsoid, or somewhat corymbose. Involucres narrow, few-flowered: bracts narrow, the inner much longer than the outer. Ray-flowers 1–3: corollas with a long tube and a yellow ligule. Diskcorollas with a funnelform throat and a tube of about equal length: lobes lanceolate. ovate. Anthers longer than the filaments. Stigmas of the disk-corollas lanceolate. Pappus of 1 or 2 series of brownish capillary bristles.—One species.

1. C. pauciflosculosa (Michx.) Greene. Stem 3–9 dm. tall: leaf-blades grayish-green, linear-spatulate to linear-oblong, 3–6 cm. long: involucres 4–6 mm. long, the inner bracts linear-lanceolate: ligules of the ray-corollas 4–6 mm. long: achene 3–4 mm. long.—Sandy soil, Coastal Plain, Fla. to Miss. and S. C.

30. SOLIDAGO L.[1] Perennial caulescent herbs, with long horizontal stolons often well-developed. Leaves alternate, the basal ones often in very large and conspicuous tufts (rosettes). Blades various, mostly toothed. Heads usually relatively small, sometimes medium sized or even large, paniculate or thyrsoid, or umbellate. Involucre campanulate, turbinate, or cylindric, few—many-flowered: bracts (tegules) in several series, the inner narrow, at least relatively so, and longer or much longer than the outer. Ray-flowers few to many: corolla with a slender tube and a yellow or very rarely a white ligule. Diskcorollas with a tube which is usually abruptly dilated into a funnelform or campanulate throat nearly or quite as long: lobes lanceolate, spreading. Anthers nearly or quite as long as the filaments. Stigmas mostly lanceolate, rarely elongate-lanceolate. Pappus of 1 or 2 series of capillary bristles.— About 125 species, mostly North American.—GOLDENRODS.

Stigmas several times as long as wide: heads large or very large, not unilaterally racemose (not secund): plant without long horizontal stolons: leaf-blades not triple-ribbed: achene sparsely silky above.   I. MACROPHYLLAE.
Stigmas lanceolate, 1–3 times as long as wide.
    Achene glabrous at maturity, sometimes sparsely hairy when young: plant without long horizontal stolons: heads not unilaterally racemose (not secund): leaf-blades not triple-ribbed.
      Main lateral veins of leaf-blades on the lower side elevated: leaf-blades not coriaceous.
        Involucral bracts, at least the outer ones, with spreading tips.   II. SQUARROSAE.
        Involucral bracts with tips not spreading.   III. HISPIDAE.
      Main lateral veins of leaf-blades on the lower side imbedded: leaf-blades coriaceous.   IV. CONFERTAE.
    Achene permanently hairy, or if (rarely) glabrate, the heads unilaterally racemose (secund).

[1] Contributed by Kenneth Kent Mackenzie.

Plant without long horizontal stolons.
  Thyrse spicate or umbel-like, the heads not uni-
    laterally racemose (not secund).   V. Virga-Aureae.
  Thyrse paniculate, usually with many of the
    heads unilaterally racemose (secund).
    Leaf-blades strongly pellucid-punctate.   VI. Odorae.
    Leaf-blades not pellucid-punctate.
      Basal rosettes wanting: stem-leaves
        gradually reduced upward.   VII. Ulmifoliae.
      Basal rosettes usually present, very large
        and conspicuous: lower stem-leaves
        much larger than the upper.
        Larger leaf-blades cordate at the
          base, triple-ribbed from near the
          base: petioles amplexicaule.   VIII. Notabiles.
        Leaf-blades not cordate at the base:
          petioles not amplexicaule.
          Leaf-blades not triple-ribbed.
            Longer petioles not or scarcely
              clasping at the base: dry
              ground plant.   IX. Argutae.
            Longer petioles strongly clasp-
              ing at the base.
              Leaf-blades crenate-serrate
                or serrate, not coria-
                ceous: plants of swamps.   X. Uliginosae.
              Leaf-blades thick and cori-
                aceous, entire: plants
                of sea-beaches or salt-
                marshes.   XI. Sempervirentes.
        Leaf-blades, at least partially
          triple-ribbed.   XII. Nemorales.
Plant with long horizontal stolons.
  Basal rosettes and basal leaves conspicuous,
    the blades much larger than the abruptly
    reduced upper leaves.
    Leaf-blades with the veins not impressed,
      serrate or crenate-serrate.   XIII. Vernae.
    Leaf-blades with impressed veins, entire or
      shallowly crenate-serrate.   XIV. Petiolatae.
  Basal rosettes wanting or very inconspicuous.
    Thyrse with the lower heads in axillary
      clusters, the upper spicate: leaf-blades
      not triple-ribbed.   XV. Flexicaules.
    Thyrse paniculate, the heads unilaterally
      racemose (secund), at least on the
      lower branches: leaves very numer-
      ous, gradually reduced upward.
      Leaf-blades not triple-ribbed.   XVI. Altissimae.
      Leaf-blades triple-ribbed.   XVII. Serotinae.

I. Macrophyllae

  Plant with basal rosettes large and conspicuous: heads 10–15 mm. high, the
lower ones in clusters, the upper forming a spike-like thyrse: stigmas much elongate
and conspicuous, somewhat flattened.   1. *S. glomerata.*

II. Squarrosae

  Plant with heads medium-sized or large, 6–12 mm. high, borne in a narrow
terminal thyrse, which is sometimes much contracted, more or less interrupted
below: involucral bracts, at least of the outer ones with spreading tips: stigmas
strongly flattened, 2–3 times as long as wide: achene glabrous, dark-brown or yellowish-brown or blackish at maturity, more or less compressed, sometimes sparingly
hairy when young.

Basal rosettes conspicuous: blades of the lower stem-leaves
    and those of the basal rosettes 6–12 cm. long, 3–5 cm.
    wide, their petioles as long as or longer than the blades.   2. *S. squarrosa.*
Basal rosettes usually wanting: blades of the lower leaves
    2–12 cm. long, 0.8–5 cm. wide, their petioles very
    short (up to 6 mm. long).
    Leaf-blades thick, oblong-oval, firm, shallowly crenate-
      serrate, the larger mostly 6–8 cm. long, 1.5–2 cm.
      wide: stem closely short hispid above: involucral
      bracts loose.   3. *S. Milleriana.*
    Leaf-blades thin, oblong-obovate or oblong-oblanceolate,
      strongly crenate-serrate the larger mostly 8–12 cm.
      long, 2.5–5 cm. wide: stem pilose above: involucral
      bracts closely appressed.   4. *S. Buckleyi.*

III. Hispidae

Plant with heads medium-sized or smallish to large, 4–11 mm. high, borne in a dense narrow terminal thyrse, only the lowermost (rarely more) in axillary clusters: involucral bracts with tips not spreading: stigmas strongly flattened, 2–3 times as long as wide: achene linear or linear-cylindric, or cylindric-clavate, glabrous at maturity, dull or blackish in color, not compressed.

Involucral bracts obtuse.
  Stem copiously pubescent.
    Ligules of the ray cream-color, veinless or obscurely
      veined: achene columnar.   5. *S. bicolor.*
    Ligules of the ray orange-yellow, strongly veined:
      achene broadened upward.   6. *S. hispida.*
  Stem glabrous or minutely puberulent.
    Involucre 4–5.5 mm. high: bracts minutely puberulent:
      achene yellowish.   7. *S. erecta.*
    Involucre 5–7.5 mm. high: bracts strigillose: achene
      blackish.   8. *S. Porteri.*
Involucral bracts, at least the inner, acute to acuminate.
  Stem closely puberulent or short-pubescent: involucral
    bracts with the midrib obsolete or obscure.
    Blades of the leaves about the middle of the stem
      oblong-obovate, hispidulous above all over: inner
      involucral bracts gradually narrowed, oblong-
      lanceolate, nearly 1 mm. wide.   9. *S. puberula.*
    Blades of the leaves about the middle of the stem
      oblanceolate, strongly hispidulous above on mid-
      rib, slightly so elsewhere; inner involucral bracts
      rather abruptly narrowed above middle, very nar-
      rowly lanceolate, about 0.5 mm. wide.   10. *S. pulverulenta.*
  Stem glabrous or sparingly loosely pubescent: involucral
    bracts mostly 3-ribbed.   11. *S. roanensis.*

IV. Confertae

Plant with heads medium-sized to large, 6–10 mm. high, borne in a narrow or large terminal thyrse: involucral bracts appressed: stigmas strongly flattened, 2–3 times as long as wide: achene linear or linear-oblong, slightly dilated upward, glabrous and dark-tinged at maturity, truncate at the apex.

Inflorescence-branches hairy: basal leaves with narrowly to
  broadly lanceolate to obovate blades; leaf-blades with
  main lateral veins conspicuous: rootstocks not forming hard ligneous masses.
  Involucre cylindric; bracts narrowly linear-oblong, obtuse
    to acutish: achene as long as pappus.   12. *S. Harperi.*
  Involucre campanulate; bracts oblong, very obtuse:
    achene half length of pappus.
    Ligules of the ray light-yellow: thyrse large and
      broad, not strict: involucral bracts with midvein
      little thickened, strongly dilated, minutely hispidu-
      lous: leaf-blades 2.5–10 cm. wide: basal rosettes
      conspicuous.   13. *S. conferta.*
    Ligules of the ray deep-yellow: thyrse narrow or
      broad, strict, or not strict: involucral bracts thick,
      with conspicuous thick central oil-tube, glabrous:
      leaf-blades 1–3 cm. wide: basal rosettes usually
      inconspicuous.   14. *S. rigidiuscula.*
Inflorescence-branches nearly glabrous: basal leaves with
  linear-spatulate blades: rootstocks forming very hard
  ligneous masses.   15. *S. plumosa.*

V. Virga-Aureae

Plant with heads medium-sized or large, 5–10 mm. high, usually not very numerous, often few, borne in a thyrse (sometimes markedly corymbiform): involucral bracts appressed: stigmas strongly flattened, 2–3 times as long as wide: achene narrow, pubescent, often dilated upward, truncate at the apex.
                                    16. *S. spithamaea.*

VI. Odorae

Plant without long horizontal stolons: basal rosettes wanting or very inconspicuous: leaves very numerous; blades not triple-ribbed, entire, pellucid-punctate, anise-scented, sessile or slightly petioled: heads unilaterally racemose, usually numerous, 4 mm. high, few-flowered: involucre cylindric; bracts thin, narrow, acute: stigmas flattened, longer than wide: achene hairy, dilated upward, truncate at the apex.

Stem pubescent in lines: leaf-blades linear-lanceolate or
  linear: pappus not exceeding the involucre at flowering
  time.   17. *S. odora.*

Stem usually pubescent all over: leaf-blades oblong-ovate,
lanceolate, or linear-oblong: pappus markedly exceeding
involucre at flowering time.   18. *S. Chapmanii.*

VII. ULMIFOLIAE

Plant without long horizontal stolons: basal rosettes wanting or very inconspicuous: leaves gradually reduced upwards; blades not triple-ribbed, not pellucid-
punctate, the larger serrate or crenate-serrate, prominently ribbed and veined beneath, sub- or very short-petioled: heads unilaterally racemose, on widely spreading
branches, small or medium sized, 4–6 mm. high: involucral bracts very unequal:
stigmas flattened, longer than wide: achene hairy, cylindric, obconic, conspicuously
ribbed, rounded at the apex.   19. *S. ulmifolia.*

VIII. NOTABILES

Plant without long horizontal stolons: leaf-blades triple-ribbed, the stem-leaves
strongly amplexicaule: inflorescence with rather few widely spreading branches or
the branches sometimes short and inflorescence contracted: heads not secund, small,
4 mm. high, few-flowered: achene linear-cylindric, enlarged upward, grayish, hirsutulous, strongly about 10-ribbed, the pappus rather sparse, as long or somewhat
shorter.   20. *S. notabilis.*

IX. ARGUTAE

Plant without long horizontal stolons: basal rosettes often very large and conspicuous: leaves much reduced upward; blades not triple-ribbed, not pellucid-punctate, not grayish-canescent, thin, prominently ribbed and veined beneath, the larger
serrate or doubly serrate and long-petioled: heads small or medium sized, 4.5–8 mm.
high, unilaterally racemose, on widely spreading branches or rarely the branches
erect: stigmas flattened, longer than wide: achene pubescent, sometimes sparsely
so or glabrate in age, ribbed, truncate at the apex.

Inflorescence-branches glabrous: achene not blackish, 1.5
    mm. long: (leaves of basal tufts with ovate-lanceolate
    or obovate-lanceolate blades).   21. *S. juncea.*
Inflorescence-branches pubescent: achene 1.75–2.5 mm. long.
    Achene not blackish: basal tufts of leaves often poorly
      developed, blades lanceolate, oblong-oval, ovate-
      lanceolate, oval-obovate or ovate, singly serrate or
      crenate-serrate.
      Stem glabrous beneath the inflorescence.
        Involucre 2–4 mm. high.
          Leaf-blades glabrous below, glabrous or spar-
            ingly pustular-hairy above, thickish, firm,
            serrate.   22. *S. Boottii.*
          Leaf-blades pustular-hairy on both sides, espe-
            cially on the veins, thin, shallowly-serrate.   23. *S. strigosa.*
                                              24. *S. yadkinensis.*
        Involucre 5–6 mm. high.
      Stem strongly and closely short-pubescent: leaf-blades
        glabrous (or strigillose above).   25. *S. brachyphylla.*
    Achene blackish, 2.25 mm. long: basal tufts of leaves very
      strongly developed, their blades ovate, more or
      less doubly serrate.
      Leaf-blades much lighter-green beneath than above,
        thin: mature achene glabrate: pappus 3–4 mm.
        long: involucre 3–4.5 mm. high, 2–2.5 mm. thick;
        inner bracts linear-oblong.   26. *S. arguta.*
      Leaf-blades little lighter-green beneath than above,
        firm: mature achene hairy: pappus 2.5–3.5 mm.
        long: involucre 4–6 mm. high, 2.5–4 mm. thick;
        inner bracts oblong-obovate.   27. *S. Harrisii.*

X. ULIGINOSAE

Plant without long horizontal stolons: basal rosettes very large and conspicuous: leaves much reduced upwards; blades not triple-ribbed, not pellucid-
punctate, not grayish canescent, thin or moderately fleshy, prominently ribbed and
veined beneath, the larger serrate or crenate and long-petioled: the petioles strongly
clasping at the base: heads small or medium-sized, 4.5–8 mm. high, unilaterally
racemose on widely spreading branches or sometimes the branches erect: stigmas
flattened, longer than wide: achene pubescent, sometimes sparsely so, ribbed, truncate
at the apex.

Internodes of the stem terete or essentially so: leaf-blades
    not very rough (retrorsely scabrous) above.
    Leaf-blades serrate with conspicuous callus-tipped teeth.
      Involucre narrowly campanulate: pedicels and inflores-
        cence-branches usually more or less hairy.   28. *S. uniligulata.*
      Involucre broadly campanulate: pedicels and inflores-
        cence-branches usually glabrous.   29. *S. austrina.*
    Leaf-blades crenate-serrate.   30. *S. flavovirens.*

Internodes of the stem prominently angled below the leaves,
(the leaves being decurrent) : leaf-blades very rough
(retrorsely scabrous) above.

Involucre broadly campanulate, 4.5–5 mm. high, about 3
mm. thick : achene two-thirds length of the pappus.   31. *S. rigida.*

Involucre campanulate to narrowly campanulate, 4 mm.
high, 2.5 mm. thick ; achene equalling the pappus.   32. *S. salicina.*

XI. Sempervirentes

Plant without long horizontal stolons : basal rosettes large and conspicuous :
leaves gradually much reduced upwards ; blades not triple-ribbed, not pellucid-punctate, not grayish-canescent, thick or fleshy, glabrous on both sides, entire, the midrib
prominent, the lateral largely obscure, the veins prominent, the lower petioles 1–3
times length of blades, strongly clasping at the base : infloresence large, the branches
spreading, the heads unilaterally racemose, small to rather large, 5–9 mm. high :
stigmas flattened, longer than wide : achene silky-pubescent, obscurely or obsoletely
ribbed, gray, or at maturity blackish, truncate at the apex.   33. *S. mexicana.*

XII. Nemorales

Plants without long horizontal stolons : basal rosettes conspicuous : leaf-blades
at least partially triple-ribbed : heads small or middle-sized, 3–8 mm. high, unilaterally racemose : stigmas triangular-lanceolate flattened : achene hairy at least above.

Stem glabrous : branches of inflorescence glabrous : achene
about equalling the pappus.

Cauline leaves abruptly smaller from near the base of the
stem : involucral bracts with obscure midribs or ribless : involucre narrowly campanulate.   34. *S. Gattingeri.*

Cauline leaves not abruptly smaller above the base of
the stem : involucral bracts with conspicuous midribs : involucre cylindric.   35. *S. pinetorum.*

Stems closely pubescent : branches of inflorescence pubescent :
achene little more than half the length of the pappus.

Upper leaves with oblanceolate or spatulate blades : involucre campanulate, the pedicel little bracteolate : involucral bracts rather thin : veins of leaf-blades little
anastomosing beneath ; the hairs little pustular.   36. *S. nemoralis.*

Upper leaves with oval, ovate, or obovate blades : involucre turbinate, the pedicels strongly bracteolate :
involucral bracts thickish : veins of leaf-blades
strongly anastomosing beneath ; the hairs strongly
pustular.   37. *S. radula.*

XIII. Vernae

Plant with long slender horizontal stolons : basal rosettes conspicuous : blades
of the lower leaves with ovate or ovate-cordate blades ; not triple-ribbed, not pellucid-
punctate, firm, serrate or crenate-serrate, the veins not impressed : inflorescence
paniculate, the branches nearly naked below, the lower heads more or less unilateral : heads small to rather large, 5–8 mm. high : ligules of the ray bright-yellow,
conspicuous : style not or but little exserted : stigmas flattened, triangular : achene
somewhat dilated upward, appressed-pubescent.

Leaf-blades tomentose beneath ; petioles strongly margined :
involucre 4–4.5 mm. high.   38. *S. verna.*

Leaf-blades glabrous ; petioles margined above only ; involucre 5–7 mm. high.   39. *S. tarda.*

XIV. Petiolatae

Plant with long slender horizontal stolons : basal rosettes conspicuous, the
leaves much the larger : leaves abruptly and very conspicuously reduced upward ;
blades of the lower leaves with linear to spatulate blades ; all blades firm, glabrous,
not triple-ribbed, not pellucid punctate, entire or shallowly crenate-serrate, the
lateral veins beneath scarcely impressed : inflorescence spike-like or narrowly
paniculate with the heads unilateral on long and widely spreading branches, glabrous or nearly so : heads small to rather large, 5–9 mm. high : style not or but
little exserted : stigmas flattened, triangular : achene linear, sparsely pubescent.

Heads numerous to very numerous : involucral bracts thin,
except at the midrib, glabrate : blades of the basal
leaf linear to oblong-elliptic or spatulate or lanceolate,
the petioles not markedly uneven.

Heads in a narrow terminal thyrse and secund at the
end of 2–5 very long branches : blades of the lower
stem-leaves shallowly crenate-serrate : ligules of the
ray one, or wanting.   40. *S. gracillima.*

Heads in a narrow thyrse, the lower branches short,
sometimes recurved or spreading : blades of the stem-
leaves entire, or shallowly crenate-serrate : ray-flowers
several with conspicuous ligules.   41. *S. petiolata.*

Heads few (5–15) : involucral bracts firm, thickish, strigillose : blades of the basal leaf spatulate to oblanceolate,
the inner much shorter-petioled than outermost.   42. *S. pulchra.*

XV. FLEXICAULES

Plant with long slender horizontal stolons : basal rosettes wanting or very
inconspicuous : leaf-blades gradually reduced upward, not triple-ribbed, not pellucid-
punctate, the lateral veins well developed : lower heads in axillary clusters, the
upper spicate ; all small, medium sized or rarely rather large 4–8 mm. high : stigmas
triangular-lanceolate : achene silky-pubescent.

Involucral bracts one-ribbed or essentially so (the lateral
ribs wanting or developed towards base only).
  Stem, inflorescence-branches, and involucre glabrous or
  nearly so.
    Stem and branches bluish-gray and more or less
    glaucous (before too old), the stem terete, or
    very obscurely angled, not zig-zag : leaf-blades
    usually more than twice as long as wide :
    achene slenderly about 10-ribbed.
      Leaf-blades round-tapering at the base, firm, 0.5–3
      cm. wide : petioles 1–2 mm. long : involucre
      3.5–4 mm. high, 1.5–2 mm. wide.   43. *S. caesia.*
      Leaf-blades cuneate-tapering at the base, thin, 1.5–
      5.5 cm. wide : petioles 1–5 mm. long : involucre
      4–4.5 mm. high, 2.5–3.5 mm. wide.   44. *S. latissimifolia.*
    Stem and branches green, not glaucous, the stem
    strongly angled, usually zig-zag : leaf-blades
    broadly ovate, 2.5–10 cm. wide, less than twice as
    long as wide : achene with ribs concealed by
    pubescense.   45. *S. flexicaulis.*
  Stem, inflorescence-branches, and involucre pubescent :
  upper part of the thyrse spike-like : involucre 3–4.5
  mm. high : stem terete below, not glaucous.   46. *S. pubens.*
Involucral bracts 3–5-ribbed.
  Involucre narrowly campanulate, 3–4.5 mm. high.   47. *S. Curtisii.*
  Involucre broadly campanulate, 5–6 mm. high.   48. *S. lancifolia.*

XVI. ALTISSIMAE

Plant with long slender horizontal stolons : basal rosettes wanting or very
inconspicuous : leaf-blades not triple-ribbed, often conspicuously veined : heads small
to rather large, 3.5–8 mm. high ; at least the lower heads unilaterally racemose :
stigmatic appendages triangular-lanceolate : achene pubescent, not strongly ribbed.

Leaf-blades narrowly linear-oblong, linear-lanceolate, or
  oblong-lanceolate, channeled, with the lateral veins
  usually very obscure, those of the lower leaves at least
  recurved-spreading or recurved, and more or less twisted
  at the base.   49. *S. tortifolia.*
Leaf-blades wider, neither markedly channeled, recurved-
  spreading, or twisted at the base, with the lateral
  veins very prominent.
  Leaf-blades oblong-oblanceolate or oblong-lanceolate, sessile, with a broad, somewhat clasping base, with few
  teeth or entire : stem strongly white-hirsute above.   50. *S. fistulosa.*
  Leaf-blades oblong-oblanceolate or elliptic or broader,
  petioled or sessile, not clasping, with many teeth.
    Heads mainly in a strict thyrse and not secund, but
    sometimes all except upper ones secund on strongly
    developed widely spreading branches.   51. *S. dispersa.*
    Heads strongly secund on widely spreading branches.
    Stem strongly hairy above : dry-ground plants.
      Leaf-blades not cordate, short-petioled, acute
      or acuminate, mostly over thrice as long as
      wide : the pubescence of pustular hairs : in-
      volucre cylindric, the pedicel moderately
      bracteolate.   52. *S. altissima.*
      Well-developed leaf-blades shallowly cordate,
      sessile or very short-petioled, obtuse or
      short-acute, mostly about twice as long as
      wide, the pubescence on the stem of weak
      not or scarcely pustular hairs : involucre
      turbinate-cylindric, the pedicel usually very
      strongly bracteolate.   53. *S. celtidifolia.*
    Stem glabrous below the inflorescence or sparingly
    hairy above : wet-ground or damp-ground
    plants.

Leaves somewhat fleshy: involucres nearly cylindric, the bracts thick, the outer ovate, the
inner with erect tips.   54. *S. Elliottii.*
Leaves not fleshy: involucres broadly cam-
panulate or cylindric, the bracts thin or
chaffy, the outer lanceolate or ovate-
lanceolate.
    Involucre broadly campanulate, 5 mm. high:
    bracts thin, but firm, the outer ovate-
    lanceolate, acutish, the inner with erect
    tips.   55. *S. Edisoniana.*
    Involucre cylindric, 6 mm. high; bracts thin
    and chaffy, the outer lanceolate, acumi-
    nate, the inner with inflexed or in-
    curved tips.   56. *S. mirabilis.*

XVII. Serotinae

Plant with long horizontal stolons: basal rosettes wanting or very inconspicuous: stem closely leafy, the leaf-blades triple-ribbed, usually serrate: heads very
small to medium-sized, 2–7 mm. high, unilaterally racemose in our species: stigmas
triangular-lanceolate: achene pubescent.

Branches of the inflorescence glabrous.   57. *S. glaberrima.*
Branches of the inflorescence pubescent.
    Stems glaucous, glabrous (minutely pulverulent): head
    4.5–6 mm. high.   58. *S. serotina.*
    Stems not glaucous.
        Involucre 2–3 mm. high: achene about the length of
        the pappus: main stem glabrous or hairy.   59. *S. canadensis.*
        Involucre 3–5 mm. high: achene half the length of the
        pappus: main stem conspicuously hairy at
        least at the bases of the petioles.
            Larger leaf-blades narrowly lanceolate or oblanceo-
            late: stem pubescent below the petioles.   60. *S. Leavenworthii.*
            Larger leaf-blades of a lanceolate or oblong-
            lanceolate type: stem pubescent all over.   61. *S. hirsutissima.*

1. S. glomerata Michx. Stem stout, 3–11 dm. tall, glabrous, conspicuously
angled: blades of the basal leaves thin, 8–15 cm. long, 2.5–5 cm. wide, ciliate,
sharply serrate, the petiole about as long:
stem-leaves reduced; blades contracted into
a petiole-like base, the upper less serrate: involucral bracts firm, thickish, hispidulous, the
midrib conspicuously dilated at apex: disk-
corollas 6.5–7.5 mm. long.—Cliffs and rocky
woods, high altitudes, Blue Ridge, N. C. and
Tenn.—Sum.-fall.

2. S. squarrosa Muhl. Stem stout, 4–15 dm.
tall, white-pubescent above: basal rosettes
conspicuous, their leaves with thin but firm
blades, 6–12 cm. long, 3–5 cm. wide, crenate,
hispidulous above, sparsely pubescent beneath, the petiole as long or longer: stem-
leaves reduced, the lower more sharply serrate, the upper entire or nearly so:
heads 10–12 mm. high: involucral bracts lanceolate, pubescent, acute, all except
inner with strongly squarrose tips.—Rocky woodlands and hillsides, various
provinces N of Coastal Plain, "Ga." and N. Car. to Ind., Ont., and N. B.—
Sum.-fall.

3. S. Milleriana Mackenzie. Stem 3–12 dm. tall, strict, closely short-hispid
above, glabrate towards base: basal rosettes wanting: leaf-blades oblong-oval,
the larger mostly 6–8 cm. long, 1.5–2 cm. wide, scabrous-hispidulous above,
sparsely pubescent beneath, thick, firm, those of the lower leaves shallowly and
sparingly crenate-serrate, those of the upper ones with entire blades: petioles
1–2 mm. long: heads 7–8 mm. high: involucral bracts lanceolate, acute, appressed-pubescent, all except the inner with spreading tips. ["*S. petiolaris*
Ait."]—Sandy pinelands, acid soils, mostly Coastal Plain, Fla. to Ala. and
N. C.—Sum.-fall.

4. S. Buckleyi T. & G. Stem 6–12 dm. tall, strict, strongly pilose above, sparsely so below: basal rosettes wanting: leaf-blades oblong-obovate or oblong-oblanceolate, mostly 8–12 cm. long, 2.5–5 cm. wide, hispidulous on veins above, sparingly pilose below, thin, those of the lower leaves strongly crenate-serrate, those of the upper entire or nearly so; petioles 1–5 mm. long: heads 7–8 mm. high: involucral bracts oblong-lanceolate, acute or acutish, hispidulous and ciliate, the tips of the outer only spreading: achene blackish, somewhat compressed.—Dry woodlands in limestone regions, Appalachian Plateau, Ala. to Ill. and Mo.—Sum.-fall.

5. S. bicolor L. Stem usually 5–8 (2–12) dm. tall, white-hirsute; lower leaves with ovate or oblong-ovate blades 5–10 cm. long, 2.5–5 cm. wide, crenate-serrate, white-pubescent or -hirsute on both sides; petioles ½ to length of blades: heads 4–6 mm. high; involucral bracts oblong, chartaceous, nearly smooth, usually whitish-yellow with the greenish midrib conspicuously dilated above.—Dry banks, woods and thickets usually in acid soils, various provinces, Ga. to Mo., Ont., and N. B.—Sum.-fall.

6. S. hispida Muhl. Similar to *S. bicolor* in habit, but with the heads usually slightly larger: involucral bracts narrowly oblong, firm, strigillose, subherbaceous, usually greenish-stramineous, with the green midrib obscurely to strongly dilated above.—Rocky banks and dry hillsides in limestone soils, various provinces N of Coastal Plain, Ga. to Ark., Man., and Newf.—Sum.-fall.

7. S. erecta Pursh. Stem usually 5–10 (3–13) dm. tall; lower leaves 6–9 cm. long, 1.8–3 cm. wide, the blades broadly oblanceolate, essentially glabrous on both sides, shallowly crenate: heads 8–10 mm. high: involucre campanulate: achene columnar, narrowly linear.—Dry open woodlands, acid soils, various provinces, Ga. to Miss., Wis., and Conn.

8. S. Porteri Small. Stem 6–14 dm. tall, glabrous below, sparsely pubescent above, short-pubescent in the inflorescence: leaf-blades oblong-oblanceolate, 8–18 cm. long, 2.5–4.5 cm. wide, crenate-serrate, sparsely hairy on both sides: involucral bracts oblong; achene linear-clavate, blackish.—Dry woods, Piedmont of Ga.—Sum.-fall.

9. S. puberula Nutt. Stem 3–10 dm. tall: basal rosettes conspicuous, their leaf-blades spatulate, 3–10 cm. long, 1.5–2.5 cm. wide, crenate-serrate, sparsely hispidulous-puberulent on both sides; petioles as long or longer: involucral bracts thin, the midrib obsolete: ligules of the ray rarely white: achene olive-green, slightly dilated upward.—Dry open woodlands, acid soils, various provinces, Fla. to Miss., Tenn., Que., and P. E. I., most common near the coast. —Sum.-fall.

10. S. pulverulenta Nutt. Stem 4–12 dm. tall: lower leaf-blades oblong-obovate or oblanceolate, 3–8 cm. long, 1.2–2.5 cm. wide, crenate-serrate, the petiole as long or longer: involucral bracts thin, with the midrib obscure: achene somewhat dilated upward.—Dry pinelands, acid soils, Coastal Plain, Fla. to Ala. and N. C.—Sum.-fall.

11. S. roanensis Porter. Stem 2–8 dm. tall, pubescent above and in the inflorescence only, or sparingly loosely pubescent: basal rosettes conspicuous: lower leaf-blades oblong-obovate or obovate, 3–10 cm. long, 2–5 cm. wide, crenate-serrate or serrate, hispidulous above and pubescent beneath mostly on the veins; petiole usually shorter: involucral bracts glabrous: achene linear, obscurely ribbed. [*S. monticola* T. & G. not Jordon *S. Maxoni* Pollard *S. alleghaniensis* House]—Dry woods, in acid soils, Blue Ridge to Appalachian Plateau, "Ga." to "Ala.," W. Va., and Md.—Sum.-fall.

12. S. Harperi Mackenzie. Stem 10–15 dm. tall: lower leaf-blades oblong-elliptic, 6–12 cm. long, 1.5–2.5 cm. wide, glabrous, entire, dull-green above, lighter beneath: thyrse narrowly ovoid, 2–3 dm. long, 8–12 cm. wide, its branches hirsutulous: heads 7–9 mm. high: involucral bracts minutely ciliolate, thickish, firm, not keeled.—Dry woods, Coastal Plain and more northern provinces, Ga. to E Tenn.—Fall.

13. S. conferta Mill. Stem 8–20 dm. tall: lower leaf-blades oblong-obovate or oblanceolate, 1.2–2.5 dm. long, crenate or crenate-serrate; petioles usually somewhat shorter: branches of the thyrse hirsutulous: heads 7–10 mm. high: involucral bracts ciliate. [*S. speciosa* Nutt.]—Dry woodlands, various provinces N of Coastal Plain, N. C. to Okla., Minn., and Mass., and introduced northeastward.—Fall.

14. S. rigidiuscula (T. & G.) Porter. Stem 6–12 dm. tall: lower leaf-blades narrowly lanceolate to ovate-lanceolate, 5–10 cm. long, entire or sometimes crenate; petioles short: thyrse with hirsutulous branches: heads 6–8 mm. high: involucral bracts ciliate.—Dry sunny places, various provinces, Ga. to Tex., S. Dak., and Minn.—Sum.-fall.

15. S. plumosa Small. Stem 4–10 dm. tall: lower leaf-blades linear-spatulate, 4–10 cm. long, 7–14 mm. wide, glabrous, sparingly crenate-serrate above, dull-green on both sides: thyrse oblong, 1.5–3 dm. long, 5–10 cm. wide, its branches nearly glabrous: heads 8–10 mm. high: involucre campanulate; bracts glabrous, thick, linear-lanceolate, obtusish: achene half the length of the pappus.—Crevices of rocks, at the junction of the Coastal Plain and the Piedmont, Yadkin River, N. C.—Sum.-fall.

16. S. spithamaea M. A. Curtis. Stem 0.5–3.5 dm. tall, pubescent especially above: lower stem-leaves with blades narrowly oblong-obovate, 4–10 cm. long, 1.2–2.5 cm. wide, sessile, crenate-serrate or serrate, sparingly hairy on the veins: heads 7–9 mm. high, in a flat-topped or rounded corymbiform thyrse: involucral bracts lanceolate, acute, thin, ciliate, hispidulous.—Sunny exposures, high altitudes, Blue Ridge, N. C. and Tenn.—Sum.-fall.—A very well marked species. Our only representative of a most widely distributed group of goldenrods, which is abundant northward, especially in alpine localities.

17. S. odora Ait. Stem 5–13 dm. tall: leaf-blades linear-lanceolate or linear, the larger 4–16 cm. long, 4–16 mm. wide, the margins ciliolate: heads 4–5.5 mm. high, 2 mm. thick: involucral bracts yellow, glabrous, not exceeded by the pappus at flowering time.—(Sweet-goldenrod)—Dry acid woodlands, especially in pinelands, various provinces, Fla. to Tex., Okla., and Me.—Sum.-fall. —Sometimes erroneously referred to *S. suaveolens* Schoepf. which is apparently *Euthamia graminifolia* (L.) Nutt.

18. S. Chapmanii T. & G. Stem 2–14 dm. tall: leaf-blades linear-oblong, lanceolate, or oblong-ovate, the larger 3–6 cm. long, 1–1.8 mm. wide, the margins revolute, ciliolate: heads 6–7 mm. high, 2–3 mm. thick: involucral bracts light-yellowish, glabrous, ciliate, markedly exceeded by the pappus at flowering time. —Pinelands and sandy hammocks, Fla. to S. Ga.—Sum.-fall.

19. S. ulmifolia Muhl. Stem 6–15 dm. tall, glabrous or nearly so below inflorescence: leaf-blades ovate or obovate or narrower, the larger 6–14 cm. long, 2–4.5 cm. wide, serrate, thin, sparsely hairy especially below: inflorescence-branches few, widely spreading, the longer not flower-bearing towards base: heads 4–6 mm. high: involucral bracts narrow, acute, the inner lanceolate or oblong-lanceolate: achene 1.5 mm. long, slightly enlarged upward.—Dry or rocky soil, open woods and thickets, various provinces, rarely Coastal Plain, Ga. to Tex., Minn., and N. S.—Sum.-fall.

20. **S. notabilis** Mackenzie. Stem 3–8 dm. tall, closely short white-pubescent: lower leaf-blades ovate or cordate, 4–8 cm. long, 3–5 cm. wide, sharply serrate, closely hispidulous above, closely short white-pubescent beneath, the petiole about length of blade, the larger strongly cordate: upper stem-leaves oblong-lanceolate or oblong-ovate, frequently entire, strongly amplexicaul, often abruptly contracted below the middle: inner involucral bracts much the longer, narrowly linear, acute. ["*S. amplexicaulis* Martens."] — Dry woodlands, Coastal Plain and adj. provinces, Fla. to Tex., Ark., and Tenn.—Sum.–fall.

21. **S. juncea** Ait. Stem 4–15 dm. tall, glabrous: larger leaf-blades ovate-lanceolate or obovate-lanceolate, 8–15 cm. long, 3–6 cm. wide, glabrous, sharply serrate, the upper gradually reduced: panicle-branches flower-bearing to much below the middle: heads usually strongly secund, 4.5–6 mm. high: involucral bracts linear-oblong, acutish, the midrib conspicuous: achene 5-ribbed, brownish, finely short-pubescent.—Dry fields and open woodlands, various provinces, Ga. to "Mo." "Sask." Que., and N. S.—Sum.–fall.

22. **S. Boottii** Hook. Stem 5–15 dm. tall, glabrous below the inflorescence: larger leaf-blades of an oval-obovate type, 5–10 cm. long, 2.5–3.5 cm. wide, serrate, thickish, firm: inflorescence-branches widely spreading, the longer ones flower-bearing towards the end only: heads about 6 mm. high: involucral bracts thin, linear-oblong, obtuse or acutish: achene 1.75 mm. long, dilated upward.— Dry woodlands, various provinces, Fla. to Tex., Tenn., and Md.—Sum.–fall.

23. **S. strigosa** Small. Stem 6–12 dm. tall, glabrous below the inflorescence: larger leaf-blades of an oblong-oval type, 10–18 cm. long, 5–8 cm. wide, hispidulous or strigose especially on the veins, thin, sharply, but shallowly singly serrate: inflorescence-branches several, widely spreading, the longer ones flower-bearing above the middle: heads 4.5–5.5 mm. high: involucral bracts thickish, oblong, obtuse or acutish: achene 2.5 mm. long, strongly clavate, conspicuously ribbed.—Dry woodlands, Coastal Plain, Ga. to La., Ark., and SE Mo.—Sum.–fall.

24. **S. yadkinensis** (Porter) Small. Stem 5–14 dm. tall, glabrous except in the inflorescence: lower leaf-blades ovate, 8–15 cm. long, 6–9 cm. wide, thickish, singly serrate, minutely hispidulous, otherwise glabrous; petiole much shorter than the blade: inflorescence with ascending stiff branches, flower-bearing to the base: heads 7–9 mm. high: involucral bracts oblong, obtuse: achene linear-clavate, ribbed. [*S. arguta caroliniana* A. Gray *S. Vaseyi* Heller]—Woods and low grounds, Coastal Plain and Piedmont, Fla. to Ala. and N. C.—Sum.–fall.

25. **S. brachyphylla** Chapm. Stem 5–13 dm. tall, closely short pubescent, closely leafy throughout: larger leaf-blades oblong-oval or oval-obovate, 3–7 cm. long, 1.2–2.5 cm. wide, crenate-serrate: branches of inflorescence much elongate, often not flower-bearing on lower part: heads few-flowered, 5 mm. high: involucre cylindric; bracts oblong, obtuse, firm: achene 2.25 mm. long, strongly dilated upward, 8–10-ribbed. [*S. pallescens* C. Mohr]—Dry woodlands, Coastal Plain, Fla. to Miss. and S. Car.—Sum.–fall.

26. **S. arguta** Ait. Stem 6–12 dm. tall, glabrous except in the inflorescence: lower leaf-blades ovate, 8–15 cm. long, 5–8 cm. wide, thin, sharply more or less doubly serrate, deep-green above, much lighter-green beneath, the petioles as long as the blades or longer: inflorescence large and loose, the branches flower-bearing at the ends: involucre 3–4.5 mm. high, 2–2.5 mm. thick; inner bracts linear-oblong: stigmas strongly exserted, conspicuous in the disk: achene glabrate or nearly so; pappus 3–4 mm. long.—Dry woodlands, various provinces, N. C. to "Ala.," "Miss.," Ky., and Me.—Sum.–fall.

27. S. Harrisii Steele. Stem 6–12 dm. tall, glabrous except in the inflorescence: lower leaf-blades ovate, 6–18 cm. long, 3–9 cm. wide, firm, sharply more or less doubly serrate, little lighter-green beneath than above; petioles as long as the blades or longer: inflorescence large and loose, the branches widely spreading, flower-bearing at the tips: involucre 4–6 mm. high, 2.5–4 mm. thick; inner bracts oblong-obovate: stigmas partially exserted, inconspicuous in the disk: achene hairy: pappus 2.5–3.5 mm. long. [*S. Vaseyi* (Fl. SE. U. S.)]—Dry woodlands, Blue Ridge and adj. provinces, "Ga." and "Ala." to Ky. and W. Va.—Sum.-fall.

28. S. uniligulata (DC.) Porter. Stem 6–15 dm. tall, glabrous below the inflorescence: leaves numerous, strongly decreasing in size upwards; blades of the larger ones lanceolate or oblong-lanceolate, 1.5–3 dm. long, 1–3 cm. wide, shallowly serrate, firm or thickish, glabrous: heads very numerous to few, in a large to small thyrse, the lower branches hirsute, spreading, usually short, with the upper heads closely bunched: heads 6–8 mm. high: involucral bracts oblong, obtuse, with a conspicuous midrib: achene 1.5–2 mm. long, linear, dilated upward, ribbed. [*S. neglecta* T. & G.]—Acid swamps and bogs, various provinces, N. C. to Wis. and Newf.—Sum.-fall.—A related species, *S. uliginosa* Nutt., was apparently erroneously recorded from N. C. in Fl. SE. U. S. 1194.

29. S. austrina Small. Stem 8–15 dm. tall, glabrous usually even in the inflorescence: leaf-blades lanceolate, 6–10 cm. long, 1–2 cm. wide, glabrous, firm, serrate, tapering to a margined petiole which is usually shorter than the blade: thyrse narrow, elongate, the branches short-spreading, flower-bearing to base or nearly so: heads 7–8 mm. high: involucral bracts oblong, acutish or obtuse: achene 2.5 mm. long, ribbed.—Swamps, sometimes brackish, Coastal Plain and Piedmont, Ga. to Va.—Sum.-fall.

30. S. flavovirens Chapm. Stem 5–20 dm. tall, glabrous even in the inflorescence: larger leaf-blades oblong-ovate or oblanceolate, 1–2 dm. long, 2–5 cm. wide, glabrous, firm, thickish, crenate-serrate, tapering to a margined petiole, which varies from much shorter than the blade to nearly as long: thyrse narrow, long, the branches short, spreading, flower-bearing to base or nearly so: heads 7–9 mm. high: involucral bracts narrow, acutish: achene 2–2.5 mm. long, ribbed.—Brackish marshes, Apalachicola, Florida.

31. S. rigida L. Stem 5–20 dm. tall, stout, glabrous except in inflorescence: lower leaf-blades oblong-ovate, 1.2–2 dm. long, 5–9 cm. wide, firm but not thick, closely crenate-serrate, very rough above with minute retrorse hispid hairs, smooth and glabrous beneath: inflorescence elongate and loose, the branches recurved-spreading or occasionally erect, the heads often crowded towards the ends: heads 6–8 mm. high: involucre broadly campanulate; bracts oblong, obtuse: achene 2.5–3 mm. long, 10-ribbed, sparsely pubescent. [*S. patula* Muhl.]—Swampy woodlands and thickets, various provinces, Ga. to Mo., Ont., and Me.—Sum.-fall.

32. S. salicina Ell. Stem 6–15 dm. tall, scarcely stout, glabrous, except in the inflorescence: lower leaf-blades oblong-ovate to oblong-lanceolate, 0.5–2 dm. long, 1.5–3 cm. wide, thin but stiff, crenate-serrate or serrate, dull-green and strongly retrorsely scabrous above, smooth and light-green beneath: inflorescence elongate and narrow, the heads in few-flowered clusters or short racemes, not at all secund: heads 6–8 mm. high: involucre campanulate to narrowly campanulate; bracts linear-oblong, acute to obtusish: achene 2.5 mm. long, obscurely ribbed, sparsely pubescent.—Low grounds, Coastal Plain and adj. provinces, Fla. to La. and N. C.—Sum.-fall.

33. S. mexicana L. Stem 8–20 dm. tall, stout, glabrous below the inflorescence: lower leaf-blades oblong-lanceolate to linear-lanceolate, 1–2.2 dm.

long, 1.2–3 cm. wide, obtuse or acutish, hispid-ciliolate, entire: heads 5–7 mm. high, in an elongate narrow panicle, the branches short: involucral bracts narrowly oblong-lanceolate: rays 7–10, the ligules 2.5 mm. long, oblong-oval: achene 2.5 mm. long, ⅔ length of pappus, not narrowed above or scarcely so.— Salt-marshes, beaches, coastal sand-dunes, and banks of tidal rivers, coastal Fla. to Tex. and Del.; S Calif. (*W. I., Mex.*)—Sum.-fall or all the year S.—This species replaces *S. sempervirens* L. of northern regions, in the SE States.

34. S. Gattingeri Chapm. Stem 6–15 dm. tall, smooth and glabrous throughout: lower leaf-blades oblanceolate or narrowly spatulate, remotely shallowly serrate or entire: upper leaf-blades much smaller, linear-oblanceolate, entire: panicle ample, the branches widely spreading, glabrous, flower-bearing above the middle: heads 4–5 mm. high: involucral bracts thick, narrowly oblong: achene sparingly silky above.—Limestone barrens, various provinces N of Coastal Plain, Tenn. to Tex. and Mo.—Sum.-fall.

35. S. pinetorum Small. Stem 4–11 dm. tall, smooth and glabrous throughout: lower leaf-blades narrowly oblanceolate, crenate-serrate above the middle: upper leaf-blades smaller, narrower and entire: panicle medium-sized, the branches widely spreading, glabrous: heads 4–5 mm. high: involucral bracts linear-oblong, the midrib dilated at apex: achene sparingly silky.—Pinewoods, Piedmont, N. C.—Sum.-fall.

36. S. nemoralis Ait. Stem and rest of plant grayish-green, 1–9 dm. tall, erect, depressed, or rarely prostrate, closely short-pubescent: lower leaf-blades oblanceolate or spatulate, 4–15 cm. long, 1–2.5 cm. wide, thick, crenate or crenate-dentate, rough grayish-pubescent on both sides, the petiole longer than the blade: upper leaf-blades much smaller, narrower and entire: panicle medium-sized, the branches spreading or recurved: peduncles sparingly bracteolate: heads very numerous, 3–4 mm. high, 1.5 mm. thick: involucral bracts rather thin: ligules of the ray short.—Dry sunny situations, roadsides, banks, open woodlands, and especially in fields, various provinces, Fla. to Tex., Sask., and N. S.—Sum.-fall.—One of the most widely distributed and abundant species of *Solidago*.

37. S. radula Nutt. Stem 3–11 dm. tall, erect or ascending, roughly short-pubescent: lower leaf-blades oblong-obovate, oblanceolate, or oblong-lanceolate, 4–8 cm. long, 1–2.5 cm. wide, firm, rough-hairy on both sides, not at all hoary, strongly reticulate-veined beneath, crenate-dentate, usually shallowly so, or nearly entire: upper leaf-blades moderately smaller: inflorescence narrow to ample, the branches short, erect to recurved-spreading: heads 4–6 mm. high: involucral bracts narrow, obtuse, firm; ligules of the ray short.—Dry limestone ledges, various provinces, N. C., La. to Tex., Mo., and Ill.—Sum.-fall.

38. S. verna M. A. Curtis. Stem 5–9 dm. tall, softly pubescent, sometimes almost villous: lower leaf-blades 4–9 cm. long, 2–5 cm. wide, tomentose beneath, hispidulous above, acute, closely serrate; petioles as long as the blades or twice or thrice as long, strongly margined: inflorescence very lax, the heads conspicuously pedunceled: involucre broadly campanulate, 4–4.5 mm. high; bracts linear, acutish: ray-flowers 10–12, the ligules linear-oblong, bright-yellow.— Pinelands, Coastal Plain, E N. C. and NE S. C.—Spr.—A very local species; rarely collected.

39. S. tarda Mackenzie. Stem 5–9 dm. tall, glabrous below the inflorescence: lower leaf-blades 4–9 cm. long, 3–5 cm. wide, acute, glabrous on both sides, dull-green above, lighter-green beneath, closely crenate-serrate, inequilaterally rounded at the base; petioles as long as the blades or up to thrice as long, margined above only: inflorescence typically somewhat lax, sometimes congested, the heads rather short-peduncled: involucre campanulate, 5–7 mm. high; bracts oblong, acutish: ray-flowers 8–10, the ligules oblong, bright-yellow.— Pinelands, Coastal Plain, Ga.—Sum.–fall.

40. S. gracillima T. & G. Stem 4–10 dm. tall, slender; lower leaf-blades oblanceolate or spatulate, 2–8 cm. long, 8–12 mm. wide, dull-green above, lighter beneath, shallowly crenate-serrate except near base; petioles equalling or 2–3 times as long as the blades: stem-leaves numerous, much reduced; blades entire or nearly so: inflorescence with a terminal narrow spike-like portion, and 2–5 very long and slender spreading branches with the heads secund on the upper third only: heads 5–6 mm. high, few-flowered: involucral bracts short, oblong, obtuse: ray-flowers mostly wanting, sometimes solitary: achene linear, short-pubescent, dark-colored.—Sandy soil, Coastal Plain, Fla. and Ga.—Sum.–fall.— Rarely collected.

41. S. petiolata Mill. Stem 2.5–20 dm. tall, strict, slender: lower leaf-blades narrowly linear-oblanceolate to lanceolate, 6–15 cm. long, 0.6–2.5 cm. wide, entire or shallowly crenate-serrate; petioles one-fourth as long as the blade to as long: stem-leaves abruptly much reduced, very numerous, entire, sessile, appressed or spreading: heads in a strict spike-like thyrse or sometimes the lower branches short spreading and the heads unilateral, 6–7 mm. high: involucre turbinate-campanulate; bracts linear, acute, thin, erose ciliolate: ray-flowers several; ligules elliptic, conspicuous: achene linear-obconic, silky, dark-colored. [*S. stricta* Ait. *S. virgata* Michx. *S. angustifolia* Ell. *S. Chrysopsis* Small]—Wet pinelands, acid soils, Coastal Plain and rarely adj. provinces, Fla. to La., Tenn., and N. J.—(*W. I.*)—Sum.–fall.—A very variable species southward. Possibly representing more than one species, as here interpreted.

42. S. pulchra Small. Stem 2.5–4 dm. tall, glabrous, very slender: lower leaf-blades spatulate or oblanceolate, 2–5 cm. long, 8–14 mm. wide, entire, obtuse, glabrous, even the edges eciliate; petioles margined above, one-half to three times length of blade: stem-leaves abruptly much reduced, appressed, sessile, mostly 5–10 mm. long and 1–2.5 mm. wide: heads 5–15 in a simple narrow somewhat one-sided thyrse 2–8 cm. long, strongly peduncled, 6–8 mm. high: involucre campanulate or turbinate-campanulate; bracts oblong, acutish, strigillose: ray-flowers 5 or 6, the ligules ovate, bright-yellow, 4–5 mm. long: achene linear obconic, appressed silky.—Moist sandy soil, Coastal Plain, E N. C.—Fall.

43. S. caesia L. Stem 3–11 dm. tall, slender, straight, terete, with a bluish-gray glaucous bloom which is often obscure in age: leaf-blades oblanceolate, lanceolate, oblong-oblanceolate, or oblong-lanceolate, 0.5–1 dm. long, 0.5–3 cm. wide, glabrous, sharply shallowly serrate, firm, long-acuminate, round-tapering at base; petioles 1–2 mm. long: heads 4–6 mm. high: involucre 3.5–4 mm. high, 1.5–2 mm. wide; bracts obtuse: achene linear, 10-ribbed.—Woodlands, usually dry but sometimes damp soil, various provinces, Fla. to Tex., Wis., Ont., and Que.—Sum.–fall.

44. S. latissimifolia Mill. Stem 5–13 dm. tall, slender, straight, terete or sometimes obscurely angled, glabrous below, sparingly pubescent above, with a slight bluish-gray glaucous bloom: leaf-blades broadly oblanceolate to obovate, 6–20 cm. long, 1.5–5.5 cm. wide, thin, strongly acuminate, very sparingly hirsutulous, sharply and deeply serrate, cuneate-tapering at base; petioles 1–5 mm. long: heads 4.5–5.5 mm. high: involucre 4–4.5 mm. high, 2.5–3.5 mm. wide; bracts obtuse: achene oblong, enlarged upward. [*S. flaccidifolia* Small *S. asterifolia* Small]—Dry woodlands, Coastal Plain to Appalachian Plateau, Ga. to La.—Sum.–fall.

45. S. flexicaulis L. Stem 3–10 dm. tall, slender, strongly angled, usually zig-zag, glabrous, not glaucous: leaf-blades broadly ovate, rather abruptly acuminate, 0.5–1.8 dm. long, 2.5–10 cm. wide, thin, very sharply and deeply serrate, glabrous above, sparingly pubescent beneath, abruptly narrowed at the base, many times the length of the short margined petioles: heads 6 mm. high: involucral bracts acute or obtusish: achene hirsute-pubescent.—Deep woods especially among loose rocks along small streams, various provinces, Tenn. to Kans., S. Dak., and N. S., and Va.—Sum.–fall.

46. S. pubens M. A. Curtis. Stem 4–15 dm. tall, slender, pilose; leaf-blades narrowly oblanceolate to broadly oblanceolate, 6–16 cm. long, 2.5–4.5 cm. wide, sharply serrate, thin, hirsutulous above, pilose beneath on the veins; petioles 1–3 mm. long: heads 5–6 mm. high, in short or even long axillary racemes, the lower racemes much exceeded by the leaves, the upper aggregated and forming a short thyrse: involucre 3–4.5 mm. high; bracts hispidulous, ciliate, obscurely few-ribbed at the base: achene appressed-hirsutulous.—Rich woods, Blue Ridge, Ga. to Tenn. and N. Car.—Sum.–fall.

47. S. Curtisii T. & G. Stem 5–14 dm. tall, slender, glabrous below, pubescent above: leaf-blades narrowly oblanceolate to broadly oblanceolate, 8–20 cm. long, 1.5–4 cm. wide, thin, sharply serrate, glabrous or nearly so, long-acuminate, long-tapering at the base; petioles 1–10 mm. long: heads 5–6 mm. high, in axillary clusters or short racemes, all except the uppermost exceeded by leaves, even the uppermost scarcely forming a spike: involucre narrowly campanulate, 3–4.5 mm. high; bracts narrowly oblong, ciliolate, strongly 3–5-ribbed: achene appressed-hirsutulous.—Rich dry soil in open upland woods, Blue Ridge to Appalachian Plateau, Ga. to Ala., Tenn., Ky., and Va.—Sum.–fall.

48. S. lancifolia T. & G. Stem 8–15 dm. tall, stoutish or stout, glabrous below, sparingly pubescent above: leaf-blades lanceolate, 8–20 cm. long, 2–3 cm. wide, thin, sharply and deeply serrate, glabrous to very sparingly hirsutulous, long-acuminate, strongly cuneate-tapering at the base; petioles 2–6 mm. long: heads 6.5–8 mm. high, in elongate axillary racemes, the upper forming a narrow terminal thyrse: involucre broadly campanulate, 5–6 mm. high; bracts oblong, obtuse, ciliolate, granular-puberulent or hispidulous, strongly 3–5-ribbed: achene appressed-hirsutulous.—Rich woodlands, slopes and summits, Blue Ridge, Ga. to Tenn. and N. C.—Sum.–fall.

49. S. tortifolia Ell. Stem 3–11 dm. tall, closely roughly short-pubescent: leaves very numerous; blades narrowly linear-oblong, linear-lanceolate, or oblong-lanceolate, 1.5–8 cm. long, 2.5–6 mm. wide, channeled, those of the lower leaves, at least, recurved-spreading and slightly twisted at the base, shallowly serrate above the middle, hispidulous on the midvein and margins, sessile, with the lateral veins usually obscure: thyrse 6–15 cm. long, nearly as wide, the branches widely spreading: heads secund, 3.5–4.5 mm. high: involucre cylindric: achene sparsely and minutely pubescent.—Dry sandy soil, pinelands, Coastal Plain, Fla. to Tex. and Md.—Sum.–fall, or all year S.

50. S. fistulosa Mill. Stem 6–20 dm. tall, strongly white-hirsute above, glabrate towards the base: leaves very numerous; blades oblong-lanceolate or oblong-oblanceolate, 5–12 cm. long, 1.7–2.5 cm. wide, sparingly and shallowly crenate-serrate or entire or nearly so, sessile, thin, prominently veined, pubescent at least on the veins, with the broad base somewhat clasping: thyrse 0.5–2 dm. long, the branches numerous, spreading, usually flower-bearing nearly to the base: heads 5–7 mm. high, secund, long-peduncled: involucre cylindric-campanulate; bracts linear-lanceolate, acute, thin: achene pubescent. [*S. aspericaulis* A. H. Moore]—Moist sunny localities, low pine-lands, acid soils, Coastal Plain, La. to Fla. and N. J.—Sum.–fall.

51. S. dispersa Small. Stem 7–12 dm. tall, glabrous or sparingly hirsutulous especially in the inflorescence: lower leaf-blades oblong-oblanceolate, 8–15 cm. long, glabrous or sparingly hairy on the veins, strongly crenate-serrate, shining green above, duller beneath, tapering to a margined petiole-like base; upper leaves much reduced: thyrse long and narrow, the heads little secund, or with a few long widely spreading branches, flower-bearing towards the end and the heads secund: heads 6–7 mm. high: involucre turbinate-campanulate; bracts linear-oblong, firm, obtuse: achene short-pubescent, obscurely ribbed.—Low sandy open woods, Coastal Plain, Miss. to Tex.—Sum.–fall.

52. S. altissima L. Stem 3–25 dm. tall, strongly pubescent above, with the hairs stiff, pustular, glabrate towards the base, closely leafy: larger leaf-blades oblanceolate or oblong-lanceolate, 5–10 cm. long, 1.5–2 cm. wide, sharply-serrate, acute or acuminate, thin, prominently veined and sparingly hairy beneath, not cordate: thyrse variable, 0.4–3 dm. long, the branches few to many: peduncles moderately bracteolate: heads small, 3–4 mm. high: involucre cylindric: involucral bracts few, rather thin, the inner linear, mostly obtusish: achene appressed-hairy, obscurely few-ribbed. [*S. rugosa* Mill. *S. Earlei* Small]—Thickets, fields, and woodlands, dry soil, often very abundant, various provinces, Fla. to Tex., Mo., Ont., and Newf.—Sum.–fall.—One of our most abundant and widely distributed species of *Solidago*.

53. S. celtidifolia Small. Stem 6–20 dm. tall, closely leafy, closely and densely short pubescent above, glabrate towards base, the stem-hairs weak, not or scarcely pustular: larger leaves with oblong-ovate to ovate blades, 3–8 cm. long, 1.5–2.5 cm. wide, crenate-serrate, obtuse or short-acute, shallowly cordate, sessile or very short-petioled, very conspicuously veined especially below, the petiole somewhat glandular: thyrse variable, usually very large: peduncles usually strongly bracteolate: heads small, 4–5 mm. high, involucre turbinate-cylindric; bracts few, firm, the inner linear, acutish: achene hairy, obscurely few-ribbed.—Sandy soil or dry woodlands, Coastal Plain, Fla. to Tex., Ark., and Ga.—Sum.–fall.

54. S. Elliottii T. & G. Stem 8–18 dm. tall, glabrous, striate or striate-angled, usually simple below the inflorescence: cauline leaves numerous; blades elliptic or nearly so, 5–10 cm. long, acute or slightly acuminate, bluntly serrate, thick, glabrous, sometimes scabrous on the margins, somewhat veiny, sessile or nearly so: thyrse rather crowded, the branches glabrous or nearly so, with broad, entire or obscurely toothed, acute, foliaceous bracts among the secund heads: peduncles glabrous or nearly so: involucre nearly cylindric, 5–6 mm. high; bracts thick, the outer ovate, obtuse or acutish, the inner linear or slightly linear-spatulate, with obtuse erect tips: ray-flowers about 8; disk-flowers about 4, usually 2 or 3, fewer than the ray-flowers; achenes very sparingly hispidulous, sharply ribbed.—Damp rich soils, Parris Island, S. C., and doubtless at other points along the southern Atlantic coast.—Fall.—This species seems to be known only from the original specimen from Parris Island, S. C. Specimens ranging all the way from eastern Georgia to eastern Canada have been erroneously referred it.

55. S. Edisoniana Mackenzie. Stem 12–50 dm. tall, glabrous below, often sparingly pubescent and rather prominently ridged above, often irregularly branched: cauline leaves very numerous; blades elliptic, sometimes elliptic-oblanceolate on the lower part of the stem and elliptic-lanceolate above, 5–17 cm. long, usually acuminate, shallowly serrate, glabrous above, pubescent with scattered hairs beneath, finely veined, sessile: thyrse densely flowered, the branches closely fine-pubescent, with rather narrow finely toothed and scabrous-margined acute bracts among the secund heads: peduncles minutely pubescent: involucre broadly campanulate, 5 mm. high; bracts thin but firm, the outer ovate-lanceolate, acutish, the inner narrowly linear, with obtuse erect tips; ray-flowers about 10: disk-flowers about 7: achenes sparingly hispidulous, ribbed.—Hammocks, near Ft. Mead, Fla.—Peculiar among our goldenrods of this and the next group in that it holds its lower cauline leaves throughout the growing season.

56. S. mirabilis Small. Stem 15–30 dm. tall, glabrous, ridged or rather sharply angled, simple or nearly so below the inflorescence: cauline leaves numerous; blades narrowly elliptic, varying to elliptic-oblanceolate or elliptic-lanceolate, 6–15 cm. long, acuminate, sharply serrate, except often the acuminate tip, thin, hispidulous on the veins and veinlets beneath, rather veiny, somewhat narrowed at the ciliate base, but sessile: thyrse usually ample, but not crowded, the branches hispidulous, with narrow, serrate, acuminate bracts among the secund heads: peduncles hispidulous, involucre cylindric 6 mm. high; bracts thin, the outer lanceolate, acuminate, the inner narrowly linear, with minute, acuminate, inflexed or incurved tips: ray-flowers 5–7; disk-flowers 3–5, usually 2 or 3 fewer than the ray-flowers: achene sparingly hispidulous, sharply ribbed.—Low hammocks, E coast of Fla., N of Cape Canaveral.—Sum.-fall.

57. S. glaberrima Martens. Stem 5–15 dm. tall, glabrous, rather slender, very leafy: middle leaf-blades narrowly lanceolate, 5–10 cm. long, 6–12 mm. wide, firm, rigid, thickish, acute or acuminate, sessile, narrowed and long-tapering at the base, remotely shallowly serrate or entire, reticulate-veined beneath; lower leaf-blades more spatulate, petioled: thyrse rather short, broad, the branches usually spreading or recurved, sometimes erect, glabrous: heads usually secund, 4–6 mm. high: involucral bracts thickish, oblong, obtuse: achene silky. [*"S. missouriensis* Nutt."]—Dry open places, prairies, and barrens, calcareous districts, various provinces N of Coastal Plain, Tex. to Minn. and Tenn.—Sum.-fall.

58. S. serotina Retz. Stem 6–25 dm. tall, appearing glabrous below inflorescence, but minutely pulverulent, glaucous-tinged, closely leafy: larger leaf-blades lanceolate, 6–12 cm. long, 1–2 cm. wide, firm, acuminate, very short-petioled, tapering at the base, sharply closely serrate, glabrous throughout, or hairy on the veins beneath: thyrse large, the branches spreading or recurved, hairy: heads 4.5–6 mm. high, secund: involucre campanulate; bracts narrowly linear, acute: achene sparsely silky. [*S. gigantea* Ait.]—Moist thickets and woodlands, various provinces, Fla. to Tex., Ore., B. C., Ont., and N. B.—Sum.-fall.—One of our most widely distributed species of *Solidago*.

59. S. canadensis L. Stem 5–20 dm. tall, slender, glabrous or pubescent below, strigillose above, and strigose in inflorescence, closely-leafy: larger leaf-blades linear-oblanceolate or linear-lanceolate, 5–10 cm. long, 7–15 mm. wide, thin but firm, sharply acuminate, sharply remotely shallowly serrate, glabrous or pubescent, deep-green above; petioles 3–15 mm. long: thyrse large, the branches spreading or recurved: heads 3.5–4 mm. high, secund: involucre cylindric-campanulate; inner bracts narrowly lanceolate, acute, thickish: achene appressed-pubescent. [*S. rupestris* Raf.]—Rocky banks, various provinces N. of Coastal Plain, S. C. to Tex., N. Dak., and Newf.—Sum.-fall.—As here treated the species includes plants varying widely in pubescence, but all having very small heads.

60. S. Leavenworthii T. & G. Stem 5–12 dm. tall, glabrate towards the base, pubescent above in lines below the petioles, closely short-pubescent in the inflorescence, closely leafy: larger leaf-blades narrowly oblanceolate or lanceolate, 6–18 cm. long, 5–12 (typically about 8) mm. wide, triple-ribbed, but sometimes with the lateral veins little developed, long-acuminate, sessile, sharply serrate or crenate-serrate or nearly entire, short-hispidulous on the midvein above, otherwise glabrous, dull-green above: thyrse large, the branches widely spreading, flower-bearing nearly to the base: heads 5–6 mm. high, secund: involucral bracts linear, thickish: achene minutely appressed-pubescent.   [*S. Nashii* Small]—Damp soil, Coastal Plain, Fla. to S. Car.—Sum.–fall.

61. S. hirsutissima Mill.   Stem 8–30 dm. tall, stout, closely hirsute or pubescent, closely-leafy, much-branched above: larger leaf-blades lanceolate or oblong-lanceolate, 4–10 cm. long, 8–15 mm. wide, strongly triple-ribbed, acute or acuminate, hirsutulous above, pubescent also beneath, sharply but not closely serrate, subpetiolate or sessile: thyrse large, the branches widely spreading, not flower-bearing at the base: heads 4.5–6 mm. high, secund: involucral bracts narrowly linear, acute or obtusish: achene appressed-hairy.   [''*S. canadensis* (Fl. SE. U. S.). ''*S. altissima* L.'']—Dry sunny places, fields, woodlands, and banks, various provinces, Fla. to Tex. and Me.—Sum.–fall.—One of our most widely distributed, abundant, and variable species of *Solidago*. As here treated both it and *S. canadensis* are probably aggregates.

31. EUTHAMIA Nutt.   Perennial, herbaceous plants.   Leaves alternate: blades elongate, herbaceous.   Heads many, in corymbs.   Involucre narrow, few-several-flowered: bracts various, the outer ones linear or nearly so.   Ray-flowers more numerous than those of the disk: corolla yellow, with a slender tube and a very small ligule.   Disk-corollas with a funnelform throat, and tube of about equal length: lobes lanceolate.   Anthers as long as the filaments or longer.   Stigmas lanceolate.   Pappus of capillary bristles.—About 10 species, North American.

Leaf-blades manifestly 3–5-ribbed: ray-flowers 15–20.   1. *E. graminifolia.*
Leaf-blades 1-ribbed: ray-flowers 5–12.
  Leaf-blades mostly over 3 mm. wide: disk-flowers 3 or 4, the
    corollas 5–5.5 mm. long.   2. *E. leptocephala.*
  Leaf-blades mostly less than 3 mm. wide: disk-flowers 5 or
    6, the corollas 3–3.5 mm. long.   3. *E. minor.*

1. E. graminifolia (L.) Nutt.   Plant 13–14 dm. tall: leaf-blades linear, mainly over 4 mm. wide: heads in dense clusters: involucre campanulate, the inner bracts 3.5–4 mm. long: achene pubescent.—Rich soil, fields and thickets, various provinces, Fla. to Miss., Sask., and N. S.— Late sum.–fall.

2. E. leptocephala (T. & G.) Greene. Plant 4–11 cm. tall: leaf-blades linear, mostly over 3 mm. wide: involucre turbinate, the inner bracts 5.5–6 mm. long: filaments shorter than the anthers.—Moist soil, Coastal Plain and adj. provinces, Miss. to Tex. and Mo.—Sum.–fall.

3. E. minor (Michx.) Greene.   Plant 2–8 dm. tall: leaf-blades narrowly linear or linear-filiform, mostly less than 3 mm. wide: involucre cylindric to turbinate-cylindric, the inner bracts 4.5–5.5 mm. long.—Moist sandy soil and low-pinelands, Coastal Plain, Fla. to Tex. and Va.—Sum.–fall, or all year S.

32. OLIGONEURON Small.   Perennial herbs, pubescent at least in the inflorescence.   Leaves alternate: blades entire or nearly so.   Heads in a terminal corymb.   Involucre campanulate, several-flowered: bracts broad, rounded at the apex, the inner much longer than the outer.   Ray-flowers few: corollas with a very long tube and a yellow ligule. Disk-corollas with a funnelform throat and a shorter tube: lobes lanceolate. Filaments nearly as long as the anthers or longer. Stigmas elliptic or ovate-elliptic. Achene stout, glabrous ribbed. Pappus of many capillary bristles.—About 6 species, North American.—Sum.–fall.

Involucre over 5 mm. thick: achene about 3 mm. long. 1. *O. grandiflorus.*
Involucre less than 5 mm. thick: achene about 2 mm. long. 2. *O. Jacksonii.*

1. O. grandiflorus (Raf.) Small. Stem 4–15 dm. tall, rough-pubescent: leaf-blades thick, those of the upper stem-leaves elliptic to ovate, 2–13 cm. long, closely pubescent, shallowly toothed or essentially entire: bracts of the involucre pubescent, the outer ovate: disk-corollas 5.5–6.5 mm. long: achene 12–15-ribbed. [*Solidago rigida* authors not L.].—Dry sandy soil and gravelly banks, various provinces N of Coastal Plain, Ga. to Tex., Man., and Md., and extending E to Mass. Nat. of W N. A.—Fall.

2. O. Jacksonii (Kuntze) Small. Stem 3–12 dm. tall, glabrous or nearly so below: leaf-blades thinnish, those of the upper stem-leaves elliptic to ovate, 2–9 cm. long, serrulate, somewhat scabrous above: bracts of the involucre glabrous, the outer elliptic-ovate. [*Solidago corymbosa* Ell.].—Dry banks and stony soil, Appalachian Plateau and adj. provinces, Ga. to Ala. and Ohio.

33. BRACHYCHAETA T. & G. Perennial herbs, resembling species of *Solidago.* Leaves alternate: blades broad, toothed. Heads numerous, thyrsoid.

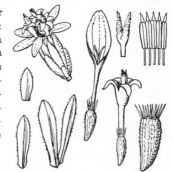

Involucre narrow, few-flowered: bracts various, the outer ones broad, the inner longer and relatively narrower. Ray-flowers few: corollas with a very slender tube and a small yellow ligule. Disk-corollas with a campanulate throat and a tube nearly as long as the throat: lobes triangular-lanceolate. Anthers about as long as the filaments: appendages slender. Stigmas lanceolate. Achene 8–10-ribbed. Pappus of scale-like bristles shorter than the achene.—One species.

1. B. sphacelata (Raf.) Britton. Stem 6–15 dm. tall, pubescent: leaf-blades orbicular-ovate to ovate on the lower part of the stem, ovate to oval or elliptic above: involucre 3.5–4 mm. long. [*B. cordata* T. & G.]—(FALSE GOLDENROD.)—Woods, various provinces N of Coastal Plain, Ga. to Ala., Ind., and S. Va.—Sum.–fall.

34. ASTRANTHIUM Nutt. Annual or perennial, caulescent herbs. Leaves alternate: blades commonly broadened upward, entire or toothed.

Heads solitary or several terminating branches. Involucre broadly campanulate or hemispheric, many-flowered: bracts in 2 or 3 series, rather broad. Ray-flowers numerous: corollas with a very short tube and a white, pink, purple, or violet ligule. Disk-corollas yellow, with a funnelform throat and a very short tube: lobes deltoid. Anthers longer than the filaments. Stigmas triangular. Achene nerved near the margins. Pappus wanting or obsolete.—About 7 species, in Mexico and SC. United States.

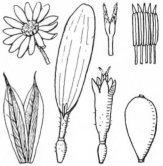

1. **A. integrifolium** (Michx.) Nutt. Stem 0.5–4 dm. tall: leaf-blades spatulate to elliptic, 1–4 cm. long, entire: bracts of the involucre elliptic-lanceolate, 2.5–3 mm. long, or 4 mm. long at maturity: ligules of the ray pale-purple or pale-violet, 6–14 mm. long. [*Bellis integrifolia* Michx.] —(DAISY.)—Low grounds, various provinces N of Coastal Plain, Ala. to Tex., Ark. and Ky.—Spr.–sum.

35. **APHANOSTEPHUS** DC. Annual or biennial, or probably perennial sparingly branched, aster-like herbs. Leaves alternate: blades narrow, some of them toothed or pinnatifid. Heads few, terminating branches. Involucre hemispheric, many-flowered: bracts in few series, rather narrow. Ray-flowers several: corollas with a very short tube and a narrow white, violet, or purple ligule. Disk-corollas yellow, with a cylindric-funnelform throat and a short tube: lobes deltoid. Anthers longer than the filaments. Stigmas obtuse. Achene ribbed. Pappus an entire, toothed, or ciliate crown.—About 5 species, North American.

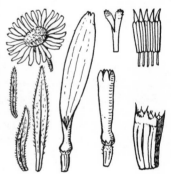

1. **A. skirrobasis** (DC.) Trelease. Stem 1–4 dm. tall, cinerous-pubescent: leaf-blades spatulate to elliptic or linear, 1.5–6 cm. long, sharply toothed or incised below: larger bracts of the involucre 5–6 mm. long, acuminate.—(WHITE-DAISY.)—Dry soil, various provinces, Tex. to Kans.; also Fla.—Spr.–sum.

36. **BOLTONIA** L'Her. Perennial tall, aster-like herbs. Leaves alternate: blades entire, sessile or decurrent. Heads many, widely panicled. Involucre broadly campanulate to hemispheric, many-flowered: bracts narrow or sometimes partly dilated. Ray-flowers often numerous: corollas with a short tube and narrow ligules. Disk-corollas with a narrowly funnelform throat and short tube: lobes triangular. Anthers as long as the filaments or longer. Achene flattened, broadest above the middle, the margins sometimes winged. Pappus a series of short scales usually accompanied by 2–4 bristles.—About 5 species, North American.

Disk about 4–5 mm. broad at maturity: corolla-tube very short.   1. *B. diffusa.*
Disk 7–12 mm. broad at maturity: corolla-tube nearly as long
   as the throat.   2. *B. asteroides.*

1. B. diffusa Ell. Plant 1–2 m. tall: blades of the upper leaves linear to linear-
subulate, 2.5–8 cm. long: outer bracts of the involucre subulate, about 1.5 mm.
long, the inner linear, about twice as long:

ligules linear-elliptic to spatulate, white or
purplish, 5–7 mm. long, white: disk achene
about 4–5 mm. wide: corolla 1–1.5 mm. long,
the throat 2–3 times longer than the tube:
1.5 mm. long. — (DOLL'S-DAISY.) — Low
grounds, Coastal Plain and adj. provinces,
Fla. to Tex., Ill., and S. C.—(*Mex.*)—Fall.

2. B. asteroides (L.) L'Her. Plant 1–2 m.
tall: blades of the upper leaves oblong to
linear, 3–12 cm. long: outer bracts of the
involucre linear-lanceolate, 2–3 mm. long, the
inner slightly longer: ligules linear, white or
pale, 5–6.5 mm. long: disk 7–12 mm. wide:
corolla about 2 mm. long, the throat about
as long as the tube: achene about 2 mm. long.—Stream-banks, and sandy or
gravelly shores, various provinces, Fla. to La., Minn., and Conn.—Sum.-fall.

37. SERICOCARPUS Nees. Perennial low, aster-like herbs. Leaves
alternate: blades entire or toothed. Heads in corymbs. Involucre campanulate to cylindric, several-flowered: bracts broad, or the inner ones sometimes
rather narrow. Ray-flowers several: corollas with a long tube and a narrow,
white or pink ligule. Disk-corollas with a narrowly funnelform throat and a
long tube: lobes lanceolate. Anthers slightly longer than the filaments or
shorter: appendages lanceolate. Achene flattened, 1-nerved. Pappus of
numerous scabrous bristles.—Four species as follows.—WHITE-TOPPED ASTERS.
RAGGED-ASTERS.

Leaf-blades entire.
  Foliage glabrous or nearly so.   1. *S. linifolius.*
  Foliage manifestly pubescent.
    Bracts of the involucre obtuse, firm: peduncles rigid,
     stout.   2. *S. bifoliatus.*
    Bracts of the involucre acute, lax: peduncles weak,
     slender.   3. *S. acutisquamosus.*
Leaf-blades toothed.   4. *S. asteroides.*

1. S. linifolius (L.) B.S.P. Stem glabrous or nearly so, 2–7 dm. tall: blades
of the upper leaves linear, 2–6 cm. long: involucre 4–6 mm. long; inner bracts
often erose at the green tips: disk-corollas

4–5 mm. long: ligules 5–6 mm. long: pappus
whitish. [*S. solidagineus* Nees.] — Acid,
sandy thickets and dry banks, various provinces, Ga. to La., Ohio, and Me.—Sum.-fall.

2. S. bifoliatus (Walt.) Porter. Stem 3–7
dm. tall: blades of the upper leaves spatulate to obovate, 1–3 cm. long: involucre
about 6 mm. high; inner bracts linear-elliptic: disk-corollas over 6.5 mm. long: anthers
longer than the filaments. [*S. tortifolius*
Nees.]—Dry pinelands, Coastal Plain and
rarely adj. provinces, Fla. to La. and Va.—
Sum.-fall, or all year southward.

3. **S. acutisquamosus** (Nash) Small. Similar to *S. bifoliatus* in habit: blades of the upper leaves elliptic-spatulate, 1–3.5 cm. long: involucre longer than that of *S. bifoliatus*; inner bracts linear: disk-corollas less than 6.5 mm. long: anthers shorter than the filaments.—Pinelands, Fla.—Sum.

4. **S. asteroides** (L.) B.S.P. Stem pubescent, 3–8 dm. tall: blades of the upper leaves ovate, elliptic-ovate, or lanceolate, 1.5–4 cm. long: involucre 6–9 mm. long; inner bracts broadly linear, rough-edged above: disk-corollas 5–6 mm. long: ligules whitish, 6–8 mm. long: pappus brownish. [*S. conyzoides* Nees.]—Rocky or sandy, usually dry, woods and thickets, various provinces, Fla. to Miss., Ohio and Me.—Sum.

38. **ASTER** [Tourn.] L.[1] Perennial herbs, various in habit, or rarely annual, occasionally shrubby or spinescent. Leaves alternate: blades broad or narrow, often enlarged and cordate at the base, entire or toothed. Rootstock often horizontal and bearing for several years a subterminal tuft of leaves. Lower, middle and upper cauline leaves often gradually transitional to each other in form, often of dissimilar types. Heads with both tubular and radiate flowers, either corymbed, racemed, or panicled and borne on erect, spreading or secund ultimate branchlets. Involucre hemispheric, campanulate, cylindric, or turbinate: bracts imbricate in several series: the outer usually smaller or shorter than the inner, and somewhat herbaceous or otherwise much modified at or toward the apex. Receptacle flat or convex, alveolate and often delicately fimbrillate. Ray-flowers pistillate, with white, pink, purple, blue, or violet ligules. Disk-flowers perfect, consisting of a tubular base (the tube), swollen above into a throat and 5 short lobes: disks typically yellow, usually changing to red, brown, or purple. Achenes columnar or more or less flattened nerved or ribbed. Pappus-bristles usually numerous, slender, in one series or rarely in two series, the tips of the inner ones sometimes thickened.—About 250 species, mostly North American.—ASTERS.

Blades of the basal and lower cauline leaves cordate and definitely petioled : those of the upper cauline leaves shorter petioled or even sessile or cordate-clasping.
  Blades of the leaves petioled or sessile, not clasping.
    Ligules of the ray white or occasionally roseate.   I. DIVARICATI.
    Ligules of the ray violet, purple, or blue.
      Radical leaves coarse: the blades larger than those of the cauline: foliage (except in *A. mirabilis*) glandular.   II. MACROPHYLLI.
      Radical leaves with blades smaller than those of the cauline: foliage not glandular.   III. HETEROPHYLLI.
  Blades of the upper cauline leaves sessile and cordate clasping.   IV. DIVERSIFOLII.
No leaves at once with cordate and definitely petioled blades.
  Blades, at least of the lower leaves abruptly narrowed or constricted below the middle, the base clasping.
    Plant herbaceous, neither woody nor vine-like.   V. PUNICEI.
    Plant a woody, trailing or climbing vine.   VI. CAROLINIANI.
  Blades of the leaves not abruptly narrowed or constricted below the middle, either clasping, sessile or wing-petioled.
    Blades of the cauline leaves with cordate or auriculate-clasping bases.
      Chief involucral bracts rigid, closely appressed unless at the tip.
        Stem glabrous below the inflorescence (sparsely pubescent in No. 46) : leaves firm, sleek or subsucculent.   VII. LAEVES.

[1] Based on the treatment of the late Edward Sandford Burgess, revised in part for the present work by Edward Johnston Alexander.

Stem and leaves pubescent with short hair.   VIII. PATENTES.
Chief involucral bracts thin, loosely appressed
   and at least the upper half spreading.   IX. SQUARROSI.
Blades of the cauline leaves gradually narrowed or
   rounded at the base, but not clasping.
Leaves not fleshy or succulent.
   Basal and lower cauline leaves not grass-like.
     Inflorescence paniculate, racemose, or ter-
      minating elongate branches.
       Leaf-blades silky or canescent on both
        sides, short, entire or nearly so.   X. SERICEI.
       Leaf-blades glabrous or pubescent, but
        not silky or canescent.
        Blades of the basal leaves nar-
         rowed to winged petioles.   XI. SPECTABILES.
        None of the leaf-blades petioled.
         Inflorescence widely and loosely
          paniculate, the heads scat-
          tered and not arranged uni-
          laterally on the branches.
          Involucral bracts acute or
           acuminate.
           Plants relatively tall,
            spreading by stolonif-
            erous rootstocks.   XII. PANICULATI.
           Plants relatively low, not
            stoloniferous.
            Outer i n v o l u c r a l
             bracts with acu-
             minate, green tips.   XIII. RAMOSISSIMI.
            Outer i n v o l u c r a l
             bracts with obtus-
             ish or merely acute
             tips.   XIV. DUMOSI.
          Involucral bracts very ob-
           tuse, bristle-pointed.   XV. MULTIFLORI.
        Inflorescence much branched,
         but the heads in unilaterally
         racemose arrangement.   XVI. DIFFUSI.
     Inflorescence in a terminal, umbellike
      corymb.
      Leaf-blades usually entire, linear-lance-
       olate; thick.   XVII. PTARMICOIDES.
      Leaf-blades coarsely toothed, broadly
       oblanceolate to broadly elliptic, acu-
       minate; thin.   XVIII. ACUMINATI.
   Basal and lower cauline leaves grass-like.
     Leaf-blades entire or sparingly hack-ser-
      rate above.   XIX. PALUDOSI.
     Leaf-blades with several spinuliform
      teeth, especially near the base.   XX. ERYNGIIFOLII.
Leaves fleshy or succulent.
   Stem solitary, herbaceous, its base not woody :
     plant unarmed.
     Plant perennial : heads mostly over 12
      mm. wide.   XXI. TENUIFOLII.
     Plant annual : heads less than 10 mm.
      wide.   XXII. SUBULATI.
   Stems rush-like, several from a woody base :
     plant spine-armed.   XXIII. SPINOSI.

I. DIVARICATI

Dominant leaves with long-acuminate blades, the teeth
   very sharp : inflorescence broadly corymbose.
Blades of the dominant leaves incurved-acuminate, the
   teeth very salient, curving backward.
Blades of the dominant leaves ovate-lanceolate,
   those of the upper axile leaves short or not
   greatly prolonged.   1. *A. divaricatus.*
Blades of the dominant leaves more elliptic, larger,
   darker, those of the upper axiles or some of them
   greatly prolonged.   2. *A. tenebrosus.*
Blades of the dominant leaves straight-acuminate, the
   teeth straight-backed.   3. *A. stilettiformis.*
Dominant leaves not long-acuminate.
   Inflorescence-clusters convex.
     Sinus (of cordated leaves) deep, enlarged : leaf-
     blades elliptic-lanceolate, curvescent-serrate : disk
     often crimson.   4. *A. excavatus.*

Sinus usually absent: leaf-blades ovate-lanceolate,
    slit-serrate: disk often chestnut color.   5. *A. castaneus.*
Inflorescence narrow, irregular or scant.
    Involucral bracts very broad and short, scale-like.   6. *A. chlorolepis.*
    Involucral bracts narrowly linear.
        Leaf-sinus broad, enlarged: leaf-blades chiefly
            elliptic-acuminate.   7. *A. Boykinii.*
        Leaf-sinus sharp: leaf-blades ovate-acute.   8. *A. flexilis.*

II. MACROPHYLLI

Plant not very rough: leaf-blades not very thick: glandu-
    lar hairs minute-tipped.
    Blades of the lower leaves serrate; sinus deep, narrow.   9. *A. multiformis.*
    Blades of the lower leaves coarsely dentate; sinus shal-
        low, broad.   10. *A. riciniatus.*
Plant extremely rough: leaf-blades very thick: glands
    broadly capitate.
    Leaf-sinus strongly developed: involucral bracts neither
        squarrose nor slender.   11. *A. macrophyllus.*
    Sinus usually absent: involucral bracts squarrose.
        Bracts acute.   12. *A. commixtus.*
        Bracts obtuse.   13. *A. mirabilis.*

III. HETEROPHYLLI

Leaf-blades entire or chiefly so, thick or firm.
    Involucre broadly campanulate: bracts mainly linear,
        thin: leaf-blades dull and scabrous above.   14. *A. Shortii.*
    Involucre cylindric-campanulate; bracts mainly linear-
        subulate, rigid: leaf-blades lustrous and smooth
        above.   15. *A. Camptosorus.*
Leaf-blades serrate or otherwise toothed, at least the lower
    ones.
    Leaf-blades not rough, or not rough on both sides,
        membranous.
        Involucral bracts linear-obtuse or obtusish (acute in
            in a variety of No. 17).
            Leaves with smooth firm blades and the chief
                petioles winged; inflorescence loosely narrow-
                panicled.   16. *A. Lowrieanus.*
            Leaves with thin blades rough above and the
                chief petioles not winged: inflorescence broad
                panicled.   17. *A. cordifolius.*
        Involucral bracts linear-acute or subulate.
            Leaf-blades downy-pubescent or glabrous.
                Plant 6–15 dm. high: blades of the chief leaves
                    ovate-lanceolate, thin, the sinus open: heads
                    compound-racemed.   18. *A. sagittifolius.*
                Plant about 3 dm. high: blades of the chief
                    leaves falcate-lanceolate, the sinus obso-
                    lescent: heads thyrsoid.   19. *A. plumarius.*
            Leaf-blades canescent or hispid above, velvety-   20. *A. trigonicus.*
                hispidulous beneath.
    Leaf-blades rough on both sides, of a spongy crumbling
        texture.
        Blades of the chief leaves elliptic-lanceolate,
            shallow-serrate.   21. *A. azureus.*
        Blades of the chief leaves grass-like.   22. *A. poaceus.*

IV. DIVERSIFOLII

Polymorphous leaf-forms present, no one type strongly
    dominant.
    Leaves not delicate, pubescent beneath, rough when dry:
        inflorescence broad, divergently compound.   23. *A. undulatus.*
    Leaves delicate, firm, rough, with little hair: inflores-
        cence narrowly racemose.   24. *A. Proteus.*
Some dominant leaf-form present.
    Blades of the dominant leaves broad, not greatly
        elongate.
        Blades of the dominant leaves tomentulose beneath,
            ovate-elliptic, thick and rough, diminutive.   25. *A. asperifolius.*
        Blades of the dominant leaves sparse-pubescent
            beneath, petioled, short-cordate, thinnish.   26. *A. sylvestris.*
    Blades of the dominant leaves elongate.
        Blades of the dominant leaves triangular-attenuate.
            Slender plant: leaf-blades chiefly petioled and
                clasping.   27. *A. truellius.*

Robust plant, when fully developed : leaf-blades
chiefly sessile.
Leaf-bases broad : leaf-axils usually foliose.   28. *A. corrigiatus.*
Leaf-bases narrow : leaves very rough.   29. *A. triangularis.*
Blades of the dominant leaves not triangular.
Blades of the dominant leaves ovate-elliptic to
elongate-lanceolate.
Leaf-blades firm, crisp : stem bearing stalked
glands : inflorescence irregular, narrow,
often clavate in outline.   30. *A. claviger.*
Leaf-blades thinnish : plant without glands :
inflorescence somewhat thyrsoid.   31. *A. gracilescens.*
Blades of the dominant leaves linear-elliptic
with straight sides.
Leaf-blades soft, thinnish, many with long
strap-like petioles : inflorescence usually
racemose.   32. *A. linguiformis.*
Leaf-blades very rough, thick, usually ses-
sile : inflorescence decompound.
Plant not glandular : leaves strap-shaped
or thong-like.   33. *A. loriformis.*
Plant somewhat glandular : leaves grass-
like, narrow.   34. *A. Mohrii.*

V. PUNICEI

Leaf-blades entire.   35. *A. puniceus.*
Leaf-blades sharply serrate (except the basal and lower
cauline of No. 36).
Inflorescence irregularly congested or corymbed : pubescence often scanty.
Upper leaves little clasping : bracts of the involucre
with linear-elliptic or linear subulate tips.   36. *A. Elliottii.*
Upper leaves sheathing the axils : bracts of the in-
volucre with deltoid tips.   37. *A. conduplicatus.*
Inflorescence broadly panicled, diffuse, leafy : heads
somewhat remote.
Leaves contracted into a broad petiolar portion : hair
present in lines on the upper stem.   38. *A. prenanthoides.*
Leaves with nearly straight sides, little constricted
below.
Tubercular-based hair scattered over the stem.   35. *A. puniceus.*
No tubercular-based hair on the stem.   58. *A. novi-belgii.*

VI. CAROLINIANI

A woody vine with trailing or climbing stems and branches,
flowering the year round.   39. *A. carolinianus.*

VII. LAEVES

Involucre campanulate.
Leaves glabrous except the edges.
Involucral bracts elliptic-linear with broad rhomboid
or deltoid green tips.
Cauline leaf-blades elliptic, oblanceolate, or ovate :
inflorescence tending to the racemose panicle.   40. *A. laevis.*
Cauline leaf-blades linear to elongate-lanceolate :
inflorescence tending to the corymbose panicle.   41. *A. concinnus.*
Involucral bracts linear, their green tips narrowly
lanceolate.
Cauline leaves linear or narrowly lanceolate.   42. *A. purpuratus.*
Cauline leaves very narrowly linear : heads very
small.   43. *A. attenuatus.*
Leaves glabrous above, often with minute hair beneath.
Leaf-blades entire, short, elliptic, remote.   44. *A. ursinus.*
Leaf-blades often coarsely toothed, prolonged, linear
in type.   45. *A. falcidens.*
Involucre turbinate : leaf-blades scarcely clasping.   46. *A. turbinellus.*

VIII. PATENTES

Stem low : leaves rough : inflorescence broad.
Involucre turbinate-campanulate or turbinate.
Heads 3–4 cm. broad, few and scattered : involucral
bracts pubescent, thick.
Leaf-blades thinnish : heads 6–8 mm. high.   47. *A. continuus.*
Leaf-blades very thick : heads 10–12 mm. high.   48. *A. georgianus.*
Heads about 2 cm. broad, numerous, crowded : in-
volucral bracts merely ciliate, thin.   49. *A. fontinalis.*

Involucre campanulate;
  Bracts linear-elliptic: branches divaricate.   50. *A. patens.*
  Bracts narrow-linear or linear: branches diffuse.   51. *A. tenuicaulis.*
Stem tall: leaves soft pubescent beneath: inflorescence
  narrow.   52. *A. phlogifolius.*

IX. Squarrosi

Heads less than 2.5 cm. broad.
  Stem closely set with small scale-like leaves: involucral
    bracts but slightly spreading.
    Leaves erect and adnate to the stem and its
     branches.   53. *A. adnatus.*
    Leaves more or less reflexed, not adnate to the stem.   54. *A. Walteri.*
  Cauline leaves not markedly, if at all scale-like, not
    closely set: involucral bracts very squarrose.   55. *A. oblongifolius.*
Heads over 2.5 cm. broad.
  Inflorescence widely branched: stem leaves reflexed, not
    elongate, very small.   56. *A. grandiflorus.*
  Inflorescence compact: stem-leaves not reflexed, elon-
    gate.
    Leaves soft-pubescent: broadly clasping: plant little
     branched below the inflorescence.   57. *A. novae-angliae.*
    Leaves not soft-pubescent: but slightly clasping:
     plant much branched.
     Stem rigid: leaves lanceolate, elliptic-lanceolate,
      or linear-lanceolate.   58. *A. novi-belgii.*
     Stem weak: leaves bayonet-like, narrowly linear.   59. *A. elodes.*

X. Sericei

Heads corymbose-paniculate: outer bracts of the involucre
  elliptic, ovate-lanceolate, or lanceolate: achene glabrous.   60. *A. sericeus.*
Heads virgately racemed: bracts linear-elliptic to linear-
  lanceolate: achene pubescent.
  Involucral bracts erect.
    Cauline leaves with elliptic or narrowly elliptic
     blades.   61. *A. concolor.*
    Cauline leaves with linear-elliptic to linear-lanceo-
     late blades.   62. *A. simulatus.*
  Involucral bracts loosely spreading or recurved.   63. *A. plumosus.*

XI. Spectabiles

Upper cauline leaves with broad, chiefly ovate, blades.
Upper cauline leaves with narrow, narrowly elliptic, vary-
  ing to oblanceolate, lanceolate, or linear blades.
  Involucre hemispheric, campanulate, or turbinate-hemi-
    spheric.
    Tips of the involucral bracts foliaceous.   64. *A. Curtisii.*
    Tips of the involucral bracts merely spreading or
     squarrose.
     Bracts of the involucre glandular.
      Involucral bracts mucronate or obtuse: cau-
       line leaves numerous.   65. *A. Smallii.*
      Involucral bracts tapering to acutish tips:
       cauline leaves few.   66. *A. spectabilis.*
     Bracts of the involucre glabrous or merely ciliate.
      Involucral bracts mucronate.   67. *A. surculosus.*
      Involucral bracts acute.
       Stem rigid: leaves narrowly elliptic-lance-
       olate.   58. *A. novi-belgii.*
       Stem weak: leaves narrowly linear.   59. *A. elodes.*
  Involucre narrowly turbinate.   68. *A. gracilis.*

XII. Paniculati

Heads over 16 mm. broad.
  Ligules of the ray white, often fading pink or purplish.
    Leaves glabrous or nearly so.   69. *A. Lamarckianus.*
    Leaves and stem pubescent.   70. *A. missouriensis.*
  Ligules of the ray lavender or violet.
    Rameal leaves with elliptic, rather broad blades:
     inflorescence crowded.   71. *A. salicifolius.*
    Rameal leaves with narrowly linear to subulate
     blades: inflorescence widely branched, the
     heads usually solitary.
     Bracts of the involucre obtuse.   46. *A. turbinellus.*
     Bracts of the involucre acute.   72. *A. Simmondsii.*

Heads less than 16 mm. broad.
　Ligules of the ray white, often fading pink or purplish.
　　Cauline leaves with oval or elliptic blades. 　　　　73. *A. spatelliformis.*
　　Cauline leaves with narrow blades.
　　　Heads abundant, closely panicled. 　　　　　　　74. *A. Tradescanti.*
　　　Heads remotely panicled or sparse. 　　　　　　75. *A. agrostifolius.*
　Ligules of this ray lavender or violet. 　　　　　　　76. *A. pinifolius.*

XIII. RAMOSISSIMI
Ligules of the ray white, sometimes becoming purplish.
　Heads numerous, 8–15 mm. broad.
　　Upper cauline leaves with linear-subulate blades:
　　　plant glabrous or nearly so. 　　　　　　　　　77. *A. ramosissimus.*
　　Upper cauline leaves with linear to narrowly ellip-
　　　tic blades: plant more or less villose. 　　　　　78. *A. pilosus.*
　Heads more scattered, 12–18 mm. broad.
　　Branches divaricate, rigid, prolonged: rameals sub-
　　　ulate. 　　　　　　　　　　　　　　　　　　79. *A. juniperinus.*
　　Branches often upturned or subcorymbose: rameals
　　　flat, linear. 　　　　　　　　　　　　　　　80. *A. Faxoni.*
Ligules of the ray violet, purple or reddish (rarely white). 　81. *A. Priceae.*

XIV. DUMOSI
Rameal leaves merely firm: most peduncles not over 3 cm.
　long. 　　　　　　　　　　　　　　　　　　　82. *A. dumosus.*
Rameal leaves rigid, very conspicuous but minute: pe-
　duncles often 10 cm. or more long.
　Rameal leaves spreading or somewhat recurved: blades
　　obtuse. 　　　　　　　　　　　　　　　　　　83. *A. coridifolius.*
　Rameal leaves erect and usually appressed; blades
　　acute. 　　　　　　　　　　　　　　　　　　84. *A. gracilipes.*

XV. MULTIFLORI
A much branched low-growing plant, with very numerous
　white-liguled heads of flowers. 　　　　　　　　　85. *A. ericoides.*

XVI. DIFFUSI.
Cauline leaves with linear to linear-lanceolate, often min-
　utely hack-toothed blades.
　Involucral bracts very short, not exceeding the achenes. 　86. *A. brachypholis.*
　Involucral bracts exceeding the achenes.
　　Plant sparsely branched, and with few heads. 　　　87. *A. racemosus.*
　　Plant profusely branched: heads very numerous. 　　88. *A. vimineus.*
Cauline leaves with elliptic or lanceolate, more or less
　dentate or serrulate blades.
　Stem and branches sparingly pubescent or glabrate. 　　89. *A. lateriflorus.*
　Stem and branches villous, as also the midrib of the
　　leaf-blades beneath. 　　　　　　　　　　　　　90. *A. hirsuticaulis.*

XVII. PTARMICOIDES
Plant with narrow, entire leaf-blades and a flat-topped
　corymbose inflorescence. 　　　　　　　　　　　91. *A. ptarmicoides.*

XVIII. ACUMINATI
Gregarious plant with thin, deeply toothed leaf-blades, ap-
　pearing as if whorled, and a somewhat corymbose-pan-
　iculate inflorescence. 　　　　　　　　　　　　92. *A. acuminatus.*

XIX. PALUDOSI
Involucral bracts long-ciliate and pubescent: inflorescence-
　branches densely pubescent. 　　　　　　　　　93. *A. paludosus.*
Involucral bracts glabrous, the margins merely scabrose-
　ciliate: inflorescence-branches sparingly pubescent if
　at all so.
　Outer involucral bracts linear to narrowly elliptic but
　　not acuminate: leaf-blades linear to narrowly el-
　　liptic.
　　Plant from a woody, corm-like rootstock, not stolon-
　　　iferous.
　　　Outer involucral bracts usually longer than or
　　　　at least as long as the inner bracts, elongate
　　　　linear-lanceolate, only the innermost abruptly
　　　　acute: bracts numerous. 　　　　　　　　94. *A. pedionomus.*
　　　Outer involucral bracts somewhat shorter than
　　　　the inner, all bracts except the outermost ab-
　　　　ruptly acute: bracts few. 　　　　　　　　95. *A. Gattingeri.*
　　Plant from a stoloniferous, wiry or woody rootstock. 　96. *A. hemisphericus.*
　Outer involucral bracts narrowly linear-acuminate:
　　leaf-blades nearly filiform from a triangular base. 　97. *A. verutifolius.*

XX. ERYNGIIFOLII

Heads sessile and subremote in the upper axils.   98. *A. spinulosus.*
Heads terminal, solitary or clustered.   99. *A. eryngiifolius.*

XXI. TENUIFOLII

Ligules of the ray 5–7 mm. long: heads 4–6 mm. high.   100. *A. Bracei.*
Ligules of the ray 10–20 mm. long: heads 6–8 mm. high.
  Involucral bracts broad: ligules of the ray violet:
  leaves chiefly basal.   101. *A. Chapmani.*
  Involucral bracts linear: ligules of the ray pale-violet
  or nearly white: leaves scattered.   102. *A. tenuifolius.*

XXII. SUBULATI

Involucre campanulate to broadly turbinate.
  Inner bracts of the involucre 5–6 mm. long, acuminate:
  rays fewer than the disk flowers.   103. *A. exilis.*
  Inner bracts of the involucre 3–5 mm. long, acute or
  short acuminate: rays more numerous than the disk-
  flowers.   104. *A. inconspicuus.*
Involucre cylindric to narrowly turbinate.   105. *A. subulatus.*

XXIII. SPINOSI

A rush-like, much branched plant with scattered, white-
rayed heads of flowers, the stem and branches spinescent. 106. *A. spinosus.*

1. **A. divaricatus** L. Stems tufted, 4–6 dm. tall, flexuous, brittle, terete,
glabrate: leaf-blades thin, smoothish, slender-petioled, ovate-lanceolate, closely
and saliently dentate with sharp teeth, in-
curved-acuminate, the basal sinus moderately large, broad and deep: leaves of the
inflorescence (*bracteals*) typically small, sessile, short, ovate-acute to short-oval, nearly
entire: corymb broad, flattish, repeatedly
and widely forked, the slender branches long,
divergent: heads 18–25 mm. broad: ray-
flowers chiefly 6–9; ligules white, or rarely
roseate or slightly crimson: young involucre
short-cylindric; bracts broad, ciliate, the
rounded or subtruncate tips with a broad
green spot: disk turning reddish brown.—
Rich woodlands and thickets, in rather dry
soil, various provinces, Ga. to Ala., Man.,
and N. S.—Fall.

2. **A. tenebrosus** Burgess. Stem glabrate, striate, wide-branched: leaf-
blades large, very thin and smooth, broadly elliptic and conspicuously cut with
coarse remote acuminate curvescent teeth, then abruptly long-acuminate and
entire; most leaves with a broad rounded sinus and slender petiole; those of the
inflorescence prolonged, lanceolate, subentire and sessile: inflorescence broadly
corymbose, often proliferously branched: rays usually 9–12: disk pale-yellow,
turning purplish-brown: outer bracts green, acute, elongate-triangular, the
others linear, obtusish.—Moist, shaded places, Blue Ridge and more N provinces, N. C. to Ohio and Mass.—Late sum.-fall.—Resembles *A. divaricatus*, but
differs in being larger and thinner in all its parts, and in having a different leaf-
form.

3. **A. stilettiformis** Burgess. Stem greenish, slender, weak and often decumbent: predominant leaf-blades deep-green, often roughened above, linear-
elliptic and long-acuminate, with subtruncate base and short petioles, and
closely set with conspicuous sharp straight-backed teeth; some lower leaves
broader, ovate-acuminate with moderate sinus and with double-curved or couch-
ant teeth; axile leaves divaricate, straight-tapered from a sessile truncate base,
everywhere closely slit-toothed, suggesting a barbed stiletto: inflorescence

remotely diffused, but with short pedicels: bracts lingual, nearly uniform, green or mostly so: rays often 7; ligules sometimes reddening at the tips: disk turning brownish-red.—Shaded banks, Blue Ridge and more N provinces, S. C. to Tenn. and Mass.—Fall.—Differs from *A. divaricatus*, especially in stem, leaf-form, and bracts.

4. A. excavatus Burgess. Stem as in *A. divaricatus* L.: leaf-blades thin, smooth, all nearly alike, elliptic-lanceolate with the rounded base abruptly excavated into a deep narrow sinus; their margins continuously low-serrate with curvescent teeth; petioles very short and slender, shorter than the leaf-breadth, replaced by short broad wings at the principal axils; the upper axils often clasped by divaricate triangular-linear bracteals: heads forming convex clusters borne on long suberect branches or reduced to a few distant enlarged heads: bracts ciliate, smooth-backed, pale and thin, short-oblong and obtuse on some subsolitary heads, narrow and acutish on the smaller clustered heads, the inner attenuate and without green tips: ligules of the ray white, or sometimes reddened: disk broad, turning usually purplish-crimson.—Mountain or hillside woods, Blue Ridge and more N provinces, Ga. to N. Y.—Early fall.—Resembles *A. divaricatus*, but the narrower, less-attenuate, more uniform leaf-blades differ in outline, sinus, and teeth.

5. A. castaneus Burgess. Stem glabrate, terete, graceful and wandlike, reddish-brown or greenish, with about 12 delicate straight darker striae, and becoming sinuous in the inflorescence: predominant leaf-blades dull-green, remote, very thin, of a dense and hard texture, minutely granular-roughened when dry, ovate-lanceolate, closely slit-serrate, often unequally decurrent upon the short slender petiole; the lowest leaves much shorter, ovate-acuminate, coarsely serrate and with a moderate sinus; rameal leaves lanceolate-attenuate or often all crescent-like and decurved, sessile by a short cuneate base: inflorescence nearly naked, narrow, composed of several upcurved slender unequal branches bearing close convex clusters, all in flower at once and very short-lived: pedicels long, filiform, upcurved, sometimes bearing small circular bracteals or discules: bracts narrow, linear-obtuse, pale, with bright-green tips: rays often 9; ligules linear, snow-white, excessively thin, and soon pendulous: disk soon turning to rose-brown, sienna, or chestnut-color.—Clayey spots in swamps, various provinces N of Coastal Plain, N. C. to Ohio, also SE N. Y. and Conn.—Early fall.—Resembles *A. divaricatus*; differs in all the above characters, especially in the leaves, bracts, and inflorescence.

6. A. chlorolepis Burgess. Stem strong, glabrate, brownish, terete below, angulate-striate above: leaf-blades large, smooth, very thin, brownish-green, pale beneath, ovate-acute, very coarsely serrate with outflung teeth; sinus deep and sharp; petioles short, slender: axile leaves also large, elliptic-lanceolate, serrate with long forward-directed teeth, the upper ones sessile: inflorescence loose and irregular: heads large, long-peduncled, inclined to be widely separated: ligules of the ray nearly twice the length of the involucre: bracts quite uniform, thick, broad, short and scale-like, with very little ciliation or hair, chiefly golden brown with a short dark-green rounded tip: disk turning crimson. —Mt. woods, Blue Ridge and more N provinces, N. C. to W. Va. and N. Y.— Fall.—Resembles *A. tenebrosus* in the large heads, leaves, teeth, and bracts; differs especially in having the sinus sharp and the bracts rounded, and in the absence and greatly prolonged entire bracteals.

7. A. Boykinii Burgess. Stem slender, greenish and glabrate, much flexed; leaf-blades ovate to elliptic-acuminate, with broad enlarged sinus, set with strong and somewhat outflung teeth; petioles slender: inflorescence lax and irregular, of short branches given off at a wide angle, often continued in clusters among the lower axils; the upper axils often conspicuous with ovate or subcircular sessile bracteals: disk turning reddish brown: ligules of the ray shorter than in its ally, *A. divaricatus* L., from which it differs especially in its more straggling habit, narrow irregular inflorescence, and less-coarsely toothed less prolonged leaves.—Mt. slopes, Blue Ridge, Ga.—Sum.

8. A. flexilis Burgess. Stem low, slender, smooth, and virgate: leaf-blades small, short, thin, dull, dark-green, ovate-acute with the broad double-rounded base bisected by a deep sharp sinus; margins crenate-serrate with low obscure teeth; petioles short: inflorescence scanty, tuft-like, or of a few slim-peduncled heads: bracts narrowly linear, obtuse, quite uniform: plant almost destitute of hair (under lens); otherwise much as *A. divaricatus* L.—Mt. woods, Blue Ridge, Ga.—Sum.—Differs from *A. Boykinii* (with which it grows), especially in its smaller, shorter dull leaf-blades, the sharp sinus, crenate margins, and the obtuse bracts.

9. A. multiformis Burgess. Stem 3–6 dm. high, minutely glandular, erect, slender, terete, or angular-striate in drying: radical leaves usually 2, their blades large, cordate-oblong; cauline leaves of several forms, their blades sharply serrate, rough above, minutely puberulent beneath, those of the lower ones ovate, acuminate, usually with a narrow sinus, those of the upper oval to ovate-lanceolate, petioled, the uppermost elliptic-lanceolate, serrulate, sessile or nearly so: corymb small, its branches upwardly directed: heads 30–40 mm. broad: ray-flowers about 13: ligules rounded and retuse at the apex: bracts green: inflorescence-glands few, almost hidden by the minutely strigose pubescence of the peduncles.—Moist, shaded places, various provinces N of Coastal Plain, N. C. to Pa. and Me.—Sum.-fall.—Resembles *A. macrophyllus*; but its leaves thinner, narrower, more polymorphous, with narrower sinus, and much less harsh; glands fewer, smaller, pale, less continuous down the stem: inflorescence more level-topped, obconic when past: rays bluer, though fading out early.

10. A. riciniatus Burgess. Stem smooth, red, terete, often 3 dm. high: radical leaves usually two, unequal; blades deltoid-cordate or ovate-cordate, with long low curvescent or crenate teeth; basal leaf smaller, the blade orbicular-ovate, without sinus; lower cauline leaves ovate in type, with slight broad open sinus; the others lanceolate or elliptic, with sessile tapered base; leaf-margins dentate below, becoming sharp-serrulate above; petioles slender or with narrow strap-like wings: inflorescence a small loose terminal tuft, with slender ascending pedicels: bracts uniform, lingual: ligules of the ray rose-purplish and then transiently violet, soon turning whitish, linear-biacuminate.—Moist mountain woods, Blue Ridge, N. C.—Late sum.—Plant very smooth and pale; much purplish-red occurs on stem and veins and especially along the bracts; glandular-pubescence very short, with small capitate glands, continuing down the stem to the base; strigose pubescence discoverable by lens on the upper leaves. Resembles *A. multiformis*, but the whole plant smoother and paler, with more red and less violet; leaves smaller, shorter, and often dentate; bracts narrower and more uniform; its colors neither sharp nor dull, but as if seen through a veil.

11. A. macrophyllus L. Stem 6–9 dm. high, reddened, angular: radical leaves developed in large colonies, usually 3 to each rootstock, larger and coarser than the similarly shaped lower cauline leaves (which are developed a subsequent year from the same rootstock); blades broad, cordate with a large irregular sinus, rough above, harsh, thick, the teeth broad, curved, somewhat crenate: upper stem-leaves with oblong blades and short broadly winged petioles, those of the uppermost sessile, acute: inflorescence strigose and glandular, broadly corymbose, irregular: heads 15–30 mm. broad: peduncles short, rigid, thickish: ray-flowers about 12–16; ligules 10–14 mm. long, chiefly lavender, sometimes violet, or rarely pale: bracts conspicuously green-tipped, the outer acute, the inner elliptic, obtuse: disk turning reddish-brown.—Moderately dry, sterile soil, in shaded places, various provinces, rarely Coastal Plain, N. C. to Minn. and N. S.—Sum.

12. **A. commixtus** (Nees) Kuntze. Stem 5–6 dm. high, rather robust, glandular-pubescent over the upper half and strigose above: leaf-blades rough, thick, dull-green, paler beneath, ovate-acute in type, low-serrate or with curvescent teeth, and with slender petioles; only the basal leaves, if any, slightly cordate: upper leaves diminished, finally lanceolate and sessile; bracteals oval, small and few: inflorescence loosely corymbose, with long-ascending pedicels: bracts narrow and acute or subulate, ciliate and minutely puberulent, the apex squarrosely recurved: ligules of the ray pale-violet becoming white: disk becoming copper-brown.—Dry woods, Appalachian provinces, Ga. and Ala.—Late sum.–fall.—From its congeners A. mirabilis and the northern A. Herveyi, this is ·distinguished by the long acumination of its squarrose bracts; and from A. mirabilis by its capitate glands.

13. **A. mirabilis** T. & G. Stem 3–7 dm. tall, sparingly branched above, manifestly pubescent, the branches and especially the branchlets closely and finely pubescent: leaves various, the basal and lower cauline little known, the upper cauline rather remote; blades ovate to oblong-ovate, 2.5–9 cm. long, or those on the branchlets smaller, mostly acute, firm, serrate with appressed subcrenate teeth, mainly sessile, rough-pubescent, with appressed scattered hairs, those of the upper surface fewer, shorter, often spinescent: heads solitary or few in terminal clusters: involucre 8–10 mm. high; bracts firm, linear-elliptic to linear, pubescent without and ciliate, the recurved herbaceous broadly obtuse tips pubescent on both sides: ray-flowers about 20; ligules violet, 1.5–3 cm. long: achene about 3.5 mm. long, glabrous or nearly so, shorter than the tawny pappus whose inner bristles are thickened at the apex.—Near Columbia on the line between the Piedmont and Coastal Plain, S. C.—Fall.—Resembles A. multiformis Burgess, but the bracts squarrose and leaves hispidulous above; cordation seems wanting but will probably yet be found on some basal leaves.

14. **A. Shortii** Hook. Stem 6–12 dm. high, roughish or smooth, slender, paniculately branched above: leaf-blades thick, glabrous or nearly so above, finely and sparingly pubescent beneath; those of the basal and lower cauline leaves ovate or ovate-lanceolate, cordate, rounded or even acuminate at the base, often wholly entire, 5–15 cm. long, dull and scabrous above, borne on slender naked petioles; those of the upper cauline leaves lanceolate, entire, sessile or with short petiole-like bases, not cordate, those of the branches small and scale-like: heads numerous, 25–30 mm. broad: involucre broadly campanulate: bracts mainly linear, acute, puberulent, their green tips appressed: ray-flowers 10–15; ligules linear, violet, 10–12 mm. long: pappus tawny.—Banks and edges of woods, various provinces N of Coastal Plain, Ga. to Ala., Tenn., Ill., and Pa.—Fall.

15. **A. Camptosorus** Small. Stem 4–8 dm. tall, simple and glabrous below the inflorescence, slightly flexuous: leaf-blades lanceolate, attenuate, 6–16 cm. long, resembling those of Camptosorus rhizophyllus, entire, undulate and sometimes crisped, dark-green, smooth and lustrous above, paler and hispidulous beneath, those of the lower cauline leaves deeply cordate at the rounded auricled base, slender-petioled, those of the upper cauline subcordate or truncate at the base: heads relatively few, 25–30 mm. broad: peduncles minutely scaly, scabrous-pubescent: involucre cylindric-campanulate and more or less constricted at the middle, or turbinate when dry; bracts mainly linear-subulate, incurved, the middle and the acute tip deep-green: ray-flowers numerous; ligules deep-purple, about 1 cm. long.—Open woods, Coastal Plain and adj. provinces, Ga. to Ala. (Miss.)? and Tenn.—Fall.—Resembles A. Shortii, but leaf-blades narrower, darker, and shining.

16. A. Lowrieanus Porter. Stem 3–12 dm. tall, glabrous or nearly so through-out, branched: leaf-blades thickish, firm, a little succulent, those of the basal leaves slender-petioled, ovate to ovate-lanceolate, cordate, acute or obtusish, serrate, 5–15 cm. long, those of the cauline leaves ovate to elliptic, often cordate, contracted into winged petioles, the uppermost lanceolate: heads usually not very numerous, 15–25 mm. broad, loosely panicled: involucre turbinate; bracts obtuse or obtusish, appressed: ray-flowers 12–20; ligules light-blue, 6–8 mm. long, but variable in length.—Woods, various provinces N of Coastal Plain, Ala. to Ky., Ia., Conn., and N. C.—Fall.—Resembles *A. cordifolius*, but leaf-blades smooth and glabrous, more wing-petioled, and inflorescence less pubescent.

17. A. cordifolius L. Stem 3–15 dm. high, glabrous or nearly so, much-branched and bushy: leaf-blades thin, rough mainly above, pubescent, sharply serrate, acuminate, those of the basal and lower cauline leaves slender-petioled, broadly ovate-cordate, 5–12 cm. long, those of the upper cauline leaves short-petioled or sessile, ovate or lanceolate: heads very numerous, small, 12–18 mm. broad, handsome: involucre turbinate to cylindric; bracts elliptic-linear, obtuse or obtusish, green-tipped, appressed: ray-flowers 10–20; ligules 6–8 mm. long, blue or violet, sometimes pale, rarely white: pappus whitish.—Rich woods and thickets, various provinces, rarely Coastal Plain, Ga. to Miss., Minn., and N. B.—Late sum.–wint.—*A. cordifolius albearius*, ranging from N. C. and Tenn. to Mass., has the thin leaf-blades usually smoothish, cordate, triangular-lanceolate or broader: inflorescence dense, thyrsoid, not leafy, in form resembling that of the lilac: bracts linear, acute: heads medium-sized: ligules blue.

18. A. sagittifolius Willd. Stem rather slender, 6–15 dm. high, strict, glabrous, or sparingly pubescent above, the inflorescence tall and paniculate with ascending branches: leaf-blades thin, glabrous above or but slightly roughened, usually glabrate beneath, those of the basal and lower leaves ovate-lanceolate to lanceolate, with cordate or rarely sagittate base, sharply serrate, acuminate, 7–15 cm. long, with slender naked or narrowly margined petioles: blades of the upper cauline leaves lanceolate, sessile, or on short and usually margined petioles, serrate or entire, those of the branches very much smaller, linear-subulate: heads 16–20 mm. broad, numerous, crowded, racemose: involucre turbinate; bracts linear-subulate, glabrous or nearly so, their tips green and slightly spreading: ray-flowers 10–15; ligules light-blue or purplish, 6–8 mm. long: pappus whitish.—Dry soil, various provinces N of Coastal Plain, Ala. to Miss., Kans., N. D., N. B., and N. C.—Late sum.–fall.—Resembles *A. cordifolius* L.; but its bracts narrower, subulate-acuminate, and its inflorescence almost without leafiness, the axile leaves being reduced, narrowed and stringy rather than foliaceous.—*A. sagittifolius dissitiflorus*, ranging from Fla. to Miss., Okla., and N. Y., differs from the typical form in its broader looser pyramidal inflorescence, its somewhat larger and longer-peduncled heads, and less serrate leaf-blades none of which may be cordate.

19. A. plumarius Burgess. Plant about 3 dm. high, chiefly composed of the dense plume-like violet inflorescence: stem smooth, zigzag: leaf-blades very smooth and firm, thickish, chiefly lanceolate-acuminate and slit-serrate, inclined to be strongly falcate at apex and unequal at the slightly cordate broadish base, measuring 7 x 1.5 cm. or less; veins strongly incurved; petioles narrow-margined; lower axile leaves conspicuous, but rapidly diminished, soon becoming narrowly falcate-lanceolate and entire, sessile by a taper subcuneate base: inflorescence otherwise naked, ovate-lanceolate in outline: bracts narrow, acute, their distinct enlarged green tips chiefly spatulate.—Mountain tops, chiefly on balds at 4,800–5,000 ft., Blue Ridge, N. C.—Fall.—Resembles a dwarf *A. sagittifolius*, but differs in leaves, bract-tips, and absence of bracteals.

20. A. trigonicus Burgess. Plant profusely branched, with rigid glabrate brownish stems and long flagellate ascending branches, which are closely short-branched or are spiciform and beset with small remotish subsessile heads: stem 8 dm. high or less: leaf-blades thick and heavy, somewhat canescent or hispid above, velvety-hispidulous below; leaf-form elongate triangular; the truncate base slightly rounded at the corners, and sometimes a little subcordate; leaf-blades 3 x 1 cm. or more, acute or obtusish, the sides straight, serrate or crenate; petiole short, forming a narrow cuneate wing: rameals stiff, very numerous, overlapping and appressed, linear-elliptic: heads small, hardly 2 cm. broad: bracts linear-acute, the green tip lanceolate.—Plains and prairies, various provinces, Ala. to Tex. and Kans.—Fall.

21. A. azureus Lindl. Stem 3–12 dm. high, slender, stiff, rough, with numerous ascending or patent branches: leaf-blades thick, of a peculiar crusty texture when dry, scabrous on both sides, those of the basal and lower cauline leaves cordate, ovate to elliptic-lanceolate in type, shallow-serrate, usually acute, 5–15 cm. long, with slender often pubescent petioles; those of the upper cauline leaves with short petiole-like bases or sessile, lanceolate or linear, entire; those of the branches reduced to small appressed scales: heads numerous, 20–25 mm. broad: involucre turbinate; bracts glabrous, linear-oblong, abruptly acute, imbricate, their broad sharp green tips appressed: ray-flowers 10–20; ligules bright-blue, 6–8 mm. long: pappus tawny.—Prairies and borders of woods, various provinces, rarely Coastal Plain, Ga. to Tex., Kans., Minn., and N. Y.—Sum.-fall.—Resembles *A. undulatus* L.; but leaves hispidulous on both surfaces: flowers smaller; rays darker and bluer; pubescence scanty.—*A. azureus scabrior*, ranging from La. to Mo., Minn., and Ont., has an extremely rough stem with more erect branches and principal leaves with elliptic-lanceolate, entire, long-petioled, noncordate blades.

22. A. poaceus Burgess. Stem diffusely and repeatedly much-branched, 8 dm. high or less: leaves very rough and stiff, of grass-like form; chief leaf-blades linear-elongate or falcate, often 13 cm. long, 0.5 cm. in uniform breadth, usually also with a narrow-margined petiole of 2–5 cm., apt to be erect, and with stout papillose-based bristles; radicals elliptic, measuring 8 x 1 cm. or less: inflorescence irregular, on very long and straggling branches, which are often for 1.5 to 3 dm. clothed with minute subulate sub-appressed bractlets: heads small, little over 1 cm. broad: bracts of the involucre linear, with long sharp tips.—Plains and prairies, various provinces, Ala. to Tex., Okla., and Mo.—Sum.-fall.—Represents the extreme of attenuation among the kindred of *A. azureus*.

23. A. undulatus L. Stem stiff, 3–10 dm. high, closely rough-pubescent, divaricately branched above: leaf-blades usually thick, rough on both sides when dry, pubescent beneath, dentate, undulate or entire, acute or acuminate, those of the radical leaves small, orbicular to ovate, soft-downy; the lower cauline leaves ovate, with cordate base, 5–12 cm. long, the naked petioles expanding into a clasping base, at least in some leaves; middle cauline leaves similar, lanceolate or elliptic; upper cauline leaves sessile or clasping, chiefly lance-elliptic; branch-leaves subulate, small and suddenly reduced: heads numerous, racemose and somewhat secund on the spreading branches, 16–20 mm. broad: involucre broadly turbinate: bracts of the involucre linear-elliptic, slightly pubescent, acute or acutish, their broad green tips appressed: ray-flowers 8–15; ligules usually pale-violet, 6–10 mm. long: pappus whitish.—Dry soil, various provinces, Fla. to Miss., Ark., Ont., and N. B.—*A. Baldwinii* T. & G., based on the upper part of a specimen of one of the undulatus group, cannot definitely be placed under any species on account of the absence of lower leaves, so that the name is best dropped from this treatment.

24. A. Proteus Burgess. Plant small, racemose, with many cordated leaves, of firm roughish texture but with little hair: stem slender, apt to be glabrate, and 3 dm. high, sometimes 7 dm., virgate and little branched, but sometimes forking near the base: leaves somewhat remote; blades delicate, polymorphous, not thick or thin; radicals numerous, resembling violet leaves, 4.5 x 2.5 cm. or less, cordate-ovate, almost acute, finely subcrenate, often nodding on their prolonged and very slender petioles: cauline leaves tend to assume about 4 types; the first, or basal, all similar to the radical, but with straighter sides, narrowly cordate-triangular and acutish, minutely serrulate, soon becoming entire; second form, triangular-lanceolate, sloping into a distinct winged petiole; third, narrowly linear or lanceolate, sessile by a short broad taper base; fourth, elliptic-acute, sessile by a broad base or with very short broad wing, numerous, much-reduced and disappearing among the middle axils: inflorescence nearly nude, a simple open raceme with spreading heads, or each head replaced by a racemose subsecund branch: ligules of the ray violet: disks not so dark as in related species: bracts linear, briefly acuminate, closely imbricate, the green tips conspicuous, narrow diamond-form or narrow lanceolate.—Dry ground, Coastal Plain, Fla. to Miss. and N. C.—Sum.–fall.

25. A. asperifolius Burgess. Plant small, racemose, minutely tomentulose throughout, very rough and heavy in texture: stem often but 3 dm. high: leaves subcoriaceous; blades hispid, subentire, obtuse, ovate-elliptic and longer than their short petioles; rameal leaves minute, adnate, subulate-filiform; radical leaves and chief caulines sometimes subcordate; petioles slender, naked or narrowly margined; amplexicaul dilation absent or rare: inflorescence a loose simple or compound naked receme, or several racemes which may become more short-peduncled and leafly: heads smaller than in *A. undulatus*: bracts of the involucre fewer, slightly pubescent, appressed, linear-elliptic, acute, with distinct rhomboid green tips. [*A. asperulus* T. & G., not Wall.]—Dry or sandy soil, Coastal Plain, Fla. to La. and S. C.—Fall.—The most hispid-pubescent and rounded-leaved of the southern correlatives of *A. undulatus*.

26. A. sylvestris Burgess. Stem slender, scabrous, erect, pale-green, usually 4 dm. high, minutely pubescent: leaves resembling *A. undulatus*, but blades broader, shorter, thinner, deeper-green, more uniformly petioled; predominant leaf-form broadly short-cordate, acute, with rounded basal lobes, deep or excavated sinus, broadly crenate or entire margin: petioles narrow, long and numerous, dilated at the base, seldom otherwise winged: upper leaves elliptic-acute, soon sessile; rameals uniform and spreading as in *A. undulatus*, oval to linear-elliptic; radicals small, orbicular, short-petioled; pilose and webby hair present on the leaves beneath but not velvety: inflorescence irregularly spreading or ascending, of long racemose branches: heads rather few: pedicels distinct, often 3 cm. long: ligules of the ray violet: bracts of the involucre linear, triangular-acute at apex, with large and broad rhomboid green tips.—Open woodlands, various provinces N of Coastal Plain, S. C. to Ala. and N. Y.—Fall.

27. A. truellius Burgess. Plant small, erect, with little hair: stem erect, strong but slender, rough: leaves subentire 5 x 2 cm., thickish, firm, rough, typically triangular-lanceolate with sides straight-tapered from the prominently shouldered truncate or cordate base, in form suggesting a mason's trowel: plant remarkable for its numerous short narrow petioles with large basal dilation, and above these, its strap-like petioles with slight basal dilation; radicals cordate-orbicular, crenate, somewhat velvety; axiles often deflexed, narrow-ovate; rameals spreading: ligules of the ray short, purplish-blue: disks soon reddish-brown: bract-tips diamond-shaped, broad and bright-green.—Sandy thickets, various provinces, rarely Coastal Plain, Ga. to Ala., Ky., and Vt.—Fall.

28. A. corrigiatus Burgess. Plant tall, robust, rough, with little hair, with predominantly narrow spearhead-shaped much-ruffled sessile leaves, foliose in the axils, and with long and high inflorescence, small blue-violet heads and lozenge-tipped bracts: stem about 12 dm. high, or more, brown, terete-striate, rough, with short scattered strigose hair above: leaves tending to be narrowly lanceolate and broad-based, slanting straight both ways from near the base, tending to the form of an acute narrow spearhead, about 7 or 12 x 2 cm., very slowly diminished through the inflorescence; radicals small, short and broad, somewhat cordate-oval; a very few lower cauline leaves develop obscure cordation and a narrow petiole; rameals not conspicuous, linear-acute, somewhat appressed: inflorescence irregularly compound-racemose, long and rather narrow, disproportionately large for the plant; its branches tend to be spreading and short, its peduncles long or at least distinct, its heads medium-sized or less, its rays much darker than in typical *A. undulatus.*—Dry hillsides, various provinces, Ala. to La., Ohio, N. Y., and Conn.—Fall.—Peculiar in its strong tendency to become corrigiate, or cross-tied, by developing two conspicuous divaricate narrow-lanceolate leaf-blades (branch-form leaves) in the lower or middle axils of the cauline leaves.

29. **A. triangularis** Burgess. Plant cinereous green, tall, robust, very rough, with little or no obvious hair, like *A. corrigiatus;* but with leaves ovate-triangular-acuminate, thicker and with very pronounced acumination: stem dull reddish-brown, somewhat terete, 9 dm. high or more: leaves very numerous, sometimes foliosely corrigiate in the axils; blades not ciliate, beneath with slight short scattered strigose hair, on the upper surface close-set with pale slender rigid aculei pointing away from the midrib and thickened at the base; leaf-form ovate-triangular, long-acuminate, suddenly contracted at the sessile base, subclasping only: inflorescence rather narrow, of loosely-ascending branches with a brushy top, uniformly close-set or catenate with conspicuous appressed overlapping elliptic chain-like bracteals: heads small: ligules of the ray purple-blue: bracts of the involucre linear-elliptic, their tips apt to be of broad diamond form. [*A. undulatus triangularis* Burgess]—Open sandy slopes, various provinces, S. C. to Ala. and N. Y.—Fall.

30. **A. claviger** Burgess. Plant wand-like, apt to spring several from a common base, with glandular pubescence along the middle of the stem, and with leaves of a crisp firm texture: stem greenish, moderately and finely pubescent, or glabrate, smooth to the eye, about 6 dm. high or more: leaves quite uniform; blades ovate-elliptic, thickish sub-entire or crenulate, acute, chiefly with a short strap-like wing broadest at its base; the slight pubescence becoming a little rough in drying and the leaves spongy-coriaceous; a very few basal leaves cordate: inflorescence irregular and narrow-elliptic or clavate, sometimes narrowly pyramidal: heads rather small: ligules of the ray violet or purplish-violet: bracts linear-acute with the medium-sized tips broad-lanceolate to diamond-form; scattered capitate glandular hairs are mingled on the stem with dry strigose hair and also with broken down strigose hairs which become irregularly glandular-thickened; the definitely formed capitate glands are colored violet, only slightly thicker than their stiff stub-like stalks.—Wood borders, various provinces N of Coastal Plain, Ala. to N. Y. and Conn.—Fall.

31. **A. gracilescens** Burgess. Plant slender and less pubescent, less rough and more thyrsoid than its congener *A. undulatus:* stem slender, often 6 dm. high and somewhat arching: leaves quite uniform; blades large and conspicuous, thin, soft, elongate-lanceolate, chiefly sessile, 12 x 4 cm. or less, scantily soft-pubescent, not velvety like *A. undulatus,* only a little rough when dry, subentire, pale-green with paler midrib; axiles narrow-ovate, rameals elliptic-linear or spreading; cordation of leaf-base and dilation of petiole-base usually little developed; radicals sagittiform-cordate with acute sinus: inflorescence loose, ovoid or thyrsoid, with distinct pedicels 3 cm. long or less: heads larger and remoter than in its relative *A. undulatus:* bracts of the involucre linear-elliptic,

suddenly acute, the tips chiefly conspicuous, short, incurved-triangular-aculeate.
—On "balds," in half-shade, or edges of rich woods, Blue Ridge and more
N Provinces, S. C. to N. Y.—Quite common and rather showy.—Late Sum.—
Fall.

32. A. linguiformis Burgess. Small racemose plants with little hair, or cordation, of soft thin texture, tending to great development of elongate linguiform
leaves, partly with long strap-like winged petioles, and the upper ones sessile by
a broad auricled base; stem 4–5 dm. high, minutely pubescent only; leaves tend
to be remarkably entire and obtuse, sage-green, closely approximate; radicals
few, narrowly ovate-elliptic, but slightly cordated, with rather long slender
petioles; lower caulines lance-elliptic, 7 x 2 cm. or less, abruptly rounded and
obtuse at base and apex, often surpassed by the strap-like petiole; other caulines
and branch-leaves sessile-auriculate, prolonged linear-oblong or pandurate-
elliptic, often rounded-truncate at apex; axiles linear-acutish: inflorescence
usually a loose and nearly simple raceme with small distinct long-pedicelled
heads: bracts of the involucre lax, linear, acute, the green tips rhomboid.—
Dry, fertile thickets, near Jacksonville, Fla.—Sum.—Fall.

33. A. loriformis Burgess. Plant rough, with but little hair, tall, narrow,
with strap-like leaves seldom developing petioles or cordation: stem somewhat
purple, terete, erect, brittle, slender, and 4–6 dm. high, or stout and even 12
dm. high: leaves dull-green; blades thick, rigid when dry, rough, only minutely
pubescent beneath, their type linear-elliptic and obtuse, with sides nearly
straight from a sessile clasping base; margins apt to be much ruffled, often
minutely and closely erose, occasionally gashed with a few coarse remote blunt
protruding teeth; petioles slightly developed, though often a few lower leaves
slope into a strap-like petiole; radicals apt to be oval-elliptic, with little or no
cordation; upper caulines and axiles linear-lanceolate, acutish, more contracted
at the base: as in *A. corrigiatus*, the inflorescence is tall and narrow, the heads
smaller than in *A. undulatus* and the ligules of the ray a more blue-purple:
bracts of the involucre narrower, the green tips diamond-form or lanceolate.
[*A. undulatus loriformus* Burgess]—Sand-barrens, Coastal Plain and adj.
provinces, Fla. to Ala. and Mass.—Fall.

34. A. Mohrii Burgess. Plant profusely and flagellately branched with very
naked bushy inflorescence: stem rough, rigid, with many small dark capitate
slender-stalked glands intermixed among strigose hairs; many of the latter are
viscid, becoming broken down and irregularly incrassate: leaf-blades long, narrowly linear and grass-like, thickish, harsh, of uniform breadth, minutely
rugulose above, or slightly acute; petioles obscure, slender or winged; occasional
radical or basal leaves are shorter, broader, somewhat cordate-lanceolate, and
at the slightly shouldered base are contracted into a distinct petiole; with
but obscure or rare sinus and amplexicaul enlargement; axile leaves and rameal
chiefly linear-oblong, clasping by a broad base: heads small, long-peduncled
(5–7 cm.) racemosely compounded: bracts of the involucre linear-elliptic,
acute, green-tips prominent, lance-elliptic: ligules of the ray reddish-purple,
12–15 or less. [*A. Baldwinii* β T. & G.]—Sandy soil, Coastal Plain, Fla. to La.
and Ga.—Fall.—Fine strigose tomentum extends down the peduncles and much
of the stem. Represents the extreme attenuation of the *A. undulatus* types.

35. A. puniceus L. Stem 9–25 dm. tall, usually stout, purplish, broadly
corymbosely or racemosely branched above, hispid with rigid hairs rising from
a reddened tubercular base: leaf-blades lanceolate to elliptic-lanceolate, 7–15
cm. long, acuminate, sessile and clasping by a broad or narrowed base, sharply
serrate (or some upper ones entire), usually very rough above, pubescent on the
midrib beneath: heads generally numerous, 2–4 cm. broad: involucre nearly
hemispheric; bracts linear or elliptic, attenuate, imbricate in about 2 series,

glabrous or ciliate, green, loose, spreading, nearly equal, sometimes broadened: ray-flowers 20–40; ligules light-violet (sometimes purplish or pale), 10–14 mm. long, showy: pappus nearly white: achene pubescent.—Swamps and ditches, various provinces, Ga. to Ala., Minn., Ont., and N. S.—Sum.-fall.

36. **A. Elliottii** T. & G. Stem 5–11 dm. tall, glabrous or pubescent in lines, corymbosely paniculate above: leaves rather numerous; blades thickish, various, those of the basal and lower cauline elliptic to oblanceolate, 2–3 dm. long, with shallow appressed or rounded teeth, narrowed into broad petiole-like bases, those of the upper cauline elliptic to elliptic-lanceolate, appressed-serrate, acute or acuminate, sessile or with petiole-like bases: heads numerous, chiefly crowded at the end of each branch: bracts of the involucre very narrow, lax and often recurved, their tips linear-elliptic or linear-subulate, and spreading: ray-flowers numerous; ligules narrowly linear, 9–11 mm. long, bright-purple: achene glabrous or nearly so.—Swamps, Coastal Plain, Fla. to N. C.—Fall.—Resembles *A. puniceus*, but inflorescence more corymbosely crowded and level-topped: bracts more attenuate and more spreading: ligules of the ray deeper-colored: hairs tubercular at the base or wanting.

37. **A. conduplicatus** Burgess. Stem purple-red, nearly smooth, but with some lines of straggling thick-based bristles; branches short, rigidly spreading, congested toward their ends with irregularly crowded heads: leaf-blades sessile, spatulate-linear, thick, smooth beneath, very rough above, without obvious veins except the pale-green midrib, entire or remotely crenulate-serrulate above the middle; axils sheathed by the conduplicate bases of the upper leaves: rameal leaves short, crowded, spreading and irregular: heads almost sessile: ligules of the ray blue or violet, fading whitish: bracts of the involucre linear, with triangular-acute apex, white scarious edges and bright-green conspicuous deltoid tip.—Moist soil near Biltmore, in the Blue Ridge of N. C.—Fall.—Allied also to *A. novi-belgii* and *A. puniceus*.—Plant chiefly pale-green and smooth.

38. **A. prenanthoides** Muhl. Stem 3–6 dm. high, glabrous below, pubescent above, flexuous, much-branched: leaf-blades thin, elliptic to ovate-lanceolate, 7–15 cm. long, sharply and coarsely serrate, scabrous above, glabrous or nearly so beneath, acuminate, abruptly narrowed below into a broad-margined entire petiole, the base dilated and auriculate-clasping: heads usually numerous, 25 mm. broad or more: involucre hemispheric; bracts linear, acute, green, spreading, imbricate in 3 or 4 series, the outer shorter: ray-flowers 20–30; ligules violet, 8–12 mm. long: pappus tawny: achene pubescent.—Moist soil, various provinces N of Coastal Plain, Tenn. to Ia., Wis., and Mass.—Sum.-fall.—Unlike other asters in its leaf-form, characteristically a suborbicular base and an ovate-acuminate tip, connected by a strap-like middle.

39. **A. carolinianus** Walt. Stem shrubby, widely or diffusely branched, 1–4 m. long, arching or climbing, finely and softly more or less grayish pubescent: leaves relatively few, those of the stem and main branches with elliptic or elliptic-lanceolate entire blades 4–11 cm. long, acute or acuminate at the apex and usually somewhat sagittate and clasping at the base, minutely pubescent: heads solitary or clustered at the ends of spreading conspicuously leafy branches: involucre hemispheric, 6–8 mm. high; bracts narrow, the outer more or less spatulate, the inner linear, all with spreading or recurved and more or less foliaceous dark-green tips minutely pubescent within and without: ray-flowers numerous; ligules pale-purplish or pinkish, 1.5–2 cm. long: achene glabrous.—In and about swamps, Coastal Plain, Fla. to S. C.—Fall, continuing in flower the year round.

40. **A. laevis** L. Stem 6–12 dm. high, usually stout, glabrous, often glaucous, branched or simple: leaf-blades thick and almost leathery, very smooth, entire

or serrate, slightly rough-margined, the upper all sessile and strongly cordate-clasping elliptic-lanceolate, oblanceolate or ovate, acute or obtusish, 2–10 cm. long; those of the basal and lower cauline leaves gradually narrowed into winged petiolar bases, those of the branches often small and scale-like: heads usually numerous, about 25 mm. broad: involucre campanulate; bracts of the involucre rigid, acute, appressed, broadly green-tipped, imbricate in several series: ray-flowers 15–30; ligules blue or violet: pappus tawny: achene glabrous or nearly so.—Dry, or stony soil, various provinces, Ga. to La., Kans., N. D., Ont. and Me.—Fall.—Remarkable among asters for its smooth, cool, polished surfaces.

41. A. concinnus Willd. Similar to narrow-leaved forms of *A. laevis* in habit, the stem glabrous or sparingly pubescent above, 3–9 dm. high, paniculately branched: leaf-blades elongate-lanceolate to linear, entire (or sometimes serrulate), 2–7 cm. long, those of the upper cauline leaves sessile, somewhat clasping, those of the basal and lower cauline leaves spatulate, or elliptic, narrowed into margined petiole-like bases: heads usually numerous, about 25 mm. broad: bracts of the involucre with rhomboid acute herbaceous tips: ray-flowers with violet to purple ligules.—Open woods or dry soil, various provinces N of Coastal Plain, N. C. to Ark. and Conn.—Fall.—Resembles *A. laevis*, but more corymbed, the heads smaller and leaves narrower.

42. A. purpuratus Nees. Stem 4–12 dm. high, slender, glabrous, simple, or branched above, the branches sometimes puberulent: leaf-blades firm, glabrous, dark-green, entire, the upper sessile and clasping at the base, elongate-lanceolate or long-linear, 5–12 cm. long, acuminate; basal and lower cauline leaves petioled, elliptic-lanceolate, obtusish; those of the branches very small: heads rather few, loosely racemose, 16–25 mm. broad: involucre broadly campanulate: bracts coriaceous, lance-acuminate, appressed, imbricate in several series, the green tips lanceolate: ray-flowers 5–10, their ligules blue or violet, 6–10 mm. long: pappus tawny: achene glabrous.—Dry soil and open woods, various provinces, Ga. to Tex., Ark., and Va.—Late Sum.—Fall.—Resembles *A. laevis*, but its heads more racemed, apt to be solitary on long branches, the bracts narrower-tipped, the leaves greatly narrowed, the blades long-linear.

43. A. attenuatus Lindl. Stem glabrous, 6 dm. high or less: leaf-blades very narrowly linear with straight sides almost from the sessile base to the acute apex, very smooth but with hispid revolute margin, 1.5 dm. long or less, about 1 cm. broad, mostly sessile: inflorescence spicate-racemose, attenuate: bracts as in *A. purpuratus* in form, from which it differs in its leaves, its smaller heads, more narrowed inflorescence of short branches, and somewhat squarrose lower bracts which pass gradually into spreading bractlets on the pedicels. [*A. virgatus* γ T. & G.]—Dry soil, Coastal Plain, Ala. to La.—Fall.

44. A. ursinus Burgess. Stem stout, smooth, glabrous below the inflorescence, very peculiar in the crowded nodes of its base and inflorescence, there 1 cm. or less apart, and in the abruptly remote nodes of the stem between, nearly 10 cm. apart: leaves elliptic, chiefly fascicled at the base and there often short-lanceolate or spatulate, sometimes serrulate and 1–2 cm. broad, with ciliate petioles; minute stubby pubescence covers some even of the larger leaves beneath, and occurs on the main stem and branches throughout the inflorescence, which tends to ellipsoid and broadly racemose type: heads chiefly solitary on virgate branches, twice the size of *A. attenuatus*, 3 cm. broad, 1 cm. high: pedicels shaggy with conspicuous uniform closely-imbricate bractlets, which are 1 cm. long, each appressed half-way and with outcurved tip; upper bractlets more spreading and furry and passing indistinguishably into the bracts of the involucre; involucre loose, broad and short; bracts chiefly linear-attenuate, tapering from the base, their green tips large, lanceolate, and conspicuous. [*A. virgatus* β T. & G. not Banks]—Mountain slopes, Blue Ridge, Ga.—Late sum.-fall.

45. A. falcidens Burgess. Plant of firm smooth texture like *A. laevis*, with similar rays and bracts: stem slight or delicate, not rigid, generally arcuate, terete, reddened, usually under 5 dm. high; leaf-blades very thin, of linear type, apple-green, glaucescent, of dense opaque texture, remarkable for the absence of veins (unless under a strong lens), varying from exceedingly smooth and glabrous (even with the margin without ciliation or roughness) to leaves with minute hair beneath and some scabrous hair at the margins: radical leaves very pale and glaucous, with oval or obovate blades, the apex rounded or obtuse, a few acutish, their petioles narrow and longer; lower cauline leaf-blades lance-elliptic, entire, 7 x 2 cm., equalled by the narrow petiole (and resembling *Pogonia ophioglossoides*); middle caulines linear, often 2 dm. long by only 1 cm. broad, sessile, short-acuminate, frequently with several large projecting teeth which are nearly opposite or remotely scattered; these notches may be increased till the leaf is pinnatifid, or reduced to many shallow crenations, or may be replaced by prolonged oblanceolate-linear entire leaves: upper cauline leaves often numerous, 10–15 or more, ascending or spreading entire, linear, straight-sided, tapering slightly to each end but not acuminate, 15 cm. by 1.5 cm., finally becoming short, linear-acute and erect, until 5 cm. long: axiles subulate, rapidly reduced, leaving the inflorescence nearly naked: rameals minute, mostly erect-appressed, almost overlapping, broadly subulate or seta-ceous; branches ascending, short and filiform, reaching 5 cm. and bearing a single head, or 10 cm. and bearing several: heads often few, forming a short raceme: ligules of the ray pale-blue: disks early turning deep-crimson: bracts of the involucre linear-elongate, suddenly acute, their green tips rhomboid. [*A. gracilentus* T. & G., not Banks.]—Upland woods, Blue Ridge and more N provinces, Ala. to Ark., Pa., and N. C.—Fall.—Differs from the allied *A. laevis*, *A. concinnus* and close relatives, in its longer linear straight-sided leaf-blades and the coarse teeth.

46. A. turbinellus Lindl. Stem 6–9 dm. high, slender, paniculately branched, glabrous below, puberulent above: leaf-blades firm, lanceolate, or elliptic-lanceo-late, 5–7 cm. long, entire, ciliate, acute or acuminate, those of the basal and lower cauline petioled, those of the upper sessile, those of the branches much smaller: heads about 25 mm. broad, mostly solitary at the ends of the branches: involucre turbinate; bracts elliptic, coriaceous, obtuse, appressed, imbricate in 5 or 6 series, their tips green only at the apex: ray-flowers 10–20; ligules 6–10 mm. long, violet: pappus tawny: achene finely pubescent.—Dry soil, especially on prairies, various provinces, La. to Ark., Kans., and Ill.—Sum.–fall.

47. A. continuus Small. Stem 5–11 dm. tall, pubescent, much branched above: leaf-blades spreading, more or less fiddle-shaped or oblong, 2–5 cm. long, acute, shallowly serrate or nearly entire, ciliolate, scabrous-pubescent on both sides, sessile and clasping at the base: heads showy, solitary or clustered at the end of the spreading closely pubescent branches: involucre turbinate-campanulate or tur-binate; bracts numerous, linear or nearly so, erect or with slightly spreading green tips, acute, passing into the numerous scales of the peduncle: ray-flowers 12–15; ligules violet, 1–1.5 cm. long: achenes pubescent. Resembles *A. patens* Ait., but its bracteals closer; the involucre narrowly turbinate.—Dry soil, often in open woods, various provinces, Ala. to Tex., Kans., and Ark.—Fall.

48. A. georgianus Alexander. Stem 4.5–8 dm. tall, rough-pubescent, spar-ingly branched: leaf-blades sessile, elliptic to obovate, rough pubescent and very thick, stiff-spreading, auriculate-clasping at the base, entire, acute or obtuse, 3–7 cm. long; leaves of the branches much smaller, sometimes bract-like: heads 3–4 cm. broad, solitary at the ends of branches or branchlets; involucre turbinate-campanulate; bracts linear, somewhat acute, pubescent, the elliptic green tips spreading: ray-flowers 20–30; ligules violet, about 15 mm. long: pappus tawny.—Dry or open woods, inner Coastal Plain and Piedmont, Ga. and S. C.—Fall.

49. **A. fontinalis** Alexander. Stem 3–9 dm. tall, pubescent, much branched: leaf-blades sessile, linear-elliptic, rough-pubescent, stiff-spreading, auriculate-clasping at the base, entire, abruptly acute, 1.5–3 cm. long; lower cauline and radical leaves not seen, those of the branches small and bract-like: heads about 2 cm. broad, or more, at the ends of the numerous branches and branchlets; involucre turbinate-campanulate; bracts linear, with narrowly spatulate, green tips, remarkably thin for this group, but closely appressed and not at all spreading, glabrous, and ciliate margined: ray-flowers 15–30; ligules purplish-blue, 7–9 mm. long: pappus whitish.—Damp, wooded slopes, and moist soil, Fla.—Late fall.

50. **A. patens** Ait. Stem 3–9 dm. tall, slender, rough, divergently branched: leaf-blades sessile, ovate-elliptic or oval, rough-pubescent, thick and somewhat rigid, strongly auriculate-clasping at the broad base, entire, acute, or the lower ones obtuse, 2.5–7.5 cm. long, those of the branches much smaller and bract-like, their margins rough-ciliate: heads 25 mm. broad or more, solitary at the ends of the branches: involucre campanulate; bracts linear-elliptic, finely pubescent or scabrous, often somewhat glandular, imbricate, their green acute tips spreading: ray-flowers 20–30; ligules purplish-blue or deep-violet, 8–12 mm. long: pappus tawny: achene pubescent.—Dry, open places, often in acid soil, various provinces, Fla. to Tex., Minn., and Mass.—Sum.–fall.

51. **A. tenuicaulis** (C. Mohr) Burgess. Resembles *A. patens;* but its branches long and slender, flagelliform and diffuse when well developed: leaves and heads smaller: pedicels longer, often 1–4 cm.: bracts and their tips much narrower, narrowly linear; bractlets mucronate-acute, catenate or forming a chain-like series along the pedicels, appressed or slightly spreading. [*A. patens gracilis* Hook. *A. patens tenuicaulis* C. Mohr.]—Dry soil, Coastal Plain and adj. provinces, Ga. to Tex., Okla., and Ky.—Sum.–fall.

52. **A. phlogifolius** Muhl. Similar to *A. patens* in habit, but when well developed, much taller, more slender and soft: leaves larger; blades lanceolate to elliptic-lanceolate, entire, thin or membranous, acuminate at the apex, strongly auriculate, clasping at the base, roughish above, pubescent beneath, usually narrowed below the middle, sometimes 15 cm. long: heads usually numerous, 3–5 cm. broad, panicled or somewhat racemose on the branches: involucre campanulate; bracts lanceolate, glabrate, rather loose, with herbaceous tips: ray-flowers numerous; ligules purple-blue.—Woods and thickets, various provinces N of Coastal Plain, Ga. to Tenn., Ohio, and Mass.—Late sum.–fall.—Resembles *A. patens*, but less harsh and taller; heads larger: inflorescence narrow: leaf-blades elongate.

53. **A. adnatus** Nutt. Stem 2–8 dm. tall, hispidulous, virgately more or less branched, especially above: leaves various, the basal few, with obovate thinnish blades 1.5–2.5 cm. long, the cauline very numerous, approximate on the lower part of the stem, more or less imbricate above and on the branches; blades elliptic to lanceolate, 3–12 mm. long, firm, scabrous, erect and partly adnate to the stem and branches, sessile: heads relatively few, scattered, singly terminating the scaly branchlets: involucre 4–6 mm. high; bracts linear or slightly broadened upward, the dark-green tips slightly spreading: ray-flowers numerous; ligules 7–10 mm. long, violet: achene glabrous.—Dry pinelands, Coastal Plain, Fla. to Miss. and Ga.—Fall.—Remarkable among asters in its minute adnate scale-like leaves.

54. **A. Walteri** Alexander. Stem 2–6 dm. tall, loosely branched above or throughout, nearly glabrous: leaves very numerous, the basal spatulate to cuneate, entire, the cauline approximate or contiguous, rigid, reflexed; blades elliptic-lanceolate to ovate or subulate-ovate, 2–9 mm. long, ciliate, serrate, closely sessile: heads few, widely scattered, terminating scaly branchlets: involucre 5–6

mm. high; bracts broadened upward, the dark green acute or acutish tips slightly spreading: ray-flowers 14–24; ligules 6–9 mm. long, violet: achene glabrous. [*A. squarrosus* Walt.]—Dry pinelands, Coastal Plain, Fla. to N. C.— Fall.

55. A. oblongifolius Nutt. Stem much-branched, 3–7 dm. high, hirsute-pubescent, smooth with age, the branches divaricate or ascending; leaves numerous, often crowded; blades elliptic or elliptic-lanceolate, sessile by a broad or slightly clasping base, usually rigid, entire, mucronulate at the apex, rough or hispidulous on both sides, rough margined, those of the stem 3–5 cm. long, 4–8 mm. wide, those of the branches gradually smaller: heads corymbose, nearly 25 mm. broad: involucre hemispheric; bracts much imbricate, glandular-aromatic, linear or linear-elliptic, the acute green tips spreading: ray-flowers 20–30; ligules violet-purple, rarely rose-pink, 6–10 mm. long: pappus becoming light-brown: achene canescent.—Prairies and bluffs, often in calcareous soil, various provinces mostly N of Coastal Plain, Ala. to Tex., N. D., and Pa.—Sum.-fall.—*A. Kumleinii* Fries is not known in the east, the eastern specimens having been referred to *A. oblongifolius.*

56. A. grandiflorus L. Stem 3–7 dm. high, rather stiff, divaricately much branched, hispid with short hairs: leaf-blades elliptic, linear, or somewhat spatulate, rigid, sessile by a broad sometimes slightly clasping base, reflexed, entire, obtusish, hispid, the larger 5 cm. long, those of the branches very numerous 4–10 mm. long: heads about 5 cm. broad, terminating the branches: involucre hemispheric; bracts very squarrose and foliaceous, imbricate in 5–7 series, linear, or linear-elliptic, glandular, the outer obtusish, the inner acute: rays very numerous; ligules deep-violet, nearly 25 mm. long, 3 mm. wide: pappus becoming brownish: achene ribbed, canescent.—Dry soil, Coastal Plain and adj. provinces, Fla. to Va.—Sum.-fall.—Resembles *A. oblongifolius,* but heads larger and fewer, more glandular.

57. A. novae-angliae L. Stem stout, 6–25 dm. high, hispid-pubescent, corymbosely branched above, very leafy: leaf-blades elliptic-lanceolate, entire, acute, pubescent, 5–12 cm. long, 12–25 mm. wide, each clasping by an auriculate base: heads numerous, 3–5 cm. broad, clustered at the ends of the branches: involucre hemispheric; bracts linear-subulate, somewhat unequal, green, spreading, pubescent and more or less glandular-viscid: ray-flowers 40–50; ligules linear, 10–16 mm. long, violet-purple (typically a royal-purple, rarely replaced by rose-color, or white): achene pubescent: pappus becoming reddish-white.—Fields and neutral soil swamp margins, various provinces, rarely Coastal Plain, S. C. to Miss., Ark., Colo., Alta., and Que.—Sum.-fall.

58. A. novi-belgii L. Stem slender, 3–9 dm. high, usually much-branched, glabrous or slightly pubescent above: leaf-blades lanceolate, elliptic-lanceolate or linear-lanceolate, 5–12 cm. long, firm, entire, or slightly serrate, glabrous or very nearly so, acuminate at the apex, narrowed, sessile, and more or less clasping at the base, those of the lower ones petioled: heads corymbose-paniculate, usually numerous, 2–3 cm. broad: involucre hemispheric to campanulate; bracts linear, acute, green, somewhat spreading, in 3–5 series, the outer shorter: ray-flowers 15–25; ligules violet, 8–10 mm. long: pappus whitish: achene glabrous or nearly so.—Swamps and acid bogs, Coastal Plain and adj. provinces, Ga. to Ala. and Newf.—Sum.-fall.—Several forms have been distinguished: *A. novi-belgii litoreus* with low and spreading, more or less fleshy, much-branched stems: leaf-blades shorter and broader, thicker, acute, 3–6 cm. long: principal bracts of the involucre obtuse, loose, spatulate, ranges in salt-marshes, from Ga. to E Can. *A. novi-belgii atlanticus* with lanceolate leaf-blades tapering from the middle to an acuminate apex and base: heads usually fewer: inflorescence racemose-corymbose, ranges in swamps, from N. C. to Mass.

59. A. elodes T. & G. Stem up to 7 dm. tall, slender, smooth, little-branched, terete, pale and reddened: leaf-blades narrowly linear, entire, shining and firm, smooth and coriaceous when dry, 5–15 cm. long, often not more than 1 cm. broad, scarcely clasping by the contracted sessile base, divaricately spreading and becoming deflexed; rameal leaves very numerous, approximate, elliptic-oval to linear, divaricate-recurvate, with abruptly contracted base and apex, diminished to 1 cm. long on the pedicels: leaves (especially the rameal) with their margins hardened, thickened, minutely spinulose and revolute: inflorescence loosely panicled, with domed, flattened or irregular top: heads often approximate; chief bracts of the involucre closely imbricate, rigid, erect, their tips lanceolate, erect or spreading, with pale or purple margin; some green spreading foliaceous outer bracts occur, but they are usually few or inconspicuous.—Swamps, especially in pinelands, Coastal Plain and adj. provinces, N. C. to Mass.—Sum.–fall.

60. A. sericeus Vent. Stem 3–6 dm. high, slender, paniculately or corymbosely branched, stiff, glabrous, leafy: basal and lowest leaves oblanceolate, narrowed into margined petioles; cauline leaves sessile, with a broad base, elliptic, entire, mucronate, 1–4 cm. long, erect or ascending, with a dense silvery-white silky pubescence on both sides: heads numerous, about 35 mm. broad: involucre turbinate; bracts elliptic, or the inner lanceolate, canescent, imbricate in 3 or 4 series, their tips green, acute, spreading: ray-flowers 15–25; ligules reddish-violet, becoming violet-blue, 12–16 mm. long: pappus tawny: achene glabrous.—Dry, open soil, various provinces N of Coastal Plain, Tenn. to Tex., Man., and Ill.—Late sum.–fall.

61. A. concolor L. Stem 3–7 dm. high, leafy, simple, or with few erect branches: leaf-blades elliptic or linear-elliptic, finely and densely canescent on both sides, or the lower glabrate, sessile, obtuse or mucronate, 4–5 cm. long: heads in an elongated narrow raceme resembling that of species of *Laciniaria*: involucre broadly turbinate; bracts linear or linear-elliptic, appressed, canescent, imbricate in 4 or 5 series, their tips green, acute, the outer shorter: ray-flowers 10–15; ligules lilac, drying violet-blue, 6–8 mm. long: pappus tawny: achene villous.—Dry sandy, often acid, soil, Coastal Plain and adj. provinces, Fla. to La., Tenn., and Mass.—Late sum.–fall.—Resembles *A. sericeus*, but more wand-like and spicate, and more canescent than silky.

62. A. simulatus Small. Stem 2–15 dm. tall, wand-like or with few virgate branches, pale-pubescent, the branches, especially near the tips, villous-silky: leaf-blades linear-elliptic to lanceolate or linear-lanceolate, 1–2.5 mm. long or somewhat scale-like and smaller above, more or less silky, acute, entire, sessile; heads in virgate racemes or panicles, showy: involucre turbinate-campanulate: bracts broadly linear to linear-lanceolate, imbricate in several series, the outer with deltoid green tips, the inner 6–7 mm. long, with lanceolate green acute tips, all appressed, copiously pubescent with appressed white hairs; ray-flowers 10–13; ligules violet, 6–7 mm. long: pappus whitish: achene copiously silky.—Pinelands, Everglade Keys, Fla.—Fall–wint.

63. A. plumosus Small. Stem 1 m. tall or less, branched above, finely pubescent, the branches more closely pubescent than the stem, villous-hirsute near the tips: leaf-blades various, those of the lower part of the stem not seen, those above linear or nearly so, those of the branches linear-elliptic to lanceolate, mostly 1 cm. long or less, acute, all sessile, finely pubescent on both sides: heads showy, in loose racemes; involucre turbinate-campanulate; bracts linear-acuminate to narrowly linear-lanceolate, imbricate in several series, the inner 6.5–7.5 mm. long, the loosely spreading or recurved green tip with copious long white hairs: ray-flowers about 10; ligules violet, 7–8 mm. long; pappus tawny: achene silky-villous.—Dry woods, Apalachicola River region, Fla.—Fall.

64. A. Curtisii T. & G. Stem 4–18 dm. tall, glabrous, at least below the inflorescence, angled, corymbose or paniculate above, the panicle sometimes raceme-
like: leaves various, sometimes all with linear or nearly linear blades and entire
or partly serrate, sometimes the lower cauline with lanceolate, elliptic, oval or
ovate sharply serrate blades and petiole-like base and the upper cauline linear
and less toothed, occasionally all of them relatively broad, all thickish, dark-
green and glabrous: heads solitary or clustered at the end of the stem or its
branches: involucre hemispheric, 6–9 mm. high, conspicuous; bracts often
slightly ciliolate, pale below the more or less dilated dark-green spreading, or
reflexed tips: ray-flowers 18–28; ligules violet-purple, often brilliant, 1–3 cm.
long: achene glabrous, shorter than the sordid pappus.—Mountain woods, Blue
Ridge and Appalachian provinces, Ga. to Tenn. and N. C.—Fall.—Resembles
A. spectabilis, but leaves more polymorphous: stem taller: head more diffused:
glands lacking.

65. A. Smallii Alexander. Stem 5–6 dm. tall, glandular-pubescent, especially
above, unbranched below the rather compact inflorescence; leaves rather numerous 5–12 cm. long; blades glabrous but rough-margined, oblanceolate, the
cauline ones tapering to a wing-petioled base, the upper ones sessile at the
broad base, all, even the floral bracts sharp-serrate and acutish: heads borne
in a dense, somewhat corymbose cluster: involucre campanulate: bracts
glandular, especially the outer, broadly linear, abruptly mucronate or obtuse, the
tips recurved: ray-flowers purplish: pappus pale-tawny: achene pubescent.—Dry
woods, Blue Ridge, N. C.—Fall.—Resembles *A. surculosus*, but differs mainly in
its glandular involucral bracts and numerous approximate leaves.

66. A. spectabilis Ait. Stem stiff, 3–6 dm. tall, simple, or corymbosely
branched above, puberulent, or rough below, more or less glandular above: leaf-
blades firm, thickish, those of the basal and lower cauline leaves oval, acute or
acutish, 7–12 cm. long, 2–4 cm. wide, sparingly serrate with low teeth, narrowed
at the base into slender petioles; blades of the upper cauline leaves sessile,
entire or very nearly so, acute, linear-elliptic: heads several or numerous, about
35 mm. broad, corymbose, very showy: involucre nearly hemispheric: bracts
linear-elliptic or slightly spatulate, glandular, imbricate in about 5 series, the
acute or acutish tips spreading: ray-flowers 15–30; ligules bright-violet, 12–20
mm. long: pappus whitish: achene slightly pubescent.—Dry, often acid, sandy
soil, Coastal Plain and N. E. Coast, N. C. to Mass.—Late sum.–fall.

67. A surculosus Michx. Stem 2.5–4.5 dm. tall, slender, from elongate-
filiform rootstocks, minutely scabrous-pubescent, corymbosely branched above:
leaf-blades firm, lanceolate or linear, those of the lower cauline petioled, 5–7
cm. long, rough-margined, slightly scabrous above, sparingly dentate, those of
the upper narrower, sessile, entire: heads few, or sometimes solitary, about 3
cm. broad: involucre turbinate-hemispheric; bracts coriaceous, imbricate in
about 5 series, ciliate, but scarcely glandular, their green tips spreading: ray-
flowers 15–30; ligules violet: pappus whitish: achene nearly glabrous.—Sandy
or gravelly soil, various provinces, Ga. to Ala., Ky., and N. C.—Sum.–fall.

68. A. gracilis Nutt. Stem slender, 3–4 dm. highly, finely puberulent and scabrous, corymbosely branched above: leaf-blades minutely scabrous, those of the
basal and lower cauline leaves elliptic, acute or obtusish, 5–7 cm. long, toothed,
narrowed into slender petioles, those of the upper leaves linear, linear-elliptic, or
slightly oblanceolate, acute, entire, sessile or a little clasping: heads usually
numerous, 12–20 mm. broad: involucre narrowly turbinate; bracts coriaceous,
glabrous or very nearly so, imbricate in about five series, their tips green and
spreading, obtusish: ray-flowers 9–15; ligules violet, 6–9 mm. long: pappus
nearly white: achene minutely pubescent.—Dry, often acid, sandy soil, various
provinces, N. C. to Tenn., Ky., and N. J.—Sum.–fall.

69. A. Lamarckianus Nees. Stem 6–25 dm. high, glabrous or nearly so, paniculately much-branched: leaf-blades lanceolate to elliptic-lanceolate, 7–15 cm. long, acuminate at the apex, narrowed to a sessile or slightly clasping base, glabrous, thin, roughish margined, those of the cauline leaves sparingly serrate in the middle, or sometimes very nearly entire, the upper and those of the branches gradually smaller: heads numerous, 16–20 mm. broad: involucre nearly hemispheric, 6–8 mm. high; bracts narrowly linear-lanceolate, acute or acuminate, appressed, green-tipped, imbricate in 4 or 5 series: ray-flowers numerous; ligules white (or faintly tinged with violet), 6–8 mm. long: pappus white or nearly so: achene minutely pubescent. [*A. paniculatus* Lam.]—Moist soil, various provinces, Fla. to La., Mont., Ont., and Va.—Late sum.–fall.—A very variable species. A form ranging from N. C. and Tenn. to Kans., and Man., with narrowly linear entire or remotely appressed-serrate leaf-blades acuminate at both ends and numerous rather densely clustered heads on ascending inflorescence-branches, is *A. Lamarckianus bellidiflorus.*

70. A. missouriensis Britton. Whole plant pubescent, much-branched: stem 6 dm. high or more: leaf-blades thin, oblanceolate and acute in type, dull or cinereous-green, sharply serrate above the middle, with long-tapering entire sessile base, finely pubescent beneath: heads irregularly panicled or scattered along leafy branches: bracts of the involucre linear, acute, closely imbricate.—Moist places, various provinces, Tenn. to Tex., S. D., and Mich.—Fall.—Differs from *A. Lamarckianus* Nees. especially in its pubescence.

71. A. salicifolius Lam. Stem 6–15 dm. high, rather slender, paniculately much-branched, usually very leafy, glabrous, or somewhat pubescent above: leaf-blades somewhat firm, lanceolate or linear-lanceolate, 5–10 cm. long, rough-margined, acute or acuminate, narrowed and sessile or slightly clasping at the base, entire or sparingly dentate with low teeth, glabrous or nearly so, those of the lower leaves sometimes with petiole-like bases, those of the branches gradually smaller: heads numerous, 16–25 mm. broad: involucre broadly turbinate; bracts linear-elliptic, appressed, imbricate in 4 or 5 series, their green tips acute or obtusish: ray-flowers numerous; ligules violet, or violet-purple, or sometimes white, 6–8 mm. long: pappus white: achene minutely pubescent.—Moist soil, various provinces, Miss. to Tex., Mont., Ont. and Me.—Late sum.–fall.—The following form may be distinguishable: *A. salicifolius subasper*, with scabrous stem and leaves, ranges from La. to Tex., Mo., and Md.

72. A. Simmondsii Small. Stem 1–12 dm. tall, minutely pubescent, usually with erect or spreading branches: leaf-blades linear, oblanceolate, or elliptic, glabrous, sessile; those of the lower leaves serrate; those of the upper serrate or entire, the rameal ones narrowly linear, entire: head solitary or paniculate: involucre campanulate to campanulate-turbinate; bracts linear with spatulate green tips and scarious margins below, acute or acutish, the inner 4–7 mm. long: ligules of the ray 7–11 mm. long, pale-lilac or pink-purple: achene finely pubescent: pappus cream-color. [*A. Sulznerae* Small.]—Moist or dry soil, pen. Fla.—Fall.–wint.—A very variable species which may contain one or more distinct species.—As in the case of related species the Seminoles use an infusion of the plant to bathe victims of sunstroke.

73. A. spatelliformis Burgess. Stem much-branched, glabrous, 6 dm. high or more: leaf-blades dull-green and crenate, thickish, glabrous, the upper surface usually finely impressed with reticular veins: leaf-form suggesting a small rounded spatula, oval with a rounded apex, tapering into a short entire cuneate-winged petiole; basal and rameal leaves as well as cauline all of nearly the same type, 5 x 3 cm. or less; the axiles half as large and oval-elliptic, with a short cuneate base; the rameals half as large as the axiles, but very uniform, numerous and characteristic: heads small, scattered along the prolonged or sarmentose branches, usually short-pedicelled: bracts of the involucre rigid, linear, with whitish sides and acute apex, the narrow dark-green tips lance-triangular.—Swamp margins, Jacksonville, Fla.—Fall.

74. A. Tradescanti L. Stem 6–15 dm. tall, slender, paniculately branched, the branches usually ascending and often pubescent in lines: cauline leaves numerous; blades linear-lanceolate or lanceolate, 7–15 cm. long, acuminate, narrowed to the sessile base, glabrous or nearly so on both sides, commonly thin, sharply serrate in the middle with low teeth, or sometimes entire: heads very numerous, racemose but not secund on the branches, 10–16 mm. broad: involucre hemispheric to broadly turbinate, 4–6 mm. high; bracts linear, acute, appressed, green-tipped, imbricate in 4 or 5 series: ray-flowers numerous; ligules white or nearly so, 4–6 mm. long: pappus white: achene minutely pubescent.—Fields and swamps, various provinces, Fla. to Miss., Minn., N Y Terr., and Ont.—Late sum.–fall.

75. A. agrostifolius Burgess. Stem terete, greenish or stramineous, 6 dm. or often 8 dm. high, slender, erect or straggling, sparingly but widely branched: leaves grass-like, dull-green above and beneath; blades very thin, chiefly entire, linear-acuminate, tapering to the sessile base and especially to the apex, 10 cm. or even 15 cm. long, by 1 cm. wide; some lower cauline leaves become broader, lanceolate or oblong and slightly appressed-serrulate; axils generally corrigiate or occupied by two little divaricate branch-leaves: heads very small and pale, about 1.5 cm. broad: bracts of the involucre linear-acuminate, very pale, with narrow linear green tips: ligules of the rays whitish.—Low grounds under light shade and about copse-borders, Coastal Plain and adj. provinces, Fla. to Ark., and S E Mass.; also river banks, Knoxville, in the Appalachian valley of Tenn.—Fall.

76. A. pinifolius Alexander. Stem 6–12 dm. tall, glabrous or sparingly pubescent, with more or less erect branches: leaf-blades linear to subulate, glabrous, sessile; those of the lower leaves narrowly linear, entire or sparingly hack-serrate; those of the upper linear-subulate, the rameals subulate: heads few or many, paniculate: involucre campanulate-turbinate to turbinate; bracts linear, acutish, the inner 5–7 mm. long: ligules of the ray 7–11 mm. long, pale-violet: pappus cream-color: achene finely pubescent.—Moist soil, Fla.—Fall.-wint.—A variable species which may contain one or more distinct species.

77. A. ramosissimus Mill. Stem 3–9 dm. tall, usually glabrous, paniculately branched, usually bushy, the branches racemose, and the branchlets often somewhat secund: leaf-blades firm or rigid; those of the basal leaves spatulate, obtuse, dentate, narrowed into margined petioles, glabrous or ciliate; those of the cauline leaves narrowly linear, acute, entire, 2–7 cm. long, those of the branches linear-subulate, numerous: heads usually very numerous, 8–12 mm. broad: involucre campanulate to hemispheric; bracts coriaceous, closely appressed, lanceolate or linear-lanceolate, abruptly acute or acuminate, green-tipped, imbricate in about 3 series: ray-flowers 15–25; ligules white or purplish-tinged: pappus white: achene finely pubescent. [*A. ericoides* (Fl. SE. U. S.)].—(SPRAY-ASTER.)—Dry soil, various provinces, Fla. to Miss., Wis., Ont., and Me.—Fall.-wint.

78. A. pilosus Willd. Stem up to 1 m. tall, pubescent, very much branched and bushy, the branchlets somewhat secund: leaf-blades firm, typically with long scattered hairs on both surfaces; those of the basal leaves spatulate or oblanceolate, obtuse, somewhat dentate, pubescent; those of the cauline leaves linear to elliptic, acute, entire, 2–8 cm. long; those of the branches linear to narrowly elliptic: heads typically numerous, 10–15 mm. broad: involucre campanulate to hemispheric; bracts linear to linear-lanceolate, with coriaceous, acuminate, green tips: ray-flowers with ligules typically white, but sometimes pink or purplish-tinged: pappus white: achene pubescent. [*A. ericoides pilosus* (Willd.) Porter, *A. ericoides villosus* (Michx.) T. & G., *A. ericoides platyphyllus* T. & G.]—Dry soil, various provinces, Ga. to Miss., Mo., Ia., and Pa.

79. A. juniperinus Burgess. Stem robust, brittle, glabrous, pale brown, about 6 dm. high, the branches numerous, prolonged, chiefly horizontal and parallel, sometimes 4 dm. long: cauline leaves dull-green; blades thin, linear-acuminate, 10 x 1 cm.; rameal and ramular leaves subulate and all nearly alike, wide-spreading, juniper-like, greatly reduced and very numerous and crowded, diminishing rapidly on the elongate pedicels and passing insensibly into the small spreading green outer bracts of the broad hemispherical head; the other bracts longer and broader, linear with triangular-acuminate summit, coriaceous and very smooth, bright-white except the broadly deltoid, sharp-angled, green tip: heads small: ligules of the ray white: disk turning reddish-brown.—Loose sandy soil, in sunny places, various provinces, Ala. to Md.—Late sum.-fall.—Unlike *A. Faxoni* in its tendency to divaricate, not corymbose, branching. Unlike its congener *A. ramosissimus* in its numerous heads solitary on long branches or branchlets.

80. A. Faxoni Porter. Stem 6–15 dm. high, glabrous throughout, paniculately or corymbosely branched, rather stout: cauline leaves various; blades lanceolate or linear-lanceolate, 5–12 cm. long, acute or acuminate, narrowed to a sessile base or those of the lower ones into margined petioles, entire or nearly so, firm, those of the branches gradually smaller: basal leaves with elliptic to spatulate, obtuse, dentate blades: heads 12–18 mm. broad: involucre hemispheric, nearly 8 mm. high; bracts linear-lanceolate, acute or subulate, green-tipped or green on the back, imbricate in about 3 series, the outer shorter: ray-flowers numerous; ligules bright-white, 6–8 mm. long: pappus white: achene minutely pubescent.—Rocky river banks, and moist cliffs, Blue Ridge and more N provinces, Ala. to Wis., Vt., and Mass.—Late sum.-fall.—*A. ericoides Reevesii* A. Gray is probably best considered as the southern form of this species.

81. A. Priceae Britton. Stem 3–7 dm. high, pubescent, widely branched: basal leaves with oblanceolate obtuse or acutish entire petioled blades, 3–7 cm. long, the petioles ciliate, broad: cauline leaves relatively few; blades linear-lanceolate, sessile, ciliate, acuminate, 2–5 cm. long, those of the branches similar but smaller: involucre nearly hemispheric, about 6 mm. high; bracts linear, the outer gradually acuminate, green, the inner a little broader, abruptly acuminate, acute, or obtusish: heads about 2.5 cm. broad: ray-flowers numerous; ligules bright crimson-purple or pink.—Dry soil, Blue Ridge to Appalachian Plateau, N. C. to Ky.—Fall.

82. A. dumosus L. Stem 3–9 dm. high, glabrous or very nearly so throughout, paniculately much-branched: leaf-blades firm, those of the stem linear or linear-lanceolate, 2–7 cm. long, entire, acute or obtusish, roughly margined, often reflexed, those of the branches very numerous, small and scale-like, those of the basal leaves spatulate, dentate: heads 8–14 mm. broad, terminating the usually divergent slender branches and branchlets, usually numerous: involucre broadly campanulate; bracts linear-subulate, appressed, imbricate in about four series, obtuse in type, with green spatulate tips tapered at their apex: ray-flowers 15–30; ligules white (rarely pale-pink or pale-violet), 4 mm. long: pappus white: achene minutely pubescent.—Sandy woods or swamps, often acid, various provinces, Fla. to La., Mo., Ont., and Me.—Late sum.-fall.—The following forms may be distinguished: *A. dumosus subulaefolius*, more rigid and long straggling branches: heads somewhat larger: rameal leaves with linear blades subulate at the apex, rigid and sharp, even pungent, erect or slightly spreading: bracts acute, their narrow green bracts lanceolate to spatulate, ranging in pinelands and copse borders from Fla. to Tex. and S. C.: *A. dumosus strictior*, with few ascending branches often aggregated above: leaf-blades acuminate and entire, ranges in moist thickets from Tenn. to Mass.

83. A. coridifolius Michx. Resembles *A. dumosus*, but the stem more rigid, diffusely decompound with slender flagellate branches and branchlets; cauline leaves as in *A. dumosus;* rameal and ramular leaves uniform, and minute, greatly and abruptly reduced from the cauline, spreading or divaricate or reflexed, linear, usually not over 1 cm. long, very numerous, crowded and bract-like, giving the plant its characteristic aspect: heads small, many of them solitary on prolonged branchlets: bracts of the involucre more rigid, obtusish, their tips broad-spatulate, rounded and then apiculate.—Pinelands and sandy barrens, Coastal Plain and adj. provinces, Fla. to La. and Mass.—Sum.–fall.

84. A. gracilipes (Wiegand) Alexander. Stem 3–8 dm. tall, glabrous or nearly so, with erect-spreading branches and branchlets: leaf-blades firm, those of the stem narrowly linear, 2–15 cm. long, entire and rough-margined, the margins usually inrolled, those of the long, spreading branchlets not very numerous, but short, erect or appressed, acute or acutish, those of the basal leaves spatulate, often sparingly dentate: heads 10–15 mm. broad, solitary at the ends of the long branchlets, fairly numerous: involucre broadly campanulate; bracts linear-spatulate, appressed, acute or acutish with spatulate green tips: ray-flowers 14–20; ligules white, or rarely pale-violet or pinkish, 5–7 mm. long: pappus stramineous: achene sparingly pubescent or nearly glabrous. [*A. dumosus gracilipes* Wiegand].—Pinelands, sandy barrens, and moist places, Fla. (to La.?).—Fall.

85. A. ericoides L. Stem 3–20 dm. high, strict, much branched and bushy, the branches ascending or spreading: leaf-blades rigid, linear, entire, mostly obtuse, sessile or slightly clasping at the base, strigose or glabrate, those of the cauline leaves 1–2.5 cm. long; those of the branches very small and crowded: heads 6–8 mm. broad, densely crowded, nearly sessile: involucre turbinate, 4–6 mm. high; bracts coriaceous, pubescent, in 3 or 4 series, their short green tips obtuse or mucronate, spreading: ray-flowers 10–20; ligules white, 3–4 mm. long: pappus becoming brownish-white: achene puberulent. [*A. multiflorus* Ait.].—Dry, open places, various provinces, Ga. to Tex., S. Dak., Ont., and Me.—Late sum.–fall.

86. A. brachypholis Small. Stem 5–6 dm. high, finely pubescent especially above, with few, spreading branches: leaf-blades thin and fragile, as is the entire plant: those of the stem linear, fairly numerous, 2–7 cm. long, blades entire, those of the branchlets exceedingly numerous, mostly reflexed, acute, those of the basal leaves narrowly elliptic-spatulate, dentate: heads 8–10 mm. broad, secund on long, spreading branches, numerous: involucre narrowly campanulate: bracts linear, very short (no longer than the achenes), 0.5–1 mm. long, obtuse, ciliate, without green tips: ray-flowers about 12: ligules white or whitish, 3–4 mm. long: disk-flowers becoming purple: pappus white: achene elliptic, pubescent, about 1 mm. long.—Wooded slopes, often on damp rocks, Apalachicola River bluffs, Fla.—Fall.

87. A. racemosus Ell. Stem apparently tall, somewhat scabrous-pubescent on the ascending rather slender branches: leaves firm; blades linear or nearly so, relatively small, acute, the upper entire: heads not very numerous, racemosely or spicately disposed, rather crowded toward the ends of the branches, distant below: involucre about 4 mm. high; bracts firm, subulate to narrowly linear, acuminate: ray-flowers few; ligules purplish, 2–3 mm. long: achene minutely pubescent.—Beaches and sandy woods, Coastal Plain, Fla. to La. and S. C.—Sum.–fall.

88. A. vimineus Lam. Stem 6–15 dm. high, glabrous or nearly so, slender, divergently branched: cauline leaves linear-acuminate, 7–12 cm. long, regularly minutely hack-serrate, slightly narrowed at the sessile base, those of the branches much smaller: heads very numerous, 6–10 mm. broad, generally densely racemose-secund, short-peduncled: involucre broadly turbinate; bracts linear, acute or acutish, green-tipped, appressed: ray-flowers numerous: ligules about 4 mm. long, narrowly linear, white, often roseate in fading: pappus white: achene minutely pubescent.—Moist soil, various provinces, Fla. to Ark., Kans., Minn., and Mass.—Late sum.–fall.

89. A. lateriflorus (L.) Britton. Stem 3–15 dm. tall, puberulent or nearly glabrous, slender, divergently branched, often bushy: basal leaves few; blades ovate, short-petioled; cauline leaves numerous; blades broadly lanceolate or elliptic-lanceolate, 5–12 cm. long, mostly acuminate, serrate, those of the branches smaller, elliptic or linear-elliptic: heads 6–10 mm. broad, racemosely unilateral on the branches, short-peduncled or sessile, usually numerous and crowded: involucre turbinate; bracts linear-elliptic, obtuse or acutish, imbricate in about 4 series, their short green tips appressed or slightly spreading: ray-flowers numerous; ligules short, whitish or pale-purple, rounded at the apex: disk-flowers purple: pappus white: achene minutely pubescent. [*A. diffusus* Ait.]—Dry or moist soil, various provinces, Ala. to Tex., Ark., Ont., N. S., and N. C.—Late sum.–fall.—The following forms may be distinguished: *A. lateriflorus glomeratus*, with the stem chiefly unbranched: leaves hispidulous above, the blades elliptic-lanceolate, dull green, with sharp straight teeth: heads glomerate in the axils or spicate above, or scattered on short branches, ranges in woodlands, from N. C. to N. Y.: *A. lateriflorus thyrsoideus* with ashy-puberulent ascending branches which bear crowded or thyrsoid-paniculate heads: leaf-blades ovate to lanceolate, ranges in open thickets from Tenn. to Ill., Ont., and N. Y.: *A. lateriflorus horizontalis*, with long divaricate branches: leaves firm succulent, those of the branches very small, mostly entire: heads very numerous, ranges from Va. to Ark., and S N. Y.: *A. lateriflorus pendulus*, with long slender, horizontal or drooping branches and drooping leaves, the blades narrowly linear-elliptic, remotely appressed-serrulate: heads long-peduncled, ranges in thickets from Ala. to N. C. and N. Y.

90. A. hirsuticaulis Lindl. Stem 4–9 dm. tall, slender, erect, pubescent, nearly or quite to the base; branches usually short spreading or ascending: leaf blades thin, glabrous above, usually densely pubescent on the midvein beneath, serrate with a few appressed teeth, or entire, of linear type, sometimes 15 cm. long, sessile or the basal ones spatulate and petioled: heads more or less secund on the branches, chiefly loosely clustered, often also solitary or few in the lower axils: involucre narrow; bracts in 3 or 4 series, linear-lanceolate, acuminate or acute: ray-flowers several; ligules white, about 4 mm. long, narrow.— Woods and thickets, various provinces N of Coastal Plain, Tenn. to Pa. and Me.—Late sum.–fall.—Unlike *A. lateriflorus* in its hirsute stem and its long linear straight-sided leaf-blades which are hirsute on the midrib beneath.

91. A. ptarmicoides (Nees) T. & G. Stem tufted, 3–6 dm. high, slender, rigid, usually rough above, corymbosely branched near the summit: leaf-blades linear-lanceolate, 3-ribbed, entire, or with a few distant teeth, firm, shining, rough-margined or ciliate, sometimes scabrous, acute, narrowed to a sessile base, or those of the lower leaves petioled; the lowest and basal ones 7–15 cm. long, the upper smaller, those of the branches linear subulate: heads 16–25 mm. broad, terminating the branches of the corymb: involucre nearly hemispheric, 4–6 mm. high; bracts linear-oblong, obtuse, appressed, nearly green, imbricated in about 4 series: ray-flowers 10–20; ligules snow-white, narrow, 6 mm. long: pappus white, achene glabrous.—Dry or rocky soil, various provinces, Ga. to Ark., Colo., N W Terr., Ont., and Mass.—Sum.–fall.—Remarkable among asters for its profuse linear shining, rough-edged leaf-blades and small level-topped white heads.—A usually taller form from Ga. and Ark., with lower leaves 15–18 cm. long, and often denticulate, and smaller heads, is *A. ptarmicoïdes georgianus.*

92. **A. acuminatus** Michx. Stem 3–9 dm. high, pubescent or puberulent zigzag, corymbosely branched, often leafless below: leaf-blades thin, broadly oblong or elliptic, 7–15 cm. long, acuminate at the apex, narrowed to a cuneate sessile base, sharply and coarsely dentate, strongly pinnately veined, glabrous or pubescent above, pubescent at least on the veins beneath, in low shaded plants often approximate above, and appearing whorled: heads several or numerous, 25–37 mm. broad: involucre nearly hemispheric; bracts subulate-linear, acuminate, the outer much shorter: ray-flowers 12–18; ligules narrow, 12–16 mm. long, white or slightly purplish: pappus copious, soft and fine, very white: achene pubescent.—Moist woods, often in acid soil, Blue Ridge and more N provinces, Ga. to Ont. and Lab.—Sum.–fall.—Remarkable for its soft-pubescent, limp subviscid leaves and its decurved buds becoming erect and fragrant in flower. The rootstocks are very slender.

93. **A. paludosus** Ait. Stem 3–7 dm. tall, roughish or rough-pubescent, especially above, slender, virgate and simple, or somewhat branched above, pale or purplish: leaf-blades linear-acuminate or nearly so, 5–15 cm. long, entire or sparingly hack-serrate, glabrous or nearly so, rather rigid, mostly 1-veined, acute, the lower part either narrowed and sheathing or somewhat auriculate, the margins rough or ciliate: heads few or several, paniculate, 3–5 cm. broad: involucre broadly campanulate; bracts imbricate in about 3–4 series, ciliate and pubescent, the upper half more or less foliaceous; the inner bracts very thin, varying from linear to spatulate, sometimes on the same plant; the outer bracts lanceolate, acute, usually exceeding the inner, often thickened-subulate at the tip: ray-flowers 20–30; ligules deep blue-violet, 10–15 mm. long: pappus tawny: achene glabrous or nearly so.—Moist, sandy soil, Coastal Plain and Piedmont, Ga. to N. C.—Fall.

94. **A. pedionomus** Alexander. Stem 3–8 dm. (rarely 1 m.) tall, from a woody corm-like rootstock, glabrous or sparingly short-pubescent above, slender and simple, but branched above, pale or purplish: leaf-blades linear to narrowly elliptic, glabrous, scabrate-margined, rigid, mostly 1-veined, acute, but slightly narrowed at the sessile or sheathing base: heads few or several, paniculate, 3.5 cm. broad: involucre nearly hemispheric; bracts imbricate in several series, the upper half squarrose, somewhat leathery in texture, the outer very long and linear-lanceolate, the inner linear or slightly spatulate: ray-flowers 20–30; ligules deep-violet, 10–20 mm. long: pappus tawny: achene somewhat pubescent. —Hard, dry soil, prairies, hillsides and woods, various provinces, Fla. and Ga. to Tex., Kans., and Tenn.—Fall.

95. **A. Gattingeri** Alexander. Stem 3–6 dm. tall, from a woody corm-like rootstock, glabrous, or sparingly short-pubescent above, slender and simple, pale or purplish: leaf-blades linear, 4–12 cm. long, entire, glabrous, scabrate margined, rather rigid, 1-veined, acute, narrowed to a sheathing base: heads sessile or short-peduncled, in a racemiform inflorescence, 3–4 cm. broad: involucre nearly hemispheric; bracts imbricate in 4–5 series, the tips spreading scabrous-ciliolate, the outer foliaceous above, somewhat shorter than the inner, the inner very thin, purple tipped, as wide as the outer: ray-flowers 20–30; ligules violet, 10–12 mm. long: pappus tawny: achene slightly pubescent.—Dry, sandy soil, Coastal Plain and adj. provinces, Ala., and Miss. to Tenn.—Early fall.

96. **A. hemisphericus** Alexander. Stem 1–7 dm. tall, from a long-stoloniferous, wiry or woody rootstock, which usually forms colonies; glabrous, or sparsely pubescent above; slender, simple or sometimes branched in the inflorescence,

pale or purplish: leaf-blades linear, linear-elliptic or oblanceolate, usually scabrate on both sides, the margin especially so, acute, somewhat narrowed to a half-clasping base: heads few to several, somewhat racemiform (rarely spiciform or racemo-paniculiform), 3–6 cm. broad: involucre hemispheric or nearly so; bracts imbricate in several to many series, only the tips spreading, leathery or foliaceous, the inner much the longer, each outer series gradually becoming shorter, the outermost linear, acute, the remainder abruptly acute, the innermost very narrow: ray-flowers 15–30; ligules blue-violet or violet, 15–25 mm. long: pappus tawny: achenes somewhat pubescent.—Dry soil, hillsides, woods and prairies, various provinces, Ala. to Tex., Kans., and Mo.—Fall.—Markedly distinct from *A. pedionomus* in its gregarious habit.

97. **A. verutifolius** Alexander. Stem up to 9 dm. tall, glabrous or nearly so, slender and sparingly branched, purplish: leaf-blades most unusual for an *Aster*, with a triangular, half-sheathing base, abruptly contracted to a nearly filiform, rapier-shaped blade, 8–10 cm. long, or longer, glabrous, entire, not very rigid: heads principally on long peduncles in a loose panicle whose branches begin far down the stem, with a few short-peduncled heads in the leaf-axils, 3–4 cm broad: involucre nearly hemispheric; bracts imbricate in about 5 series, scabrose-ciliolate, the outer narrowly linear-acuminate from a broad base, the inner rather oblong or narrowly elliptic with acuminate tips: ray-flowers 20–25; ligules violet, 12–15 mm. long: pappus tawny: achene not seen mature, but probably slightly pubescent.—Moist soil near Ocean Springs, Miss.—Fall.

98. **A. spinulosus** Chapm. Plant nearly or quite smooth to the touch, and almost without hair: stem pale, slender, 5–6 dm. high, from a short erect tuberous rootstock shaggy with marcescent leaf-bases: basal leaves tufted, very numerous, long and slender, linear and attenuate below, often 3 dm. long, with occasional long slender teeth; stem-leaves bract-like, erect, 4 cm. long or commonly half that: axile leaves upcurved, stiff and pungent: heads sessile and subremote in the upper axils, each subtended by an upturned carinate pungent involucral leaf: ligules of the ray violet, little over 1 cm. long, broader, the disk-flowers fewer and the bracts paler-margined than in *A. paludosus*, which this otherwise resembles: pappus tawny, becoming ferruginous.—Wet pinelands, Apalachicola River region, N Fla.—Sum.—Unlike *A. paludosus* in its smaller spicate heads, longer narrower basal leaves, more pungent upper cauline leaves and less conspicuous teeth.

99. **A. eryngiifolius** T. & G. Plant nearly smooth to the touch, sparsely villous above: rootstock tuberous-thickened: stem rigid, erect, 3–7 dm. high, unbranched, with one terminal head or sometimes several large heads closely approximate: leaves grass-like, linear-acute with narrowed base, the numerous basal leaves spreading chiefly 1 dm. long or less, the others soon reduced to one-third the length, suberect, subulate-linear, sessile and bract-like; both set below the middle with long slender subremote subulate teeth: involucre subremote broadly hemispheric; bracts nearly of the same length but of many series, linear-subulate, flat, and appressed, the upper third slender, bristle-like and spreading: ligules of the ray 3 cm. long, tapering below, light violet, blue or white: disk-flowers very numerous: pappus becoming ferruginous in the herbarium: alveolae deep and pronounced.—Low pinelands, M Fla., and adj. Ga.—Sum.

100. **A. Bracei** Britton. Plant perennial: stem rather wiry, 2–9 dm. tall: upper leaves more or less spreading; blades narrowly linear to linear-subulate: heads corymbose: involucre campanulate-turbinate; bracts stout, the inner ones not reaching to the top of the disk—Low hammocks, Florida Keys.—Fall to Spr.—(*W. I.*)

101. A. Chapmanii T. & G. Plant perennial: stem rigid, arising from a short caudex, glabrous, usually with few slender or nearly filiform branches above: leaves mainly crowded on the caudex, 1–3 dm. long, glabrous, the linear or linear-spatulate blades longer or shorter than the slender petiole-like base, entire, obscurely veined in drying; lower cauline-leaves nearly like the basal, the upper gradually reduced to subulate-filiform erect scales, and subulate on the branches: heads few, solitary at the ends of the branches; involucre campanulate, 7–8 mm. high; bracts firm, elliptic-lanceolate to broadly linear and linear-oblanceolate, erect, acute, sometimes abruptly pointed: ray-flowers numerous; ligules 1.5–2 cm. long, violet: achene glabrous.—Pineland swamps, Apalachicola River region, N Fla. and rare in peninsular Fla.—Fall.

102. A. tenuifolius L. Plant perennial, glabrous and fleshy. Stem 3–6 dm. tall, flexuous, striate, at least when dry, sparingly and loosely branched: cauline leaves linear, 5–15 cm. long, entire, sessile, or slightly clasping at the base, the lowest lanceolate-linear, those of the branches minute, scale-like, appressed: heads rather few, 12–25 mm. broad, terminating the branches: involucre turbinate, about 8 mm. high; bracts lanceolate, acuminate or mucronate, glabrous, green on the back or tips, appressed, imbricate in about 5 series, the outer shorter: ray-flowers numerous; ligules longer than the pappus, pale-purple or nearly white: pappus tawny; achene hispid-pubescent, 5-nerved.—Salt marshes, coast of Fla. to Miss. and Mass.—Sum.-fall.

103. A. exilis Ell. Plant annual, glabrous, fleshy: stem 3–12 dm. tall, slender, usually much-branched, the branches usually divergent: cauline leaves linear to linear-lanceolate, 2–10 cm. long, entire, sessile, acute or acuminate, or the lower narrowly elliptic, 6–8 mm. wide, usually petioled, those of the branches subulate: heads numerous, panicled, about 1 cm. broad: involucre campanulate, about 6 mm. high; bracts linear-subulate, appressed, imbricate in 3 or 4 series: ray-flowers mostly fewer than those of the disk; ligules purplish, about 4 mm. long, longer than the pappus: achene somewhat pubescent.—Moist or wet soil, especially in saline situations, various provinces, Fla. to Tex., Kans., and S. C.—Sum.-fall.

104. A. inconspicuus Less. Plant annual, glabrous or obscurely glandular in the inflorescence: stem mostly 1 m. tall or less, rather copiously branched above, the stem and branches flexuous: cauline leaves mostly 1–1.5 dm. long; blades elliptic or nearly so, varying to broadest above or below the middle, acute, shallowly toothed, those of the branches much narrower: heads much smaller than those of *A. exilis* and *A. subulatus:* involucre campanulate, 3.5–5 mm. high; bracts linear-lanceolate to narrowly linear: ray-flowers 20–30, more numerous than the disk-flowers; ligules mostly pale-lilac, about 2 mm. long.—Edges of hammocks or salt-marshes, Key West, Fla.—(*W. I.*)—Fall-wint.—Differs from *A. exilis* in the numerous ray-flowers with small ligules and from *A. subulatus* in the broad toothed blades of the cauline leaves.

105. A. subulatus Michx. Plant annual, glabrous and fleshy: stem 3–18 dm. tall, paniculately branched, flexuous above, slightly angled, sometimes 25 mm. in diameter at the base, but usually smaller: cauline leaves linear-lanceolate, 5–8 cm. long, acute, entire, sessile by a broad or slightly clasping base, those of the branches very small and subulate: heads numerous, 6–10 mm. broad: involucre cylindric to narrowly turbinate, 4–6 mm. high; bracts linear-subulate, green, imbricate in 3 or 4 series, the outer shorter: ray-flowers 20–30, more numerous than the disk-flowers; ligules purplish, scarcely exceeding the nearly white, soft, copious pappus: achene compressed, minutely pubescent.—Salt marshes, coast of Fla. to Ala., and N. H.—Sum.-fall.

106. A. spinosus Benth. Stem woody at the base, divided into striate pliable bright-green branches, 1–2.5 m. tall, these branches paniculate: leaves inconspicuous, those of the main branches linear or linear-spatulate, mainly 2–4 cm. long, those of the branchlets reduced to subulate scales or obsolete, all or some of them with soft subulate spines in or above their axils: heads scattered: involucre turbinate, 4–4.5 mm. high; bracts lanceolate-subulate, attenuate: ray-flowers few; ligules about 4 mm. long, white: achene glabrous.—Sand flats, river valleys and moist soil, various provinces, La. to Tex., and Calif.—Late sum.–wint.—(*Mex.*)

39. **DOELLINGERIA** Nees. Perennial, relatively tall, aster-like herbs. Leaves alternate: blades relatively broad, veiny, entire or nearly so. Heads in a terminal corymb. Involucres campanulate to hemispheric, several–many-flowered: bracts various, the inner scarcely wider than the outer but much longer. Ray-flowers few or several: corollas with a long tube and a white or cream-colored ligule. Disk-corollas with a funnelform throat and a long tube: lobes lanceolate. Pappus of 2 distinct series, the outer series of short bristles or scales, the inner of elongate capillary bristles.—About 5 species, eastern North American.—WHITE-TOPPED ASTERS.

Ray-flowers with linear ligules over 10 mm. long: inner bracts of the involucre acuminate.   1. *D. reticulata.*
Ray-flowers with oblong ligules less than 10 mm. long: inner bracts of the involucre merely acute or obtuse.
    Achene nearly terete, ribless, less than 1 mm. wide.
        Involucral bracts acute or acutish, the inner linear, ciliate at the tip.   2. *D. umbellata.*
        Involucral bracts obtuse, the inner elliptic, eciliate.   3. *D. humilis.*
    Achene much flattened, ribbed, over 1 mm. wide.   4. *D. infirma.*

1. **D. reticulata** (Pursh) Greene. Stem 3–12 dm. tall, fastigiate-corymbose above: blades of the upper leaves elliptic to obovate, obtuse or merely acutish, reticulate: inner bracts of the involucre 6–7 mm. long. [*Aster reticulatus* Pursh.]— Low pinelands, Coastal Plain, Fla. to S. C.— Spr.–sum.

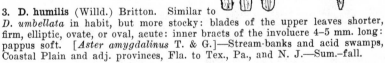

2. **D. umbellata** (Mill.) Nees. Stem 6–25 dm. tall, corymbose above: blades of the upper leaves membranous, elliptic, usually narrowly so, or linear-lanceolate, usually acuminate: inner bracts of the involucre 3–4 mm. long: pappus soft. [*Aster umbellatus* Mill.]—Shaded banks and in thickets, various provinces, Ga. to Ia., Sask., and Newf.—Sum.–fall.

3. **D. humilis** (Willd.) Britton. Similar to *D. umbellata* in habit, but more stocky: blades of the upper leaves shorter, firm, elliptic, ovate, or oval, acute: inner bracts of the involucre 4–5 mm. long: pappus soft. [*Aster amygdalinus* T. & G.]—Stream-banks and acid swamps, Coastal Plain and adj. provinces, Fla. to Tex., Pa., and N. J.—Sum.–fall.

4. **D. infirma** (Michx.) Greene. Stem 4–12 dm. tall, often widely branched: blades of the upper leaves elliptic to oval, varying to broadest above or below the middle, short-acuminate: inner bracts of the involucre 3–4 mm. long: disk-corollas 3–4 mm. long: pappus rigid. [*Aster infirmus* Michx.]—Dry woods and banks, various provinces, rarely Coastal Plain, La. to Ala., Tenn., and Mass.— Sum.–fall.

40. IONACTIS Greene. Perennial, low, rigid, widely creeping herbs. Leaves alternate: blades narrow, entire. Heads few in a corymb or rarely solitary, conspicuously radiate. Involucres campanulate to turbinate, many-flowered: bracts narrow, the inner ones several times longer than the outer. Ray-flowers several, with bright-colored elongate ligules. Disk-corollas yellow, with a slender tube and a longer funnelform throat, the lobes deltoid. Pappus of slender bristles in 2 indistinct series, the outer bristles the shorter.—Three species, North American.

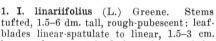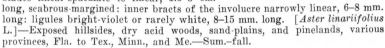

1. I. linariifolius (L.) Greene. Stems tufted, 1.5–6 dm. tall, rough-pubescent: leaf-blades linear-spatulate to linear, 1.5–3 cm. long, scabrous-margined: inner bracts of the involucre narrowly linear, 6–8 mm. long: ligules bright-violet or rarely white, 8–15 mm. long. [*Aster linariifolius* L.]—Exposed hillsides, dry acid woods, sand-plains, and pinelands, various provinces, Fla. to Tex., Minn., and Me.—Sum.–fall.

41. ERIGERON L. Annual, biennial, or perennial, caulescent, aster-like herbs. Leaves alternate, sometimes mostly basal: blades entire or toothed. Heads solitary or numerous, conspicuously radiate. Involucres broad, many-flowered: bracts narrow, the inner broader than the outer ones. Ray-flowers numerous: corollas with a slender tube and a narrow pink, violet, purple, or white ligule. Disk-corollas with a funnelform throat and a usually shorter tube: lobes deltoid. Anthers usually as long as the filaments. Stigma short. Pappus of numerous capillary bristles or bristles and scales.—About 130 species, widely distributed, but most abundant in America.—FLEABANES.

Plant perennial often with rosulate offsets ; pappus single.
 Heads with 30 ray-flowers or fewer : stem scape-like.   I. VERNI.
 Heads with 50 ray-flowers or more : stem leafy.
  Ray-flowers less than 75 ; ligules narrowly linear.   II. PULCHELLI.
  Ray-flowers over 100 ; ligules linear-filiform.   III. PHILADELPHICI.
Plant annual or biennial : pappus double.   IV. ANNUI.

I. VERNI
Plant glabrous, with a corymb terminating the scape.   1. *E. vernus.*

II. PULCHELLI
Plant pubescent, with one or several large heads terminating the stem.   2. *E. pulchellus.*

III. PHILADELPHICI
Longer involucral bracts less than 4 mm. long : ligules of the ray-flowers less than 5 mm. long.   3. *E. quercifolius.*
Longer involucral bracts over 4 mm. long : ligules of the ray-flowers over 5 mm. long.   4. *E. philadelphicus.*

IV. ANNUI
Upper stem-leaves with sharply toothed blades : ray-flowers with pink, or rarely purplish or white ligules.   5. *E. annuus.*
Upper stem-leaves with entire blades : ray-flowers with white or rarely pale pink ligules.   6. *E. ramosus.*

1. E. vernus (L.) T. & G. Stem 1–6 dm. tall, glabrous or nearly so: blades of the basal leaves spatulate, elliptic or oval: ray-flowers 20–30, white or

pink. [*E. nudicaulis* Michx.]—Moist pinelands and shallow ponds, Coastal Plain, Fla.
to La. and Va.—Spr.–sum.

2. E. pulchellus Michx. Stem 1–5 dm.
tall, villous or hirsute-villous: blades of the
basal leaves obovate, spatulate or elliptic:
outer bracts of the involucre finely pubescent; inner bracts acuminate, 5–5.5 mm.
long: ray-flowers 50–65; ligules violet or
bluish-purple: disk-corollas 4–4.5 mm. long.
[*E. bellidifolius* Muhl.] — (ROBIN'S-PLAN-
TAIN.)—Woods and banks, various provinces,
Fla. to La., Ont., and N. S.—Spr.

3. E. quercifolius Lam. Stem 1–7 dm. tall,
pubescent: blades of the basal leaves spatulate, oblanceolate, or oblong, pinnatifid or sinuate-pinnatifid: involucres manifestly pubescent; inner bracts prolonged into slender tips: ray-flowers numerous: disk-corollas 3.5–4 mm. long.—
Pinelands, grassy banks, and open woods, Coastal Plain and adj. provinces,
Fla. to Tex., Tenn., and S. C.—(*W. I.*)—Spr.–sum.

4. E. philadelphicus L. Stem 1–12 dm. tall, softly hirsute: blades of the
basal leaves spatulate to oblong, coarsely toothed: outer bracts of the involucre
minutely hispidulous; inner bracts acute, 2.5–3 mm. long: ray-flowers 100 or
more; ligules pink or rose-purple: disk-corollas 1.5–2 mm. long.—Thickets,
fields, and low pastures, various provinces, Fla. to Tex., Calif., B. C., Ont.,
and Lab.—Spr.–sum.

5. E. annuus (L.) Pers. Stem 3–12 dm. tall, loosely pubescent: blades of the
basal leaves oval, elliptic, or lanceolate, coarsely toothed or incised: bracts of
the involucre with few long hairs: ligules of the ray pink, purplish or rarely
white: disk-corollas less than half the length of the larger involucral bracts.—
(DAISY-FLEABANE. SWEET-SCABIOUS.)—Waste-places, in fields, and thickets,
various provinces, Ga. to Miss., Mo., Man., and N. S.—(*W. I.*)—Sum.—Often
a weed.

6. E. ramosus (Walt.) B.S.P. Stem elliptic, 2–10 dm. tall, appressed-pubescent: blades of the basal leaves spatulate to elliptic, shallowly toothed: bracts
of the involucre with many short hairs: ligules of the ray white or rarely pale-
pink: disk-corollas over half the length of the larger involucral bracts. [*E.
strigosus* Muhl. *E. strigosus Beyrichii* A. Gray.]—(DAISY-FLEABANE.)—Woods,
fields, and roadsides, nearly throughout N. A.—Spr.–sum.—Commonly a weed.

42. LEPTILON Raf. Annual or biennial, weedy herbs. Leaves alternate: blades narrow, entire or sparingly toothed. Heads several or numerous, inconspicuously radiate or discoid. Involucres usually campanulate or
cylindric, few-flowered: bracts very narrow, the inner much longer than the
outer ones. Ray-flowers few: corollas with a very slender tube and a minute
ligule. Disk-corollas with a campanulate or a cylindraceous throat and a long
tube: lobes deltoid. Pappus of many brittle capillary bristles in 1 series.—
About 20 species, American and Asiatic.

Inner bracts of the involucre glabrous or nearly so.
　Stem usually simple below the inflorescence: ray-flowers with white ligules.
　　Stem-leaves with mainly entire or merely few-toothed blades.
　　　Plant glabrate or hirsute: involucral bracts green
　　　　throughout.　　　　　　　　　　　　　　　1. *L. canadense.*

Plant glabrous or nearly so: involucral bracts purple
tipped.   2. *L. pusillum.*
Stem-leaves with mainly pinnatifid or pinnatifid-toothed
blades.   3. *L. bonariense.*
Stem diffusely branched at the base: ray-flowers with purplish ligules.   4. *L. divaricatum.*
Inner bracts of the involucre copiously pubescent.   5. *L. linifolium.*

1. L. canadense (L.) Britton. Stem 3–20 dm. tall, paniculate above, pubescent or sparingly hirsute: leaf-blades spatulate to linear or nearly so, ciliate
near the base: longer bracts of the involucre
3–3.5 mm. long: disk-corollas 2.5–3 mm.
long. [*Erigeron canadensis* L.]—(HORSE-
WEED. BUTTER-WEED.)—Common, fields and
waste-places, nearly throughout the U. S.—
Sum.–fall.

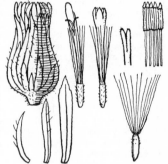

2. L. pusillum (Nutt.) Britton. Stem as in
L. canadense, but glabrous or nearly so: leaf-
blades narrowly spatulate to linear; petioles
sometimes ciliate: longer bracts of the involucre 3–4 mm. long: disk-corollas 2.5–3
mm. long.—Fields, roadsides, and waste-
places, Fla. to La., Tenn., and Mass.—(*W. I.,
Mex., C. A., S. A.*)—Sum.–fall.

3. L. bonariense (L.) Small. Similar to *L. canadense* in habit: leaf-blades
finely pubescent: longer bracts of the involucre 5–6 mm. long: disk-corollas
3.5–4 mm. long.—Waste-places, Fla.—Nat. of S. Am.—Spr.–fall.

4. L. divaricatum (Michx.) Raf. Stem 1–3 dm. tall, diffuse, hirsute and
somewhat cinereous: leaf-blades narrowly linear to subulate, 1–4.5 cm. long,
entire: disk-corollas less than 3 mm. long. [*Erigeron divaricatus* Michx.]—
Dry soil, waste-places, meadows, and fields, various provinces, Ala. to Tex.,
Minn., and Ill.—Sum.–fall.

5. L. linifolium (Willd.) Small. Stem racemose or paniculate above, 2–7
dm. tall, hirsute: leaf-blades narrowly spatulate to linear, 1.5–10 cm. long,
those of the lower incised or laciniate: disk-corollas mostly over 3 mm.
long. [*Erigeron linifolius* Willd.]—Waste-places, Coastal Plain, Fla. to Miss.
and S. C.—(*W. I., Mex., C. A., S. A.*)—Spr.–fall.

43. BACCHARIS L. Shrubs with much-branched, sometimes fastigiate
stems. Leaves alternate: blades leathery, entire or toothed. Heads dioecious,
often clustered, discoid. Involucres ovoid to campanulate, many-flowered:
bracts of the staminate involucre smaller than those of the pistillate. Corollas
greenish, various, those of the staminate with a funnelform throat and a long
tube, the lobes lanceolate: those of the pistillate flowers filiform or slightly enlarged upward. Pappus of the staminate flowers shorter than that of the pistillate. Achenes nearly terete, many-ribbed, glabrous.—About 300 species, American.

Leaf-blades broadest above the middle.
  Leaf-blades entire.   1. *B. dioica.*
  Leaf-blades mostly toothed.
    Inner bracts of the pistillate involucres acute: heads in
      peduncled panicled clusters.   2. *B. halimifolia.*
    Inner bracts of the pistillate involucres obtuse: heads
      in sessile or nearly sessile axillary clusters.   3. *B. glomeruliflora.*
Leaf-blades narrowly linear.   4. *B. angustifolia.*

1. B. dioica Vahl. Shrub 8–25 dm. tall: leaf-blades spatulate, often broadly so, to obovate-spatulate, 1–3 cm. long: pistillate involucres with ovate-obtuse outer bracts and linear-lanceolate acuminate inner bracts: achene 1–1.5 mm. long.—Hammocks, Everglade Keys, Fla.—(*W. I.*)—All year.

2. B. halimifolia L. Shrub 9–40 dm. tall, resinous: leaf-blades suborbicular to elliptic or linear-elliptic, some of them, at least, coarsely toothed: pistillate involucres about 6 mm. long; inner bracts linear: achenes 1.5 mm. long.—(GROUNDSEL-TREE. SILVERLING.) —Shore-hammocks, sea-beaches, and salt-marshes, and low grounds inland, Coastal Plain and rarely adj. provinces, Fla. to Tex. and Mass.—(*W. I., Mex., C. A.*)—Sum.-fall.

3. B. glomeruliflora Pers. Shrub 8–30 dm. tall, barely resinous: leaf-blades spatulate to cuneate-obovate, 2–5 cm. long, often sharply toothed: pistillate involucres 5–6 mm. long; inner bracts oblong-spatulate: achene 1.5 mm. long.—Salt-marshes and swamps, Coastal Plain, Fla. to N. C. and hammocks in the interior of the Fla. peninsula.—(*W. I.*)—Fall-wint. or all year S.

4. B. angustifolia Michx. Shrub 5–25 dm. tall, resinous: leaf-blades narrowly linear, 1–8 cm. long, entire or nearly so: pistillate involucres 4–5 mm. long; inner bracts elliptic: achene 1–1.5 mm. long.—(FALSE-WILLOW.)—Salt marshes, brackish swamps, and low hammocks, Coastal Plain, Fla. to Tex. and N. C.—(*W. I.*)—Fall or all year S.

44. PLUCHEA Cass. Herbs with often conspicuously pubescent and camphor-scented foliage, or shrubs. Leaves alternate: blades usually toothed, often prominently veined. Heads borne in corymb-like or glomerate cymes. Involucres turbinate, campanulate, or hemispheric, rather many-flowered: bracts unequal, the inner much longer and much narrower than the outer. Flowers pink to rose-purple. Pistillate flowers marginal: corollas filiform. Perfect flowers central: corollas with a funnelform or campanulate throat: lobes triangular lanceolate. Pappus a single series of capillary bristles.—About 35 species, in warm and temperate regions.—MARSH-FLEABANES.

Plant perennial.
  Leaf-blades entire: stem woody.   I. ODORATAE.
  Leaf-blades toothed: stem herbaceous.   II. FOETIDAE.
Plant annual.
  Leaves not decurrent, the stem terete, not winged.   III. CAMPHORATAE.
  Leaves decurrent, the stem thus winged.   IV. SUBDECURRENTES.

I. ODORATAE
Shrubby much-branched plant with heads in erect rather dense corymbs.   1. *P. odorata.*
II. FOETIDAE
Outer bracts of the involucres acuminate.
  Leaf-blades broad at the base, and cordate-clasping. 2. *P. foetida.*
  Leaf-blades acute or merely rounded at the base, not clasping.   3. *P. tenuifolia.*
Outer bracts of the involucres obtuse or merely acute.
  Pappus white: upper stem-leaves little shorter than the lower.   4. *P. longifolia.*
  Pappus buff: upper stem-leaves much shorter than the lower.   5. *P. imbricata.*

III. Camphoratae

Bracts of the involucre thin, sparingly pubescent.   6. *P. petiolata.*
Bracts of the involucre thick, densely pubescent.
  Involucres 4–5 mm. high; inner bracts abruptly acuminate.   7. *P. purpurascens.*
  Involucres 6–8 mm. high; inner bracts long-acuminate.   8. *P. camphorata.*

IV. Subdecurrentes

Erect herb with corymbosely branched stem, the branches
  winged as well as the stem: leaf-blades shallowly toothed.   9. *P. Quitoc.*

1. P. odorata Cass. Plant mostly 1 m. tall or less: leaf-blades elliptic or nearly so, 8–15 cm. long: inner bracts of the involucres 3.5–4 mm. long, obtuse. Hammocks and waste-grounds, S Pen. Fla. and the Keys. Nat. of Tr. Am.—(*W. I.,* *Mex., C. A., S. A.*)—Spr.–sum.

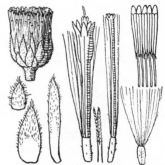

2. P. foetida (L.) DC. Plant 3–10 dm. tall, the stem usually scurfy-tomentulose: leaf-blades cuneate to elliptic, ovate-elliptic or ovate, 3–8 cm. long, thick, rather coarsely veined, denticulate or serrulate with prominently gland-tipped teeth: inner bracts of the involucre mostly 4–5 mm. long. [*P. bifrons* DC.]—Low grounds and shallow ponds, Coastal Plain and adj. provinces, Fla. to Tex., Mo., and N. J.—(*W. I., Mex.*)— Spr.-sum. or all year S.

3. P. tenuifolia Small. Plant 4–11 dm. tall, the stem thinly pubescent: leaf-blades elliptic to elliptic-lanceolate, 4–12 cm. long, thin, finely veined, sharply and coarsely serrate with slightly glandular teeth: inner bracts of the involucre 5–6 mm. long.—Pinelands, Coastal Plain, Fla. to La.—Sum.–fall.

4. P. longifolia Nash. Plant 6–10 dm. tall: leaf-blades elliptic, 5–16 cm. long: inner bracts of the involucre 7–19 mm. long: staminate corollas 6.5–7.5 mm. long.—Swamps, Fla.—Sum.

5. P. imbricata (Kearney) Nash. Plant 9–25 dm. tall: leaf-blades ovate-elliptic to triangular-ovate, 3–6 cm. long: inner bracts of the involucre 6–7 mm. long: staminate corollas 5–6 mm. long.—Swamps and pond-borders, Coastal Plain, Fla. to Ga. and S. C.—Sum.–fall.

6. P. petiolata Cass. Plant 5–12 dm. tall: leaf-blades mainly elliptic, 8–25 cm. long: outer bracts of the involucre ovate; intermediate bracts acuminate. [*P. foetida* DC.]—Stream-banks, swamps and ditches, various provinces, Fla. to Miss., Kans. and S Va.—Sum.–fall.

7. P. purpurascens (Sw.) DC. Plant 3–14 dm. tall: leaf-blades ovate-lanceolate to elliptic, 4–10 cm. long: outer bracts of the involucre ovate, acute; intermediate bracts abruptly pointed.—Hammocks and moist sandy thickets, Coastal Plain, Fla. to Tex. and Ga.—(*W. I., Mex., C. A., S. A.*)—Sum.–fall.

8. P. camphorata (L.) DC. Plant 3–15 dm. tall: leaf-blades elliptic or lanceolate, 3–15 cm. long: outer bracts of the involucre elliptic, acute: intermediate bracts acuminate.—Salt marshes, Coastal Plain and adj. provinces, Fla. to Tex. and Mass.—(Mex.)

9. P. Quitoc DC. Plant 7–20 dm. tall: leaf-blades oblong, elliptic, lanceolate or linear-lanceolate, 4–16 cm. long: outer bracts of the involucre obtuse.— Marsh places, W Fla.—Nat. of trop. Am.—Spr.–fall.

P. adnata (H. & B.) C. Mohr, Mexican, with winged stem and branches: narrowly lanceolate leaf-blades; lanceolate-acuminate involucral bracts; and said to have a perennial rootstock has been reported as adventive on ballast in Ala.

45. **SACHSIA** Griseb. Perennial, inconspicuously pubescent, slender herbs. Leaves alternate, mostly basal: blades toothed. Heads scattered in open corymbs. Involucres campanulate: bracts very unequal, the inner much longer and somewhat narrower than the outer. Flowers yellow, the pistillate marginal: corollas filiform. Perfect flowers central: corollas narrowly tubular-funnelform: lobes ovate. Pappus a single series of very slender bristles. —Four species, West Indian.

1. **S. bahamensis** Urban. Plant 1–6 dm. tall: blades of the basal leaves firm, spatulate, 3–7 cm. long, those of the stem-leaves much smaller: involucres peduncled; bracts various, the outer membranous, the inner chaffy, 5–6 mm. long, very narrowly linear: achene 2.5 mm. long.—Pinelands, Everglade Keys, Fla. and Florida Keys.—(*W. I.*)—Spr.-sum.

46. **PTEROCAULON** Ell. Perennial, tomentose or woolly, stout herbs. Leaves alternate: blades entire or shallowly toothed, decurrent. Heads borne in contiguous or separated glomerate cymes. Involucres rather narrow, densely flowered: bracts unequal, the inner narrower than the outer. Pistillate flowers marginal: corollas filiform. Perfect flowers central: corollas with a funnelform throat and a long tube; lobes linear or lanceolate. Anthers shorter than the filaments. Pappus a single series of capillary bristles. [*Chlaenobolus* Cass.] —About 12 species, mostly American.

1. **P. undulatum** (Walt.) C. Mohr. Plant 2–7 dm. tall: leaf-blades elliptic to lanceolate, 4–12 cm. long, undulate: involucre 3.5–4 mm. high: flowers whitish or cream, lobes of the staminate corollas linear.— [*P. pycnostachya* (Michx.) Ell.]—(BLACK-ROOT.)—Pinelands, Coastal Plain, Fla. to Miss. and N. C.—Spr.-fall.—The thick black root gives this plant its common name.

47. **ANTENNARIA** Gaertn. Perennial woolly, stoloniferous herbs. Leaves alternate, those of the short caudex different from those of the flowering stem: blades entire. Heads in a terminal cluster, or rarely solitary. Involucres turbinate to campanulate, many-flowered: bracts with petaloid tips, those of the staminate involucres larger than those of the pistillate. Flowers whitish, dioecious or polygamo-dioecious. Pappus-bristles united at the base.—

About 50 species, natives of the north temperate zone and southern South America.—Spr.—EVERLASTINGS. LADIES'-TOBACCOS.

Heads corymbose or racemose: stolons more or less ascending and distantly leafy, their leaves gradually increasing in size towards the ends, with oblanceolate or spatulate blades.
  Pistillate heads 6–8 mm. high: staminate heads 5–7 mm. high.
    Blades of the basal leaves obovate or oval.   1. *A. plantaginifolia.*
    Blades of the basal leaves oblanceolate.   2. *A. caroliniana.*
  Pistillate heads 9–12 mm. high: staminate heads 6–8 mm. high.
    Blades of the basal leaves broadest below the middle, in age subcoriaceous: pistillate heads rather long-peduncled, in age often racemose.   3. *A. calophylla.*
    Blades of the basal leaves mostly broadest above the middle, thin: pistillate heads short-peduncled, corymbose.   4. *A. fallax.*
Heads solitary: stolons prostrate, their leaves, except those of the terminal rosette, with small or inconspicuous linear blades.   5. *A. solitaria.*

1. A. plantaginifolia (L.) Richards. Basal leaves 5–9 cm. long; blades about equalling the petioles, 1.5–4 cm. wide, loosely floccose, but in age glabrate above, white-tomentose beneath, obovate or nearly oval, distinctly 3-ribbed: blades of the stem leaves linear-lanceolate, acuminate: flowering stem of pistillate plants 6–20 cm. tall, of the staminate 5–12 cm. tall: pistillate heads corymbose, 6–8 mm. high, floccose at the base; bracts linear-lanceolate, acute, bright olive-green or brownish at the base, white at the tip; staminate heads more loosely clustered, 5–7 mm. high, their bracts somewhat darker at the base with elliptic, obtuse, white tips. [*A. plantaginea* R. Br. *A. decipiens* Greene *A. arkansana* Greene]—Dry soil, various provinces, Fla. to Tex., Minn., and Me.—Spr.—*A. nemoralis* Greene from E Tenn. with thinner more rounded leaf-blades may belong here; pistillate plant unknown.

2. A. caroliniana Rydb. Basal leaves 4–8 cm. long; blades often longer than the petioles, 1–2 cm. wide, loosely floccose, but soon glabrate above, white-tomentose beneath, oblanceolate, rounded to acutish at the apex, gradually tapering at the base, distinctly 3-ribbed; blades of the stem-leaves linear-lanceolate, acuminate: flowering stem 1–1.5 dm. tall: heads corymbose, short-peduncled; the pistillate 6–7 mm. high, their bracts linear-lanceolate, acute, greenish or brownish below, white at the tip; staminate heads about 5 mm. high, their bracts yellowish, with elliptic, obtuse, white tips.—Dry soil, Coastal Plain and Piedmont, Ala. to S. C.—Spr.

3. A. calophylla Greene. Basal leaves 5–10 cm. long: blades usually as long as the petioles, 2–5 cm. long, loosely floccose above, but glabrate in age, finely and densely white-tomentose beneath, broadly ovate or oval, usually broadest a little below the middle, rounded or mucronate at the apex, abruptly contracted at the base, subcoriaceous in age, distinctly 3–5-ribbed: blades of the stem-leaves linear-lanceolate, acuminate: flowering stems of pistillate plants 3–4 dm. tall: heads 10–12 mm. high, corymbose or in age often racemose, the peduncles 1–3 cm. long: bracts of the involucre linear-lanceolate, acuminate, brownish at the base, white at the tip: staminate heads densely corymbose, 7–8 mm. high, dark-brown below, with elliptic or oval white tips.—Wooded hills, various provinces, La. (or Ga.?) to Okla., Ill., and Ky.—Spr.

4. A. fallax Greene. Basal leaves 5–9 cm. long; blades sometimes shorter than the petioles, 2–4 cm. wide, loosely floccose and glabrate above, densely and closely white tomentose beneath, obovate-spatulate, rounded and mucronate or acutish at the apex, abruptly narrowed at the base, distinctly 3–5-ribbed: blades of the stem-leaves linear-lanceolate, acuminate: flowering stem of pistillate plants 2–4 dm. tall, that of the staminate 1–1.5 dm. tall: pistillate heads 9–12 mm. high, corymbose, the peduncles rarely 2 cm. long; bracts of the involucre linear-lanceolate, acuminate, brownish below, white at the tip: staminate heads 6–7 mm. high, corymbose, their bracts light-brown or greenish-brown below the elliptic obtuse white tips. [*A. ambigens* (Greene) Fernald.]—Woods and fields, various provinces, rarely Coastal Plain, Ga. to Mo., Minn., and Me.— The leaf-blades are broader and more rounded at the apex in the southern form than in the northern.

5. A. solitaria Rydb. Basal leaves 4–10 cm. long; blades much longer than the petioles, 1.5–4 cm. wide, somewhat floccose above when young, in age minutely tomentulose beneath, obovate to oblanceolate-spatulate, rounded at the apex, distinctly 3–ribbed; blades of the stem-leaves linear to elliptic: flowering stem of the pistillate plant 1–2 dm. tall, that of the staminate 0.5–1 dm. tall: heads solitary, the pistillate one about 1 cm. high; bracts linear-lanceolate, attenuate, purplish-brown except the very tips: staminate heads smaller; bracts often wine-colored, except the brownish-white spatulate tips.—Wooded slopes, often in rather acid soil, Coastal Plain and adj. provinces, Ga. to La., Ind., and Pa.—Spr.

48. ANAPHALIS DC. Perennial, conspicuously pubescent, erect herbs. Leaves alternate: blades narrow, entire. Heads in a terminal corymb. Involucres broad, turgid, many-flowered: bracts pearly-white, obtuse. Flowers whitish, dioecious, the staminate with a slender or filiform corolla. Pappus-bristles of the fruit-producing flowers distinct, that of the sterile flowers not thickened at the apex.—About 35 species, natives of the north temperate zone.

1. A. margaritacea (L.) Benth. & Hook. Plant woolly, 2–8.5 dm. tall: leaf-blades linear or nearly so, 5–15 cm. long, attenuate: involucres pearly white; outer bracts elliptic, the inner spatulate: staminate corollas 3.5–4 mm. long.—(PEARLY-EVER-LASTING.)—Dry woods, hillsides, and clearings, in sterile and often somewhat acid soil, various provinces, in Coastal Plain only N, N. C. to Alas., Ont., and Newf.

49. GNAPHALIUM L. Annual, biennial, or perennial, pubescent herbs. Leaves alternate: blades entire, sometimes decurrent. Heads in open or glomerate cymes, panicles, or corymbs. Involucres ovoid to cylindric, several–many-flowered: bracts various, the inner longer and usually narrower than the outer. Flowers white or cream. Pistillate flowers marginal: corollas filiform. Perfect flowers central: corollas with a cylindric-funnelform throat and a slender tube: lobes ovate to deltoid. Anthers mostly longer than the filaments. Pappus a series of capillary bristles.—About 120 species, widely distributed.— Sum.—CUDWEEDS. EVERLASTINGS.

Pappus-bristles distinct, falling away separately : achene glabrous.   I. OBTUSIFOLIA.
Pappus-bristles united at the base, falling away together : achene
   pubescent.   II. PURPUREA.

I. OBTUSIFOLIA
Leaf-blades merely sessile.
   Foliage pubescent, not viscid.   1. *G. obtusifolium.*
   Foliage glandular-viscid.   2. *G. Helleri.*
Leaf-blades decurrent on the stem.   3. *G. Macounii.*

II. PURPUREA
Leaf-blades manifestly more pubescent beneath than above,
   spatulate, sometimes broadly so.
   Leaf-blades thin : stem cobwebby : involucre-clusters co-
     piously woolly.   4. *G. spathulatum.*
   Leaf-blades thick : stem densely woolly or felty : involucre-
     clusters sparingly woolly.   5. *G. purpureum.*
Leaf-blades almost equally pubescent on both sides, linear-
   spatulate below, linear or mostly so above.   6. *G. falcatum.*

1. **G. obtusifolium** L. Plant 2–6 dm. tall: cauline leaves 2–10 cm. long;
blades elliptic-linear to linear, the upper surface glabrous or glabrate: heads
corymbose-paniculate: involucre 6–7 mm.
high; inner bracts glabrous.   [*G. poly-
cephalum* Michx.] — (RABBIT-TOBACCO.)—
Woods, fields, and thickets, various provinces, Fla. to Tex., Man., and N. S.—Sum.-
fall.

2. **G. Helleri** Britton. Plant 2–9 dm. tall:
leaf-blades linear to elliptic, 3–11 cm. long:
involucre 5–6 mm. high; outer bracts obtuse.—Sandy woods, various provinces, Ga.
to Miss., Ky., and N. J.—Sum.-fall.

3. **G. Macounii** Greene. Plant 2–9 dm. tall:
leaf-blades linear or slightly broadened upward, 6–12 cm. long: involucre 4–5 mm.
high; outer bracts acute. [*G. decurrens* Ives,, not L.].—Dry soil, edges of woods
and clearings, Blue Ridge and more N provinces, Tenn. to Tex., Ariz., B. C., N.
S., and Pa.—Sum.-fall.

4. **G. spathulatum** Lam. Plant thinly gray-pubescent, 2–4 dm. tall: leaf-
blades spatulate, 2–8 cm. long: outer bracts of the involucre broadly linear.—
Waste-places, cult. grounds, roadsides, and pastures, Coastal Plain and Piedmont, Fla. to Tex.—(*W. I.*)—Spr.-fall.

5. **G. purpureum** L. Plant white-woolly or silvery, 1–4 dm. tall: leaf-blades
spatulate to linear, 2–8 cm. long: heads in sessile axillary clusters, these in
virgate panicles: outer bracts of the involucre elliptic.—Woods, cult. grounds,
and waste-places, various provinces, Fla. to Tex., Kans., and Me.—(*W. I.*,
Mex., C. A., S. A.)—Spr.-fall

6. **G. falcatum** Lam. Plant more slender than in *G. purpureum*, densely
white-woolly, 1–4 dm. tall: leaf-blades linear-spatulate to linear, 2–6 cm. long:
outer bracts of the involucre elliptic-ovate.—Pinelands and cult. grounds,
Coastal Plain and adj. provinces, Fla. to Tex. and Tenn.—(*S. A.*)—All year.

G. uliginosum L. related to the species of group I in its distinct pappus-
bristles; differing from them in its low diffuse habit and the congested or
capitate inflorescence, has been reported from Tenn.

   50. FACELIS Cass. Annual, small, pubescent herbs. Leaves alternate:
blades narrow, entire. Heads borne in the axils or in terminal clusters. In-

volucres ellipsoid to ovoid, few-flowered: inner bracts much narrower and longer than the outer. Flowers whitish, the pistillate flowers marginal: corollas slender, truncate or nearly so. Perfect flowers central: corollas with a cylindric throat and a long tube. Anthers longer than the filaments. Pappus of numerous very long capillary bristles concreted at the base.—About 3 species, South American.

1. F. apiculata Cass. Plant 2–20 cm. tall, lanate: leaf-blades linear-spatulate to linear, 0.5–1 cm. long: involucre narrow; inner bracts 5–7.5 mm. long: achene long-hairy.—Roadsides and waste-places, Coastal Plain and Piedmont, Fla., Ala., and Ga.—Nat. of S S. Am.—Sum.-fall.

51. GIFOLA Cass. Annual, caulescent herbs resembling *Gnaphalium*. Leaves alternate: blades narrow, entire. Heads discoid, in small dense, sometimes proliferous, clusters. Involucres narrow, sessile: bracts scarious, in several series. Receptacle subulate to conic, chaffy. Flowers whitish, the pistillate marginal, fruit-producing, with filiform corollas and rudimentary or no pappus. Perfect flowers central, few, with tubular corollas and capillary pappus. Anthers sagittate at the base. Achene terete or slightly flattened.—About 10 species, in warm and temperate regions.

1. G. germanica (L.) Dumort. Plant silvery-pubescent, 5–35 cm. tall, the stem or branches usually proliferous above: leaves numerous, erect; blades lanceolate to linear, 1–2 cm. long, acute: involucre 3–3.5 mm. high; bracts ovate-lanceolate to elliptic-lanceolate, acuminate or cuspidate: achene about 0.8 mm. long.—(HERBA-IMPIA. COTTON-ROSE.)—Dry fields and waste-places, various provinces, Ga. to N. Y.—Nat. of Eu.—Spr.-fall.

52. FILAGINOPSIS T. & G. Annual or sometimes perennial woolly herbs. Leaves alternate: blades entire, commonly narrow. Heads in dense involucrate clusters, discoid. Involucre broad: inner bracts longer than the outer ones. Flowers whitish, the pistillate marginal, with filiform corollas. Perfect flowers few: corollas with a cylindraceous or narrowly funnelform throat and a narrow tube. Pappus wanting.—About 12 species, natives of warm and temperate regions.

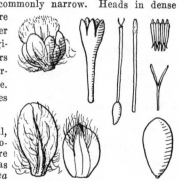

1. F. nivea Small. Plant 2–15 cm. tall, whitish: leaf-blades oblong to oblong-lanceolate, 5–12 mm. long: bracts of the involucre barely 2 mm. long or less: staminate corollas less than 1.5 mm. long. [*Filago nivea*

Small.]—(Poverty-weed. Rabbit-tobacco.)—Dry plains or stony soil, Coastal Plain and adj. provinces, Ga. to Tex. Naturalized E.—Spr.–sum.

53. **INULA** L. Perennial, often large, pale-pubescent herbs. Leaves alternate: blades broad, toothed, often clasping. Heads in open panicles or corymbs, terminating long peduncles, usually showy. Involucre hemispheric, very many-flowered: bracts, at least the outer ones broad, somewhat foliaceous. Ray-flowers numerous: corollas with a long tube and a narrow elongate yellow ligule. Disk-flowers numerous: corolla with narrowly funnelform throat above a narrow tube with a dilated base: lobes lanceolate. Anthers longer than the filaments. Achene columnar, ribbed. Pappus of several or many capillary scabrous bristles.—About 90 species, Eurasian and African.

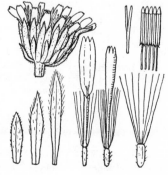

1. **I. Helenium** L. Stem, 2 m. tall or less, softly pubescent: leaf-blades pale beneath, those of the basal leaves lanceolate to elliptic-lanceolate, 1–3 dm. long, petioled, those of the cauline leaves elliptic, oval, or ovate, sessile and clasping, mostly 9–20 cm. long, all toothed: involucre hemispheric, 1.5–1.7 cm. high; bracts various, the outer ovate or oval, the inner narrowly linear, about 2 cm. long: ligules yellow, narrowly linear, 2–3 cm. long: achene 4–5 mm. long, finely ribbed.—(Elecampane.)—Roadsides, fence-rows, and fields, various provinces N of Coastal Plain, N. C. to Mo., Ont., and N. S. Nat. of Eu.—Sum.

54. **VICOA** Cass. Annual or perennial herbs with much-branched stems. Leaves alternate: blades narrow, shallowly toothed, at least the upper ones auricled at the base and clasping. Heads several or numerous, often radiate, rather slender-peduncled. Involucre hemispheric-campanulate, many-flowered: bracts very narrow, numerous. Ray-flowers few: corolla with a very slender tube and a short rather broad ligule. Disk-flowers numerous: corolla with a slender tube and an elongate cylindric throat: lobes triangular-lanceolate. Anthers longer than the filaments. Achene cylindric, not ribbed. Pappus of few capillary bristles.—About 8 species, Asiatic and African.

1. **V. auriculata** Cass. Annual, 1 m. tall or less, widely branched, finely pubescent and partly viscid: leaf-blades lanceolate to elliptic-lanceolate, 3–11 cm. long or much reduced on the branchlets, acute, sometimes toothed: heads erect: involucre 4–4.5 mm. high; bracts linear-lanceolate to narrowly linear, the inner ones about 5 mm. long, acuminate, sparingly glandular-pubescent, ciliate: ligules yellow, rather obcuneate, about 3 mm. long: achene about 0.8 mm. long, pubescent: pappus-

bristles several times longer than the achene.—Waste-places and roadsides, W Fla. Nat. of E. I.—Sum.

55. CUPULARIA Godr. & Gren. Perennial, much-branched, partly woody plants. Leaves alternate: blades rather narrow, toothed, clasping, more or less auricled at the base. Heads numerous, panicled, short-peduncled. Involucre campanulate, many-flowered: bracts narrow, not foliaceous. Ray-flowers few: corolla with slender tube and a short rather broad ligule. Disk-flowers rather numerous: corolla with a slender tube and a narrowly funnelform throat; lobes triangular-lanceolate. Anthers longer than the filaments. Achene of a cylindric-ellipsoid type, not ribbed. Pappus of several capillary scabrous bristles. —About 3 species, Eurasian and African.

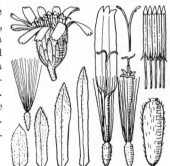

1. C. viscosa (Ait.) Godr. & Gren. Stem 1 m. tall or less, glandular-pubescent: leaf-blades elliptic to lanceolate or linear-lanceolate, 2–12 cm. long, serrate, sessile: involucre 8–9 mm. high, glandular; bracts ovate to linear or linear-spatulate, the inner 6–7 mm. long, short-acuminate: ligules yellow, elliptic, 5–7 mm. long: achene narrowly ellipsoid or slightly broadened upward, about 2 mm. long, finely pubescent.—Roadsides and waste-places, W Fla. Nat. of Eu.—Sum.–fall.

56. SMALLANTHUS Mackenzie. Perennial herbs. Leaves opposite: blades very broad, palmately veined. Heads conspicuously radiate. Involucre large, the outer series of bracts foliaceous, the inner narrower. Ray-flowers conspicuous, the corollas with pubescent tubes and long yellow ligules. Disk-flowers with short abortive ovaries, the corollas with cylindraceous throats and short, ciliate lobes. Stigma slender, not thickened under the appendage. Achene somewhat laterally compressed, oblique, finely striate. —One species.

1. S. Uvedalia (L.) Mackenzie. Stem 1–3 m. tall: leaves 1–5 dm. long; blades 3–5-lobed or angled: outer bracts of the involucre ovate to elliptic, 9–14 mm. long: ray-flowers with yellow ligules 15–20 mm. long: achene 5–6 mm. long. [*Polymniastrum Uvedalia* (L.) Small]—(BEAR-FOOT.)—Rich soil, edges of woods, thickets, and stream-banks, various provinces, Fla. to Tex., Mo. and N. Y.—Sum.–fall.

57. POLYMNIA L. Perennial, widely branched herbs. Leaves opposite or mainly so: blades broad, pinnately veined. Heads inconspicuously radiate. Involucre small, double, the outer series of bracts loose, the inner ones variously shaped. Ray-flowers inconspicuous, the corollas with pubescent tubes and white, greenish, or pale-yellow, wide ligules. Disk-flowers with long abortive ovaries, the corollas with broadly funnelform throats and relatively long, ciliate lobes. Stigma stout, thickened under the tip. Anther-body broader than the appendage. Achene slightly obcompressed, not oblique, 3- or 5-ribbed, with a rounded tip. Pappus wanting.—About 10 species, American.—Sum.-fall.—LEAF-CUPS.

Foliage manifestly or copiously pubescent: achene 3-ribbed or angled.
   Ray-flowers evident; ligules 5–10 mm. long.   1. *P. radiata.*
   Ray-flowers inconspicuous; ligules 1–2 mm. long.   2. *P. canadensis.*
Foliage glabrous or the stem with merely puberulent nodes:
   achene 5-ribbed.
                                         3. *P. laevigata.*

1. P. radiata (A. Gray) Small. Stem 5–15 dm. tall: leaves 1.5–3 dm. long; blades elliptic to oval or elliptic-ovate: intermediate bracts of the involucre rather long-acuminate: ligules of the ray white, conspicuous cuneate to oval-cuneate: achene about 5 mm. long, sharp-angled.— Rich woods, often over calcareous rocks, various provinces N of Coastal Plain, Ga. to Mo., Wis., and N. Y.

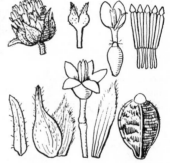

2. P. canadensis L. Stem 5–15 dm. tall: leaves 1–2 dm. long; blades elliptic, oval, or ovate: intermediate bracts of the involucre short-acuminate: ligules of the ray greenish or whitish, inconspicuous, or obsolete: achene about 3 mm. long, obtuse-angled.—Stream-banks, ravines, hillsides, and thickets, various provinces, rarely Coastal Plain, La. to Mo., Ont., and Vt.

3. P. laevigata Beadle. Stem 5–12 dm. tall: leaves 1–2.5 dm. long; blades oval to ovate or deltoid: intermediate bracts of the involucre acute: ligules of the ray, white, broad: achene barely 3 mm long.—Mt. slopes, often in somewhat acid soil over siliceous rocks, Appalachian Plateau, Ga. and Tenn.

58. ACANTHOSPERMUM Schrank. Annual, coarse herbs. Leaves opposite: blades broad, toothed. Heads inconspicuously radiate. Involucre double: bracts of the inner series becoming bur-like, each one surrounding an achene. Ligules of the ray-corollas concave or hooded, yellowish, inconspicuous with short pubescent tubes. Disk flowers with long abortive ovaries, the corollas with campanulate throats, short tubes, and lobes. Achene slightly flattened, fusiform or obovoid, smooth. Pappus wanting.—About 3 species, tropical American.—Spr.-fall.

Involucral bracts uniformly prickly: petioles not broadly winged.   1. *A. australe.*
Involucral bracts with 2 large spines in addition to the prickles:
   petioles broadly winged or leaf-blades cuneately sessile.
   Leaf-blades wing-petioled, incised: involucral bracts 3–4 mm.
     long.   2. *A. humile.*
   Leaf-blades sessile by a cuneate base: involucral bracts 4–5
     mm. long.   3. *A. hispidum.*

1. A. australe (L.) Kuntze. Stem branched at the base, the branches prostrate or creeping: leaf-blades ovate, oval, or rhombic, 1–2.5 cm. long: disk-corollas about 2 mm. long: mature involucre starfish-like.—Pinelands, waste-grounds, and roadsides, Coastal Plain and Piedmont, Fla. to La., and Va. Nat. of trop. Am.

2. A. humile (Sw.) DC. Stem or branches erect or ascending: leaf-blades deltoid-ovate to pandurate, 1–3 cm. long: disk-corollas about 1 mm. long: mature involucre spinescent.—Sandy roadsides and pinelands, Fla. to Ala., and at Atlantic seaports. Nat. of trop. Am.—(*W. I., Mex., C. A., S. A.*).

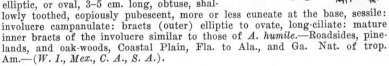

3. A. hispidum DC. Stem erect, 1 m. tall or less, widely branched: leaf-blades ovate, elliptic, or oval, 3–5 cm. long, obtuse, shallowly toothed, copiously pubescent, more or less cuneate at the base, sessile: involucre campanulate: bracts (outer) elliptic to ovate, long-ciliate: mature inner bracts of the involucre similar to those of *A. humile.*—Roadsides, pinelands, and oak-woods, Coastal Plain, Fla. to Ala., and Ga. Nat. of trop. Am.—(*W. I., Mex., C. A., S. A.*).

59. SILPHIUM L. Perennial, erect, usually large herbs. Leaves alternate or opposite: blades entire, toothed, or pinnately or pedately parted, sometimes connate-perfoliate. Heads erect. Involucre campanulate or hemispheric, many-flowered: bracts distinct, relatively broad. Ligules of the ray-corollas yellow or rarely white, conspicuous, the tube short. Disk-flowers with long abortive ovaries, the corollas with short tubes, tubular throats, and short lobes. Achene conspicuously flattened, winged. Pappus of two awns beside the apical teeth of the wings, which usually form a U- or V-shaped sinus, or wanting. —More than 30 species, North American.—ROSIN-WEEDS. ROSIN-PLANTS.

Leaf-blades or their petiole-like bases connate-perfoliate: stem square, sharply angled. | I. PERFOLIATA.
Leaf-blades not connate-perfoliate: stem terete or obtusely quadrangular.
 Plants with scape-like flower-stems, the leaves basal or near the base of the stem: leaf-blades pinnately or pedately parted or lobed, or very coarsely toothed.
  Heads borne in a raceme at the top of the stem, very large, the involucre 3–4 cm. wide. | II. LACINIATA.
  Heads borne in terminal effuse or diffuse panicles, or individually solitary, relatively small, the involucre 1–3 cm. wide. | III. COMPOSITA.
 Plants with leafy flower-stems: leaf-blades toothed or entire.
  Bracts of the involucre ciliate, otherwise glabrous or nearly so. | IV. DENTATA.
  Bracts of the involucre with pubescent surfaces as well as ciliate margins. | V. INTEGRIFOLIA.

I. PERFOLIATA

Tall often much-branched plant, with a square stem and finely rough-pubescent toothed leaf-blades. 1. *S. perfoliatum.*

II. LACINIATA

Ray-flowers with yellow ligules: wings of the achene prolonged into short lacerate teeth. 2. *S. laciniatum.*

III. COMPOSITA

Heads relatively small, the involucre less than 2 cm. broad.
 Blades of the basal leaves coarsely toothed or sometimes also shallowly lobed. 3. *S. reniforme.*

Blades of the basal leaves deeply lobed or parted:
  Blades mostly pedately lobed: involucre about 1
    cm. wide.
  Blades pinnately lobed or pinnate: involucre 1–1.5   4. *S. compositum.*
    cm. wide.
    Heads small; involucre about 1 mm. broad.
      Leaf-blades very scabrous: bracts of the
        involucre with spreading or recurved tips.   5. *S. lapsuum.*
      Leaf-blades smooth or nearly so: bracts of
        the involucre with erect or appressed tips.   6. *S. orae.*
    Heads rather large: involucre about 2 cm. broad.
      Basal leaves with petioles as long as the
        blades or longer: apical tips of the
        achene-wings obtuse.   7. *S. ovatifolium.*
      Basal leaves with petioles scarcely half as
        long as the blades: apical tips of the
        achene-wings acute.   8. *S. venosum.*
Heads large, the involucre over 2 cm. broad: ligules of
  the ray-flowers 1.5–3 cm. long.
  Leaf-blades merely toothed.
    Outer bracts of the involucre broader than long:
      leaf-blades narrowed at the base.   9. *S. rumicifolium.*
    Outer bracts of the involucre longer than broad:
      leaf-blades cordate.   10. *S. terebinthinaceum.*
  Leaf-blades pinnatifid, except a form with narrow
    undulate-toothed or undulate leaf-blades.   11. *S. pinnatifidum.*

IV. Dentata

Leaves, at least on the lower part of the stem, whorled
  in threes.   12. *S. trifoliatum.*
Leaves alternate or opposite, often both on the same
  plant.
  Blades of the basal and lower cauline leaves narrowed
    at the base; those of the upper cauline leaves
    short-petioled or sessile.
    Stem smooth and glabrous or essentially so, ex-
      cept sometimes near the top.
      Leaf-blades smooth except the margins, or
        slightly scabrous.
        Leaves regularly disposed along the stem;
          blades smooth.   13. *S. glabrum.*
        Leaves mainly crowded at the base of the
          stem; blades scabrous near the edges.   14. *S. confertifolium.*
      Leaf-blades very rough-pubescent.
        Leaf-blades entire.   15. *S. Elliottii.*
        Leaf-blades coarsely toothed.   16. *S. dentatum.*
    Stem rough-pubescent.
      Leaves mainly cauline, often numerous on the
        stem, opposite or alternate or both.
        Achene with a U-shaped sinus at the top,
          the wings produced into two teeth
          above the apex.
          Leaves several or numerous, usually
            scattered along the stem, often rather
            close together; blades short-petioled
            or sessile.   17. *S. Asteriscus.*
          Leaves few, usually remote on the stem;
            blades of the upper ones, and petiole-
            like bases of the lower ones more or
            less clasping.   18. *S. Simpsonii.*
        Achene truncate at the apex, the very nar-
          row wings not produced into teeth at the
          apex.   19. *S. nodum.*
      Leaves mainly basal or approximate at the
        base of the stem, the stem with few re-
        mote opposite or alternate leaves, often
        scape-like: achenes with large apical
        teeth.
        Blades of the basal leaves very coarsely
          toothed: achenes 7–8 mm. long.   20. *S. incisum.*
        Blades of the basal leaves shallowly toothed:
          achenes 9–10 mm. long.   21. *S. gracile.*
  Blades of the basal and lower cauline leaves cordate
    or truncate at the base; those of the upper cauline
    leaves manifestly petioled.   22. *S. brachiatum.*

V. INTEGRIFOLIA

Stem pubescent with short, stiff hairs, often very rough.
  Upper leaves sessile, cordate or clasping.
    Achenes with very short apical teeth, the sinus
      broadly U-shaped.   23. *S. asperrimum.*
    Achenes with long apical teeth, the sinus narrowly
      U-shaped.   24. *S. integrifolium.*
  Upper leaves narrowed or rounded at the base, short
    petioled.   25. *S. scaberrimum.*
Stem at least above, and involucral bracts shaggy-hispid
  or hispid.
  Involucral bracts appressed towards the base: leaf-
    blades relatively narrow.   26. *S. Gatesii.*
  Involucral bracts loose and spreading: leaf-blades
    relatively broad.   27. *S. Mohrii.*

1. S. perfoliatum L. Stem 8–26 dm. tall, often branched above, smooth and glabrous: leaf-blades lanceolate to ovate, 2–6 dm. long, dentate-serrate, the lower ones narrowed into broad petiole-like

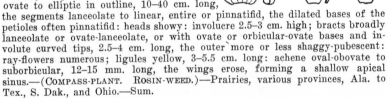

bases: heads showy: involucre 1–2 cm. high, broader than high; bracts ovate-lanceolate to ovate or oval, subreniform, or the inner broadly spatulate or cuneate: ray-flowers mostly 15–25; ligules bright-yellow, 2.5–3 cm. long: achene obovate, narrowly winged, 11–14 mm. long, emarginate by slight projections of the wings at the apex.—(CUP-PLANT.)—Prairies and moist soil, various provinces, Ga. to La., Ont., and Neb. Also naturalized E.—Sum.

2. S. laciniatum L. Stem 10–35 dm. tall, coarsely hispid: blades of the basal leaves ovate to elliptic in outline, 10–40 cm. long, the segments lanceolate to linear, entire or pinnatifid, the dilated bases of the petioles often pinnatifid: heads showy: involucre 2.5–3 cm. high; bracts broadly lanceolate or ovate-lanceolate, or with ovate or orbicular-ovate bases and involute curved tips, 2.5–4 cm. long, the outer more or less shaggy-pubescent: ray-flowers numerous; ligules yellow, 3–5.5 cm. long: achene oval-obovate to suborbicular, 12–15 mm. long, the wings erose, forming a shallow apical sinus.—(COMPASS-PLANT. ROSIN-WEED.)—Prairies, various provinces, Ala. to Tex., S. Dak., and Ohio.—Sum.

3. S. reniforme Raf. Stem 8–20 dm. tall, glabrous or nearly so: blades of the basal leaves ovate to reniform, 10–35 cm. long, obtuse, coarsely dentate, deeply cordate at the base; petioles longer than the blades on the lower part of the stem: involucre campanulate, 6–8 mm. high; bracts ovate or broadly elliptic to elliptic, ciliate, otherwise glabrous, the obtuse tips spreading or recurved: ray-flowers several; ligules yellow, 1–1.5 cm. long: achene suborbicular or orbicular-obovate, 7–8 mm. long; wing-tips forming a shallow apical sinus.—Dry or stony soil, Blue Ridge, N. C. and Appalachian shale slopes, Va.—Sum.

4. S. compositum Michx. Stem 9–20 dm. tall, glabrous, glaucous: blades of the basal leaves 10–30 cm. long, not conspicuously veined, mostly somewhat pedately parted, the segments broad; petioles longer than the midribs: heads often numerous: involucre campanulate, 7–8 mm. high; bracts ovate to broadly elliptic or oval, obtuse, ciliolate, otherwise glabrous, the tips erect: ray-flowers several; ligules bright-yellow, 14–20 mm. long: achene cuneate or cuneate-obovate, 7–9 mm. long, the wing-tips broad, erose, forming a U-shaped apical sinus.—Dry woods and pinelands, Coastal Plain and adj. provinces, Ga. to Ala., Tenn., and N. C.—Sum.–fall.

5. S. lapsuum Small. Stem 9–22 dm. tall, glabrous, green or glaucescent: blades of the basal leaves pinnatifid or pinnately parted, the segments coarsely toothed or pinnatifid, usually very scabrous on both sides, the lower ones often long-stalked: heads few to several: involucre hemispheric, 8–10 mm. high; bracts orbicular-ovate to obovate or orbicular-obovate, obtuse, ciliolate, often veiny, the tips spreading or recurved: ray-flowers mostly 6–8; ligules 8–10 mm. long: achene obovate, 8–9 mm. long, the wing-tips coarsely toothed forming a U-shaped sinus.—Sandhills and oak-woods, Coastal Plain and Piedmont, near the Fall Line, Ga., and S. C.—Sum.

6. S. orae Small. Stem 6–21 dm. tall, glabrous, glaucescent: blades of the basal leaves 8–16 cm. long, more or less pinnately parted, ciliate, with scattered hairs, but not rough, the lower segments sometimes long-stalked: heads rather numerous: involucre campanulate, 8–9 mm. high; bracts ovate to obovate, obtuse, ciliolate, the tips erect or appressed: ray-flowers mostly 6–9; ligules yellow, 11–16 mm. long: achene obovate to orbicular-obovate, 6–7 mm. long, the wing-tips toothed, forming a small U-shaped sinus at the top.—Sandy woods, Coastal Plain, S. C. to N. C.—Sum.

7. S. ovatifolium (T. & G.) Small. Stem 5–20 dm. tall, glabrous or nearly so, glaucescent: blades of the basal leaves ovate to elliptic-ovate, 10–30 cm. long pinnately lobed or pinnately parted, the lobes coarsely toothed, rounded or acute; petioles longer than the midribs on the lower part of the stem: involucre campanulate, or hemispheric-campanulate, about 1 cm. high; bracts ovate to elliptic, oval, or elliptic-obovate, ciliolate, rounded at the apex, the tips erect or nearly so: ray-flowers several; ligules yellow, 1–1.5 cm. long: achene suborbicular, about 10 mm. broad; the wing-tips irregularly toothed forming a usually V-shaped sinus.—Sandy woods, Coastal Plain, Fla. to Ga.—Spr.-sum.

8. S. venosum Small. Stem 8–12 dm. tall, glabrous or nearly so, glaucous: blades of the basal leaves ovate to elliptic, 9–30 cm. long, conspicuously red-veined, deeply pinnatifid or pinnately parted, the segments linear to linear-elliptic, coarsely and irregularly toothed or incised; petioles about ½ as long as the blades, dilated at the base: heads few, showy, corymbose: involucre campanulate, about 1 cm. high; bracts ovate or broadly elliptic to orbicular-oval, or spatulate, rounded at the apex, ciliolate: ray-flowers several; ligules yellow, 1–1.5 cm. long: achene suborbicular or rhombic-orbicular about 10 mm. long, the wing-tips forming a narrow U-shaped sinus, nearly entire.—Pinelands, Coastal Plain, Ga.—Spr.-sum.

9. S. rumicifolium Small. Stem 4–8 dm. tall: blades of the basal leaves elliptic to elliptic-ovate or obovate, 9–15 cm. long, rounded at the apex, repand-undulate, smooth, red-veined above, rather cuneate at the base; petioles shorter than the blades, dilated and sheathing at the base: involucre hemispheric, fully 2 cm. broad; bracts various, the outer suborbicular, broader than long, the inner broadly elliptic to cuneate or spatulate, rounded at apex: ray-flowers several; ligules yellow, 1.5–2 cm. long: achene cuneate to elliptic-obovate, 9–10 mm. long, narrowly winged, nearly truncate or slightly notched at the top.—Dry, sterile soil, in the Appalachian Valley near Knoxville, Tenn.—Sum.-fall.

10. S. terebinthinaceum Jacq. Stem 9–30 dm. tall: blades of the basal leaves ovate to elliptic, 9–60 cm. long, coarsely dentate, with more or less prolonged teeth, usually cordate at the base: heads showy, relatively few: involucre broadly campanulate, 2–3 cm. broad; bracts various, the outer ovate, oval, or obovate, the inner elliptic, much broader than the outer, all obtuse and longer than broad: ray-flowers 15–25; ligules yellow, 2–3 cm. long: achene obovate-cuneate, 9–11 mm. long, narrowly thick-winged, truncate or notched at the top.—Dry hills and prairies, various provinces, Ga. to La., Ia., and Mich.—Sum.-fall.

11. **S. pinnatifidum** Ell. Stem 5–30 dm. tall, pubescent: blades of the basal leaves pinnatifid or pinnately parted, the segments entire or incised, or rarely some of them merely undulate; petioles shorter than the blades: heads showy: involucre hemispheric, 2–3 cm. broad; bracts various, the outer suborbicular, the inner elliptic to elliptic-lanceolate, about twice as long as the outer, all obtuse: ray-flowers 12–20; ligules yellow, 1.5–2 cm. long: achene cuneate to obovate-cuneate or cuneate, 9–10 mm. long, with a small notch at the top.—Open grounds, Appalachian provinces and Interior Low Plateaus, Ga. to Ala., and Ohio.—Sum.—An apparent extreme form with narrow (lanceolate) undulate-toothed or undulate leaf-blades is *S. chickamaugense* Canby (*S. lanceolatum* Canby, not Nutt.).

12. **S. trifoliatum** L. Stem 9–22 dm. tall, glabrous, glaucous: leaves in whorls of 3, or rarely opposite or alternate above; blades lanceolate to ovate-lanceolate or linear-lanceolate, 8–20 cm. long, remotely serrate or nearly entire, acute or slightly acuminate, scabrous on both sides: heads several or numerous, rather showy: involucre campanulate, 10–12 mm. high; bracts ovate to ovate-lanceolate and elliptic, the tips often lax or somewhat spreading, ciliate, the outer acutish, the inner obtuse: ray-flowers few; ligules yellow, 2–2.5 cm. long: achene obovate or elliptic-obovate, 8–10 mm. long, narrowly winged, the wing-tips often toothed.—Hillsides, in sterile soil, various provinces, rarely Coastal Plain, Ala. to Ohio, Pa., and Md.—A form with scabrous-pubescent stems occurs in S. C.

13. **S. glabrum** Eggert. Stem 9–15 dm. tall, smooth, often glaucescent: leaves opposite or the upper ones sometimes alternate; blades ovate-lanceolate, 8–20 cm. long, acute or short-acuminate, remotely dentate, smooth and glabrous except along the margins: heads few to several: involucre campanulate, 9–12 mm. high; bracts elliptic-lanceolate to ovate or elliptic, obtuse, ciliate, spreading at the tip or slightly recurved: ray-flowers several; ligules yellow, 2–2.5 cm. long: achene obovate, 7–9 mm. long, rather narrowly winged, the wing-tips short with acute or lacerate teeth.—Dry soil, various provinces, rarely Coastal Plain, Ga. to Miss., Tenn., and N. C.—Sum.-fall.

14. **S. confertifolium** Small. Stem 1–6 dm. tall, glaucous, smooth and glabrous: leaves mainly on the lower part of the stem, and there approximated or crowded at the base; blades firm, elliptic to ovate-lanceolate, 6–12 cm. long, acute or cuspidate, ciliate, nearly entire or shallowly toothed, slightly scabrous except near the center: involucre campanulate, 7–10 mm. high; bracts broadly ovate, elliptic or elliptic-obovate to somewhat cuneate, obtuse, merely ciliate, with spreading or recurving tips at maturity: ray-flowers several; ligules yellow, 1.5–2 cm. long: achene orbicular-cuneate to orbicular-obovate, 6–8 mm. long, margined, the wings-tips ascending.—Dry soil, Choctaw Co., on the Coastal Plain of Ala.; also Ga. (?)—Sum.

15. **S. Elliottii** Small. Stem 8–13 dm. tall, glabrous, often red or reddish: leaves alternate, or few sometimes opposite; blades lanceolate to broadly elliptic-lanceolate elliptic ovate or rarely oval, 6–12 cm. long, entire, or occasionally with few indistinct teeth, conspicuously ciliate; petioles of the lower leaves more conspicuously ciliate than the blades: heads showy, often in terminal clusters: involucre 10–12 mm. high; bracts ovate or ovate-elliptic to suborbicular and obovate, merely ciliate, obtuse, or the outer sometimes acutish: ray-flowers several; ligules 1.5–2 cm. long, yellow: achene obovate or cuneate-obovate, 7–10 mm. long, narrowly winged, the wing-tips short, broad, rather widely separated.—Dry soil, woods and river-banks, Coastal Plain and adj. provinces, Ga. to Ala., and N. C.—Sum.

16. **S. dentatum** Ell. Stem 6–15 dm. tall, glabrous, or sparingly pubescent near the top: leaves opposite or the upper rarely alternate, or in whorls of 3;

blades elliptic to lanceolate or ovate-lanceolate, 5–15 cm. long, acute, commonly coarsely dentate or dentate-serrate; heads corymbose: involucre about 1 cm. high; bracts ovate-lanceolate to suborbicular, oblong or oblong-cuneate, merely ciliate, the outer ones acute, the inner obtuse: ray-flowers several; ligules yellow, 2–3 cm. long: achene obovate to oval, 6–8 mm. long, narrowly winged, the wing-tips rounded, or the sinus nearly obsolete.—Sandy soil, Coastal Plain, Fla. to Ala., and S. C.—Sum.–fall.

17. S. Asteriscus L. Stem 6–15 dm. tall, scabro-pubescent: leaves mostly alternate, approximate or scattered; blades elliptic to elliptic-lanceolate, ovate-lanceolate, 4–15 cm. long, more or less distinctly serrate, those of the lower leaves petioled: heads showy, solitary or few: involucre campanulate, about 1 cm. high: bracts ovate, elliptic-lanceolate to oval and elliptic, obtuse, or the outer ones acutish, merely ciliate: ray-flowers 11–15; ligules 1.5–2 cm. long: achene oval or obovate-oval, 8–9 mm. long, the wing-tips rather broad forming a rather broad sinus.—Dry soil, various provinces, Fla. to Miss., Ohio, and Va.—Sum.–fall.

18. S. Simpsonii Greene. Stem 9–12 dm. tall, less densely pubescent above than below: leaves opposite, the pairs rather remote; blades various, those of the basal leaves spatulate to spatulate-elliptic, 10–15 cm. long, on short-margined petioles, those of the upper part of the stem elliptic to lanceolate or ovate, 3–10 cm. long, sessile and clasping by broad bases, all coarsely crenate-serrate or slightly repand: heads few or solitary: involucres 1–1.5 cm. high ovate-orbicular or sub-orbicular or ovate to orbicular-obovate, merely ciliolate: ray-flowers 12–16; ligules yellow, 2.5–3 cm. long; achene broadly obovate or orbicular-obovate, 10–13 mm. long, broadly winged, the wing-tips erect, blunt, forming a deep U-shaped sinus.—Sandy pinelands, S pen. Fla.—Sum.

19. S. nodum Small. Stem mostly less than 1 m. tall, hispid: leaves opposite, the pairs distant; blades elliptic, oval, or broadly ovate, 5–8 cm. long, shallowly and remotely dentate-serrate, obtuse or sometimes abruptly pointed, of the lower ones with short petiole-like bases: heads solitary or few together: involucre broadly campanulate, about 1 cm. high; bracts ovate or orbicular-ovate to obovate, obtuse, ciliate: ray-flowers few, ligules 1.5–2 cm. long: achene obovate or oval, 7–8 mm. long, narrowly winged, contracted into more or less of a neck at the top and truncate, the wing-tips obsolete or obscure.—Sandy soil, about Charleston, S. C.—Sum.

20. S. incisum Greene. Stem about 6 dm. tall, perhaps up to 1 m., hirsute: leaves opposite and alternate; blades of the basal ones ovate to ovate-lanceolate, 9–21 cm. long, coarsely dentate-serrate, abruptly narrowed or truncate at the base, on long hirsute petioles, those of the remote cauline leaves lanceolate or elliptic-lanceolate, somewhat acuminate, coarsely few-toothed, short-petioled or sessile: heads usually few: involucre broadly campanulate, about 1 cm. high; bracts elliptic-ovate to broadly ovate, ciliate, sparingly pubescent, obtuse or merely acutish, with more or less recurved tips: ray-flowers few; ligules yellow: achene obovate, 7–8 mm. long, narrowly winged, the wing-tips broad, forming a rather broad U-shaped sinus.—Appalachian provinces, Ga.—Sum.

21. S. gracile A. Gray. Stem 3–9 dm. tall, hirsute: leaves opposite; blades of the basal leaves elliptic-lanceolate to ovate-laneolate, 5–30 cm. long, acute at both ends or slightly acuminate or rarely obtuse, remotely dentate-serrate, those of the remote cauline leaves elliptic to lanceolate: heads solitary or few, showy: involucre 1–1.5 cm. high; bracts ovate or orbicular-ovate to elliptic-ovate, oval, or obovate, ciliolate, obtuse, or the often inconspicuously pubescent outer ones acutish, ciliolate: achene suborbicular or orbicular-oval, 9–10 mm. long, or rarely larger, very broadly winged, the wing-tips broad, forming a rather shallow sinus.—Rocky soil, woods or prairies, Coastal Plain and adj. provinces, Ala. to Tex.—Sum.

22. S. brachiatum Gattinger. Stem 8–20 dm. tall, glabrous: blades of the basal leaves triangular-hastate, 8–15 cm. long, repand, the lower cauline ones triangular-hastate, truncate subcordate, or cordate at the base, repand-toothed or coarsely dentate-serrate, acute, with petioles sometimes half as long as the blades, conspicuously ciliate, blades of the upper leaves ovate-lanceolate to lanceolate, entire or nearly so: heads several or numerous, usually on long, slender, glaucous peduncles: involucre campanulate, about 1 cm. high; bracts ovate, orbicular-ovate to elliptic, or ovate-elliptic obtuse, ciliate, the tips often somewhat spreading: ray-flowers several; ligules yellow, 1–1.5 cm. long: achene suborbicular, 7–8 mm. long, narrowly winged, emarginate at the apex, the wing-tips very short and broad.—Hillsides, Appalachian Plateau, Tenn.—Sum.

23. S. asperrimum Hook. Stem 6–15 dm. tall, scabro-pubescent: leaves opposite or sometimes alternate, especially above; blades ovate, ovate-lanceolate, elliptic-lanceolate, or lanceolate, 4–14 cm. long, acute or somewhat acuminate, entire or shallowly toothed, rounded at the base, sessile and more or less clasping: heads few or several, showy: involucre hemispheric 1.5–2 cm. high; bracts pubescent, the outer ovate or lanceolate, the inner broadly ovate, acute or obtuse, ciliate, the tips often lax or recurved: ray-flowers several or numerous; ligules 2.5–3.5 cm. long, yellow: achene obovate or oval-obovate, 9–14 mm. long or rarely smaller, the wing-tips forming a broadly U-shaped sinus.— Woods, prairies, and old fields, various provinces, Ala. to N. M., Okla., and Mo.—Sum.–fall.

24. S. integrifolium Michx. Stem 8–15 dm. tall, scabro-pubescent: leaves opposite or mainly so; blades ovate to broadly lanceolate, often nearly uniform in size, 7–12 cm. long, scabrous on both sides, acute, often shallowly toothed, especially on the lower part of the stem, mostly entire above: heads in rather open corymbs: involucre 1–1.5 cm. high; bracts more or less pubescent, the outer triangular-ovate to lanceolate, acute, the inner broader, obtuse, all often with recurved tips: ray-flowers 15–23; ligules bright-yellow, 2–3 cm. long: achene narrowly obovate, about 1 cm. long, broadly winged only near the top, the wing-tips broad, long, forming a narrowly U-shaped sinus.—Plains and prairies, various provinces, Miss. to Tex., Wis., and Ill.—Sum.–fall.

25. S. scaberrimum Ell. Stem 9–15 dm. tall, pubescent, sometimes sparingly so: leaves opposite or alternate: blades elliptic-lanceolate, ovate-lanceolate or narrowly ovate, or those of the basal leaves lanceolate, 8–20 cm. long, or rather shorter high up on the stem, acute or somewhat acuminate, sharply serrate, scabrous on both sides; heads usually few, showy: involucre campanulate, about 1 cm. high; bracts ovate-lanceolate to ovate or elliptic, not conspicuously pubescent, but ciliate, obtuse or the outer ones acutish, the inner with recurved tips: ray-flowers several; ligules about 1.5 cm. long, yellow: achene suborbicular, 5–7 mm. broad, broadly winged, the wing-tips forming a deep apical notch.— Open woods, fields, and pinelands, Coastal Plain and adj. provinces, Ga. to Miss., Tenn., and S Va.—Sum.

26. S. Gatesii C. Mohr. Stem 6–15 dm. tall, hispid: leaves alternate, often rather numerous; blades broadly linear to elliptic-lanceolate or lanceolate, 5–14 cm. long, acute, entire or remotely shallowly toothed, scabrous-pubescent, the lower ones petioled: heads showy; involucre campanulate, about 1 cm. high; bracts ovate-lanceolate to ovate, hispid, the outer acute and short-acuminate, coarsely hairy, the inner obtuse: ray-flowers several; ligules yellow, 12–20 mm. long: achene suborbicular or broader than high, the wing-tips forming a broad sinus.—Dry soil, various provinces N of Coastal Plain, Ala., and Tenn., to Mo.—Spr.–sum.

27. S. Mohrii Small. Stem 6–12 dm. tall, shaggy-hispid: leaves alternate; blades ovate-lanceolate to narrowly ovate, 5–28 cm. long, acuminate, remotely serrate with prominent teeth except near the base, or merely undulate: heads showy, but relatively few: involucre campanulate or hemispheric, 1–1.5 cm. high; bracts lanceolate to ovate-lanceolate, acute or slightly acuminate, densely hispid and conspicuously long-ciliate: ray-flowers several; ligules yellow, 10–14 mm. long: achene obovate, about 7–9 mm. long, the wing-tips acutish or blunt, widely separated.—Dry soil, Interior Low Plateaus and Appalachian Provinces, Ga. to Ala., and Tenn.—Sum.-fall.

60. CHRYSOGONUM L. Perennial, depressed, stoloniferous herbs. Leaves opposite: blades toothed. Heads erect. Involucre hemispheric: bracts distinct, the outer foliaceous. Ligules of the ray yellow. Disk-flowers with short abortive ovaries and corollas with a very short tube and funnelform throat. Filaments less than half as long as the anthers. Style glabrous. Achene wingless. Pappus a half cup-shaped crown.—Two or three species.

Leaf-blades truncate or abruptly cuneate at the base, deltoid-ovate: plant eventually caulescent.	1. *C. virginianum.*
Leaf-blades gradually tapering at the base, elliptic: plant acaulescent.	2. *C. australe.*

1. C. virginianum L. Stem hirsute, prostrate, sometimes 6 dm. long: leaf-blades light-green, deltoid-ovate, 2.5 cm. long, long-petioled, short-pubescent on both surfaces: involucre hirsute: outer bracts 7–10 mm. long: ligules of the ray mostly 9–11 mm. long: achene 4–4.5 mm. long.—Dry woods and hillsides, Coastal Plain to Blue Ridge, Fla. to La., Tenn., and Pa.—Spr.

2. C. australe Alexander. Stem a mere caudex, giving off hirsute stolons which form new plants at their tips: leaf-blades dark-green, elliptic, 3–7 cm. long, tapering at the base to a long petiole, hirsute on both surfaces: involucre hirsute; outer bracts 8–9 mm. long: ligules of the ray 10–15 mm. long: mature achene not seen.—Dry woods, various provinces Fla. to Ala. and N. C.—Spr.

61. BERLANDIERA DC. Perennial, erect herbs, with large roots. Leaves alternate: blades toothed or pinnatifid. Heads more or less nodding. Involucre somewhat depressed: bracts broad, often veiny. Ligules of the ray-corollas yellow. Disk-flowers with long abortive ovaries and corollas with a very short tube and a funnelform throat. Filaments nearly as long as the anthers. Style pubescent. Achene wingless, 1 ribbed within. Pappus obsolete or of 2 caducous-awns.—About 8 species, North American.—Sum.-fall, or all year S.—Green-eyes.

Leaf-blades merely toothed or slightly pinnatifid near the base, often gray-woolly or tomentose.	
Plants with stem leafy to near the inflorescence.	1. *B. pumila.*
Plants with scapes.	2. *B. humilis.*
Leaf-blades pinnatifid throughout: stem hispidulous.	3. *B. subacaulis.*

1. B. pumila (Michx.) Nutt. Stem 2–9 dm. tall, gray-woolly: leaf-blades elliptic, ovate, or oval, 4–10 cm. long, obtuse, crenate, truncate or subcordate

at the base or rarely narrowed, pubescent
with gray wool beneath, the upper ones sessile or nearly so: involucre flattish, 2–2.5 cm.
broad; bracts elliptic, oval, or obovate, obtuse, ciliolate: ligules of the ray yellow,
1–1.5 cm. long: disk-corolla 3–3.5 mm. long:
achene 6 mm. long, ciliate. [*B. tomentosa*
Nutt.]—Sandy soil, Coastal Plain, Fla. to
Ala., and N. C.

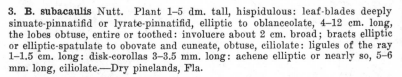

2. B. humilis Small.   Plant 1–2 dm. tall,
tomentose: leaf-blades elliptic to ovate, 3–8
cm. long, rounded at the apex, unevenly
crenate, pale beneath, more or less lyrate-
pinnatifid near the base, or some of them
merely cordate: scape simple or corymbosely
branched, the heads thus solitary or several together: involucre 1.5–2 cm. broad;
bracts elliptic or lanceolate to ovate or orbicular, closely soft-pubescent: ligules
of the ray 1.5–2 cm. long: achene obovate, 5–6 mm. long, woolly.—Pinelands
and sandy woods, Fla.

3. B. subacaulis Nutt.   Plant 1–5 dm. tall, hispidulous: leaf-blades deeply
sinuate-pinnatifid or lyrate-pinnatifid, elliptic to oblanceolate, 4–12 cm. long,
the lobes obtuse, entire or toothed: involucre about 2 cm. broad; bracts elliptic
or elliptic-spatulate to obovate and cuneate, obtuse, ciliolate: ligules of the ray
1–1.5 cm. long: disk-corollas 3–3.5 mm. long: achene elliptic or nearly so, 5–6
mm. long, ciliolate.—Dry pinelands, Fla.

62. PARTHENIUM L.   Coarse herbs, or shrubs, usually pale-pubescent.
Leaves alternate: blades toothed, pinnatifid, or dissected.   Heads inconspicuously radiate.   Involucre depressed to globular: bracts appressed, broad.   Ray-
flowers usually 5: ligules inconspicuous, white or whitish.   Lobes of the disk-
corollas ovate, ciliate.   Anthers longer than the filaments.   Achene flattened.
Pappus of 2 or 3 scales or awns.—About 12 species, American.

Leaf-blades 1–2-pinnatifid: heads not firm at maturity.   1. *P. Hysterophorus.*
Leaf-blades merely toothed: heads very firm at maturity.   2. *P. integrifolium.*

1. P. Hysterophorus L.   Plant annual, 3–7 dm. tall: leaf-blades elliptic to
ovate in outline: involucre saucer-like, 4–5 mm. broad: disk-corollas, 1–1.5
mm. long: achene 1–1.5 mm. long.—(Rag-
weed.) — Pinelands, waste-places, cult.
grounds, and roadsides, Coastal Plain and
adj. provinces, Fla. to Tex., Mo., and Pa.

2. P. integrifolium L.   Plants perennial,
4–12 dm. tall: blades of the basal leaves
elliptic to lanceolate: involucre campanulate,
becoming globular, 4–6 mm. broad: disk-
corollas, 2.5–3 mm. long: achene 3.5–4 mm.
long.—Dry soil, woods and hillsides, various
provinces, Ga. to Tex., Minn., and Md.—
Spr.–sum.—*P. hispidum* Raf., with rough-
pubescent foliage and coarsely toothed or
incised leaf-blades, known to range from
Tex. to Kans. and Mo. is to be expected from
W. Tenn.

63. ZINNIA L.[1] Annual or perennial, erect herbs, or shrubby plants. Leaves opposite: blades entire or sparingly toothed, 3-ribbed. Heads showy, on usually clavate peduncles. Involucre hemispheric to somewhat cylindric: bracts broad except the inner elongate ones. Ray-flowers few: ligules red, purple, yellow, or variegated, conspicuous. Lobes of the disk-corollas lanceolate to linear, ciliate. Anthers shorter than the filaments, the appendages deltoid or lanceolate. Achene of the ray 3-angled. Pappus of 1-few awns, or wanting.—About 15 species, natives of western America.

Involucre cylindric-campanulate: chaff of the receptacle with erose or lacerate tips.
  1. *Z. pauciflora.*
Involucre hemispheric: chaff of the receptacle with long-fringed, appendage-like tips.
  2. *Z. elegans.*

1. Z. pauciflora L. Stem 1–6 dm. tall: leaf-blades linear-elliptic to ovate, 2–5 cm. long: outer bracts of the involucre ovate, the inner bracts linear-elliptic to slightly broadened upward, 11–13 mm. long: ligules of the ray 10–15 mm. long: lobes of the disk-corollas linear. [*Z. multiflora* L.]—Dry soil, Fla. to Ariz. and N. C. Nat. of trop. Am., but possibly native in the SW U. S.—(*W. I., Mex., C. A., S. A.*)—Sum.–fall.

2. Z. elegans Jacq. Stem 1–6 dm. tall: leaf-blades elliptic to ovate, 2–10 cm. long: outer bracts of the involucre broadly obovate, the inner bracts elliptic, slightly broadened upward, 9–12 mm. long: ligules of the ray, 10–20 cm. long: lobes of the disk-corollas linear.—Waste-places, roadsides and cult. grounds, Fla. Native of Mex. and S. A., and widely cult. (*W. I., Mex., S. A.*)—Sum.–fall. The common zinnia of gardens is a cultivated form of *Z. elegans*, sometimes hybridized with *Z. pauciflora* and other species, as is shown by the varying shape of the involucre as well as the color of the ray-flowers.

64. HELIOPSIS L. Perennial or rarely annual, *Helianthus*-like herbs. Leaves opposite: blades serrate, petioled. Heads showy. Involucre flattish: bracts in 2 or 3 series, the outer more or less spreading. Ray-flowers several: ligules yellow, conspicuous. Disk-corollas longer than the ovaries. Stigmas long. Achene of the ray with a pappus of 2–4 teeth or a crown, or the pappus obsolete.—About 6 species, American.—Spr.–fall.—Ox-EYES.

Foliage, especially the leaf-blades, very scabrous.
  1. *H. scabra.*
Foliage, especially the leaf-blades, smooth or very slightly scabrous.
  Heads usually over 1 cm. high: achene glabrous.
  2. *H. helianthoides.*
  Heads usually less than 1 cm. high: achene pubescent above.
  3. *H. minor.*

1. H. scabra Dunal. Stem 8–14 dm. tall: leaf-blades thick, deltoid or broadly lanceolate, 5–15 cm. long, serrate, cuneate to truncate at the base:

[1] Revised by Edward Johnston Alexander.

heads showy, with broadly conic disks:
bracts of the involucre linear-elliptic to
elliptic, acutish or obtuse: ray-flowers several; ligules of the ray 2–2.5 cm. long,
bright-yellow: bractlets slightly dilated and
barely erose at the tip: achene pubescent on
the margins, at least when young, each with
a pappus of 1–3 short awns, or a laciniate
crown.—Fields, roadsides, and woods, various provinces, Tenn. to Ark., B. C., Ont.,
Me., and N. J.

2. **H. helianthoides** (L.) B. S. P. Stem
3–15 dm. tall: leaf-blades thinnish, ovate to
lanceolate, 8–20 cm. long, sharply serrate,
cuneate to truncate at the base: heads
showy, with a rounded disk usually over 1 cm. high: bracts of the involucre
elliptic-lanceolate to elliptic, ciliate, acute or acutish, the outer with spreading
or reflexed tips: ray-flowers several; ligules of the ray bright-yellow, 2–3 cm.
long: bractlets dilated and erose at the apex: achene glabrous, truncate or
obscurely 2–4-toothed at the apex. [*H. laevis* Pers.]—Banks, thickets, and
open woods, various provinces, Fla. to Miss., Ont., and N. Y.

3. **H. minor** (Hook.) C. Mohr. Stem 2–7 dm. tall: leaf-blades thinnish,
lanceolate, elliptic or elliptic-lanceolate, 3–10 cm. long, sharply serrate, cuneate,
rounded, or truncate at the base: heads with disks usually less than 1 cm. high:
bracts of the involucre ovate or lanceolate to elliptic, rather obtuse, the outer,
at least, with spreading or reflexed tips: ray-flowers few; ligules bright-yellow,
1–2 cm. long: achene 2.5–3 mm. long: pappus short. [*H. gracilis* Nutt.]—
Pinelands, woods, and hillsides, Coastal Plain and adj. provinces, Fla. to
Ark. and Ga.

65. **TETRAGONOTHECA** L. Perennial, erect, stout herbs. Leaves
opposite: blades broad, repand, saliently toothed or pinnatifid, sessile or connate-perfoliate. Heads large, resembling
those of *Silphium*. Involucre with thin partially united foliaceous outer bracts, and
narrower and shorter inner ones. Ray-flowers several: ligules narrow, yellow. Disk-
flowers numerous: corollas with a short tube
and a longer throat: lobes deltoid or triangular. Anthers mostly longer than the
filaments, the appendages ovate. Stigmas
slender. Achene very thick, broadened upward, striate or angled. Pappus wanting.—
About 5 species, American.

1. **T. helianthoides** L. Stem 3–10 dm. tall,
pubescent: blades of the upper leaves elliptic to oval, 8–15 cm. long, remotely
toothed: outer involucre 4–6 cm. broad; inner bracts slenderly acuminate:
ligules 3–4 cm. long: achene 5–6 mm. long.—(PINELAND-GINSENG).—Dry soil,
pinelands and woods, Coastal Plain and adj. provinces, Fla. to Miss. and Va.—
Spr.–fall.

66. **VERBESINA** L. Annual diffuse herbs. Leaves opposite, blades
narrow, entire or sparingly toothed. Heads small, inconspicuously radiate.

Involucre hemispheric or campanulate: bracts broad, those of the outer series scarcely larger than those of the inner. Ray-flowers several: ligules white, inconspicuous. Disk-flowers numerous: corollas with a short tube and a longer funnelform throat: lobes deltoid. Anthers ellipsoid, longer than the filaments, the appendages ovate. Stigmas broad. Achene stout, 3–4-angled, or somewhat flattened in the disk. Pappus wanting or minute.—About 4 species, tropical.

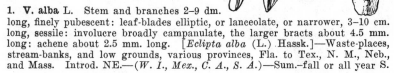

1. **V. alba** L. Stem and branches 2–9 dm. long, finely pubescent: leaf-blades elliptic, or lanceolate, or narrower, 3–10 cm. long, sessile: involucre broadly campanulate, the larger bracts about 4.5 mm. long: achene about 2.5 mm. long. [*Eclipta alba* (L.) Hassk.]—Waste-places, stream-banks, and low grounds, various provinces, Fla. to Tex., N. M., Neb., and Mass. Introd. NE.—(*W. I., Mex., C. A., S. A.*)—Sum.-fall or all year S.

67. MELANTHERA Rohr.[1] Perennial, erect herbs. Leaves opposite: blades entire, toothed, or hastate-lobed. Heads discoid, appearing gray on account of the dark anthers. Involucre hemispheric or depressed: bracts often broad, in 2 or 3 series. Throat of the white corolla much longer than the tube. Filaments generally as long as the black-tipped anthers or nearly so. Stigmas often flattened, mostly subulate. Achene compressed-quadrangular, somewhat obpyramidal, truncate.—About 12 species, tropical American.

Leaf-blades ovate to deltoid in outline.
  Involucral bracts and chaff acute, obtusish, or merely short-acuminate.
    Leaf-blades less than 5 cm. long: chaff short-acuminate.
      Middle lobe of the leaf-blade very narrow and long
        with a roundish few toothed tip.   1. *M. parvifolia.*
      Middle lobe of the leaf-blade, if present, broad and
        short with an expanded many toothed tip.   2. *M. radiata.*
    Leaf-blades over 5 cm. long: chaff acute or bluntly tipped.   3. *M. deltoidea.*
  Involucral bracts and chaff long-acuminate.   4. *M. hastata.*
Leaf-blades elliptic to linear in outline.
  Involucral bracts fully as long as the disk, linear-lanceolate.   5. *M. ligulata.*
  Involucral bracts shorter than the disk, rhombic-ovate.   6. *M. angustifolia.*

1. **M. parvifolia** Small. Stems often several together, 3–8 dm. tall, very rough-hispidulous, slender, sparingly branched: leaf-blades prominently hastate, 2–5 cm. long, or longer, the lateral lobes prominent, coarsely toothed or entire, the middle lobe elongate, contracted between the lateral lobes and the dilated apex, usually coarsely few-toothed above, the petioles rather short: heads few, usually very long-peduncled: larger bracts of the involucre 5–7 mm. long.—Pinelands and coastal sand-dunes, S pen. Fla. and the Keys.—All year.

2. **M. radiata** Small. Stems radially spreading from a woody root, 1–4 dm. long: leaf-blades ovate, 1–4 cm. long, entire and coarsely serrate, or hastately lobed and irregularly toothed, the middle lobe often obovate: larger bracts of the involucre ovate,

[1] Contributed by Edward Johnston Alexander.

5.5–6.5 mm. long, obtuse: corolla mostly about 6 mm. long.—Pinelands, Everglade Keys, Fla. and Florida Keys.—All year.

3. **M. deltoidea** Michx. Stem 8–24 dm. tall, somewhat rough-pubescent, often stout, considerably branched: leaf-blades ovate to deltoid or ovate-hastate or deltoid-hastate, 5–15 cm. long, obtuse or acute, crenate, or serrate, the petioles rather long: heads several or numerous, mostly rather short-peduncled: larger bracts of the involucre 3.5–5 cm. long: pappus of 2–3 bristles with a shorter fringe-like crown at their base.—Hammocks and coastal sand-dunes, S pen. Fla. and the Keys.—(*W. I.*)—All year.

4. **M. hastata** Michx. Stem 8–18 dm. tall, scabrous or hispidulous: leaf-blades 8–15 cm. long, ovate to deltoid in outline, often hastate or hastately lobed, crenate to serrate: larger bracts of the involucre 8–10 mm. long, acuminate as is also the receptacle chaff: corollas 3–4 mm. long. [*M. nivea* (Fl. SE. U. S.) *M. lobata* Small.]—Along lake and stream shores and in damp soil, Coastal Plain, Fla. to La. and S. C.—Sum.

5. **M. ligulata** Small. Stem erect, 4–7 dm. tall, finely pubescent: leaf-blades elongate-linear, mainly 8–16 cm. long, irregularly toothed, sometimes saliently so at the base: larger bracts of the involucre linear-lanceolate, 9–13 mm. long, acuminate: corolla 5–6 mm. long.—Pinelands, S pen. Fla.—Spr.

6. **M. angustifolia** A. Rich. Stem 2–8 dm. tall, strigillose: leaf-blades linear to linear-oblanceolate, 4–8 cm. long: larger bracts of the involucre rhombic-ovate, acute, 4–5 mm. long: corolla about 4 mm. long. [*M. lanceolata* (Fl. SE. U. S.)]—Everglades and low pinelands, pen. Fla.—(*W. I.*)—Spr.–fall.

68. **SPILANTHES** Jacq. Annual or perennial (ours), diffuse or creeping herbs, or partly woody plants. Leaves opposite: blades relatively broad, often toothed. Heads radiate, often inconspicuous, long-peduncled; the disk protruding high above the involucre by the elongation of the receptacle. Involucre campanulate or flat: bracts broad, narrowed to the apex. Ligules of the ray-corollas white or yellow. Disk-flowers inflated by the bractlets: corollas yellow, the throat often somewhat inflated: lobes deltoid. Filaments very short. Achene of the disk flattened, margined. Pappus one or several awns.—About 30 species, of warm and tropical regions.

1. **S. Americana** (Mut.) Hieron. Stem 2–8 dm. long, often creeping: leaf-blades ovate to lanceolate, 2–6 cm. long, toothed: bracts of the involucre lanceolate to elliptic or ovate-lanceolate, 4–5 mm. long: ligules of the ray about 5 mm. long: disk ovoid: achene 1.5 mm. long. [*S. repens* (Walt.) Michx.]—Low grounds, Coastal Plain and adj. provinces, Fla. to Tex., Mo., and N. C.—Spr.–fall or all year S.

69. **ECHINACEA** Moench. Perennial, caulescent herbs. Leaves normally alternate: blades simple, entire or toothed. Heads radiate, solitary or few, conspicuous. Involucres many-flowered, rather flat: bracts in 2–4 series, narrow. Receptacle depressed, hemispheric, chaffy. Ray-flowers several, neutral, often with imperfect styles: ligules spreading or drooping, purple or rose, rarely yellow or white. Disk-flowers perfect, fruit-producing: chaff awned, surpassing the flowers, persistent. Achene acutely 4-angled, stout.

Pappus a crown, more or less produced into triangular teeth at the angles. [*Brauneria* Neck.]—Six species, North American.—CONE-FLOWERS.

Awn of the chaff about as long as the body : root horizontal or horizontally inclined, fibrous.   I. PURPUREAE.
Awn of the chaff shorter than the body : root vertical, fusi-
form.   II. ANGUSTIFOLIAE.

I. PURPUREAE
Rather coarse herb, with leaf-blades ovate lanceolate.   1. *E. purpurea.*
II. ANGUSTIFOLIAE
Plant glabrous or glabrate.   2. *E. laevigata.*
Plant hirsute or hispid.
  Ray-flowers with drooping ligules 4–8 cm. long.   3. *E. pallida.*
  Ray-flowers with spreading ligules 1.5–2.5 cm. long.   4. *E. tennesseensis.*

1. **E. purpurea** (L.) Moench. Stem scabrous-pubescent, 6–12 dm. tall: leaf-blades ovate to lanceolate, 5–12 cm. long, serrate or dentate-serrate: bracts of the involucre linear to linear-lanceolate, hispidulous: ligules of the ray 2.5–5 cm. long, or rarely shorter, purple or somewhat crimson or whitish. [*B. purpurea* Britton.] Rich soil, woods, and fields, various provinces, Ala. to La., Mo., S Va., and N. C.—Sum.–fall.

2. **E. laevigata** (Boynton & Beadle) Small. Stem glabrous, about 10 dm. tall: blades of the basal and lower cauline leaves 1.5–3.5 cm. wide: bracts of the involucre lanceolate to elliptic-lanceolate, merely ciliate: ligules of the ray 3–6 cm. long, rose-color. [*B. laevigata* Boynton & Beadle.]—Woods and fields, Piedmont of S. C.—Sum.–fall.

3. **E. pallida** Nutt. Stem hispid, 5–10 dm. tall: leaf-blades broadly linear to narrowly elliptic, 5–20 cm. long: bracts of the involucre lanceolate, hispid: ligules of the ray 4–8 cm. long, pale or deep rose-color. [*B. pallida* Britton.] —Dry soil, prairies, barrens, and hillsides, various provinces, Ala. to Tex., Minn., and Mass.—Spr.–sum.

4. **E. tennesseensis** (Beadle) Small. Stem shaggy-hispid, 2–3 dm. tall: leaf-blades linear, 5–18 cm. long: bracts of the involucre lanceolate, bristly: ligules of the ray 1.5–2.5 cm. long, purplish. [*B. tennesseensis* Beadle.]—Gravelly hillsides, Interior and Ozark Plateaus, Tenn. and Ark.—Spr.–sum.

70. **VIGUIERA** H.B.K. Annual herbs. Leaves alternate: blades narrow, entire. Heads conspicuously radiate, the disk elongating in age. Involucre campanulate or hemispheric: bracts lax, narrow, unequal. Receptacle conic, becoming columnar. Ray-flowers several: ligules yellow. Disk-corollas with a very short tube and a broadly campanulate throat: lobes lanceolate, longer than the throat. Anthers slightly longer than the filaments. Achene turgid. Pappus obsolete or wanting.—About 150 species, natives of the Western Hemisphere.

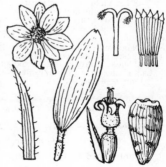

1. **V. Porteri** (A. Gray) Blake. Annual, 2–12 dm. tall, hispid: leaf-blades narrowly linear to narrowly linear-lanceolate, 3–15

cm. long: heads showy: outer bracts of the involucre linear or linear-lanceolate, 6–10 mm. long, acuminate: ligules 1–2 cm. long: achene 2.5–3 mm. long. [*Gymnolomia Porteri* A. Gray.]—Granite outcrops, Stone Mt. and vicinity in the Piedmont of Ga.—Sum.–fall.

71. RUDBECKIA L.[1] Perennial or sometimes annual or biennial, often pubescent herbs. Leaves alternate: blades entire, toothed, or pinnatifid. Heads erect. Involucre hemispheric or depressed, many-flowered: bracts spreading or reflexed, often unequal. Receptacle conic or convex. Ray-flowers several: ligules yellow, rarely discolored or crimson, spreading or drooping. Disk-flowers crowded: corollas with a short tube and a longer throat: lobes deltoid or ovate. Anthers longer than the filaments. Achene 4-angled, flat-topped. Pappus merely a low crown or obsolete.—About 40 species, North American.—CONE-FLOWERS.

Stigmas with short obtuse tips: pappus present except in *R. mollis.*
  Chaff of the receptacle acute, mucronate or obtuse.
    Chaff canescent or pubescent at the apex.
      Leaf-blades, at least those of the lower leaves,
        deeply lobed or divided.   I. LACINIATAE.
      Leaf-blades entire or merely toothed.
        Disk globose-ovoid, ovoid-conic, or hemispheric:
          plant pubescent: corolla-lobes reflexed after
          anthesis.   II. HELIOPSIDES.
        Disk cylindric or conic-cylindric at maturity:
          plant glabrous: corolla-lobes erect after
          anthesis.   III. LAEVIGATAE.
    Chaff ciliate or fimbriate, denticulate or entire at the
      apex.
      Chaff ciliate or fimbriate.   IV. FULGIDAE.
      Chaff with entire, hyaline, or erose-denticulate
        tips.
        Leaf-blades various, but not elongate-linear.   V. SPECIOSAE.
        Leaf-blades elongate-linear.   VI. GRAMINIFOLIAE.
  Chaff of the receptacle aristate or subulate.   VII. TRILOBAE.
Stigmas with slender subulate tips: pappus wanting.
  Plant annual or biennial.   VIII. BICOLORES.
  Plant perennial.   IX. HIRTAE.

I. LACINIATAE

Plant glabrous or glabrate.   1. *R. laciniata.*
Plant cinereous-pubescent.
  Disk greenish-yellow.   2. *R. heterophylla.*
  Disk brown-purple, anise-scented.   3. *R. subtomentosa.*

II. HELIOPSIDES

Cauline leaves with petioled blades.
  Heads small, the disk about 1 cm. in diameter.   4. *R. Heliopsidis.*
  Heads large, the disk 1.5–2.5 cm. in diameter.
    Stem glabrous or glabrate.   5. *R. alismaefolia.*
    Stem hispid or scabrous.   6. *R. grandiflora.*
Cauline leaves with closely sessile or partly clasping blades.   7. *R. mollis.*

III. LAEVIGATAE

Leaves glaucous; blades oval, broadly ovate, or elliptic.   8. *R. maxima.*
Leaves lustrous; blades narrower.
  Leaf-blades ovate-spatulate to lanceolate-elliptic.   9. *R. nitida.*
  Leaf-blades elongate-lanceolate to linear-lanceolate, at-
    tenuate at both ends.   10. *R. glabra.*

IV. FULGIDAE

Blades of the basal and lower cauline leaves cordate or trun-
  cate.
  Chaff of the disk 1.5–2.5 mm. wide, densely ciliate at the
    tip.   11. *R. umbrosa.*
  Chaff of the disk narrower, sparsely ciliate at the tip.   12. *R. Chapmanii.*

[1] Contributed by Charles Lawrence Boynton and Chauncy Delos Beadle.

Blades of the basal and lower cauline leaves not cordate or
truncate.
  Involucral bracts ciliate, glabrous above: leaves larger,
    with long-acuminate blades.
    Stem glabrate or glabrous.   13. *R. palustris.*
    Stem strigose.   14. *R. acuminata.*
  Involucral bracts ciliate, pubescent above: leaves small
    or medium, with acute or short-acuminate blades.
    Upper leaves with cuneiform or elliptic-lanceolate
      blades.
      Well-developed disks 1–1.5 cm. in diameter: ligules
        of the ray relatively short.   15. *R. fulgida.*
      Well-developed disks smaller: ligules relatively
        large.   16. *R. foliosa.*
    Upper leaves with conspicuously dilated blade.   17. *R. spathulata.*

V. Speciosae

Ligules of the ray large and showy, much exceeding the
diameter of the disk.
  Leaf-blades laciniate or very coarsely dentate.
    Prevailing leaves with blades of an ovate type.   18. *R. Sullivantii.*
    Prevailing leaves with blades of a narrower type.   19. *R. speciosa.*
  Leaf-blades remotely and shallowly dentate or entire.
    Plant glabrous or nearly so.   20. *R. truncata.*
    Plant densely hirsute.   21. *R. missouriensis.*
Ligules short, often less than the diameter of the disk.   22. *R. tenax.*

VI. Graminifoliae

Plant pubescent: ligules of the ray crimson.   23. *R. graminifolia.*
Plant glabrous: ligules yellow.   24. *R. Mohrii.*

VII. Trilobae

Blades of the lower cauline leaves, or some of them pal-
mately 3-lobed.
  Disk 5–13 mm. wide: ray-flowers with ligules 1.5–2.5 cm.
    long.   25. *R. triloba.*
  Disk 15–20 mm. wide: ray-flowers with ligules 2–3.5 cm.
    long.   26. *R. rupestris.*
Blades of the lower cauline leaves, or some of them pinnately
5–7 lobed.
  Bracts of the involucre, or most of them, as long as the
    ligules of the ray: Alleghenian species.   27. *R. Beadlei.*
  Bracts of the involucre, or most of them, not half as long
    as the ligules: Floridian species.   28. *R. pinnatiloba.*

VIII. Bicolores

Plant hispid: ligules of the ray brown-purple at the base.   29. *R. bicolor.*

IX. Hirtae

Well-developed disks 1 cm. in diameter or more: ligules of
the ray large and showy.
  Blades of the upper cauline leaves not of an ovate type.
    Petioles of the basal leaves not exceeding 1 dm. in
    length.
      Leaf-blades broader than linear.
        Main axis or stem not divergently branched.
          Upper cauline leaves elliptic-lanceolate or
            lanceolate, or narrower.   30. *R. hirta.*
          Upper cauline leaves elliptic, subcordate-
            clasping.   31. *R. amplectens.*
        Main axis or stem divergently branched,
          usually from near the base.   32. *R. divergens.*
              33. *R. sericea.*
      Leaf-blades linear or linear-lanceolate, elongate.
    Petioles of the basal leaves, or some of them, con-
      spicuously elongate.   34. *R. longipes.*
  Blades of the upper cauline leaves, or some of them, of
    an ovate type.
    Blades of the basal leaves 5–6 cm. wide: involucral
      bracts often foliaceous.   35. *R. Brittonii.*
    Blades of the basal leaves narrower: involucral bracts
      not foliaceous.   36. *R. monticola.*
Well-developed disks smaller: ligules of the ray short.   37. *R. floridana.*

1. R. laciniata L. Stem 6–20 dm. tall, glabrous or nearly so: blades of the upper leaves less deeply lobed than those of the lower, or merely cleft: bracts of the involucre elliptic to lanceolate: ligules of the ray 2–4 cm. long: disk becoming cylindric or long-conic.—Rich woods, thickets, and meadows, various provinces, N. Fla. to La., Man., and Que.—Sum.–fall.—Cult. in several forms.—A full double form is common in cultivation under the name *Golden-glow*.

2. R. heterophylla T. & G. Stem 4–16 dm. tall, cinereous-pubescent: blades of the upper leaves coarsely toothed, or lobed: bracts of the involucre elliptic to elliptic-lanceolate: ligules of the ray 1–2.5 cm. long: disk subglobose.—Swamps, woods, and damp places, N. Fla.—Sum.

3. R. subtomentosa Pursh. Stem 6–15 dm. tall, cinereous-pubescent: blades of the upper leaves mostly undivided: bracts of the involucre linear or nearly so: ligules of the ray 2–3 cm. long: disk hemispheric to ovoid-conic.—Dry soil and low grounds, various provinces, Tenn. to Miss., Tex., Kans., Ia., and Ill.—Sum.–fall.

4. R. Heliopsidis T. & G. Stem 3–7 dm. tall, glabrate or softly pubescent: leaf-blades elliptic-ovate to ovate-lanceolate, 3–10 cm. long, serrate: bracts of the involucre elliptic to linear-lanceolate: ligules of the ray 1.5–2.5 cm. long: disk subglobose, about 1 cm. in diameter: pappus nearly obsolete.—Woods and low grounds, Piedmont to Appalachian Plateau, Ga. and Ala.—Sum.–fall.

5. R. alismaefolia T. & G. Stem 5–9 dm. tall, hispidulous or scabrous above: leaf-blades oval or elliptic, 5–12 cm. long, repand-denticulate to nearly entire: bracts of the involucre linear to elliptic: ligules of the ray 3–4 cm. long: disk subglobose, 1.5–2 cm. in diameter: pappus prominent.—Pine-woods and prairies, Coastal Plain and adj. provinces, La. to Tex. and Ark.—Sum.–fall.

6. R. grandiflora C. G. Gmel. Stem scabrous or hispid throughout: leaf-blades ovate-elliptic to lanceolate, 6–15 cm. long, usually shallowly toothed: bracts of the involucre linear: ligules of the ray 3–4 cm. long: disk ovoid or ovoid-globose, 1.5–2.5 cm. in diameter: pappus prominent.—Dry prairies, Coastal Plain and adj. provinces, La. to Tex. and Mo.—Sum.

7. R. mollis Ell. Stem 3–10 dm. tall, gray-hirsute: leaf-blades elliptic-spatulate to elliptic, 1.5–6 cm. long, crenate or nearly entire: bracts of the involucre linear to linear-lanceolate: ligules of the ray 2–3.5 cm. long: disk hemispheric, 1.5–2 cm. in diameter: pappus wanting.—Pinelands and dry soil, Coastal Plain, Fla., also E Ga.—Spr.–sum.—Little known.

8. R. maxima Nutt. Stem 9–30 dm. tall, glaucous: leaf-blades elliptic, oval, or ovate, or sometimes pandurate, 6–30 cm. long, dentate or repand-dentate: bracts of the involucre linear to linear-lanceolate: ligules of the ray 1.5–4 cm. long: disk ellipsoid to conic-cylindric, 3–4.5 cm. long: pappus conspicuous.—Moist soil, various provinces, La. to Tex., Okla., and Mo.—Spr.–sum.

9. R. nitida Nutt. Stem 6–12 dm. tall, glabrous: leaf-blades ovate-spatulate to lanceolate-elliptic, 8–15 cm. long, nearly entire to repand-dentate: bracts of the involucre linear to linear-lanceolate: disk cylindric to conic-cylindric, 3–4.5

cm. long.—Low pinelands and pond-margins, Coastal Plain, Fla. to Tex. and Ga.—Spr.–fall.

10. **R. glabra** DC. Stem 6–12 dm. tall, glabrous: leaf-blades elongate-lanceolate to linear-lanceolate, 9–30 cm. long, repand-dentate or undulate, veiny: bracts of the involucre linear: ligules of the ray 3–5 cm. long: disk cylindric or conic-cylindric, 2–4 cm. long.—Low grounds, Coastal Plain, Fla. to Tex. and Ga.—Spr.–fall.

11. **R. umbrosa** Boynton & Beadle. Stem 4–10 dm. tall, pubescent: blades of the lower leaves ovate, coarsely serrate: bracts of the involucre elliptic to linear-elliptic, 10–15 mm. long: ligules of the ray 1.5–2 cm. long.—Moist soil, Appalachian provinces and Interior Low Plateaus, Ga. to Ky.—Sum.

12. **R. Chapmanii** Boynton & Beadle. Stem 4–10 dm. tall, glabrous or glabrate: blades of the lower leaves ovate-lanceolate, dentate or coarsely crenate-dentate: bracts of the involucre linear or linear-elliptic, 6–12 mm. long: ligules of the ray 1.5–2.5 cm. long.—Mt. slopes, Blue Ridge, Ga. and Ala.—Sum.

13. **R. palustris** Eggert. Stem 5–7 dm. tall, glabrous or glabrate, at least below: blades of the lower leaves ovate-lanceolate, remotely serrate or dentate, or nearly entire: bracts of the involucre linear to linear-oblong, mostly obtuse: ligules of the ray 1–2 m. long—Low grounds, wet banks, and cedar-glades, Interior and Ozark Plateaus, Tenn. to Mo. and Ky.—Sum.–fall.

14. **R. acuminata** Boynton & Beadle. Stem 5–8 dm. tall, strigose: blades of the lower leaves lanceolate, remotely serrate with low teeth or entire: bracts of the involucre lanceolate, acute: ligules of the ray 1–2.5 cm. long.—Woods, Interior Low Plateau, Tenn.—Sum.

15. **R. fulgida** Ait. Stem 3–7 dm. tall, hirsute or somewhat hispid: blades of the lower leaves lanceolate, elliptic-lanceolate, or cuneiform, remotely toothed or entire: bracts of the involucre linear to linear-lanceolate: ligules of the ray 9–15 mm. long: disk 1–1.5 cm. wide.—Woods, thickets, meadows, low grounds, and swamps, various provinces, rarely Coastal Plain, Ala. to Miss., Tenn., W. Va., Pa., and N. C.—Fall.

16. **R. foliosa** Boynton & Beadle. Stem 3–7 dm. tall, pubescent or some-what hispid: leaf-blades lanceolate, elliptic-lanceolate, elliptic or cuneiform, sparingly serrate or entire: bracts of the involucre linear to elliptic-linear: ligules of the ray 1–1.5 cm. long: disk mostly less than 1 cm. wide.—Woods and thickets, mostly in marly places, Coastal Plain and Piedmont, Fla. to N. C.—Sum.–fall.

17. **R. spathulata** Michx. Stem 3–7 dm. tall, minutely pubescent: blades of the lower leaves lanceolate, elliptic, or oblanceolate, entire, or minutely and remotely toothed: bracts of the involucre linear, mostly acute: ligules of the ray 1–2 cm. long; disk about 1 cm. wide.—Woods, and along streams, various provinces, rarely Coastal Plain, Ga. to Ala., Tenn., and N. C.—Sum.–fall.

18. **R. Sullivantii** Boynton & Beadle. Stem 5–10 dm. tall, hispid or glabrate: blades of the lower leaves oval, ovate, or ovate-lanceolate, irregularly coarse-toothed: bracts of the involucre linear-elliptic, obtuse: ligules of the ray 2–4 cm. long: disk 12–18 mm. wide.—Low grounds, various provinces N of Coastal Plain, Ala. to Mich.—Sum.–fall.

19. **R. speciosa** Wenderoth. Stem 5–10 dm. tall, hirsute or somewhat hispid: blades of the lower leaves elongate-lanceolate, often falcate, irregularly coarse-

toothed: bracts of the involucre linear to linear-lanceolate: ligules of the ray 2–3.5 cm. long: disk 13–20 mm. wide.—Woods and low grounds, various provinces N of Coastal Plain, Ga. to Ala., Mo., and Pa.—Sum.–fall.

20. R. truncata Small. Stem 3–8 dm. tall, glabrous or nearly so: blades of the lower leaves narrowly lanceolate to elliptic or elliptic-linear, remotely and shallowly dentate or entire: bracts of the involucre linear to linear-lanceolate: ligules of the ray 1.5–2 cm. long: disk 10–15 mm. wide.—Woods and low grounds, Blue Ridge to Appalachian Plateau, Ga. to Ala. and Tenn.—Fall.

21. R. missouriensis Engelm. Stem 4–6 dm. tall, hirsute: blades of the lower leaves linear-lanceolate to linear, entire: bracts of the involucre linear to linear-elliptic: ligules of the ray 1.5–2.5 cm. long: disk 10–15 mm. wide.—Dry hills and rocky soil, La. to Mo.—Sum.–fall.

22. R. tenax Boynton & Beadle. Stem 4–8 dm. tall, sparingly pubescent, often hirsute: blades of the lower leaves ovate-lanceolate to lanceolate, remotely shallow-dentate or entire: bracts of the involucre elliptic to lanceolate: ligules of the ray 6–12 mm. long; disk 10–18 mm. wide.—Woods and fields, Interior Low Plateau, Ala. and Tenn.—Sum.–fall.

23. R. graminifolia (T. & G.) Boynton & Beadle. Stem 6–8.5 dm. tall, pubescent: blades of the lower leaves elongate-linear, grass-like, entire, the midrib alone prominent: bracts of the involucre mostly lanceolate: ligules of the ray 8–12 mm. long: disk hemipheric to elliptic-ovoid. [*Echinacea?* *atrorubens graminifolia* T. & G.]—Pineland ponds, Coastal Plain, N Fla. and Ga.—Spr.–sum.

24. R. Mohrii A. Gray. Stem 4–12 dm. tall, glabrous: blades of the lower leaves linear or elongate-linear, several-ribbed: bracts of the involucre linear to linear-lanceolate: ligules of the ray 15–30 mm. long: disk ovoid-conic to conic-cylindric. [*R. bupleuroides* Shuttlew.]—Pineland ponds and moist pinelands, Coastal Plain, N Fla. and Ga.—Sum.

25. R. triloba L. Stem 6–15 dm. tall, hispid or hirsute: blades of the upper leaves ovate-lanceolate to lanceolate: bracts of the involucre linear to linear-lanceolate: ligules of the ray 15–25 mm. long: disk subglobose to conic-globose, 5–13 mm. broad.—Moist soil, rocky woods, old fields, and thickets, various provinces, Ga. to Tex., Kans., Mich., and N. J.—Sum.–fall.

26. R. rupestris Chickering. Stem 7–15 dm. tall, sparingly pubescent: blades of the upper leaves ovate: bracts of the involucre lanceolate to elliptic-lanceolate: ligules of the ray 20–35 mm. long: disk hemispheric to ovoid-conic, 15–20 mm. broad. [*R. triloba rupestris* A. Gray.]—Rocky slopes, Roan Mt. and adj. peaks, in the Blue Ridge of N. C. and Tenn.—Sum.–fall.

27. R. Beadlei Small. Stem 6–15 dm. tall, hirsute: blades of the upper leaves lanceolate: bracts of the involucre linear to linear-lanceolate: ligules of the ray 11–20 mm. long: disk 5–10 mm. wide.—Rocky slopes, above 1,000 m., in the Blue Ridge of N. C.—Sum.

28. R. pinnatiloba (T. & G.) Beadle. Stem 6–12 dm. tall, softly hirsute: blades of the upper leaves ovate-lanceolate: bracts of the involucre linear to linear-lanceolate: ligules of the ray 10–15 mm. long: disk 6–9 mm. broad. [*R. triloba pinnatiloba* T. & G.]—Calcareous soil, W Fla.—Sum.–fall.

29. R. bicolor Nutt. Stem 3–9 dm. tall, hispid: blades of the upper leaves elliptic to lanceolate, sometimes narrowly so: bracts of the involucre elliptic-lanceolate to linear: ligules of the ray 15–25 mm. long, brown-purple at the base.—(NIGGER-TEATS. THIMBLE-FLOWER.)—Woods, dry hills, and sandy soil, various provinces, Ala. to Tex., Ark., and Tenn.—Spr.–sum.

30. R. hirta L. Stem 3–7 dm. tall, hirsute or hispid: blades of the upper leaves elliptic, oblong, or lanceolate, or nearly linear: bracts of the involucre linear-lanceolate or linear-elliptic: ligules of the ray 20–35 mm. long: disk 10–18 mm. wide.—(YELLOW-DAISY. BLACK-EYED SUSAN.)—Fields, roadsides, and woods, various provinces, Fla. to Okla., S. Dak., and Que. Native mainly W.—Sum.

31. R. amplectens T. V. Moore. Stem 3–6 dm. tall, hispidulous: blades of the upper leaves elliptic: bracts of the involucres linear-elliptic to linear-lanceolate: ligules of the ray 10–20 mm. long.—Dry soil, Piedmont, Ga., and S. C. —Sum.

32. R. divergens T. V. Moore. Stem 3–10 dm. tall, hirsute or hispid: blades of the upper leaves elliptic to lanceolate or almost linear: bracts of the involucre linear or linear-lanceolate: ligules of the ray 15–30 mm. long: disk 12–18 mm. wide.—Pinelands and fields, Coastal Plain, Fla. to S. C.—Spr.—sum.—This and related species are used by the Seminoles as a cold infusion in cases of fever and headache.

33. R. sericea T. V. Moore. Stem 5–12 dm. tall, hispid: blades of the upper leaves linear-lanceolate to linear, shallowly toothed: bracts of the involucre linear to elliptic-linear or lanceolate: ligules of the ray 20–40 mm. long: disk 12–20 mm. long.—Dry woods and fields, various provinces N of Coastal Plain, Ga. to Ala., Mo., and S. Dak.—Sum.

34. R. longipes T. V. Moore. Stem 3–10 dm. tall, hispid: blades of the upper leaves lanceolate to elliptic-lanceolate, entire or toothed bracts of the involucres linear-lanceolate to elliptic-lanceolate: ligules of the ray 20–35 mm. long: disk about 15 mm. wide.—Woods and fields, various provinces, rarely Coastal Plain, Ala. to Miss., Ia., and N. Y.—Sum.–fall.

35. R. Brittonii Small. Stem 5–8 dm. tall, hispid or hirsute-hispid: blades of the upper leaves mostly ovate to elliptic-ovate, rather coarsely toothed or shallowly crenate: bracts of the involucre elliptic to lanceolate: ligules of the ray 25–35 mm. long.—Wooded hill-sides, various provinces N of Coastal Plain, Ala. to Tenn.—Sum.

36. R. monticola Small. Stem 3–10 dm. tall, hirsute or hispid: blades of the upper leaves ovate or ovate-lanceolate, mostly serrate: bracts of the involucre linear to linear-lanceolate, 10–14 mm. long; ligules of the ray 20–35 mm. long.—Woods, Blue Ridge to Appalachian Plateau, Ga. to Ala., Tenn., and Pa.—Sum.–fall.

37. R. floridana T. V. Moore. Stem 3–6 dm. tall, hispid: blades of the upper leaves elliptic, lanceolate, or narrowly pandurate (very narrow in *R. floridana angustifolia*): bracts of the involucre elliptic to linear-elliptic, 6–10 mm. long: ligules of the ray 10–20 mm. long, yellow, fading greenish.—Sandy soil, Coastal Plain, Fla. to Tex. and Ark.—Spr.–fall.

72. DRACOPIS Cass. Annual, glaucous herbs. Leaves alternate: blades entire or slightly toothed, clasping. Heads erect. Involucre of few

somewhat foliaceous bracts which are ultimately reflexed. Ray-flowers few: ligules
yellow, drooping, often discolored. Disk-
flowers crowded: corollas relatively long
with a short tube and a longer throat, ultimately deciduous, leaving the erect cone-like
disk. Anthers usually about as long as the
filaments. Stigmas slender. Achene terete,
striate and transverse-wrinkled. Pappus
wanting.—One species.

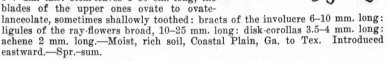

1. D. amplexicaulis (Vahl.) Cass. Stem
3–7 dm. tall: stem-leaves 4–10 cm. long, the
blades of the upper ones ovate to ovate-
lanceolate, sometimes shallowly toothed: bracts of the involucre 6–10 mm. long:
ligules of the ray-flowers broad, 10–25 mm. long: disk-corollas 3.5–4 mm. long:
achene 2 mm. long.—Moist, rich soil, Coastal Plain, Ga. to Tex. Introduced
eastward.—Spr.–sum.

73. RATIBIDA Raf. Annual, biennial, or perennial, pubescent herbs.
Leaves alternate: blades pinnately parted or divided, or lyrate. Heads erect,
usually showy. Involucre flat: bracts mostly spreading or reflexed, narrow.
Ray-flowers several: ligules broad or narrow, often discolored. Disk-flowers
crowded on the elongate receptacle: corollas stout, with a very short tube and
a longer relatively wide throat; lobes ovate or deltoid. Anthers longer than
the filaments. Stigmas stout or slender. Achene flattened, margined or
winged, deciduous with bractlets. Pappus of 2 awns or wanting.—About 6
species, North American.

Stigmas with lanceolate-subulate tips: ligules of the ray elongate, linear to linear-
    spatulate.   1. *R. pinnata.*
Stigmas with short obtuse tips: ligules of the ray relatively
    short, elliptic to oval.   2. *R. columnaris.*

1. R. pinnata (Vent.) Barnhart. Stem strigillose and scabrous, 6–15 dm. tall,
often with elongate branches: leaves 5–20 cm. long; blades pinnately 3–7-folio-
late or -parted, the segments linear to lanceo-
late, entire or toothed: heads showy: disk
subglobose to oval, 1–2 cm. long: ray-flowers
few; ligules bright yellow, 3–5 cm. long,
early drooping: achene 2–2.5 mm. long.—
Dry, often calcareous soil, various provinces,
Fla. to Tex., Ia., and N. Y.—Sum.–fall.

2. R. columnaris (Sims) D. Don. Stem 3–
7 dm. tall, scabrous-strigose, often branched
at the base and sometimes above: leaves 5–
12 cm. long; blades pinnately parted, the
segments mostly linear, lanceolate, or oblanceolate, often pinnatifid or 2–3-cleft:
heads showy: disk cylindric or columnar,
2.5–4 cm. long: ray-flowers few; ligules yel-

low (or brown-purple at the base in *R. columnaris pulcherrima*), 2–4 cm. long,
drooping: achene 2–2.5 mm. long.—(NIGGER-HEAD)—Dry soil, prairies, plains,
and hills, Tenn. to Tex., Ariz., Sask., and Minn.—Sum.–fall.—Often cult.

74. **WEDELIA** Jacq. Perennial, caulescent, diffusely branching and creeping herbs. Leaves opposite: blades typically or predominantly of a cuneate type, coarsely few-toothed or -lobed. Heads erect, peduncled, radiate. Involucre broad, somewhat foliaceous: bracts in 2 or 3 unequal series, the outer mostly longer than the inner. Ray-flowers few: corollas with broad yellow, 3-lobed ligules. Disk-corollas with a cylindric-funnelform throat longer than the tube; lobes deltoid. Anthers sagittate at the base, with deltoid appendages. Stigmas stout-tipped. Achene of the ray 3-angled, turgid, tuberculate. Pappus a fimbriate crown, deciduous.—About 40 species, of warm and tropical regions.

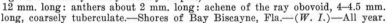

1. **W. trilobata** (L.) A. Hitchc. Stem and branches creeping, fleshy: leaf-blades cuneate or elliptic and cuneate at the base, 3–10 cm. long, coarsely few-toothed, or 3–5-lobed, more or less auricled at the base, or abruptly narrowed into a short petiole-like base: outer bracts of the involucre elliptic to ovate, lax: ligules of the ray mostly broadly elliptic, 8–12 mm. long: anthers about 2 mm. long: achene of the ray obovoid, 4–4.5 mm. long, coarsely tuberculate.—Shores of Bay Biscayne, Fla.—(W. I.)—All year.

75. **STEMMODONTIA** Cass. Perennial, caulescent, *Helianthus*-like herbs or partly woody plants. Leaves opposite: blades of a lanceolate or an ovate type, entire or shallowly toothed. Heads erect, peduncled, radiate. Involucre rather broad, somewhat foliaceous: bracts in 3 or 4 unequal series, the outer mostly longer than the inner. Ray-flowers few: corolla with broad yellow, often 2-lobed ligules. Disk-corollas with a nearly cylindric throat much longer than the tube; lobes ovate-lanceolate. Anthers sagittate at the base, with ovate appendages. Stigmas capillary-tipped. Achene of the ray flattened, thick-margined, pubescent. Pappus a fimbriate crown, persistent. —About 6 species, tropical American.

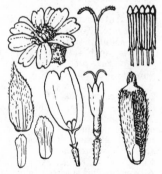

1. **S. calycina** (L. C. Rich.) O. E. Schulz. Stem and branches erect, mostly 2 m. tall or less, partly woody: leaf-blades lanceolate to ovate-lanceolate, 4–15 cm. long, serrate or crenate-serrate, rough-pubescent, gradually narrowed or rounded at the base: outer bracts of the involucre mostly elliptic to lanceolate, lax: ligules of the ray narrowly elliptic: anthers about 3 mm. long: achene of the ray elliptic-cuneate, about 4 mm. long, appressed-pubescent.—Waste-places, Coastal Plain, Ala. Nat. of W. I.—Sum.–fall.

76. **PASCALIA** Ortega. Perennial, caulescent herbs. Leaves opposite: blades entire, toothed, or somewhat lobed. Heads erect, radiate. In-

volucre hemispheric: outer bracts herbaceous, the inner membranous. Ray-flowers pistillate: ligules yellow, spreading. Disk-flowers perfect: corollas with a very short tube, a long throat and deltoid lobes. Anthers much longer than the filaments. Achene various, those of the ray 3-angled, those of the disk 4-angled. Pappus of scales, which are often accompanied by awns.—One species.

1. P. glauca Ortega. Stem mostly 1 m. tall or less, glaucous: leaf-blades 3-ribbed, 1 dm. long or shorter on the upper part of the stem, those of the lower cauline leaves ovate-lanceolate or narrowly ovate, shallowly toothed, those of the upper cauline often linear-lanceolate or narrowly lanceolate, repand or entire: involucre 1.5–2 cm. wide; bracts lanceolate to linear, the larger ones 8–15 mm. long: ligules of the ray-flowers bright-yellow, 1–1.5 cm. long: achene 5–6 mm. long.— Waste-places and roadsides, coast of N Fla. Nat. of Chile.—Spr.–fall.

77. BORRICHIA Adans. Fleshy, maritime, erect herbs or shrubs. Leaves opposite: blades thick, entire, or toothed. Heads erect, on stiff peduncles. Involucre hemispheric or flattish: bracts fleshy or leathery. Ray-flowers yellow, few. Disk-corollas with a cylindric-funnelform throat and a very short tube: lobes eciliate. Free portions of the filaments much longer than the corolla-tube. Pappus crown-like.—About 5 species, American.— Sea ox-eyes.

Outer bracts of the involucre spreading or reflexed at maturity: bractlets of the
    receptacle spine-tipped.   1. *B. frutescens.*
Outer bracts of the involucre appressed at maturity: bractlets
    of the receptacle obtuse or barely mucronate.   2. *B. arborescens.*

1. B. frutescens (L.) DC. Plant 2–7 dm. tall: leaf-blades linear-spatulate to obovate, 2–6 cm. long: outer bracts of the involucre acute, the inner ones subulate-tipped.—Shores, sand-dunes, prairies, and salt-marshes, Coastal Plain, Fla. to Tex. and S Va.—(*W. I., Mex.*)— Sum.–fall, or all year S.

2. B. arborescens (L.) DC. Plant 2–12 dm. tall: leaf-blades oblanceolate or spatulate-oblanceolate, 3–6 cm. long: outer bracts of the involucre acute, the inner ones rounded at the apex.—Shores, sand-dunes, and low waste hammocks, pen. Fla. and Fla. Keys.—(*W. I., Mex., C. A., S. A.*)— All year.—This species is much more variable than the preceding one. The plants become very robust and succulent in strictly saline localities. The foliage various from glabrous and glossy green to densely pale silky-canescent. The glabrous form has been described as *B. glabrata* Small and may be specifically distinct from the pubescent and larger form.

78. TITHONIA Desf. Annual, *Helianthus*-like herbs. Leaves alternate: blades entire or three lobed. Heads large, erect, on peduncles swollen just below the involucre. Involucre hemispheric or broadly campanulate: bracts in two series, the other short and appressed, the inner long, appressed at the base and somewhat foliaceous above. Ray flowers several, neutral: ligules yellow, showy. Disk flowers perfect: corollas yellow, with a short villous tube dilated into a long throat: lobes lanceolate. Stigmas slender, hirsute. Achene broadened upward, flattened, four-angled, wingless, embraced by the bractlets. Pappus of 2 awns or scales, caducous or persistent, accompanied by several shorter, always persistent, scales.—Four or five species, native of Mexico, Central America and the West Indies.

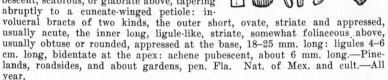

1. T. diversifolia (Hemsl.) Gray. Plant up to 4.5 m. tall, with a branching, woody stem, slightly pubescent or glabrate: leaf-blades ovate in outline, 3–5 lobed, or entire on the upper stem, serrate, pubescent beneath, pubescent, scabrous, or glabrate above, tapering abruptly to a cuneate-winged petiole: involucral bracts of two kinds, the outer short, ovate, striate and appressed, usually acute, the inner long, ligule-like, striate, somewhat foliaceous above, usually obtuse or rounded, appressed at the base, 18–25 mm. long: ligules 4–6 cm. long, bidentate at the apex: achene pubescent, about 6 mm. long.—Pinelands, roadsides, and about gardens, pen. Fla. Nat. of Mex. and cult.—All year.

77. HELIANTHUS L.[1] Annual or perennial, coarse, erect or diffuse herbs. Leaves various, the first ones opposite, sooner or later the succeeding ones becoming alternate, or in a few species very rarely all alternate: blades simple, 3-veined, but sometimes obscurely so. Flowers in involucrate, radiate heads, the rays usually conspicuous, the ligules always yellow, sterile and in one series; flowers of the disk perfect, with tubular corollas and the corolla 5-lobed, the tube short, the lobes yellow, red-purple, or brownish. Achene obovate, slightly compressed, surmounted by a pappus of two scale-like awns on the long diameter, the bases of the awns expanded and often lacerate, sometimes with accessory and intermediate scales, the whole pappus readily caducous; each flower subtended by a conduplicate, chaffy bractlet on the receptacle. Bracts of the involucre in 3 or 4 series, green.—About 100 species, American.—Sum.-fall, unless otherwise stated.—SUNFLOWERS.

Disk-corollas with red, purple, or brown lobes.	I. RUBRI.
Disk-corollas with yellow lobes.	II. FLAVI.

I. RUBRI

Ray-flowers with ligules more than 5 mm. long.
 Leaves more or less pubescent, but not densely white-hairy.
  Blades of the cauline leaves of a long-linear type, 2–8 mm. wide.

Heads many : leaves alternate.	1. *H. angustifolius.*
Head solitary : leaves opposite.	2. *H. heterophyllus.*

[1] Contributed by Elba Emanuel Watson.

Blades of the cauline leaves of a lanceolate to ovate
type.
  Leaves opposite.
    Bracts of the involucre linear, mucronate:
      leaves chiefly basal.   3. *H. atrorubens.*
    Bracts of the involucre lanceolate, not mucro-
      nate: leaves cauline.   4. *H. rigidus.*
  Leaves alternate.
    Disk more than 3 cm. in diameter.   5. *H. annuus.*
    Disk less than 3 cm. in diameter.
      Chaff toward center of disk, conspicuously
        white-bearded.   6. *H. petiolaris.*
      Chaff not thus bearded.
        Leaf-blades decurrent on the petiole
          nearly or quite to its base:
          Blade conspicuously bristly ciliate
            toward the base: annual.   7. *H. agrestis.*
          Blade not thus ciliate (often undu-
            late): perennial.   8. *H. floridanus.*
        Leaf-blades obviously petioled.
          Stem, especially the branches, con-
           spicuously white-villous.   9. *H. vestitus.*
          Stem more or less pubescent, but not
           as above.
            Plant erect: stems more or less
              mottled.   10. *H. cucumerifolius.*
            Plant prostrate: stems not con-
              spicuously mottled.   11. *H. debilis.*
Leaves densely white-pubescent, especially beneath.   12. *H. argophyllus.*
Ray-flowers wanting or minute, the ligules less than 3 mm.
long.   13. *H. radula.*

II. Flavi

Leaves verticillate.   14. *H. verticillatus.*
Leaves not verticillate.
  Leaf-blades of a linear type, some or all more than 10
    times as long as broad.
    Leaves cauline; blades usually less than 5 mm. wide,
      revolute and pubescent.   15. *H. simulans.*
    Leaves mostly basal; blades usually more than 7 mm.
      wide.
      Head solitary: disk about 1.5 cm. wide.   16. *H. carnosus.*
      Heads several: disk about 1 cm. wide.   17. *H. longifolius.*
  Leaf-blades of a linear, lanceolate or ovate type, less than
    10 times as long as broad.
    Leaf-blades linear to lanceolate, never broadly so.
      Leaf-blades densely white-pubescent both sides.   18. *H. Schweinitzii.*
      Leaf-blades more or less pubescent but not as above.
        Branches of the inflorescence and leaves below
          it opposite.
          Leaves strumose-hispid: bracts hispidulous,
            longer than the disk and recurved.   19. *H. stenophyllus.*
          Leaves and bracts almost or quite glabrous,
            latter about equal to disk and erect, or leaf-
            blades strumose-setose above.   20. *H. Eggertii.*
        Branches of the inflorescence and leaves below
          it alternate.
          Mature cauline leaf-blades deeply and irregu-
           larly serrate.   21. *H. grosse-serratus.*
          Cauline leaf-blades entire or serrate, but not
           as above.
           Bracts longer than the disk, very loose.
            Leaves evenly tomentulose; blades
              copiously resin-dotted and much
              lighter beneath.   22. *H. tomentosus.*
            Leaves not tomentulose; blades not
              copiously resin-dotted beneath.
            Leaf-blades firm, conduplicate,
              densely scabrous-hispidulous: 23. *H. Maximiliani.*
              ligules of the ray deep-yellow.
            Leaf-blades thinnish, flat, remotely
              pubescent: ligules of the ray
              light-yellow.   24. *H. giganteus.*
           Bracts about as long as the disk, not con-
            spicuously loose.
            Leaf-blades with revolute margins,
             usually undulate, fine-tomentose be-
             neath.   8. *H. floridanus.*

Leaf-blades not revolute-margined, not undulate, not tomentulose beneath.

Leaf-blades serrate, the lower surface glabrous except on the nerves.   25. *H. montanus.*

Leaf-blades entire, at most, obscurely denticulate, long-hispid beneath.   26. *H. alienus.*

Leaf-blades of a broadly lanceolate to ovate type.

Heads small : disk less than 8 mm. wide.

Leaves, stems, and bracts entirely glabrous.   27. *H. laevigatus.*

Some or all of these parts more or less pubescent.

Leaf-blades firm, copiously resin-dotted beneath : stem dark and conspicuously glaucous.   28. *H. glaucus.*

Leaf-blades thin, remotely if at all resin-dotted beneath : stem light, at most faintly glaucous.

Bracts of the involucre linear, abruptly curled : peduncles short.   29. *H. decapetalus.*

Bracts of the involucre loose but not reflexed : peduncles long and very slender.   30. *H. microcephalus.*

Heads larger : disk more than 8 mm. wide.

Leaf-blades broadly decurrent on the petiole, lateral nerves confluent only a little below the middle of the blade, the petiole from the confluence often as long as the blade.

Basal leaves numerous, approximate and persistent ; cauline leaves few and greatly reduced.   31. *H. occidentalis.*

Basal leaves often fugacious ; cauline leaves more evenly disposed on the stem and not greatly reduced.   32. *H. Dowellianus.*

Leaf-blades sessile or petiolate ; if decurrent, the petiole (from the confluence of the lateral nerves) much less than half the length of the leaf.

Bracts of the involucre about as long as the disk.

Leaves opposite ; blades sessile and often clasping : branches conspicuously erect.   33. *H. mollis.*

Leaves opposite or alternate ; blades not clasping : branches spreading.

Base of leaf-blade obtuse, cordate or roundish ; petiole distinct or blade only briefly decurrent.

Leaves opposite and divaricate.   34. *H. divaricatus.*

Leaves alternate (rarely opposite), not divaricate.   35. *H. saxicola.*

Base of leaf-blade more pointed, decurrent, but petiole partly distinct.

Leaves mostly or all alternate, light green, evenly, short-hispid above, short-hirsute beneath, not glaucous beneath.   36. *H. tuberosus.*

Leaves mostly opposite, dark green above, glabrous beneath, except on the nerves, and glaucous.   37. *H. strumosus.*

Bracts of the involucre longer than the disk.

Leaves opposite (sometimes alternate above in *H. decapetalus* and *H. reindutus*) ;

Blade decurrent to the base of the petiole.   38. *H. reindutus.*

Blade not decurrent to the base of the petiole, distinctly petiolate.

Leaf-blades thin, ovate, very sparingly pubescent : branches of the inflorescence and rarely the uppermost leaves alternate.   29. *H. decapetalus.*

Leaf-blades firm, broadly lanceolate, densely rough-pubescent : branches of the inflorescence opposite.   39. *H. hirsutus.*

Leaves alternate (lower cauline rarely opposite in *H. doronicoides*) ;

Blades densely tomentose beneath.

Leaf-blades sessile, broadly decurrent to the base of the petiole.   40. *H. doronicoides.*

Leaf-blades apparently short-petiolate, less broadly decurrent and not quite to the base of the petiole.   22. *H. tomentosus.*

Blades more or less pubescent, but not
densely tomentose or tomentulose.
Leaf-blades conspicuously resin-dotted
beneath, finely tomentulose.
Leaf-blades thin, lower surface
little if any lighter than the
upper.   41. *H. resinosus.*
Leaf-blades firm, lower surface
lighter than the upper.   22. *H. tomentosus.*
Leaf-blades not conspicuously resin-
dotted beneath.
Leaf-blades tapering at the base,
decurrent almost to the base of
the petiole: bracts loose.   42. *H. validus.*
Leaf-blades roundish, or at least
broad toward the base, not decurrent to the base of the peti-
ole: bracts erect.   43. *H. laetiflorus.*

1. H. angustifolius L. Perennial: stem 1–2 m. high, slender, simple to the inflorescence, hispid: leaves alternate: blades varying in width from 2–4 mm. in sunny, exposed places to about 1 cm. in moist, shady habitats, usually 8–15 cm. long, revolute except when very wide: ray-flowers with bright yellow ligules: lobes of the disk-corollas red-purple.—Moist ground, wet pine-lands, woods, and prairies, Coastal Plain and adj. provinces, Fla. to Tex., Mo., and N. Y. —A showy plant, often in large masses.

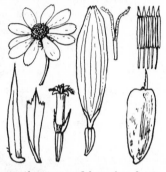

2. H. heterophyllus Nutt. Perennial: stem slender, simple, about 1 m. high, rarely with long, ascending branches, usually rough: leaves of two kinds, the basal with broadly ovate to elongate, narrowly oblan-ceolate blades, the cauline narrowly linear, all very coarse in texture and scabrous-hispid, the hairs often very long: heads solitary on the stem and branches, large, disk often 2 cm. wide, corollas of the disk very dark.—Wet clay soil, low pine-lands, edges of swamps, and marshes, Coastal Plain, Fla. to La. and N. C.— There are no crown buds nor rhizomes; the longer of the fibrous roots produce a bud about 2 cm. from the tip, which grows at once, the daughter plants often blooming the same season.

3. H. atrorubens L. Perennial: stem about 1.5 m. high, slender, very coarsely hispid, simple to the inflorescence: basal leaves large, approximate, opposite: blades mainly ovate, oval, or elliptic; the cauline leaves alternate, broadly ovate, obtuse, the blades abruptly contracted below to a long, winged petiole, often as long as the blade, rough, coarse, hispid: heads few, rarely more than 6–7: bracts of the involucre oblong, glabrous: ray-flowers with short, deep yellow ligules: disk-flowers with very dark-red corollas.—Open woods, creek-banks, and shaded mountain sides, various provinces, Fla. to La., Mo., and Va.—Vegetative propagation is from axillary buds at the base of the stem.

4. H. rigidus (Cass.) Desv. Perennial: stem 0.7–1.75 m. high, rough, simple or branched, mostly purple: leaves opposite: blades lanceolate, rarely ovate, obtuse, mostly entire, thick, firm, rough both sides, dark-green: heads large, very compact, solitary on the stem and branches: bracts of the involucre ovate, appressed, obtuse, glabrous, ciliate: disk-corollas with red-purple lobes: the pappus usually with many small intermediate scales. [*H. scaberrimus* Ell. *H. subrhomboideus* Rydb.]—Dry sandy soil, usually on prairies, various provinces, Ga. to Tex.—The root stocks have swollen tips which bear abundant rootlets.

5. **H. annuus** L. Annual, similar to the preceding, but taller, more branched, and less pubescent: disk-corollas shorter than in the preceding, and the lobes brownish-red rather than magenta-colored or in cultivated forms the lobes of the disk-corollas frequently yellow.—Dry plains, various provinces, Tex. to Sask. and Minn.; also cult. grounds, waste-places, and fields throughout the E U. S.

6. **H. petiolaris** Nutt. Annual: stem simple or, in vigorous plants, much branched, rough: leaves alternate; blades lanceolate to ovate, mostly entire, distinctly petiolate, very variable in size, 4–15 cm. long, in normal plants about 7 cm. long, densely appressed-scabrous on both sides, blue-green: inflorescence terminal and axillary, profuse, the heads very showy: bracts of the involucre broadly lanceolate, about as long as the disk, erect, densely hispidulous, often without cilia: ray-flowers with oval ligules, about 2 cm. long: disk 1–2.5 cm. wide: lobes of disk corollas red-purple.—Plains, hills, river-bottoms, and rocky banks, various provinces, Tex. to Ariz., Ore., Sask., and Minn.; also waste-places and cult. grounds in the E U. S.

7. **H. agrestis** Pollard. Annual: stem 1–2 m. high, light-green, glabrous, sulcate, in vigorous plants much branched: leaves alternate; blades broadly elliptic-lanceolate, very light-green, hispid on both sides, the midrib beneath and the margin toward the base with long, rather remote bristly cilia: heads few but very showy: bracts of the involucre lanceolate, glabrous, erect: ray-flowers with bright-yellow ligules: disk-corollas deep-violet. [*H. Curtissii* Fernald.]— Pinelands, scrub, and prairies, often along ditches, pen. Fla.

8. **H. floridanus** Gray. Perennial: stem 1–2 high, hispid, simple: leaves alternate toward the top of the stem (opposite in small individuals); blades lanceolate, sessile or subsessile, scabrous above, mostly fine-tomentose beneath, revolute, often unevenly so and apparently undulate, mostly 6–8 cm. long: inflorescence one to four or five heads in a loose panicle: bracts of the involucre about as long as the disk: disk-corollas mostly with red-brown lobes, rarely yellow. [*H. undulatus* Chapm.]—Woods, thickets, and edges of fields, Coastal Plain, Fla. to La.

9. **H. vestitus** E. E. Watson. Annual: stem 6–7.0 dm. high, lax, densely white-villous, profusely branched: leaves alternate, crowded; blades deltoid-lanceolate, mostly about 6 cm. long, deeply irregularly serrate, or lobed, hispid-hirsute beneath, especially on the veins appressed-hispid above, distinctly petioled, the petioles long, slender, very hirsute: heads terminal on the stem and branches: bracts of the involucre linear-lanceolate, attenuate, longer than the disk, densely hispidulous, very loose; ray-flowers with oval ligules 1.5 cm. long; disk 1 cm. wide; lobes of the disk-corollas purple: achene villous.— Sandy places, Hog Island, Fla.

10. **H. cucumerifolius** T. & G. Annual: stem erect, 1–2 m. tall somewhat rough above, with ascending branches mostly above the middle: leaves alternate; blades deltoid-ovate, 5–8 cm. long, acute, irregularly serrate, strumose-setose above, scabrous-hispid beneath, cordate; petioles about as long as the blades: heads 1–3 terminating the stem and the branches: bracts of the involucre narrowly lanceolate, longer than the disk, scabrous, scarcely ciliate: disk about 2 cm. wide, its corollas with red-purple lobes.—Sandy places near the coast, La. and Tex.; naturalized in Fla. through cult.—Sum.–fall.—Cult. forms have yellow disks.

11. **H. debilis** Nutt. Annual: stem more or less branched at the base, the branches decumbent or horizontal, up to 1 m. long, subglabrous to hispid: leaves alternate; blades deltoid-ovate, acute, 5–8 cm. long, irregularly serrate, scabrous-setose and deep-green on both sides, broadly cuneate to cordate; petioles sca-

brous, about one-third as long as the blades: heads terminating the stem and the branches: peduncles hispid: bracts of the involucre narrowly lanceolate, longer than the disk, scabrous, scarcely ciliate: ray-flowers with light-yellow ligules about 1.5 cm. long: disk about 1.5 cm. wide, its corollas with red-purple lobes.—Coastal sand-dunes and rarely introduced into sandy places inland, Coastal Plain, Fla. to Tex. and Ga.—All year.

12. H. argophyllus T. & G. Annual: stem 1–2 m. high, branched, densely white-tomentose, especially on younger parts: leaves alternate: blades ovate, mostly entire, 1–2 dm. long, the petiole a little shorter, densely pubescent: heads large, very showy: bracts of the involucre ovate-acuminate, white-tomentose: disk 2–3 cm. in diameter; lobes of the disk-corollas magenta-red.— Sandy places, wood and chaparral, various provinces, Tex., often cultivated and readily escaping and persistent through the southeast.—Similar to *H. annuus*, but shorter and less branched. The leaf-buds are densely long, white-pubescent.

13. H. radula (Pursh) T. & G. Perennial: stem erect from an ascending base, about 0.5–1 m. high, hirsute below, simple to the inflorescence: leaves opposite, the basal ones crowded into a rosette, with obovate or suborbicular blades 5–21 cm. in diameter; cauline leaves much reduced, rough-hispid: flower-stem rising from beneath the basal rosette: peduncles 1-flowered, heads large: ray-ligules minute, 1–2 mm. long: disk 2–3 cm. in diameter, like the whole head, often including the glabrous involucral bracts, suffused with purple.— Sandy pinelands, flat-woods, and oak-ridges, Coastal Plain, Fla. to Ala. and Ga.—There are no rootstocks, and vegetative propagation is by crown-buds.

14. H. verticillatus Small. Perennial: stem slender, less than 2 m. high, glabrous: leaves verticillate in 4's, blades lanceolate, narrowly sessile, about 9 cm. long, scabrous above, finely short-pubescent and paler beneath: inflorescence a cyme: bracts of the involucre lanceolate, sub-glabrous, a little longer than the disk: disk-corollas yellow.—Wet sandy soil, Interior Low Plateaus, Tenn.

15. H. simulans E. E. Watson. Perennial: stem erect, simple to the inflorescence, scabrous-strigose: leaves alternate, crowded; blades linear, mostly about 14 cm. long, revolute, rough-scabrous above, tomentulose beneath: heads showy: bracts of the involucre linear-lanceolate, longer than the disk, thinly pubescent, scarcely ciliate: the ray-flowers with ligules deeply 2–3-dentate at the apex, 2–3 cm. long: corollas of the disk yellow.—Wet muck, low woods, and pinelands, Coastal Plain, Fla. to La.—Differs from *H. angustifolius*, with which it is often confused, by its yellow disk.

16. H. carnosus Small. Perennial: stem 0.8–1 m. high, slender, glabrous, arising from a mass of basal leaves surmounting a bulbous base: basal leaves with blades varying from ovate-spatulate to narrowly linear-oblanceolate, 4–17 cm. long; cauline leaves alternate; blades glabrous, succulent: inflorescence a single terminal head on the main stem: bracts of the involucre oblong-lanceolate 4–5 mm. wide, a little longer than the disk and glabrous: ray-flowers with ligules about 2 cm. long and 2–3-dentate at the apex: disk 1.5 cm. wide; corollas yellow.—Wet sandy soil, mostly about ponds, N Fla.—The main stem arises from one side of the bulbous base and the basal clump of leaves from the other side; rootstocks none, propagation is from crown buds.

17. H. longifolius Pursh. Perennial, similar to the preceding species: stem simple to the much branched inflorescence, often purplish: leaves opposite or the upper alternate; blades narrowly linear-oblanceolate, the longest being 25 cm. long, chiefly basal and sheathing the stem: inflorescence an open panicle: heads smaller than in *H. carnosus;* bracts of the involucre narrowly lanceolate, about as long as the disk, glabrous, scarcely ciliate: disk rarely more than 1 cm. wide, its corollas yellow: ray-flowers with ligules about 1.5 cm. long.—Wet sandy or rocky glades and sandhill bogs, Coastal Plain and adj. provinces, Ga. and Ala.

18. **H. Schweinitzii** T. & G. Perennial: stem erect, branched, 1–2 m. high, strigose or glabrescent in age, purple: leaves alternate above; blades lanceolate, acuminate, revolute, narrowly sessile, scabrous above, densely white-pubescent beneath: heads few, on short, slender peduncles, small: bract of the involucre lanceolate, a little shorter than the disk, pubescent: disk about 6 mm. wide, the corollas yellow.—Dry, often sandy and rocky woods, various provinces, Ga. to Ala. and N. C.

19. **H. stenophyllus** (T. & G.) E. E. Watson. Perennial, with stout branched rootstocks 1–3 dm. long: stem 0.5–1 m. high, slender, simple, scabrous-hispid, light-green; leaves opposite; blades narrowly lanceolate, attenuate, acute, 10–15 cm. long, pointed at the base, thick, densely strumose-hispid above, scabrous-hispid beneath, the petioles more or less winged by the decurrence of the blade: inflorescence cymose, bracts of the involucre linear-lanceolate, longer than the disk, loose, recurved, densely hispidulous; ray-flowers with ligules deep-yellow, 2.5 cm. long, disk 1–2 cm. wide, its corollas yellow, the lobes pubescent.—La. to Tex., and Okla. Perhaps not east of the Mississippi River.

20. **H. Eggertii** Small. Perennial: stem erect, slender, purplish, glabrous, glaucous, 1–2 m. high: leaves opposite, or the uppermost alternate in vigorous plants; blades lanceolate, acute, thinnish, glaucous on both sides, conspicuously so beneath, strumose-setose above, glabrous beneath, obscurely serrulate broadly decurrent to the base of the petiole, about 12 cm. long: inflorescence a few heads on short peduncles from the axils of the alternate upper leaves; involucre cylindrical; bracts broadly lanceolate, acuminate, not very loose, a little longer than the disk, glabrous: ray-flowers with ligules about 1.5 cm. long: disk about 1.2 cm. wide, its corollas yellow.—Dry, often rocky hills, Interior Low Plateau, Tenn.

21. **H. grosse-serratus** Martens. Perennial, with abundant, often branched rootstocks and woody roots: stem 1–3.5 m. high, simple to the inflorescence, glabrous, glaucous; leaves alternate; blades broadly linear-lanceolate, grossly and saliently serrate, often very large, 15–25 cm. long, thinly strumose-setulose above, with fine, soft, short, straight hairs beneath, abruptly contracted to a stout petiole which is 4–8 cm. long, the upper leaves smaller and less deeply serrate: inflorescence a many headed-panicle: heads large and showy: involucre campanulate; bracts linear-lanceolate, attenuate, longer than the disk, loose but not reflexed, very dark green, subglabrous; ray-flowers with bright yellow ligules, 2.5–4 cm. long: disk 1–2 cm. wide, its corollas yellow.—Rich soil, fields, pastures, meadows, and waste-places, various provinces, Tenn. to Tex., N. M., Wyo., Sask., Me., and Va.

22. **H. tomentosus** Michx. Perennial, with rootstocks 3–4 cm. long and numerous crown-buds: stems 1–2 m. high, usually 3–5 together, very variable in pubescence, always more or less hispid, rarely subglabrous or tomentose: leaves alternate toward the inflorescence; blades usually broadly lanceolate, often very narrowly so, and rarely ovate, decurrent to the base of the petiole, dark-green and hispid above, subglabrous to densely tomentose beneath, usually sparingly tomentose, always resin-dotted: inflorescence a small panicle, the peduncles slender; heads showy: bracts of the involucre linear-lanceolate, loose, reflexed, hispidulous, resin-dotted, longer than the disk: ray-flowers with ligules about 2 cm. long, bright-yellow, pubescent and resin-dotted on lower surface: disk 1–2.5 cm. wide, its corollas yellow, pubescent, resin-dotted.—Woods and hillsides, Piedmont and adj. Blue Ridge, Ga. to Ala., and Va.

23. H. Maximiliani Schrad. Perennial: stem 1–2 m. high, very scabrous, often several from one root: leaves alternate; blades lanceolate, conduplicate, densely scabrous-hispidulous on both sides, both stem and leaves light gray-green: inflorescence normally racemose, with 2 or 3 heads on very short peduncles in the axils of the upper leaves, occasionally the peduncles are 1–1.5 dm. long, and bear 1–3 heads: heads showy: bracts of the involucre narrowly linear-lanceolate, densely scabrous-hispidulous, attenuate, longer than the disk, loose, but not reflexed: ray-flowers with many, but short ligules, distinctly cupped: disk large, often 2 cm. wide, its corollas yellow.—Rather dry and rocky soil, plains and prairies, various provinces, Tex. to Man., and Minn.; also adv. in the E U. S.—The Texan specimens are often coarsely hispid-scabrous.

24. H. giganteus L. Perennial with numerous short rootstocks and crown-buds: stem stout, simple to the inflorescence, usually rough-hispid, 1.5–3.5 m. tall: leaves alternate; blades lanceolate, pointed at both ends, but very narrowly sessile, rather thin, serrate, sharply scabrous above, the lower surface paler, with remote, long, ascending hairs: inflorescence a many-flowered panicle: heads showy: bracts of the involucre linear or linear-lanceolate, much longer than the disk, dark green, glabrous, but conspicuously ciliate: ray-flowers with ligules about 1.5 cm. long, oval, light-yellow: disk relatively large, about 1.5 cm. wide, its corollas yellow.—Swamps and wet thickets, various provinces, N. C. to Colo., Sask., Ont., and Me.

25. H. montanus E. E. Watson. Perennial: stem 1–2 m. high, glabrous, purple, striate, more or less glaucous, branching above: leaves alternate, blades lanceolate, about 12 cm. long, serrate, slightly revolute, upper surface strumose-scabrous, lower surface paler and glabrous except on the hispid nerves, the petiole narrowly winged almost to its base: inflorescence of 2 or 3 heads on slender branches from the upper axils: involucral bracts lanceolate, nearly or quite glabrous, erect but loose, about as long as the disk: disk about 1 cm. wide, its florets yellow, the rays about 2 cm. long, the achene slender and glabrous, chaff 3-cuspidate.—Stony or sandy soil, various provinces, Fla. and Ga.

26. H. alienus E. E. Watson. Perennial, with coarse woody roots: stem 1–1.5 m. high, stout, scabrous toward the apex, purplish, sulcate: leaves alternate; blades lanceolate, obscurely denticulate, very narrowly sessile, 11–15 cm. long, thickish, densely scabrous above, sparingly but long-hispid beneath, the veins prominent: inflorescence few-flowered: heads showy: bracts of the involucre linear-lanceolate, about as long as the disk, densely hispidulous, spreading-ciliate: ray-flowers with ligules about 1.7 cm. long: disk about 1.3 cm. wide, its corollas yellow, the chaff entire.—Woods, Blue Ridge, N. C. to Va.

27. H. laevigatus T. & G. Perennial, with rootstocks rarely more than 3 cm. long: stem slender, erect, glabrous, 1–2 m. high: leaves mostly opposite, or alternate above in vigorous plants; blades narrowly, or often very broadly, lanceolate, pointed at both ends, glabrous on both sides: inflorescence a few-flowered panicle: heads small: bracts of the involucre lanceolate, glabrous, a little longer than the disk; disk rarely exceeding 8 mm. in diameter: ray-flowers with ligules 1–2 cm. long: disk-corollas yellow.—Woods, Blue Ridge and adj. provinces, N. C. to Ky. and Va.

28. H. glaucus Small. Perennial, with rootstocks 2–5 cm. long: stem purple, branched, glabrous, glaucous, up to nearly 2 m. high; leaves alternate above, though often all opposite: blades ovate to lanceolate, firm, scabrous above, tomentulose and very resin-dotted beneath, the veins conspicuously brown: heads many, small: bracts of the involucre lanceolate, about as long as the disk: disk about 7 mm. wide, the corollas yellow.—Dry woods, various provinces, Fla. to Miss., Ark. (?), and N. J.

29. H. decapetalus L. Perennial, with long rootstocks: stem slender, light-green, glabrous, simple to the inflorescence: leaves opposite to the inflorescence (branches of the latter mostly alternate); blades ovate, serrate, broadly decurrent on the usually long petiole, very thin, dark-green, remotely setose above, sparingly pubescent beneath: heads very showy: bracts of the involucre linear or linear-lanceolate, longer than the disk, very loose, often curling about, subglabrous: ray-flowers with ligules often 2.5 cm. long: disk 0.7 to 1.5 cm. wide; corollas yellow.—Rich woods, river-banks, and roadsides, various provinces, Ga. to Tenn., Mich., and Que.

30. H. microcephalus T. & G. Perennial, with rootstocks about 1 dm. long, the crown buds numerous: stem very slender, light-green, glabrous, simple: leaves opposite, or sometimes the upper alternate: blades very thin and delicate, light-green, broadly oblong-lanceolate, thinly pubescent beneath, remotely short-hispid above: heads few, very small: disk rarely exceeding 5 mm. in diameter: bracts of the involucre lanceolate, subglabrous, a little longer than the disk.— Woods, thickets, and fence-rows, various provinces, Ga. to Ky. and Pa.

31. H. occidentalis Riddell. Perennial, with rootstocks 2–3 dm. long, the terminal bud producing a daughter plant during the season, and numerous fine-fibrous roots: stem arising from a basal rosette which is not always persistent, simple to the inflorescence, scabrous; leaves opposite, crowded toward the base of the stem; blades oval in outline, either very narrowly or very broadly so, exceedingly variable in size, obtuse, entire or serrulate, rough above, hispid beneath, the base gradually contracted into a long, margined petiole which is as long as or often longer than the blade: inflorescence a panicle, or often only a single head in small plants; heads showy: bracts of the involucre narrowly lanceolate, acute, not longer than the disk, sparingly pubescent, ciliate: ray-flowers with ligules about 1.8 cm .long: disk about 1 cm. wide, its corollas yellow.—Dry or moist clay or sandy soil, woods, plains, and prairies, various provinces, Fla. to Tex., Minn., Ohio, and N. C.—The plants are large and vigorous in black, rich soil, smaller, but no less abundant in dry, sandy soil.

32. H. Dowellianus M. A. Curtis. Perennial, with rootstocks 1–3 dm. long and fibrous roots: stem 1–2.5 m. high, usually simple, rarely branched, appressed-pubescent or subglabrous: leaves more numerous and more approximate towards the base of stem, opposite below, alternate above; blades ovate, acute, rather densely short-hispid beneath, dark-green, concolor, contracted at the base to a long, margined petiole, the latter about as long as the blade: bracts of the involucre lanceolate, acuminate, a little longer than the disk, finely appressed-pubescent, the cilia short and very fine: ray-flowers with light yellow ligules about 2 cm. long: disk about 1 cm. wide, its corollas yellow: achene pubescent at the apex and on the angles.—Open woods, rocky banks, and sandy bottoms, various provinces, Ga. to Ill., and D. C.

33. H. mollis Lam. Perennial, with stout rootstocks about 15 cm. long, the terminal bud very large, and numerous crown-buds, the roots fine-fibrous: stems 0.5–1 m. high, more or less tufted, scabrous-hirsute, usually simple, if branched, the branches closely ascending, even parallel to the main stem, the pubescence of two kinds, long, scabrous, spreading hairs, and short, closely appressed hairs: leaves opposite, or in very vigorous plants the upper sometimes alternate: blades ovate, sessile, often clasping, 7–9 cm. long, densely pubescent on both sides: inflorescence a single terminal head, or else racemose in the upper axils, in the latter case, the peduncles short: heads very showy: bracts of the involucre broadly linear-lanceolate, about as long as the disk, densely pubescent: ray-flowers numerous, with ligules 2–3 cm. long: disk 2–3 cm. wide, its corollas yellow.—Prairies, barrens, woods, and fields, various provinces, Ga. to Tex., Kans., Ia., and Mass.—Frequently cultivated.

34. H. divaricatus L. Perennial, with numerous rootstocks 1–7 dm. long and few roots: stem simple to the inflorescence, or very vigorous plants often branched, subglabrous, usually purple if exposed to the sun, enlarged and woody at the base: leaves opposite; blades lanceolate, usually broadly so, rarely very narrow or very broad, round at the base, subsessile, rough above, sparingly pubescent beneath, with remote, long, ascending hairs, divaricate: inflorescence a single, terminal head or else a cyme: heads not very showy; bracts of the involucre lanceolate, a little longer than the disk, subglabrous, erect with very loose tips: ray-flowers with narrow ligules about 2.0 cm. long: disk about 1 cm. in width, its corolla yellow.—Dry woods and old fields, various provinces, Fla. to La., Man., Ont., and Me.

35. H. saxicola Small. Perennial: stem slender, 0.8–1.5 m. high, glabrous, glaucous, reddish, simple; leaf arrangement unstable, alternate or opposite; blades ovate, acuminate, serrulate, rounded at the base to a short distinct petiole 2–3 cm. long, dark-green and rough above, paler and glabrous beneath, the main veins sometimes slightly short-hispid: inflorescence solitary or few-flowered: heads showy; bracts of the involucre broadly lanceolate, a little longer than the disk, glabrous or subglabrous, somewhat reflexed: ray-flowers with ligules 2–2.5 cm. long: disk about 1.5 cm. wide, its corollas yellow.—Rocky and sandy soil, Blue Ridge, Ga. to N. C.

36. H. tuberosus L. Tall, perennial, with tuber-bearing rootstocks: stem simple or branched, robust, hispid, rough, often 2–3 cm. thick at the base, light-green: leaves alternate above the middle of the stem, in plants often all opposite: blades ovate, thinnish, short-hispid above, short-hirsute beneath, soft to the touch, abruptly contracted below to a margined petiole, 10–20.0 cm. long inflorescence paniculate: heads very showy: bracts of the involucre lanceolate or linear-lanceolate, sparingly pubescent, often glabrous, erect, the tips recurving slightly, very dark green: ray-flowers with ligules 2.5–4 cm. long: disk relatively small, rarely more than 1 cm. wide, the disk-corollas yellow.—(ARTI-CHOKE. JERUSALEM-ARTICHOKE.)—Moist or dry rich soil, various provinces, Fla. to Tex., Sask., Ont., and N. S.—The plant is commonly cultivated for its edible tubers, which accounts for its wide distribution, as it is native only in the western part of its range.

37. H. strumosus L. Perennial, with an often very long branched root-stock, the roots coarse: stem tall, erect, glabrous or subglabrous, sometimes a little pubescent toward the apex, mostly simple, sometimes, when very vigorous, a little branched: leaves mostly opposite: blades broadly lanceolate, rarely ovate, acuminate at the apex, serrate or serrulate, rounded at the base, the petiole partly distinct, 10–15 cm. long, strumose-setose above, the strumae becoming conspicuously white in dry specimens, much paler beneath, and (in the southern states) pubescent beneath only on the main veins: inflorescence cymose, the main branches opposite, usually all opposite: ray-flowers with ligules 2–3 cm. long: disk 1–2 cm. wide, its corollas yellow: bracts of the involucre broadly lanceolate; bracts usually glabrous, never more than very sparingly pubescent, ciliate, loose but erect.—Dry woods, hillsides, and fields, various provinces, Ga. to Ark., Minn., and Me.

38. H. reindutus (Steele) E. E. Watson. Perennial with rootstocks 7–8 cm. long, the crown buds numerous: stem reddish, especially above, glabrous, rarely a little rough, 1–2 m. high: leaves opposite or sometimes alternate above; blades lanceolate, serrulate, narrowly sessile, firm, glabrous or remotely setose above, very remotely scabrous beneath, the scabra usually large and blunt, the margins usually appressed hispid-ciliate below: inflorescence a profusely branched, open panicle, the branches very slender: heads showy: bracts of the involucre lanceolate, longer than the disk, loose, often reflexed, scarcely ciliate:

disk 1–1.5 cm. wide, its florets yellow.—Woods and shale-barrens, Blue Ridge and Appalachians, N. C. and Va.—Similar to *H. laevigatus*, but differs by its profuse inflorescence, and its pubescent leaves.

39. H. hirsutus Raf. Perennial, with stout abundant profusely branched rootstocks 1–3 dm. long: stem stout, 0.5–1.7 m. high, hispid, often branched, the pubescence spreading or retrorse: leaves opposite; blades ovate to ovate-lanceolate, thick, rounded or obtuse at the base, on short, stout petioles 1–2 cm. long, densely scabrous above, hispid-hirsute, often densely beneath: inflorescence cymose, its branches rarely more than 10–15 cm. long: bracts of the involucre lanceolate attenuate, very loose, longer than the disk, recurved, densely hispidulous: ray-flowers with oval ligules 2 cm. long: disk 1–2 cm. wide, its corollas yellow.—Open, often rocky woods, river-banks, prairies, and old fields, various provinces, Ga. to Tex., Kans., Wisc., and Pa.

40. H. doronicoides Lam. Perennial, with short stout rootstocks with woody roots: stem stout, 1–2 m. high, usually densely, softly pubescent: leaves opposite below the middle of stem, alternate above, or all opposite in weak plants; blades broadly oval-lanceolate, serrate, obtuse, narrowly sessile, densely tomentose both sides, but more so beneath: inflorescence a lax, open panicle, the peduncle 1–4-flowered: bracts of the involucre linear-lanceolate, loose, reflexed, longer than the disk, densely pubescent: ray-flowers with oval ligules, 2–3 cm. long, light-yellow: disk about 1.7 cm. wide, its corollas yellow, the lobes puberulent.—River bottoms, prairies, and woods, various provinces, Ala. to Ark. (?), Mo., and Ohio.

41. H. resinosus Small. Perennial: stem 1–2 m. high, slender retrorsely hispid: leaves opposite below but alternate above, or in small plants all opposite; blades ovate or oblong-ovate, narrowly sessile, hispid with rather long hairs above, tomentulose, but not densely so, and copiously resin-dotted beneath. thin in texture: heads few on long peduncles, either cymose or paniculate: bracts of the involucre linear-lanceolate, longer than the disk, reflexed, pubescent, resin-dotted: ray-flowers with ligules 2–2.5 cm. long: disk 1–1.6 cm. wide, its corollas yellow, both rays and disk florets copiously resin-dotted.—Woods, N Fla.—Very similar to *H. tomentosus* but more delicate.

42. H. validus E. E. Watson. Perennial: stem slender, 1–2 m. high, branched toward the apex, rough with very fine scabra: leaves alternate; blades broadly lanceolate-elliptic, obscurely serrulate, acute at both ends, 10–12 cm. long, scabrous-setose above, sparingly hispid and resin-dotted beneath: inflorescence of 3–4 rather large heads which are solitary on leafy peduncles on the stem and branches: bracts of the involucre linear-lanceolate, sparingly short-pubescent or puberulent, scarcely ciliate, longer than the disk, loose but erect: ray-flowers with ligules 1.5 cm. long: disk 1.5–2 cm. wide, its corollas yellow.—Blue Ridge, N. C.

43. H. laetiflorus Pers. Perennial, with numerous profusely branched rootstocks: stem erect, rough but shining, 1–2 m. high, simple to the inflorescence: leaves opposite, or alternate on the upper part of stem in vigorous plants: blades broadly lanceolate, narrowly decurrent to the base of the petiole, usually thick, firm, shining, very rough, very variable in size: heads on very long, stout, ascending, not very leafy branches, very handsome: bracts of the involucre linear-lanceolate, subglabrous, usually with 2–3 dark brown lines: ray-flowers with ligules 2–3 cm. long, deep-yellow: disk 1.5–2.5 cm. wide, its corollas yellow.—Creek-bottoms, woods, and banks, various provinces, Ga. to Mo., and Ill.

80. PHOEBANTHUS Blake. Perennial, *Helianthus*-like herbs, the stems arising from horizontal tubers. Leaves alternate or opposite: blades typically narrow. Heads erect or nearly so, radiate. Involucre hemispheric or depressed: bracts narrow or broad, ultimately lax. Ray-flowers several: corolla with a very short tube and a long yellow ligule. Disk-corollas with a cylindric-funnelform throat abruptly narrowed into the short tube. Filaments slightly shorter than the anthers. Stigmas linear-lanceolate. Pappus sometimes of several scales between chaffy awns or teeth.—Two species, as follows:

Leaf-blades linear or linear-lanceolate: involucral bracts appressed: ray-flowers 16–20.   1. *H. grandiflora.*
Leaf-blades linear-filiform: involucral bracts spreading: ray-flowers 10–15.   2. *H. tenuifolia.*

1. P. grandiflora (T. & G.) Blake. Stem 6–13 dm. tall, simple or sparingly branched above: leaves mostly alternate; blades linear to linear-lanceolate, 2–6 cm. long, acute, entire, somewhat revolute: heads showy: involucral bracts linear-subulate to lanceolate or cuneate, or oblong with lanceolate or ovate tips, hispidulous, the tips rather lax: ray-flowers 16–20; ligules yellow, 3–4.5 cm. long: disk 1.5–2 cm. broad: achene 5–6 mm. long, narrowly margined or wing-margined, strongly ribbed, pubescent about the upper edge, each side surmounted by a tooth, and one or both sometimes prolonged into an awn. [*Helianthella grandiflora* T. & G.]—Pinelands, oak-woods, and stream-banks, pen. Fla.—Spr.–fall.

2. P. tenuifolia (T. & G.) Blake. Stem 3–11 dm. tall, simple or sparingly branched above: leaves alternate or opposite or whorled on the lower part of the stem; blades linear-filiform, 3–8 cm. long, acute, entire, revolute, very scabrous: heads showy: involucral bracts linear-subulate to linear-lanceolate, attenuate, spreading: disk 1–2 cm. wide: achene unequally 4-angled, 3–4 mm. long, often minutely pubescent, the margins prolonged into triangular scales. [*Helianthella tenuifolia* T. & G.]—Sandhills and pinelands, N Fla.—Spr.–Fall.

81. XIMENESIA Cav. Annual, caulescent herbs. Leaves alternate or sometimes opposite: blades toothed or somewhat laciniate. Heads peduncled, often showy. Involucre flat, or flattish. Bracts rather narrow and elongate. Ray-flowers numerous: corollas with a slender tube and yellow ligules. Disk-corollas with a narrowly funnelform throat and a short tube: lobes triangular or lanceolate-triangular. Filaments nearly as long as the anthers. Pappus of short awns.—About 4 species, American.

1. X. encelioides Cav. Plant 3–7 dm. tall, pale-pubescent: leaf-blades deltoid or lanceolate, 5–10 cm. long, serrate or incised, the broader petiole-bases appendaged at the base: larger bracts of the involucre linear to linear-lanceolate, 15–20 mm. long: ligules cuneate, 1–2 cm. long: achene 6–7 mm. long, broadly winged.—(SKUNK-DAISY.)—Hammocks and waste-places, Key West, Fla., and several points in Ala. Nat. from Tex. to Ariz., and Colo.

82. PHAETHUSA Gaertn. Perennial herbs or shrubby plants. Leaves alternate or opposite: blades entire or toothed, more or less decurrent. Heads numerous and clustered. Involucre narrow or broad: bracts not slender-tipped. Ray-flowers 4 or 5, pistillate and fertile, with an often short or obsolete corolla-tube, the ligules white or yellow, or wanting. Disk-corollas with a campanulate throat, contracted into a shorter tube: lobes lanceolate to triangular-lanceolate. Filaments slightly shorter than the anthers. Pappus of 1–3 awns.—About 35 species, American.—CROWNBEARDS.—The stem is ridged or winged.

Leaves alternate: ray-flowers with white ligules.
    Leaf-blades undulate, sinuate, or serrate.   1. *P. virginica.*
    Leaf-blades pinnatifid or pinnately lobed.   2. *P. laciniata.*
Leaves opposite: ray-flowers with yellow ligules.   3. *P. occidentalis.*

1. P. virginica (L.) Small. Stem 6–18 dm. tall, tomentulose or puberulent: leaf-blades membranous, lanceolate to oval or ovate, 5–21 cm. long: larger bracts of the involucre about 7 mm. long: disk-corollas about 5 mm. long: achene winged, 5 mm. long. [*Verbesina virginica* L.]—(FROST-WEED. TICKWEED. INDIAN-TOBACCO.)—Dry soil, various provinces, Fla. to Tex., Mo., and Pa.

2. P. laciniata (Poir.) Small. Stem 7–16 dm. tall, tomentulose: leaf-blades ovate to elliptic-ovate in outline, 5–22 cm. long, the segments sometimes repand: larger bracts of the involucre about 6 mm. long: disk-corollas about 5 mm. long: achene obovate, 5–6 mm. long: achene with wings as broad as the body, 5–7 mm. long. [*Verbesina laciniata* (Poir.) Nutt.] — Pineland and sandy hammocks, Coastal Plain, Fla. to S. C.

3. P. occidentalis (L.) Small. Stem 9–20 dm. tall, smooth and glabrous: leaf-blades ovate to elliptic-lanceolate, 5–20 cm. long: larger bracts of the involucre about 6 mm. long, broadly linear: ligules 10–15 mm. long: achene with very long pappus bristles and wingless or nearly so, 5–6 mm. long. [*Verbesina occidentalis* (L.) Walt.]—Rich soil, various provinces, Fla. to Miss., Ill., and Pa.

83. PTEROPHYTON Cass.[1] Perennial caulescent herbs. Leaves alternate or opposite: blades entire or toothed, decurrent or sessile. Heads solitary or few together, long-peduncled. Involucre broad: bracts shorter than the disk. Ray-flowers when present 5–10 pistillate or neutral, but always sterile, the ligules yellow or whitish. Disk corollas with a campanulate throat, contracted into a shorter tube: lobes triangular-lanceolate to lanceolate. Filaments shorter than the anthers. Pappus of 1–3 very short, slender awns or wanting.—About 15 species, American.

Stem winged: leaves decurrent.   I. HETEROPHYLLA.
Stem wingless: leaves merely sessile.   II. NUDICAULIA.

I. HETEROPHYLLA

Leaf-blades hirsute beneath, very acute: stem leafy to the inflorescence.   1. *P. helianthoides.*

[1] Contributed by Edward Johnston Alexander.

Leaf-blades hispidulous beneath, somewhat blunt: stem sparingly scaly above the middle.　　　　　　　　　　　　　　　2. *P. heterophyllum.*

II. NUDICAULIA

Foliage scabrous: leaf-blades elliptic or broadest slightly above the middle: heads rayless.　　　　　　　　　　　　　3. *P. pauciflorum.*
Foliage hirsute or hispid: leaf-blades broadest at or below the middle: heads with rays.　　　　　　　　　　　　　　　4. *P. aristatum.*

1. P. helianthoides (Michx.) Alexander. Stem 5–11 dm. tall, finely pubescent: leaves mostly alternate; blades lanceolate to elliptic, 4–12 cm. long: larger bracts of the involucre about 8 mm. long, linear: ligules 20–30 mm. long: achene with short, slender pappus-bristles, usually narrowly winged, 5 mm. long. [*Verbesina helianthoides* Michx.]—Open woods and thickets, various provinces, Ga. to Tex., Ia., and Ohio.

2. P. heterophyllum (Chapm.) Alexander. Stem 5–12 dm. tall, scabro-hispidulous: leaves mostly opposite; blades elliptic, or elliptic-lanceolate, 2–6 cm. long, serrate-dentate: larger bracts of the involucre about 7 mm. long, elliptic-lanceolate: ligules 15–20 mm. long: achene with short pappus-bristles, broadly winged, 5–6 mm. long. [*Verbesina heterophylla* (Chapm.) A. Gray.]—Dry pinelands, Fla.

3. P. pauciflorum (Nutt.) Alexander. Stem 3–7 dm. tall, scabrous: leaves scattered; blades elliptic or slightly broadest above the middle, 3–9 cm. long, lucid: involucre about 1 cm. high: ray-flowers wanting: achene with no pappus, narrowly winged, 5–6 mm. long. [*Actinomeris pauciflora* Nutt. *Verbesina Warei* A. Gray.]—Low pinelands, W Fla.

4. P. aristatum (Ell.) Alexander. Stem 5–12 dm. tall, hirsute to hispid: leaves remote; blades elliptic to elliptic-ovate or elliptic-lanceolate, 3–10 cm. long, scabrous: involucre 5–6 mm. high: ray-flowers 7–12: achene with short pappus-bristles, very broadly winged, 4–5 mm. long. [*Verbesina nudicaulis* (Nutt.) A. Gray. *V. aristata* (Ell.) Heller.]—Pinelands, Coastal Plain and adj. provinces, Fla. to Ala., and Ga.

84. RIDAN Adans. Perennial, rather coarse, tall herbs. Leaves alternate or opposite: blades usually toothed and decurrent. Heads several or numerous. Involucre narrow: bracts few, spreading or recurving, becoming lax. Ray-flowers few: ligules yellow or wanting. Disk-corollas many, with a funnelform throat rather abruptly contracted into the shorter tube: lobes lanceolate. Filaments slightly shorter than the anthers. Pappus of 2 more or less spreading awns, accompanied by 2 or 3 smaller awns, or scales. [*Actinomeris* Nutt.]—Sum.-fall.—Two species, as follows:

Ray-flowers 2–8: disk-corollas yellow.　　　　　　　　　　　1. *R. alternifolia.*
Ray-flowers wanting: disk-corollas white.　　　　　　　　　2. *R. paniculata.*

1. R. alternifolia (L.) Britton. Plant 6–25 dm. tall: leaf-blades elliptic, 9–30 cm. long: disk-corollas 5 mm. long: achene-body with ciliate wings.

[*Actinomeris alternifolia* (L.) DC.]—Rich woods, moist thickets, and roadsides, various provinces, Fla. to La., Ia., and N. J.

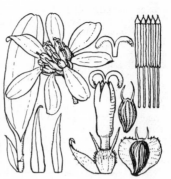

2. **R. paniculata** (Walt.) Small. Plant 6–24 dm. tall: leaf-blades linear to elliptic or narrowly elliptic, 8–31 cm. long: disk-corollas 4 mm. long: achene-body with toothed wings. [*Athanasia paniculata* Walt.]—Alluvial soil, Coastal Plain, Fla. to La. and S. C.—The typical habitat of these species is the alluvial flood-plains of creeks and river. There the plants grow very tall and in dense colonies.

85. **SYNEDRELLA** Gaertn. Annual, pubescent, erect herbs. Leaves opposite: blades usually toothed. Heads inconspicuous. Involucre simple, narrow, several-flowered, with 1 or 2 herbaceous and several chaffy bracts. Ray-flowers few: corolla with a very slender tube and a yellow ligule. Disk-corollas with a cylindraceous throat and a slender tube nearly or quite as long: lobes broad. Filaments much shorter than the linear anthers. Pappus of 2 or 3 awns becoming longer than the corolla in the disk.—Two species, tropical American.

1. **S. nodiflora** (L.) Gaertn. Plant 3–8 dm. tall: leaf-blades ovate to elliptic, 5–10 cm. long, serrate, the petiole-like bases hispid-ciliate: involucre 7–9 mm. high; larger bracts narrow: disk-corollas about 4 mm. long: achene 4–5 mm. long, those of the ray elliptic, with ascending marginal bristles, those of the disk columnar or clavate.—Sandy soil and wet places, Fla. Nat. of trop. Am.—(*W. I., Mex., C. A., S. A., O. W.*)—All year.

85a. **CALYPTOCARPUS** Less. Annual, pubescent, erect, herbs. Leaves opposite: blades toothed. Heads inconspicuous radiate. Involucre several-flowered: bracts various, with 3 herbaceous and several chaffy. Ray-flowers few: corolla with a tube shorter than the yellow ligule. Disk-corollas with a funnelform throat and tube: lobes narrow. Anthers somewhat longer than the filaments. Pappus of 2 or 3 awns with a rim at the base.—The following species:

Involucral bracts not ciliate: leaf-blades abruptly tapering at
  the cuneate or subcordate base, broadest below the middle.   1. *C. vialis.*
Involucral bracts long-ciliate: leaf-blades long-tapering to a
  cuneate base, broadest above the middle.   2. *C. blepharolepis.*

1. **C. vialis** Less. Stem 1–4 dm. long, branched at the base, the branches erect or prostrate: leaf-blades ovate, 1–3 cm. long, serrate, the petiole-like bases

shorter than the blade, hispid: involucre 5–7
mm. high; larger bracts broad: disk-corollas
about 4 mm. long: achene 4–5 mm. long,
those of the ´ray and disk alike wingless,
minutely muricate.—Dry soil and waste-
places, S La. to S Tex. (*W. I., Mex., C. A.*)
—All year.

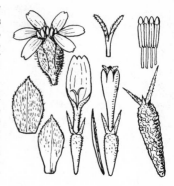

2. C. blepharolepis B. L. Robinson. Stem
branched at the base, branches opposite,
spreading: leaf-blades 2–3 cm. long, obovate,
entire or nearly so: involucre about 5 mm.
high: ligules of the ray corollas very short:
achenes of the ray apparently glabrous and
smooth, those of the disk muricate.—Ten-
saw, Ala. — Sum.–fall. — Apparently introduced, but nativity unknown.

86. COREOPSIS L.[1] Annual, or perennial herbs. Leaves various.
Heads conspicuously radiate. Involucre campanulate to hemispheric: bracts
distinct or nearly so, the outer narrow. Ray-flowers several: corollas with
yellow, discolored, or pink ligules. Disk-corollas with a funnelform throat
and a stout or slender tube. Filaments mostly shorter than the anthers. Achene
with entire or pinnate wings, or wingless.—About 5 species, American, African,
and Australian.—Dye-flowers. Tickweeds.

Stigmas with acute or cuspidate tips.
 Leaf-blades or their divisions with entire margins.
  Stigma-tips cuspidate: chaff of the receptacle with broad bases and attenuate
   filiform tips: leaf-blades simple or pinnately lobed.
   —Subgenus Eucoreopsis.   I. Lanceolatae.
  Stigma-tips acutely conic: chaff of the receptacle
   linear or with slightly dilated tips: leaf-blades
   palmately lobed.—Subgenus Anacis.   II. Palmatae.
 Leaf-blades evenly toothed.—Subgenus Silphidium.   III. Latifoliae.
Stigmas with truncate or obtusely conic tips.—Subgenus
  Calliopsis.
 Achene wingless.   IV. Tinctoriae.
 Achene winged.
  Leaves with flat blades or divisions, not rush-like.   V. Angustifoliae.
  Leaves thick, rush-like.   VI. Nudatae.

I. Lanceolatae

Achene with broad outspread wings (entire or fimbriate).
 Stem leafy near the base, bearing long, naked, peduncle-
  like branches.
  Ligules uniformly yellow.
   Plant glabrous except the ciliate bases of the
    leaves.   1. *C. lanceolata.*
   Plant pubescent except near the inflorescence.   2. *C. crassifolia.*
  Ligules with dark markings near the base.   3. *C. nuecensis.*
 Stem leafy to near the summit: peduncle short.
  Leaf-blades of the main stem broad, simple or with 1–5
   small lateral lobes.   4. *C. pubescens.*
  Leaf-blades of the main stem pinnately parted into
   narrow divisions.
   Achenes with entire wings: petioles ciliate near
    the base.   5. *C. grandiflora.*
   Achenes with fimbriate wings: petioles and entire
    plant glabrous.   6. *C. saxicola.*
Achene with strongly incurved entire wings, which become
 callous-thickened at maturity.   7. *C. auriculata.*

II. Palmatae

Leaves with petioled blades.
Leaves with sessile blades.   8. *C. tripteris.*

[1] Contributed by Frank Ellis Boynton.

Disk-flowers with yellow corollas.
  Leaf-segments entire, elliptic-lanceolate or lanceolate.   9. *C. major.*
  Leaf-segments 1-2-pinnately parted, very narrowly
    linear or filiform.   )   10. *C. verticillata.*
Disk-flowers with purple-brown corollas.
  Divisions of the leaf-blades comparatively few, 2-4
    mm. broad : internodes longer than the leaves.   11. *C. delphinifolia.*
  Divisions of the leaf-blades very numerous, appearing
    in dense fascicles, 1-2 mm. broad: internodes
    mostly shorter than the leaves.   12. *C. pulchra.*

III. LATIFOLIAE

Plant with ovate or ovate-lanceolate leaf-blades.   13. *C. latifolia.*

IV. TINCTORIAE

Ligules of the ray yellow with crimson-brown base: flowers
  of the disk with dark-red corollas.
  Outer involucral bracts much shorter than the inner:
    achene linear-elliptic, thin, flat.   14. *C. tinctoria.*
  Outer involucral bracts mostly about as long as the
    inner: achene obovate, thick, convex.   15. *C. Drummondii.*
Ligules of the ray pink: flowers of the disk with yellow
  corollas.   16. *C. rosea.*

V. ANGUSTIFOLIAE

Achenes with entire scarious margins.
  Pappus of minute teeth or wanting.
    Ligules of the ray discolored.   17. *C. cardaminefolia.*
    Ligules of the ray uniformly yellow.   18. *C. stenophylla.*
  Pappus of conspicuous awns.
    Leaf-blades, or some of them, lobed: internodes
      mostly shorter than the leaves.   19. *C. Leavenworthii.*
    Leaf-blades simple and entire: internodes mostly
      much longer than the leaves.   20. *C. Lewtonii.*
Achenes with fimbriate or dissected winged margins.
  Blades of the larger leaves of an elliptic, lanceolate, or
    narrower type.
    Lower leaves little longer than the internodes.   21. *C. angustifolia.*
    Lower leaves much longer than the internodes.
      Blades of the basal leaves linear. lanceolate, or
        linear-elliptic, mostly pointed.
        Leaf-blades simple and entire: achene obovate
          or spatulate, about 4 mm. long, the wing
          about one-third as wide as the body.   22. *C. longifolia.*
        Leaf-blades often lobed: achenes elliptic, about
          5 mm. long, the wing as wide as the body.   23. *C. falcata.*
      Blades of the basal leaves elliptic or oblanceolate,
        obtuse.   24. *C. gladiata.*
  Blades of the larger leaves of an ovate or ovate-lanceolate
    type.
    Leaves opposite; petioles and blades (when young)
      ciliate-margined.   25. *C. integrifolia.*
    Leaves alternate; margins naked.   26. *C. helianthoides.*

VI. NUDATAE

Plant with long-tapering leaves and pink-purple ligules.   27. *C. nudata.*

1. C. lanceolata L. Plant 2-6 dm. tall: blades of the lower leaves spatulate
to linear-oblanceolate, and rarely with 1 or 2 lateral lobes (in *C. lanceolata*
glabella the leaves with narrow blades or
crowded at the base of the stem): outer involucral bracts lanceolate: achene orbicular,
2.5-3 mm. long.—Dry soil, pinelands, barrens, woods, and stony fields, various provinces, Fla. to La. and Ont.—Spr.-sum.

2. C. crassifolia Ait. Plant 2-4 dm. tall:
blades of the lower leaves obovate-spatulate
to elliptic, entire, usually pubescent at
least beneath: outer involucral bracts lance-
ovate: achene elliptic-orbicular, 2.5-3 mm.
long.—Dry soil, woods, and old fields, Coastal
Plain and adj. provinces, Ga. to La., Ill.,
and N. C.—Spr.-sum.

3. C. nuecensis Heller. Plant up to 1 m. tall, usually glabrous: blades of the lower leaves ovate to elliptic in outline, usually pinnately lobed, the lobes elliptic: outer involucral bracts lanceolate: ligules cuneate, with several dark markings near the base of each, together appearing as a corona: achene suborbicular, about 5 mm. long, the body with a reniform callosity at either end within, the wings nearly as broad as the body.—Moist soil, Coastal Plain, S Tex., also escaped from cultivation eastward.

4. C. pubescens Ell. Plant 6–12 dm. tall, pubescent: leaf-blades ovate to elliptic-lancolate, the lobes small when present: outer involucral bracts linear-lanceolate: achene orbicular, about 3 mm. long.—Dry woodlands, thickets, and old fields, various provinces, Fla. to Miss., Ill., and Va.—Sum.–fall.

5. C. grandiflora Hogg. Plant 3–6 dm. tall, glabrous except the leaf-bases: blades of the lower leaves spatulate or lanceolate, sometimes lobed: outer bracts of the involucre lanceolate, 6–9 mm. long: achene orbicular, 2.5 mm. long.—Dry soil, woods and fields, various provinces, rarely Coastal Plain, Ga. to Tex., N. Mex., and Md.—Spr.–sum.

6. C. saxicola Alexander. Plant up to 1 m. tall, glabrous throughout: leaf-blades pinnately dissected into linear-elliptic segments: outer bracts of the involucre ovate-lanceolate to lanceolate 7–10 mm. long: achene suborbicular, 2–3 mm. long, with stalked glands on the inner face, the wings more or less fimbriately dissected.—Dry soil, on and about Stone Mtn. in the Piedmont of Ga., also Tallapoosa Co., in the Piedmont of Ala.—Sum.

7. C. auriculata L. Plant 2–5 dm. tall, more or less pubescent: leaf-blades round-oval to elliptic-ovate, sometimes with 1 or 2 small basal lobes: outer involucral bracts linear-elliptic, 7–9 mm. long: achene oval, 2–2.5 mm. long.—Dry soil, woods, thickets, and waste-places, various provinces, Fla. to Miss., Tenn., W. Va., and Va.—Spr.–sum.

8. C. tripteris L. Plant 8–30 dm. tall, glabrous or nearly so: leaf-blades deeply 3–5-divided, the divisions elliptic-lanceolate or lanceolate, or those of the upper leaves entire: outer involucral bracts linear, 2–3 mm. long: ligules elliptic, yellow: achene elliptic, 5–6 mm. long.—Woods, river-shores, and old fields, various provinces, Fla. to La., Tenn., and Pa.—Sum.–fall.

9. C. major Walt. Plant 5–9 dm. tall, pubescent (or glabrous in *C. major Oemleri*); leaf-blades with elliptic-lanceolate or lanceolate lobes (or lobes very long and narrow in *C. major rigida*): outer involucral bracts linear-elliptic, 5–6 mm. long: achene elliptic, 5–6 mm. long. [*C. senifolia* Michx.]—Dry woods, various provinces, Fla. to Miss., Tenn., W. Va., and Va.—Sum.–fall.

10. C. verticillata L. Plant 5–9 dm. tall, glabrous: leaf-blades with the divisions once or twice pinnately parted into linear-filiform lobes: outer involucral bracts linear, 5–6 mm. long: achene elliptic-obovate, 4–5 mm. long.—Dry acid soil, rocky places, woods, and pinelands, various provinces, rarely Coastal Plain, Ala. to Kans., Nebr., Ont., N. J., and N. C.—Sum.–fall.

11. C. delphinifolia Lam. Plant 8–15 dm. tall, glabrous: leaf-blades with the middle division parted into 3–5 linear lobes: outer involucral bracts linear, 5–6 mm. long: achene elliptic, 5–6 mm. long.—Dry woods, pinelands, and low grounds, various provinces, Ga. to Ala. and Va.—Sum.

12. C. pulchra F. E. Boynton. Plant 4–7 dm. tall, glabrous: leaf-blades with the primary divisions parted into linear lobes: outer involucral bracts linear,

5-6 mm. long: achene narrowly winged, elliptic-obovate, about 4 mm. long.—Rocky woodlands, N Ala.—Sum.

13. C. latifolia Michx. Plant 9-15 dm. tall, pubescent or glabrate: leaf-blades ovate to ovate-lanceolate, coarsely toothed: outer involucral bracts narrowly linear, about 5 mm. long: achene wingless, narrowly elliptic, about 7 mm. long.—Wooded slopes, Blue Ridge, N. C. and Tenn.—Sum.

14. C. tinctoria L. Plant 6-12 dm. tall, glabrous: blades of the lower leaves twice pinnately parted, the lobes linear-lanceolate or linear: outer involucral bracts triangular-lanceolate, about 2 mm. long: achene linear-elliptic about 2 mm. long.—Moist soil, prairies, and fields, various provinces, La. to Ariz., Sask., and Minn.; also cult. and naturalized eastward.—Sum.-fall.

15. C. Drummondii (D. Don) T. & G. Plant 2-4 dm. tall, pubescent or nearly glabrous: blades of the lower leaves ovate, oval, or lanceolate, frequently entire, or like the upper ones with elliptic or linear-lanceolate lobes (or with very narrow lobes in *C. Drummondii Wrightii*): outer involucral bracts linear-lanceolate, 5-9 mm. long: achene obovate, about 2 mm. long.—Dry soil, and sandy prairies, Tex., also escaped from cultivation eastward.—Sum.

16. C. rosea Nutt. Plant 2-5 dm. tall, glabrous: leaf-blades linear and entire, or with 2 or 3 linear lobes: outer bracts of the involucre lanceolate, 2-3 mm. long: achene wingless, narrowly elliptic, about 2 mm. long.—Moist, or wet, acid soil, Coastal Plain, and occasionally other provinces, Ga. to Mass. and E Tenn.—Sum.

17. C. cardaminefolia (DC.) T. & G. Plant 2-5 dm. tall, glabrous: blades of the lower leaves once or twice pinnately divided into elliptic or linear-lanceolate lobes; blades of the upper leaves few-lobed or entire and linear: outer involucral bracts lanceolate, 3-4 mm. long: achene elliptic, 2.5-3 mm. long.—Low grounds, various provinces, Miss. to Tex., Ariz., and Kans.—Sum.

18. C. stenophylla F. E. Boynton. Plant 4-8 dm. tall, glabrous: blades of the lower leaves entire and sometimes 2 mm. wide, or with 1 or 2 narrow lobes, those of the upper leaves narrowly linear to filiform, and sometimes with filiform lobes: outer involucral bracts lanceolate, 1-2 mm. long: achene elliptic, 1.5-2 mm. long, the wing ⅓ as wide as the body.—Pinelands, La.—Sum.-fall.

19. C. Leavenworthii T. & G. Plant 5-15 dm. tall, glabrous: blades of the lower leaves mostly with 2 or more narrow lobes, usually very narrow, (or broad in *C. Leavenworthii Garberi*), those of the upper leaves mostly entire and narrow: outer involucral bracts subulate-lanceolate, 1-2 mm. long: achene roundish oval, 2.5-3 mm. long, the wing as broad as the body.—Pinelands and moist prairies, pen Fla. and the Keys.—All year.—A hot infusion of this plant is used externally by the Seminoles in cases of heat prostration.

20. C. Lewtonii Small. Plant 3-5 dm. tall: blades of the lower leaves linear or narrowly cuneate, entire: outer involucral bracts suborbicular, about 2 mm. long: achene not seen.—Low grounds, pen. Fla.—Sum.

21. C. angustifolia Ait. Plant 5-7 dm. tall: blades of the lower leaves spatulate or oblanceolate, entire: outer involucral bracts ovate, 2-3 mm. long: achene oval, 2.5-3 mm. long.—Low pinelands and swampy places, Coastal Plain, Fla. to Tex. and N. C.—Sum.-fall.

22. C. longifolia Small. Plant 7–10 dm. tall: blades of the lower leaves linear-elliptic, linear-lanceolate, or linear, entire: outer involucral bracts lanceolate, 2–4 mm. long: achene obovate or spatulate in outline, about 4 mm. long.—Low woods and thickets, Coastal Plain, Fla. and Ga.—Fall.

23. C. falcata F. E. Boynton. Plant 8–12 dm. tall: blades of the lower leaves scythe-shaped, entire or with 1 or 2 narrow lobes: outer involucral bracts lanceolate, 5–7 mm. long: achene elliptic, about 5 mm. long.—Swamps and pineland ponds, Coastal Plain, N. C.—Early sum.

24. C. gladiata Walt. Plant 6–12 dm. tall: blades of the lower leaves elliptic or oblanceolate, entire: outer involucral bracts broadly triangular, 3–4 mm. long: achene elliptic, about 3.5 mm. long.—Swamps and low pinelands, Coastal Plain, Fla. to Miss. and N. C.—Fall.

25. C. integrifolia Poir. Plant 6–9 dm. tall: blades of the lower leaves ovate, entire: outer involucral bracts elliptic, 4–6 mm. long: achene not seen.—Moist soil, Coastal Plain, Fla. and Ga.—Fall.

26. C. helianthoides Beadle. Plant 5–12 dm. tall: blades of the lower leaves ovate to ovate-lanceolate, entire: outer involucral bracts lanceolate, 5–9 mm. long: achene spatulate, about 3 mm. long.—Low grounds, bogs, and woods, Coastal Plain, N Fla. and Ga.—Fall.

27. C. nudata Nutt. Plant 6–12 dm. tall: leaves terete: outer involucral bracts lanceolate, 4–6 mm. long: rays pink-purple: achene elliptic, about 3 mm. long.—Wet pinelands and cypress ponds, Coastal Plain, Fla. and Ga.—Spr.–sum.

87. BIDENS L.[1] Annual or biennial, or rarely perennial, herbs. Leaves opposite or the upper ones sometimes alternate: blades entire, toothed, or divided. Heads erect or nodding. Involucre double, the outer bracts foliaceous, the inner appressed. Ray-flowers few and with white or yellow ligules, or wanting. Disk-corollas with a short tube and a longer throat: lobes mostly deltoid. Achene flat, terete, or 4-angled. Pappus of 2–4 rigid barbed awns or these much reduced and tooth-like.—About 75 species, of wide geographic distribution.—BUR-MARIGOLDS. BEGGAR-TICKS.

Achene spindle-shaped, gradually tapering above: ligules of the ray white or yellowish white.   I. LEUCANTHAE.
Achene flattened, broadest above the middle: ligules of the ray, when present, yellow.
  Ray-flowers inconspicuous and caducous or wanting.   II. VULGATAE.
  Ray-flowers showy or conspicuous.
    Leaf-blades undivided: pappus-awns 2–4, retrorsely barbed.   III. CERNUAE.
    Leaf-blades pinnately divided or individually simple: pappus-awns 2 or none.   IV. AUREAE.

I. LEUCANTHAE

Leaves 1–3-pinnately dissected, the divisions incised or lobed: ray-flowers with inconspicuous, mostly entire ligules.   1. *B. bipinnata*.
Leaves 1-pinnate or undivided, the segments evenly crenate-serrate: ray-flowers with showy and lobed ligules.   2. *B. pilosa*.

II. VULGATAE

Leaves usually undivided: pappus awns 3 or 4.
  Disk-corollas pale, 4-lobed: achene-margins strongly, retrorsely barbed throughout; involucre long.   3. *B. comosa*.

[1] Contributed by Karl McKay Wiegand.

Disk-corollas orange, 5-lobed: barbs of the achene-margins
few, directed both ways: involucre short.   4. *B. connata.*
Leaves 3–5-divided: pappus-awns 2.
  Awns long, usually retrorsely barbed: achene-body 5–11 mm.
    long.
    Outer involucral bracts 10–16, ciliate, the inner con-
    stricted at the tip: disk-corollas pale.   5. *B. vulgata.*
    Outer bracts 6–8, nearly glabrous, the inner not con-
    stricted: disk-corollas orange.   6. *B. frondosa.*
  Awns short, erect-barbed: achene-body 4–5.5 mm. long:
    leaf-blades long-acuminate.   7. *B. discoidea.*

III. Cernuae

Outer involucral bracts exceeding the disk, foliaceous: ray-
flowers with ligules twice the length of disk or less: achene
dilated at the summit.   8. *B. cernua.*
Outer bracts rarely exceeding the disk: ray-flowers with ligules
2–4 times the length of disk: achene not dilated above.
  Blades of the upper cauline leaves elliptic-lanceolate to
  lanceolate, acuminate, mostly sharply serrate.   9. *B. laevis.*
  Blades of the upper cauline leaves spatulate, obovate, oval
  or elliptic, obtuse, abruptly pointed or acutish, nearly entire, shallowly serrate, or crenate-serrate.   10. *B. Nashii.*

IV. Aureae

Achene 6–8 mm. long, ciliate,
In fruit obovate.
  Involucre nearly glabrous: pappus-awns slender or
  wanting.   11. *B. aristosa.*
  Involucre hispid: achene bidentulate.   12. *B. involucrata.*
In fruit narrowly cuneate, 2–2.5 mm. wide, short-awned.   13. *B. coronata.*
Achene 2–4 mm. long, not ciliate, the awns very short.   14. *B. mitis.*

1. B. bipinnata L. Stem 3–17 dm. tall, glabrous or nearly so, 4-angled,
branched and rather slender: primary leaf-segments thin, deltoid, the ultimate
one lanceolate, incised or lobed: outer in-
volucral bracts 7–10, linear, shorter than the
acute inner ones: rays few, the ovaries awnless and glabrous, the ligules yellowish-
white, about equaling the disk, nearly entire: disk-corolla 5-lobed: stamens included:
achenes spindle-shaped, much longer than the
involucre, the outer slightly shorter; awns
3–4, yellow, retrorsely barbed.—(SPANISH-
NEEDLES.)—Rich soil, and a weed in waste-
places, various provinces, Fla. to Ariz.,
Nebr., and R. I.—(*W. I., Mex., C. A.,
S. A.*)—Sum.–fall.

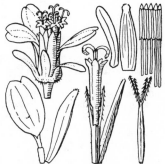

2. B. pilosa L. Stem 4–12 dm. tall,
branched, 4–10 dm. high, nearly or quite
glabrous: leaf-segments ovate or ovate-lanceolate, 2–8 cm. long, evenly crenate-
serrate: outer bracts of the involucre about 8, linear-elliptic, usually shorter
than the inner: rays white, the ligules 1–2 cm. long, broadly cuneate, 2–3-lobed,
the ovaries awnless, few-barbed toward summit: disk-corollas 5-toothed: stamens
barely exserted: achene spindle-shaped, very unequal, the inner much longer
than the involucre; awns 2–4, short, yellow, retrorsely barbed. [*B. leucantha*
L.]—(SHEPHERD'S-NEEDLE.)—Sandy soil, cult. grounds, roadsides, and waste-
places, Coastal Plain, Fla. and sporadically in S Ga. and Ala.—(*W. I., Mex., C.
A., O. W.*)—All year.

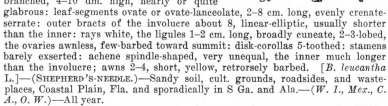

3. B. comosa (A. Gray) Wiegand. Stem 3–8 dm. tall, pale throughout,
stout, glabrous, the branches short, stout: leaves undivided, 8 cm. long: blades
elliptic-lanceolate, regularly serrate, acute, each attenuate into a margined
petiole, or the upper sessile: heads large: peduncles short and stout: outer

bracts of the involucre 6–8, often 2–5 times the length of the disk, erect: rays wanting: disk-corollas funnelform, pale-yellow, 4-lobed: stamens included: achene large, flat, 8–10 mm. long, 3 mm. wide, brown or olive, nearly smooth and glabrous, margined to the base, the 3 long awns retrorsely barbed.—Damp soil, rich banks, and sandy shores, various provinces, Ga. to La., Minn., and Me.—Fall.

4. B. connata Muhl. Stem 3–14 dm. tall, sparingly branched, glabrous, bright-green: leaf-blades undivided or some of the lower deeply parted, lanceolate to elliptic, acuminate, tapering to the petiole, coarsely and saliently serrate: heads medium; outer bracts of the involucre 4–5, linear-spatulate, rarely exceeding the disk, glabrous: rays rarely present, the ligules one-half longer than the disk, the ovaries awnless, and hairy: disk-corollas campanulate above, 5-lobed, orange: achene 4–6 mm. long, rather narrow and thick, nearly black, covered with yellowish warts; some or all marginal barbs erect; awns 4, slender, with retrorse, nearly erect barbs.—(SWAMP BEGGAR-TICKS.)—Swamps and ditches, various provinces, N. C. to Mo., Minn., and N. H.—Fall.

5. B. vulgata Greene. Stem 7–15 dm. tall, much branched, nearly glabrous: leaf-blades commonly 5-divided, the segments lanceolate, straight-veined, acute, serrate with numerous regular sharp or bluntish teeth: heads large, 15–25 mm. wide: outer bracts of the involucre 10–16, unequal, usually longer than the disk, ciliate, the inner with abruptly narrowed tips: rays pale-yellow, the ligules equaling the disk, the ovaries awnless and nearly glabrous: disk-corollas funnelform, pale, 4–5-lobed: stamens included: achene large; body 6–11, 7.5–9 mm. long, 3.5–5 mm. wide, very flat, brown or olive, nearly smooth, the 2 long awns and the upper part of the achene-margins retrorsely barbed.—(STICK-TIGHT.)—Damp soil, waste-places, and roadsides, various provinces, rarely Coastal Plain, N. C. to Mo., Calif., B. C., and Ont.—Fall.

6. B. frondosa L. Stem 5–12 dm. tall, slender, bushy-branched, nearly glabrous: leaf-blades pinnately 3-divided or rarely 5-divided, the segments lanceolate, serrate with sharp spreading teeth, acuminate: heads not large: outer bracts of the involucre 6–8, subequal, spatulate, sparsely ciliate, usually exceeding the disk: rays usually present, golden-yellow, the ligules equaling the disk, the ovaries hairy and with 2 short retrorsely barbed awns: disk-corollas orange, 5-lobed: stamens exserted: achene black; body 5–9 mm. long, 2–4.5 mm. wide, cuneate, flattish, sparsely hairy and often tuberculate, the barbs on the margins erect, those on the 2 awns reflexed or rarely erect.—Damp soil, often a weed, various provinces, Fla. to Tex., Nebr., and N. B.—Sum.-fall.

7. B. discoidea (T. & G.) Britton. Stem 3–15 dm. tall, slender, diffusely branched, nearly or quite glabrous: leaf-blades 3-divided, the segments lanceolate or ovate-lanceolate, 4–9 cm. long, sharply and coarsely serrate below the entire long-acuminate tip: heads very small and numerous, 8–10 mm. broad: outer bracts of the involucre mostly 4, spatulate-linear, rarely exceeding the disk, glabrous: rays none: disk-corollas orange, 5-lobed: achene small body 4–5.5 mm. long, black, cuneate, thickish, tuberculate or nearly smooth, hairy, the margins and the 2 short awns erect-barbed.—Swamps, wet banks, and low woods, various provinces, Ala. to Tex., Mich., Mass., and N. C.—Late sum.-fall.

8. B. cernua L. Stem 2–7 dm. tall, low, pale-green, nearly glabrous; the branches very short, decreasing down the stem: leaf-blades undivided, 6–16 cm. long, lanceolate or linear-lanceolate, more or less connate by the broad bases, acuminate, serrate with coarse distant teeth: heads very large, broader than high, nodding in fruit: outer bracts of the involucre 7–8, unequal, exceeding the disk and spreading: rays usually present, bright-yellow, the ligules about one-half longer than the disk, the ovaries glabrous except the margin, and awnless: disk-corollas orange, 5-lobed: achene narrowly cuneate, slightly dilated at the summit, 4-angled, the margins retrorsely barbed and tuberculate, the awns 4, slender, retrorsely barbed.—(STICK-TIGHT.)—Swamps and wet meadows, various provinces, rarely Coastal Plain, N. C. to Mo., Ore., and N. S.—(*O. W.*)—Sum.–fall.

9. **B. laevis** (L.) B. S. P. Stem 5–14 dm. tall, glabrous, 5–10 mm. high, the branches all toward the summit of the stem, slender, ascending: leaf-blades undivided, 7–13 cm. long; blades elliptic-lanceolate, serrate with small inconspicuous teeth, acute, contracted toward the sessile base: heads medium, nearly globular, erect or nodding in fruit: outer bracts of the involucre 7–8, rarely longer than the disk: rays very large, the ligules 2–3 cm. long, golden-yellow, the ovaries as in the next preceding species: disk-corollas orange, 5-lobed: achene cuneate, neither dilated nor contracted at the top, not tuberculate, the margins and 2–4 awns retrorsely barbed. [*B. chrysanthemoides* Michx.]— (WILD-GOLDENGLOW.)—Swamps and low woods, Coastal Plain and adj. provinces, Ga. to Ala., Tenn., N. Y., and Pa.—Sum.–fall.

10. **B. Nashii** Small. Similar to the next preceding species but slightly succulent, less branched: leaves ascending; blades broader and thicker, elliptic-lanceolate or oblanceolate, with very broad but scarcely connate bases, finely serrate or entire: achene slightly contracted at the summit.—Swamps, Coastal Plain, Fla. to Tex.—Sum.–fall. The plants of this and of the next preceding species are slightly fleshy.

11. **B. aristosa** (Michx.) Britton. Stem 3–10 dm. high, much-branched: leaf-blades pinnately 5–7-divided, the segments lanceolate, acuminate, serrate, incised or pinnatifid, slightly pubescent beneath: heads numerous, 2–5 cm. broad: outer bracts of the involucre 8–10, linear-spatulate, rarely ciliate, not surpassing the inner: rays 6–10, the ligules golden-yellow, the ovaries ciliate and awnless: achene obovate, flat, strigose and hispid-ciliate; awns 2, slender, as long as the achene-body or shorter, the barbs erect or reflexed (or the pappus-awns wanting in *B. aristosa mutica*).—Swamps, various provinces, rarely Coastal Plain, Tex. to Kans., Minn., and Ohio, and adv. eastward.—Sum.–fall.

12. **B. involucrata** (Nutt.) Britton. Stem 3–10 dm. high, much-branched, minutely pubescent: leaf-blades pinnately divided, the segments narrow, linear-lanceolate, incised or pinnatifid, long-acuminate: heads 3–5 cm. broad: outer bracts of the involucre 12–20, linear, acutish, hispid on back and margins, mostly surpassing the inner: rays several, the ligules golden-yellow, the ovaries awnless, ciliate throughout: disk-corollas 5-lobed: stamens exserted: achene very flat, obovate, slightly contracted at the top, strigose-ciliate, bidentulate.— Swamps, various provinces, Tex. to Kans. and Ill., and adv. eastward.—Sum.–fall.

13. **B. coronata** (L.) Britton. Stem 9–20 dm. tall, glabrous, much-branched: leaf-blades pinnately divided, with 4–8 narrowly lanceolate, serrate or incised, acute or acuminate segments: heads 4–6 cm. broad: outer bracts of the involucre linear-spatulate, rarely ciliate, equaling the disk: rays several, the ligules bright-yellow, 12–25 mm. long, the ovaries bidentulate at the summit: disk-corollas deep yellow, 5-lobed: stamens exserted: achene narrowly cuneate, slightly strigose-ciliate above; awns 2, about equaling the breadth of the achene, erect-barbed. [*B. trichosperma* (Michx.) Britton.]—Swamps, various provinces, Fla. to Miss., Ill., and Mass.—Sum.–fall.

14. **B. mitis** (Michx.) Sherff. Stem 3–10 dm. tall, glabrous or nearly so, branched: leaf-blades 7–12 cm. long, 3–5-divided or rarely mostly simple, the

segments lanceolate, acuminate, serrate (narrowly linear and almost or quite entire, and achenes awnless, in *B. mitis leptophylla*), the lateral much smaller: heads 2–5 cm. broad: outer bracts of the involucre linear-spatulate, equaling the disk, glabrous, the inner usually black-punctate: rays-several, the ligules 1–3 cm. long, golden-yellow, the ovaries glabrous and awnless: disk-corollas 5-lobed: stamens exserted: achene very small, 2–4 mm. long, glabrous; awns very short, tooth-like. [*B. coronata* (L.) Britton.]—Wet soil, often in brackish marshes, Coastal Plain, Fla. to Miss. and Va.—Sum.–fall.

88. **COSMOS** Cav.[1] Annual or perennial, usually tall, widely branched herbs. Leaves opposite: blades entire, lobed, or 2–3-pinnately dissected. Heads peduncled, showy. Involucre nearly hemispheric: bracts unequal, the outer sometimes smaller than the inner. Ray-flowers few: corollas with pink, purple, yellow, or orange-yellow ligules. Disk-corollas yellow in our species, with a funnelform throat and a shorter tube. Filaments as long as the anthers or nearly so, sometimes pubescent. Achene beaked. Pappus of 2–4 barbed awns, or a crown.—About 20 species, tropical American.—Spr.–fall or all year S.

Leaf-segments broad, elliptic, lanceolate, or linear.
  Ligules pink or rose, mostly less than 2 cm. long.   1. *C. caudatus.*
  Ligules orange-yellow, mostly over 2 cm. long.   2. *C. sulphureus.*
Leaf-segments filiform or linear-filiform.   3. *C. bipinnatus.*

1. **C. caudatus** H. B. K. Stem 7–14 dm. tall: leaf-blades 2-pinnately parted, the segments lanceolate or linear: involucral bracts linear or nearly so: ray-flowers 7–12; ligules pink or rose-colored, 1–2 cm. long: achene fusiform, about 2 cm. long, the beak nearly or quite as long as the body.—Waste-places and cult. grounds, Key West, Fla. Nat. of trop. Am. and cult.

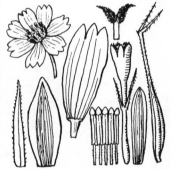

2. **C. sulphureus** Cav. Stem 2–21 dm. tall, often pubescent, much-branched: leaf-blades 2-pinnately parted, the segments elliptic or lanceolate: involucral bracts linear: ray-flowers 8–10; ligules orange-yellow, 2–3 cm. long: achene fusiform, 2–2.5 cm. long, the beak as long as the body or nearly so.— Pinelands, edges of hammocks, and waste-places, pen. Fla. Nat. of trop. Am. and cult.

3. **C. bipinnatus** Cav. Stem 3–30 dm. tall, usually glabrous or nearly so: leaf-blades 2-pinnately divided, the segments remote and filiform or linear-filiform: involucral bracts of two kinds, the outer ovate-acuminate, the inner elliptic: ray-flowers 8–10; ligules pink crimson or white, 2–4 cm. long: achene fusiform, 1–1.5 cm. long, the beak shorter than the body.—Pinelands, waste-places, and cult. grounds, Fla. Nat. of trop. Am. and cult.

89. **ENDORIMA** Raf. Perennial or biennial, usually simple-stemmed herbs. Leaves alternate, few: blades narrow, entire. Involucre thick: bracts herbaceous, the outer ones broad, the inner ones longer and narrower. Ray-flowers numerous: corollas with narrow yellow or purple ligules. Disk-corollas

[1] Revised by Edward Johnston Alexander.

with a narrowly funnelform throat and a shorter tube. Filaments nearly as long as the anthers. Pappus of 7–9 elliptic or lanceolate scales. Achene pubescent.—Two species; as follows:

Disk dark-purple: lower cauline leaves 10–12 cm. long.   1. *E. atropurpurea.*
Disk yellow: lower cauline leaves 4–6 cm. long.   2. *E. uniflora.*

1. **E. atropurpurea** (Harper) Small. Plant 6–8 dm. tall: leaf-blades linear-spatulate; narrower bracts of the involucre 8–9 mm. long: ligules linear-cuneate: corollas of the disk mostly less than 6.5 mm. long: filaments much shorter than the anthers. [*Baldwina atropurpurea* Harper] Moist pinelands, Coastal Plain, S. Ga.—Fall.

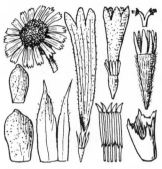

2. **E. uniflora** (Nutt.) Barnhart. Plant 3–9 dm. tall: leaf-blades spatulate to linear: narrower bracts of the involucre 10–11 mm. long: ligules spatulate: corollas of the disk mostly over 6.5 mm. long: filaments nearly as long as the anthers. [*Balduina uniflora* Nutt.]—Low pinelands, Coastal Plain, Fla. to La. and N. C.—Sum.–fall.— *Endorima* and *Actinospermum* are peculiar in having the bractlets of the receptacle partly concreted into honeycomb-like structure which partly surrounds the achenes.

90. **ACTINOSPERMUM** Ell. Annual or biennial, branching herbs. Leaves alternate, often numerous: blades very narrow, entire. Involucre thick: bracts in several series, in the inner narrower and longer than the outer. Ray-flowers numerous: corollas with rather broad yellow ligules. Disk-corollas with a cylindric-campanulate throat and a very short or obsolete tube: lobes lanceolate. Filaments shorter than the anthers. Pappus of 7–12 obovate-orbicular scales. Achene pubescent.—One species.

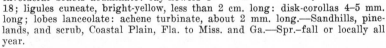

1. **A. angustifolium** (Pursh) T. & G. Plant 2–5 dm. tall: leaf-blades narrowly linear or slightly broadened upward: heads showy: involucral bracts acuminate: ray-flowers 8– 18; ligules cuneate, bright-yellow, less than 2 cm. long: disk-corollas 4–5 mm. long; lobes lanceolate: achene turbinate, about 2 mm. long.—Sandhills, pinelands, and scrub, Coastal Plain, Fla. to Miss. and Ga.—Spr.–fall or locally all year.

91 **MARSHALLIA** Schreb. Perennial, rigid herbs. Leaves alternate: blades entire. Heads discoid. Involucre campanulate or hemispheric: bracts broad or narrow. Ray-flowers wanting. Disk-corollas white, pink, or purple, with a campanulate or obsolete throat and a long slender tube: lobes linear or nearly so. Filaments somewhat shorter than the anthers. Pappus of 5 or 6 nearly equal scales.—About 10 species, natives of the southeastern United States.—BARBARA'S-BUTTONS.

Bracts of the involucre attenuate or subulate-tipped.
Bracts of the involucre obtuse or merely acute or apiculate.

I. GRAMINIFOLIAE.
II. OBOVATAE.

I. GRAMINIFOLIAE

Basal and lower cauline leaves with spatulate, elliptic to elliptic-ovate, obtuse blades.

1. *M. graminifolia.*

Basal and lower cauline leaves with elongate linear-attenuate 3-ribbed blades.

Heads few-flowered: longer involucral bracts less than 6 mm. long: pappus-scales ovate.

2. *M. laciniarioides.*

Heads many-flowered: longer involucral bracts over 6 mm. long: pappus-scales lanceolate.

3. *M. Williamsonii.*

II. OBOVATAE

Corolla-throat long (3–3.5 mm.), half as long as the tube or nearly so.

Outer bracts of the involucre acute: upper cauline leaves broad, markedly acuminate.

4. *M. trinervia.*

Outer branches of the involucre obtuse or abruptly pointed: upper cauline leaves narrow acute or slightly acuminate.

5. *M. grandiflora.*

Corolla-throat very short (1–1.5 mm.).

Bractlets of the receptacle spatulate or markedly clavate-spatulate, spine-tipped.

6. *M. obovata.*

Bractlets of the receptacle linear, or sometimes slightly enlarged near the tip, not spine-tipped.

Blades of the upper cauline leaves linear, thick: bracts of the involucre obtuse or abruptly acutish.

7. *M. ramosa.*

Blades of the upper cauline leaves lanceolate or elliptic-lanceolate, thinnish: bracts of the involucre somewhat acuminate.

8. *M. Mohrii.*

1. M. graminifolia (Walt.) Small. Plant 2–11 dm. tall, the stem simple or with few erect branches: basal and lower cauline leaves 3–12 cm. long, with narrowly spatulate or linear-spatulate mostly obtuse blades: upper cauline leaves much smaller, with linear blades: outer bracts of the involucre linear or linear-lanceolate, 4–6 mm. long, with narrow margins, acuminate: corolla-tube 5–6 mm. long: achene 2.5–3 mm. long: pappus-scales ovate, very short. [*M. angustifolia* Pursh *M. angustifolia cyananthera* Ell.] Moist pinelands and prairies, Coastal Plain, Fla. to La. and N. C.—Sum.

2. M. laciniarioides Small. Plant 3–4 dm. tall, the stem usually with few erect branches above: basal and lower cauline leaves 3–17 cm. long, with spatulate to linear, mostly acute or acuminate blades; upper cauline leaves smaller, several or many, with narrowly linear blades: outer bracts of the involucre ovate-lanceolate, 5–6 mm. long, with broad margins, rather abruptly narrowed to a long tip: corolla-tube less than 5 mm. long: achene 1–1.5 mm. long. Sandy soil, Coastal Plain, Ga. to S. C.—Sum.

3. M. Williamsonii Small. Plant similar to that of *M. laciniarioides* but larger, and leaves fewer: blades of the basal and lower cauline leaves 8–21 cm. long, with linear-spatulate to linear acuminate blades: upper cauline leaves few, with narrowly linear blades: outer bracts of the involucre lanceolate, 7–8 mm. long, with rather wide margins, acuminate: corolla-tube 6–7 mm. long: achene 2.5–3 mm. long.—Sandy pine woods, Coastal Plain, S. C. and N. C.—Spr.–fall.

4. M. trinervia (Walt.) Porter. Plant 3–9 dm. tall, the stem typically simple, rarely with one or few erect branches: basal and lower cauline leaves 5–14 cm. long with spatulate or elliptic obtuse or acute 3-veined blades narrowed into long petiole-like bases; upper cauline leaves with elliptic, elliptic-ovate or lanceolate markedly acuminate blades: outer bracts of the involucre ovate-lanceolate or lanceolate, acute or acuminate, 7–10 mm. long, strongly ribbed: corolla-tube 7–8 mm. long: achene 3–4 mm. long, the pappus scales subulate-tipped, about half as long as the achene.—Pinelands and damp woods, Coastal Plain and adj. provinces, Ala. to Miss., Tenn., and Va.—Spr.–sum.

5. M. grandiflora Beadle & Boynton. Plant 2–10 dm. tall, thirteen typically simple basal and lower cauline leaves 3–19 cm. long, with elliptic, spatulate, or oval obtuse blades; upper cauline leaves with linear-elliptic to lanceolate-acute or slightly acuminate blades: outer bracts of the involucre linear lanceolate to elliptic, obtuse or abruptly pointed, 8–11 mm. long, narrowly margined: corolla-tube 8–11 mm. long: achene 3.5–4 mm. long, the pappus-scales fully half as long as the achene.—Sandy river-banks and open woods, Blue Ridge and Appalachian Plateau, N. C. to W. Va. and Pa.—Spr.–sum.

6. M. obovata (Walt.) Beadle & Boyton. Plant 1–7 dm. tall, the stem typically simple: basal and loweral cauline leaves 2–12 cm. long, with linear, spatulate, elliptic-ovate or obovate mostly obtuse blades; upper cauline leaves rarely present: outer bracts of the involucre elliptic or linear-elliptic, 6–8 mm. long, obtuse or abruptly pointed, very narrowly margined: corolla-tube 7–8 mm. long: achene 3–3.5 mm. long, the pappus-scales less than half as long as the achene. [*M. obovata platyphylla* (M. A. Curtis) Beadle & Boynton]—Pinelands and dry woods, Coastal Plain and adj. provinces, Fla. to Ala. and N. C.—Spr.–sum.

7. M. ramosa Beadle & Boynton. Plant 1.5–6 dm. tall, the stem corymbosely branched above: leaves many; blades of the basal and lower cauline 3–21 cm. long, narrowly spatulate to linear, obtuse or acutish, those of the upper cauline linear or narrowly linear-lanceolate: outer bracts of the involucre linear, lanceolate, or narrowly elliptic, 5–7 mm. long, obtuse or acutish, narrowly margined: corolla-tube about 5 mm. long: achene about 4 mm. long, the pappus-scales about half as long as the achene.—Pinelands and moist rocks, Coastal Plain and Piedmont, Ga.—Spr.–sum.

8. M. Mohrii Beadle & Boynton. Plant 2–7 dm. tall, the stem sparingly corymbosely branched above: leaves few, blades of the basal and lower cauline spatulate to narrowly elliptic, those of the upper cauline elliptic-lanceolate to lanceolate: outer bracts of the involucre elliptic to lanceolate, 5–9 mm. long, acute, rather obscurely margined: corolla-tube 6–8 mm. long: achene about 4 mm. long, the pappus scales fully half as long as the achene.—Low grounds and pine-woods, Appalachian Plateau, Ga. and Ala.—Spr.–sum.

92. GALINSOGA R. & P. Annual, tender herbs. Leaves opposite: blades toothed. Heads radiate. Involucre campanulate or hemispheric: bracts relatively broad. Ray-flowers 4 or 5: corollas with a pubescent tube and broad white to purple ligule. Disk-corollas with a campanulate throat and a tube of about the same length. Anthers ellipsoid. Achene nearly or quite as long as tne corolla. Pappus of the ray of several bristles or wanting, of the disk of lacerate or fimbriate bristles.—About 5 species, of tropical and temperate America.

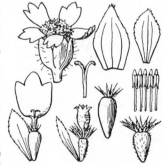

1. G. ciliata (Raf.) Blake. Plant 1–7 dm. tall, often branched, the pubescence coarse and spreading, often glandular: leaf-blades ovate to ovate-lanceolate, 2–5 cm. long, petioled: involucre 2–2.5 mm. high; outer bracts ovate, obtuse: ligules white, 1–1.5 mm. wide: disk-corollas about 1.5 mm. long: achene less than 2 mm. long: pappus scales minutely fimbriate and aristate. [*G. parviflora* (Fl. SE. U. S.)]—Roadsides, cult. grounds, and waste-places, throughout U. S. and S Can. Nat. of S. Am.—(*W. I., Mex., C. A.*)—Sum.–fall.—A particularly pestiferous weed of such rapid growth and seeding as to make eradication extremely difficult.

G. parviflora Cav. with much smaller ray-flowers, appressed pubescence, and pappus scales fimbriate, but not aristate, often occurs with *G. ciliata* north of our range, and may be looked for in N. C. and Tenn. or further S.

93. **TRIDAX** L. Perennial, caulescent, decumbent herbs. Leaves opposite: blades incised-toothed or pinnately dissected. Heads radiate. Involucre ovoid to campanulate: bracts various, the inner broader than the outer. Ray-flowers few: corollas with a slender glabrous tube and a broad yellow or pale ligule. Disk-corollas with a narrowly funnelform throat and a short tube. Anthers linear. Achene much shorter than the corolla. Pappus of numerous plumose-ciliate scales.—About 12 species, tropical American.

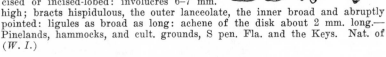

1. **T. procumbens** L. Plant branched at the base, the branches hirsute: leaf-blades ovate to ovate-lanceolate, 2–5 cm. long, incised or incised-lobed: involucres 6–7 mm. high; bracts hispidulous, the outer lanceolate, the inner broad and abruptly pointed: ligules as broad as long: achene of the disk about 2 mm. long.—Pinelands, hammocks, and cult. grounds, S pen. Fla. and the Keys. Nat. of (*W. I.*)

94. **HYMENOXYS** Cass. Annual, biennial, or perennial, erect, caulescent herbs. Leaves alternate: blades pinnatifid or pinnatisect, the segments usually narrow. Heads radiate, or (in ours) discoid, peduncled. Involucre often campanulate or hemispheric: bracts in 2 series, the outer smaller than the inner, firm and more or less united at the base. Ray-flowers, when present yellow or orange, few or several, pistillate, fruit-producing: ligules 3-lobed. Disk-flowers numerous, perfect, fruit-producing: corollas yellow, with a short tube and a cylindric or funnelform throat of equal length or longer; lobes deltoid. Anthers very minutely appendaged at the base. Stigmas blunt. Achene obpyramidal, 5-angled, pubescent. Pappus of 5 scales.—Seven species, North American.

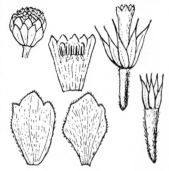

1. **H. anthemoides** (Juss.) Cass. Stem branched throughout, the branches ascending or diffuse: leaf-segments narrowly linear or linear-filiform: peduncles erect, fluted, enlarged under the head: involucre broadly

campanulate; bracts finely pubescent, the outer ovate, tubercled at the base, the inner elliptic or elliptic-obovate, 4–5 mm. long, longer than the outer: achene 2–2.5 mm. long, densely appressed-pubescent: pappus-scales acuminate, shorter than the achene.—Waste-places, Coastal Plain, Ala. Nat. of S. A.—Sum.

95. HELENIUM L. Annual, biennial, or perennial, bitter, caulescent herbs. Leaves alternate: blades entire, toothed, or pinnatifid, often decurrent. Heads solitary, few, or numerous. Involucre flattish: bracts spreading or reflexed. Receptacle conic, ellipsoid, or subglobose. Ray-flowers several, the corollas with cuneate yellow or red-stained ligules. Disk-corollas with broadly ovate lobes. Achene ribbed. Pappus of 5–8 acuminate or awn-tipped scales. —About 25 species, North American.—SNEEZEWEEDS.

Ray-flowers pistillate, or wanting.
  Plant annual or rarely biennial.
    Leaves with narrowly linear or linear-filiform blades,
      not decurrent.   I. TENUIFOLIA.
    Leaves with broader blades, more or less decurrent.   II. QUADRIDENTATA.
  Plant perennial.   III. AUTUMNALES.
Ray-flowers neutral or sterile.
  Heads corymbose.   IV. NUDIFLORA.
  Heads solitary or 2 or 3 on long peduncles.   V. HELENIA.

I. TENUIFOLIA
Leaves numerous ; blades entire : pappus-scales awn-tipped.   1. *H. tenuifolium.*

II. QUADRIDENTATA
Leaves few ; blades of the lower ones pinnately lobed :
  pappus-scales rounded.   2. *H. quadridentatum.*

III. AUTUMNALES
Disk mostly over 1 cm. wide : disk-corollas about 3 mm.
  long.   3. *H. latifolium.*
Disk mostly less than 1 cm. wide : disk-corollas about 2.5
  mm. wide.   4. *H. parviflorum.*

IV. NUDIFLORA
Disk yellow.   4. *H. parviflorum.*
Disk purplish or dark-brown.
  Upper part of the stem and branches with wings 1 mm.
    wide or less : upper cauline-leaves much smaller than
    the lower ones.   5. *H. nudiflorum.*
  Upper part of the stem and branches with wings 2 mm.
    wide or more : upper cauline leaves not conspicuously
    smaller than the lower ones.   6. *H. polyphyllum.*

V. HELENIA
Disk yellow.
  Receptacle ovoid or ovoid-conic : disk subglobose to
    hemispheric : bracts of the involucre early reflexed.
    Pappus-scales dissected into bristle-like segments :
      disk about 1.5 cm. wide.   7. *H. fimbriatum.*
    Pappus-scales entire or merely erose : disk about 2
      cm. wide.   8. *H. Curtisii.*
  Receptacle and disk depressed-hemispheric or convex :
    bracts of the involucre spreading or tardily recurved.
    Achene glabrous or merely glandular-granular.   9. *H. Helenium.*
    Achene pubescent on the ribs.   10. *H. vernale.*
Disk purplish or brown.   11. *H. brevifolium.*

1. **H. tenuifolium** Nutt. Plant 2–4 dm. tall: leaves numerous; blades 1–5 cm. long: involucral bracts linear-subulate to subulate, 4–7 mm. long: ligules

7–12 mm. long: pappus-scales prolonged into slender awns.—(YELLOW-DICK. BITTER-WEED. SPANISH-DAISY.)—Fields, roadsides, and waste-places, various provinces, Fla. to Tex., Mo., and S Va.; adventive NE to Pa. and Mass.—Sum.-fall.

2. **H. quadridentatum** Labill. Plant 3–10 dm. tall, loosely branched: blades of the lower leaves 8–15 cm. long, pinnatifid: involucral bracts linear to linear-subulate, becoming 4–6 mm. long: ligules 3–5 mm. long: pappus-scales orbicular-oval.—Low grounds, Coastal Plain, Fla. to Tex. and S. C.—Spr.-fall.

3. **H. latifolium** Mill. Plant 2–9 dm. tall: leaf-blades elliptic or slightly broadest above the middle or below it, 3–12 cm. long, rather prominently toothed: involucral bracts linear-lanceolate or narrower, 5–7 mm. long: ligules 10–20 mm. long: disk yellow; corollas about 3 mm. long. [*H. autumnale* L. in part]—Swamps and low grounds, various provinces, Fla. to Tex., Minn., Que., and Conn.—Sum.-fall.

4. **H. parviflorum** Nutt. Plant 2–8 dm. tall, much branched: leaf-blades elliptic to elliptic-lanceolate, 3–12 cm. long, shallowly toothed: involucral bracts linear-subulate or narrower, 6–9 mm. long: ligules 6–10 mm. long: disk yellow; corollas about 2.5 mm. long.—Low grounds, Coastal Plain and adj. provinces, Fla. to Tex., Ark., Tenn., and Ga.—Sum.-fall.

5. **H. nudiflorum** Nutt. Plant 2–10 dm. tall, corymbosely branched above: leaf-blades oblanceolate to elliptic or linear, 2.5–12 cm. long, those of the lower leaves often toothed: involucral bracts narrowly linear to linear-subulate, 5–7 mm. long: ligules 10–15 mm. long.—Low grounds, prairies, and flat-woods, various provinces, Fla. to Tex., Mo., and Md.; adv. NE to Conn.—Spr.-fall.

6. **H. polyphyllum** Small. Plant 3–8 dm. tall: leaf-blades elliptic to linear-lanceolate, 2–10 cm. long, undulate or remotely toothed: involucral bracts narrowly linear to linear-subulate, 5–8 mm. long: ligules 6–12 mm. long: disk purplish: corollas 2 mm. long.—Fields, meadows, and thickets, Appalachian provinces, Ga. and Tenn.—Sum.-fall.

7. **H. fimbriatum** (Michx.) A. Gray. Plant 4–8 dm. tall: leaf-blades linear-spatulate to broadly linear, 4–12 cm. long, entire: involucral bracts linear-subulate, 7–10 mm. long, reflexed: ligules 1.5–2 cm. long: disk corollas 5 mm. long: achene 1 mm. long.—Low pinelands, Coastal Plain, Fla. to Tex.—Sum.-fall.

8. **H. Curtisii** A. Gray. Plant 5–9 dm. tall: leaf-blades oblanceolate to linear, 4–10 cm. long, undulate: involucral bracts lanceolate to lance-subulate, 5–8 mm. long; ligules 1.5–2 cm. long: disk corollas 4.5–5 mm. long: achene 1.5 mm. long.—Low pinelands and marshes, Coastal Plain, N. C.—Spr.-sum.

9. **H. Helenium** (Nutt.) Small. Plant 3–7 dm. tall: leaf-blades linear or nearly so, 5–15 cm. long, undulate or coarsely few-toothed: involucral bracts linear or linear-lanceolate, 5–9 mm. long: ligules 9–17 mm. long: disk corollas 4.5 mm. long: achene 1–1.5 mm. long. [*H. incisum* (T. & G.) Wood]—Marshes, low pinelands, and about ponds, Coastal Plain, Fla. to La. and S. C.—Spr.-fall.

10. **H. vernale** Walt. Plant 3–7 dm. tall: leaf-blades spatulate to linear, 6–15 cm. long, toothed or incised-pinnatifid: involucral bracts lance-subulate, 5–6 mm. long, spreading: ligules 1 cm. long: disk corollas 4–4.5 mm. long:

achene 1.5–2 mm. long. [*H. pinnatifidum* (Schw.) Rydb.]—Low pinelands and swamps, Coastal Plain, Fla. to Miss. and N. C.—Spr.–sum.

11. H. brevifolium (Nutt.) A. Gray. Plant 3–8 dm. tall: leaf-blades spatu-late to linear, 2–8 cm. long, entire, or undulate: involucral bracts linear-lanceolate to linear, 8–10 mm. long: ligules 1–1.5 cm. long: disk-flowers 4 mm. long: achene 1.5 mm. long.—Wet pinelands, Coastal Plain and adj. provinces, Fla. to Miss. and N. C.—Spr.–sum.

96. GAILLARDIA Foug. Annual, biennial, or perennial, often diffuse herbs. Leaves alternate: blades entire, toothed, or pinnatifid. Heads erect, radiate and showy, or sometimes discoid. Involucre broad or flat: bracts ultimately spreading or reflexed. Ray-flowers several, the corollas with prominently lobed yellow, orange, red, or purple ligules, or wanting. Disk-corollas with a short tube, a longer throat, and deltoid, triangular-lanceolate or caudate-acuminate lobes. Achene 5-ribbed. Pappus of 6–12 awned, 1-nerved scales.—About 20 species, all except one North American.—BLANKET-FLOWERS. FIRE-WHEELS. BANDANA-DAISIES.

Fimbrillae of the receptacle obsolete or very small tooth-like projections: lobes of the
    disk-corollas caudate-acuminate from a broad base.   I. LANCEOLATAE.
Fimbrillae of the receptacle subulate or setiform, longer than
    the achenes: lobes of the disk-corollas short-acuminate.   II. PULCHELLAE.

I. LANCEOLATAE
Disk light-yellow.   1. *G. chrysantha.*
Disk purplish or purplish-brown.   2. *G. lanceolata.*

II. PULCHELLAE
Plant herbaceous: leaf-blades thin.   3. *G. Drummondii.*
Plant partly woody: leaf-blades fleshy.   4. *G. picta.*

1. G. chrysantha Small. Plant annual or biennial, finely pubescent, 3–6 dm. tall, usually with few elongate more or less spreading branches: leaf-blades spatulate or elliptic-spatulate on the lower part of the stem to linear or elliptic-linear above, 2–8 cm. long, undulate or remotely sinuate-toothed: heads long-peduncled: in-volucral bracts 7–11 mm. long, the outer triangular or lanceolate-triangular, the inner lanceolate: ligules of the ray-flowers yellow, 1–1.5 cm. long, 3-cleft, the middle lobe the narrowest: disk light-yellow, 1.5–2 cm. broad: achene about 2 mm. long.—Pine-lands and sandy prairies, Coastal Plain, Ala. to Tex. and Ark.—Spr.–fall.

2. G. lanceolata Michx. Plant annual or sometimes biennial, cinereous-pubescent, 3–7 dm. tall, loosely branched, the branches long and spreading: leaf-blades spatulate to elliptic or linear, 1.5–8 cm. long, acute, entire or remotely serrate, sessile, at least above the base of the stem: heads long-peduncled: involucral bracts oblong to lanceolate, 8–12 mm. long, acute or acuminate: ligules of the ray-flowers yel-low, 1.5–2 cm. long, 3-cleft: disk purplish or purplish-brown, 1.5–2 cm. broad: receptacle naked or nearly so: achene 1.5–2 mm. long.—Pinelands, dry woods, rocky banks, and prairies, various provinces, Fla. to Tex., Kans., and S. C.—Spr.–sum.

3. G. Drummondii (Hook.) DC. Plant annual, 6 dm. tall or less, the branches puberulent and somewhat villous: leaf-blades spatulate to oblanceolate and undulate to pinnatifid on the lower part of the stem, lanceolate to linear-lanceolate above, entire, undulate, or distantly toothed, sessile: heads slender-peduncled: involucral bracts 12–20 mm. long, or rarely shorter, linear-lanceolate, usually narrowly so, long-attenuate, hirsute and ciliate; ligules of the ray-flowers 15–22 mm. long, usually purple, except the yellow tips: achene 2.5 mm. long or nearly so, strigose.—Dry soil, prairies, open woods, and cult. grounds, Coastal Plain, S Fla. and Tex.—(*Mex.*)—Spr.–fall, or all year S.

4. **G. picta** Sweet. Plant perennial, but flowering the first year, becoming woody below, 3 dm. tall or less, the branches puberulent and densely long-hairy: leaf-blades spatulate and pinnatifid on the lower part of the stem, linear to lanceolate and mostly entire on the upper part and sessile: heads long-peduncled: involucral bracts narrowly lanceolate, mostly 9–15 mm. long, acuminate, copiously pubescent and ciliate: ligules of the ray-flowers 15–24 mm. long, purple or sometimes yellow-tipped: achene about 2 mm. long, strigose.—Coastal sands, Fla. to Tex. and S. C.—Spr.–fall.

97. **HYMENOPAPPUS** L'Her. Biennial or perennial, erect herbs. Leaves alternate: blades pinnatifid or dissected, or rarely entire. Heads discoid, corymbose. Involucral bracts peta-loid. Disk-corollas white or pink, becoming purplish-red the second day, pubescent, with a campanulate or urceolate throat and spreading or recurved lobes. Anther-appendages deltoid-ovate. Achene broadened upward, pubescent all over. Pappus of several scales shorter than the achene, or obsolete.—About 7 species, North American.

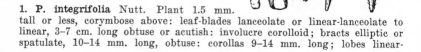

1. **H scabiosaeus** L'Her. Stem 3–7 dm. tall, glabrate or thinly tomentose: leaf-segments rather coarse, elliptic to linear, entire or with ovate to elliptic teeth: bracts of the involucre narrowly elliptic to oval, varying to somewhat obovate: achene 3.5–4 mm. long, or sometimes smaller: pappus-scales obovate, about 0.5 mm. long.—Dry sandy soil, various provinces, Fla. to Tex., Kans., and S. C.—Sum.

98. **POLYPTERIS** Nutt. Perennial, tall, branching, rigid herbs. Leaves alternate, or opposite on the lower part of the stem: blades entire, thick. Heads corymbose, scattered, discoid. Involucre turbinate: bracts rather numer-ous and broad, scarious above the base, mainly in 2 series. Receptacle naked. Ray-flowers wanting. Disk-corollas white or pink, with a campanulate throat and a long slender tube. Anthers longer than the fila-ments. Achene 4-angled, rather stoutly enlarged upward, pubescent. Pappus of several slender pubescent awn-like scales.—One species.

1. **P. integrifolia** Nutt. Plant 1.5 mm. tall or less, corymbose above: leaf-blades lanceolate or linear-lanceolate to linear, 3–7 cm. long obtuse or acutish: involucre corolloid; bracts elliptic or spatulate, 10–14 mm. long, obtuse: corollas 9–14 mm. long; lobes linear-

lanceolate: achene narrowly obpyramidal, 4–5 mm. long.—Dry pinelands, Coastal Plain, Fla. and Ga.—Sum.-fall or all year S.

99. PALAFOXIA Lag. Annual or perennial, sometimes partly woody plants. Leaves alternate or opposite: blades narrow, entire. Heads corymbose. Involucre campanulate to ellipsoid: bracts narrow, herbaceous. Disk-corollas with a cylindric throat much longer than the tube. Achene 4-angled, slenderly enlarged upward, pubescent. Pappus of 4–8 short broad scales.—About 6 species, North American.

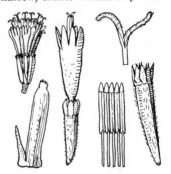

1. **P. Feayi** A. Gray. Slender shrubby plant 6–35 dm. tall minutely pubescent: leaves evergreen; blades elliptic to elliptic-lanceolate, 2–7 cm. long: involucre 7–8 mm. long; bracts obtuse: corollas white, 7–8 mm. long: achene clavate, 5–6 mm. long.—Pinelands and scrub, pen. Fla.—All year S.

100. FLAVERIA Juss. Annual, glabrous or pubescent, erect but often bushy-branched, somewhat succulent herbs. Leaves opposite: blades entire or toothed, sessile, sometimes connate. Heads individually inconspicuous. Involucre narrow, prismatic: bracts few, 1–8, mostly nearly equal. Ray-flowers mostly solitary and ligule yellow, or wanting. Disk-flowers 1–15. Achene narrow, 8–10-ribbed. Pappus wanting, or rarely of 2–4 scales.— About 10 species, all except 1 American.—Spr.-fall or all year S.

Receptacle naked: involucre of more than 2 bracts: heads 2–20-flowered: disk-corollas with a funnelform throat.
Involucre of 3 bracts or rarely of 4.   1. *F. bidentis.*
Involucre of 5–7 bracts.
  Heads 2–8-flowered.
    Stem with long internodes below and usually simple at the base: leaves herbaceous: plant annual.   2. *F. latifolia.*
    Stem with short internodes below and usually branched at the base: leaves fleshy: plant perennial (?).   3. *F. linearis.*
  Heads 10–15-flowered.   4. *F. floridana.*
Receptacle setose: involucre of 1, 2, or 3 bracts: head usually 1-flowered: disk-corollas with a campanulate throat.   5. *F. trinervia.*

1. **F. bidentis** (L.) Kuntze. Stem 10 dm. tall or less, angled, glabrous or sparingly villous on the angles and the nodes: leaf-blades lanceolate-elliptic, linear-lanceolate, or linear-elliptic, 3–8 cm. long, serrate, 3-ribbed, glabrous, slightly connate: inflorescence with scorpioid branches: heads 2–9-flowered: bracts of the involucre 3, with 1 or 2 additional scale-like ones at the base, oval to ovate, concave 3–4 mm. long, obtuse: ligule about 1 mm. long, narrow: disk-flowers 1–8, the corolla 2–3 mm. long: achene 1.5 mm. long. [*F. chilensis* Gmel.]—Waste-places and road-sides, Coastal Plain, Fla. to Ala. and Ga.— (*Mex., S. A.*)

2. **F. latifolia** (J. R. Johnston) Rydb. Stem 10 dm. tall or less, striate, glabrate: leaf-blades linear-lanceolate to linear, 2.5–10

cm. long, entire or serrulate, connate: corymb open: heads in small clusters: bracts of the involucre 5, narrowly elliptic, 3.5–4.5 mm. long: ligule 2.5–3 mm. long: disk-flowers 2–5, the corolla 2.5 mm. long: achene about 1.5 mm. long.— Low pinelands, wet prairies, and mangrove swamps, pen. Fla. and the Keys.

3. F. linearis Lag. Stem 2–9 dm. long, sometimes decumbent, corymbose above, striate, glabrous: leaf-blades narrowly linear, often narrowly so, 3–10 cm. long, narrowed above the connate bases, entire: corymbs irregular: heads numerous: bracts of the involucre mostly 5, 3.5–4 mm. long, elliptic, or lanceolate: ray-flowers usually solitary; ligule elliptic to oval, 2–3.5 mm. long: disk-flowers usually 5–10, the corollas 2.5–3.5 mm. long: achene about 2 mm. long. [*F. pinetorum* Blake.]—Coastal sands, hammocks, marshes, and low pinelands, pen. Fla. and the Keys.—(*W. I., Mex.*)

4. F. floridana J. R. Johnston. Stem 10 dm. tall or less, striate, glabrous: leaf-blades linear-lanceolate to linear, 2.5–8 cm. long, entire or rarely denticulate, slightly connate: heads 10–13-flowered, in compact clusters which are often subtended by a whorl of leaves: bracts of the involucre about 4 mm. long: ligule oval, about 2 mm. long: disk-corollas 2.5 mm. long: achene about 1.5 mm. long.—Sandy shores, pen. Fla.

5. F. trinervia (Spreng.) C. Mohr. Stem 2–12 dm. tall, widely branched, glabrate: leaf-blades linear-elliptic to lanceolate or broadly linear, 3–10 cm. long, acute or somewhat acuminate, serrate, 3-ribbed, narrowed to the sessile but connate bases: heads usually 1-flowered, in axillary or involucrate clusters: bracts 1–3, or sometimes accompanied by a few accessory ones: corolla of the pistillate flowers 1.5 mm. long, the ligule oblique: corolla of the perfect flower 2 mm. long: achene clavate, about 2 mm. long.—Waste-places and cult. grounds, various provinces, Ala. to Ariz.—(*W. I., Mex., C. A., S. A.*)

101. TAGETES L. Annual or rarely perennial, strong-scented, erect, caulescent herbs. Leaves mostly opposite: blades pinnately divided. Heads erect. Involucre narrow: bracts partly united. Ray-flowers several, the corollas with elongate tubes and broad colored, often variegated, ligules. Disk-corollas elongate, the slender tube and narrow throat about equal in length. Achene elongate, somewhat 4-angled. Pappus of unequal narrow scales.—About 20 species, of warm and tropical America.—MARIGOLDS.

Heads solitary at the ends of the branches: involucre campanulate: ray-flowers 5–8; ligules obovate, 1 cm. long or more.   1. *T. erecta.*
Heads in compact corymbose cymes: involucre fusiform: ray-flowers usually 3; ligules suborbicular, usually 5 mm. long or less.   2. *T. minuta.*

1. T. erecta L. Plant mostly 2–15 dm. tall, the branches spreading or ultimately more or less decumbent: leaf-divisions linear-lanceolate, elliptic, mostly 1–2 cm. long, sharply and rather coarsely serrate: peduncles elongate, markedly clavate: involucre 15–18 mm. long; lobes ovate, short-acuminate: ligules obovate, orange or pale-yellow, 1–2 cm. long: disk-corollas 11–16 mm. long; lobes lanceolate: achene nearly linear, 7–9 mm. long, about as long as the longer pappus-scale.—(AFRICAN MARIGOLD.)—Roadsides, fields, and waste-places, Fla. Nat. of Mex.— (*W. I., C. A., S. A., O. W.*)—All year.

2. T. minuta L. Plant 3–10 dm. tall, the branches erect or nearly so: leaf-divisions linear to linear-lanceolate, finely but sharply serrate: peduncles short, slender: involucre about 1 cm. long; lobes deltoid, obtuse or merely acutish: ligules yellowish, suborbicular, usually less than 5 mm. long: disk-corollas 3–4 mm. long; lobes ovate: achene 5–6 mm. long, much longer than the longer pappus-scale.—Sandy waste-places, Coastal Plain, N. C. Nat. of Chile.—Sum.–fall.

102. BOEBERA Willd. Annual or perennial, glandular-dotted, strong-scented herbs. Leaves alternate or opposite: blades commonly parted or dissected. Heads inconspicuous, usually corymbose. Involucre turbinate or campanulate: bracts broad, thin-margined. Receptacle flat or nearly so. Ray-flowers yellow, few, the corollas with minute ligules. Disk yellow. Achene 3–5-angled. Pappus of 10 or more partly united narrow scales.— About 3 species, North American.

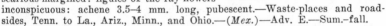

1. B. papposa (Vent.) Rydb. Plant annual, pubescent, 1–4 dm. tall: leaves opposite; blades 1–3 cm. long, pinnately 1- or 2-parted: involucre 6–8 mm. high; bracts scarious-margined: ligules of the ray-flowers inconspicuous: achene 3.5–4 mm. long, pubescent.—Waste-places and road-sides, Tenn. to La., Ariz., Minn., and Ohio.—(*Mex.*)—Adv. E.—Sum.–fall.

Thymophylla tenuiloba (DC.) Small, a native of Tex. and adj. Mex., is adventive at Miami, Fla. It has finely cut leaf-blades and yellow heads.

103. PECTIS L. Slender or wiry glandular-dotted herbs, the stems usually pubescent in lines. Leaves opposite: blades narrow, usually ciliate near the base. Heads clustered or solitary. Involucre narrow, few-several-flowered: bracts gland-bearing. Ray-flowers few: corollas with yellow ligules. Styles pubescent. Stigmas of the disk-flowers very short.—About 75 species, American.

Heads sessile or nearly so, mostly in clusters.
  Leaves with scattered glands; blades oblanceolate to linear-
    spatulate.   1. *P. prostrata*
  Leaves with 2 rows of glands beneath; blades narrowly
    linear.   2. *P. linearifolia.*
Heads distinctly peduncled, solitary in the branch-forks and
  at the ends of the branches.   3. *P. leptocephala.*

1. P. prostrata Cav. Stem usually branched at the base, the branches procumbent or prostrate, 0.5–2 dm. long: leaf-blades oblanceolate to linear-spatulate, 1–3 cm. long, entire, with 5–9 pairs of bristles: heads sessile or nearly so, more or less clustered: involucre 5–7 mm. long; bracts 5, elliptic to linear-elliptic, concave and keeled: ray-flowers 5: disk-flowers 4–15, with corollas 2–2.5 mm. long: achene 3–4 mm. long or rarely smaller: pappus-scales of the ray 2, narrowly lanceolate, accompanied by 1–3 bristles; of the disk 5, unequal.—Waste-places and cult. grounds, various provinces, Fla. to Ariz.—(*W. I., Mex., C. A., S. A.*)

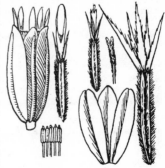

2. P. linearifolia Urban. Stem 1–4 dm. tall, erect or diffusely branched, puberulent in lines: leaf-blades linear or nearly so, over

1 mm. wide, acute, entire, 3–6 pairs of bristles near the base: heads sessile or nearly so, few in clusters: involucre prismatic, 4–5 mm. high; bracts 4–6, linear or linear-lanceolate: ray-flowers 2–3; ligules 2–2.5 mm. long: disk-flowers 6 or 7, with corollas about 2.5 mm. long: achene 3 mm. long or nearly so: pappus-scales of the ray 2, narrowly lanceolate and aristate-attenuate, of the disk 5. [*P. ciliaris* Fernald, not L.]—Sandy woods and cult. grounds, pen. Fla.—(*W. I.*).

3. P. leptocephala (Cass.) Urban. Stem more or less diffusely branched, slender, 1–4 dm. long, the branches prostrate, forming mats, finely pubescent in lines: leaf-blades narrowly linear, commonly 1–3 cm. long, mostly less than 1 mm. wide, acute, entire, with 2–4 pairs of bristles below the middle: heads solitary on filiform peduncles, 1–2.5 cm. long: involucre narrow, 4–5 mm. high; bracts 5, linear or nearly so: ray-flowers 5; ligules 2–2.5 mm. long: disk-flowers 4–7, with corollas 2–2.5 mm. long: achene slender, 2.5–3 mm. long: pappus-bristles of the ray 2, with an incised lanceolate base and a slender awn, of the disk 5, or rarely 4. [*P. linifolia* Less. *P. Lessingii* Fernald.]—Pine-lands and sand-dunes, S pen. Fla. and the Keys.—(*W. I.*).

104. ACHILLEA (Vaill.) L. Perennial, usually copiously pale-pubescent, herbs. Leaves alternate: blades coarsely toothed to thrice-pinnatifid. Heads several or numerous, rather small, in corymbs or corymbiform panicles. Involucre hemispheric, campanulate, or obovoid: bracts imbricate in 3 or 4 series, the outer the smaller. Receptacle conic or convex, chaffy, the chaff membranous, broad. Ray-flowers 5–12, pistillate, fruit-producing: corollas with short and broad, white, pink or purple, or rarely yellow ligules. Disk-flowers 15–75, perfect, fruit-producing: corollas yellowish-white or straw-colored, the tube equaling or longer than the throat. Achene ellipsoid or obovoid, callous-margined. Pappus wanting.—About 75 species, in the Northern Hemisphere, mostly in the Old World.—Spr.–fall.—MILFOILS. YARROWS.

Ultimate leaf-segments linear or nearly so: ligules of the ray white. — 1. *A. occidentalis.*
Ultimate leaf-segments ovate or lanceolate.
  Ligules of the ray purplish: leaf-blades conspicuously punctate, the ultimate segments strongly callous-thickened toward the apex. — 2. *A. asplenifolia.*
  Ligules of the ray white or rarely pink: leaf-blades not conspicuously punctate, the ultimate segments not callous-thickened toward the apex. — 3. *A. Millefolium.*

1. A. occidentalis Raf. Stem 3–10 dm. tall, silky-villous, mostly simple: leaves sparingly villous; rachis merely margined; ultimate segments linear or nearly so: bracts of the involucre elliptic, often broadly so, to elliptic-lanceolate, the outer obtuse, the inner acute, all erose-ciliate at the apex: ligules 2 mm. wide: disk-corollas 2–2.5 mm. long: achene narrowly cuneate, nearly 2 mm. long.—Open woods, clearings, roadsides, and waste-places, various provinces, Fla. to Ark., Colo., Minn., and Mass.

2. A. asplenifolia Vent. Stem 2.5–6 dm. tall, nearly glabrous or sparingly silky-villous, sometimes branched above: leaves glabrous above, sparingly villous beneath; rachis winged; ultimate segments lanceolate: bracts of the involucre ovate to elliptic, sometimes narrowly so, all obtuse, ciliate at the apex: ligules nearly 2 mm. wide: disk-corollas about 2 mm. long: achene ellipsoid, less than 2 mm. long.— (YAR.)—Roadsides, fields, and woods, various provinces N of Coastal Plain, N. C. to S. Dak. and N. S. Nat. of Eu.

3. A. Millefolium L. Stem 2–7 dm. tall, sparingly villous, sometimes branched above: leaves sparingly villous; rachis winged; ultimate segments ovate or ovate-lanceolate: bracts of the involucre ovate to elliptic, all obtuse, ciliate at the apex: ligules about 2 mm. wide: disk-corollas fully 2 mm. long: achene ellipsoid or slightly broadened upward, fully 2 mm. long.—Dry hillsides, woods, pastures, and roadsides, various provinces, Fla. to Miss., Ill., Yukon, and N. S.—(*W. I., O. W.*)—Often a weed.

105. ORMENIS Cass. Annual, diffusely branched herbs. Leaves alternate: blades pinnatifid, the segments rather broad. Heads solitary at the ends of the branches. Involucre saucer-shaped: bracts in 2 or 3 series, rather broad. Receptacle conic, chaffy, the chaff cartilaginous, boat-shaped, surrounding the achenes. Ray-flowers perfect, fruit-producing; corollas with yellow ligules, or white and yellow at the base. Disk-flowers numerous, perfect, fruit-producing, the tube produced into an appendage at the base. Achene ellipsoid or obovoid, prominently 3-ribbed on the inner side. Pappus wanting.—One species.

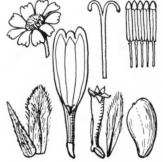

1. O. mixta (L.) Dum. Stem 1–4 dm. tall, usually branched at the base, the branches spreading, villous: leaf-blades cuneate or spatulate to linear in outline, 1–3 cm. long, the rachis broad, the segments triangular to lanceolate on the lower part of the blade, often broadened upward toward the apex: peduncles slightly thickened under the head: bracts of the involucre ovate to elliptic and linear, 3–4 mm. long, villous: ligules cuneate, 5–8 mm. long, yellow at the base: achene obovoid, fully 1 mm. long.—Waste-places and cult. grounds, various provinces, Fla. to B. C. and N. J. Nat. of Medit. Reg.—Spr.–fall.

106. ANTHEMIS L. Annual or perennial, branched, leafy herbs. Leaves alternate: blades pinnatifid or bipinnatifid, the segments rather narrow. Heads solitary at the ends of the branches. Involucre saucer-shaped: bracts in about 3 series, usually thin. Receptacle conic to hemispheric, chaffy, the chaff membranous, with a midrib. Ray-flowers pistillate, fruit-producing: corollas with white ligules. Disk-flowers numerous, perfect, fruit-producing: corolla yellow, the tube equalling or longer than the throat, the lobes ovate. Achene subcylindric or somewhat obovoid, with filiform ribs. Pappus wanting or a minute crown.—About 80 species, Eurasian and African.

Receptacle with cuspidate-acuminate chaff : achene equally 10-nerved.   1. *A. arvensis.*
Receptacle with obtuse chaff : achene 3-nerved on the inner side.   2. *A. nobilis.*

1. A. arvensis L. Annual or sometimes biennial, not strong-scented: stem 1–5 dm. tall, finely pubescent: leaf-blades 2–5 cm. long, pinnatifid or bipinnatified, the segments linear-lanceolate to subulate: bracts of the involucre pubescent, the outer lanceolate, acute, the inner elliptic, obtuse: ligules 7–12 mm. long: achene subcylindric, 1.5–2 mm. mm. long: pappus a minute border. — Waste-places, roadsides, and fields, various provinces, Fla. to Ore., B. C., and Que. Nat. of O. W.—Spr.–fall.

2. **A. nobilis** L. Perennial, aromatic: stem 1–3.5 dm. tall, pubescent, sometimes decumbent: leaf-blades 1–4 cm. long, pinnatifid or bipinnatifid, the segments linear to subulate: bracts of the involucre pubescent, the outer ovate-lanceolate, obtuse, the inner elliptic, rounded at the apex: ligules 6–10 mm. long: achene somewhat pyriform, 1–1.5 mm. long: pappus wanting. —Waste-places and about gardens, various provinces, N. C. to Tenn. and R. I. Nat. of Eu.—Sum.–fall.

107. **MARUTA** Cass. Annual, branching, usually very leafy herbs. Leaves alternate: blades pinnatifid, the segments narrow. Heads solitary at the ends of the branches. Involucre saucer-shaped: bracts in 2 series, rather broad. Receptacle conic, chaffy toward the apex, the chaff subulate, rather persistent. Ray-flowers 10–15, neutral: corollas with white ligules. Disk-flowers perfect, fruit-producing: corollas greenish-yellow, the tube longer than the throat, the lobes ovate. Achene nearly cylindric, 10-ribbed, glandular-tubercled. Pappus wanting.—About 12 species, natives of the Old World.

1. **M. Cotula** (L.) DC. Plant strong-scented: leaf-blades thrice pinnately dissected, the segments very slender: disk-flowers near the center of the receptacle with chaff; coróllas mostly 2.5 mm. long: achene tuberculate-roughened: pappus wanting. [*Anthemis Cotula* L.]—(MAY-WEED. DOG'S-CAMOMILE. DOG-DAISY. DOG-FENNEL.)—Fields, roadsides, cult. grounds, and waste-places, various provinces, Fla. to Calif., Alas., and Newf. Nat. of O. W.—Sum.–fall.

108. **CHAMOMILLA** [Hall.] Gilib. Annual herbs, resembling *Anthemis* and *Maruta*. Leaves alternate: blades once to thrice pinnatifid, the segments narrow. Heads solitary or corymbose. Involucre saucer-shaped to hemispheric: bracts somewhat imbricate in 2–4 series, scarious-margined. Receptacle conic, hemispheric, or subglobose, naked. Ray-flowers, if present, pistillate, fruit-producing: corollas with white ligules. Disk-flowers numerous, perfect, fruit-producing: corollas yellow, the tube equaling or slightly longer than the throat, the lobes lanceolate to ovate. Achene asymmetric, the back nerveless, the face 3–5-ribbed. Pappus a crown or a mere border.—About 50 species, mostly natives of the Old World.

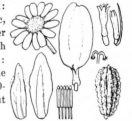

1. C. maritima (L.) Rydb. Stem and branches 1–3 dm. tall, often decumbent: leaf-blades 2–4 cm. long; blades bipinnatifid, the segments spreading, fleshy: involucre 10–12 mm. wide; bracts elliptic, obtuse, brown-margined: ray-flowers 15–20; ligules white, 8–11 mm. long: achene cuneate, 2–2.5 mm. long, rugose on the back and between the corky ribs: pappus-crown toothed.—Ballast and waste-places, Coastal Plain and adj. provinces, Ala. to Pa. and Mass. Nat. of Eu.—Spr.–fall.

109. MATRICARIA [Tourn.] L. Annual or perennial, branching herbs, but sometimes partly woody. Leaves alternate: blades lobed, dissected, or pinnately divided. Heads corymbose. Involucre saucer-shaped to hemispheric: bracts somewhat imbricate in 2–4 series, narrow. Receptacle convex, naked. Ray-flowers usually present, several, pistillate, fruit-producing: corollas with narrow or broad ligules, white in our species. Disk-flowers numerous, perfect, fruit-producing: corollas often yellow, the tube and throat slightly differentiated, the lobes deltoid. Achene subcylindric, 5–10-angled or 5–10-ribbed. Pappus in both ray and disk a lobed crown. —About 100 species, widely distributed.

1. M. Parthenium L. Stem 2–7 dm. tall, striate: leaf-blades broad, those of the lower ones at least, twice pinnately parted, the divisions incised: involucre 7–10 mm. wide; outer bracts linear-lanceolate, acute; inner bracts linear-elliptic, 2.5–3 mm. long, acute or obtuse: ligules white, 3–8 mm. long: disk cream-colored: achene 1.5 mm. long, 8–10-ribbed: pappus a toothed crown. [*Chrysanthemum Parthenium* (L.) Bernh.]—(FEVERFEW.)—Roadsides, fence-rows, and waste-places, various provinces, Ga. to Ohio and N. B.; also Calif. to Wash. Nat. of Eu.—(*W. I., Mex., C. A.*)—Sum.–fall.

110. LEUCANTHEMUM [Tourn.] Mill. Perennial herbs with root-stocks. Leaves alternate: blades toothed or entire, or sometimes pinnatifid. Heads solitary at the ends of the stem and branches. Involucre saucer-shaped: bracts somewhat imbricate in 2–4 series, narrow. Receptacle flat or convex, naked. Ray-flowers usually present, 10–25, pistillate and fruit-producing: corollas with white ligules. Disk-flowers numerous, perfect, fruit-producing: corollas yellow, the tube usually shorter than the throat, the lobes lanceolate. Filaments adnate to the tube. Achene cylindric or nearly so, 10-ribbed or 10-angled. Pappus wanting or obsolete, or in the ray a mere crown.—About 20 species, natives of the northern hemisphere.

1. **L. Leucanthemum** (L.) Rydb. Plant 2–9 dm. tall, glabrous or nearly so: leaf-blades spatulate to linear, 2–15 cm. long, serrate or pinnatifid: involucre 12–18 mm. wide; outer bracts linear-lanceolate, acute: inner bracts elliptic, 5.5–6.5 mm. long, obtuse: ray-flowers numerous; ligules white or pink, 1–2.5 cm. long: disk yellow: achene cylindric, about 1.5 mm. long: pappus obsolete. [*Chrysanthemum Leucanthemum* L.]—(WHITE-DAISY. OX-EYE DAISY. WHITE-WEED.)—Fields, roadsides, woods, and waste-places, nearly throughout U. S. and Can. Nat. of O. W.—(*W. I.*)—Sum.-fall.—Widely distributed in the Southern States during the Civil War. In the mountains, when abundant, the plants, especially the ripe heads, are much eaten by sheep.

111. CHRYSANTHEMUM L. Annual herbs, suggesting coarse-leaved *Maruta* or *Cotula*. Leaves alternate: blades toothed to pinnatifid. Heads solitary at the ends of the branches. Involucre hemispheric or nearly so: bracts thin, imbricate in about 3 series, broad. Receptacle convex, naked. Ray-flowers 10–20, pistillate, fruit-producing: corollas with yellow ligules. Disk-flowers numerous, perfect, fruit-producing: corollas yellow, the tube and throat about equal in length, the lobes ovate. Achenes various, those of the ray short and obpyramidal, with 2 or 3 wing-angles, those of the disk prismatic or cylindric, 8–10-ribbed. Pappus wanting.—About 15 species, natives of the Old World.

Leaf-blades dissected, bipinnatifid: achenes of the ray 3-angled, the median angle with the broader wing-margin.   1. *C. coronarium.*
Leaf-blades toothed or merely pinnately lobed: achenes of the ray with 2 lateral wings.   2. *C. segetum.*

1. **C. coronarium** L. Stem 3–6 dm. tall, glabrous: blades of the cauline leaves obovate outline 3–6 cm. long, mostly bipinnatifid, sessile and auricled, the ultimate segments linear-lanceolate: heads on peduncles mostly over 5 cm. long: involucre 1 cm. high or less; bracts ovate to elliptic, with broad light-brown margins: ray-flowers 15–20, the ligules 1–1.5 cm. long: disk-corollas about 5 mm. long: achenes of the ray 3-angled, the middle angle winged, those of the disk 4-angled, the inner angle produced into a spur.—Waste-places and roadsides, various provinces, Ala. to Ont. Nat. of Medit. Reg.—(*W. I.*)—Spr.-fall.

2. **C. segetum** L. Stem 2–5 dm. tall, glabrous: blades of the cauline leaves spatulate to elliptic or lanceolate, pinnately lobed, toothed, or entire, the segments oblanceolate to cuneate: heads on peduncles mostly less than 5 cm. long: involucre about 1 cm. high; bracts elliptic, often broadly so, with broad brown margins: ray-flowers 12–15, the ligules 1–2 cm. long: disk-corollas about 5 mm. long: achenes of the ray with two lateral wings, those of the disk cylindric, 10-ribbed.—(CORN-MARIGOLD. CORN-CHRYSANTHEMUM.)—Waste-places, fields, and cult. grounds, various provinces, Fla. to Ala., N. Y., and N. B.; also Calif. and Ore. Nat. of O. W.—Sum.-fall.

112. TANACETUM [Tourn.] L. Perennial rather coarse erect herbs with rootstocks or rarely annuals. Leaves alternate: blades once to thrice pinnatifid. Heads corymbose. Involucre hemispheric to saucer-shaped: bracts in 2 or 3 series, usually narrow, often partly similar. Receptacle convex, naked. Ray-flowers 5–20, pistillate, fruit-producing: corollas with erect or spreading, inconspicuous, yellow ligules. Disk-flowers numerous, perfect, fruit-producing: corollas with the tube and throat only slightly differentiated. Achenes subcylindric, those of the ray mostly 3-angled, those of the disk 5-angled. Pappus a crown-like border.—About 30 species, widely distributed in the Northern Hemisphere.

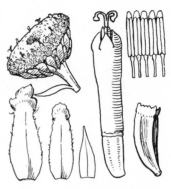

1. **T. vulgare** L. Plants perennial, 3–10 dm. tall, acrid-aromatic: leaf-blades 5–20 cm. long, with the ultimate segments sharply toothed: involucre 6–8 mm. wide, the inner bracts 4–5 mm. long: ray-flowers scarcely exceeding the disk and so inconspicuous as to make the heads appear discoid; corollas yellow: achene about 2 mm. long.—(TANSY.)—Fields, roadsides, and about gardens, various provinces, Ga. to Miss., Calif., Wash., and N. S. Nat. of O. W.—Sum.

113. ARTEMISIA L. Annual or perennial, often copiously branched herbs, or shrubs. Leaves alternate: blades dissected, lobed, or toothed, or entire. Heads relatively small, mostly in panicles, usually nodding before maturity, apparently discoid, the marginal flowers without ligules or wanting. Involucre campanulate to hemispheric: bracts in 2–4 series, the inner longer and thinner than the outer. Receptacle convex or conic, naked or hairy. Flowers yellowish or greenish. Marginal flowers (functionally ray-flowers) pistillate, fruit-producing: corollas various, sometimes oblique, or wanting. Disk-flowers few, perfect, often fruit-producing: corollas campanulate, funnelform, or trumpet-shaped. Achene ellipsoid, terete. Pappus wanting.—About 250 species, in the Northern Hemisphere and South America.—WORMWOODS.

Disk-flowers not producing fruits: stigmas united or very short and erect: receptacle naked.   I. DRACUNCULOIDES.
Disk-flowers fruit-producing, their stigmas elongate and recurved.
  Receptacle hairy.   II. FRIGIDAE.
  Receptacle naked.
    Annual or biennial herbs.   III. ANNUAE.
    Perennial plants.
      Leaf-blades with broad lobes.   IV. VULGARES.
      Leaf-blades bipinnatifid, the segments very narrow or filiform.   V. PONTICAE.

I. DRACUNCULOIDES

Plant biennial: heads mostly erect.   1. *A. caudata.*
Plant perennial: heads mostly nodding.   2. *A. campestris.*

II. FRIGIDAE

Woody perennial: leaf-blades with linear to ovate obtuse teeth.   3. *A. Absinthium.*

III. ANNUAE

Heads in dense axillary spikes, not nodding.   4. *A. biennis.*
Heads in lax racemes or panicles, nodding.   5. *A. annua.*

IV. VULGARES

Perennial with broad-lobed leaf-blades: heads in simple or compound spikes.　　　　　　　　　　　　　　　　　　　　　　6. *A. vulgaris.*

V. PONTICAE

Perennial with narrow lobed leaf-blades: heads in simple or compound racemes.　　　　　　　　　　　　　　　　　　7. *A. Abrotanum.*

1. A. caudata Michx. Stem, glabrous, at least at maturity, 5–18 dm. tall, often with ascending branches at the base: leaves numerous; blades once to thrice pinnately divided, the segments linear-filiform to nearly filiform: heads very numerous in elongate panicles: involucre with the disk-flowers perfect but not producing fruit, 3–4 mm. high; bracts ovate to oval or broadly elliptic: ray-flowers 6–8: corollas 1.5 mm. long: achene about 1 mm. long.—Sandy soil, various provinces, Fla. to Tex., Wyo., and N. B.—Sum.–fall.

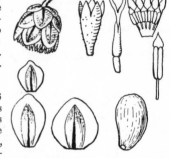

2. A. campestris L. Stem, glabrous, 3–6 dm. tall, usually branched, striate: leaves clustered at the base of the stem; blades mostly once or twice pinnately divided, the segments linear-filiform: heads numerous, in open panicles: involucre with the disk-flowers perfect, but not producing fruits, 2–2.5 mm. high; bracts ovate to oval: ray-flowers 6–10: corollas 1 mm. long: achene fully 0.5 mm. long.—Sandy woods and dry banks, various provinces, S. C. to Conn. Nat. of Eu.—Sum.–fall.

3. A. Absinthium L. Stem, more or less woody, 4–12 dm. tall, finely cinereous-pubescent, much-branched: leaf-blades once, twice, or thrice pinnately divided, the segments linear, lanceolate, or ovate: heads numerous in leafy panicles, nodding: involucre 3–3.5 mm. high, with the central flowers fruit-producing; bracts lanceolate to ovate: ray-flowers about 10: corollas 1.5 mm. long: achene fully 1 mm. long.—(WORMWOOD.)—Fields, roadsides, and banks, various provinces, N. C. to Utah, B. C., Ont., and Newf. Nat. of Eu.—Sum.–fall.

4. A. biennis Willd. Plant glabrous, inodorous, insipid, 2–11 dm. tall, the stem nearly simple or sparingly branched: leaves numerous; blades once or twice pinnately divided, the segments lanceolate or linear, incised-pinnatifid or pinnatifid: panicle-branches ending in spikes: heads not drooping, crowded in axillary clusters: involucre 2–3 mm. high, with the central flowers perfect and fruit-producing; bracts elliptic to elliptic-lanceolate: ray-flowers 10–15; disk-flowers 10–15; corollas yellow, about 1 mm. long: achene about 1 mm. long.—Gravelly banks and rocky soil, various provinces N of Coastal Plain, Tenn. to Mo., B. C., N. S., and Pa.; naturalized eastward.—(*O. W.*)—Sum.–fall.

5. A. annua L. Plant, glabrous, very aromatic, 4–10 dm. tall, the stem much-branched: leaf-blades once, twice, or thrice pinnately divided, the segments elliptic or incised, or pinnatifid: panicle-branches ending in loose racemes: heads subglobose, scattered, nodding: involucre about 1.5 mm. high, with the central flowers perfect and fruit-producing; bracts mostly elliptic, the outer narrower than the inner: ray-flowers 5 or 6; corollas greenish-yellow, less than 1 mm. long: disk-flowers 5 or 6; corollas yellow, 1 mm. long: achene 1 mm. long.—Fields, roadsides, and waste-places, various provinces, Tenn. to Ark., Ont., N. B., and Va.; also Calif. Nat. of O. W.—Sum.

6. A. vulgaris L. Herbaceous, lanate-tomentose, 3–12 dm. tall, the stems paniculately branched: leaf-blades various, white-woolly beneath, twice pin-natifid or pinnately parted, the segments lanceolate or linear: heads first nodding, soon erect, in a leafy panicle: involucre 4–5 mm. high, with the central flowers fruit-producing; bracts ovate to elliptic or elliptic-lanceolate: ray-flowers 6–12; corollas 2 mm. long: disk-flowers 5–15; corollas 2.5 mm. long: achene 1.5 mm. long or more.—(MUGWORT. WHITE-SAGE.)—Roadsides, stream-banks, cult. grounds, and waste-places, various provinces, Ga. to Ala., B. C., Ont., and Newf. Nat. of Eu.—(*W. I.*)—Sum.–fall.

7. A. Abrotanum L. Shrub 1 m. tall or less, puberulent or glabrous, the stem much-branched, the branches erect or ascending: leaf-blades twice pin-nately divided, the segments linear-filiform, revolute: heads numerous, nod-ding, in leafy panicles: involucre about 3 mm. high; bracts linear-lanceolate to elliptic, arachnoid-canescent: ray-flowers about 10; corollas 1.5 mm. long: disk-flowers 15–20; corollas nearly 2 mm. long: achene about 1 mm. long.—(SOUTHERNWOOD.)—Waste-places and roadsides, various provinces, N. C. to Colo. and N. B. Nat. of Eu.—Sum.–fall.

114. SOLIVA R. & P. Annual, caulescent, diminutive herbs. Leaves alternate: blades pinnately twice divided, the ultimate segments deeply lobed. Heads sessile on the stem or on the branches, green, discoid, the flowers mostly pistillate and apetalous, the few perfect ones with 2–6–lobed corollas. Involucre hemispheric: bracts broad in 2 series. Anthers broad, mostly rounded at the base. Achene much flattened, winged, the wings, often broadly pandurate, smooth, usually prolonged into a short spine on either side of the larger terminal spine. Pappus none. —About 3 species, South American.

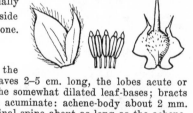

1. S. sessilis R. & P. Plant depressed, the stem and branches, at least, villous: leaves 2–5 cm. long, the lobes acute or acuminate, ciliate: involucre sessile in the somewhat dilated leaf-bases; bracts ovate, about 4 mm. long, acute or sharp acuminate: achene-body about 2 mm. long, the broad wings ciliolate, the terminal spine about as long as the achene-body.—Lawns and banks, N Fla. to La. Nat. of S. Am.—Spr.–fall.

115. GYMNOSTYLES A. Juss. Annual, caulescent, diminutive, often matted stoloniferous herbs. Leaves alternate: blades once or twice pin-nately divided, the ultimate segments entire or toothed. Heads sessile at the base of the plant, green, discoid, the flowers as in *Soliva*. Involucre hemi-spheric, becoming flattish: bracts narrow, in 1 or 2 series. Anthers narrow, somewhat sagittate at the base. Achene somewhat flattened, with callous cor-rugated margins and a terminal spine. Pappus none.—About 3 species, South American.

Leaf-blades 2-pinnate: achene-callous corrugated up to the base of the rounded top:
  heads much depressed, 8–10 mm. wide.   1. *G. anthemifolia.*
Leaf-blades 1-pinnate: achene-callous corrugated up to the truncate or notched top: heads subglobose, 3–6 mm. wide.   2. *G. nasturtiifolia.*

1. G. anthemifolia A. Juss. Plant somewhat depressed, light-green, the branches often creeping: leaves erect or nearly so, 4–14 cm. long, the lobes acute or acuminate, long-hairy: bracts of the involucre elliptic-lanceolate, 4.5–5.5 mm. long, usually somewhat acuminate: achene-body ellipsoid-cuneate, about 2 mm. long, the margins bluntly corrugated.—In dense tufts, bayou-banks, roadsides, ditch-banks, paths, fields, yards and waste grounds, Coastal Plain, N Fla. to Tex. Nat. of S. Am.—Spr.

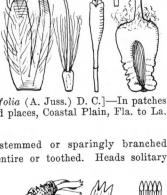

2. G. nasturtiifolia A. Juss. Plant much depressed, dark-green, the branches creeping: leaves prostrate or spreading, 1.5 cm. long or less, the lobes obtuse or acutish, short-hairy: bracts of the involucre lanceolate to linear-spatulate, 2.5–3 mm. long, acute or acuminate: achene-body cuneate, 1.5–2 mm. long, the margin sharply corrugated. [*Soliva nasturtiifolia* (A. Juss.) D. C.]—In patches or carpets, low, moist, or damp, partly shaded places, Coastal Plain, Fla. to La. and N. C. Nat. of S. Am.—Early spr.

116. ARNICA L. Perennial simple-stemmed or sparingly branched herbs. Leaves typically opposite: blades entire or toothed. Heads solitary or several. Involucre mostly turbinate or campanulate, or broader in age: bracts nearly equal, narrow. Ray-flowers with yellow ligules. Corollas of the disk-flowers tubular, the lobes very short. Achene ribbed. Pappus a single series of slender bristles.—About 45 species, in the Northern Hemisphere.

1. A. acaulis (Walt) B. S. P. Plant 2–10 dm. tall, hirsute: leaves mainly basal and spreading on the ground; blades elliptic to oval or ovate, 5–12 cm. long, shallowly toothed or nearly entire: bracts of the involucre 9.5–11 mm. long, acute: ligules 1.5–2.5 cm. long: achene 4 mm. long. [*A. nudicaulis* Nutt.]—(LEOPARD'S-BANE.)—Pinelands and low open woods, in acid soil, Coastal Plain and adj. provinces, Fla. to Pa.—Sum.—Rather rare.

117. EMILIA Cass.[1] Annual or perennial, tender herbs. Leaves alternate, but often mostly basal: blades entire toothed, or lyrate-pinnatifid. Heads solitary or in lax corymbs. Involucre swollen at the base: bracts in one series and without accessory ones at the base. Ray-flowers wanting. Disk-corollas golden, purple, or red, with a cylindric throat and a slender tube, the lobes lanceolate. Filaments slender. Achene 5-ribbed.—About 5 species, natives of the Old World Tropics.

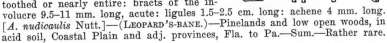

Corollas scarlet or orange: heads stout: involucre campanulate, usually over 1 cm. long.   1. *E. coccinea.*

Corollas lilac or pale-purplish: heads slender: involucre cylindric-campanulate, usually less than 1 cm. long.   2. *E. sonchifolia.*

[1] Revised by Edward Johnston Alexander.

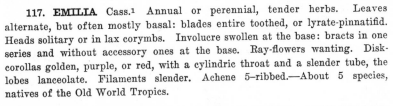

1. E. coccinea (Sims) Sweet. Plant moderately slender, mostly 1–8 dm. tall: leaf-blades rather succulent, those of the lower leaves spatulate, those of the upper leaves lanceolate to linear, auricled at the base, all sinuate-dentate: heads long-peduncled: involucral bracts linear, 10–12 mm. long: corollas 9–11 mm. long: achene 4 mm. long. [*E. sonchifolia* (Fl. SE. U. S.)]— Cult. grounds, waste-places, fields, and roadsides, pen. Fla. and Florida Keys. Nat. of O. W. trop.—(*W. I., Mex., C. A., S. A.*)—All year.

2. E. sonchifolia (L.) DC. Plant very slender, 1–5 dm. tall: leaf-blades spatulate in outline below, above lanceolate to elliptic, all auricled at the base, the lower narrowed to a wing-like petiole between the blade and the auricled base, all sinuate-dentate, or somewhat pinnatifid: heads long-peduncled: involucral bracts linear, 8–10 mm. long: corollas 7–8 mm. long: achene 3 mm. long.—Cult. grounds, waste-places, fields, and roadsides, pen. Fla. and Florida Keys. Nat. of O. W. trop.— (*W. I., Mex., C. A., S. A.*)

118. GYNURA Cass. Annual or perennial, rather coarse herbs or subshrubs. Leaves alternate; blades entire, toothed, pinnatifid or pinnately parted. Heads solitary to many. Involucre campanulate or cylindric, with several subtending bractlets: bracts flat. Heads discoid. Corollas yellow or orange to red, with a long, narrow funnel-form throat, and triangular or ovate lobes. Anthers entire or minutely sagittate at the base. Style-branches slender with long, subulate, pubescent appendages. Achene terete, 5–10-ribbed. Pappus copious, white.—About 20 species, natives of Asia, Africa, East Indies, and Australia.

1. G. aurantiaca (Blume) DC. Plant up to 1 m. tall, the stem densely velvety with long purple hairs, often widely branched: leaf-blades simple, with flaring teeth; the lower petioles expanding into an auriculate base; upper leaves sessile by an auriculate base: bracts subtending the involucre narrowly linear to filiform; involucre 10–15 mm. high: corollas yellow-orange: achene pubescent.—(VELVET-PLANT.)—Pinelands, roadsides and waste-places, S pen. Fla. Nat. of E. I. (*W. I.*)—Spr.

119. MESADENIA Raf. Perennial, somewhat leafy herbs. Leaves alternate: blades undulate, toothed, or somewhat lobed. Heads in corymb-like clusters but centrifugal. Involucre cylindric to cylindric-ovoid: bracts sometimes winged or keeled. Flowers white or pinkish; disk-corollas with linear or linear-lanceolate lobes longer than the campanulate throat. Filaments filiform. Achene ribbed, glabrous. [*Cacalia* L. in part]—About 30 species, North American.—Sum. or Spr.-fall S.—INDIAN-PLANTAINS.

Bracts of the involucre wingless.
    Leaf-blades pedately or digitately veined, those of the lower leaves wider than long. I. RENIFORMES.

Leaf-blades parallel-veined or subpinnately veined: stem
terete.   II. LANCEOLATAE.
Bracts of the involucre winged along the midrib.   III. TUBEROSAE.

I. RENIFORMES

Leaves green on both sides or glaucous beneath; blades
pedately veined.
   Leaves green: stem furrowed.   1. *M. reniformis.*
   Leaves glaucous beneath: stem terete.   2. *M. atriplicifolia.*
Leaves glaucous on both sides: blades digitately veined.   3. *M. maxima.*

II. LANCEOLATAE

Leaf-blades ovate, commonly broadly so.   4. *M. Elliottii.*
Leaf-blades linear to lanceolate.   5. *M. lanceolata.*

III. TUBEROSAE

Stem terete, merely striate: blades of the upper stem-leaves
hastate.   6. *M. diversifolia.*
Stem channeled or angled: blades of the upper stem-leaves not
hastate.
  Lower leaves with 7–9-veined entire or crenate blades.
    Leaf-blades entire or nearly so.   7. *M. tuberosa.*
    Leaf-blades crenate.   8. *M. floridana.*
  Lower leaves with 3–5-veined sinuate-dentate blades.   9. *M. sulcata.*

1. M. reniformis (Muhl.) Raf. Stem 9–30 dm. tall: blades of the cauline
leaves reniform, 10–60 cm. wide: involucral bracts 8–11 mm. long: achene
about 5 mm. long. [*C. reniformis* Muhl.]—
(GREAT INDIAN-PLANTAIN.)—Rich banks,
woods, and thickets, various provinces,
rarely Coastal Plain, Ga. to Ala., Tenn.,
Minn., and N. J.

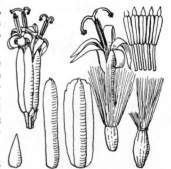

2. M. atriplicifolia (L.) Raf. Stem 9–20
dm. tall: blades of the cauline leaves ovate
to triangular, or narrower above, angulate-
lobed or sharply and coarsely toothed: involucral bracts 8–11 mm. long: achene 4–4.5
mm. long. [*C. atriplicifolia* L.]—(PALE
INDIAN-PLANTAIN.) — Woods, various provinces, Fla. to Kans., Minn., and N. J.

3. M. maxima Harper. Stem about 15
dm. tall: blades of the cauline leaves broadly ovate or narrower above, coarsely
sinuate-toothed involucral bracts 9–11 mm. long: achene not seen.—Dry pinelands, Sumter Co., near inner edge of Coastal Plain of Ga.

4. M. Elliottii Harper. Stem 8–12 dm. tall: blades of the cauline leaves
ovate to oval, entire or repand-undulate: involucral bracts 8–10 mm. long:
achene 6–6.5 mm. long. [*Cacalia ovata* (Chapm. Fl.) *M. ovata* (Fl. SE.
U. S.)]—Swamps, low pinelands, and damp woods, Coastal Plain, Fla. to
La. and Ga.—Late sum.

5. M. lanceolata (Nutt.) Raf. Stem 8–15 dm. tall: blades of the cauline
leaves linear, narrowly lanceolate, or linear-elliptic, entire or repand-denticulate: glaucous (or merely yellowish-green in *M. lanceolata virescens*): involucral bracts 8–10 mm. long: achene about 5 mm. long. [*C. lanceolata*
Nutt.]—Everglades and wet pinelands, Coastal Plain, Fla. to La. and N. C.

6. M. diversifolia (T. & G.) Greene. Similar to *M. atriplicifolia* in habit,
but not glaucous: stem angled, bracts keeled: corolla-lobes but little longer
than the throat. [*C. diversifolia* T. & G. *M. difformis* Small.]—Swamps,
Coastal Plain, W Fla. and SW Ga.

7. M. tuberosa (Nutt.) Britton. Stem 6–12 dm. tall: blades of the cauline leaves ovate, oval, elliptic-lanceolate, or narrowly elliptic, 5–20 cm. long: bracts of the involucre 8–10 mm. long: achene 4.5–5 mm. long. [*C. tuberosa* Nutt.]— Prairies, various provinces, Ala. to La., Minn., and Ont.

8. M. floridana (A. Gray) Greene. Stem 7–12 dm. tall: leaf-blades ovate, oval, or elliptic, crenate: involucral bracts 10–12 mm. long: corolla-lobes slightly longer than the throat: achene about 5 mm. long.—Dry pinelands, E Fla.—Spr.–sum.

9. M. sulcata (Fernald) Small. Stem 9–15 dm. tall: leaf-blades ovate to elliptic-ovate, narrowly elliptic, or elliptic-lanceolate: involucral bracts 8–10 mm. long: corolla-lobes twice as long as the throat: achene 5.5–6 mm. long.— Bogs or wet woods, Coastal Plain, N Fla. to Ala. and Ga.—Sum.–fall.

120. SYNOSMA Raf. Perennial, copiously leafy herbs. Leaves alternate: blades triangular to hastate, toothed. Heads corymbose. Involucre nearly cylindric: bracts narrow. Flowers white or pinkish: disk-corollas with lanceolate lobes shorter than the funnelform throat. Filaments enlarged below the anthers. Achene ribbed, glabrous.—One species.

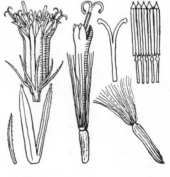

1. S. suaveolens (L.) Britton. Plant 6–15 dm. tall: leaves numerous; blades hastate, 8–20 cm. long, serrate or dentate-serrate: larger bracts of the involucre 10–11 mm. long: corollas 11–12 mm. long: achene slender, 7–9 mm. long. [*Cacalia suaveolens* L.]—Rich woods, thickets, and shaded banks, various provinces, Fla. to Tenn., Minn., and Mass.—Sum.–fall.

121. ERECHTITES Raf. Annual herbs. Leaves alternate: blades toothed or pinnatifid. Heads corymbose or paniculate. Involucre narrow and somewhat swollen at the base: bracts narrow, flat. Disk-corollas with triangular-lanceolate or deltoid lobes shorter than the narrow throat. Filaments longer than the anthers. Achene ribbed. Pappus of many white bristles.—About 12 species, American and Australian.

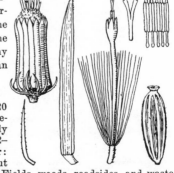

1. E. hieracifolia (L.) Raf. Plant 2–20 dm. tall, watery: leaf-blades spatulate-elliptic to lanceolate, 5–20 cm. long, coarsely toothed, incised, or pinnatifid: involucre 12–15 mm. long; bracts narrowly linear: corollas 8–9 mm. long, white: achene about 1.5 mm. long.—(FIREWEED. PILEWORT.)—Fields, woods, roadsides, and waste-places, various provinces, Fla. to La., Sask., and Newf.—Sum. or all year S.— A rather tender, but also somewhat coarse herb varying greatly in habit and with almost endless leaf-forms.

122. SENECIO [Tourn.] L. Annual or perennial herbs. Leaves alternate: blades entire, toothed, pinnatifid, or pinnately parted. Heads solitary or many. Involucre campanulate to cylindric: bracts flat. Ligules of the ray yellow, when present, in our species. Disk-corollas yellow with a funnelform throat and triangular or ovate lobes. Filaments often enlarged below the anthers. Achene 5–10-ribbed, pubescent or papillose.—About 1,500 species, widely distributed.—Spr.—SQUAW-WEEDS. RAGWORTS. RAGWEEDS. GROUNDSELS.

Plant annual or perhaps biennial: pubescence, if present, arachnoid.
  Ray-flowers present: achene pubescent on the angles.   I. LOBATI.
  Ray-flowers wanting: achene pubescent all over.   II. VULGARES.
Plant perennial: foliage, if pubescent, woolly or floccose.
  Heads large, the involucres over 1 cm. high: ray-flowers
    none.   III. NUDICAULES.
  Heads small, the involucres less than 1 cm. high: ray-
    flowers normally present.
    Blades of the basal leaves toothed or partly and slightly
      lyrate-pinnatifid.   IV. AUREI.
    Blades of the basal leaves pinnately parted and twice
      or thrice pinnatifid or dissected.   V. MILLEFOLIA.

I. LOBATI

Plant with pinnately parted leaf-blades: involucre 4–5 mm.
high; bracts light-green.   1. *S. glabellus.*

II. VULGARES

Plant with pinnatifid leaf-blades: involucre 6–8 mm. high;
bracts, as well as the small bracts at their bases, dark-green
or black.   2. *S. vulgaris.*

III. NUDICAULES

Stem usually bearing 3–5 pedunculate somewhat racemose
heads: heads very many-flowered.   3. *S. Rugelia.*

IV. AURIE

Blades of the basal leaves cordate or truncate at the base.
  Blades of the basal leaves predominantly lanceolate or
    elliptic-lanceolate, sharply serrate.   4. *S. Robbinsii.*
  Blades of the basal leaves predominately orbicular or
    ovate, crenate.
    Involucres over 5 mm. high.   5. *S. aureus.*
    Involucres less than 5 mm. high.   6. *S. gracilis.*
Blades of the basal leaves gradually narrowed or cuneate at
  the base.
  Blades of the basal leaves scarcely longer than broad.   7. *S. rotundus.*
  Blades of the basal leaves manifestly or markedly longer
    than broad.
    Blades of the basal leaves wholly, or predominately,
      narrowly or broadly spatulate: achene glabrous.   8. *S. obovatus.*
    Blades of the basal leaves wholly, or predominately,
      elliptic, oval, or lanceolate: achene pubescent.
      Foliage more or less copiously arachnoid; often
        densely so, the base of the stem and petioles of
        the basal leaves usually copiously silky-tomen-
        tose.
        Involucre 4–6 mm. high: blades of the basal
          leaves elliptic or oval, varying to broadest
          above or below the middle, or oblanceolate
          to lanceolate.
          Blades of the basal leaves elliptic to oval,
            varying to ovate or obovate: involucre 5–6
            mm. long.   9. *S. pauperculus.*
          Blades of the basal leaves narrowly lanceolate
            to oblanceolate: involucre 4–5 mm. long.   10. *S. Smallii.*
        Involucre 6–7 mm. high: blades of the basal leaves
          triangular-ovate to broadly lanceolate, triangu-
          lar-lanceolate, or ovate.   11. *S. tomentosus.*
      Foliage nearly glabrous, the base of the stem, petioles,
      and inflorescence inconspicuously arachnoid.   12. *S. alabamensis.*

V. MILLEFOLIA

Primary leaf-divisions 1–2-pinnatifid.   13. *S. Memmingeri.*
Primary leaf-divisions dissected, the ultimate divisions mainly
  linear.   14. *S. Millefolium.*

1. **S. glabellus** Poir. Plant annual, glabrous, the stem, 1–9 dm. tall: leaf-blades 3–20 cm. long, the lateral lobes cuneate to suborbicular, coarsely toothed, the terminal lobe rather large: involucre 4–6 mm. long; bracts narrowly linear to linear-lanceolate: ligules 4–8 mm. long: achene 1.5–2 mm. long, pubescent on the ribs. [*S. lobatus* Pers.]—Wet soil and river bottoms, various provinces, Fla. to Tex., Mo., Ill., and N. C.—(*Mex.*)—Spr.-fall.—The form with few-lobed broad terminal leaf-segments has been described as *S. mississippianus.*—Sometimes called BUTTER-WEED.

2. **S. vulgaris** L. Plant annual, sparingly pubescent, the stem 5 dm. tall or less, hollow, corymbosely branched: leaf-blades mostly 1 dm. long or less; the lobes and rachis

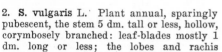

toothed, the terminal lobe relatively small: involucre 6–8 mm. long; bracts narrow, acuminate: ligules wanting: achene about 2.5 mm. long, minutely pubescent all over.—(COMMON-GROUNDSEL.)—Cult. grounds and waste-places, various provinces, rarely Coastal Plain, N. C. to Tex., S. Dak., Ont., and Newf.; also Pacific Coast. Nat. of Eu.—Spr.-fall.—*Senecio viscosus* L., coarser than *S. vulgaris* and strong-scented, with wholly green involucral bracts and inconspicuous ray-flowers, has been reported from N. C. It is a native of Eu.

3. **S. Rugelia** A. Gray. Plant 2–5 dm. tall: leaf-blades ovate to elliptic-oval, 8–15 cm. long, denticulate or dentate: bracts of the involucre linear-lanceolate, 12–13 mm. long: disk-corollas 7–8 mm. long: achene about 6 mm. long.—High mt. slopes, Blue Ridge, N. C. and Tenn.—Sum.

4. **S. Robbinsii** Oakes. Plant 3–10 dm. tall: blades of the basal leaves 3–8 cm. long, acute: involucre 6–8 mm. long; bracts narrowly linear: ligules 4–5 mm. long: achene pubescent.—Mt. meadows, Roan Mt. in the Blue Ridge of N. C. and Tenn., and more N provinces, N. Y. to Que. and N. B.—Sum.

5. **S. aureus** L. Plant 3–7 dm. tall: blades of the basal leaves 2–12 cm. long, rounded at the apex: involucre 6–7 mm. long; bracts linear, fully 1 mm. wide: ligules narrow, 5.5–7.5 mm. long: achene glabrous.—Low grounds, swamps, and wet woods, various provinces, Fla. to Tex., Ont., and Newf.—Spr.-sum.

6. **S. gracilis** Pursh. Plant similar to that of *S. aureus* in habit, but smaller and more slender: involucre 3.5–4.5 mm. long; bracts narrowly linear, scarcely 1 mm. wide: ligules broad, 3.5–5 mm. long.—Wet grounds, various provinces, Ga. to Pa.—Spr.

7. **S. rotundus** (Britton) Small. Plant 3–6 dm. tall: blades of the basal leaves suborbicular to orbicular-ovate, coarsely crenate-serrate: involucre 4–5 mm. long; bracts linear-subulate to linear-lanceolate: ligules 8–10 mm. long.—Low grounds or wet rocks, various provinces, La. to Tex., Mo., and Ohio.—Spr.

8. **S. obovatus** Muhl. Plant 1–5 dm. tall: blades of the basal leaves spatulate to obovate, coarsely toothed or some of them lyrate-pinnatifid: involucre 4–5 mm. long: bracts narrowly linear or subulate-linear: ligules 5–7 mm. long. —Thickets and dry hillsides, various provinces, W Fla. to Tex., Vt., and Me.—Spr.-sum.

9. **S. pauperculus** Michx. Plant 2–6 dm. tall: blades of the basal leaves elliptic to oval, varying ovate or obovate, serrate, incised-serrate or partly

pinnatifid: heads typically few, not crowded: involucre 5–6 mm. long; bracts glabrous or nearly so: ligules of the ray mostly 7–9 mm. long: achene 2.5–3 mm. long.—Stony woods, dry pastures, hillsides, and meadows, various provinces, Ga. to Tex., B. C., Ont., and Newf.—Spr.–sum.—*Senecio Earlei* Small seems to be a more robust and broader leaved form of this species in the southern part of its range.

10. S. Smallii Britton. Plant 3–6 dm. tall: blades of the basal leaves narrowly lanceolate to oblanceolate, serrate, incised-serrate, or incised or pinnatifid near the base: heads typically numerous and often crowded: involucre 4–5 mm. long; bracts glabrous or nearly so: ligules of the ray mostly 4–5 mm. long: achenes 1.5–2 mm. long.—Sandy fields, ditches, pinewoods, and dry woods, various provinces, Fla. to Miss., Tenn., and Pa.—Spr.

11. S. tomentosus Michx. Plant 2–7 dm. tall, the foliage typically and persistently floccose-tomentose: blades of the basal leaves triangular-ovate to broadly lanceolate, triangular-lanceolate, or ovate, crenate or crenate-serrate, abruptly narrowed or truncate at the base: heads few, at least relatively so. ultimately not crowded: involucre 6–7 mm. long; bracts densely white-pubescent when young: ligules of the ray 5–8 mm. long: achene 2–2.5 mm. long.—Sandy fields, banks, roadsides, and prairies, Coastal Plain and adj. provinces, Fla. to Tex., Ark., and N. J.—Spr.

12. S. alabamensis Britton. Plant similar to *S. tomentosus* in habit, but nearly glabrous up to the inflorescence where the peduncles are arachnoid: blades of the basal leaves ovate, triangular-ovate, or ovate-lanceolate, crenate, dentate, or nearly entire, often inequilateral at the abruptly narrowed or truncate base; heads rather few, not crowded, except when young: involucre 6–7 mm. long: bracts slightly arachnoid or nearly glabrous: ligules 5–8 mm. long: achene about 2.5 mm. long.—Moist pine woods, Coastal Plain, Ala.—Spr.

13. S. Memmingeri Britton. Plant 3–6 dm. tall: blades of the basal leaves bipinnatifid: involucre 5–6 mm. long; bracts linear: ligules 5–6 mm. long.— Cliffs and dry soil, Blue Ridge to Appalachian Plateau, Ala. to N. C.—Spr.–sum.

14. S. Millefolium T. & G. Plant 3–7 dm. tall: blades of the basal leaves bipinnately dissected into narrowly linear segments: involucre 5–6 mm. long; bracts linear and usually lanceolate at the tip: ligules 2–4 mm. long: disk-corollas 4 mm. long.—Cliffs, Blue Ridge, S. C. and N. C.—Sum.

123. ARCTIUM L. Biennial, coarse herbs. Leaves alternate: blades often ample, mainly entire or repand. Heads solitary in the axils or clustered, not conspicuous. Involucre with many narrow bracts, each hooked at the tip. Filaments glabrous. Pappus of short, rigid or scale-like bristles.—About 6 species, Eurasian.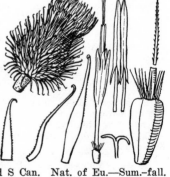

1. A. minus Schk. Plant 4–16 dm. tall, often widely branched: leaf-blades ovate, those of the lower cauline leaves 2–4.5 dm. long, all undulate or shallowly toothed: inner bracts of the involucre mostly 7–8 mm. long: corollas purple, pink, or white: achene cuneate to elliptic-obovate, 5–6 mm. long or rarely smaller. — (BURDOCK. BEGGAR'S-BUTTONS. CLOTBUR.) — Waste-places, cult. grounds, and roadsides throughout U. S. and S Can. Nat. of Eu.—Sum.–fall.

124. CIRSIUM [Tourn.] Hill. Annual, biennial or perennial, large or coarse herbs. Leaves alternate: blades toothed, lobed, or pinnatifid, usually spiny. Heads erect, often showy. Involucre with the outer bracts, at least, spine-tipped or spiny margined. Flowers violet, purple, lilac, or yellowish, or rarely white. Filaments mostly pubescent. Pappus of elongate capillary, plumose bristles in several series.—More than 200 species, widely distributed in the Northern Hemisphere.—Sum.–fall or all year S.—THISTLES. BULL-THISTLES.

Heads not involucrate, but sometimes approximate to 1 or few bract-like leaves.
  Bracts of the involucre not spine-tipped.
    Heads solitary or few, large, the involucre over 2 cm.
      in diameter.   I. MUTICA.
    Heads numerous, small, the involucre less than 2 cm.
      in diameter.   II. ARVENSIA.
  Bracts of the involucre, at least the outer spine-tipped.
    Spines of the involucral bracts appressed or erect.   III. REPANDA.
    Spines of the involucral bracts spreading.
      Inner bracts of the involucre narrow, with soft
        flattened tips.   IV. ALTISSIMA.
      Inner bracts of the involucre, as well as outer spine-
        tipped.   V. LANCEOLATA.
Heads involucrate, surrounded by a whorl of spinescent
  bracts.   VI. HORRIDULA.

I. MUTICA

Rather tall plant with woolly involucral bracts and deeply pinnatifid leaf-blades.   1. *C. muticum.*

II. ARVENSIA

Very spiny erect or diffuse plant with clusters of numerous small, lilac-colored, heads of flowers.   2. *C. arvense.*

III. REPANDA

Body of the involucre 2 cm. thick or less.
  Leaf-margins densely spiny: glutinous line of the involu-
    cral bracts narrow.   3. *C. repandum.*
  Leaf-margins not densely spiny: glutinous line of the in-
    volucral bracts broad.   4. *C. LeContei.*
Body of the involucre 3 cm. thick or more.   5. *C. odoratum.*

IV. ALTISSIMA

Involucre less than 1.5 cm. thick.
  Leaf-blades densely lanate-tomentose beneath.
    Leaf-blades merely spiny toothed: spines of the involu-
      cral bracts slender, over 2 mm. long.   6. *C. virginianum.*
    Leaf-blades pinnatifid or sinuate- pinnatifid: spines of
      the involucral bracts stout, less than 2 mm. long.   7. *C. revolutum.*
  Leaf-blades thinly lanate-tomentose beneath.
    Leaf-blades with weak, rather few, marginal spines:
      spines of the involucral bracts over 2 mm. long.   8. *C. flaccidum.*
    Leaf-blades with long and stout, very numerous mar-
      ginal spines: spines of the involucral bracts less than
      2 mm. long.   9. *C. Nuttallii.*
Involucre over 1.5 cm. thick.
  Leaf-blades, except those near the heads, merely toothed.   10. *C. altissimum.*
  Leaf-blades 1–2-pinnatifid.   11. *C. discolor.*

V. LANCEOLATA

Very spiny plant with decurrent leaves: heads of flowers bril-liant-violet.   12. *C. lanceolatum.*

VI. HORRIDULA

Involucral bracts all serrulate-ciliate.
  Basal leaves with narrow spine-margined blades: anthers
    twice as long as the filaments.   13. *C. vittatum.*
  Basal leaves with broad pinnatifid blades: anthers about
    as long as the filaments.   14. *C. Smallii.*
Involucral bracts puberulent or pubescent, but not ciliate.   15. *C. horridulum.*

1. C. muticum Michx. Stem 8–25 dm. tall, angled, lanuginous or glabrate: leaf-blades elliptic to elliptic-ovate, 1–2-pinnatifid, mainly 17–40 cm. long, rather weakly spine-armed: outer bracts of the involucre obtuse or cuspidate, the inner ones narrowly linear, short-acuminate, 27–29 mm. long: corollas lilac, mostly 28–30 mm. long.—(SWAMP-THISTLE.)—Swamps, meadows, fields, and roadsides, various provinces, Fla. to Tex., Sask., and Newf.—Sum.–fall.

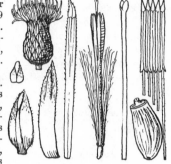

2. **C. arvense** (L.) Scop. Stems 2–10 dm. tall, glabrous or nearly so: leaf-blades spatulate, elliptic, or lanceolate in outline, pinnatifid, 4–16 cm. long, rigidly spine-armed, pubescent beneath or sometimes nearly glabrous: outer bracts of the involucre acute, the inner ones narrowly linear, short-acuminate, 9–12 mm. long: corollas lilac to rosy-purple or white, mostly 12–15 mm. long.—(CANADA-THISTLE.)—Fields, pastures, waste-places, and roadsides, various provinces, N. C. to Kans., B. C., and Newf.—Sum.—Nat. of Eu.—Plants are imperfectly dioecious.

3. **C. repandum** Michx. Stem 1.5–5 dm. tall, webby-lanate: leaf-blades spatulate to narrowly elliptic or broadly linear, pinnately many-lobed and copiously spiny: outer bracts of the involucre long-acuminate, the inner ones with curled tips: corollas rosy-purple.—Pinelands and sand-hills, Coastal Plain, Fla. to N. C.—Sum.

4. **C. LeContei** T. & G. Stem 6–11 dm. tall, floccose-woolly: leaf-blades oblanceolate to lanceolate, pinnatifid and relatively sparingly spiny: outer bracts of the involucre short-acuminate, the inner ones with erect tips: corollas rosy-purple.—Low pinelands, Coastal Plain, Fla. to La. and N. C.—Sum.–fall.

5. **C. odoratum** (Muhl.) Petrak. Stem 3–10 dm. tall, tomentulose: leaf-blades oblanceolate, 1 or 2-pinnatifid: outer bracts of the involucre lanceolate, slender-tipped, the inner bracts 25–35 mm. long: corollas rosy-purple, 40–50 mm. long.—(PASTURE-THISTLE.)—Pastures, fields, and low grounds, various provinces N of Coastal Plain, N. C. to Pa. and Me.—Sum.–fall.

6. **C. virginianum** (L.) Michx. Stem 5–11 dm. tall, arachnoid: leaf-blades linear to linear-elliptic, or spatulate at the base of the stem, spiny-toothed: outer bracts of the involucre with slender tips nearly as long as the body, the inner bracts 12–14 mm. long: corollas lilac to rosy-purple, 16–19 mm. long.—Woods and thickets, Fla. to Miss., Ky., and Va.—Spr.–sum.

7. **C. revolutum** Small. Stem 5–20 dm. tall, floccose: leaves rigid; blades thick, revolute, rigidly spine-armed, densely white-woolly or tomentose beneath: outer bracts of the involucre short-tipped, the inner bracts 12–20 mm. long, narrowly linear: corollas lilac to rosy-purple, 20–25 mm. long.—Low pinelands, Coastal Plain, Fla. to N. C.—Sum.–fall.

8. **C. flaccidum** Small. Stem 7–16 dm. tall, floccose: leaves pliable; blades thin, flat, weakly spine-armed, thinly gray tomentose-woolly beneath: outer bracts of the involucre with slender tips nearly as long as the body, the inner bracts long-tipped, 12–16 mm. long: corollas lilac to rosy-purple, 19–21 mm. long.—Woods and banks, Coastal Plain and adj. provinces, Ga. to Tex. and Mo.—Late spr.–sum.

9. **C. Nuttallii** (DC.) A. Gray. Stem 9–40 dm. tall, early glabrate: blades of the basal and the lower cauline leaves elliptic to elliptic-spatulate, 2-pinnatifid: outer bracts of the involucre short-tipped, the inner bracts abruptly short-tipped, 15–20 mm. long: corollas lilac to rosy-purple, 20–25 mm. long.—Dry soil, Coastal Plain, Fla. to Miss. and S. C.—Spr.–fall or all year S.

10. **C. altissimum** (L.) Spreng. Stem 9–30 dm. tall, downy: blades of the basal or lower cauline leaves elliptic, or broadest above or below the middle, densely white-tomentose beneath: outer bracts of the involucre with tips about ½ as long as the body, the inner bracts 28–30 mm. long: corollas purple to lilac, 37–40 mm. long.—(ROADSIDE-THISTLE.)—Thickets and fields, various provinces, Fla. to Tex., Minn., and Mass.—Sum.–fall.

11. **C. discolor** (Muhl.) Spreng. Similar to *C. altissimum* in habit, but seldom over 20 dm. tall: leaf-blades mainly elliptic-lanceolate to ovate-lanceolate, densely white-tomentose beneath: outer bracts of the involucre with tips about as long as the body, the inner bracts 25–28 mm. long: corollas, lilac to purple, 28–30 mm. long.—(FIELD-THISTLE.)—Thickets and roadsides, various provinces, rarely Coastal Plain, Ga. to Miss., Mo., Ont., and N. B.—Sum.–fall.

12. **C. lanceolatum** (L.) Hill. Stem 8–15 dm. tall, pubescent: leaves crowded; blades lanceolate, 1 or 2 pinnatifid, grayish-woolly beneath: outer bracts of the involucre gradually narrowed into slender tips, the inner bracts very narrowly linear and attenuate: corollas, brilliant violet, 32–35 mm. long. —(COMMON-THISTLE. BULL-THISTLE.)—Fields, pastures, and roadsides, various provinces, Ga. to Nebr., Calif., Ore., Minn., and Newf.; mostly a weed. Nat. of Eu.—Sum.–fall.

13. **C. vittatum** Small. Stem 2–7 dm. tall, thinly pubescent: leaf-margins undulate or sinuate, with mostly ascending spines: inner bracts of the involucre 30–35 mm. long: corollas yellow or cream, about 30 mm. long: anthers much longer than the filaments.—Everglades and low pinelands, Everglade Keys, Fla.—Spr.–sum.

14. **C. Smallii** Britton. Stem 4–9 dm. tall, thinly pubescent: leaf-segments with the terminal spines directed forward: inner bracts of the involucre 25–30 mm. long: corollas yellow or cream, 30–40 mm. long: anthers about as long as the filaments. [*C. pinetorum* Small not Greenm.]—Pinelands and sand-dunes, Coastal Plain, Fla. to S. C.—(*W. I.*)—Wint.–late spr.

15. **C. horridulum** Michx. Stem 3–40 dm. tall, woolly: leaf-segments with spreading spines: inner bracts of the involucre 40–45 mm. long: corollas 40–43 mm. long, yellow, (or purple in *C. horridulum Elliottii*): anthers mostly shorter than the filaments. [*Carduus spinosissimus* Walt.]—(YELLOW-THISTLE.)—Low grounds, swamps, and pastures, Coastal Plain and adj. provinces, Fla. to Tex. and Me.—Spr.–sum.—Often a weed.

125. **ONOPORDUM** [Vaill.] L. Annual or biennial, caulescent, coarse herbs, the stems and branches winged. Leaves alternate: blades sinuate or pinnatifid, prickle-armed, decurrent. Heads erect, many-flowered. Involucre ovoid, globular, or depressed: bracts numerous, narrow, spine-tipped. Receptacle honeycombed. Flowers numerous, all alike, perfect, tubular. Corollas elongate, with a slender tube and a shorter campanulate throat: lobes linear or

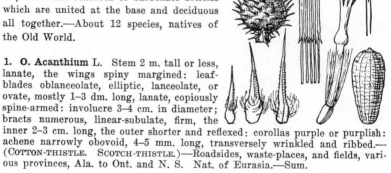

nearly so. Anthers sagittate at the base, with subulate appendages. Achene stout, broadened upward. Pappus of many capillary-attenuate scabrous or barbellate bristles which are united at the base and deciduous all together.—About 12 species, natives of the Old World.

1. **O. Acanthium** L. Stem 2 m. tall or less, lanate, the wings spiny margined: leaf-blades oblanceolate, elliptic, lanceolate, or ovate, mostly 1–3 dm. long, lanate, copiously spine-armed: involucre 3–4 cm. in diameter; bracts numerous, linear-subulate, firm, the inner 2–3 cm. long, the outer shorter and reflexed: corollas purple or purplish: achene narrowly obovoid, 4–5 mm. long, transversely wrinkled and ribbed.— (COTTON-THISTLE. SCOTCH-THISTLE.)—Roadsides, waste-places, and fields, various provinces, Ala. to Ont. and N. S. Nat. of Eurasia.—Sum.

126. **MARIANA** [Vaill.] Hill. Annual or biennial, tall, thistle-like herbs, the stem not winged. Leaves alternate: blades sinuate-lobed or pinnatifid, prickle-armed, not decurrent. Heads erect, many-flowered, not radiate. Involucre depressed-globose: bracts conspicuous, spiny-ciliate, with broad bases and firm spreading or reflexed spine-armed tips. Receptacle flattish, densely bristly. Flowers all alike, perfect, tubular. Corollas elongate, with a very slender tube and a short campanulate throat: lobes linear. Anthers slightly sagittate at the base, with lanceolate appendages. Achene stout. Pappus of numerous capillary-attenuate barbellate bristles which are united at the base and deciduous all together from the ring-like top of the achene.—One species.

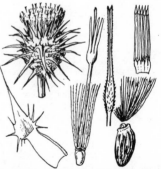

1. **M. Mariana** (L.) Hill. Stem 1.5 m. tall or less, sparingly branched: leaf-blades pinnately lobed and spinescent on and near the margins, those of the basal leaves with stout petiole-like bases, those of the cauline auriculate-clasping, mostly 1–4 dm. long: involucre mostly 4–6 cm. in diameter; bracts with suborbicular, ovate, or elliptic bodies and equally as long or longer tips: corollas purple or purplish, mostly 2.5–3 cm. long: achene more or less oblique, ellipsoid-obovoid, 5.5–6.5 mm. long, glabrous, with a blunt protuberance within the ring-like top.—(MILK-THISTLE.)—Roadsides and waste-places, locally in various provinces, Ala. to Ont.; also on Pacific Coast. Nat. of Eu.—Spr.–sum.

127. **CENTAUREA** L. Annual (ours), or perennial herbs. Leaves alternate: blades entire, toothed, or pinnatifid. Heads relatively small. Involucre with irregularly toothed or fimbrillate outer bracts, the intermediate ones, at least, often armed with spines. Anthers sagittate at the base, with appendages at least ½ as long as the sacs. Achenes flattened or 4-angled. Pappus

of scales or bristles in several series, or obsolete.—About 350 species, mostly natives of the Old World.—Sum.—STAR-THISTLES.

Corollas yellow: stem and branches winged.
    Stem woolly: spines of the involucre yellowish.   1. *C. solstitialis.*
    Stem: spines of the involucre purplish.   2. *C. melitensis.*
Corollas purple: stem and branches wingless.   3. *C. Calcitrapa.*

1. C. solstitialis L. Stem 3–6 dm. tall, woolly: blades of the stem-leaves elliptic-lanceolate or linear, entire or merely toothed: involucres ovoid or sub-globose, about 1.5 cm. long; bracts various, the intermediate ones with long, slender, yellow spines: corollas yellow.—(BARNA-BY'S-THISTLE.)—Waste-places, fields, and roadsides, various provinces, Fla. to Calif., Ia., Ont., and Mass. Nat. of Eu.

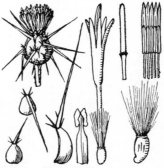

2. C. melitensis L. Stem 1 m. tall or less, arachnoid, usually sparingly branched: leaf-blades various, those of the basal leaves spatulate, toothed or pinnatifid, those of the stem-leaves oblanceolate, elliptic or linear, narrowly decurrent on the stem: heads ses-sile or short-peduncled: involucre ovoid, the outer and middle bracts with slender apical prickles: corollas yellow.—Various prov-inces, Ga. to Ala., N. Mex., Calif., Mo., and Mass. Nat. of Eu.

3. C. Calcitrapa L. Stem 3–4 dm. tall: blades of the stem-leaves 1–2-pin-natifid: corollas purple.—Waste-places, various provinces, Ala. to N. C. and Mass.; also on Pacific Coast. Nat. of Eu.

Centaurea Cyanus L. An annual, native of Europe, with white-floccose foliage, narrow entire leaves, white, pink, blue, or purple heads, and spineless involucral bracts, has escaped from cultivation in the eastern United States. It is known as CORN-FLOWER, BLUEBOTTLE, BACHELOR'S-BUTTON, or RAGGED-ROBIN.

128. CNICUS L. Annual, caulescent, widely branched herbs. Leaves alternate: blades sinuate-pinnatifid and spiny-margined or merely spiny-pin-natifid, veiny. Heads erect, many-flowered, sessile. Involucre ovoid, leafy-involucrate: bracts narrow, rigid, some of them pectinate-spiny near the tip, appressed. Receptacle with capillary bristles. Flowers various, the marginal ones sterile, the central fruit-producing. Corollas elongate, with a slender tube and a shorter cylindric-campanulate throat: lobes narrow, unequal. Anthers minutely tailed at the base, with lanceolate appen-dages. Achene stout, oblique, many striate-ribbed, with a scalloped crown. Pappus double, the outer row of long slender-sub-ulate bristles, the inner of short-subulate bristles.—One species.

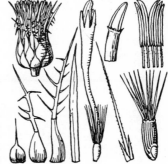

1. C. benedictus L. Stem usually less than 1 m. tall, finely hirsute or villous: leaf-blades mostly 5–15 cm. long, coarsely reticu-late, the upper ones somewhat clasping: in-volucre 1.5–2 cm. in diameter; larger bracts lanceolate, with pectinate spinescent tips: corollas mainly yellow: achene nearly cylindric, 7–9 mm. long, with many prominent ribs, thus fluted; teeth of the crown deltoid: longer pappus-bristles exceeding the achene.—(BLESSED-THISTLE.)—Waste-places, roadsides, and fields, various provinces, Ga. to Ala. and N. S. Nat. of Eu.—Spr.–sum.

129. CHAPTALIA Vent. Perennial, scapose, small herbs, woolly throughout. Leaves alternate, all basal: blades undulate to lyrate-pinnatifid. Heads nodding, at least when young, solitary. Involucre mostly narrow: bracts herbaceous, ultimately reflexed. Flowers white, sometimes purple-stained without. Marginal corollas ligulate. Anthers long-tailed at the base: appendages lanceolate. Achene mostly beaked or narrowed at the apex.— About 25 species, natives of warm-temperate and tropical America.—SUN-BONNETS.

Involucre becoming 1–1.5 cm. long: achene narrowed into a short neck; only the pistillate perfect.   1. *C. tomentosa.*
Involucre becoming 2 cm. long: achene with a beak fully as long as the body; all perfect.   2. *C. dentata.*

1. C. tomentosa Vent. Leaves in rosettes; blades elliptic to oblanceolate, 4–10 cm. long, apiculate, entire or remotely denticulate, green and glabrous above, densely white tomentose beneath: scapes 1–3 dm. tall, sometimes tufted, simple: involucral bracts subulate to linear, the inner becoming 10–15 mm. long: ligules of the ray-flowers purple without, white or ivory within, 7–10 mm. long: achene of the pistillate flowers perfect, glabrous, 3 mm. long, each constricted into a short neck. [*Thyrsanthema   semiflosculare*   (Walt.) Kuntze.]—Moist pinelands, Coastal Plain, Fla. to Tex. and N. C.

2. C. dentata (L.) Cass. Leaves spreading; blades spatulate to oblanceolate, 3–11 cm. long or more, undulate or denticulate, evergreen, floccose above or glabrous in age, lanate-tomentulose beneath: scape slender, 1–3 dm. tall, floccose: involucre lanate, the inner bracts becoming 18–21 mm. long, narrowly linear: inner corollas 7–8 mm. long: achene slender, the body 3.5–4.5 mm. long, the beak as long or longer than the body. [*Thyrsanthema dentata* (L.) Kuntze.]—Pine-lands, Everglade Keys, Fla.—(*W. I.*)—Spr.

FAMILY 3. **CICHORIACEAE** — CHICORY FAMILY

Annual, biennial, or perennial herbs, or partially woody plants. Leaves alternate: blades entire, toothed, or parted. Flowers perfect, all alike, borne in heads. Corolla ligulate, the 1-sided limb mostly 5-lobed at the apex. Stigmas unappendaged. Achene smooth, papillose, muriculate, or spiny.—About 70 genera and 1,500 species, of wide geographic distribution.

Pappus wanting or obsolete.   1. SERINEA.
Pappus present.
    Pappus of plumose bristles.
        Receptacle not chaffy: plant caulescent.   2. TRAGOPOGON.
        Receptacle chaffy: plant scapose.   3. HYPOCHAERIS.

Pappus not plumose.
Pappus consisting, at least in part, of scales which
  sometimes are united into a crown.
  Involucre single: pappus of both scales and
    bristles: corolla yellow.
    Pappus of 5 broad scales and 5–10 bristles:
      plant annual.   4. KRIGIA.
    Pappus of 10–15 minute narrow scales and
      10–15 bristles or more: plant perennial.   5. CYNTHIA.
  Involucre double: pappus crown-like, of numer-
    ous scales in 2 or more series: corolla blue.   6. CICHORIUM.
Pappus consisting of capillary bristles, not plumose.
  Achene not flattened, cylindric or prismatic.
    Achene not beaked.
      Corolla rose or purplish.
        Achene tapering to the apex: plant
          with rush-like stems and narrow
          leaf-blades.   7. LYGODESMIA.
        Achene tapering to the base: plant
          with cane-like stems and broad leaf-
          blades.   8. NABALUS.
      Corolla yellow, cream-colored, or white.
        Ligules cream-colored.   8. NABALUS.
        Ligules yellow.
          Pappus tawny, or white in *H.*
            argyraeum: leaf-blades not pin-
            natifid.   9. HIERACIUM.
          Pappus white: leaf-blades pin-
            natifid.   10. CREPIS.
    Achene beaked at the apex, the beak long and
      slender or short and stout.
      Achenes, at least the marginal ones slen-
        der beaked.
        Achene smooth, merely nerved or ribbed.
          Bracts of the outer involucre ap-
            pressed: pappus white: achene
            attached by a narrowed base.   10. CREPIS.
          Bracts of the outer involucre lax:
            pappus sordid: achene attached
            by a disk-like base.   11. SITILIAS.
        Achene tuberculate and spinulose.   12. LEONTODON.
      Achenes with short stout beaks.   13. BRACHYRHAMPHUS.
  Achene flattened.
    Achene narrowed at the apex or beaked.
      Achene thin, prolonged into a slender,
        often filiform beak.   14. LACTUCA.
      Achene thickish, narrowed at the apex,
        but not beaked.   15. MULGEDIUM.
    Achene truncate at the apex.   16. SONCHUS.

1. **SERINEA** Raf. Annual, pale, tender, caulescent herbs. Leaves often numerous: blades narrow, entire, repand, or lyrate-pinnatifid. Heads long-peduncled, small (1–1.5 cm. broad). Involucre campanulate: bracts rather broad, ribbed, erect at maturity. Corollas yellow. Achene obovoid, 8–10-ribbed. Pappus want-ing or obsolete.—Three species, North American.

1. **S. oppositifolia** (Raf.) Kuntze. Stem 5–30 cm. tall, slender, sometimes sparingly glandular-pubescent: leaf-blades spatulate to linear, 2–12 cm. long, very irregular, those of the lower leaves often toothed or pinnatifid and with petiole-like bases, those of the upper entire and sessile: bracts of the involucre ovate to lanceolate, becoming 4–5 mm. long: achene 1.5 mm. long, prominently ribbed.—Moist soil, fields, and waste-places, various provinces, Fla. to Tex., Kans., and S. C.—Spr.

2. TRAGOPOGON [Tourn.] L. Biennial or perennial erect caulescent, rather coarse herbs. Leaf-blades narrow, long-attenuate, often sheathing at the base. Heads erect. Involucres relatively narrow: bracts elongate, often surpassing the disk. Achene terete or 5-angled, the inner at least slender-beaked.—About 35 species, natives of the Old World.

Bracts of the involucre surpassing the ligules: corollas purple.   1. *T. porrifolius.*
Bracts of the involucre as long as the ligules or shorter: corollas yellow.   2. *T. pratensis.*

1. T. porrifolius L. Stem 4–15 dm. tall: leaf-blades clasping or sheathing at the base: peduncles gradually enlarged upward: bracts of the involucre linear-lanceolate, 30–60 mm. long: achene slender-fusiform, 3.5–4 cm. long, the beak longer than the body.—(SALSIFY. OYSTER-PLANT.)—Fence-rows and roadsides, various provinces, Ga. to Calif. and Ont. Nat. of Eu.—Sum.

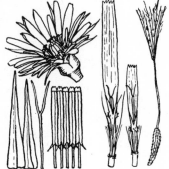

2. T. pratensis L. Similar to *T. porrifolius* in habit: peduncle abruptly thickened under the head: bracts of the involucre lanceolate, 25–35 mm. long: achene stout-fusiform, 1.5–2 cm. long, the beak shorter than the body.—(GOAT'S-BEARD.)—Fields and waste-places, various provinces, Ga. to Ont. Nat. of Eu.

3. HYPOCHAERIS L. Perennial or rarely annual, scapose herbs, the scapes often minutely scaly. Leaf-blades entire, toothed, or pinnatifid. Heads showy, erect, long-peduncled. Involucres cylindric to campanulate: bracts in several unequal series, the outer ones very small, the inner ones with dorsal crests near the apex. Corollas yellow. Stigmas slender, filiform or short. Achenes, the inner ones, at least, slender-beaked. Pappus single, the bristles plumose.—About 50 species, Eurasian and South American.—CAT'S-EARS.

Achenes uniform, all beaked: corollas much exceeding the involucre.   1. *H. radicata.*
Achenes of 2 kinds, the outer beakless, the inner beaked: corollas slightly exceeding the involucre.   2. *H. glabra.*

1. H. radicata L. Plant perennial, 2–6 dm. tall: leaves mostly 4–17 cm. long, hirsute; blades spatulate in outline, coarsely toothed or pinnatifid: heads 2.5–4 cm. wide: corollas with very narrow ligules: achenes fusiform, the bodies 3–3.5 mm. long, spinulose, those of the inner ones at least shorter than the filiform beaks.—Waste-places, fields, and wet pastures, various provinces, S. C. to Tex., Ont., and N. J.; Colo., and Pacif. St.—Nat. of Eu.—Spr.-sum.·

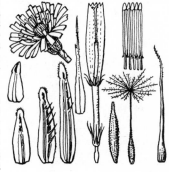

2. H. glabra L. Plant annual, 2–5 dm. tall: leaves mostly 6–14 cm. long, glabrous or nearly so; blades spatulate to linear-spatulate in outline, pinnatifid or pinnately toothed: heads smaller than in *H. radicata:* corollas with narrow but relatively short ligules: achenes various, the inner fusiform with bodies 3–4 mm. long and slender beaks, the outer about 3 mm. long, beakless.—Roadsides, lawns, and grassy places, various provinces, N Fla. to Ohio and Me. Nat. of Eu.—Spr.–fall.

4. **KRIGIA** Schreb. Annual herbs. Leaves mainly basal: blades narrow, toothed or pinnatifid. Heads slender-peduncled. Involucre narrow: bracts narrow, reflexed at maturity. Corollas light-yellow. Achene oblong or broadened upward. Pappus of 5 scales about ½ as long as the achene and also of 5 or 10 barbellate bristles.—One species.

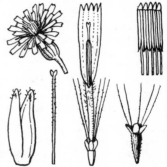

1. **K. virginica** (L.) Willd. Plant 0.3–4 dm. tall: leaf-blades spatulate to nearly linear, 2–12 cm. long: involucres mostly less than 7 mm. long: corollas 6–7 mm. long: achenes fully 1.5 mm. long, finely ribbed. [*Adopogon carolinianus* (Walt.) Britton.] —(DWARF-DANDELION.)—Open sandy places, and woods, various provinces, Fla. to Tex., Ont., and Me.—Spr.

5. **CYNTHIA** D. Don. Perennial herbs. Leaves mainly basal: blades narrow or broad, entire, repand, or pinnatifid. Heads long-peduncled. Involucre stout: bracts narrow, reflexed at maturity. Corollas bright-yellow. Achene not broadened upward. Pappus of 10–15 minute scales and as many or more numerous barbellate bristles.—Four species, North American.

Plant caulescent, the roots not tuber-bearing: pappus-scales not attenuate: heads 2–many.
  Pappus-scales very short: stem erect, sparingly leafy: leaves with dilated blades.   1. *C. virginica.*
  Pappus-scales about ¼ the length of the achene: stem decumbent or reclining, very leafy: leaves with narrow blades.   2. *C. montana.*
Plant acaulescent, the roots tuber-bearing: pappus-scales attenuate: heads solitary.   3. *C. Dandelion.*

1. **C. virginica** (L.) D. Don. Stem 1–7 dm. tall: leaf-blades spatulate, elliptic, or oval, not elongate, entire or repand or slightly lyrate-pinnatifid: involucres mostly over 8 mm. long: corollas 10–12 mm. long: achene 2 mm. long, coarsely ribbed.—Moist banks and meadows, various provinces, rarely Coastal Plain, Ga. to Kans., Man., and Mass.—Spr.–fall.

2. **C. montana** (Michx.) Standley. Stem 1–4 dm. tall, branched, diffuse at maturity: leaf-blades linear to linear-spatulate, elongate, entire or irregularly pinnatifid: peduncles usually solitary: achene slightly broadest above the middle, 2.5–3 mm. long, ⅓ as long as the pappus-bristles: pappus-scales about ¼ as long as the achene.— Cliffs and rocky slopes, in rather acid soil, Blue Ridge, Ga. to Tenn. and N. C.— Sum.–fall.

3. **C. Dandelion** (L.) DC. Scape 0.5–5 dm. tall, simple: leaf-blades spatulate to linear-oblong or linear, 5–15 cm. long, entire, repand, or irregularly

pinnatifid: head solitary: achene slightly broadest above the middle, nearly 2.5 mm. long, about ⅓ as long as the pappus-bristles: pappus-scales ¼–⅕ as long as the achene.—Moist or dry soil, often in woods, various provinces, Fla. to Tex., Kans., and N. J.—Spr.–sum.

6. CICHORIUM [Tourn.] L. Perennial rigid herbs. Leaf-blades toothed or pinnatifid, or crisped. Heads sessile or nearly so. Involucre firm or rigid: outer bracts spreading, the inner erect. Achene 5-ribbed or 5-angled. Pappus of 2 or 3 rows of scales.—About 8 species, in the Old World.—CHICORIES. SUCCORIES.

1. **C. Intybus** L. Tap-root elongate, tough. Stem 3–15 dm. tall, rigidly wide-branched: blades of the stem-leaves oblong to lanceolate, pinnatifid, toothed, or entire: involucres 10–12 mm. long; bracts lanceolate to linear, the outer glandular-ciliate: corollas sky-blue or white: ligules 10–20 mm. long: achene 2–2.5 mm. long.—(COMMON-CHICORY. BLUE-SAILORS.)—Fields, fence-rows, and roadsides, various provinces, Fla. to Tex., Calif., Wash., Ont., and N. S. Nat. of Eu.—(*W. I.*)—Sum.–fall.

7. LYGODESMIA D. Don. Annual or perennial caulescent herbs or partly woody plants, the stems rush-like. Leaf-blades narrow, entire or remotely pinnate-toothed, or scale-like. Heads erect. Involucre cylindric. Achene not flattened.—About 6 species, North American.

1. **L. aphylla** (Nutt.) DC. Stem erect or ascending, 3–8 dm. tall, solitary or tufted by the branching base, rush-like, naked or nearly so, sometimes forking above: leaves wanting or represented by narrow scales, or a few elongate linear blades at base of stem: involucres cylindric, about 2 cm. long; bracts various, the outer small, 1–3 mm. long, the inner linear or nearly so: ligules rose-colored or rarely white, 1.5–2 cm. long, toothed at the apex: achene narrow, 10–13 mm. long, nearly as long as the white pappus.—(FLOWERING-STRAWS. ROSE-RUSH.)—Dry pinelands and scrub, Coastal Plain, Fla. and Ga.—Spr.–fall.

8. NABALUS Cass. Perennial caulescent herbs. Leaf-blades toothed, lobed, pinnatifid, or divided. Heads nodding. Involucre cylindric or nearly so: main bracts nearly equal in length. Achene ellipsoid to columnar.— About 25 species, American and Asiatic.—Sum.–fall.—RATTLESNAKE-ROOTS. WHITE-LETTUCES. LION'S-FOOT. GALL-OF-THE-EARTH.

Heads 8–18-flowered, in thyrsoid or virgate racemiform panicles.
   Achene minutely, sometimes obscurely striate and also sometimes 3- or 4-ribbed:
      involucre glabrous or nearly so.   I. ALBI.

Achene 5–15-nerved and sometimes angled by 4 or 5 of the
stronger nerves : involucre copiously pubescent.   II. Racemosi.
Heads 20–35-flowered, in corymb-like panicles.   III. Crepidinei.

I. Albi

Heads 5–7-flowered : involucre slender, less than 3 mm. thick ;
bracts light-green : pappus stramineous.   1. *N. altissimus.*
Heads 8–16-flowered : involucre stout, over 3 mm. thick, deep-
green, glaucous, or purple.
Pappus deep cinnamon-colored.   2. *N. albus.*
Pappus stramineous or light-brown.
    Leaf-blades merely toothed or somewhat incised.
        Larger bracts of the outer involucre lanceolate :
        lower leaf-blades elliptic to oval, not cordate.   3. *N. integrifolius.*
        Larger bracts of the outer involucre ovate : lower
        leaf-blades hastate, cordate.   4. *N. roanensis.*
    Leaf-blades, at least some of them, pinnatifid, lobed, or
    divided.
        Inflorescence paniculate.
        Panicle broadened upward : bracts of the in-
        volucre, at least the longer ones, glabrous.
        Larger bracts of the outer involucre lanceo-
        late : pappus exceeding the inner involu-
        cral bracts.   5. *N. serpentarius.*
        Larger bracts of the outer involucre ovate to
        triangular-ovate : pappus and inner in-
        volucral bracts about equal.   6. *N. trifoliatus.*
        Panicle cylindric : bracts of the involucre spar-
        ingly hairy.   7. *N. cylindricus.*
        Inflorescence racemiform.   8. *N. virgatus.*

II. Racemosi

Leaf-blades entire or rather finely toothed : branches of the
inflorescence very short and close together.   9. *N. asper.*

III. Crepidinei

Leaf-blades finely or coarsely toothed or incised : branches of the
inflorescence elongate and distant.   10. *N. crepidineus.*

1. N. altissimus (L.) Hook. Stem 9–21 dm. tall, glabrous, glaucous: leaf-
blades denticulate, or lobed or divided and with denticulate or lobed divisions:
involucres less than 3 m. thick, the outer
bracts of the involucre deltoid to ovate, 1–2
mm. long, the inner ones 9–10 mm. long,
light-green, glabrous: ligules greenish or
yellowish.—Woods and low thickets, various
provinces, rarely Coastal Plain, Ga. to Miss.,
Tenn., Man., and Newf.

2. N. albus (L.) Hook. Stem 3–16 dm.
tall, glabrous, glaucous: leaf-blades, or the
divisions, coarsely toothed: outer bracts of
the involucre ovate, 2–3 mm. long, the inner ones 10–12 mm. long, dark-green,
glabrous: ligules dull-white or cream-
colored.—Rich banks, woods, and thickets,
various provinces, rarely Coastal Plain, Ga.
to Tenn., Sask., and Me.

3. N. integrifolius Cass. Stem 4–18 dm. tall, glabrous, at least in age;
leaf-blades oblong, varying to broadest above or below the middle, finely or
coarsely dentate, those of the lower leaves cuneate to subcordate at the base:
outer bracts of the involucre lanceolate, hirsute on the back: pappus dirty-
brown.—Woods, various provinces N of Coastal Plain, Ga. to N. Y.

4. N. roanensis Chickering. Stem 3–5 dm. tall, pubescent: leaf-blades
ovate to hastate, denticulate, the basal lobes directed backwards or sidewards:

inner bracts of the involucre 8–9 mm. long, sparingly hirsute on the back with long hairs: pappus dingy straw-colored.—Mt. peaks, Blue Ridge, N. C. and Tenn.

5. N. serpentarius (Pursh) Hook. Stem 3–12 dm. tall, glabrous: larger leaf-blades pinnately lobed: inner bracts of the involucre 9–11 mm. long, often ciliate at the tip: pappus straw-colored.—(LION'S-FOOT.)—Fields, woods, and thickets, various provinces, Fla. to Miss., Ont., and Mass.

6. N. trifoliatus Cass. Stem 8–26 dm. tall, glabrous: larger leaf-blades pedately lobed: inner bracts of the involucre 9–11 mm. long, wholly glabrous: pappus light-brown.—(GALL-OF-THE-EARTH.)—Woods and thickets, various provinces, rarely Coastal Plain, N. C., and Tenn.

7. N. cylindricus Small. Stem 3–9 dm. tall, glabrous: larger leaf-blades pinnately 3–5-lobed: inner bracts of the involucre 9–10 mm. long, with scattered hairs on the back: pappus pale-brown.—Mt. slopes, Blue Ridge to Appalachian Plateau, N. C. to Tenn. and Ky.

8. N. virgatus (Michx.) DC. Stem 6–12 dm. tall, glabrous: leaf-blades spatulate to lanceolate in outline, pinnatifid, the lobes sometimes toothed: outer bracts of the involucre ciliate, the inner ones 9–10 mm. long, glabrous: ligules white or pink: pappus straw-colored.—Pinelands, Coastal Plain, Fla. to Miss. and N. J.

9. N. asper (Michx.) T. & G. Stem 9–20 dm. tall, pubescent: leaf-blades obovate, oblong or lanceolate, undulate to coarsely toothed: bracts of the involucre hirsute, the inner ligules cream-colored: pappus sordid-brown or pale straw-colored.—Dry soil, various provinces, La. to Tenn., S. Dak., and Ohio.

10. N. crepidineus (Michx.) DC. Stem 9–21 dm. tall, finely pubescent at least when young: leaf-blades ovate to ovate-hastate, finely or coarsely toothed: bracts of the involucre strigose-hirsute, the inner 9–10 mm. long: ligules cream-colored: pappus dirty-brown.—Rich soil and thickets, various provinces N of Coastal Plain, Tenn. to Kans., Minn., and N. Y.

9. HIERACIUM L. Perrennial caulescent or scapose herbs. Leaf-blades entire or toothed. Heads erect, paniculate or corymbose. Involucres usually narrow: main bracts unequal in length, often in 2 or 3 series, with a calyculum. Corolla yellow, rarely white or orange. Achenes fusiform or columnar, ribbed. Pappus of 1 or 2 series of sordid or brownish fragile bristles, or rarely white.—About 300 species, natives of the north temperate zone and South America.—HAWKWEEDS.

Flowering stem leafy.	I. PANICULATA.
Flowering stem leafless.	II. VENOSA.

I. PANICULATA

Achene columnar.	
Inflorescence more or less elongate, not flat-topped.	
Panicle lax: heads few- (10–20) flowered.	1. *H. paniculatum.*
Panicle stiff: heads many- (40–50) flowered.	2. *H. scabrum.*
Inflorescence corymbiform.	
Heads many- (20–40) flowered: peduncles densely pubescent.	3. *H. marianum.*
Heads few- (10–15) flowered: peduncles glaucous.	4. *H. Scribneri.*
Achene fusiform.	
Inflorescence elongate, paniculate.	5. *H. Gronovii.*
Inflorescence corymbiform.	
Pappus brown.	6. *H. megacephalon.*
Pappus white.	7. *H. argyraeum.*

II. Venosa

Inflorescence-branches glabrous or sparingly pubescent: bracts of the involucre glabrous or with scattered fine short glandular hairs. 8. *H. venosum.*

Inflorescence-branches tomentulose and hispid: bracts of the involucre tomentulose and also with long black glandular hairs. 9. *H. Greenii.*

1. **H. paniculatum** L. Plant pale-green or glaucescent, 3–12 dm. tall, the stem sometimes villous at the base: blades of the cauline leaves elliptic-spatulate to elliptic or elliptic-lanceolate, mostly 3–13 cm. long, sinuate-toothed, glabrous, acute or acuminate, sessile: peduncles very slender, nearly filiform, usually glabrous: inner bracts of the involucre 5–6 mm. long, glabrous or obscurely pubescent: achene about 2.5 mm. long.—Banks, woods, and thickets, various provinces, Ga. to Ala., Mich., and N. S.—Sum.

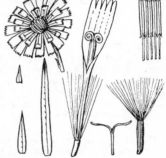

2. **H. scabrum** Michx. Plant bright-green, 3–14 dm. tall, the stem pubescent throughout: blades of the cauline leaves spatulate to elliptic, oval, or ovate, 3–16 cm. long, entire or repand-denticulate, pubescent, obtuse or acutish, the upper ones sessile: peduncles rather stout, copiously glandular-pubescent: inner bracts of the involucre 7–9 mm. long, glandular-pubescent: achene 2–2.5 mm. long.—Clearings, dry woods, pastures, and roadsides, various provinces, Ga. to Miss., Kans., Minn., and N. S.—Sum.-fall.

3. **H. marianum** 'Willd. Plant bright-green, 3–8 dm. tall, the stem glabrous or softly hirsute near the base: basal leaves often persistent; blades spatulate to obovate, mostly 10–15 cm. long, with more or less shaggy-pubescent petiole-like bases: cauline leaves few; blades obovate, oblanceolate, or elliptic, entire or repand-denticulate, obtuse or abruptly pointed, sessile: peduncles usually finely white-tomentulose and also glandular-pubescent: inner bracts of the involucre 7–9 mm. long, sparingly glandular-pubescent: achene 2.5–3 mm. long, or rarely longer.—Woods, clearings, and banks, various provinces, Fla. to Miss., Ohio, and N. H.—Spr.

4. **H. Scribneri** Small. Plant glaucous, 3–8 dm. tall, the stem glabrous or hirsutulous at the more or less purple-tinged base: basal leaves often persistent; blades spatulate to elliptic, 5–15 cm. long, with shaggy-pubescent petiole-like bases: cauline leaves few; blades oblanceolate, elliptic, lanceolate, or linear-lanceolate, undulate or repand-denticulate, acuminate or acute, sessile: peduncles glabrous or sparingly glandular-pubescent: inner bracts of the involucre 7–9 mm. long, glabrous or sparingly glandular pubescent: achene 2–2.5 mm. long or rarely larger.—Rocky slopes, wooded hillsides, and bluffs, Blue Ridge to Interior Low Plateaus, Ga. to Ala. and Ind.—Sum.

5. **H. Gronovii** L. Plant 2–12 dm. tall, very variable in habit, bright-green, the stem pubescent on the lower part or near the base: basal leaves sometimes persistent; blades obovate to spatulate, 3–16 cm. long, sparingly shaggy-pubescent at the edges or sometimes only sparingly pubescent: cauline leaves few to many; blades spatulate, obovate, elliptic, or ovate, mostly sessile or clasping: peduncles glandular-pubescent: inner bracts of the involucre 6–7 mm.

long, glandular-pubescent: achene 3–3.5 mm. long.—Dry woods, barren hill-sides, and pinelands, various provinces, Fla. to Tex., Ont., and Mass.—Sum.-fall.—The plant with broad based sessile leaf-blades extending nearly to the base of the stem, from Florida, has been described as *H. floridanum.*

6. H. megacephalon Nash. Plant 2–7 dm. tall, the stem hirsute, sometimes sparingly so, throughout: basal leaves persistent; blades spatulate to obovate, 4–17 cm. long, more or less shaggy-pubescent: cauline leaves few; blades spatulate, obovate, elliptic, or lanceolate: peduncles finely pubescent and glandular: inner bracts of the involucre 9–11 mm. long, glandular-pubescent: achene 4.5–5.5 mm. long.—Pinelands, pen. Fla. and Coastal Plain of Ga.—All year.

7. H. argyraeum Small. Plant 1.5–5 dm. tall, the stem more or less hirsute and glandular above: basal leaves persistent; blades spatulate, obovate, or elliptic, 2–13 cm. long, more or less shaggy-pubescent: cauline leaves few; blades spatulate, obovate, elliptic, or lanceolate: peduncles closely glandular pubescent and finely tomentulose: inner bracts of the involucre 8–10 mm. long, glandular-pubescent, sometimes copiously so: achene 4–4.5 mm. long.—Hammocks and open pinelands, Fla.—All year.

8. H. venosum L. Plant 2–6.5 dm. tall, the stem (scape) usually glabrous and purple-tinged: basal leaves persistent; blades obovate to spatulate, 3–15 cm. long, undulate or repand-denticulate usually pale-green and purple-veined, sometimes purple beneath, glabrous or pubescent near the base: peduncles glabrous or sparingly glandular-pubescent: inner bracts of the involucre 6–7 mm. long: achene 2.5–3 mm. long.—(RATTLESNAKE-WEED. POOR-ROBIN'S PLANTAIN.)—Dry woods, shaded banks, and plains, often in acid soil, various provinces, Ga. to Nebr., Mass., and Me.—Sum.

9. H. Greenii Porter & Britton. Plant 3–9 dm. tall, the stem (scape) glabrous or finely pubescent, often only in lines: basal leaves persistent; blades spatulate to elliptic-spatulate, 5–20 cm. long, undulate, somewhat shaggy-pubescent, especially near the margins and at the base, bright green: peduncles finely white tomentulose and glandular-pubescent: inner bracts of the involucre 8–11 mm. long: achenes 3–3.5 mm. long.—Dry woods and open slopes, Blue Ridge and more N provinces, Ga. to Ala., Ohio, and Pa.—Spr.

10. CREPIS. L. Annual or biennial herbs, resembling *Hieracium*, with glabrous or sparingly pubescent foliage. Leaves alternate: blades mostly re-pand or pinnatifid. Heads few–many-flowered, paniculate or corymbose. In-volucres narrow: bracts usually in a single row or in several rows. Corollas yellow. Achene narrow. Pappus of white soft hairs.—About 200 species, natives of the Northern Hemisphere.

Involucre 6–8 mm. high: achenes fusiform, beakless.
  Leaf-blades runcinate-pinnatifid: involucre 6–8 mm. high: achene
    2.5–3 mm. long.   1. *C. tectorum.*
  Leaf-blades lyrate-pinnatifid: involucre 3.5–4.5 mm. high: achene
    1.5–2 mm. long.   2. *C. japonica.*
Involucre 9–12 mm. high: achene slender-fusiform, beaked, the
  marginal ones filiform-beaked.   3. *C. foetida.*

1. C. tectorum L. Plant usually branched at the base, 2–4 dm. tall, spar-ingly pubescent: leaf-blades elliptic, lanceolate, or linear-lanceolate in outline, runcinate-pinnatifid, usually sagittate-auriculate at the base: involucres 6–8 mm. high; bracts hirsute-hispid, acute: achene fusiform, 2.5–3 mm. long, ribbed.—(HAWKS-BEARD.)—Roadsides and fields, various provinces, N. C. to Nebr. and Ont. Nat. of Eu. —Fall.

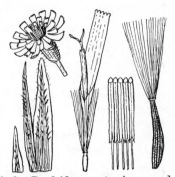

2. **C. japonica** (L.) Benth. Plant 1–6 dm. tall: stem simple below or branched at the base, finely pubescent near the base, glabrous or nearly so above and in the very slenderly branched inflorescence: leaves mainly or wholly basal; blades lyrately pinnatifid, mostly 5–15 cm. long, petioled: involucres 3.5–4.5 mm. high; bracts acuminate, glabrous: achene fusiform, 1.5–2 mm. long, ribbed.—Roadsides, waste-places, and meadows, S La. Nat. of Japan.—(W. I.)—All year.

3. **C. foetida** L. Plant 3–5 dm. tall, simple below or branched at the base, pubescent: leaf-blades mostly oblanceolate in outline, runcinate-pinnatifid or some of them coarsely sinuate-toothed, those of the stem with dilated fringed-toothed bases: involucres 9–12 mm. high; bracts acuminate, loosely hirsute: achenes various, and inner ones short-beaked, the marginal ones with filiform beaks as long as the body.—Roadsides, fields, and dunes, coastwise islands of NE Fla. and Ga.—Nat. of Eu.—Spr.–fall.

11. **SITILIAS** Raf. Biennial or perennial caulescent or scapose herbs. Leaf-blades irregularly toothed, pinnatifid, or sometimes entire. Heads erect. Involucre ovoid to campanulate: bracts in 2 unequal series, inner ones abruptly keeled near the apex. Corollas yellow or whitish. Achene with an ellipsoid body. Pappus double, the outer very short.—Six species, North American.—Spr.–fall.—FALSE-DANDELIONS.

Bracts of the outer involucres fully 1/3 to over 1/2 as long as the inner: heads fully 2.5 cm. long at maturity.   1. *S. caroliniana.*
Bracts of the outer involucres less than 1/3 as long as the inner: heads 2 cm. long at maturity or shorter.   2. *S. multicaulis.*

1. **S. caroliniana** (Walt.) Raf. Stems erect, 1–1.5 dm. tall, usually branched: leaves various; blades more or less deeply pinnatifid, sometimes merely denticulate or nearly entire, these conspicuously elongate: involucre 12–26 mm. long; inner bracts narrowly linear; outer bracts narrower, fully ⅓ to over ½ as long as the inner: ligules yellow: achene-body about 5 mm. long, ribbed, somewhat rufous. [*Pyrrhopappus carolinianus* (Walt.) DC.]—Dry soil, roadsides, waste-places and pinelands, various provinces, Fla. to Tex., Kans., and Del.—Spr.–fall.—A variety with pale cream-colored ligules, tipped with rose, and streaked rose on the under side, occurs in N Fla. A similar or the same one occurs in Ala. This may prove, upon further investigation to be a distinct species.

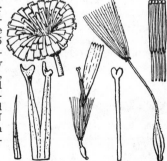

2. **S. multicaulis** (DC.) Greene. Stems solitary or tufted, ascending or spreading, 1–4 dm. long, more or less branched: leaves mainly basal, 5–15 cm. long:

blades pinnate or irregularly pinnatifid, the segments entire or toothed; upper leaves narrower, deeply pinnatifid or merely toothed; involucres 1–1.5 cm. long; inner bracts narrowly linear, acute; outer bracts linear-subulate, ¼ to nearly ⅓ as long as the inner bracts: ligules bright-yellow, 1.5–2 cm. long: achene-body 3.5–4 mm. long, reddish, transversely wrinkled.—Dry soil, hillsides, prairies, woods, and ditch-banks, various provinces, N Fla. to Tex. and Ariz.—(*Mex.*)—Spr. and sum.

12. **LEONTODON** L. Perennial low caulescent herbs. Leaf-blades sinuate-toothed or runcinate-pinnatifid, or rarely entire. Heads solitary. Involucre thick, scaly. Achene not much flattened. Pappus persistent. [*Taraxacum* Ludwig.]—About 30 species, in the Northern Hemisphere and South America.—Spr.–fall.—DANDELIONS. BLOW-BALLS.

Inner involucral bracts unappendaged: achene brown or olive-green.
                                                        1. *L. Taraxacum.*
Inner involucral bracts appendaged at the tip: achene red
    or red-brown.   2. *L. erythrospermum.*

1. **L. Taraxacum** L. Leaf-blades sinuate or coarsely pinnatifid, often lyrate, the lobes broad: heads 3–5 cm. wide, the ligules orange-yellow: involucral bracts green, the outer ones long, reflexed: achene-body bluntly spinulose near the top: pappus white. [*Taraxacum Taraxacum* (L.) Karst.]—Fields, open grounds, waste-places, and woods, throughout U. S. and S. Can.

2. **L. erythrospermum** (Andrz.) Eichw. Leaf-blades pinnatifid or pinnately divided, runcinate, the lobes narrow: heads 2–3 cm. wide, the ligules light-yellow: involucral bracts glaucous, the outer ones short, ascending or spreading: achene-body sharply spinulose near the apex: pappus dirty-white.—Fields, lawns, and waste-places, various provinces N of Coastal Plain, N. C. to Tenn., Alb., and Me. Nat. of Eu.

13. **BRACHYRHAMPHUS** DC. Annual, coarse herbs with branching stems. Leaves mainly basal or on the lower part of the stem. Leaf-blades sagittate-clasping, mostly pinnatifid or lyrate-pinnatifid. Heads erect. Involucre ovoid-conic. Achene subterete, ribbed, the ribs muriculate.—The following and perhaps a few other species, tropical.

1. **B. intybaceus** (Jacq.) DC. Stem 3–15 dm. tall, glabrous: leaf-blades bright-green, those of the lower leaves 1–3 dm. long, the edges or lobes spiny-toothed: heads solitary at the nodes, on slender scaly stalks: bracts of the involucre conspicuously scarious-margined, the outer ovate, the inner linear-lanceolate: corollas yellow or ochroleucous: achene somewhat fusiform, about 4 mm.

long: pappus bright-white.—(WILD-LETTUCE.)—Roadsides, cult. grounds, and waste-places, S Fla. Nat. of Trop. Am.—(*W. I., Mex., C. A., S. A.*)—All year.

14. **LACTUCA** L. Annual, biennial, or perennial herbs, the stems stout. Leaf-blades mostly relatively broad, entire, toothed, or pinnatifid, sometimes spiny-margined. Heads erect. Involucres cylindric to ovoid. Achene flattened, slender-beaked.—About 75 species, in the Northern Hemisphere.—Sum.–fall.—LETTUCES. WOOD-LETTUCES. WILD-LETTUCES.

Leaf-blades spiny-toothed and often spiny along the midrib beneath : corollas yellow.
  Involucres 6–12-flowered.
    Leaf-blades sinuately spiny-denticulate.   1. *L. virosa.*
    Leaf-blades deeply pinnatifid.   2. *L. Scariola.*
  Involucres 12–20-flowered.
    Involucres over 1.5 cm. high : beak fully as long as the
      body of the achene.   3. *L. ludoviciana.*
    Involucres less than 1.5 cm. high : beak shorter than the
      body of the achene.   4. *L. sagittifolia.*
Leaf-blades without spines on the margins or midribs.
  Leaf-blades entire or merely toothed.   4. *L. sagittifolia.*
  Leaf-blades, at least some of them, pinnatifid.
    Leaves glabrous.   5. *L. canadensis.*
    Leaves hirsute, at least their midribs.
      Lower leaf-blades all pinnatifid : beak of achene fully
        as long as the body.   6. *L. hirsuta.*
      Lower leaf-blades usually both entire and pinnatifid :
        beak of achene much shorter than the body.   7. *L. graminifolia.*

1. **L. virosa** L. Stem hirsute below, 6–20 dm. tall : leaf-blades oblanceolate to oblong, merely denticulate, glaucous: inner bracts of the involucre 12–15 mm. long, narrowly linear: outer corollas 11–12 mm. long : achene-body gradually narrowed at the apex.—Fields, waste-places, and roadsides, various provinces, Ga. to Tenn., Kans., and N. Y. Nat. of Eu.

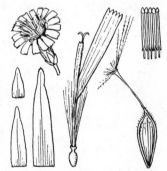

2. **L. Scariola** L. Stem nearly or quite glabrous, 4–15 cm. tall : leaf-blades oblong to lanceolate in outline, pinnatifid, bright-green: inner bracts of the involucre 8–10 mm. long, linear-oblong: outer corollas 8–9 mm. long : achene-body abruptly narrowed at the apex.—(PRICKLY-LETTUCE.)—Waste-places, fields, and roadsides, various provinces, Ga. to Miss., Mo., and Vt. Nat. of Eu.

3. **L. ludoviciana** (Nutt.) DC. Stem 4–15 dm. tall, glabrous: leaves horizontal: blades 5–20 cm. long, sinuate-lobed or pinnatifid: involucres 16–20 mm. long, the inner bracts linear-lanceolate: ligules yellow: achene-body 4–4.5 mm. long.—Dry soil, often on wooded banks, various provinces, Tenn. to Tex., N. Dak., Minn., and Ark.

4. **L. sagittifolia** Ell. Stem 9–30 dm. tall, glabrous: blades of the stem-leaves 8–30 cm. long, irregularly dentate: involucres 10–20 mm. long, the inner bracts narrowly linear or nearly so: ligules yellow or reddish: achene-body 2.5–3 mm. long, longer than the beak.—Rich soil, open woods, and shaded banks, various provinces, Ga. to Nebr., and Pa.

5. **L. canadensis** L. Stem 9–30 dm. tall, glabrous or nearly so: blades of the stem-leaves 10–30 cm. long, sinuate-pinnatifid: involucres 10–12 mm. long,

the inner ones linear-lanceolate: ligules yellow: achene-body 3–4 mm. long, about as long as the beak.—(WILD-LETTUCE. HORSE-WEED.)—Rich soil, fence-rows, thickets, and open woods, various provinces, Ga. to La., Colo., B. C., Ont., and N. S.—(*W. I.*)

6. **L. hirsuta** Muhl. Stem 6–12 dm. tall, sometimes hirsute: blades of the stem-leaves 9–20 cm. long, sinuate-pinnatifid, not elongate: involucres 12–15 mm. long, the inner bracts linear: ligules purplish yellow to white: achene-body about 4 mm. long, much shorter than the beak.—Dry soil, various provinces, Ala. to Tex., Ont., and Que.

7. **L. graminifolia** Michx. Stem 6–15 dm. tall, glabrous: blades of the stem-leaves 10–40 cm. long, entire or with few spreading or deflexed lobes, conspicuously elongate: involucres 12–15 mm. long, the inner ones linear-lanceolate: ligules purple-blue, or rarely white or yellowish: achene-body 4–4.5 mm. long. —Fields and woods, Coastal Plain and adj. provinces, Fla. to Tex. and S. C.

15. **MULGEDIUM** Cass. Herbs resembling *Lactuca* in habit. Achene thick, beakless. About 25 species, Eurasian and North American.—Sum.–fall. —LETTUCES. BLUE-LETTUCES.

Pappus bright-white: blades of the stem-leaves neither auriculate nor clasping.
    Leaf-blades toothed: achene-body not narrowed into a neck.   1. *M. villosum.*
    Leaf-blades pinnatifid: achene-body narrowed into a slender
       neck.   2. *M. floridanum.*
Pappus brown: blades of the stem-leaves auriculate and clasp-
    ing.   3. *M. spicatum.*

1. **M. villosum** (Jacq.) Small. Stem 9–20 dm. tall: blades of the stem-leaves irregularly dentate, 8–20 cm. long: inner bracts of the involucre linear-lanceolate: ligules blue: achene 4.5–5.5 mm. long.—Borders of woods, open woods, and thickets, various provinces, Fla. to La., Nebr., and N. Y.

2. **M. floridanum** (L.) DC. Stem 10–30 dm. tall: blades of the stem-leaves lyrate-pinnatifid, 2–45 cm. long: inner bracts of the involucre linear: ligules blue: achene 6–7 mm. long.—Rich soil, thickets, and banks, various provinces, Fla. to Tex., Nebr., and N. Y.—(*W. I.*)

3. **M. spicatum** (Lam.) Small. Stem 9–35 dm. tall: blades of the stem-leaves lobed or pinnatifid (merely denticulate in *M. spicatum integrifolium*): ligules white, yellowish, or bluish: achene 4–5 mm. long. —Low grounds, thickets, and open woods, various provinces, rarely Coastal Plain, N. C. to Colo., Man., and Newf.

16. **SONCHUS** [Tourn.] L. Annual or perennial, tall caulescent herbs. Leaf-blades entire, toothed, or pinnatifid, sometimes spiny margined. Heads erect. Involucres ovoid or subglobose. Achene flattened. Pappus deciduous. —About 45 species, natives of the Old World.—Spr.–fall.—SOW-THISTLES.

Leaf-auricles rounded: achenes smooth and 3-ribbed.   1. *S. asper.*
Leaf-auricles acute: achenes transverse-wrinkled and striate.   2. *S. oleraceus.*

1. **S. asper** (L.) All. Stem 2–15 dm. tall: leaf-blades with rigid-tipped teeth: achene 2–2.5 mm. long, margined, ribbed and smooth.—Waste-places, fields, and roadsides, throughout U. S. and S Can. Nat. of Eu.—(*W. I., Mex., C. A., S. A.*)

2. **S. oleraceus** L. Stem 1–18 dm. tall: leaf-blades more divided than in *S. asper*, with soft-tipped teeth: achene 2.5–3 mm. long, scarcely margined, striate and transverse-wrinkled.—Cult. grounds, waste-places, and fields, various provinces, U. S. and S Can. Nat. of Eu.—(*W. I., Mex., C. A., S. A.*)

Scolymus maculatus L., an annual, spine-armed herb, with pinnately lobed leaves, each lobe terminating in a long spine, the stem with broad spine-margined wings, the involucre not spiny, bracts thin, herbaceous, flowers yellow; achene inclosed by the chaff, has been found on ballast on the seacoast of N. C. Nat. of Eu.

APPENDIX

This appendix contains descriptions of additional plants found within the region covered by this work during the several years the book has been in press, and corrections.

Page 300, after *O. puberula,* insert:

1a. **O. nitida** (Britton) Mackenzie. Plant similar to *O. puberula* in habit, but usually smaller; leaf-blades narrowly elliptic to elliptic-lanceolate, 2–4 cm. long, thinnish, green and shining on both sides; sepals and petals 1.5–2 cm. long: capsule oval-elliptic to oval-orbicular, 1.5–1.8 cm. long.—Low pinelands, Coastal Plain, N. C. to N. J.—Differs from *O. puberula* in the smooth or nearly smooth stem-angles, the uniformly green and shining leaf-blades, the smaller flowers and the smaller and relatively broader capsules.

Page 375, at bottom of page add:

Petals very much shorter than the sepals: sepals with elongate
 involute tips: flower (and capsule) long-stalked: lip over twice
 as long as wide.   1. *I. verticillata*
Petals as long as the sepals or slightly shorter: sepals without
 involute tips: flower (and capsule) short-stalked: lip less than
 twice as long as wide.   2. *I. affinis*

Page 376, after *Isotria verticillata* add:

2. **I. affinis** (Austin) Rydb. Plant similar to *I. verticillata* in habit: scapes 1–2.5 dm. tall: blades of the whorled bracts oval to elliptic, 2.5–5 cm. long: flowers short-stalked: lateral sepals greenish-yellow, narrowly spatulate, 1–2 cm. long, without long tips: petals broadly spatulate or obovate, as long as the sepals or somewhat shorter: lip white with green crest, obovate-cuneate, 11–13 mm. long, less than twice as long as wide when spread out, with scattered hairs at the end of the median ridges, the apical lobe flabellate; capsule 2–3 cm. long, stout-stalked. [*Pogonia affinis* Aust.]—Woods, various provinces, N. C. to Pa., Vt., and Me.—Spr.—Discovered in N. C. in the summer of 1933.

Page 389, after *Pleurothallis gelida,* insert:

36a. **LEPANTHES** Sw. Epiphytic dwarf caulescent herbs. Stems clustered, slender, simple, covered with tubular or funnelform sheaths, the uppermost one of which bears a leaf-blade. Leaves solitary on a stem: blade broad, margined, coriaceous, sessile, minutely 3-toothed at the apex. Racemes axillary, solitary or sometimes clustered, slender-peduncled. Flowers few or several, minute, usually approximate, 2-ranked. Sepals spreading or erect, broad, nearly equal, the lateral more or less united. Petals minute, with the short claw adnate to the base of the column, the limb usually wider than long. Lip often slightly longer than the petals, adnate at the base or above the base to the column, entire or lobed, with the two lobes erect, parallel to the column, with the edges thickened and embracing the column. Column short. Anther terminal. Pollinia pyriform. Capsule, oval, ovoid, ellipsoid, or obovoid.—About 50 species, in continental and insular tropical America.—Differs from *Pleurothallis* in having the claws of the petals and the lip adnate to the column.—The description and drawing made partly from Jamaican specimens.

1. **L. Harrisii** Fawcett and Rendle. Stems 3–4.5 cm. tall, simple, several usually together. Leaf-sheaths contiguous, funnelform, oblique, brown-hirtellous on the ridges and on the mouth: leaf-blade elliptic or oval, 1–2 cm. long, acute or acutish, shining. Raceme overtopping the leaf, compact: bracts glabrous, acute: perianth minute, dark crimson-purple: sepals about 2 mm. long, the median one narrowly oval, the 2 lateral ½ united, lanceolate, 1-veined: petals elliptic, 0.5–0.7 mm. long, rounded at the apex: lip orbicular-ovate, entire, little over 1 mm. long, 3-veined: column about 0.5 mm. long: capsule ellipsoid or oval, 3–4 mm. long, 6-ribbed.—On trees, Big Cypress Swamp, Fla.—(*W. I.*)—Wint.

Page 396, after *Macradenia lutescens*, insert:

49a. **MAXILLARIA** R. & P. Epiphytic herbs with more or less clustered flowering branches, the pseudobulbs sometimes poorly developed, each bearing one leaf. Leaves coriaceous, 2-ranked, erect. Scapes (peduncles) arising at the bases of the pseudobulbs or in the axils of the leaves, solitary, with sheathing bracts, 1-flowered. Flowers large or medium. Sepals narrow, nearly equal, distinct, the lateral adnate to the column-foot, forming a more or less prominent chin. Petals narrower than the sepals, usually somewhat broadened upward. Lip concave, erect at the apex of the column-foot, the claw very short, or wanting, the lateral lobes shallow, erect, the terminal lobe ovate or elliptic-ovate, spreading. Column with a short foot, often slightly incurved, semiterete, not winged. Anther terminal. Pollinia 4, unappendaged. Capsule ovoid, ellipsoid, or obovoid, erect, ribbed, beakless.—About 240 species, in continental and insular tropical America.—Differs from *Macradenia* in having 4 pollinia, instead of 2, the solitary axillary flower at the base of the plant, and the slightly lobed lip.

1. **M. sessilis** (Sw.) Fawcett and Rendle. Stem very short, the branches usually clustered or approximate: pseudobulbs inconspicuous, elongate, flattened, each with a leaf at the apex. Leaves basal (except the one on the apex of the pseudobulb) erect, 2-ranked, the outer ones scale-like; inner one 1–3 dm. long, with blades conduplicate and sheating at the thickened base, linear, oblique at the apex: flowers few, clustered in two's or three's, from the axils of each leaf, the peduncle very short: pedicels about as long as the peduncle, with one sheathing bract: perianth mainly pale-yellow: sepals coriaceous, lanceolate, about 1.5 cm. long; petals linear-spatulate, about as long as the sepals, slightly curved: lip elliptic-lanceolate, 1–1.5 cm. long, with a strong midrib, acute: capsule ellipsoid, 2–3 cm. long, with 6 ribs and furrows.—On trees, Big Cypress Swamp, Fla.—(*W. I., Mex., C. A., S. A.*) —Spr.–sum.

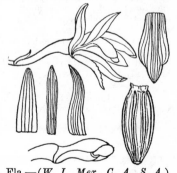

Page 430, after *Quercus coccinea*, insert:

35a. Q. Nuttallii E. J. Palmer. Tree becoming 22 m. tall, with a narrow pyramidal crown, the bark gray or slate-colored and smooth or dark brownish-gray and slightly fissured on old trunks: leaf-blades obovate or elliptic in outline, 8–16 cm. long, glabrous, except tufted vein-axils beneath, pinnately 5–7-lobed, the lobes as long as the body or shorter, all bristle-tipped, the terminal one acuminate: acorns sessile or very short-stalked; cup hemispheric above the stout stipe or deep-turbinate, 2–2.5 cm. wide; nut ovoid or cylindric-ovoid, 20–28 mm. long, ⅓ to ½ included in the cup.—Alluvial lowlands, mostly Coastal Plain, Miss. to E. Tex., to Ark. and Mo. (?)

Page 608, after *Spiraea alba*, insert:

2a. S. prunifolia S. & Z. Shrub, with slender arching branches and finely pubescent twigs: leaf-blades elliptic or oval, varying to ovate, 1–2.5 cm. long, obtuse or acute, more or less pubescent and sometimes veiny, serrulate, very short-petioled: hypanthium broadly turbinate, less than 1 mm. high: petals white, about 3 mm. long: follicles oblong, 3–3.5 mm. long. (BRIDAL-WREATH)—Roadsides and about abandoned gardens, various provinces, N. C. to Mass. Nat. of Asia.—Spr.—Differs from *S. alba* in the elliptic, oval or ovate leaf-blades, and the inflorescence which has sessile clusters scattered along the old wood of the slender branchlets.

Page 608, after *Spiraea corymbosa*, add:

6a. S. japonica L. f. Shrub 1–2 m. tall with finely pubescent twigs: leaf-blades oblong, elliptic, or oblong-lanceolate, 3–12 cm. long, acuminate, coarsely serrate, finely pubescent at least when young, cuneate at the base: corymbs many-flowered, round-topped: hypanthium broadly campanulate: petals pink or rose-colored, suborbicular, 1.5–2 mm. long, or rarely longer: follicles erect, about 3 mm. long, glabrous.—Woods, hillsides, and roadsides, various provinces, Ga. to Pa., and Conn. Nat. of e Asia.—Sum.—Differs from *S. corymbosa* in the acuminate leaf-blades and the pink or rose-colored corolla.

Page 816, in place of the description of *Ilex Amelanchier* as it now stands, insert:

14. I. Amelanchier M. A. Curtis. Shrub or small tree with more or less persistent pubescent foliage: leaf-blades elliptic to elliptic-lanceolate, 4–8 cm. long, acute or short-acuminate, inconspicuously serrate, finely reticulate above, thinly pubescent beneath, acute or rounded at the base: calyx 2–2.5 mm. broad: corolla 6–7 mm. broad: drupe globose, 7–10 mm. in diameter, red.—Swamps and shaded stream-banks, Coastal Plain, Ga. and S. C.—Spr.—This more complete description is to replace that on page 816, where the word petioles is omitted before "6–10 mm." long and to give measurements of the flowers which have only recently been collected.

Pages 1166 and 1167, under *Conradina* in place of **C. montana** Small, read **C. verticillata** Jennison, in both key and description.

LIST OF GENERA AND SPECIES PUBLISHED IN THIS MANUAL*

Sagittaria ornithorhyncha Small. Type, Fayetteville, N. C., Biltmore Herbarium, No. 5236 b, in herb. N. Y. B. G.
Philotria densa (Planch.) Small. *Egeria densa* Planch.
Cyperus Winkeleri Britton & Small. Type, Humbuggus Prairie, Dade Co., Fla., Small & Mosier, No. 5625, in herb. N. Y. B. G.
Cyperus Deeringianus Britton & Small. Type, Arch Creek Prairie, Dade Co., Fla., Small, Mosier, and Small, No. 6789, in herb. N. Y. B. G.
Cyperus multiflorus (Chapm.) Small. *Cyperus echinatus multiflorus* Chapm.
Eleocharis carolina Small. Type, South Carolina, M. A. Curtis, in herb. C. U.
Eleocharis Curtisii Small. Type, Wilmington, N. C., M. A. Curtis, in herb. C. U.
Rynchospora Rappiana Small. Type, between DeLand and New Smyrna, Fla., Rapp, Oct. 10, 1926, in herb. N. Y. B. G.
Rynchospora leptocarpa (Chapm.) Small. *Rynchospora glomerata leptocarpa* Chapm.
Rynchospora Harperi Small. Type, 3 m. sw. of Hawkinsville, Ga., Harper, No. 1377, in herb. N. Y. B. G.
Rynchospora pinetorum Britton & Small. Type, w. of Punta Gorda, Fla., Small, No. 10,912, in herb. N. Y. B. G.
Rynchospora Edisoniana Britton. Type, Everglades, w. of Miami, Fla., Small, No. 8835, in herb. N. Y. B. G.
Rynchospora saxicola Small. Type, Little Stone Mountain, Ga., Harper, No. 2308, in herb. N. Y. B. G.
Scleria Brittonii Core. *Scleria pauciflora glabra* Chapm.
Carex purpurifera Mackenzie. Type, Morley, Tenn., John Bright, May 18, 1923, in herb. N. Y. B. G.
Commelina Gigas Small. Type, e. shore of Lake Okeechobee, Fla., Small, No. 8247, in herb. N. Y. B. G.
Tillandsia simulata Small. Type, along Manatee River, Fla., Garber, June, 1878, in herb. C. U.
Tillandsia myriophylla Small. Type, s. of Brooksville, Fla., Small & Alexander, May 13, 1931, in herb. N. Y. B. G.
Xeniatrum umbellulatum (Michx.) Small. *Dracaena umbellulatum* Michx.
Tortipes Small (tortus, *twisting*, and pes, *foot*, referring to the twisted flower-stalk.)
Tortipes amplexifolius (L.) Small. *Uvularia amplexifolia* L.
Atamosco candida (Lindl.) Small. *Amaryllis candida* Lindl.
Hymenocallis keyensis Small. *Hymenocallis caribaea* Chapm., not Herb.
Hymenocallis Collieri Small. Type, Marco Island, Fla., Small, May, 1920, in herb. N. Y. B. G.
Hymenocallis Kimballiae Small. Type, Apalachicola, Fla., Kimball, May, 1921, in herb. N. Y. B. G.
Hymenocallis tridentata Small. Type, Vero, Fla., Small, Dec., 1920, in herb. N. Y. B. G.
Hymenocallis bidentata Small. Type, St. Bernard, Ala., Bede Knapke, Oct., 1920, in herb. N. Y. B. G.
Hymenocallis laciniata Small. Type, near Carbur, Fla., Small, May 6, 1925, in herb. N. Y. B. G.

* In this list C. U. = Columbia University and N. Y. B. G. = New York Botanical Garden.

Habenella odontopetala (Reichenb. f.) Small. *Habenaria odontopetala* Reichenb. f.
Spathiger stroboliferus (Reichenb. f.) Small. *Epidendrum stroboliferum* Reichenb. f.
Amphiglottis conopsea (Ait.) Small. *Epidendrum conopseum* Ait.
Micropiper leptostachyon (Nutt.) Small. *Piper leptostachyon* Nutt.
Micropiper humile (Vahl) Small. *Piperomia humilis* Vahl.
Rhynchophorum Small. *Peperomia*, subgenus *Rhynchophorum* Miq.
Rhynchophorum obtusifolium (L.) Small. *Piper obtusifolium* L.
Rhynchophorum floridanum Small. *Piperomia floridana* Small.
Rhynchophorum spathulifolium Small. *Piperomia spathulifolium* Small.
Hicoria austrina Small. Type, Shell-midden, 5 m. s. of Daytona, Fla., Small, Britton, & DeWinkeler, No. 9191, in herb. N. Y. B. G.
Salix Chapmanii Small. Type, Middle Fla., Chapman, in herb. C. U.
Parietaria nummularia Small. Type, Sanford, Fla., Rapp, Apr. 11, 1929, in herb. N. Y. B. G.
Ramium niveum (L.) Small. *Urtica nivea* L.
Acetosella Acetosella (L.) Small. *Rumex Acetosella* L.
Delopyrum filiforme Small. Type, near Douglas, Fla., Harper, No. 2010, in herb. N. Y. B. G.
Delopyrum articulatum (L.) Small. *Polygonum articulatum* L.
Persicaria mississippiensis (Sanford) Small. *Polygonum mississippiense* Sanford.
Persicaria paludicola Small. Type, Everglades, Camp Jackson to Camp Longview, Fla., Small, Carter, and Small, No. 3494, in herb. N. Y. B. G.
Gastronychia Small. (Gaster, *belly*, and *anychia*, referring to the swollen base of the flower.)
Gastronychia herniarioides (Michx.) Small. *Anychia herniarioides* Michx.
Odontonychia interior Small. Type, along the Suwanee River, e. of Old Town, Fla., Small, Small, & DeWinkeler, No. 11465, in herb. N. Y. B. G.
Torrubia globosa Small. Type, Miami Beach, Fla., Small, Small, & DeWinkeler, No. 11539, in herb. N. Y. B. G.
Claytonia media (DC.) Small. *Claytonia virginica media* DC.
Sabularia uniflora (Walt.) Small. *Stellaria uniflora* Walt.
Sabularia groenlandica (Retz.) Small. *Stellaria groenlandica* Retz.
Sabularia brevifolia (Nutt.) Small. *Arenaria brevifolia* Nutt.
Sabularia glabra (Michx.) Small. *Arenaria glabra* Michx.
Sabularia caroliniana (Walt.) Small. *Arenaria caroliniana* Walt.
Clematis micrantha Small. Type, Devil's Punch Bowl, w. of Brooksville, Fla., Small, No. 11337; for fr. Choocochatte hammock, s. of Brooksville, Fla., Small, No. 10602, in herb. N. Y. B. G.
Viorna subreticulata Harbison. Type, Garden City, Ala., Biltmore herb., No. 15011, in herb. N. Y. B. G.
Viorna Beadlei Small. Type, Currahee Mt., Ga., Small, Sept. 1–3, 1894, in herb. N. Y. B. G.
Pityothamnus Small. (πίτυς, *pine*, and θάμνυς, *shrub*, referring to the habitat of these plants.)
Pityothamnus reticulatus (Chapm.) Small. *Asimina reticulata* Chapm.
Pityothamnus incanus (Bartr.) Small. *Anona incana* Bartr.
Pityothamnus angustifolius (A. Gray) Small. *Asimina angustifolia* A. Gray.
Pityothamnus pygmaeus (Bartr.) Small. *Anona pygmaea* Bartr.
Pityothamnus tetramerus Small. *Asimina tetramera* Small.
Pityothamnus obovatus (Willd.) Small. *Anona obovata* Willd.
Neocleome Small. (νέος, *new*, and *Cleome*.)
Neocleome spinosa (L.) Small. *Cleome spinosa* L.
Neocleome serrata (Jacq.) Small. *Cleome serrata* Jacq.
Sedum vigilimontis Small. Type, Lookout Mountain, near Rising Fawn, Ga., Curtiss, No. 6798, in herb. N. Y. B. G.

Vachellia peninsularis Small. Type, Long (Pine) Key, Everglades, Fla., for fls., Small & Wilson, No. 1778; for fr., Small & Carter, No. 2975, in herb. N. Y. B. G.

Vachellia densiflora Alexander. Type, along Bayou La Fourche near Cut-off, La., for fls., Small & Alexander, Apr. 16, 1931; for fr., Small, Aug., 1931, both in herb. in N. Y. B. G.

Vachellia insularis Small. Type, Big Pine Key, Fla., for fls., Small & Mosier, No. 6018; for fr., Small, Carter, & Small, No. 3549, in herb. N. Y. B. G.

Adipera corymbosa (Lam.) Small. Cassia corymbosa Lam.

Chamaesenna didymobotrya (Forsk.) Small. Cassia didymobotrya Forsk.

Crotalaria Linaria Small. Type, Big Pine Key, Fla., Small & Mosier, No. 6034, in herb. N. Y. B. G.

Galactia prostrata Small. Type, for fls., Redlands district, Dade Co., Fla., Small, No. 8633; for fr., near Silver Palm, Dade Co., Fla., Small, Mosier & Small, No. 6453, in herb. N. Y. B. G.

Stylosanthes calcicola Small. Type, Rose-Costello hammock, Dade Co., Fla., Small, Mosier, & Small, No. 6539, in herb. N. Y. B. G.

Asemeia leiodes (Blake) Small. Polygala grandiflora leiodes Blake.

Asemeia grandiflora (Walt.) Small. Polygala grandiflora Walt.

Asemeia cumulicola Small. Polygala cumulicola Small.

Asemeia miamensis Small. Polygala miamensis Small.

Polygala aboriginum Small. Type, dunes s. of Coronado, Fla., Small, Mosier, and Matthaus, May 24, 1926, in herb. N. Y. B. G.

Pilostaxis arenicola Small. Polygala arenicola Small.

Pilostaxis lutea (L.) Small. Polygala lutea L.

Pilostaxis Rugelii (Shuttl.) Small. Polygala Rugelii Shuttl.

Pilostaxis ramosa (Ell.) Small. Polygala ramosa Ell.

Pilostaxis cymosa (Walt.) Small. Polygala cymosa Walt.

Pilostaxis Baldwinii (Nutt.) Small. Polygala Baldwinii Nutt.

Pilostaxis Carteri Small. Polygala Carteri, Small.

Chamaesyce cumulicola Small. Type, Caxambas Island, Fla., Small. No. 10490, in herb. N. Y. B. G.

Chamaesyce Moseri Small. Type, near Brogdon hammock, Dade Co., Fla., Small & Mosier, No. 6347, in herb. N. Y. B. G.

Chamaesyce Mathewsii Small. Type, dunes opposite Miami, Fla., Small, No. 4556.

Galarrhoeus floridanus (Chapm.) Small. Euphorbia floridana Chapm.

Galarrhoeus inundatus (Torr.) Small. Euphorbia inundata Torr.

Galarrhoeus telephioides (Chapm.) Small. Euphorbia telephoides Chapm.

Galarrhoeus Darlingtonii (A. Gray) Small. Euphorbia Darlingtonii A. Gray.

Galarrhoeus austrinus Small. Tithymalus austrinus Small.

Galarrhoeus trichotomus (H.B.K.) Small. Euphorbia trichotoma H.B.K.

Saccharodendron nigrum (Michx. f.) Small. Acer nigrum Michx. f.

Argentacer Small. (argentum, silver, and acer, i.e., silver-maple.)

Argentacer saccharinum (L.) Small. Acer saccharinum L.

Rufacer Small. (rufus, red, and acer, i.e., red-maple.)

Rufacer rubrum (L.) Small. Acer rubrum L.

Rufacer carolinianum (Walt.) Small. Acer carolinianum Walt.

Cardiospermum keyense Small. Type, Key Largo, Fla., Small, Mosier, & De-Winkeler, No. 10952, in herb. N. Y. B. G.

Ascyrum Edisonianum Small. Type, twenty-one m. e. of Arcadia, Fla., Hand, No. 118, in herb. N. Y. B. G.

Lechea prismatica Small. Type, scrub, e. of Sebring, Fla., Small, No. 9787, in herb. N. Y. B. G.

Lechea exserta Small. Type, w. of Halendale, Fla., Small, DeWinkeler, & Small, No. 11089, in herb. N. Y. B. G.

Lechea myriophylla Small. Type, scrub, e. of Sebring, Fla., Small & De-Winkeler, Dec. 13, 1920, in herb. N. Y. B. G.

Viola rugosa Small. Type, Telogia, Fla., Small, Apr., 1927, in herb. N. Y. B. G.
Opuntia atrocapensis Small. Type, dunes, Cape Sable (E. Cape), Small, Nov. 25, 1916, in herb. N. Y. B. G.
Opuntia polycarpa Small. Type, Caxambas Island, Fla., Small, May 11, 1922, in herb. N. Y. B. G.
Opuntia nitens Small. Type, hammock, 5 m. s. of Daytona, Fla., Small, Small, & DeWinkeler, Aug. 23, 1922, in herb. N. Y. B. G.
Opuntia cumulicola Small. Type, beach, opp. Lemon City, Fla., Small, Small, & Carter, No. 970, in herb. N. Y. B. G.
Opuntia tenuiflora Small. Type, Lignum Vitae Key, Fla. Small, Mar. 30, 1916, in herb. N. Y. B. G.
Opuntia turbinata Small. Type, St. Scorge Island, Fla., Small, Aug. 22, 1922, in herb. N. Y. B. G.
Opuntia magnifica Small. Type, s. end of Amelia Island, Fla., Small, Small, and DeWinkeler, Aug. 21, 1922, in herb. N. Y. B. G.
Brasiliopuntia brasiliensis (Willd.) Small. *Cactus brasiliensis* Willd.
Eugenia anthera Small. Type, for fls., near Roseland, Fla., Charles A. Mosier, Aug., 1928; for fr., near Roseland, Fla., Small, Dec. 27, 1927, in herb. N. Y. B. G.
Mosiera Small. (In honor of Charles A. Mosier.)
Mosiera longipes (Berg) Small. *Eugenia longipes* Berg.
Mosiera bahamensis (Kiearsk.) Small. *Eugenia bahamensis* Kiearsk.
Isnardia media Small, Alexander. Type, between Homestead and Cross Key, Fla., Small & Carter, No. 2626, in herb. N. Y. B. G.
Ludwigia spathulifolia Small. Type, Everglades, NW. of Perrine, Fla., Small & Carter, No. 2990, in herb. N. Y. B. G.
Jussiaea neglecta Small. Type, along Escambia River, near Pensacola, Fla., Small, Aug., 1930, in herb. N. Y. B. G.
Proserpinaca amblygona (Fernald) Small. *Proserpinaca palustris amblygona* Fernald.
Eryngium cuneifolium Small. Type, about Lake Nancesowee, Fla., Small & Mosier, Dec., 1927, in herb. N. Y. B. G.
Sium floridanum Small. Type, Swamps of the Chipola River, Fla., Chapman, in herb. C. U.
Zizia latifolia Small. Type, near Bristol, Fla., Curtiss, Aug. 28, in herb. N. Y. B. G.
Decachaea tomentosa Small. *Gaylussacia tomentosa* Small.
Decachaena nana (A. Gray) Small. *Gaylussacia frondosa nana* A. Gray.
Decachaena baccata (Wang.) Small. *Andromeda baccata* Wang.
Decachaena ursina (M. A. Curtis) Small. *Vaccinium ursinum* M. A. Curtis.
Lasiococcus Small. (λάσιος, hairy, and κοκκος, berry, referring to the hairy fruit.)
Lasiococcus dumosus (Andr.) Small. *Vaccinium dumosum* Andr.
Lasiococcus Mosieri Small. *Gaylussacia Mosieri* Small.
Lasiococcus orocola Small. Type, near Flat Rock, N. C., Biltmore Herbarium, No. 470b, in herb. N. Y. B. G.
Buxella Small. (Diminutive of Buxus.)
Buxella brachycera (Michx.) Small. *Vaccinium brachycerum* Michx.
Polycodium macilentum Small. Type, Vaughns Mill, Ala., Earle, No. 1632, in herb. N. Y. B. G.
Polycodium leptosepalum Small. Type, French Camp, Miss., Ida M. Clute, No. 59, in herb. N. Y. B. G.
Cyanococcus Myrsinites (Lam.) Small. *Vaccinium Myrsinites* Lam.
Cyanococcus fuscatus (Ait.) Small. *Vaccinium fuscatum* Ait.
Cyanococcus tenellus (Ait.) Small. *Vaccinium tenellum* Ait.
Cyanococcus Elliottii (Chapm.) Small. *Vaccinium Elliottii* Chapm.
Cyanococcus amoenus (Ait.) Small. *Vaccinium amoenum* Ait.
Cyanococcus virgatus (Ait.) Small. *Vaccinium virgatum* Ait.

Cyanococcus atrococcus (A. Gray) Small. *Vaccinium corymbosum atrococcum* A. Gray.
Cyanococcus simulatus Small. *Vaccinium simulatum* Small.
Cyanococcus Cuthbertii Small. Type, Augusta, Ga., Cuthbert, No. 259, in herb. N. Y. B. G.
Cyanococcus holophyllus Small. Type, for fls., Sandhills, e. of Sebring, Fla., Small, DeWinkeler, & Mosier, No. 11347; for fr., Lake Jackson, Fla., Small, Mosier, & DeWinkeler, No. 10861, in herb. N. Y. B. G.
Cyanococcus Margarettae (Ashe) Small. *Vaccinium Margarettae* Ashe.
Cyanococcus pallidus (Ait.) Small. *Vaccinium pallidum* Ait.
Cyanococcus liparus Small. Type, Bull Pasture Mtn., Va., Rydberg, No. 9007.
Cyanococcus tallapusae Coville. Type, for fls., near Tallapoosa, Ga., George E. Murrill, Nat. Herb. No. 1,582,192; for fr. one m. east of Tallapoosa, Ga., G. A. Schulze, No. 691.
Cyanococcus subcordatus Small. Type, Knoxville, Tenn., Ruth, No. 445, in herb. N. Y. B. G.
Cyanococcus hirsutus (Buckl.) Small. *Vaccinium hirsutum* Buckl.
Herpothamnus Small. ('ἔρπης, *spreads*, and θάμνος, *shrub*, referring to the trailing stems.)
Herpothamnus crassifolius (Andr.) Small. *Vaccinium crassifolium* Andr.
Bumelia lacuum Small. Type, for fls., dunes, n. of Kuhlman, Fla., Small, & DeWinkeler, No. 9965; for fr., between Avon Park and Sebring, Fla., Small, Small and DeWinkeler, No. 10666 in herb. N. Y. B. G.
Amarolea Small. (Amarus, *bitter*, and olea, *olive*, referring to the bitter olive-like fruit.)
Amarolea megacarpa Small. Type, for fls. and fr., near Lake Annie, Fla., Small & Matthaus, No. 11612, in herb. N. Y. B. G.
Lapithea capitata (Raf.) Small. *Pleienta capitata* Raf.
Acerates delticola Small. Type New Orleans, La., Ingalls in 1834, in herb. C. U.
Biventraria Small. (Bis, *two*, and venter, *belly*, referring to the inflated hoods of the flower.)
Biventraria variegata (L.) Small. *Asclepias variegata* L.
Oxypteryx Curtissii (A. Gray) Small. *Asclepias Curtissii* A. Gray.
Asclepiodella Small. (Diminutive of *Asclepias*.)
Asclepiodella Feayi (Chapm.) Small. *Asclepiodora Feayi* Chapm.
Cyclodon Small. (Κύκλος, *circle*, and 'οδούς, *tooth*, referring to the toothed crown of the flower.)
Cyclodon alabamense (Vail) Small. *Vincetoxicum alabamense* Vail.
Odontostephana Alexander. ('οδούς, *tooth*, and στέφανος, *crown*, referring to the toothed crown of the flower.)
Odontostephana decipiens Alexander. *Vincetoxicum carolinense* Authors, not *Cynanchum carolinense* Jacq.
Odontostephana carolinensis (Jacq.) Alexander. *Cynanchum carolinense* Jacq.
Odontostephana obliqua (Jacq.) Alexander. *Cynanchum obliquum* Jacq.
Odontostephana Shortii (A. Gray) Alexander. *Gonolobus obliquus Shortii* A. Gray.
Odontostephana Baldwiniana (Sweet) Alexander. *Gonolobus Baldwinianum* Sweet.
Odontostephana flavidula (Chapm.) Alexander. *Gonolobus flavidulus* Chapm.
Odontostephana floridana (Vail) Alexander. *Vincetoxicum floridanum* Vail.
Edisonia Small. (In honor of Thomas Alva Edison.)
Edisonia pubiflora (Decne.) Small. *Chthamalia pubiflora* Decne.
Evolvulus macilentus Small. Type, Big Pine Key, Ga. Small, No. 3798, in herb. N. Y. B. G.
Strophocaulos Small. (στροφή, *twist*, and καυλός, *stem*, referring to the twining stems.)
Strophocaulos arvensis (L.) Small. *Convolvulus arvensis* L.

Decemium appendiculatum (Michx.) Small. *Hydrophyllum appendiculatum* Michx.
Solanum perplexum Small.   Type, near Thomasville, Ga., Small, May 28–June 6, 1895, in herb. C. U.
Myriopus Small.   (μυρίος, *many*, and πούς, *foot*, referring to the many-flowered cymes.)
Myriopus volubilus (L.) Small. *Tournefortia volubilis* L.
Myriopus poliochrus (Spreng.) Small. *Tournefortia poliochrus* Spreng.
Stylodon carolinensis (Walt.) Small. *Verbena carolinensis* Walt.
Glandularia maritima Small. *Verbena maritima* Small.
Glandularia Lambertii (Sims) Small. *Verbena Lambertii* Sims.
Glandularia canadensis (L.) Small. *Verbena canadensis* L.
Glandularia Drummondii (Lindl.) Small. *Verbena Drummondii* Lindl.
Glandularia tampensis (Nash) Small. *Verbena tampensis* Nash.
Glandularia tenuisecta (Briq.) Small. *Verbena tenuisecta* Briq.
Glandularia peruviana (L.) Small. *Erinus peruvianus* L.
Scutellaria Cuthbertii Alexander.   Type, Augusta, Ga., Cuthbert, May 26, 1900, in herb. N. Y. B. G.
Scutellaria alabamensis Alexander.   Type, Attalla, Ala., Eggert, June 30, 1897, in herb. N. Y. B. G.
Dracocephalum leptophyllum Small. *Physostegia leptophyllum* Small.
Dracocephalum veroniciformis Small. *Physostegia veroniciformis* Small.
Koellia pauciflora Small.   Type, Albany, Ga., Small, July 9–12, 1895, in herb. C. U.
Tragiola Small & Pennell (Anagram of *Gratiola*.)
Tragiola pilosa (Michx.) Small & Pennell. *Gratiola pilosa* Michx.
Tragiola pilosa epilis (Pennell) Small & Pennell. *Gratiola pilosa epilis* Pennell.
Penstemon Brittonorum Pennell.   Type, White Rock Mountain, Va., Britton, Britton, & Vail, June 22, 1892, in herb. N. Y. B. G.
Penstemon brevisepalus Pennell.   Type, Crossville, Tenn., F. W. Pennell, No. 11311, May 30–31, 1923, in herb. Acad. Nat. Sci. Phila.
Buchnera breviflora Pennell.   Type, Robinson Island, Fla., S. M. Tracy, No. 7605, May 22, 1901, in herb. N. Y. B. G.
Calpidisca Standleyae Barnhart.   Type, near Ft. Myers, Fla., J. P. Standley, No. 406, in herb. N. Y. B. G.
Rotantha Small.   (Rota, *wheel*, and anthus, *flower*, referring to the rotate corolla.)
Rotantha floridana (S. Wats.) Small. *Campanula floridana* S. Wats.
Rotantha Robinsiae Small. *Campanula Robinsiae* Small.
Kuhnia Mosieri Small.   Type, Ross-Costello hammock, Dade Co., Fla., Small, Mosier, & Small, No. 6544, in herb. N. Y. B. G.
Laciniaria Shortii Alexander.   Type, Ohio, Short, 1842, in herb. C. U.
Laciniaria Tracyi Alexander.   Type, Gateswood, Ala., Tracy, No. 8558, in herb. N. Y. B. G.
Laciniaria Ruthii Alexander.   Type, Hiawassee Valley, e. Tenn., Ruth, No. 34, in herb. C. U.
Chrysopsis subulata Small.   Type, between Avon Park and Sebring, Fla., Small, No. 11495.
Chrysopsis arenicola Alexander.   Type, Hartsville, S. C., Coker, Oct. 9, 1909, in herb. N. Y. B. G.
Chrysopsis lanuginosa Small.   Type, Lynn Haven, Fla., A. H. Van Cleve, Dec. 3, 1920, in herb. N. Y. B. G.
Chrysopsis floridana Small.   Type, Bradenton, Fla., Tracy, No. 7344.
Pityopsis flexuosa (Nash) Small. *Chrysopsis flexuosa* Nash.
Pityopsis Tracyi Small. *Chrysopsis Tracyi* Small.
Pityopsis microcephala Small. *Chrysopsis microcephala* Small.
Pityopsis Ruthii Small. *Chrysopsis Ruthii* Small.
Pityopsis aspera Small. *Chrysopsis aspera* Small.
Pityopsis oligantha (Chapm.) Small. *Chrysopsis oligantha* Chapm.

Solidago Milleriana Mackenzie. *Solidago petiolaris* Authors, not Ait.
Solidago Harperi Mackenzie. Type, near Grier's Cave, Randolph Co., Ga., Harper, No. 1778, in herb. N. Y. B. G.
Solidago notabilis Mackenzie. *Solidago amplexicaulis* T. & G., not Martens.
Solidago tarda Mackenzie. Type, Winterville, Ga., J. H. Miller, Oct. 20, 1926, in herb. N. Y. B. G.
Solidago Edisoniana Mackenzie. Type, hammocks, near Ft. Mead, Fla.
Solidago mirabilis Small. Type, Turnbull hammock, near Titusville, Fla., Small.
Oligoneuron Jacksonianum (Kuntze) Small. *Solidago corymbosa* Ell.
Aster georgianus Alexander. Type, Augusta, Ga., Cuthbert, No. 275, in herb. N. Y. B. G.
Aster fontinalis Alexander. Type, prairie, s. of Deep Lake, Fla., Small & Buswell, Dec. 7, 1925, in herb. N. Y. B. G.
Aster Walteri Alexander. *Aster squarrosus* Walter, not All.
Aster Smallii Alexander. Type, between Hendersonville and Salola Mountain, N. C., Small & Huger, October 2–3, 1901, in herb. N. Y. B. G.
Aster pinifolius Alexander. Type, Coconut Grove, Fla., Small, No. 7958, in herb. N. Y. B. G.
Aster gracilipes (Wiegand) Alexander. *Aster dumosus gracilipes* Wiegand.
Aster brachypholis Small. Type, Aspalaga Bluff, Liberty Co., Fla., Small, DeWinkeler, & Mosier, No. 11027, in herb. N. Y. B. G.
Aster pedionomus Alexander. Type, Cheatham Co., Tenn., Eggert, Aug. 19, 1897, in herb. N. Y. B. G.
Aster Gattingeri Alexander. Type, Tullahoma, Tenn., Gattinger, Aug. 19, in herb. C. U.
Aster hemisphaericus Alexander. Type, Will's Point, Tex., Reverchon, No. 4363, in herb. N. Y. B. G.
Aster verutifolius Alexander. Type, Ocean Springs, Miss., Earle, Sept. 11, 1899, in herb. N. Y. B. G.
Pluchea tenuifolia Small. Type, 5½ miles n. of Bowling Green on road to Ft. Mead, Fla., Hand, No. 360, in herb. N. Y. B. G.
Smallanthus Mackenzie. (In honor of John Kunkel Small.) Type, *Polymnia Uvedalia* L.
Smallanthus Uvedalia (L.) Mackenzie. *Polymnia Uvedalia* L.
Silphium lapsuum Small. Type, Augusta, Ga., Cuthbert, July 17, 1898, in herb. N. Y. B. G.
Silphium orae Small. Type, Wilmington, N. C., Curtis, in herb. C. U.
Silphium confertiflorum Small. Type, Cocoa, Ala., Schuchert, Oct. 13, 1896, in herb. N. Y. B. G.
Silphium nodum Small. Type, Charleston Neck, Charleston, S. C., Gibbes & Branch in 1855, in herb. N. Y. B. G.
Chrysogonum australe Alexander. Type, Marianna, Fla., Harper, May 16, 1925, in herb. N. Y. B. G.
Echinacea tennesseensis (Beadle) Small. *Brauneria tennesseensis* Beadle.
Pterophyton helianthoides (Michx.) Alexander. *Verbesina helianthoides* Michx.
Pterophyton heterophyllum (Chapm.) Alexander. *Actinomeris heterophylla* Chapm.
Pterophyton pauciflorum (Nutt.) Alexander. *Actinomeris pauciflora* Nutt.
Pterophyton aristatum (Ell.) Alexander. *Verbesina aristata* Ell.
Ridan paniculatum (Walt.) Small. *Anthanasia paniculata* Walt.

TABLES OF THE ORDERS AND FAMILIES

	Gen.	Sp.		Gen.	Sp.
CYCADALES.			SCITAMINALES.		
1. Cycadaceae,	1	4	41. Musaceae,	1	2
PINALES.			42. Cannaceae,	1	2
2. Pinaceae,	5	18	43. Alpiniaceae,	1	1
3. Juniperaceae,	6	9	44. Marantaceae,	2	3
4. Taxaceae,	2	2	ORCHIDALES.		
PANDANALES.			45. Burmanniaceae,	2	3
5. Typhaceae,	1	2	46. Orchidaceae,	55	112
6. Sparganiaceae,	1	2	PIPERALES.		
NAIADALES.			47. Saururaceae,	1	1
7. Zannichelliaceae,	3	17	48. Piperaceae,	2	5
8. Zosteraceae,	1	1	CASUARINALES.		
9. Cymodoceaceae,	2	2	49. Casuarinaceae,	1	1
10. Naiadaceae,	1	5	JUGLANDALES.		
ALISMALES.			50. Juglandaceae,	2	16
11. Scheuchzeriaceae,	1	1	LEITNERIALES.		
12. Alismaceae,	5	28	51. Leitneriaceae,	1	1
HYDROCHARITALES.			MYRICALES.		
13. Elodeaceae,	3	7	52. Myricaceae,	3	6
14. Hydrocharitaceae,	2	2	SALICALES.		
POALES.			53. Salicaceae,	2	23
15. Poaceae,	100	476	FAGALES.		
16. Cyperaceae,	22	375	54. Corylaceae,	3	4
ARECALES.			55. Betulaceae,	2	6
17. Arecaceae,	10	15	56. Fagaceae,	3	50
ARALES.			URTICALES.		
18. Araceae,	7	11	57. Urticaceae,	7	16
19. Lemnaceae,	4	10	58. Cannabinaceae,	2	2
XYRIDALES.			59. Artocarpaceae,	4	9
20. Mayacaceae,	1	2	60. Ulmaceae,	5	15
21. Xyridaceae,	1	20	POLYGONALES.		
ERIOCAULALES.			61. Polygonaceae,	18	67
22. Eriocaulaceae,	3	13	CHENOPODIALES.		
COMMELINALES.			62. Chenopodiaceae,	11	25
23. Commelinaceae,	7	25	63. Scleranthaceae,	1	1
24. Pontederiaceae,	4	7	64. Basellaceae,	1	1
25. Bromeliaceae,	6	18	65. Amaranthaceae,	9	34
LILIALES.			66. Corrigiolaceae,	8	16
26. Melanthiaceae,	16	23	67. Phytolaccaceae,	4	5
27. Juncaceae,	2	35	68. Petiveriaceae,	1	1
28. Nartheciaceae,	1	2	69. Batidaceae,	1	1
29. Alliaceae,	3	10	70. Allioniaceae,	4	6
30. Liliaceae,	7	16	71. Pisoniaceae,	2	6
31. Convallariaceae,	13	19	72. Tetragoniaceae,	6	8
32. Aloaceae,	1	1	73. Portulacaceae,	3	13
33. Dracaenaceae,	2	9	74. Alsinaceae,	11	31
34. Trilliaceae,	2	20	75. Caryophyllaceae,	6	17
35. Roxburghiaceae,	1	1	RANALES.		
36. Smilacaceae,	2	18	76. Ceratophyllaceae,	1	3
AMARYLLIDALES.			77. Ranunculaceae,	24	92
37. Leucojaceae,	7	35	78. Annonaceae,	4	14
38. Tamaceae,	1	5	79. Magnoliaceae,	5	13
39. Ixiaceae,	7	119	80. Menispermaceae,	4	4
40. Haemodoraceae,	2	2	81. Cabombaceae,	2	2

	Gen.	Sp.
82. Nelumbonaceae,	1	1
83. Nymphaeaceae,	2	13
84. Podophyllaceae,	4	4
85. Berberidaceae,	1	1
PAPAVERALES.		
86. Papaveraceae,	5	8
87. Fumariaceae,	4	10
88. Brassicaceae,	31	94
89. Capparidaceae,	5	8
90. Moringaceae,	1	1
SARRACENIALES.		
91. Droseraceae,	1	5
92. Dionaeaceae,	1	1
93. Sarraceniaceae,	1	8
ROSALES.		
94. Podostemaceae,	1	2
95. Sedaceae,	7	13
96. Penthoraceae,	1	1
97. Parnassiaceae,	1	3
98. Saxifragaceae,	9	27
99. Hydrangeaceae,	3	12
100. Iteaceae,	1	1
101. Rosaceae,	25	93
102. Hamamelidaceae,	2	5
103. Altingiaceae,	1	1
104. Grossulariaceae,	2	6
105. Platanaceae,	1	1
106. Calycanthaceae,	1	4
107. Malaceae,	7	53
108. Amygdalaceae,	6	25
109. Mimosaceae,	11	24
110. Cassiaceae,	14	30
111. Krameriaceae,	1	1
112. Fabaceae,	74	304
GERANIALES.		
113. Geraniaceae,	2	8
114. Oxalidaceae,	4	19
115. Linaceae,	2	12
116. Tropaeolaceae,	1	1
117. Balsaminaceae,	1	3
118. Limnanthaceae,	1	1
119. Zygophyllaceae,	3	5
120. Malpighiaceae,	1	1
121. Rutaceae,	8	20
122. Surianaceae,	1	1
123. Simarubaceae,	4	4
124. Burseraceae,	1	1
125. Meliaceae,	2	2
POLYGALALES.		
126. Polygalaceae,	5	37
EUPHORBIALES.		
127. Euphorbiaceae,	30	127
128. Callitrichaceae,	1	6
SAPINDALES.		
129. Buxaceae,	1	1
130. Empetraceae,	1	1
131. Spondiaceae,	6	16
132. Cyrillaceae,	2	4

	Gen.	Sp.
133. Aquifoliaceae,	1	19
134. Celastraceae,	7	10
135. Hippocrateaceae,	1	1
136. Dodonaeaceae,	1	3
137. Staphyleaceae,	1	1
138. Aesculaceae,	1	4
139. Aceraceae,	5	11
140. Sapindaceae,	6	9
RHAMNALES.		
141. Frangulaceae,	9	18
142. Vitaceae,	5	23
MALVALES.		
143. Tiliaceae,	3	19
144. Malvaceae,	20	63
145. Buettneriaceae,	6	7
HYPERICALES.		
146. Canellaceae,	1	1
147. Clusiaceae,	1	2
148. Elatinaceae,	1	1
149. Tamaricaceae,	1	1
150. Hypericaceae,	6	45
151. Theaceae,	4	4
152. Turneraceae,	2	5
153. Cistaceae,	3	26
154. Violaceae,	2	42
PASSIFLORALES.		
155. Papayaceae,	1	1
156. Passifloraceae,	1	7
OPUNTIALES.		
157. Loasaceae,	1	1
158. Opuntiaceae,	10	44
BEGONALES.		
159. Begoniaceae,	1	1
PROTEALES.		
160. Proteaceae,	1	1
THYMELEALES.		
161. Daphnaceae,	1	1
162. Elaeagnaceae,	1	2
163. Lauraceae,	8	12
164. Cassythaceae,	1	1
MYRTALES.		
165. Melastomaceae,	2	15
166. Lythraceae,	7	16
167. Punisaceae,	1	1
168. Terminaliaceae,	4	4
169. Myrtaceae,	6	13
170. Rhizophoraceae,	1	1
171. Epilobiaceae,	14	66
172. Gunneraceae,	2	8
AMMIALES.		
173. Nyssaceae,	3	14
174. Hederaceae,	3	7
175. Ammiaceae,	41	92
ERICALES.		
176. Clethraceae,	1	3
177. Monotropaceae,	3	7
178. Pyrolaceae,	2	4
179. Ericaceae,	22	50

	Gen.	Sp.		Gen.	Sp.
180. Vacciniaceae,	10	41	212. Pinguiculaceae,	9	22
181. Diapensiaceae,	1	2	213. Orobanchaceae,	4	4
182. Galacaceae,	2	2	214. Bignoniaceae,	6	7
PRIMULALES.			215. Pedaliaceae,	2	2
183. Armeriaceae,	2	6	216. Martyniaceae,	1	1
184. Primulaceae,	9	22	PLANTAGINALES.		
185. Theophrastaceae,	1	1	217. Plantaginaceae,	1	9
186. Ardisiaceae,	2	2	SANTALALES.		
EBENALES.			218. Loranthaceae,	1	3
187. Ebenaceae,	1	2	219. Santalaceae,	4	4
188. Sapotaceae,	7	15	220. Olacaceae,	2	2
189. Symplocaceae,	1	1	RUBIALES.		
190. Styracaceae,	2	6	221. Rubiaceae,	25	70
OLEALES.			222. Caprifoliaceae,	9	35
191. Oleaceae,	7	26	VALERIANALES.		
GENTIANALES.			223. Valerianaceae,	2	7
192. Spigeliaceae,	6	11	224. Morinaceae,	1	1
193. Gentianaceae,	11	37	ARISTOLOCHIALES.		
194. Menyanthaceae,	1	2	225. Asaraceae,	3	17
ASCLEPIADALES.			CAMPANULALES.		
195. Apocynaceae,	12	21	226. Cucurbitaceae,	11	18
196. Asclepiadaceae,	20	53	227. Campanulaceae,	5	8
POLEMONIALES.			228. Lobeliaceae,	1	22
197. Dichondraceae,	1	1	229. Brunoniaceae,	1	1
198. Convolvulaceae,	15	52	230. Calyceraceae,	1	1
199. Cuscutaceae,	1	14	CARDUALES.		
200. Hydroleaceae,	7	19	231. Ambrosiaceae,	5	22
201. Polemoniaceae,	3	17	232. Carduaceae,	129	698
202. Solanaceae,	12	67	233. Cichoriaceae,	16	50
203. Borraginaceae,	11	23			
204. Ehretiaceae,	3	5	Orders		
205. Heliotropiaceae,	8	14	58		
206. Verbenaceae,	14	41		Families	
207. Avicenniaceae,	1	1		233	
208. Phrymaceae,	1	1			Genera
209. Lamiaceae,	41	159			1518
210. Rhinanthaceae,	39	122			Species
211. Acanthaceae,	10	25			5557

INDEX[1]

Aaron's-beard cactus, 911
Aaron's-rod, 674
Abama, 287
Abelmoschus, 857
Abies, 3, 8
Abildgaardia, 155
Abrus, 742
Abizzia, 653
Abutilon, 847
Acacia, 653, 654
Acaciella, 654
Acalypha, 785, 786, 787
ACANTHACEAE, 1225
Acanthocereus, 914, 915,
   915
Acanthospermum, 1407,
   1408
Acanthoxanthium, 1301
ACANTHUS FAMILY, 1225
Acer, 823, *824, 825*
ACERACEAE, 823
Acerates, 1066, 1067
Acetosella, 445, 446
Ache, 982
Achillea, 1466, 1467
Achroanthes, 386
Achyranthes, *475*, 476
Acicarpha, 1296
Acmispon, 687
Acnida, 474, 475
Acoeloraphe, 242
Aconites, 515
Aconitum, 515, 516
Acorus, 244
Actaea, 513
Actinomeris, 1444, 1445
Actinospermum, 1455
Acuan, 655, 656
Adam-and-Eve, 388
Adam's-needle, 303
Adam's-pitcher, 581
Adder's-tongue, 292
Adelia, 1040, 1041
Adenoropium, 791
Adenoplea, 1047
Adicea, 433
Adipera, 660
Adlumia, 549
Adonis, 523
Adonis-flower, 523
Adopogon, 1489
Adzuk-bean, 724
Aegopodium, 974
Aeschynomene, 727, 728,
   729
AESCULACEAE, 822
Aesculus, 822, 823
Aethusa, 982
African bowstring - hemp,
   301
African-marigold, 1464
Afzelia, 1213
Agalinis, 1216
   aphylla, 1220
   decemloba, 1220
   divaricata, 1221
   erecta, 1220
   fasciculata, 1219
   filicaulis, 1221
   filifolia, 1219
   Gattingeri, 1221

georgiana, 1219
   Harperi, 1218
   keyensis, 1220
   laxa, 1219
   linifolia, 1221
   maritima, 1219
   oligophylla, 1220
   pinetorum, 1218
   Plukenetii, 1220
   pulchella, 1219
   purpurea, 1218
   setacea, 1219
   stenophylla, 1219
   tenella, 1220
   tenuifolia, 1221
   virgata, 1218
Agastache, 1153
Agati, 703
Agave, 319, 320
Agdestis, 485
Ageratum, 1319
Agrimonia, 615
   Bicknellii, 616
   Eupatoria, 615, 616
   Eupatoria mollis, 616
   gryposepala, 616
   hirsuta, 616
   incisa, 616
   microcarpa, 616
   mollis, 616
   parviflora, 615
   platycarpa, 616
   pubescens, 616
   pumila, 616
   rostellata, 616
   striata, 615
Agrimony, 615
Agropyron, 136
Agrostemma, 508
Agrostis, 104
   alba, 105
   altissima, 106
   arachnoides, 106
   borealis, 105
   canina, 105
   Elliottiana, 105
   hiemalis, 105
   novae-angliae, 106
   perennans, 105
   rubra, 105
   scabra, 105
   Scribneriana, 106
   vulgaris, 105
Ague-tree, 923
Ague-weed, 1052
Ailanthus, 763
Air-plants, 269, 272
Aira, 107, 108
Albizzia, 653
Alchemilla, 614
Aldenella, 575
Alder
   Black, 814
   Green, 419
   Hazel, 419
   Mountain, 419
   Red, 419
   Russet, 419
   Speckled, 419
   Tag, 419
Alders, 418

Aletris, 315, 316
Alfalfa, 682
Alfileria, 745
Alicia, 730
Alisma, 21
ALISMACEAE, 20
ALISMALES, 20
Alkali-grasses, 128
Allamanda, 1063, 1064
   Pink, 1066
Allegheny-barberry, 545
Allegheny Mountain-spurge,
   806
Allegheny-vine, 549
ALLIACEAE, 288
Alligator-apple, 533
Alligator-bonnet, 543
Alligator-buttons, 540
Alligator-lily, 324
Alligator-pear, 921
Alligator-tree, 601
Allionia, 488
ALLIONIACEAE, 487
Allium, 288, 289
Almond
   Indian, 933
   West Indian, 933
Alnus, 418, 419
ALOACEAE, 301
ALOE FAMILY, 301
Aloe, 302, 316
Alopecurus, 100
ALPINIACEAE, 360
Alsatian-clover, 685
Alsike-clover, 685
ALSINACEAE, 496
Alsine, 497
   aquatica, 497
   Baldwinii, 498
   brevifolia, 499
   fontinalis, 498
   glabra, 499
   groenlandica, 499
   longifolia, 498
   media, 497
   Michauxii, 499
   patula, 499
   pubera, 498
   squarrosa, 499
   tennesseensis, 498
Alsinopsis, 498
Alternanthera, *476, 477*
ALTINGIACEAE, 601
Alum-roots, 923
Alvaradoa, 763, 764
Alysicarpus, 736
Alyssum, 565
Amaranth, 473
AMARANTHACEAE, 470
AMARANTH FAMILY, 470
Amaranthus, 471
   albus, 473
   blitoides, 473
   chlorostachys, 473
   crassipes, 472
   crispus, 473
   cruentus, 472
   deflexus, 473
   gracilis, 473
   graecizans, 473
   hybridus, 473

[1] In the cases of genera with less than ten species the latter have not been indexed.